Handbook of Anion Determination

To
Dr Anne Pauline Williams

Handbook of Anion Determination

W John Williams

School of Chemistry, University of Bath

Butterworths

London Boston Sydney Wellington Durban Toronto

United Kingdom London	Butterworth & Co (Publishers) Ltd 88 Kingsway, WC2B 6AB
Australia Sydney	Butterworths Pty Ltd 586 Pacific Highway, Chatswood, NSW 2067 Also at Melbourne, Brisbane, Adelaide and Perth
Canada Toronto	Butterworth & Co (Canada) Ltd 2265 Midland Avenue, Scarborough, Ontario, M1P 4S1
New Zealand Wellington	Butterworths of New Zealand Ltd T & W Young Building, 77–85 Customhouse Quay, 1, CPO Box 472
South Africa Durban	Butterworth & Co (South Africa) (Pty) Ltd 152–154 Gale Street
USA Boston	Butterworth (Publishers) Inc 10 Tower Office Park, Woburn, Massachusetts 01801

First published 1979

ISBN 0 408 71306 2

British Library Cataloguing in Publication Data

Williams, W J
Handbook of anion determination.
1. Electrochemical analysis
2. Anions
I. Title
545 QD115 78-40553

ISBN 0-408-71306-2

Typeset & Printed by Page Bros (Norwich) Ltd

Preface

The story related by the late Professor C.L. Wilson at the Birmingham Conference on Analytical Chemistry in 1969 has some bearing on the purpose of this book. Mr F.E. Smith (later Lord Birkenhead), the famous legal advocate, dealing with a 'difficult' judge, offered an explanation in a lengthy speech.

> Judge: 'Mr Smith, I have listened to you patiently, but I am no wiser'.
> F.E. Smith: 'No, my Lord, merely better informed.'

This book is concerned with providing information as to how a wide range of anions can be determined in a variety of circumstances. That there is a need for such a book would be disputed by few. Anions feature significantly in many areas of science and technology and, accordingly, their determination is important.

Several factors were taken into account when deciding to write this book. There was no single text in which the determination of anions was the main purpose. There are some general texts and monographs which include a treatment of selected anions, but in these theoretical principles or specific techniques usually form the central theme, with the treatment of anions as a by-product. Reviews have appeared on the determination of certain anions: but some are restricted in scope and others are no more than catalogues, simply indicating techniques and with little critical information.

The most important feature of the book is the determination of anions and each anion is treated separately rather than as a member of a group. All other considerations take a secondary role. The length of each anion section is related to its importance. Whilst the main disadvantage of the arrangement is a degree of repetition in the case of similar anions, I feel that this drawback is far outweighed by the benefits.

Experience in helping both chemists and non-chemists with analytical problems has convinced the author that more care is required to present analytical chemistry in such a way that an effective choice of method can be made. If there is a basic principle on which the book has been based, it is this. It is perhaps pertinent to list some of the questions that might be asked when attempting to choose the best method for solving a particular problem.

> Over what range is the method applicable?
> What is its accuracy?

How long does it take?
Does it require special expertise?
Is it suitable for large numbers of samples?

Even for chemists themselves, deciding on the best analytical method from the seemingly endless list of available methods can be difficult. For those with little training in chemistry, the situation is far worse. The techniques of analytical chemistry are now used in several areas outside the confines of chemistry itself. In the author's experience increasing numbers of biologists, physicists, metallurgists and engineers find that they need to carry out chemical analyses. The present book is written as much for them as for the chemist with a knowledge of analytical work, and the general level of presentation has been adapted to meet this need.

A conscious effort has been made to avoid producing an extensive catalogue of methods which lack sufficient detail. Instead, a number of methods have been selected which contain useful analytical information on range, interferences and accuracy. Deciding what to include or reject has not been easy and has also posed the problem of how much of the past literature to include. Although of historical interest, much of the older work bears little relation to current analytical practice. There seemed no point in digging up the bones yet again to move them to a new cemetery. Anyone wishing to consult the earlier literature should find this possible by following up the reviews quoted.

Each anion section is similarly structured, the sequence being: separations, gravimetry, titrimetry, spectroscopic methods, electroanalytical methods, followed by catalytic, kinetic, radiochemical and thermal methods. The order has been chosen to standardize presentation and facilitate locating information and does not imply an order of importance. In the case of a composite method, the final procedure is used in assigning the category. The inclusion of gravimetric methods requires comment. Some chemists exhibit dismay bordering on disbelief that this analytical coelacanth is still not extinct. The evidence indicates that it continues to find limited use in cases where other methods are unsatisfactory. The high-precision analysis of pure chemicals and the determination of tungstate or silicate are examples.

In view of the excellent monographs on decomposition techniques for inorganic[1] and organic[2] samples, this aspect of anion determination has been omitted; that is, samples are assumed to be already in solution. Separation methods, still a fundamental aspect of analysis, have been treated at some length.

Over 110 practical procedures have been included. In a rapidly changing subject, the problem of recommending methods is not easy. The last 10 or 15 years have seen the introduction of several new techniques into anion determination; for instance, ion-selective electrodes, atomic absorption spectroscopy and gas-chromatography. These, no doubt, have affected the status of many hitherto standard methods. The guiding principles in selecting practical procedures have been wide applicability and an evidence of acceptance by analysts.

Equations and structures are important features of analytical chemistry and both have been employed throughout the text. With the increasing use of Molarity rather than Normality, full equations become necessary in evaluating the results. Practical procedures which originally employed Normalities have been modified to include the corresponding concentrations in Molarities.

In writing the book, considerable use was made of *Analytical Abstracts*, published by the Chemical Society. References to these are included for the more inaccessible journals.

It is a pleasure to record my appreciation of the assistance and encouragement I have received from many sources. Often it was specific advice such as that given by Mr R. Witty and Mr S. Greenfield on the citrate and orthophosphate sections respectively At other times it was of a more indirect nature, such as that derived from nine years membership of the Analytical Methods Committee (Analytical Division, Chemical Society) under the able chairmanship of Dr D.C. Garratt. Another important influence has been that of my colleagues in the Western Region of the Analytical Division, who have shared their experience of analytical methods and have provided critical comments on several aspects of anion determination. Needless to say, none of the above must in any way be held responsible for any errors in the book.

I am indebted to Dr R.A. Chalmers whose enthusiasm did much to get the project under way. Finally, I am especially grateful to my wife, Anne, for continuous encouragement and forbearance despite long and often intense exposure to anions.

1. DOLEZAL, J., POVONDRA, P. and SULCEK, Z., *Decomposition Techniques in Inorganic Analysis*, Iliffe, London (1966)
2. GORSUCH, T.T. *The Destruction of Organic Matter*, Pergamon, Oxford (1970)

Acknowledgement

The procedure
Spectrophotometric determination of sulphide (in steam condensate) by the methylene blue method
on pages 578–580 is taken from BS 2690 Part 14 and is reproduced by permission of BSI, 2 Park Street, London W1A 2BS.

Contents

Part 1 General Anions

Part 2 Halogen Anions

Part 3 Phosphorus Oxyanions

Part 4 Sulphur Anions

Part 1

General Anions

Acetate

Separations

Acetic acid and other volatile fatty acids may be separated by steam distillation[1]. The procedure may be used as a preliminary step before the determination of acetic acid by gas-chromatography[2]. Lester[3] has separated acetic acid from biological material by vacuum distillation, this being followed by gas-chromatography.

Gas-chromatography is now used extensively both for separation and subsequent determination of acetic acid. Experimental details of some of the procedures are given in *Table 1*.

Table 1 Gas-chromatographic procedures for analysis of acetic acid

Substances from which acetic acid is separated	*Experimental conditions*	*Ref.*
Propionic, butyric, iso-butyric, valeric, and iso-valeric acids	10% SP-1200 on Chromosorb W (80–100 mesh). 150 °C.	4
Formic, propionic, and butyric acids	10.5% ethylene glycol adipate and 1.75% phosphoric acid on Anakrom-110/120 mesh. 100 °C. Argon carrier	2
Acetaldehyde, acetone, vinyl acetate, paraldehyde, acetic anhydride, and ethylidene diacetate	Tetrapentyl silane supported on celite 545. 95 °C. Helium carrier	5
Biological material	20% 2,2-dimethylpropane 1,3-diol succinate and 1.7% phosphoric acid. 165 °C. Nitrogen carrier	6

Dittman[7] finds that formic, acetic, oxalic, tartaric, and citric acids can be separated from other carboxylic acids by TLC on cellulose. Data on the solvent systems and the relevant R_f values are given in the section on citrate. Paper chromatography may be used to separate acetate and formate[8].

A solvent extraction procedure using the triphenylstannonium ion, Ph_3Sn^+, enables acetate to be 100 per cent extracted at pH 1–2.4 using benzene as solvent[9].

Another technique for separation is diffusion. This has been investigated by Lundquist, Fugmann and Rasmussen[10] who apply it to the analysis of blood and tissues. The separation is time-consuming.

Determination

The British Standards Institution have published specifications for acetic acid and its analysis[11].

Once separated from interferences, several methods are available for determination of acetate, the final choice depending on the amount present and the accuracy desired. Some methods give a degree of selectivity that enables acetate to be determined in the presence of other carboxylic acids.

Titrimetric methods

1. Acid-base

In common with several other carboxylic acids acetic acid can be titrated in aqueous solution with standard NaOH, the equivalence point being at pH 8.23. Phenolphthalein, thymol blue, or tetrabromophenolphthalein serve as indicators. The method is non-selective.

Erdey, Pickering and Wilson[12] have recommended mixed chemiluminescence indicators, for example, fluorescein plus lucigenin (10,10′-dimethyl-9,9′-biacridinium dinitrate). The indicator action is reversible if the titration is begun at 60 °C.

2. Iodimetric methods

A direct iodimetric procedure based on the reaction

$$IO_3^- + 5I^- + 6H^+ \rightarrow 3I_2 + 3H_2O$$

is not possible. Neither is it possible to enhance the acid strength by addition of Ca, Ba, Mg or Zn salts as in the case of citric or tartaric acids because acetic acid contains no hydroxy group. It is, however, possible to add excess of thiosulphate to a solution of acetic acid containing KIO_3 and KI and titrate the excess after a suitable interval[13].

Iodimetric determination of acetate

Procedure

To about 20 mℓ 0.1 M solution of acetic acid add 1 g KI, 5 mℓ 3% KIO_3 and 25 mℓ 0.1M thiosulphate. After 15–30 min titrate the excess of thiosulphate with standard iodine.

---

3. *Miscellaneous methods*

For the determination of acetic and formic acids when present together Jaiswal and Chandra[14] utilize the fact that both acids are oxidized by copper(III) on boiling for 30 min. Unconsumed copper(III) is determined by arsenic(III) and iodine. Formic acid alone is oxidized by cerium(IV) on refluxing for 1.5 h in the presence of chromium(III). Unconsumed cerium(IV) is titrated with iron(II) using N-phenylanthranilic acid as indicator.

Microcosmic salt (ammonium sodium hydrogen phosphate) has been suggested recently for titration of milligram amounts of acetate with aqueous bromocresol purple as indicator[15].

Coetzee and Frieser[16] have attempted to make anion liquid–liquid membrane electrodes based on dissolving the appropriate salts of the methyl tricaprylyl ammonium ion in 1-decanol. In the case of acetate the response was found to be approximately Nernstian with $mv/\log C = 53.0$. The useful life span of the electrode is one month, or longer in the absence of mechanical defects.

When sub-microgram amounts of acetate have to be determined a catalytic method may be used[17]. The method depends on decolorization of indigo carmine by acetic acid in the presence of hydrogen peroxide.

The diffusion separation method mentioned earlier was followed by an enzymatic estimation of acetate based on its reaction with sulphanilamide in the presence of pigeon-liver enzyme. Unreacted sulphanilamide was determined colorimetrically at 540 nm using N-naphthyl-ethylene diamine and sulphamic acid. The method is suitable for 1–15 μg acetate in a volume of less than 3 mℓ, and appears to be specific.

Colorimetric methods have been described[18, 19].

References

1. *Official Methods of Analysis of the Association of Official Agricultural Chemists,* Washington U.S.A., 10th edn, 274 (1965)
2. SHELLEY, R.N., SALWIN, H. and HOROWITZ, W. *J. Ass. off. agric. Chem.*, **46**, 486 (1963)
3. LESTER, D., *Analyt. Chem.*, **36**, 1810 (1964)
4. OTTENSTEIN, D.M. and BARTLEY, D.A., *Analyt. Chem.*, **43**, 952 (1971)
5. SMITH, B. and DAHLEN, J., *Acta chem. scand.*, **17**, 801 (1963); *Analyt. Abstr.*, **11**, 1001 (1964)
6. MEDZIHRADSKY, F. and LAMPRECHT, W., *Hoppe-Seyler's Z. physiol. Chem.*, **343**, 35 (1965); *Analyt. Abstr.*, **14**, 2702 (1967)
7. DITTMAN, J., *J. Chromat.*, **34**, 407 (1968)
8. JONG, E. DE and MCCULLOUGH, T., *Chemist Analyst*, **56**, 80 (1967)
9. BOCK, R., NIEDERAUER, H-T. and BEHRENDS, K., *Z. analyt. Chem.*, **190**, 33 (1962)
10. LUNDQUIST, F., FUGMANN, U. and RASMUSSEN, H., *Biochem. J.*, **80**, 393 (1961)
11. British Standard 576: (1969) London
12. ERDEY, L., PICKERING, W.F. and WILSON, C.L., *Talanta*, **9**, 371 (1962)
13. KOLTHOFF, I.M., *Chem. Weekbl.*, **23**, 260 (1926)
14. JAISWAL, P.K. and CHANDRA, S., *Microchem. J.*, **14**, 289 (1969)
15. SAXENA, A.K., *Microchem. J.*, **15**, 171 (1970)
16. COETZEE, C.J. and FREISER, H., *Analyt. Chem.*, **40**, 2071 (1968)
17. KRAUSE, A. and SLAWEK, J., *Chemia analit.*, **13**, 1329 (1968); *Analyt. Abstr.*, **18**, 2500 (1970)
18. BRADA, Z., *Chemiké Listy*, **37**, 289 (1943); *Chem. Abstr.*, **44**, 5762d (1950)
19. KIMURA, K., IKEDA, N. and NOMURA, M., *Bull. chem. Soc. Japan*, **26**, 119 (1953); *Chem. Abstr.*, **48**, 3201c (1954)

Arsenate and Arsenite

In solution, arsenic may be in the form of un-ionized molecules or in anionic form (arsenate, arsenite, or complex anions). After pre-treatment of samples, it is usually present as arsenic(V); if a separation or determination is to be made involving an arsenic(III) compound, prior reduction is required. This may be effected by passing SO_2 through the solution. Excess SO_2 is removed with CO_2. Care should be taken not to boil the solution if hydrochloric acid is present or loss of arsenic due to the volatility of the trichloride may result.

Separation and concentration

1. Distillation

Distillation of arsenic either as the trichloride or tribromide remains one of the most important methods for separation of arsenic. Arsenic trichloride boils at 130 °C but is quite volatile at 110 °C. A variety of reagents may be used for reduction to the tervalent state before distillation. Of these, hydrazine sulphate has the advantage of also removing oxides of nitrogen, which might affect the subsequent determination of arsenic.

Nitrate ion interferes with the separation of arsenic by distillation, and the same applies to other oxidizing agents.

A number of elements, including Sb, Ge, Sn, Te, Se, Hg, Re, and Mo form volatile chlorides. Germanium tetrachloride boils at 86 °C, $SnCl_4$ at 115 °C and $SbCl_3$ at 220 °C, though the last mentioned is appreciably volatile at 130 °C. If the distillation is carried out at not greater than 108 °C, arsenic is separated from most elements, those still interfering being Ge, Hg and Se. Selenium and Te may be reduced to the elemental form by boiling under reflux with H_2SO_3 and hydrazine hydrochloride prior to the distillation. The precipitates are filtered off. A stream of CO_2 may be used to carry over the $AsCl_3$.

Numerous modifications of the distillation procedure have been described to suit particular cases, e.g. organic matter[1], food[2], pesticides[3]. The basic form of the apparatus is shown in *Figure 1*. A second receiving flask may be coupled to the first.

Separation of macro amounts of arsenic by distillation

Procedure

To the sample, containing up to 0.4 g As, in a 500-mℓ flask, add about 6 g NaBr and 1–2 g hydrazine sulphate. Make the solution 1:1 in HCl and add 1:1 HCl until the total volume is about 200 mℓ.

Distil until 130–150 mℓ has been collected, add more 1:1 HCl (about 80 mℓ) to the flask, and continue the distillation until the total distillate is about 240 mℓ (until the volume in the distillation flask has been reduced to about 40 mℓ). Wash down the condenser adding the washings to the distillate. Make up to known volume for analysis.

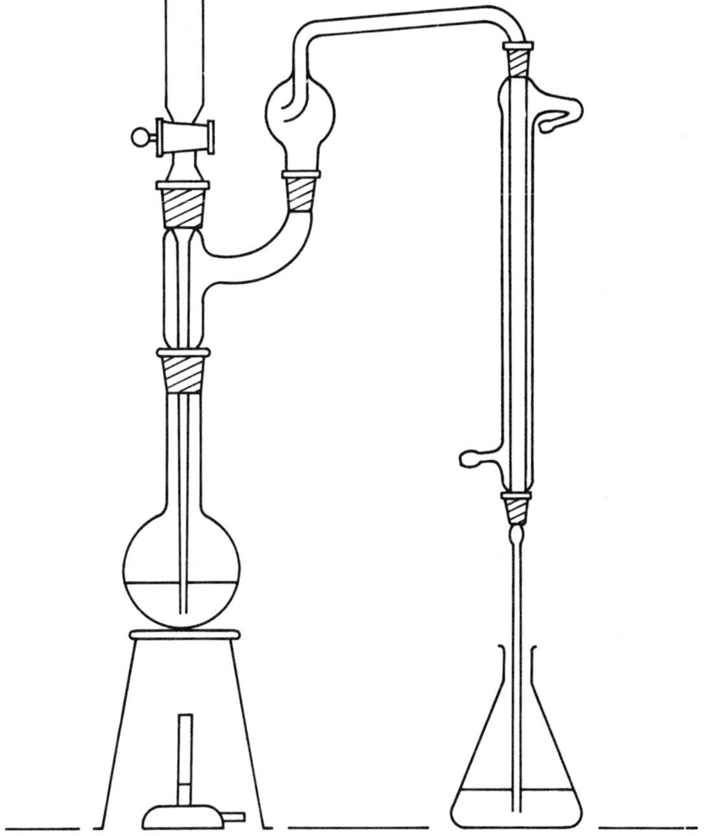

Figure 1 *Basic distillation apparatus for separation of arsenic. A second receiving flask may be coupled to the first*

If two receivers are used, combine the contents of both for analysis.

For small amounts of arsenic in organic matter including foodstuffs the apparatus shown in *Figure 2* is recommended[1]. 1–25 μg As may be distilled as the tribromide and later determined by the molybdenum blue spectrophotometric method.

2. *Solvent extraction*

A detailed account of the separation of P, As, Si and Ge by solvent extraction of their heteropolyacids is given in the section on orthophosphate (p. 447). *Table 45* in that account summarizes the present range of separations possible. It will be noted that arsenic may be reduced to heteropoly blue in the aqueous phase after removal of phosphorus. The subsequent determination of arsenic may also be made by Atomic Absorption Spectroscopy.

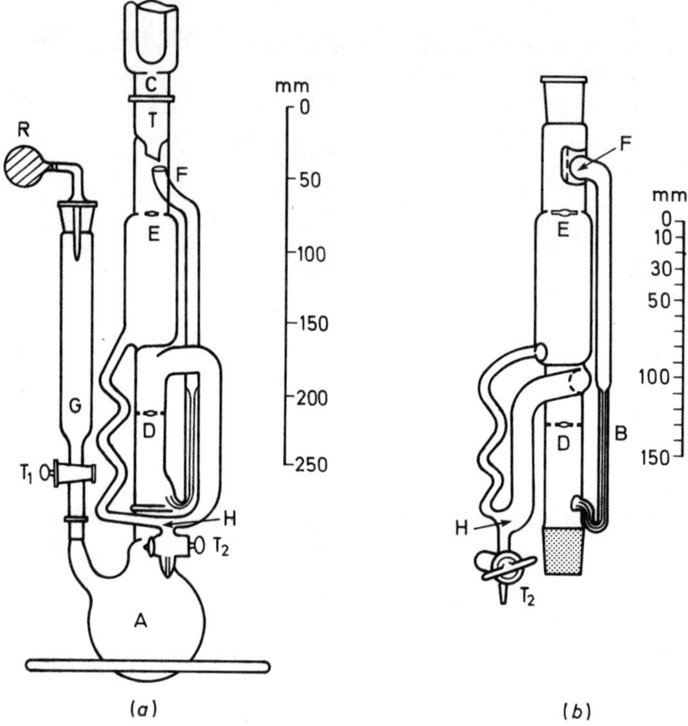

Figure 2 *Distillation apparatus for arsenic: (a) complete assembly; (b) details of trap head.*
(Reproduced with permission of *The Analyst*)

Stará and Starý[4] describe a selective method for extracting arsenic, based on earlier work by Tanaka. Arsenic(III) is extracted from H_2SO_4 containing KI into carbon tetrachloride or other non-polar solvents. Sn(IV), Ge(IV) and Sb(III) are also extracted; the extraction of antimony(III) is substantially reduced if a higher concentration of KI is used. The arsenic may be stripped into the aqueous phase and then determined by conventional methods. The above workers use 8-mercaptoquinoline which reacts with arsenic(III) iodide dissolved in carbon tetrachloride giving a strongly coloured yellow complex. The spectrophotometric procedure is applicable in the 0–30 μg As range. Only tin(II) interferes.

Nall[5], in the determination of arsenic in steel, extracts $AsCl_3$ into chloroform followed by back-extraction into water. The subsequent determination of arsenic is via the molybdo-arsenic acid spectrophotometric method. Phosphorus does not interfere. Fogg, Marriott and Thorburn Burns[6] have modified the method in an attempt to improve the British Standards method[7]. They extract the arsenic(III) as iodide rather than chloride. The same investigation indicates that use of H_2SO_4 (as in the above work by Stará and Starý) increases the rate of spontaneous re-oxidation of the arsenic(III) solution.

Two other important solvent extraction systems involve sodium diethyldithiocarbamate (*Structure 1*) and diethylammonium diethyldithiocarbamate (*Structure 2*). In the former, arsenic may be separated from Ga, In, and Tl[8] by extracting into chloroform at pH 5–6, or from Ge[9]. Chalmers and Dick[10] extract arsenic(III) and arsenic(V) into chloroform alone or mixed with acetone (5:2).

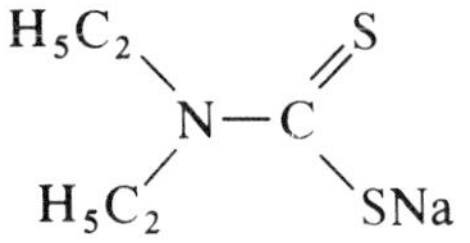

$$(H_5C_2)_2N{-}C({=}S){-}SNa$$

Structure 1 Sodium diethyldithiocarbamate

$$\left\{(H_5C_2)_2N{-}C({=}S){-}S^-\right\}\ \overset{\oplus}{N}H_2(C_2H_5)_2$$

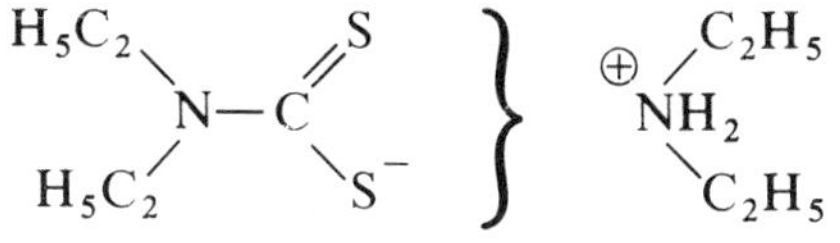

Structure 2 Diethylammonium diethyldithiocarbamate

Using diethylammonium diethyldithiocarbamate, arsenic(III) may be extracted into chloroform from mineral acid solution (0.5–5M H_2SO_4)[11]. Interfering metals are eliminated by preliminary extraction by the same reagent, with arsenic in the arsenic(V) form being retained in the aqueous phase without extraction. Bode and Newmann[12] used CCl_4 as extractant.

Separation of arsenic by solvent extraction using diethylammonium diethyldithiocarbamate[11]

Procedure

To the arsenic(V) solution in about 40 mℓ 2M H_2SO_4 add 1 mℓ 100-volume H_2O_2. Extract the interfering metals with two successive 10-mℓ portions of a 1% solution of diethylammonium diethyldithiocarbamate in chloroform.

To the separated aqueous layer add 1 mℓ of 30% H_2O_2 and boil gently for 15 min. Add 1 mℓ of bromine water. Boil off the bromine. Cool. Add 1 mℓ iodide-ascorbic acid solution (15 g KI and 2.5 g ascorbic acid/100 mℓ). Extract the arsenic(III) with two successive 10-mℓ portions of the 1% reagent in chloroform. Shake the aqueous phase with 5 mℓ chloroform and add to the main extract. The procedure does not separate arsenic from antimony(III).

---

3. Chromatography including ion-exchange

Thin-layer chromatography enables arsenic(III) and arsenic(V) to be separated from a variety of other anions as indicated in *Table 2.*

Ascending paper chromatography has been recommended by Miketukova, Kohlicek and Kacl[25] for separating arsenic(III) and arsenic(V). The solvent employed was methanol-M aq. ammonia (4:1). Ion-exchange chromatography may be used to separate arsenic both from cations and other anions. Strongly acid exchangers retain accompanying cations leaving an effluent

Table 2 Separations involving arsenic(III) and arsenic(V) by TLC

Species separated	*Adsorbent*	*Solvent*	*Ref.*
F^- NO_2^- $S_2O_3^{2-}$ SO_4^{2-} CrO_4^{2-} PO_4^{3-} AsO_4^{3-} AsO_3^{3-}	Silica gel + 5% corn starch	MeOH—*n*-Butanol—H_2O 3 : 1 : 1	13
PO_4^{3-} NO_2^- $S_2O_3^{2-}$ CrO_4^{2-} N_3^- CN^- SCN^- BO_3^{3-} S^{2-} AsO_3^{3-} AsO_4^{3-} NO_3^- SO_4^{2-}	Corn starch	Acetone—3M NH_4OH 1 : 4	14
AsO_3^{3-} AsO_4^{3-}	Silica gel with 5% $CaSO_4$	Acetone—15M H_3PO_4 50 : 1	15
CrO_4^{2-} Cl^- Br^- I^- BrO_3^- ClO_3^- $Fe(CN)_6^{4-}$ $Fe(CN)_6^{3-}$ SCN^- AsO_3^{3-} SO_3^{2-}	Circular TLC See Note (a)		16

Note (a) This is a semi-quantitative method employing a TCL apparatus described in previous papers [17,18]. The spots or rings obtained are compared with standards.

in which arsenic may be determined. Duval, Ironside and Russel[19] use the method to remove iron in the analysis of arsenic–iron alloys.

Basic exchangers find application in the separation of other anions. For example arsenic(III) and selenium(IV) may be separated on strongly basic Dowex-1 resin[20]. Here ammonium chloride is used as eluent. Arsenic(III) and arsenic(V) may be separated on a weakly basic hydroxide-form resin (Amberlite IRA-4B(OH)) eluted with water and dilute NaOH[21].

4. Gravimetric

Arsenate may be precipitated in a similar manner to phosphate, using magnesia mixture. The precipitate, magnesium ammonium arsenate, $MgNH_4AsO_4 \cdot 6H_2O$ provides a separation from Sb, Sn(IV), Mo and Ge. Many cations interfere by precipitating as oxides, hydroxides, or as basic salts, though masking with citrate or tartrate makes the separation more selective. Precipitation of arsenic in this form may also be used for its determination.

Another gravimetric separation involves the heteropolyacids. Heslop and Pearson[22], in a comparative study of quinolinium and lutidinium molybdates found that although lutidinium molybdate was less efficient than quinolinium, it was possible to precipitate phosphate leaving all the arsenate in solution.

5. Adsorption on carriers

Traces of arsenic may be collected on ferric hydroxide. A new and interesting method based on adsorption has been described by Kar and Singh[23]. Ignited $BaSO_4$ acts as carrier for both arsenic(V) and phosphorus(V). Arsenic(III) is not adsorbed so that the procedure may be used to separate arsenic(III) and arsenic(V). 1.5 g $BaSO_4$ is required for 15 µg of arsenic. The method is clean, convenient, and simple.

Note If arsenic needs to be removed (as distinct from separated—where subsequent analysis is involved), precipitation with H_2S or volatilization as the tribromide may be used. When the determination of other heteropoly-acid-forming elements is being undertaken, use can be made of the selective destruction of molybdoarsenic acid by citric acid[24].

Determination

Standard solutions

Arsenic(III): 0.025M

Dissolve about 2.47 g of pure As_2O_3 (accurately weighed) in 20 mℓ 1M NaOH. Make slightly acid to litmus paper by addition of dilute H_2SO_4 or HCl. Make up volume to exactly 500 mℓ. Calculate the factor using the theoretical weight of 2.4725 g.

Arsenic(V)

Either prepare from a standard solution of arsenic(III) by oxidation or dissolve the appropriate amount of pure disodium hydrogen arsenate (heptahydrate) in water. The water content of this compound may vary and should be checked gravimetrically where accurate work is required.

Gravimetric methods

Separation by precipitation as magnesium ammonium arsenate has already been mentioned in the context of separation of arsenic. The precipitate, $MgNH_4AsO_4 \cdot 6H_2O$ may be ignited at 415–855 °C to the pyroarsenate $Mg_2As_2O_7$ and interfering bivalent cations can be masked by EDTA. Ter- and quadrivalent cations may be masked by Tiron (1:2-dihydroxybenzene-3:5-disulphonic acid)[26].

A titrimetric variation of the method is possible in which the precipitate is dissolved in HCl, an excess of EDTA added and the excess titrated with standard $MgCl_2$ solution using Eriochrome Black T as indicator.

Determination of arsenic by precipitation as quinoline molybdoarsenate offers the same advantages as the analogous method for phosphorus. A gravimetric[27] and titrimetric[28] procedure have have been described. In the former, addition of tartaric acid prevents the precipitation of molybdic acid before the quinoline reagent is added. Unlike the yellow complex, blue molybdoarsenic acid is not destroyed by tartaric acid. The amount of arsenic is obtained by dividing the weight of precipitate by 30.127.

Where As^{5+} and As^{3+} have to be determined together, As^{3+} may be determined in one aliquot by permanganate oxidation, and the As^{5+} obtained by subtracting this from the total arsenic found gravimetrically. Phosphates, germanates, and silicates interfere as well as nitrate, and ferrous and ferric iron in amounts greater than 2 g per litre.

Arsenate is precipitated as the insoluble bismuth salt $BiAsO_4 \cdot H_2O$ and this forms the basis of another gravimetric determination. The precipitate is weighed after drying *in vacuo*. A thermogravimetric investigation of the precipitate[30] has indicated that the water of crystallization is not completely removed below 645 °C.

Gravimetric determination of arsenate[29]

Procedure

Dilute the solution containing approximately 0.1–0.2 g arsenate in alkaline solution to 100 mℓ. Acidify with 1 mℓ concentrated HNO_3. Bring to boil and add dropwise, with constant stirring, a 0.5% $Bi(NO_3)_3$ solution until the supernatant liquid no longer gives a precipitate. A large excess of reagent will cause errors and should be avoided; one or two drops in excess are sufficient.

Filter through a X4 porosity sintered filter and wash with 2% HNO_3, ethanol, and finally diethyl ether. Dry *in vacuo* and weigh as $BiAsO_4 \cdot H_2O$.

Note

The error should not exceed 0.22 per cent.

Titrimetric methods

1. Redox

Earlier work, including much of the extensive literature on this aspect of arsenic analysis, will be found in standard texts[31–33].

Several oxidizing agents have been used for the titration of arsenic(III). They include potassium bromate, iodine, potassium iodate, sodium hypochlorite, sodium chlorite, lead tetra-acetate and ceric salts. Of these, potassium bromate and iodine appear to have been the most successful.

Where arsenic has been separated by distillation, titration with standard bromate may be applied directly to the distillate after acidification. The end-point is detected visually using reversible or irreversible indicators, or potentiometrically.

$$BrO_3^- + 3As^{3+} + 6H^+ \rightarrow Br^- + 3As^{5+} + 3H_2O$$

At the end-point bromine is generated.

$$BrO_3^- + 5Br^- + 6H^+ \rightarrow 3Br_2 + H_2O$$

Of the irreversible indicators, which depend on bleaching of the dyestuffs by bromine, methyl orange (0.1% aq.)[34] or naphthol blue black (B.C.I 246: 0.2% aq.)[35] may be used. The colour changes are from colourless to yellow and green to faint pink respectively. When irreversible indicators are used extreme care is needed to avoid local excesses of reagent during the titration. Additional indicator near the end-point is recommended. α-naphthoflavone (0.5% in ethanol)[36, 37], and *p*-ethoxychrysoidine (0.1% in ethanol)[38] have been proposed as reversible indicators, the latter being the better. The colour changes are pale yellow to orange, and red to yellowish-orange respectively.

If α-naphthoflavone is used, slow titration with swirling near the end-point is essential to avoid overshooting. It has been observed that α-naphthoflavone may vary in purity, this sometimes leading to diminished colour at the end-point[39].

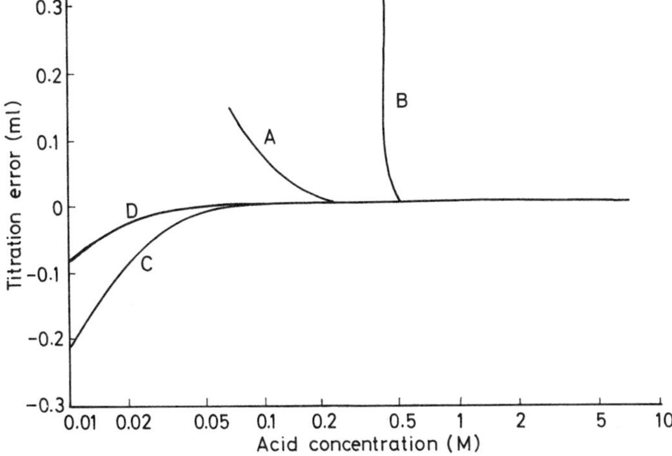

Figure 3 *Errors in potentiometric titration of 25 mℓ of 0.05M arsenic(III) with 0.01667M KBr in various media.*
A, Initial bromide concentration 0.1M; HCl;
B, Initially bromide-free; HCl,
C, Two drops of 0.01M osmic acid; HCl;
D, Two drops of 0.01M osmic acid; H_2SO_4.
(After Bhattarai and Ottaway[41])

With bromate, one important consideration is the acidity range for which the titration is analytically feasible, and this has been the subject of numerous investigations. Ottaway and Bishop[40] find positive errors at HCl concentrations below 0.55M in the absence of added Br^- and below 0.3M in the presence of 0.1M Br^-. In both instances the upper limit for HCl concentration is 2.5M when rosaniline hydrochloride is used as indicator. The reaction becomes exceedingly slow in the absence of both Cl^- and Br^- which may be considered to act as catalysts.

In order to extend the range of acidity concentration Bhattarai and Ottaway[41] have used osmium tetroxide as catalyst. The extension in acidity range is indicated in *Figure 3*. It should be noted that a potentiometric method was employed in this investigation as bromine, on which the indicator mechanism is dependent, is not generated sufficiently rapidly at the equivalence point when the acid concentration falls below 0.1M. The potentiometric titration was performed using a bright platinum wire indicator electrode with a saturated calomel reference electrode. At lower acid concentrations, a considerable time is required for a steady potential in the region of the equivalence point. At 0.1M acid and above, the maximum time is 30 s.

The above work indicated that osmic acid acts as a catalyst in the titration of arsenic(III) with bromate, and permits a wider acid range than for chloride or bromide. The recommended conditions are a solution of the arsenic(III) sample in 0.1M acid (either sulphuric or hydrochloric) with one or two drops of osmic acid, followed by a direct potentiometric titration with $KBrO_3$.

Determination of arsenic(III) by titration with $KBrO_3$

Indicator

p-ethoxychrysoidine (0.1 % in ethanol).

Procedure

Add sufficient concentrated HCl to the arsenic(III) solution to make it 1.0–1.5M. Add 1 g KBr and four drops of the indicator. Titrate with a standard $KBrO_3$ solution to an orange-yellow end-point.

Titration of arsenic(III) with standard iodine is one of the best methods for determination of arsenic.

$$H_3AsO_3 + I_2 + H_2O \rightleftharpoons HAsO_4^{2-} + 4H^+ + 2I^-$$

The reaction is reversible, with the position of equilibrium being dependent on the hydrogen-ion concentration of the solution.

In strongly acid solution the reaction goes from right to left. Strong alkalis cannot be used to promote the forward reaction for they would react with the iodine. In slightly alkaline conditions the reaction proceeds quantitatively from left to right. The pH will tend to fall during the reaction itself due to the formation of HI, so that buffering is required. Not all investigations have agreed on the exact range of pH for which accurate results may be obtained, but in general an excess of $NaHCO_3$ is used.

The titration is often used for the accurate standardization of iodine solution with highly pure arsenic trioxide as reference standard. Electrogenerated iodine may be used in a coulometric procedure. This will be dealt with in electrochemical methods.

Application of the iodimetric titration of arsenic(III) is extensive. In the British Standards method for arsenic in steel, arsenic is precipitated in elemental form by reduction with sodium hypophosphite, and subsequently determined by iodimetric titration[7].

Iodimetric determination of arsenic(III)

Procedure
Neutralize the arsenite solution if necessary, add 1 g of $NaHCO_3$ and titrate with a standard iodine solution to a faint permanent blue using starch as indicator.

As with $KBrO_3$ and I_2, KIO_3 is an old-established reagent for titration of arsenite.

$$2H_3AsO_3 + IO_3^- + 2H^+ + Cl^- \rightleftharpoons 2H_3AsO_4 + ICl + H_2O$$

The titration is based on the Andrews–Jamieson condition of a high concentration of HCl. The range of concentration for the Andrews titration will vary according to the ion being titrated; for arsenic(III) there is some disagreement on the exact range, but 3–6M appears to be satisfactory.

Oxidation by iodate under these conditions proceeds by several stages

$$IO_3^- + 6H^+ + 6e \rightarrow I^- + 3H_2O$$

$$IO_3^- + 5I^- + 6H^+ \rightarrow 3I_2 + 3H_2O$$

$$IO_3^- + 2I_2 + 6H^+ \rightarrow 5I^+ + 3H_2O$$

giving the overall reaction

$$IO_3^- + 6H^+ + 4e \rightarrow I^+ + 3H_2O$$

Several methods are available for detecting the end-point. Carbon tetrachloride will exhibit a purple colour while free iodine is present. This will disappear abruptly when the last trace of iodine has been oxidized to ICl, which is not extracted, and which gives the aqueous phase a faint yellow colour.

Since their introduction by Smith and Wilcox, a number of dyestuffs have been used as indicators[43]. Of these, Naphthol Blue Black and Amaranth are irreversibly bleached, but *p*-ethoxychrysoidine introduced by Schulek and Rozsa[44] as a bromometric indicator, was applied by Belcher and Clark[45] as a reversible indicator for titrations involving KIO_3.

Determination of arsenic(III) using KIO_3

Procedure 1 (using carbon tetrachloride)
Adjust the acidity of the arsenite solution to 4–6M in HCl. Add 5 ml CCl_4.

Titrate with 0.025M KIO_3. The CCl_4 layer becomes purple. Continue the titration until this layer is just permanently clear of colour.

Procedure 2 (using *p*-ethoxychrysoidine)
To the arsenite solution add sufficient HCl to make it about 4M. Titrate with 0.025M KIO_3 until the iodine colour has almost disappeared, and then add 12 drops of 0.1% *p*-ethoxychrysoidine (in ethanol). Continue the titration to a colour change from red to orange.

Notes
1. The reversibility of this indicator is limited by its partial destruction. Three reversals only may be carried out.
2. Just before the true end-point the indicator passes through a deep purple colour.
3. The blank value of each new batch of *p*-ethoxychrysoidine should be determined, for this may vary appreciably.

The reaction between cerium(IV) and arsenic(III) is slow, and requires a catalyst such as osmium tetroxide or ICl. Most procedures are based on the work of Gleu[46] who recommended ferroin as indicator with osmium tetroxide as catalyst. The colour change is from orange-red to very pale blue. More recently Keattch[47] has found that ruthenium tetroxide also catalyses the reaction, but when used, a potentiometric end-point is required.

While the overall reaction may be represented by the stoichiometric equation

$$2Ce(IV) + As(III) \rightarrow 2Ce(III) + As(V)$$

recent kinetic investigations indicate a complicated mechanism in which the nature of the medium has an important effect[48, 49]. An important aspect of the reaction is the accurate standardization of cerium(IV) solutions with reference to pure arsenic trioxide. In this connection, several critical studies have appeared recently[50–53]. They confirm that a small directional difference exists between the direct titration of arsenic(III) with cerium(IV), and the reverse titration. While this difference is small (~0.03%) it could be significant in very accurate work. The cause of the discrepancy is attributed to the reaction of cerium(IV) with water. The most recent of the studies[53] has indicated that iodide may be used as catalyst, but nitrate interferes (as it does in the standard procedure using osmium tetroxide or ICl).

Determination of arsenic(III) with cerium(IV)

Procedure
To the arsenite solution, which should be approximately 1M in H_2SO_4, add 0.5 mℓ of 0.005M KI and 2 drops of 0.01M ferroin (0.25%).

Titrate with 0.1M cerium(IV) sulphate to a very pale blue end-point.

Other oxidants for which redox procedures are available for arsenic(III) include hypochlorite, chlorite, lead tetra-acetate, Chloramine-T, N-bromosuccinimide and sodium peroxomolybdate. Most of these receive detailed treatment in the standard text on newer redox titrants by Berka, Vulterin and Zyka[54]. Of these reagents N-bromosuccinimide has been used for determination of arsenite in the presence of arsenate[55]. The oxidation is carried out in the presence of $NaHCO_3$.

$$\begin{matrix} CH_2\text{—}CO \\ | \\ CH_2\text{—}CO \end{matrix}\rangle NBr + NaAsO_2 + H_2O \rightarrow \begin{matrix} CH_2\text{—}CO \\ | \\ CH_2\text{—}CO \end{matrix}\rangle NH + NaAsO_3 + HBr$$

Several advantages are claimed over iodine. These include non-volatility, cheapness, and ability to determine small amounts of As_2O_3 (100 µg). However, attention has been drawn to some instability of standard solutions of the reagent[54].

Sarwar, Randa, and Hamdani[50] titrate 0.6–6.0 mg As(III) with N-bromosuccinimide using Bordeaux red as indicator.

Sodium peroxomolybdate has been introduced recently[57]. The arsenite is titrated potentiometrically using platinum and saturated calomel electrodes. Potassium iodide appears to catalyse the reaction.

2. *Compleximetric*

Several indirect compleximetric methods are available for arsenic(V), mainly based on precipitation with a bismuth nitrate solution followed by an EDTA titration of unconsumed bismuth[58, 59].

3. *Miscellaneous*

The successful method for phosphorus based on precipitation of quinoline molybdophosphate led to the development of a similar one for arsenic[60]. Precipitation is made at the boiling point in about 1M HCl with $KClO_3$ present to maintain the arsenic in the pentavalent state, and tartaric acid to prevent the precipitation of molybdic acid. As in the analogous phosphorus determination, an excess of standard NaOH is added to the washed precipitate and back-titration made with standard HCl using phenolphthalein as indicator.

Reproducibility is to within about 10 µg of arsenic; a determination takes about 20 min.

Spectroscopic methods

1. *Colorimetric*

Despite the introduction of newer methods for the determination of arsenic the older Gutzeit method finds extensive use for estimation of trace amounts in inorganic and organic materials including foodstuffs. The method depends on arsine produced by the interaction of nascent hydrogen and an arsenious solution, reacting with paper impregnated with mercuric bromide to produce a yellow-brown spot due to $H(HBr)_2As$, $(HgBr)_3As$ and Hg_3As_2. Through not very accurate, the method permits the estimation of minute traces of arsenic.

It may be used after distillation of arsenic. In most food analysis it is necessary to carry out wet oxidation before applying the method. The form of apparatus recommended by the Association of Official Analytical Chemists[61] is shown in *Figure 4*.

Figure 4 *Generator used in Gutzeit method for the determination of arsenic.* (After *Official Methods of Analysis of the A.O.A.C.*)

A report of the Analytical Methods Committee of the Society for Analytical Chemistry has described in detail the determination of arsenic in organic matter (0.5–5.0 μg As) using the Gutzeit method[62]. The method is also an official method of the British Pharmacopoeia[63].

Control of conditions is necessary if stains from the same amounts of arsenic are to be identical.

Several elements interfere, for example, forms of phosphorus giving PH_3 (e.g. hypophosphorous acids) which accompany the AsH_3, should be absent. Any H_2S produced will be retained by the lead acetate. Sulphate, phosphorus(V), and small amounts of fluoride do not interfere. Co, Ni and Cu interfere.

Hashmi and Chughtai[16] have described the semi-quantitative estimation of arsenite using thin layer chromatography and using an apparatus described in previous papers[17,18]. The procedure involves making circular spots or rings on chromatoplates. Eleven anions (including arsenite) may be determined in a single drop with an accuracy of ± 5 per cent.

2. *Spectrophotometric*

Of the spectrophotometric methods for arsenic probably the most important are those based on heteropolyacid formation. Arsenate, like phosphate, reacts with molybdate in acid solution to give the heteropolyacid which may be reduced by a variety of compounds to the blue polymeric species, molybdenum blue. The absorbance is usually measured at 840 nm. Of the many reductants proposed hydrazine sulphate appears to be the best.

The method has been criticized on the grounds that rigid adherence to conditions, including the pH, is essential for reproducible results[64].

As the method is normally subject to several interferences, particularly by phosphorus and silicon; preliminary separation of arsenic by distillation is sometimes made. Recent work has indicated that this is not always required. The method has been applied to widely differing groups of samples ranging from foodstuffs to steel. For the determination of arsenic in organic matter (which includes foodstuffs) the method has been recently re-examined and the resulting procedure subjected to collaborative testing[1]. The procedure developed is based on earlier work by Hoffman and Rowsome[65] and it is claimed that the modification is quicker and more reproducible than the standard method it replaces[66].

Two modifications of the heteropolyacid method have appeared recently for the determination of arsenic in steel[5,6]. Both involve a solvent extraction procedure before the molybdenum blue stage.

An interesting approach has been used by Chalmers and Sinclair[67] based on the fact that the heteropolyacids of As, Ge, and Si can exist in α and β forms. Stabilization of the β-forms is effected by addition of acetone. The resulting procedure is better in terms of rapidity, sensitivity and accuracy. Addition of acetone to the colourless molybdoarsenic acid causes a yellow colour. The effect is to shift the absorption spectrum to longer wavelengths. No reduction to the heteropoly blue is made, but instead, the absorbance is measured at 440 nm. Phosphorus interferes but not silicon, and Beer's law holds for up to 140 µg As/mℓ.

When arsenic is accompanied by P, Si or Ge the heteropolyacid spectrophotometric method may be modified by selective extraction or suppression of unwanted species. A more detailed discussion of this will be found in the section on orthophosphate. The pertinent factors are as follows:

(a) Citric acid destroys molybdophosphoric acid and molybdoarsenic acid, but not molybdosilicic acid.
(b) Addition of perchloric acid before the ammonium molybdate prevents the formation of molybdosilicic acid but allows the formation of the corresponding acids of arsenic and phosphorus.
(c) The heteropolyacids of P, As, Si, and Ge may exist in α and β modifications, each having different absorption and stability properties.

Table 3 shows the application of these principles to the development of specific methods for arsenic.

Table 3 Methods for determination of arsenic in the presence of P, Si and Ge

Present	*Basis of As selectivity*	*Procedure for As determination*	*Ref.*
As, P	P removed by extraction of its HPA into isobutyl acetate. As reduced to HPA blue in aq. phase	Spectrophotometric	68
As, P, Si	Addition of perchloric acid before ammonium molybdate prevents formation of Si-HPA	Spectrophotometric	24
As, P, Ge	P-HPA extracted at pH 1.0–0.8 into isobutyl acetate. Ge-HPA extracted at pH 0.4 into iso-octyl alcohol. As-HPA remains in aq. phase	Spectrophotometric	69
As, Si	Si-HPA extracted at pH < 4 into iso-octyl alcohol. As-HPA remains in aq. phase	Spectrophotometric	69
As, P, Si	P-HPA extracted into isobutyl acetate. As-HPA extracted into ethyl acetate/butanol/isoamyl alcohol. Si-HPA extracted into methyl isobutyl ketone/citrate	AAS (Mo)	70

In a recent study by Pungor and co-workers[71–73] on the α- and β-heteropolyacids it has been shown that despite the many similar characteristics of the four acids (P, As, Si and Ge) sufficient differences exist between individual acids to permit their determination without separation. For example, the absorbance of the α-molybdoarsenic acid is practically zero at 427 nm whereas that of the other three is considerable. The method requires no reduction or extraction.

An almost equally well known spectrophotometric method for arsenic uses silver diethyldithiocarbamate. Based on the red complex formed when arsine is passed into a solution of silver diethyldithiocarbamate in pyridine, it is easier to perform than the heteropolyacid method, but several disadvantages detract from its use. In a collaborative study published by the Analytical Methods Committee of the Society for Analytical Chemistry[1] wide variations were found in different batches of the reagent, this causing a variation in the wavelength of maximum absorbance (between 520 and 550 nm).

Little appears to be known about the complex itself. In a recent study of the application of the method to drinking water, unreliability was found in the presence of traces (2–500 ppb(10^9)) of Cr, Mo, and V which suppress the complex formation[74]. Copper gives high results.

Nevertheless, the method has been recommended by the A.O.A.C.[75] and British Standards Institution[76] for 1–10 μg As and has been used[77] in the analysis of industrial water for as little as 1 μg As.

3. Atomic absorption spectroscopy

Many non-metals cannot be determined directly by AAS because their resonance lines lie in the vacuum ultra-violet. Like P and Si, As can be determined indirectly by means of the molybdenum stoichiometrically associated with it in the heteropolyacid.

When this is preceded by solvent extraction of the heteropolyacid, a highly selective method is derived enabling traces of arsenic to be determined even when accompanied by P, Si and Ge[70].

The basis of the method is given in *Table 3*.

Yamamoto *et al.*[78] describe a similar method except that arsenic(III) is oxidized by iodine to arsenic(V) and the molybdoarsenic acid is extracted into methyl iso-butyl ketone. Silicate and phosphate interfere in this procedure.

4. Fluorimetry

In dilute sulphuric acid, cerium(III) exhibits a characteristic fluorescence at 350 nm using an exciting wavelength of 260 nm. This has found application in the determination of arsenic by means of the reaction:

$$2\text{Ce(IV)} + \text{As(III)} \rightarrow 2\text{Ce(III)} + \text{As(V)}$$

which is catalysed by osmium tetroxide[79]. 7.5–37.5 μg of arsenic may be determined indirectly by spectrofluorimetric measurement of the cerium(III) produced.

Another fluorimetric method depends on the simple bromo-ion association complex with arsenic(III) or arsenic(V) at $-196\,^{\circ}$C. Arsenic in the range 2×10^{-5}–10^{-4}M can be determined using the procedure, which requires a slight modification to the spectrofluorimetric cell[80].

Electroanalytical methods

The conventional polarographic determination of arsenic is complicated and inaccurate. Arsenic(III) is reduced in several waves at the electrode in acid medium, giving uncertain products. Arsenic(V) is not reduced. The large body of literature on this topic has been comprehensively reviewed recently[81].

Indirect procedures are available. In one recent example constant current polarography is carried out on peroxomolybdate, this being produced by the following sequence[82]

$$\text{As(V)} \longrightarrow \text{molybdoarsenate} \xrightarrow[\text{Oxidize with } HClO_4 \text{ and } H_2O_2]{\text{Extract with isobutyl alcohol}} \text{peroxomolybdate}$$

Certain forms of polarography are capable of reaching the ppb(10^9) range for arsenic. Myers and Osteryoung[83], using differential pulse polarography report a detection limit of 4×10^{-9}M.

Several coulometric methods have been described for determination of arsenic, based on both controlled current and controlled potential. For example Wise and Williams[84] utilize electrogenerated iodine for the titration of arsenic(III) by constant current coulometry. An excellent account of this approach to the determination of arsenic is given in the monograph by Milner and Phillips[85].

The highly successful fluoride electrode has been used[86] in an indirect procedure for arsenic(V). The arsenate, in amounts of up to 15 ppm in solution is precipitated with lanthanum at pH 8.65, and the excess of lanthanum titrated with standard fluoride using the pF electrode. In the above paper, evaluation of the arsenate is made using Gran's plot paper. Chloride and nitrate are without interference up to a molar excess of 600, but sulphate interferes giving high results. This can be prevented by prior precipitation with barium. The precision of the method is ± 5 per cent. For quantities of arsenic(V) in the milligram range, and where increased precision and accuracy is required, a potentiometric titration with lead perchlorate and using a lead ion-selective electrode is recommended in the same work.

Kinetic methods

In recent years several kinetic methods for arsenic have appeared. Krause and Slawek base their fixed-concentration method on indigo carmine and hydrogen peroxide with a spectrophotometric procedure for following the reaction[87].

A simultaneous comparison method based on molybdenum blue, and capable of giving a sensitivity of 1×10^{-6} g mℓ^{-1}, has been published by Bognar and Czekkel[88].

Burgess and Ottaway[89] base their method on the reaction:

$$As(III) + Br_2 \rightarrow As(V) + 2Br^-$$

which is extremely fast, but limited by the rate at which the bromine is generated in the reaction.

$$BrO_3^- + 5Br^- + 6H^+ \rightarrow 3Br_2 + 3H_2O$$

where

$$+\frac{d[Br_2]}{dt} = k_4[BrO_3^-][Br^-][H^+]^2$$

in which $k_4 = 489\ \ell^3\ mol^{-3}\ min^{-1}$ at 25°C and ionic strength 1M.

The completion of the arsenic(III)–Br_2 reaction is indicated visually by the bleaching of methyl orange.

Although the method is rapid and simple, arsenic(III) down to 0.005 ppm in 20 mℓ may be determined. It is, however, non-selective to reducing agents that react with bromine. This is no great disadvantage in many analytical applications.

Radiochemical methods

If microgram amounts of arsenic are precipitated as ammonium uranyl arsenate on filter paper, and an α-particle count made on the uranium associated with the arsenic, this can be used[90] for the determination of traces of arsenic in the range 1–8 μg.

Activation analysis has now been established for several years as a method for trace arsenic. In a recent paper by Byrne, arsenic at sub-microgram level in biological material is determined. Where antimony is present as well, a preliminary solvent extraction of their iodides from a H_2SO_4–KI medium with toluene is made[91].

Without doubt, the most distinguished sample to receive attention by the activation method was Napoleon's hair, in order to establish whether he died of arsenic poisoning. The account makes interesting reading and illustrates the value of analysis in forensic investigations[92,93].

References

1. Analytical Methods Committee, *Analyst*, **100**, 54 (1975)
2. British Standards 757: (1959)
3. Official Methods of Analysis of the Association of Official Agricultural Chemists, 10th edn, 35 (1965)
4. STARÁ, V. and STARÝ, J., *Talanta*, **17**, 341 (1970)
5. NALL, W.R., *Analyst*, **96**, 398 (1971)
6. FOGG, A.G., MARRIOTT, D.R. and THORBURN BURNS, D., *Analyst*, **97**, 657 (1972)
7. British Standards 1121: Part 38: (1967)
8. NAZARENKO, V.A., FLYANTIKOVA, G.V. and LEBEDEVA, N.V., *Zav. Lab.*, **23**, 891 (1957); *Analyt. Abstr.*, **5**, 2954 (1958)
9. SAITO, K., IKEDA, S. and SAITO, M., *Bull. chem. Soc. Japan*, **33**, 884 (1960); *Analyt. Abstr.*, **8**, 1485 (1961)
10. CHALMERS, R.A. and DICK, D.M., *Analytica chim. Acta*, **31**, 520 (1964)
11. WYATT, P.F., *Analyst*, **78**, 656 (1953); **80**, 368 (1955)
12. BODE, H. and NEUMANN, F., *Z. analyt. chem.*, **172**, 1 (1960)
13. KAWANABE, K., TAKITANI, S., MIYAZAKI, M. and TAMURA, Z., *Japan Analyst*, **13**, 976 (1964); *Analyt. Abstr.*, **13**, 5385 (1966)
14. CANIĆ, V.D., TURCIĆ, M.N. and BUGARSKI-VOJINOVIĆ, M.B., *Z. analyt. Chem.*, **229**, 93 (1967); *Analyt. Abstr.*, **15**, 5211 (1968)
15. OGUMA, K., *Talanta*, **14**, 685 (1967)
16. HASHMI, M.H. and CHUGHTAI, N.A., *Mikrochim. Acta*, 1040 (1968)
17. HASHMI, M.H., SHAHID, M.A. and AYAZ, A.A., *Talanta*, **12**, 713 (1965)
18. HASHMI, M.H., SHAHID, M.A., AYAZ, A.A., CHUGHTAI, F.R., HASSAN, N. and ADIL, A.S., *Analyt. Chem.*, **38**, 1554 (1966)
19. DUVAL, G.R., IRONSIDE, R. and RUSSEL, D.S., *Analytica chim. Acta*, **25**, 51 (1961)
20. KRAUSE, K.A. and NELSON, F., A.S.T.M. Symposium No. 195, Philadelphia (1958)
21. BLASIUS, E., *Chromatographische methoden in der analytischen und praparativen anorganishen chemie*, Enke Verlag, Stuttgart (1958)
22. HESLOP, R.B. and PEARSON, E.F., *Analytica chim. Acta.*, **37**, 516 (1967)
23. KAR, K.R. and SINGH, G., *Mikrochim. Acta*, 560 (1968)
24. PAUL, J., *Mikrochim. Acta*, 836 (1965)
25. MIKETUKOVA, V., KOHLICEK, J. and KACL, K., *J. Chromat.*, **34**, 284 (1968)
26. MALINEK, M. and REHAK, B., *Colln Czech chem. Commun. Engl. Edn*, **21**, 777 (1956)
27. FILIPOV, D., *Compt. Rend. Acad. Bulg. Sci.*, **16**, 61 (1963); *Chem. Abstr.*, **60**, 4797f (1964)
28. MEYER, S. and KOCH, O.G., *Z. analyt. Chem.*, **158**, 434 (1957)
29. VANCEA, M. and VOLUSNIVC, M., *Stud. Cercet. Chim. Cluj.*, **10**, 141 (1959); *Analyt. Abstr.*, **7**, 1713 (1960)

30. DUVAL, C., *Inorganic Thermogravimetric Analysis*, Elsevier, London (1963)
31. KOLTHOFF, I.M. and BELCHER, R., *Volumetric Analysis*, Vol. 3, Interscience, New York (1957)
32. WILSON, C.L. and WILSON D.W. (Eds.), *Comprehensive Analytical Chemistry*, Vol. 1B, Elsevier, Amsterdam (1960)
33. BERKA, A., VULTERIN, J. and ZYKA, J., *Newer Redox Titrants*, Pergamon Press, Oxford (1965)
34. GYÖRY, S., *Z. analyt. Chem.*, **32**, 415 (1893)
35. SMITH, G.F. and BLISS, H.H., *J. Am. chem. Soc.*, **53**, 2091 (1931)
36. UZEL, R., *Colln Czech chem. Commun. Engl. Edn*, **7**, 380 (1935); *Chem. Abstr.*, **30**, 1683 (1936)
37. SCHULEK, E., *Z. analyt. Chem.*, **102**, 111 (1935)
38. SCHULEK, E. and ROZSA, P., *Z. analyt. Chem.*, **115**, 185 (1939); *Chem. Abstr.*, **33**, 1621 (1939)
39. BELCHER, R. and NUTTEN, A.J., *Quantitative Inorganic Analysis*, 3rd edn, Butterworths, London, 251 (1970)
40. OTTAWAY, J.M. and BISHOP, E., *Analytica chim. Acta*, **33**, 153 (1965)
41. BHATTARAI, D.R. and OTTAWAY, J.M., *Talanta*, **19**, 793 (1972)
42. BISHOP, E. (Ed.), *Indicators*, Pergamon Press, Oxford (1972)
43. SMITH, G.F. and WILCOX, C.S., *Ind. Engng Chem. analyt. Edn*, **14**, 49 (1942)
44. SCHULEK, E. and ROZSA, P., *Z. analyt. Chem.*, **115**, 185 (1939)
45. BELCHER, R. and CLARK, S.J., *Analytica chim. Acta*, **4**, 580 (1950)
46. GLEU, K., *Z. analyt. Chem.*, **95**, 305 (1933)
47. KEATTCH, C.J., *Talanta*, **8**, 620 (1961)
48. RODRIGUEZ, P.A. and PARDUE, H.L., *Analyt. Chem.*, **41**, 1369 (1969)
49. HABIG, R.L., PARDUE, H.L. and WORTHINGTON, J.B., *Analyt. Chem.*, **39**, 600 (1967)
50. ZIELEN, A.J., *Analyt. Chem.*, **40**, 139 (1968)
51. SCHLITT, R.C. and SIMPSON, K., *Analyt. Chem.*, **41**, 1722 (1969)
52. ZIELEN, A.J., *Analyt. Chem.*, **41**, 1905 (1969)
53. OHLWEILER, O. A., MEDITSCH, J. O. and PIATNICKI, C. M. S., *Analytica chim. Acta*, **63**, 341 (1973)
54. BERKA, A., VULTERIN, J. and ZYKA, J., *Newer Redox Titrants*, Pergamon Press, Oxford (1965)
55. BARAKAT, M.Z. and ABDALLA, A., *Analyst*, **85**, 288 (1960)
56. SARWAR, M., RANDA, A.K. and HAMDANI, S.P., *Microchem. J.*, **16**, 184 (1971)
57. KOTKOWSKI, S. and LASSOCINSKA, A. *Chemia analit.*, (Warsaw), **11**, 789 (1966); *Analyt. Abstr.*, **14**, 6774 (1967)
58. YAMAMOTO, Y., BAN, T. and UEDA, S., *J. chem. Soc. Japan, pure Chem. Sect.*, **86**, 540 (1965); *Analyt. Abstr.*, **14**, 3935 (1967)
59. VASILIEV, R. and ANASTASESCU, G., *Rev. Chim. Bucharest*, **11**, 298 (1960); *Analyt. Abstr.*, **8**, 89 (1961)
60. MEYER, S. and KOCH, O.G., *Z. analyt. Chem.*, **158**, 434 (1957)
61. *Official Methods of Analysis of the Association of Official Agricultural Chemists*, 10th edn, 354 (1965)
62. *Analyst*, **85**, 629 (1960)
63. *British Pharmacopoeia*, A74 (1973)
64. CHARLOT, G., *Colorimetric Determination of Elements*, Elsevier, London (1964)
65. HOFFMAN, I. and ROWSOME, M., *Analyst*, **85**, 151 (1960)
66. Analytical Methods Committee of the Society for Analytical Chemistry, *Analyst*, **85**, 629 (1960)
67. CHALMERS, R.A. and SINCLAIR, A.G., *Analytica chim. Acta*, **33**, 384 (1965)
68. PAUL, J., *Mikrochim. Acta*, 830 (1965)
69. PAUL, J., *Analytica chim. Acta*, **35**, 200 (1966)
70. RAMAKRISHNA, T. V., ROBINSON, J. W. and WEST, P. W., *Analytica chim. Acta*, **45**, 43 (1969)
71. HALASZ, A. and PUNGOR, E., *Talanta*, **18**, 557 (1971)
72. HALASZ, A. and PUNGOR, E., *Talanta*, **18**, 569 (1971)
73. HALASZ, A., PUNGOR, E. and POLYAK, K., *Talanta*, **18**, 577 (1971)
74. MARTINS, H.M. and WHITNACK, G.C., *Science*, **171**, 383 (1971)
75. *Official Methods of Analysis of the Association of Official Agricultural Chemists*, 10th edn, 358 (1965)
76. British Standards 4404: (1968)
77. REES, T. D., *Proc. Soc. analyt. Chem.*, **7**, 32 (1970)
78. YAMAMOTO, Y., KUMAMARU, T., HAYASHI, Y., KANKE, M. and MATSUI, A., *Talanta*, **19**, 1633 (1972)
79. KIRKBRIGHT, G.F., WEST, T.S. and WOODWARD, C., *Analytica chim. Acta*, **36**, 298 (1966)
80. KIRKBRIGHT, G.F., SAW, C.G. and WEST, T.S., *Analyst*, **94**, 538 (1969)

81. ARNOLD, J.P. and JOHNSON, R.M., *Talanta*, **16**, 1191 (1969)
82. ASAOKA, H., *Japan Analyst*, **17**, 736 (1968); *Analyt. Abstr.*, **18**, 1602 (1970)
83. MYERS, D.J. and OSTERYOUNG, J., *Analyt. Chem.*, **45**, 267 (1973)
84. WISE, W.M. and WILLIAMS, J.P., *Analyt. Chem.*, **36**, 19 (1964)
85. MILNER, G.W.C. and PHILLIPS, G., *Coulometry in Analytical Chemistry*, Pergamon Press, Oxford (1967)
86. SELIG, W., *Mikrochim. Acta*, 349 (1973)
87. KRAUSE, A. and SLAWEK, J., *Z. analyt. Chem.*, **255**, 44 (1969)
88. BOGNAR, J. and CZEKKEL, J., *Mikrochim. Acta*, **572** (1970)
89. BURGESS, A.E. and OTTAWAY, J.M., *Analyst*, **97**, 357 (1972)
90. WILSON, A.D. and LEWIS, D.T., *Analyst*, **88**, 510 (1963)
91. BYRNE, A. R., *Analytica, chim. Acta*, **59**, 91 (1972)
92. FORSHUFVUD, S., SMITH, H. and WASSEN, A., *Nature*, **192**, 103 (1961)
93. SMITH, H., FORSHUFVUD, S. and WASSEN, A., *Nature*, **194**, 725 (1962)

Borate

In most boron-containing materials the element is in the form of borates, either soluble or insoluble. Insoluble borates are readily converted to the soluble form by treatment with acids. After such treatment they can be determined by a wide range of methods. Determination of boron in ferrous and non-ferrous alloys, minerals, ores, biological materials, foodstuffs, pharmaceutical products, soils and fertilizers is often required on a routine basis. Its uses include the manufacture of glassware, porcelain and glazes, and cleaning compositions for metals.

The distribution of boron is widespread. It has been stated that no substances have been found that do not contain measurable amounts of the element. Often its determination is required at low levels, for example its concentration in fresh water may be as low as 0.01 ppm. Boric acid (H_3BO_3) or sodium tetraborate ($Na_2B_4O_7 \cdot 10H_2O$) are generally used as reference standards.

The analytical chemistry of borate is covered in several reviews[1–3]. An account of boron determination in the context of organic microanalysis has been given by Dixon[4].

In carrying out analytical work involving boron particular care is necessary to avoid loss of the element by volatility and to prevent contamination of samples by boron-containing materials, especially glassware. Boron-free glassware should be used in accurate work. The use of platinum, porcelain or fused silica in place of glass is another way of reducing or eliminating contamination. Spicer and Strickland[5] have reported that for recovery of about 20 μg of B, only silica or platinum are satisfactory, and that trials even with alleged boron-free glassware were unsatisfactory.

Boric acid itself is volatile in steam. Boron trifluoride and HBF_4 are volatile. Methyl borate has a boiling point of 68.5 °C and forms the basis of a method for separating boron by distillation. In carrying out such operations as evaporation, ignition, and boiling acidified boron solutions, possible loss by volatility must be considered and preventive action taken. In the case of boiling this can be done by employing a reflux arrangement. Loss by evaporating acidified boron solutions have been investigated by Feldman[6].

Separations

1. Distillation as methyl borate

This is a standard method and applicable over the whole range from macro to sub-microgram amounts of boron. A general form of the apparatus is shown in *Figure 5*.

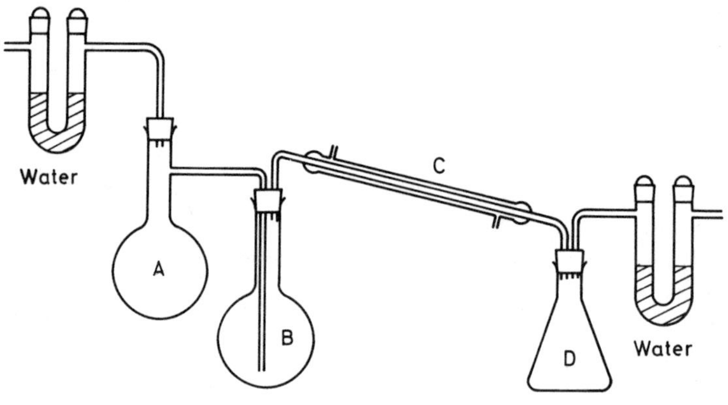

Figure 5 Separation of borate by distillation

The U-tube traps contain water. Fluoride interferes in the separation, but can be retained as the strong aluminium(III) complex in flask B by addition of $AlCl_3$. Large excesses should be avoided as they make complete recovery of boron difficult. Vanadium(V) also distils over.

Spicer and Strickland use a modified distillation apparatus for quantities of boron below 20 μg. The main apparatus is shown in *Figure 6*.

The apparatus itself is made of silica with the exception of the condenser jacket which may be of soft glass. Distillates are collected in a platinum dish. The investigation by Spicer and Strickland indicates that the methanol distillate can be evaporated without loss of boron by first adding water, NaOH and glycerol. The resulting solutions can be analysed directly by the Curcumin spectrophotometric method. Luke[7,8] has proposed a similar apparatus for the distillation. Here heating is provided by an infra-red lamp and the methyl borate swept out in a stream of nitrogen.

Separation of borate by distillation

Outline procedure

The apparatus shown in *Figure 5* is used. Up to 1 g of the solid sample is

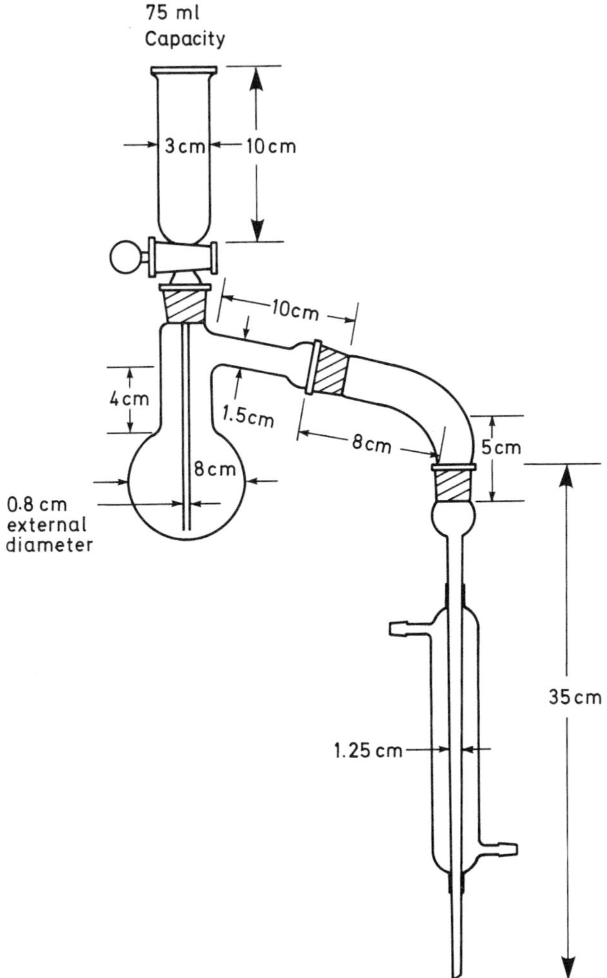

Figure 6 *Separation of sub-micro amounts of boron by distillation. The apparatus is made of silica except for the condenser jacket which may be of soft glass.* (From Spicer and Strickland[5])

dissolved in 5 mℓ of 6M HCl and introduced into flask B. If the substance is insoluble in HCl a carbonate fusion is required. Add pure anhydrous $CaCl_2$, about 1 g per mℓ of sample, to retain water. Transfer about 300 mℓ of purified methanol to flask A, then heat using a thermomantle until about 25 mℓ has condensed in flask B.

At this stage heat flask B using a water bath, so that the volume in it remains fairly constant. Collect about 180 mℓ of distillate in D and add to it the contents of the trap. The second batch can be used to check that the distilled boron is entirely in the first batch.

The distillate can now be concentrated by evaporation after first neutralizing with NaOH. The alkaline solution tends to absorb considerable amounts of CO_2. This is conveniently removed by making slightly acid and boiling for a few seconds. The solution is then neutralized again using methyl red.

---

2. *Ion-exchange*

Both cation- and anion-exchange have found application in the separation of borates. Martin and Hayes[9], in the analysis of ferro-boron, use cation-exchange to separate borate from a number of metallic ions. Iron is removed by cation exchange before the sodium hydroxide–mannitol titration of borate in a British Standards[10] method for boron in ferro-boron.

Suzuki[11] has employed a strongly basic anion-exchange resin to separate borate and silicate. Carlson and Paul[12] use an Amberlite XE-243 boron-specific resin contained in polyethylene tubing. The concentrated borates are converted to tetrafluoroborate for evaluation by ion-selective electrode.

3. *Solvent extraction*

Few solvent extraction methods appear to exist for borate. Melton, Hoover and Howard[13] find that soluble boron in fertilizers is extractable into 20% 2-ethylhexane-1,3-diol in isobutyl methyl ketone. The organic layer is analysed using atomic absorption spectroscopy. More recently Egneus and Uppstrom[14] have examined 40 potential extractants for boric acid. The results indicate that aliphatic 1,3-diols with at least six carbon atoms are the best compared with diketones, hydroxyketones and other groups of compounds. It is appropriate to mention here that several metals capable of interfering with borate analytical methods can be separated by solvent extraction of their oxine complexes.

4. *Thin-layer chromatography*

Canic and co-workers[15] have separated 13 anions (including borate) by TLC on maize-starch and using acetone-3MNH_4OH (1:4) as solvent. The total list consists of NO_2^-, $S_2O_3^{2-}$, CrO_4^{2-}, N_3^-, CN^-, SCN^-, BO_3^{3-}, S^{2-}, AsO_3^{3-}, AsO_4^{3-}, NO_3^-, SO_4^{2-} and PO_4^{3-}. Borate and oxalate can be separated on silica gel containing 5% soluble starch, using butanol saturated with 2M-HNO_3 as solvent[16].

5. *Miscellaneous methods*

Several metallic ions can be removed from borate solutions by mercury cathode electrolysis. Borate remains unaffected. Another method of removing selected metals is to precipitate them as hydroxides at pH 5.0–5.5. Borate is left in the filtrate. Oxine too can be used with the added advantage that extraction of metal oxinates is possible. Other methods of separation will be referred to later in the section.

Determination

Gravimetric methods

Earlier work on the analytical chemistry of boron produced several gravimetric procedures for its determination. They are generally regarded as inferior to the NaOH–mannitol titration, and there is little evidence of current use. Information on these methods will be found in the reviews cited earlier.

However some recent work has been reported. Akimov, Busev and Andzhaparidze[17] report the use of the antipyrine derivatives 1,1-diantipyrinylbutane and αα-diantipyrinyltoluene for gravimetric determination of 0.5–37 mg B in 0.5M HF.Using the first reagent the relative error is reported as less than 2 per cent with no interference from Al, Zn, Cd, Ti, Zr, Cu, Fe, Co or Ni, but Sb(V), Nb and Ta must be absent. A titrimetric form of the method is also reported.

Chadwick[18] has reported the use of 2,4,6-triphenylpyrylium chloride for gravimetric determination of borate. The borate solution is acidified with HCl, and the reagent added followed by HF. Borate is converted to BF_4^- which then reacts as follows:

$$(C_6H_5)_3C_5H_2O^+ + BF_4^- \rightarrow (C_6H_5)_3C_5H_2OBF_{4(s)}$$

After being allowed to stand for 20 h at room temperature and 3 h at 0 °C the precipitate is dried at 110 °C before weighing. The gravimetric factor is 0.1561. Further information on the reagent is given in the section on perchlorate where it also functions as a gravimetric reagent.

Titrimetric methods

For milligram and larger amounts the NaOH–mannitol titration is one of the most important methods. Under certain circumstances the method is applicable to the lower microgram level, but other methods are generally more effective in this region. Its use appears to date from 1899 (Gooch and Jones[19]; Jones[20]) though the effect of polyhydric alcohols on boric acid was known earlier.

The basis of the method is discussed in most analytical texts. Boric acid itself is a weak acid ($K_a = 6.4 \times 10^{-10}$), which cannot be satisfactorily titrated with standard bases. It reacts with certain polyhydroxy compounds, for example glycerol, sorbitol, and mannitol, to give much stronger acids ($K_a \sim 10^{-4}$).

$$B(OH)_3 + 2\begin{array}{c} | \\ -C(OH) \\ | \\ -C(OH) \\ | \end{array} \rightarrow \left[\begin{array}{c} | \\ -CO \\ | \\ -CO \\ | \end{array} \!\!>\!B\!<\!\! \begin{array}{c} | \\ OC- \\ \\ OC- \\ | \end{array}\right]^- H^+ + 3H_2O$$

It has been usual to use mannitol, though recent work has indicated that sorbitol is slightly more effective[21]. The procedure for boric acid on its own is to add mannitol and titrate with standard NaOH to a phenolphthalein end-point.

When boric acid is accompanied by strong acids these must first be neutralized to a strong acid end-point using methyl red or a similar indicator. After addition of mannitol the titration is continued to a phenolphthalein end-point. The volume of NaOH used between the two end-points is equivalent to the boric acid present. A potentiometric end-point is possible. This occurs at about pH 8.5. Published methods on the potentiometric form of the method quote the initial neutralization pH as being within the range 4–6. Dixon[22] has stressed the need to use the same initial pH for both the analysis itself and the standardization of the NaOH, which should be done using boric acid or borax. This is particularly important on the micro-scale if accurate results are required. Wilson and Pellegrini[23] use an 'identical pH' method in the determination of borates in fertilizers. The solution is adjusted to pH 6.3 and finally brought back to the same value with carbon dioxide-free 0.02M NaOH after addition of mannitol. This method is now recommended for fertilizer analysis[24]. Nazarenko and Ermak[25] report pH 7.75–7.9 as the optimum value for the potentiometric titration using mannitol.

Many species interfere with the NaOH–mannitol titration. Not unexpectedly, acids and bases of medium strength interfere. Phosphate, which may be carried over in the distillation, interferes. This can be removed by precipitation as magnesium ammonium phosphate or as ferric phosphate. An alternative procedure is precipitation with bismuth nitrate. Excess bismuth is removed using a slight excess of NaOH[23]. Ammonium ions interfere. These can be eliminated by boiling the solution with NaOH.

Heavy metals can mask the end-point or interfere by hydrolysis of their salts. This is eliminated by methyl borate distillation.

The NaOH–mannitol titration is now recommended as a standard method by several authorities[26–28]. In the last quoted reference, which is concerned with determination of boron in ferro-boron, the titration is carried out after cation-exchange removal of iron.

Spectroscopic methods

1. Spectrophotometric, visible and UV

The widespread distribution of boron, usually at low concentration, has given impetus to the development of adequate methods for its trace determination. In this, spectrophotometric methods have been significant, though current investigations in atomic emission spectroscopy suggest that this might provide a viable alternative.

Many of the currently used spectrophotometric reagents for boron, for example quinalizarin, carminic acid, dianthrimide and curcumin are based on anthraquinone. The colour is often produced in a medium of concentrated H_2SO_4. In such cases the colour is a function of temperature, the acid strength, duration of heating and other variables. Statements are sometimes made in the literature that one boron spectrophotometric reagent is better than others. Such judgements appear to be based on restricted criteria and are not of general validity. The essential data, including sensitivities, optimum wavelengths and reagent concentrations for 21 chromogenic reagents for borate have been published[29].

Mention should be made of another aspect of this form of boron determination, namely automatic methods. Until recently reservations were being expressed on the use of certain reagents such as quinalizarin and carminic acid in borate automatic procedures because of the concentrated H_2SO_4 medium required[30]. The advent of Acidflex and similar tubing has now overcome this difficulty. Ostling[31] has described a simplified automatic method based on curcumin. The same publication provides the essential data for eleven other automated methods for boron. Spectrophotometric methods for borate are reviewed in the monograph edited by Boltz[53] and in a more recent general review of boron analysis by Braman[3].

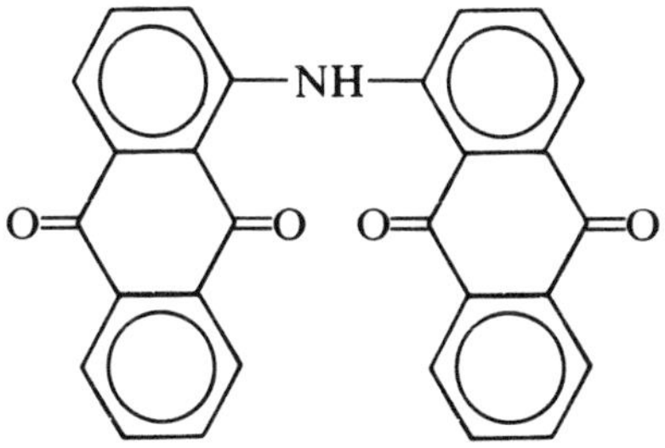

Structure 3 1,1′-Dianthrimide (1,1′-bis anthraquinoylamine)

Individual reagents will now be considered. 1,1′-Dianthrimide(1,1′-bis anthraquinoylamine) (*Structure 3*) produces a yellow colour in concentrated H_2SO_4, this becoming blue in the presence of boron. The colour is a function of temperature and is destroyed at 90 °C. Measurements are generally made at 620 nm; Beer's law is valid over the range 0.5–6 µg B. The reagent is more sensitive than either quinalizarin or carminic acid. Relatively large amounts of F^- interfere. Other interfering species are NO_3^-, NO_2^-, CrO_4^{2-}, IO_4^- and ClO_4^-, but the effects of some can be prevented. An investigation of the effects of a large number of cations has been carried out by Langmyhr and Skaar[32]. A more recent study by Gupta and Boltz[33] has indicated the optimum conditions and the effects of diverse ions on the determination of 1–10 µg B.

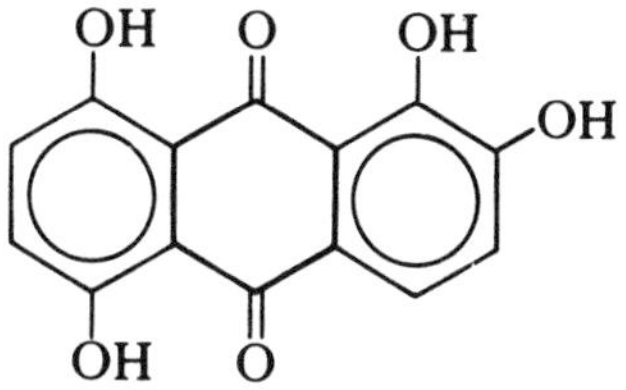

Structure 4 *Quinalizarin* (1,2,5,8-tetrahydroxyanthraquinone)

With quinalizarin (1,2,5,8-tetrahydroxyanthraquinone) (*Structure 4*) the colour change is from red-violet to blue. Absorbance measurements at 615 nm.

Nitrate and fluoride interfere. As the reagent is far more sensitive to germanium than boron, this must be absent. Again, temperature and H_2SO_4 concentration in the final solution are critical. A recent study by Gupta and Boltz[34] gives the sensitivity as 0.00037 μg mℓ$^{-1}$ B and the optimum range 0.06–0.25 ppm B. There appears to be no automatic form of the method.

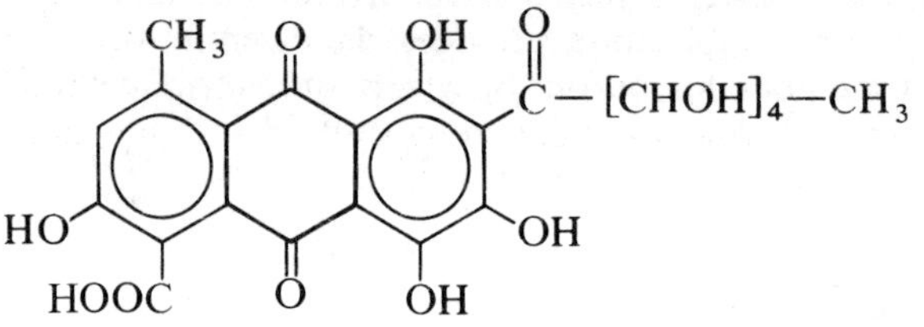

$$\text{Carminic acid: anthraquinone nucleus with } CH_3,\ HO,\ HOOC,\ OH,\ OH,\ OH \text{ and } -C(=O)-[CHOH]_4-CH_3$$

Structure 5 Carminic acid

Carmine and carminic acid (*Structure* 5), a glucoside of carmine, give the same colour reaction with borate because the glucoside radical is not conjugated with the quinoid part of the nucleus on which the colour reaction depends. Carmine in concentrated H_2SO_4 changes from bright red to purple-blue in the presence of borate. Absorbance measurements are made within the range 575–610 nm. The colour development, though slow at room temperature, becomes rapid at 90 °C. In the general form of the method interferences include F^-, NO_3^-, As(III), IO_3^-, I^-, V(V) and citrate. Beer's law holds over the range 0–20 μg B. An automated form of the method by Lionnel[35] has a limit of detection of about 0.02 mgℓ$^{-1}$ B, and a standard deviation of 0.03 mgℓ$^{-1}$ at the 3.0 mgℓ$^{-1}$ level. Application of the method was made to sewage, sewage effluents and river waters. Other automatic methods are included in the publication by Ostling cited earlier.

The carminic acid method finds wide application and has been recommended for determination of boron in feeding stuffs[27] and water[26]. A recent critical study by Gupta and Boltz[36] has provided two improved visible methods and

Table 4 Tolerances of diverse ions in the spectrophotometric determination of 4 μg B in 25 ml using carminic acid (H_2SO_4 medium; 300 nm)[36]

Ion	*Tolerance* (μg/25 mℓ)
F^-	2
Ge^{4+}	1
Ti^{4+}	1
NO_3^-	50
Fe^{2+}	10
UO_2^{2+}	50
Ce^{3+}	100
AsO_3^{3-}	150

Note: The above ions are those giving the maximum interference. Other ions tested can be tolerated in much larger amounts. A fuller list is given in the original publication[36].

a new UV method. The visible methods are carried out in 95% H_2SO_4 with absorbance measurements at 615 nm, and in H_2SO_4–acetic acid with the corresponding measurements at 548 nm. The respective sensitivities are $1.5 \times 10^{-3}\ \mu g\ m\ell^{-1}$ B and $3.8 \times 10^{-4}\ \mu g\ m\ell^{-1}$ B. The higher absorptivity in the UV region at 300 nm compared with the 600–615 nm region in the visible spectrum will be seen in *Figure 7*. The corresponding sensitivity at 300 nm is $7.0 \times 10^{-4}\ \mu g\ m\ell^{-1}$ B. A study of interferences is included in the investigation. For the determination of 4 µg of B in 25 mℓ, the tolerances of some ions is shown in *Table 4*.

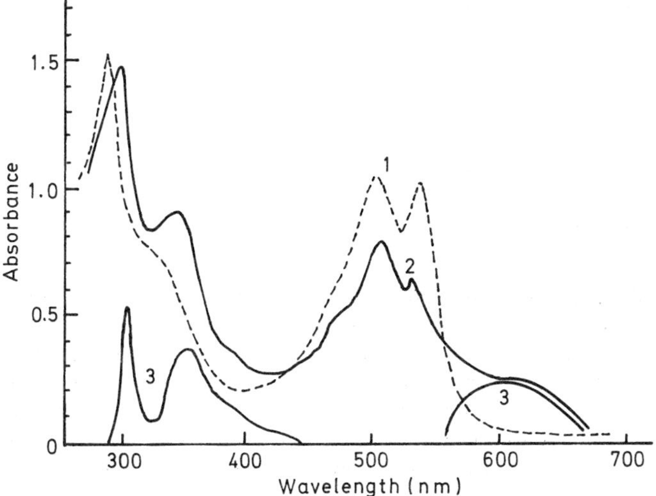

Figure 7 *Absorption spectra for carminic acid and boron–carminic acid complex in sulphuric acid medium.*

1, Reagent blank (1 mg reagent per 25 mℓ H_2SO_4) v. H_2SO_4

2, Boron–carminic acid complex (15.5 µg B per 25 mℓ H_2SO_4 solution) v. 95% H_2SO_4

3, Boron–carminic acid complex (15.5 µg B per 25 mℓ H_2SO_4 solution) v. reagent blank solution.

(After Gupta and Boltz[36])

Shelton and Reed[37] have recently investigated the method in its application to analysis of magnesites. Included in this work is a study of the effects of magnesium, the pick-up of boron from glassware, and the loss of boron by volatilization in the preliminary treatment.

```
OMe
         H      O       OH      H
         |      ||      |       |
HO-(O)-C=C — C —C=C—C=C-(O)-OH
            |       |       |
            H       H       H        |
                                    OMe
```

Structure 6 *Curcumin* (1,7-bis (4-hydroxy-3-methoxyphenyl)-1,6-heptadiene-3,5-dione)

Curcumin 1,7-bis(4-hydroxy-3-methoxyphenyl)-1,6-heptadiene-3,5-dione (*Structure 6*) was the first reagent not to require the use of concentrated H_2SO_4. The method can be used in two ways, a different complex being formed in each case. Both forms are described as the curcumin method. An excellent account of the development of modern forms of the method is given by Uppström[38].

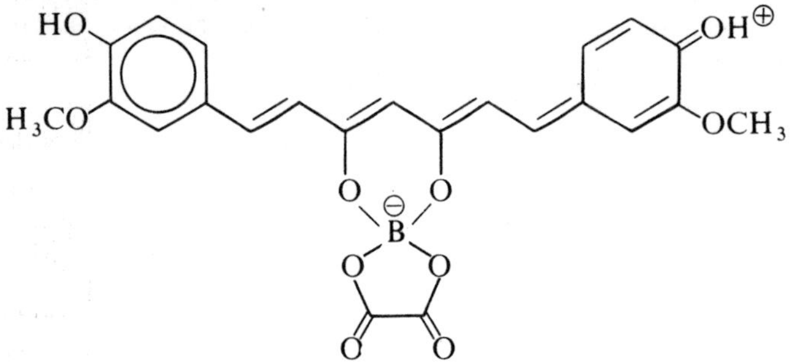

Structure 7 Rubrocurcumin

Boric acid, oxalic acid and curcumin in acetic acid form rubrocurcumin (*Structure 7*). This is relatively unstable to hydrolysis, resulting in lack of reproducibility in the analytical procedure. Strict control of water content in the reaction solution and atmospheric moisture, is essential. The boric acid–curcumin–oxalic acid complex conforms to 1:1:1 ratio. A strongly acid solution of borate reacts with curcumin under almost water-free conditions to give rosocyanin (*Structure 8*) which is very stable. Its molar absorptivity

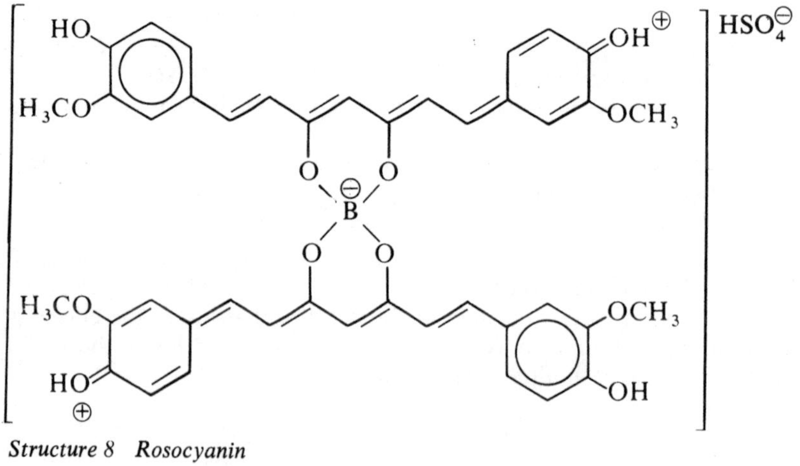

Structure 8 Rosocyanin

is about twice that for rubrocurcumin, making it a more sensitive analytical form. Here the boric acid–curcumin forms a 1:2 complex[39,40]. When applied to aqueous solutions most curcumin methods include as the first step the elimination of water, which interferes with the reaction. Earlier forms of the method achieved this by evaporation to dryness followed by baking to dryness on a water bath. The red complex was then dissolved in alcohol or acetone and its absorbance measured, generally at 560 nm. Alternative procedures are distillation of methyl borate or solvent extraction. In recent years procedures have been considerably simplified.

Boric acid and curcumin only react at a measurable rate when the curcumin molecule is protonated in the presence of a strong acid. However, in this form it is unstable. The evaporation procedure to eliminate water therefore required a delicate balance between attaining sufficient acidity to protonate the curcumin and completing the reaction before its destruction. A notable advance was made by Hayes and Metcalfe[41] who showed that the reaction can be conducted at room temperature if both components are dissolved in suitable non-aqueous solvents. Furthermore they showed that small amounts of water are permissible, though a later investigation indicates that this lowers the sensitivity. Crawley[42] studied the elimination of water by acetic anhydride, using a reaction catalysed by HCl. An important aspect of the procedure is elimination of excess curcumin–proton complex which interferes with the reaction. This can be achieved by diluting the solution with ethanol.

Uppström[38] has recommended propionic anhydride catalysed by oxalyl chloride as a means of eliminating water from the sample. This reacts in two ways,

$$(COCl)_2 + H_2O \rightarrow 2HCl + CO + CO_2$$

or

$$(COCl)_2 + 2H_2O \rightarrow (COOH)_2 + 2HCl$$

the first reaction predominating in aqueous solution. The reaction between boron and curcumin then takes place in a completely homogeneous liquid medium. Excess of protonated curcumin is destroyed with an ammonium acetate buffer. Standard procedures using this reagent are capable of borate analysis in the range 0.0033–40 $\mu g \ell^{-1}$ B. Six standard procedures are given depending on the level of borate present. At the lowest levels $4\frac{1}{2}$ h is required for a complete analysis. The reliability of the above modification of the curcumin method has been confirmed and it is now incorporated into automatic methods[43,44].

Germanium interferes directly by forming an analogue of rosocyanin. Fluoride interferes and the only satisfactory procedure in this case appears to be separation of boron. Nitrate also interferes. Up to 30 mg of NO_3^- in samples containing 0.2–5 µg B can be successfully eliminated by treatment with aniline sulphate in a platinum dish[41]. Other species that interfere either by interaction with curcumin or by retarding the colour formation are Fe(III), Mo, Ti, Nb, Ta, Zr, CrO_4^{2-}, MnO_4^-, NO_2^- and ClO_3^-.

The method has been applied to a wide range of samples. These include water[26], industrial effluents[24], food additives[45], and animal tissue[46].

1,1′-Dianthrimide, quinalizarin, carminic acid and curcumin constitute the principal borate spectrophotometric reagents. Others will now be considered. Several thionine derivatives, notably methylene blue and nile blue A form extractable species with the fluoroborate ion. Extraction of the complexes can be made into 1,2-dichloroethane, *o*-dichlorobenzene or similar solvents. The use of methylene blue was first investigated by Ducret[47].

The complex structure is given below (*Structure 9*). Earlier work on its development is discussed in the monograph by Belcher and Wilson[48]. The sensitivity is high, with Beer's law holding over the range 0.1–6 μg B per 50 mℓ. Skaar[49] has published the effects of a wide range of ions on the recovery of 25 × 10^{-9}M H_3BO_3 in 0.1M HCl, using the method. This shows that many ions

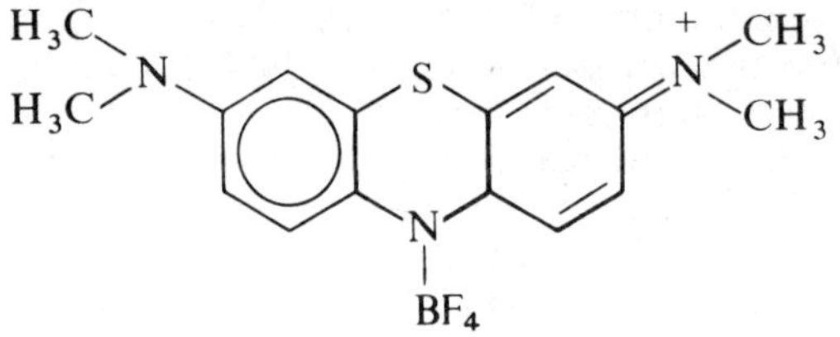

H_3C CH_3 N S N^+ CH_3 H_3C N BF_4

Structure 9 Methylene blue–fluoroborate complex

interfere to a considerable extent, the reason being that methylene blue forms slightly soluble compounds with several inorganic acids and neutral salts. Most of these are soluble in 1,2-dichloroethane and extract together with the methylene blue-BF_4^- complex. The authors point out that boron is a common impurity in many reagents even when these are of high grade quality.

Normally conversion of borate to BF_4^- takes about 18 h. Iron catalyses the reaction, reducing the time to 5–10 min. A recent application of the method to steel is described by Bhargava and Hines[50]. The lower limit is 0.2 ppm. Up to 20% Cr, 10% Ni, and 1% each of V, Mo or W (separate or together) do not interfere, making the procedure suitable for alloy steels.

The reagent azomethine H has featured in some recent spectrophotometric methods for borate. Initial studies were made by Capelle[51] with further work by Shanina Gel'man and Mikhailovskaya[52]. The reagent is available as the condensation product of H-acid (8-amino-1-naphthol-3,6-disulphonic acid) and salicylaldehyde. Its preparation has been described by Basson Bohmer and Stanton[54] who developed an automatic form of the method for determination of 1–10 μg of boron in plant tissue. Investigation of interferences was restricted to species likely to be found in plant material, and indicated that Cu, Fe and Al have effect. The first two can be masked using thioglycollic acid. Aluminium is masked with citrate or oxalate. All three may be masked using EDTA.

The reagent tends to hydrolyse, and requires storage in a refrigerator. Under such conditions its working life can be extended to 14 days. In a second publication Basson, Pille and Du Preez[55] reported the *in situ* preparation of the reagent in an automatic procedure. More recently a modified form of the method has been introduced by John, Chuah and Neufeld[56], and application made to soils and plant material. Of 15 ions studied for interference only F^-, Al^{3+}, Fe^{3+} and Cu^{2+} do so with colour development at below the 10000 ppm level in the sample. The tolerance concentrations of these ions are reported as 5000, 3000, 200 and 2500 ppm respectively.

Other spectrophotometric reagents for borate include tetrabromochrysazin, phthalein violet, chromotropic acid and victoria violet. Information on these is contained in reviews Nemodruk and Karalova[1] and Braman[3] as well as in a general review of anions by Boltz[57].

Spectrophotometric determination of borate using carminic acid[36]

Reagents

Carminic acid solution:

I. Dissolve 1.00 g of carminic acid in 1 ℓ of 95 % H_2SO_4. Keep in a refrigerator. Dilute 18 mℓ of this solution to 100 mℓ to obtain a 0.018 % solution.

II. Dissolve 1 g of carminic acid in 1 ℓ of glacial acetic acid, filter and dilute 400 mℓ of this solution to 1 ℓ with glacial acetic acid.

Sulphuric acid:

98 % S.G. 1.84

95 % Prepare from 98 % H_2SO_4. Check concentration titrimetrically.

Glacial acetic acid: 99.8 % reagent grade.

Standard boron solution I:

Dissolve 1.427 g of boric acid in 95 % H_2SO_4 and dilute to 1 ℓ with 95 % H_2SO_4. Dilute 8.80 mℓ of this stock solution to 1 ℓ with 95 % H_2SO_4 to obtain a 2.03×10^{-4}M B solution (2.20 μg B $m\ell^{-1}$).

Standard boron solution II:

Dissolve 1.4302 g of boric acid in water and dilute to 1 ℓ. Dilute 100 mℓ of this solution to 1 ℓ with glacial acetic acid. Transfer 40 mℓ of the latter solution to a 1-ℓ volumetric flask. Add 21.8 mℓ of acetic anhydride (97 %) and dilute to volume with glacial acetic acid (1 mℓ ≡ 1 μg B).

Procedure I

Transfer 1–10 mℓ of H_2SO_4 solution of borate containing 1–25 μg B to a 25 mℓ volumetric flask. If necessary dilute to 10 mℓ with 95 % H_2SO_4. Add 10 mℓ of 0.1 % carminic acid solution I for absorbance measurements at 615 nm or 10 mℓ of 0.018 % carminic acid solution I for absorbance measurements at 300 nm. Prepare a reagent blank solution. Place flasks in water maintained at 50 ± 2 °C. After heating for 15–20 min, remove the flasks, cool to room temperature and dilute to the mark with 95 % H_2SO_4. Measure the absorbance at either 300 nm or 615 nm using the reagent blank solution in the reference cell.

Procedure II

Transfer the boric acid solution in acetic to a 25-mℓ volumetric flask, add 10 mℓ of carminic acid solution II, cool in ice and add 1 mℓ of 98 % H_2SO_4 with shaking. Heat the flasks in a water bath maintained at 50 ± 2 °C for 15–20 min. Remove the solutions from the bath and allow to cool to room temperature. Dilute to volume with acetic acid. Mix and measure the absorbance at 548 nm after 1 h, using a reagent blank solution in the reference cell.

Notes

1. Although borosilicate glassware was used in the original investigation, volumetric flasks in which carminic acid–boric acid reactions were carried out were heated repeatedly with concentrated H_2SO_4 for several hours prior to use, and blanks were always prepared.
2. All solutions should be stored in polyethylene bottles.
3. Beer's law holds for 2–40 μg B per 25 mℓ when absorbance

measurements are made at 615 nm, and 0.5–8 μg B per 25 mℓ for 300 nm. The corresponding sensitivities are 1.5×10^{-3} μg mℓ$^{-1}$ B at 615 nm, 7.0×10^{-4} μg mℓ$^{-1}$ B at 300 nm both using 95% H_2SO_4, and 3.8×10^{-4} μg mℓ$^{-1}$ B using H_2SO_4–acetic with measurements at 548 nm.

---

2. *Other spectroscopic methods*

Boric acid forms a highly luminescent complex with dibenzoylmethane in a H_2SO_4-diethylether (8–96% v/v) glassy medium at 77 K[58]. This was subsequently developed into an analytical method for borate at the ng mℓ$^{-1}$ level[59]. The phosphorescence is attributed to a T→So emission from a 2:1 dibenzoylmethane–boric acid chelate. The emission is measured at 508 nm with excitation at 402 nm. Tungsten and molybdenum form similar complexes producing a positive interference. Benzoylacetone behaves similarly to dibenzoylmethane.

A fluorimetric method using hydroxy-2-methoxy-4-chloro-4′-benzophenone in concentrated H_2SO_4 has been published[60]. This uses excitation at 365 nm with emission at 490 nm and enables borate in the 10–100 ppb(10^9) range to be determined.

Atomic absorption methods can be applied. Determination of boron by this technique is limited by formation[61] of a series of highly stable oxides BO_x. Even in N_2O–acetylene flames the degree of atomization is low. A method by Harris[62] employing this flame is suitable for 0–200 μg mℓ$^{-1}$ B. Melton *et al.*[63] developed a procedure applicable to water-soluble boron in fertilizers. Here extraction is made into 2-ethyl-1,3-hexanediol and methyl isobutyl ketone mixture before analysis by AAS using the 249.7 nm line. No significant interference is given by elements commonly found in fertilizers. The method is now recommended as a standard method for fertilizer analysis[64]. In a recent atomic absorption method for use in plant tissue analysis, Elton-Bott[65] converts borate to boric acid, reacts this with methanol and atomizes the resulting methyl borate in a nitrous oxide–acetylene flame. Using a 3 g sample, a concentration of 25 mg kg^{-1} B can be determined with acceptable precision.

Flame emission methods have been described[66, 67]. A newer development in this area is a semi-automatic emission method incorporating a methanol distillation concentration step[68]. Sixty specimens can be distilled and 180 distilled specimens analysed per hour. The sensitivity is given as 0.004 mg Bℓ$^{-1}$. Another notable development in atomic emission spectroscopy is determination of boron using a hollow-cathode lamp[69]. Here the boron sample is transferred to the cathode cavity of the lamp and evaporated to dryness using an infra-red lamp. The system is evacuated and flushed, preferably with argon, before initiating the discharge. The attainable sensitivity, which is in the sub-ppb(10^9) region, compares favourably with those reported using fluorescence and other highly sensitive methods.

Electroanalytical methods

1. *Potentiometric*

Reference has already been made to potentiometric forms of the NaOH–

mannitol titration. This has been applied to determination of boric and salicylic acids in pharmaceutical preparation[70]. An indirect potentiometric method has been based on the tetrafluoroborate ion-selective electrode[12]. Borate is first converted to BF_4^- after concentration on an Amberlite XE243 boron-specific resin.

2. Coulometric

Coulometric analysis is often capable of a much higher degree of precision than other methods. The technique has been used in a highly precise absolute method for assay of boric acid[71]. M KCl–0.75M mannitol is used as supporting electrolyte. The method, applicable to macro quantities of boric acid, is capable of accuracy within 0.0033 per cent.

Thermometric methods

A comparison of potentiometric curves and thermograms for aqueous solutions of boric acid and HCl with NaOH show important differences[72]. In contrast to the well-defined inflection on the potentiometric curve for HCl, the corresponding one for boric acid is barely discernible. On the other hand, the thermograms for each are almost identical. These are shown in *Figure 8*.

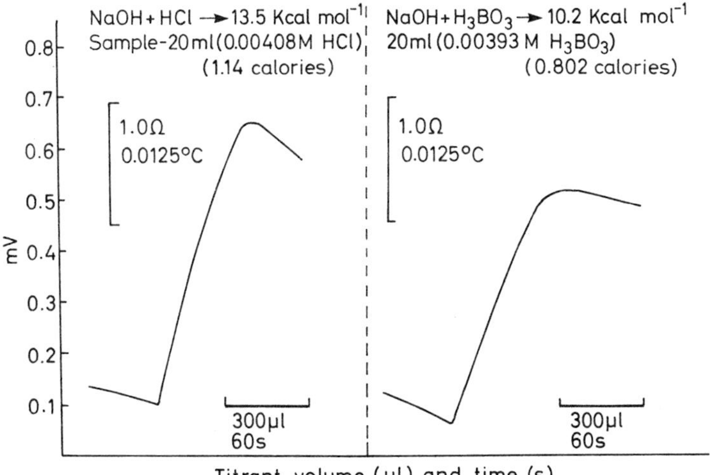

Figure 8 Thermometric titration curves of strong and weak acids. (From Jordan[71])

This results from the fact that while the acid strengths are vastly different, the heats of neutralization differ by only 30 per cent (-13.4 kcal mol^{-1} and -10.6 kcal mol^{-1}). Several thermometric procedures for borate have been published[73–75]. At the 0.3 m eq. level a standard deviation of 1 per cent is attainable. Mixtures of boric acid and H_2SO_4 or boric acid and HCl can be analysed, the stronger acid being titrated first[73, 74].

Miscellaneous methods

Borate is included in a number of anions that can be determined by gas-chromatography as the trimethylsilyl derivatives[76]. A mass-spectrometric stable isotope dilution method has been used for the determination of borate in mineral waters[77]. Highly enriched ^{10}B in the form of H_3BO_3 is added to the sample. After ion-exchange separation of borate, it is converted to $NaBF_4$ and analysed isotopically in a Nier-type spectrometer.

References

1. NEMODRUK, A.A. and KARALOVA, Z.K., *Analytical Chemistry of Boron*, Trans. by R. Kondor, Distributed by Oldbourne Press, London (1966)
2. HUDSWELL, F., in *Comprehensive Analytical Chemistry* (Ed. C.L. and D.W. Wilson), Vol. 1C, Elsevier, Amsterdam, 89 (1962)
3. BRAMAN, R.S., in *An Encyclopedia of Industrial Chemical Analysis* (Ed. F.D. Snell and C.L. Hilton), Vol. 7, Interscience, New York and London, 312 (1968)
4. DIXON, J.P., *Modern Methods in Organic Microanalysis*, Chapter 10, Van Nostrand, London (1968)
5. SPICER, G.S. and STRICKLAND, J.D.H., *Analytica chim. Acta*, **18**, 523 (1958)
6. FELDMAN, C., *Analyt. Chem.*, **33**, 1916 (1961)
7. LUKE, C.L., *Analyt. Chem.*, **30**, 1405 (1958)
8. LUKE, C.L. and FLASCHEN, S.S., *Analyt. Chem.*, **30**, 1406 (1958)
9. MARTIN, J. R. and HAYES, J. R., *Analyt. Chem.*, **24**, 182 (1952)
10. *British Standards* 1121: Part 49 (1966) London
11. SUZUKI, T., *J. chem. Soc. Japan, pure Chem. Sect.*, **82**, 696 (1961); *Analyt. Abstr.*, **9**, 4103 (1962)
12. CARLSON, R.M. and PAUL, J.L., *Analyt. Chem.*, **40**, 1292 (1968)
13. MELTON, J.R., HOOVER, W.L. and HOWARD, P.A., *J. Ass. off. analyt. Chem.*, **52**, 950 (1969)
14. EGNEUS, B. and UPPSTROM, L., *Analytica chim. Acta*, **66**, 211 (1973)
15. CANIC, V.D., TURCIC, M.N., BUGARSKI-VOJINOVIC, M.B. and PERISIC, N.U., *Z. analyt. Chem.*, **229**, 93 (1967); *Analyt. Abstr.*, **15**, 5211 (1968)
16. KAWANABE, K., TAKITANI, S., MIYAZAKI, J. and TAMURA, Z., *Japan Analyst*, **13**, 976 (1964); *Analyt. Abstr.*, **13**, 5385 (1966)
17. AKIMOV, V.K., BUSEV, A.I. and ANDZHAPARIDZE, D.I., *Zh. analit. Khim.*, **26**, 2434 (1971); *Analyt. Abstr.*, **24**, 3373 (1973)
18. CHADWICK, T.C., *Analyt. Chem.*, **45**, 985 (1973)
19. GOOCH, F.A. and JONES, L.C., *Am. J. Sci.*, **7**, 34 (1899)
20. JONES, L.C., *Am. J. Sci.*, **7**, 147 (1899)
21. BELCHER, R., TULLY, G.W. and SVEHLA, G., *Analytica chim. Acta*, **50**, 261 (1970)
22. Ref. 4, 175
23. WILSON, H.N. and PELLEGRINI, G.U.M., *Analyst*, **86**, 517 (1961)
24. *Official, Standardised and Recommended Methods of Analysis*, 2nd edn, Compiled and Edited by N.W. Hanson, The Society for Analytical Chemistry, London (1973)
25. NAZARENKO, V.A. and ERMAK, L.D., *Zav. Lab.*, **34**, 257 (1968); *Analyt. Abstr.*, **16**, 2908 (1969)
26. American Public Health Association, American Waterworks Association, and Water Pollution Control Federation, *Standard Methods for the Examination of Water and Waste-water*, 13th edn, American Public Health Association, New York (1970)
27. Ref. 24, p. 264
28. *British Standard* 1121: Part 49 (1966) London
29. GOWARD, G.W. and WIEDERKEHR, V.R., *Analyt. Chem.*, **35**, 1542 (1963)
30. BASSON, W.D., BOHMER, R.G. and STANTON, D.A., *Analyst*, **94**, 1135 (1969)
31. OSTLING, G., *Analyst*, **78**, 507 (1975)
32. LANGMYHR, F.J. and SKAAR, O.B., *Analytica chim. Acta*, **25**, 262 (1961)
33. GUPTA, H.K.L. and BOLTZ, D.F., *Analyt. Lett.*, **4**, 161 (1971)
34. GUPTA, H.K.L. and BOLTZ, D.F., *Mikrochim. Acta*, 577 (1971)
35. LIONNEL, L.J., *Analyst*, **95**, 194 (1970)

36. GUPTA, H.K.L. and BOLTZ, D.F., *Mikrochim. Acta*, 415 (1974)
37. SHELTON, N.F.C. and REED, R.A., *Analyst*, **101**, 396 (1976)
38. UPPSTRÖM, L.R., *Analytica chim. Acta*, **43**, 475 (1968)
39. DYRSSEN, D.W., NOVIKOV, U.P. and UPPSTRÖM, L.R., *Analytica chim. Acta*, **60**, 139 (1972)
40. SPICER, G.S. and STRICKLAND, J.D.H., *Analytica chim. Acta*, **18**, 523 (1958)
41. HAYES, M.R. and METCALF, J., *Analyst*, **87**, 956 (1962)
42. CRAWLEY, R.H.A., *Analyst*, **89**, 749 (1964)
43. HULTHE, P., UPPSTRÖM, L. and OSTLING, G., *Analytica chim. Acta*, **51**, 31 (1970)
44. OSTLING, G., *Analytica chim. Acta*, **78**, 507 (1975)
45. *Official Methods of Analysis of the Association of Official Analytical Chemists* (Ed. W. Horowitz), 11th edn, AOAC Washington, D.C. (1970)
46. MAIR, J.N. and DAY, H.G., *Analyt. Chem.*, **44**, 2015 (1972)
47. DUCRET, L., *Analytica chim. Acta*, **17**, 213 (1957)
48. BELCHER, R. and WILSON, C.L., *New Methods of Analytical Chemistry*, 2nd edn, Chapman and Hall, London, 222 (1964)
49. SKAAR, O.B., *Analytica chim. Acta*, **28**, 200 (1963)
50. BHARGAVA, O.P. and HINES, W.G., *Talanta*, **17**, 61 (1970)
51. CAPELLE, R., *Analytica chim. Acta*, **24**, 555 (1961)
52. SHANINA, T.M., GEL'MAN, N.E. and MIKHAILOVSKAYA, V.S., *Zh. analit. Khim.*, **22**, 782 (1967); *Analyt. Abstr.*, **16**, 204 (1969)
53. PORTER, G. and SHUBERT, R.C., in *Colorimetric Determination of Nonmetals* (Ed. D.F. Boltz), Interscience, New York and London, 339 (1958)
54. BASSON, W.D., BOHMER, R.G. and STANTON, D.A., *Analyst*, **94**, 1135 (1969)
55. BASSON, W.D., PILLE, P.P. and DU PREEZ, A.L., *Analyst*, **99**, 168 (1974)
56. JOHN, M.K., CHUAH, H.H. and NEUFELD, J.H., *Analyt. Lett.*, **8**, 559 (1975)
57. BOLTZ, D.F., *Critical Reviews in Analytical Chemistry*, 147 (1973)
58. MARCANTONATOS, M., GAMBA, G. and MONNIER, D., *Helv. chim. Acta*, **52**, 538 (1969)
59. MARCANTONATOS, M., GAMBA, G. and MONNIER, D., *Analytica chim. Acta*, **67**, 220 (1973)
60. LIEBICH, B., MONNIER, D. and MARCANTONATOS, M., *Analytica chim. Acta*, **52**, 305 (1970)
61. MAVRODINEANU, R. and BOITEUX, H., *Flame Spectroscopy*, Wiley, New York (1965)
62. HARRIS, R., *Atom. Abs. Newsl.*, **8**, 42 (1969)
63. MELTON, J.R., HOOVER, J.L., HOWARD, P.A. and AYRES, J.L., *J. Ass. off. analyt. Chem.*, **53**, 682 (1972)
64. Ref. 24, p. 597
65. ELTON-BOTT, R.R., *Analytica chim. Acta*, **86**, 281 (1976)
66. AGAZZI, E.J., *Analyt. Chem.*, **39**, 233 (1967)
67. MAECK, W.J., KUSSY, M.E., GINTHER, B.E., WHEELER, G.V. and REIN, J.E., *Analyt. Chem.*, **35**, 62 (1963)
68. PIERCE, F.D. and BROWN, H.R., *Analyt. Chem.*, **48**, 670 (1976)
69. DAUGHTREY, E.H. and HARRISON, W.W., *Analytica chim. Acta*, **67**, 253 (1973)
70. MOHAY, J. and MOHAY-FARKAS, J., *Acta. pharm. Hung.*, **37**, 71 (1967); *Analyt. Abstr.*, **15**, 3567 (1968)
71. MARINENKO, G. and CHAMPION, C.E., *J. Res. natn Bur. Stand. A*, **75**, 421 (1971)
72. JORDAN, J., *J. chem. Edn*, **40**, A5 (1963)
73. MILLER, F.J. and THOMASON, P.F., *Talanta*, **2**, 109 (1959)
74. LINDE, H.W., ROGERS, L.B. and HUME, D.N., *Analyt. Chem.*, **25**, 404 (1953)
75. PECHAR, F., *Chemiké Listy*, **59**, 1073 (1965); *Analyt. Abstr.*, **13**, 6768 (1966)
76. BUTTS, W.C. and RAINEY, W.T., *Analyt. Chem.*, **43**, 538 (1971)
77. GORENC, B., MARSEL, J. and TRAMSEK, G., *Mikrochim. Acta*, 24 (1970)

Carbonate and Bicarbonate

The need to determine carbonate arises in a wide range of materials ranging from soils and minerals to blood and dental enamel. In the last mentioned material samples may be as low as 20 μg necessitating the use of sub-micro methods. In addition to the standard titrimetric and gravimetric procedures, several other techniques are now available including spectroscopic, thermometric, conductimetric and more recently gas chromatographic.

Some of the simpler procedures, for example gasometric and manometric, are not capable of high accuracy. However, they often meet the need for rapid estimation of carbonate without using elaborate equipment. Several methods depend on measurement of evolved CO_2. Here developments in determination of carbon in steel and organic compounds has provided an extensive range of methods capable of adaption to more general use.

Non-gravimetric methods for determination of CO_2 and CO have been reviewed by Davies[1].

Sodium carbonate is generally used as reference standard. In drying this compound care is required. Loss of CO_2 is reported[2] at 400 °C. This appears to be mainly due to hydrolysis, though some reaction with quartz and borosilicate surfaces is also indicated. The compound has been investigated as a reference standard in acid–base titrimetry. A report on this which includes experimental details of its preparation in pure form, has been published by the Analytical Methods Committee of the Society for Analytical Chemistry[3].

Determination

Gravimetric methods

1. Based on loss in weight of liberated CO_2

Although the Schroedter alkalimeter method is old there is justification for including it on the grounds of its simplicity. The apparatus itself is shown in *Figure 9*. An outline procedure is given below. Pauschmann[4] has emphasized the need to flush out residual CO_2 with dry air, quoting an error of up to 30 per cent on 0.1 g of $CaCO_3$ when this step is omitted. A form of the method capable of wide application is described by Pieters[5].

Determination of carbonate using the Schroedter alkalimeter

Procedure

(a) Weigh the apparatus empty and again after introducing about 1 g of the sample into the lower chamber, and dilute HCl and concentrated H_2SO_4 into A and B respectively.

(b) Open stopper below A to allow the HCl to enter the lower chamber, then close. The CO_2 passes through the H_2SO_4 which retains any moisture, and out through the tap on B.

(c) When the effervescence has ceased, heat gently for 2–3 min.

(d) Gently flush with dry air to remove residual CO_2. This is introduced through the tube on top of A, with the taps on A and B open.

(e) Weigh the apparatus and calculate the carbonate content from the loss of CO_2.

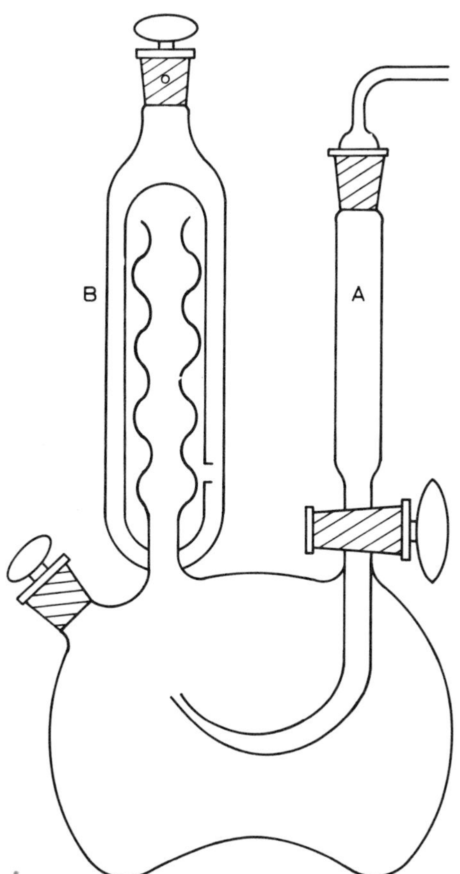

Figure 9 Schroedter alkalimeter

2. *Based on absorption and weighing of liberated CO_2*

This is a more accurate method as it permits the incorporation of a purification train before weighing the CO_2. A recent form of the method has been described by Meyrowitz[6] who applied it to micro-analysis of minerals. The products of decomposition with 1:1 HCl are passed through various traps to remove water and HCl vapours, H_2S, hydrocarbons and chlorine. The CO_2 is absorbed in Ascarite (NaOH on asbestos, soda-asbestos) for weighing. Other versions of the method are described in standard texts[7, 8]. It has recently featured in the determination of cyanide, cyanate and carbonate when present together[9]. This includes conversion of carbonate and cyanate to CO_2 after masking cyanide with $HgCl_2$. The CO_2 is subsequently determined gravimetrically after absorption in soda-asbestos.

Gasometric and manometric methods

In gasometric methods the volume of liberated CO_2 after acid treatment is measured, corrected to standard temperature and pressure, and the carbonate content of the sample calculated from this. The equipment is often simple. Leo[10] uses an all-plastic apparatus for determination of soil carbonates. The results compare well with those obtained in titrimetric procedures. In another method the volume of CO_2 is evaluated from the distance moved by a plug of mercury along a capillary tube[11]. On amounts of $BaCO_3$ in the range 2.2–4.0 mg the error is ± 5 per cent.

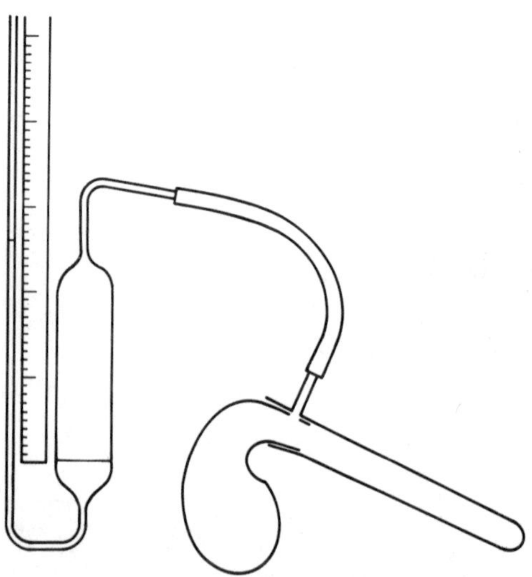

Figure 10 Simple apparatus for manometric determination of carbonate. (After Pittwell[14])

Stephenson and Hartley[12] have reported a gasometric method for bicarbonate in self-raising flour containing chalk. Here disodium diphosphate ($Na_2H_2P_2O_7$) is used instead of dilute H_2SO_4 to liberate CO_2 which is measured in a Chittick apparatus. The chalk remains undecomposed. An elegant form of the method for analysis of dental enamels has been described by Weatherell and Robinson[13]. Samples of 20–50 μg are used, the liberated CO_2 forming a single bubble. An image of this is projected on to a screen for measurement. The error is reported at ±7 per cent for 0.5–3 μg of carbonate.

Manometric procedures can be carried out using simple apparatus. Pittwell[14] uses a 25-mℓ pipette and Warburg tube as shown in *Figure 10.* Modifications can be introduced if necessary to obtain more accurate results. Jordanov[15] employs a copper sulphate solution supported on pumice to absorb any H_2S evolved with the CO_2.

Some indication of the nature of the carbonate-containing minerals can be obtained from the time taken to decompose. This has been investigated by Mueller and Gastner[16] using a 'Karbonat-Bombe' calibrated directly in percentage carbonate. The increase in gas pressure in 10–15 s is a measure of the calcite and aragonite content. After 15 min when all the carbonate including dolomite has reacted, the pressure is again read. The dolomite content is given approximately from the difference.

Titrimetric methods

1. Acid–base titration for aqueous solutions of carbonates

For soluble carbonates acidimetric titration is a standard procedure. The principles involved are discussed in standard texts[17, 18]. The method is essentially the one used in standardizing an acid using Na_2CO_3 as reference standard.

Several potential sources of error exist. The concentration of CO_2 is not reproducible, the solution becoming supersaturated as the titration proceeds. Various amounts are lost depending on the degree of shaking. The colour of methyl orange in a saturated solution of CO_2 is sensitive to the concentration of NaCl. This causes the colour to move to the acid side with increasing salt concentration. This difficulty can be overcome by employing a back-titration procedure.

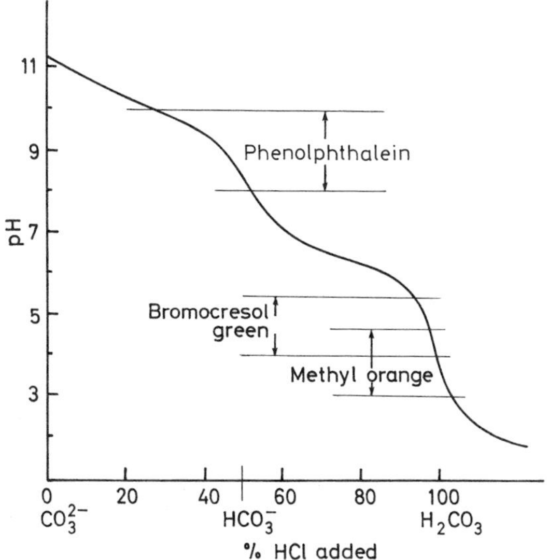

Figure 11 Titration of 0.05M Na_2CO_3 with 0.1M HCl

The form of the titration curve is shown in *Figure 11*. The titration is generally made with 0.1M HCl. It may be carried out in several ways. Standard acid can be added to give a distinct acid colour to methyl orange added as indicator (pH ~ 3). The indicator is now destroyed by adding a drop of bromide water and a back-titration made with 0.01M NaOH to a bromothymol blue or methyl red end-point.

Alternatively, a direct titration can be carried out using phenolphthalein and bromocresol green as recommended by Kolthoff *et al.*[19] This is given below. If carbonate is to be determined in the presence of bicarbonate, a titration is possible to the bicarbonate end-point (pH 8.3–8.4), though the slope of the curve is shallow at this point. Where carbonate and bicarbonate are to be determined the two-indicator method referred to above can be used. Zangen[20] has pointed out that due to variation in the pH of the equivalence point in titrating carbonate–bicarbonate mixtures, errors of 60 per cent are possible for the minor component if the carbonate ratio differs greatly from one. This study presents curves giving end-point pH as a function of carbonate: bicarbonate ratio. These permit the determination to be made to within 2 per cent.

In the determination of bicarbonate, titration to a methyl orange end-point is common with CO_2 being removed by boiling just before the end-point. Some of the published procedures omit the boiling stage[21,22]. The pH at the equivalence point varies with the concentration of H_2CO_3. This can lead to serious errors, particularly in dilute solutions. In the titration of bicarbonate, anions of other weak acids are titrated if a simple acidimetric titration to a pH 4.4 end-point is made. Rosopulo and Quentin[23] overcome this by making a gravimetric determination of total CO_2, namely free dissolved CO_2 and the gas liberated from bicarbonate. This is followed by a titration of free dissolved CO_2 only, and the bicarbonate calculated by difference.

Carbonate in the presence of hydroxyl can be determined by titration with standard HCl. Phenolphthalein is used for the first end-point, the titre being equivalent to $OH^- + \frac{1}{2}CO_3^{2-}$. Methyl orange is now added and the titration continued to a second end-point. This is equivalent to $\frac{1}{2}CO_3^{2-}$. From the two titres each constituent can be evaluated.

British Standards[24] have published a recommended method for titrimetric determination of bicarbonate in photographic grade K_2CO_3.

Titrimetric determination of carbonate using phenolphthalein and bromocresol green[19]

Procedure

Add 1 drop of phenolphthalein to the carbonate solution and titrate with 0.1M HCl until colourless. Add a few drops of bromocresol green indicator and continue the titration until it turns greenish-blue. Boil for 1–2 min to remove CO_2. The indicator now changes through blue to violet (blue of bromocresol green and red of phenolphthalein). Cool. Continue the titration to a green colour.

---

2. *Titration of CO_2 liberated from carbonate*

Carbon dioxide liberated by treating carbonate with acid can be absorbed in barium hydroxide solution (free of carbonate) and titrated with standard acid. The method was used by Schollenberger[25,26] for determination of carbonate in soils. Although the method gives precise results the time required for analysis of a resistant sample such as limestone is excessive. Watkinson[27] has recommended replacing the acid with disodium EDTA in such cases. This produces an increased reaction rate. The apparatus is shown in *Figure 12*. Details of the method are given below.

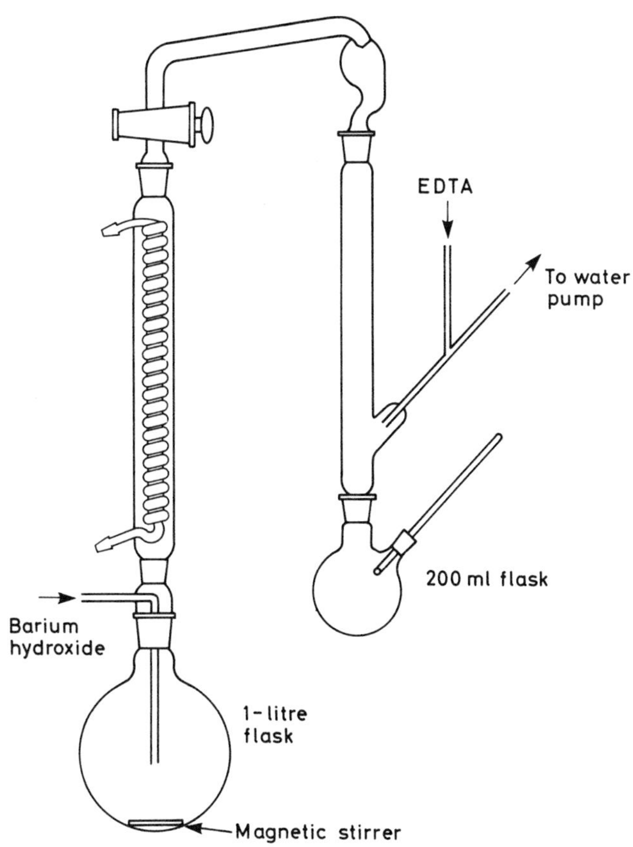

Figure 12 *Vacuum distillation apparatus for determination of carbonate in soils.* (From Watkinson[27])

In recent years several investigators have modified and extended the titrimetric procedure introduced by Blom and Edelhausen[28], in which CO_2 is absorbed in pyridine and titrated with a solution of sodium methoxide dissolved in a methanol–pyridine mixture. Such procedures have relevance in organic microdetermination of carbon and determination of carbon in steel. Pringle[29] has developed a rapid method for carbonate CO_2 in coal. The CO_2 is absorbed in benzylamine solution and the benzylamine salt titrated with potassium methoxide in methanol–benzene using thymol blue as indicator. A complete analysis excluding the weighing, requires 10 min.

Another procedure falling into this category is the Conway microdiffusion technique. This is applicable to carbonate in blood. Liberated CO_2 reacts with $Ba(OH)_2$ precipitating an equivalent amount of carbonate which is titrated acidimetrically. A modified Conway unit has been described by Holm-Jensen[30] in which 0.1 mℓ samples containing 25 mmoles of CO_2 are titrated with an accuracy of $\pm$0.8 per cent.

EDTA procedures have found application in measuring CO_2 liberated from carbonates. One such case is determination of alkali carbonate in the presence of alkali hydroxide (in ratios 10:1 to 3:10 respectively). The total alkali is titrated in one aliquot. To a second aliquot a known excess of $Sr(NO_3)_2$ is added. After removal of the $SrCO_3$ precipitate, filtrate strontium is titrated with EDTA using methyl thymol blue as indicator. From the two titres, carbonate and hydroxide may be evaluated[31].

The ultra-violet absorption of carbonate ion at 235 nm can be utilized. Underwood and Howe[32] employ this in a photometric titration of carbonate itself, and in the presence of bicarbonate and hydroxide. A higher precision is claimed than for potentiometric or visual titrations. Photometric titration has featured in a recent method for automatic determination of total carbonate and total alkalinity of seawater[33]. In this case bromothymol blue is used as indicator. The method is complex involving control of the phototitrator by a minicomputer processing system.

Vacuum-distillation method for determination of carbonate in soils[27]

Apparatus

This is shown in *Figure 12*. The $Ba(OH)_2$ is stirred continuously by a magnetic stirrer during absorption of CO_2. The condenser maintains a vacuum in the absorption flask by condensing the steam, passing in at 90–95 °C, from the first section of the apparatus. The splash-head and the tubing leading to it from the reaction flask prevent the soil suspension from 'bumping' over into the absorption flask. The tube from the EDTA solution and the water pump is sealed into a bulb on the side of the tube connecting the reaction flask and the splash head, in order to avoid direct contamination from 'bumping' splashes.

Reagents

EDTA: 0.5% w/v.
$Ba(OH)_2$: 0.02M.
HCl: 0.02M.
Thymolphthalein indicator solution: 0.1% in 96% ethanol.

Procedure

Place the finely ground soil sample containing sufficient limestone to neutralize about half the $Ba(OH)_2$ into the 200-mℓ flask. Evacuate the apparatus, and run in 25 mℓ of 0.02M $Ba(OH)_2$ and 150 mℓ of 0.5%

EDTA solution. Partly close the tap and heat the soil suspension rapidly by means of a gas burner until its temperature reaches 90 °C. Maintain the temperature at 90–95 °C, and adjust the tap so that the distillation rate does not cause the temperature in the absorption section to exceed about 40 °C. After 5 min (or less, according to the resistance of the limestone), remove the flame, and carefully open the tap fully. After a further 5 min to complete the absorption of CO_2, restore the atmospheric pressure by introducing carbon dioxide-free air. With thymophthalein as indicator, titrate the excess of $Ba(OH)_2$ against 0.02M HCl to a faint blue end-point.

Spectroscopic methods

A spectrophotometric method for bicarbonate in plasma has been based on the increase in pH of a 12.5 mM aqueous ethanolic KH_2PO_4 solution, on addition of a deproteinized ethanolic solution of plasma or serum. The increase in pH is measured by the extinction of methyl red at 520 nm. Good agreement with alternative methods is reported[34].

Infra-red methods have been used both on solid samples and for the determination of liberated CO_2. The former method enables carbonate in mineral materials to be determined[35] using the band at 1429 cm^{-1}. Analysis of evolved CO_2 at 3676 cm^{-1} and 2315 cm^{-1} using an infra-red gas cell (50–760 torr pressure) is claimed to be rapid and specific [36]. The method is sensitive to 100 ppm or less of K_2CO_3 and gives a reproducibility of ± 0.04 per cent for a 0.4% solution of K_2CO_3. A recent investigation has employed 50 μℓ samples of blood serum with direct reading by means of a digital voltmeter[37].

Electroanalytical methods

The acidimetric titration of carbonate with standard acid can be carried out potentiometrically. More recent work has been centred on ion-selective electrodes.

A CO_2 electrode has been used for blood gas analysis[38] where concentrations are above 20 $\mu g\, m\ell^{-1}$. This electrode contains a PTFE membrane which separates the sample from a film of $NaHCO_3$ solution trapped between the electrode itself and a sensitive glass electrode surface. Carbon dioxide diffuses across the membrane.

Midgley[39] has attempted to use this type of electrode (a Radiometer E 5036) to determine CO_2 in boiler feedwater, but concluded that direct application was not possible. Fogg, Pathan and Burns[40] have shown that a liquid-state perchlorate ion-selective electrode based on Brilliant Green perchlorate, responds to bicarbonate over the range 10^{-1}–10^{-3}M.

Recent work by Herman and Rechnitz[41,42] has produced a carbonate electrode which appears to have marked advantages. It is a liquid-membrane type, the active liquid phase consisting of a quaternary ammonium salt dissolved in an organic solvent. Its response to carbonate is linear over the range

10^{-7}–10^{-2}M. The pH range is 5.5–8.5. It shows good selectivity over carbonate, chloride, sulphate and phosphate. Furthermore, in the physiologically important pH region hydroxide ions do not interfere. Detailed information on the composition and properties of the active membrane phase are given in the original papers.

A successful gas-sensing electrode for CO_2 has been described by Ross, Riesman and Kruger[43].

Gas chromatography

A feature of recent advances in inorganic analysis has been the application of gas chromatographic methods. The subject has been reviewed by Rodriguez-Vazquez[44], and includes a section on anions. Carbonate has featured in several investigations. Butts and Rainey[45] report the formation of trimethylsilyl derivatives by reacting $(NH_4)_2CO_3$ with bistrimethylsilylfluoroacetamide in dimethylformamide as solvent. Carbonate may be separated and determined when present with borate, oxalate, phosphite, sulphate, arsenite, phosphate, vanadate, arsenate, and sulphamate. The separation is shown in *Figure 66* in the sulphate section. Bicarbonate gives the same peak as carbonate. A feature of the method is that the silyl derivatives are not formed from the corresponding sodium or potassium salts of the anions concerned. This is overcome by employing an ion-exchanger to convert to the ammonium form.

In another method, H_2S, SO_2 and CO_2 liberated by acid treatment of the corresponding salts, are separated by gas chromatography and determined using a thermal conductivity detector[46].

Miscellaneous methods

Thermometric titration of carbonate has been described[47]. Differential thermal analysis is claimed to be more accurate than X-ray diffraction for identification and determination of mineral carbonates, giving an error of ±2 per cent for up to 50% carbonate content[48].

A dynamic sorption method developed by Thomas and Hieftze[49] is claimed to be rapid and precise for carbonate in rocks, soils and clays. In the method, helium is used to sweep evolved CO_2 into a thermal conductivity detector. Strict control of conditions are necessary. Results giving accuracy within 0.1 per cent are quoted.

An isotopic-dilution method has been reported for carbonate in the range 10–100 μg[50].

References

1. DAVIES, D.H., *Talanta*, **16**, 1055 (1969)
2. OTTERSON, D.A., *Analyt. Chem.*, **38**, 506 (1966)
3. Analytical Methods Committee of the Society for Analytical Chemistry, *Analyst*, **90**, 251 (1965)

4. PAUSCHMANN, H., *Z. analyt. Chem.*, **207**, 14 (1965); *Analyt. Abstr.*, **13**, 2281 (1966)
5. PIETERS, H. A. J., *Analytica chim. Acta.* **2**, 263 (1948)
6. MEYROWITZ, R., *Prof. Pap. U.S. geol. Surv.*, No. 700-C, c183 (1970); *Analyt. Abstr.*, **22**, 704 (1972)
7. HILLEBRAND, W.F., LUNDELL, G.E.F., BRIGHT, H.A. and HOFFMAN, J.I., *Applied Inorganic Analysis*, Wiley, New York (1953)
8. YOUNG, R.S., *Industrial Inorganic Analysis*, Chapman and Hall, London (1953)
9. HARZDORF, C., *Z. analyt. Chem.*, **237**, 161 (1968); *Analyt. Abstr.*, **17**, 791 (1969)
10. LEO, M.W.M., *J. agric. Fd Chem.*, **11**, 452 (1963)
11. GORBENKO-GERMANOV, D.S. and ZENKOVA, R.A., *Zh. analit. Khim.*, **20**, 749 (1965); *Analyt. Abstr.*, **14**, 637 (1967)
12. STEPHENSON, W.H. and HARTLEY, A.W., *Analyst*, **80**, 461 (1955)
13. WEATHERELL, J.A. and ROBINSON, C., *Analyst*, **93**, 244 (1968)
14. PITTWELL, L.R., *Mikrochim. Acta*, 903 (1968)
15. JORDANOV, N., *Talanta*, **13**, 563 (1966)
16. MUELLER, G and GASTNER, M., *Neues. Jb. Miner. Mh.*, 466 (1971); *Analyt. Abstr.*, **23**, 1983 (1972)
17. LAITINEN, H.A., *Chemical Analysis*, McGraw-Hill, New York, 86 (1960)
18. FISCHER, R. B. and PETERS, D. G., *Quantitative Chemical Analysis*, W. B. Saunders Co. Philadelphia, 302 (1968)
19. KOLTHOFF, I.M., SANDELL, E.B., MEEHAN, E.J. and BRUCKENSTEIN, S., *Quantitative Chemical Analysis*, 4th edn. The Macmillan Co., Toronto, 778 (1969)
20. ZANGEN, M., *J. appl. Chem.*, **12**, 92 (1962)
21. British Pharmacopoeia, Pharmaceutical Press, London, 898 (1968)
22. The U.S. Pharmacopoeia, 18th Revision, 610 (1970)
23. ROSOPULO, A. and QUENTIN, K-E., *Z. analyt. Chem.*, **253**, 27 (1971); *Analyt. Abstr.*, **21**, 4449 (1971)
24. British Standard 3751: (1964); British Standards Institute, London
25. SCHOLLENBERGER, C.J., *Canad. J. Soil Sci.*, **30**, 307 (1930)
26. SCHOLLENBERGER, C.J., *Canad. J. Soil Sci.*, **59**, 57 (1945)
27. WATKINSON, J.H., *Analyst*, **84**, 659 (1959)
28. BLOM, L. and EDELHAUSEN, L., *Analytica chim. Acta*, **13**, 120 (1955)
29. PRINGLE, W.J.S., *Fuel, Lond.*, **42**, 63 (1963)
30. HOLM-JENSEN, I., *Scand. J. Clin. Lab. Invest.*, **12**, 269 (1960); *Analyt. Abstr.*, **8**, 5123 (1961)
31. SZEKERES, L. and BAKACS-POLGAR, E., *Z. analyt. Chem.*, **177**, 89 (1960); *Analyt. Abstr.*, **8**, 1891 (1961)
32. UNDERWOOD, A.L. and HOWE, L.H., *Analyt. Chem.*, **34**, 692 (1962)
33. GRANELI, A. and ANFALT, T., *Analytica chim. Acta*, **91**, 175 (1977)
34. SINNEMA, Y.A., *Pharm. Weekbl.*, **103**, 837 (1968); *Analyt. Abstr.*, **17**, 3614 (1969)
35. SHCHERBOV, D.P. and GULYAEV, A.M., *Trudy Kazakh. Nauch-Issled. Inst. Mineral Syr'ya*, 204 (1962); *Analyt. Abstr.*, **11**, 3584 (1964)
36. POBINGER, H., *Analyt. Chem.*, **34**, 878 (1962)
37. PETERSON, J.I., *Clin. Chem.*, **16**, 144 (1970); *Analyt. Abstr.*, **20**, 1820 (1971)
38. SEVERINGHAUS, J.W., *Ann. N.Y. Acad. Sci.*, **148**, 115 (1968)
39. MIDGLEY, D., *International Symposium on Selective Ion-Sensitive Electrodes*, Cardiff, Wales (1973)
40. FOGG, A.G., PATHAN, S. and BURNS, D.T., *Analytica chim. Acta.*, **73**, 220 (1974)
41. HERMAN, H.B. and RECHNITZ, G.A., *Science*, **184**, 1074 (1974)
42. HERMAN, H.B. and RECHNITZ, G.A., *Analytica chim. Acta*, **76**, 155 (1975)
43. ROSS, J.W., RIESMAN, J.H. and KRUGER, J.A., *Pure appl. Chem.*, **36**, 473 (1973)
44. RODRIGUEZ-VAZQUEZ, J.A., *Analytica chim. Acta*, **73**, 1 (1974)
45. BUTTS, W.C. and RAINEY, W.T., *Analyt. Chem.*, **43**, 538 (1971)
46. BIRK, J.R., LARSEN, C.M. and WILBOURN, R.G., *Analyt. Chem.*, **42**,273 (1970)
47. PRIESTLEY, P.T., *Analyst*, **88**, 194 (1963)
48. GITA, G. and GITA, E., *Rev. Chim. Bucharest*, **15**, 214 (1964); *Analyt. Abstr.*, **12**, 3914 (1965)
49. THOMAS, J. and HIEFTZE, G.M., *Analyt. Chem.*, **38**, 500 (1966)
50. JOHANNESSON, J. K., *Analyst*, **92**, 766 (1967)

Chromate and Dichromate

Chromium finds extensive use in electroplating, in the manufacture of alloys particularly stainless steels, and in the manufacture of corrosion inhibitors. It is through its use as a corrosion inhibitor that chromium(VI) enters the environment where its highly toxic effects are of some concern. From an analytical standpoint chromium(VI) is important as the form to which chromium is generally converted for determination.

Alkali metal chromates and dichromates are quite soluble, and this is so for several other metals. Most heavy metal chromates tend to be insoluble. This has been utilized in gravimetric procedures as well as in separating chromium.

In acid medium dichromate is a strong oxidant.

$$Cr_2O_7^{2-} + 14H^+ + 6e \rightleftharpoons 2Cr^{3+} + 7H_2O \qquad E^0 = +1.33\ V$$

The $Cr_2O_7^{2-}/Cr^{3+}$ couple does not behave reversibly. In alkaline medium the oxidizing character of Cr(VI) is greatly reduced.

$$CrO_4^{2-} + 4H_2O + 3e \rightleftharpoons Cr(OH)_{3(hyd)} + 5OH^- \qquad E^0 = -1.13\ V$$

In acid solution the main species are $Cr_2O_7^{2-}$ and $HCrO_4^-$. Above pH 8 CrO_4^{2-} predominates. The fundamental chemistry of chromium related to its analysis is discussed in the monograph by Lingane[1]. Determination of chromium(VI), though relatively straightforward in inorganic materials is notoriously difficult in organic matter. The analytical chemistry of chromium has been reviewed by Chalmers[2] and Olsen and Foreback[3].

Potassium dichromate is almost exclusively used as reference standard for chromium(VI). If necessary, it can be standardized to a very high degree of accuracy by constant current coulometry. This is discussed later in the section.

Separations

1. By precipitation

Chromate is quantitatively precipitated by Ba^{2+}, Ag^+, Hg^+ and Pb^{2+}. Anions giving insoluble compounds with these would interfere, as would cations giving insoluble chromates.

Another method of separation is to remove various interfering cations by precipitation in alkaline solution, leaving chromate in solution. This allows separation of iron, nickel and aluminium.

2. Solvent extraction

Dichromate is extracted into isobutyl methyl ketone from acid medium[4]. This separation has been used as part of a procedure for determination of chromium in biological materials. The organic extract is analysed using atomic absorption spectroscopy[5].

Tri-*n*-butyl phosphate has been used by Tuck[6]. Extraction is made into benzene and followed by spectrophotometric evaluation. No interference is given by Ni, Th(IV), UO_2(II), Cu(II), Co(II), Fe(III) or V(V).

Long-chain amines have been studied by several workers. Schevchuk and Simonova[7] reported that chromium(VI) is almost completely extracted from 0.08–1.5M H_2SO_4 by tridecylamine, didecylamine, dihexylamine and tribenzylamine in organic solvents. The same workers report complete extraction from 0.1M tribenzylamine in chloroform, dichloroethane, cyclohexanol or tributylphosphate. Tribenzylamine in dichloroethane is used by Tserkovnitskaya, Il'inskaya and Belyaev[8] to extract chromium(VI) from a perchloric acid medium. The procedure, which is applied to analysis of silicates, enables chromium(VI) to be separated from calcium and chromium(III). Adam and Pribil[9] find that chromate is very selectively extracted from 0.1–0.2M H_2SO_4 using a chloroform solution of trioctylamine or trioctylmethylammonium chloride. Here separation is effected from Fe, Ni, Co, Cu, Al, Zn, etc. Coextraction of vanadium(V) and uranium(VI) is prevented by addition of NaCl. Extraction of chromium(VI) into mesityl oxide from an HCl–KCl solution, followed by back-extraction into aqueous ammonia is reported by Shinde and Khopkar[10]. Platinum(VI), Au(III), Fe(III), SCN^-, $S_2O_3^{2-}$, CN^-, F^- and tartaric acid interfere.

Many other extraction systems have been reported[11].

3. *Ion-exchange*

Cation exchange has been used to separate chromium(VI) from Mg, Ni and Al. A critical feature of the procedure is the flow rate through the column. If too slow, chromium(VI) is reduced to chromium(III) and retained; if above 8 mℓ min^{-1}, losses are less than 1 per cent[12].

Several anion-exchange separations have been reported. Mulokozi[13] showed that whereas chromium(VI) cannot be quantitatively separated from other metals on a strongly basic exchange resin in H_2SO_4, it is retained when an alkaline solution is used. This permits the separation of chromium from such elements as aluminium which form amphoteric oxides. These dissolve and are eluted. The chromium(VI) is subsequently eluted with 8–10% Na_2CO_3 solution or with an aqueous mixture of $NaHCO_3$ and Na_2CO_3.

Chromate and sulphate can be separated on a strongly basic anion exchanger[14]. Both ions are adsorbed. Sulphate is eluted with NaCl and chromate with NaOH.

4. *Paper and thin-layer chromatography*

Galateanu[15] has reported the separation of chromium(VI) and chromium(III) by thin layer chromatography on aluminium oxide using a saturated aqueous solution of sodium sulphate as developer. Some tailing was experienced. Lederer and Polcaro[16], also using TLC on Al_2O_3 were able to separate IO_4^-, IO_3^-, BrO_3^- and CrO_4^- using various solvents. Other TLC methods in which CrO_4^{2-} is separated from large numbers of anions have been reported by Kawanabe *et al.*[17] and Canic *et al*[18].

5. High voltage paper electrophoresis
Chromium(III) and CrO_4^{2-} can be separated in 5–10 min by high voltage paper electrophoresis using 0.1M KCl as electrolyte and an applied voltage of 1–1.5 kV[19].

6. Coprecipitation
Coprecipitation has been used to separate 0.05–0.5 mg of chromium(III) from 0.05–100 mg of chromium(VI). The procedure[20] employs $Ti(OH)_4$ at pH 8.0–9.5.

Determination

Gravimetric methods

As indicated in the discussion on separations chromium(VI) is precipitated as insoluble chromates of several metals including Ag, Ba, Hg(I), and Pb. Organic precipitants can also be used.

With mercury(I), mercurous chromate can be weighed as such or after ignition to Cr_2O_3. Silver chromate can be precipitated from homogeneous solution using urea[21]. More recent work has shown that volatilization of ammonia from the silver–amine complex is effective[22]. No interference is given by Mg(II), Mn(II), Fe(III), Cu(II), Ti(IV), Zr(IV), Ni(II) or Co(II). Large amounts of sulphate can be tolerated.

In general, determination of CrO_4^{2-} gravimetrically as insoluble metal chromates suffers from the disadvantage that cations giving insoluble chromates and anions giving insoluble compounds with the precipitants, must be absent.

Precipitation using barium chloride or acetate appears to be widely used. In this case sulphate must be absent or previously separated. Gravimetric methods are discussed at some length by Chalmers[2] in the review cited earlier.

Titrimetric methods

An important aspect of the titrimetric determination of chromium(VI) is the standardization of potassium dichromate solutions for use in analysis. This compound is obtainable in a state of high purity. After drying at 150–180 °C it can be used as a secondary standard by weighing out the appropriate amount and making up to volume. It does not, however, conform to the requirements of a good primary standard, and for high-precision work dichromate solutions must be standardized. Constant current coulometry is probably the best way of doing this. If an arbitrary dichromate solution is to be standardized for general analytical purposes, methods (1) or (2) given below would be suitable.

1. Redox using iron(II)
This method consists of adding excess of a standard iron(II) solution to an acidified dichromate solution and then back-titrating with standard dichromate using a suitable indicator such as sodium diphenylamine sulphonate

or ferroin. Potassium permanganate can also be used for the back-titration.

$$Cr_2O_7^{2-} + 6Fe^{2+} + 14H^+ \rightarrow 6Fe^{3+} + 2Cr^{3+} + 7H_2O$$

Hydrochloric or sulphuric acids are suitable. Phosphoric acid is generally added to lower the potential of the iron(II)–iron(III) system by forming the stable iron(III)–phosphate complex.

The titration is widely used for determination of chromium in certain alloys. After dissolution, chromium is oxidized to chromium(VI) and the above method applied. The reaction exhibits several peculiar features. First there is the anomalous behaviour of certain redox indicators. This has been satisfactorily explained in recent years[22–24]. More important is the course of the reaction itself. Here the indication is that the mechanism is complex. For example the end-point is different according to whether the dichromate is added to iron(II) or whether the reverse is carried out. The potential change near the end-point is also different in each case. Despite many investigations these irregularities remain largely unexplained. The matter is reviewed by Laitinen[25] and Westheimer[26]. An indication of the more recent situation is given by Belcher, Chakrabarti and Stephen[27] and Spiramam[28]. The latter work includes a critical study of ferroin as indicator in the reaction.

Despite the anomalies, the reaction finds extensive use in the determination of chromium(VI).

Titrimetric determination of dichromate using standard solutions of Fe(II) and dichromate

Reagents

Ammonium ferrous sulphate, 0.1M:
Containing about 20 mℓ of concentrated H_2SO_4 per litre.
Potassium dichromate: M/60.
Sodium diphenylamine sulphonate: 0.2% aqueous.

Procedure

To the slightly acid dichromate solution in a volume of about 25 mℓ add 0.1M ammonium ferrous sulphate solution until the colour turns green, and then 5 mℓ excess, noting the exact amount added. Add sufficient 1:1 H_2SO_4 to make the solution about 2M in H_2SO_4, followed by 4–5 drops of the diphenylamine indicator and 5 mℓ of concentrated phosphoric acid. Titrate with standard M/60 $K_2Cr_2O_7$ until the indicator turns purple.

Notes

1. Standard $KMnO_4$ can be used in place of the dichromate. This form of the method is recommended by British Standards[29] for determination of chromium in steel.
2. An amperometric end-point can be used[30]. This is discussed later.

The method has been adapted by RaO and Muralikrishna[31] to analysis of $MnO_4^-/Cr_2O_7^{2-}$ mixtures. In this the solution is acidified with H_2SO_4 and Mn(II)SO_4 added as catalyst. On titration with standard sodium oxalate or oxalic acid to a colour change from orange-red to yellow, the titre represents MnO_4^- only. The titration is now continued using ammonium ferrous sulphate and standard dichromate as described above. The volume of iron(II) consumed is equivalent to dichromate in the original mixture.

Another approach to the same analysis is given in the sub-section on spectrophotometric methods.

---

2. Iodimetric

Chromium(VI) reacts with excess KI in acidified solution giving iodine which can be titrated with standard thiosulphate.

$$Cr_2O_7^{2-} + 6I^- + 14H^+ \rightarrow 2Cr^{3+} + 3I_2 + 7H_2O$$

As in the previous method, the apparent simplicity conceals a more complex situation. Earlier studies indicated the possibility of air-oxidation of hydriodic acid, this leading to positive errors. Another potential source of error is complex formation between chromium(III) and thiosulphate under certain conditions[32]. This is discussed in the standard monograph by Kolthoff and Belcher[33].

The reaction is heavily dependent on acidity. If an excessive amount of acid is present, iodine is immediately liberated but air-oxidation of iodide is possible. For accurate results, a lower acidity with a 5-min waiting period for complete liberation of iodine is recommended.

The iodimetric procedure allows CrO_4^{2-} (or MnO_4^-) to be determined[36] in the presence of iron(III). The latter is masked using $(NaPO_3)_6$. For CrO_4^{2-} in amounts equivalent to 17–88 mg Cr the error is reported as ±0.3%.

Iodimetric titration of dichromate

Procedure

Dilute the dichromate solution, which should be contained in a glass-stoppered iodine flask, to about 100 mℓ and add about 2 g of KI. Add sufficient 2M HCl, with swirling, to make the solution about 0.4M in acid. Stopper the flask and set aside in a dark place for 5 min. Dilute further by adding 50 mℓ of water, then titrate the liberated iodine with standard thiosulphate using starch as indicator.

Notes

1. The above procedure applies to dichromate solutions of strength M/60 or stronger. For solutions ten times more dilute the same procedure can be used with the HCl adjusted to about 0.6M (instead of 0.4M).
2. Iron(III), copper(II), arsenic(V), molybdenum(VI) and vanadium(V) interfere by liberating iodine. Pribil and Sykora[34] overcome interference by iron(III) and copper(II) by including EDTA at pH 1–2 which masks both.

---

3. Compleximetric

Earlier procedures involving EDTA consisted of precipitating barium chromate by adding excess standard Ba^{2+} and evaluating the excess compleximetrically[35, 36].

Other procedures have involved reduction of chromium(VI) to

chromium(III) followed by determination of the latter using EDTA. A major drawback here is the sluggish reaction between chromium(III) and EDTA. Aikens and Reilley[37] found that if the reduction is made using sodium bisulphite at pH 6.6 in the presence of EDTA, the complex is formed immediately, thus avoiding the prolonged boiling usually necessary in reacting chromium(III) with EDTA.

In more recent work, de Sousa[38] has proposed a method based on precipitation of silver chromate. This is produced in neutral or slightly acid medium, filtered, washed, and dissolved in an ammoniacal solution of potassium tetracyanonickelate as recommended by Flaschka and Huditz[39] for silver halides.

$$Ag_2CrO_4 + K_2[Ni(CN)_4] \rightarrow K_2[Ag_2(CN)_4] + Ni^{2+} + CrO_4{}^{2-}$$

The liberated Ni^{2+} ions are titrated with standard EDTA. Errors of less than 1 per cent are reported.

4. *Miscellaneous*

Kreshkov, Kuznetsov and Mezhlumyan[40] have proposed the titration of chromium(VI), molybdenum(VI) and tungsten(VI) with Ba^{2+} in a mixed solvent medium using nitchromazo as indicator. The reaction is reported to be quantitative in 80–90% acetone at a pH of 4.0–5.5 in the original aqueous solution.

Several other redox titrations have been described for dichromate. Erdey and Kasa[41] reacted $Cr_2O_7{}^{2-}$ with hexacyanoferrate(II) and then determined the resulting hexacyanoferrate(III) with standard ascorbic acid. The same procedure is suitable for other oxidants, for example $IO_3{}^-$ and $BrO_3{}^-$.

Spectroscopic methods

1. *Colorimetric and spectrophotometric—visible and UV*

Diphenylcarbazide reacts with chromium(VI) in acidic medium to give an intense red-violet complex cation[42,43]. The optimum wavelength is 540 nm and the molar absorptivity 3.14×10^4. The range for chromium is 0.1–0.005 ppm. If the acidity is below 0.05N, the reaction is slow: when above 0.2N in H_2SO_4 the complex becomes unstable.

Interference by molybdenum(VI) which also gives a violet-red complex, is masked by oxalate. Copper(II) interferes and so does iron(III) to a slight extent. Other factors that might cause erratic results include residual chromic acid on glassware after cleaning and residual oxidants used to oxidize chromium to chromium(VI). In the latter case these destroy the complex and must be removed. Though the colour develops quickly, it fades relatively quickly[44].

The method finds considerable use. In the analysis of iron and steel it is recommended by British Standards Institution[52].

Chromate or dichromate can be determined colorimetrically without addition of reagents. In the case of chromate, the optimum response is at 366 nm in the UV, at which the molar absorptivity is 4416. As an alternative, the measurement can be made at 400 nm in the visible region. In alkaline medium, if the pH is sufficiently high the chromium is entirely in the form of

CrO_4^{2-} and Beer's law holds closely. Where Cr(VI) is accompanied by manganese(VII) each may be determined. Interferences in the alkaline range include uranium(VI), cerium(IV) and other species, giving precipitates under these conditions. Interference by vanadium(V) is slight: no interference is given by molybdenum(VI) or tungsten(VI).

In the acidic region the situation is different due to the principal equilibria

$$Cr_2O_7^{2-} + H_2O \leftrightharpoons 2HCrO_4^-$$

$$HCrO_4^{2-} \leftrightharpoons H^+ + CrO_4^{2-}$$

Three species co-exist in varying amounts, namely CrO_4^{2-}, $Cr_2O_7^{2-}$ and $HCrO_4^-$, and each has a different molar absorptivity. Even if the pH is kept constant, deviation from Beer's law occurs due to the equilibrium involving $Cr_2O_7^{2-}$ being concentration-dependent. However, the curved calibration plot of absorbance as a function of dichromate concentration can be used for determination of chromium(VI) though its effectiveness is restricted. Kolthoff *et al.*[45] have discussed the effect of the three co-existing species on the colorimetric determination of chromium(VI), and have stressed the fact that $HCrO_4^-$ cannot be ignored. In dilute solution, $HCrO_4^-$ is the main species, and it becomes important to realize that dichromate solutions above about 10^{-4}M cannot follow Beer's law irrespective of acid concentration.

Other spectrophotometric methods have been reported for chromium(VI). Ramanauskas and co-workers[46] have reported the use of triphenylmethane dyes for determination of several oxidizing species including $Cr_2O_7^{2-}$. Brilliant green and crystal violet were used in this investigation. The sensitivity for $Cr_2O_7^{2-}$ is about 0.01 $\mu g\ m\ell^{-1}$.

Cheng[47] has reported the use of 3,3′-diaminobenzidine for determination of CrO_4^{2-}.

2. *Atomic absorption spectroscopy*

AAS is now well established as a method for trace determination of chromium(VI). The usual conditions include use of the 357.9 nm chromium line and a fuel-rich air–acetylene flame. In general the detection limit is about 0.1 ppm. Barnes[48] has applied the technique to analysis of low alloy steel, and has found that aluminium and NH_4Cl are effective in reducing the depressive effects of iron on chromium absorption.

A useful advantage of the method is its ability to determine the different chromium oxidation states, if combined with solvent extraction. Thus Yanagisawa, Suzuki and Takeuchi[49] use sodium diethyldithiocarbamate to extract chromium(VI) without interference from chromium(III), the latter being subsequently extracted using 8-hydroxyquinoline and theonyltrifluoracetone. In each case the extract in isobutyl methyl ketone is analysed by AAS. The method is rapid and simple.

Cresser and Margitt[50] also determine chromium(III) and chromium(VI) but combine AAS with total anion exchange. The method is applied to soil analysis.

A non-flame cell for determination of chromium by AAS was employed by L'vov[51] as early as 1961, this giving an absolute sensitivity of 1×10^{-10} g of Cr. A graphite furnace was used, and the 425.4 nm wavelength. A more recent study by Jackson, West and Balchin[53] using a carbon filament atom reservoir reports a detection limit of 1×10^{-11} g at a wavelength of 357.9 nm. Nitric and hydrochloric acids do not interfere, but H_2SO_4 causes a loss in sensitivity. Cationic interferences are not as might be expected, for example Sr, Ca and Ba show more interference than expected while others, for example Ti, V and Mn, interfere less.

3. *Infra-red*

Using the KBr disc technique, chromate in trace amounts ($\nless 20\,\mu g$) can be identified and determined in admixture with hexacyanoferrate(II), hexacyanoferrate(III), cobalticyanide, sulphate and metavanadate[54].

Electroanalytical methods

1. *Potentiometric*

The chromium(VI)–iron(II) reaction has been discussed earlier in this section. The titration can be followed potentiometrically using platinum and saturated calomel electrodes. Despite the anomalous nature of the reaction, the method is capable of giving high accuracy. Veselago[55] has found some advantage in using 8.5M H_3PO_4 as medium. The method itself is applicable to Cr, Mo and V. For chromium(VI) and vanadium(V) mixtures, a sequential titration is possible using one potential jump corresponding to the reduction of both (to chromium(III) and vanadium(IV)), and a second corresponding to reduction of vanadium(IV) to vanadium(III).

Erdey, Svehla and Weber[56] utilize the hexacyanoferrate(III)–ascorbic acid reaction for indirect potentiometric titration of dichromate. In one method 0.2–2 mg $Cr_2O_7^{2-}$ can be determined by automatic titration. A second method is adapted to the micro scale[57].

Ruzicka[58] finds that $TiCl_3$ in glycerol containing formic acid is stable for 4 days in air. The reagent is used for the potentiometric titration of chromium(VI) in alkaline medium. A visual end-point using resazurin is also possible.

2. *Amperometric*

The indirect procedure based on adding excess iron(II) to acidified chromium(VI) and back-titrating with standard chromium(VI) can be adapted to an amperometric end-point[30]. A precision of 3–5 parts per 10000 is reported.

Songina *et al.*[59] use KI as titrant in the sequential amperometric titration of manganese(VII), chromium(VI) and vanadium(V). Chromium(VI) is titrated in a medium of 3M-H_2SO_4 using a graphite disc indicator electrode maintained at +0.6 V *v.* a saturated calomel electrode. The lower limit of the determination is 40 µg of Cr in 20 mℓ of solution.

The same titrant is used by Zhdanov, Kondratova and Akent'eva[60], who employ a rotating platinum electrode at +1.2 V (*v.* a saturated calomel electrode). No interference is given by Al, Mg, Zn, Co or Cr in 600-fold excess over Cr, Mn and NO_3^- in 100-fold excess, or Cu, Cd, H_3PO_4, citric, tartaric or acetic acids in 10-fold excess. Equal amounts of Bi or Fe, and large amounts of U, Mo and Th do not interfere, but interference is given by Hg, V and Ag, a 10-fold excess of Bi, Fe or EDTA.

3. *Coulometric*

An important feature of the coulometric titration of chromium(VI) is the high precision attainable. An investigation by Marinenko and Taylor[61] using electrogenerated Fe^{2+} demonstrated that results accurate to within a few parts in 100 000 could be obtained. Relatively high precision is attained even in the sub-micro region. Christian and Feldman[62] report that in the determination of 4 ng of chromium(VI) the mean error is 3.7 per cent.

Constant current coulometry is now regarded as one of the most precise of analytical techniques. Indeed its precision is such that the coulomb has been proposed as the ultimate primary standard[63]. An investigation by Knoeck and Diehl[64] has concerned itself with the coulometric assay of reference standard $K_2Cr_2O_7$. The procedure represents one of the most precise used in modern analytical practice, and would be used only when such high precision was justified. Time was measured using a frequency standard counter calibrated against time signals from the National Bureau of Standards. Six calibration runs over elapsed times ranging from 24 to 72 h were found to agree within 1 ppm. One set of results is shown in *Table 5*.

Table 5 Coulometric assay of NBS 136b potassium dichromate[64]

Purity found (%)		*Other results (%)*	
	99.972	99.98	Certificate value NBS
	99.977		
	99.975	99.977	Marinenko and Taylor[61]
	99.974		
	99.977		
	99.974		
Average	99.975		
Standard deviation	0.002		

It will be seen that the average value of 99.975 per cent is in good agreement with the value of 99.977 per cent obtained by Marinenko and Taylor who analysed the same sample batch. Work at such high precision must take into account uncertainties in atomic masses. In the above study the standard deviation approaches the uncertainty in molecular weight of the $K_2Cr_2O_7$.

A novel coulometric method has been developed by Fleet and Ho[65] for automatic determination of $Cr_2O_7^{2-}$ and MnO_4^-. Its basis is a porous catalytic oxygen electrode whose response is almost independent of temperature and pressure. Oxygen is generated when both dichromate and permanganate react with H_2O_2 in acidic medium. The reaction in the case of dichromate can be represented by

$$\underset{\text{chromic acid anhydride}}{2CrO_3} + H_2O_2 \rightarrow \underset{\text{perchromic anhydride}}{Cr_2O_7} + H_2O$$

$$Cr_2O_7 + 4H_2O_2 \rightarrow Cr_2O_3 + 4H_2O + 4O_2$$

The actual reaction appears to be more complicated than this. A flow diagram

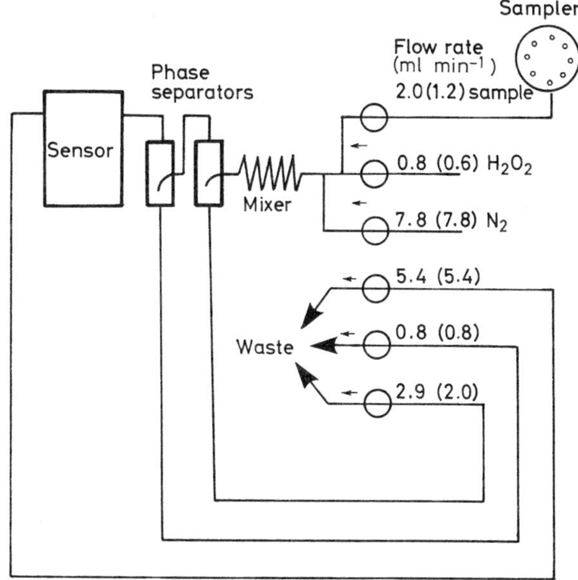

Figure 13 Flow diagram for automatic determination of dichromate using porous catalytic oxygen electrode.
(After Fleet and Ho[65])

of the method is shown in *Figure 13*. The analytical system resembles an automatic coulometric titrator, the integrated response being proportional to the dichromate concentration. An attractive feature of the method is that it provides an alternative method for determination of Chemical Oxygen Demand (C.O.D.).

4. Polarographic

Chromium(VI) is reduced in 0.1–1M NaOH giving a well-defined wave with $E_{\frac{1}{2}} = -0.85$ V *v.* S.C.E.[66] In strongly alkaline solution the reduction is in accordance with the equation

$$CrO_4^{2-} + 2H_2O + 3e \rightarrow CrO_2^- + 4OH^-$$

Polarography of chromium(VI) in neutral or unbuffered solutions of KCl as supporting electrolyte yield 4 waves with half-wave potentials at −0.3, −1.0, −1.5 and −1.7 V *v.* S.C.E. The last three correspond to chromium(III), chromium(II) and the metallic state.

The well-defined wave in alkaline solution has been utilized analytically in the determination of chromium in steel[67].

Miscellaneous methods

Several catalytic methods for chromium(VI) have appeared in the past decade. Jasinskiene and Bilidiene[68] utilize its effect on the oxidation of indigo carmine and methyl orange[69] by H_2O_2. The sensitivity ranges from 6 to 21 ng of chromium(VI) mℓ^{-1} depending on the procedure. Both employ spectrophotometric techniques.

Hadjiioannou[70] describes an automatic catalytic method based on the effect of chromium(VI) on the H_2O_2–I^- reaction in a H_2SO_4 medium. It allows 0.6–3.0 μg of chromium(VI) to be determined within 1–2% in 10–50 s.

Kreingol'd *et al.*[71] obtain a sensitivity of about 5 ng Cr mℓ^{-1} using the catalytic effect of chromium(VI) on the oxidation of methurin (1-hydroxy-3-methyl-1-phenyl urea) by $KBrO_3$ in acid medium.

Weisz and Goenner[72] have developed an amplification method for CrO_4^{2-}. Its novel feature is that the amplification cycle can be repeated until its end-product, AgCl, is in sufficient amount to be evaluated.

A radiochemical method[73] has been based on the reaction of $Cr_2O_7^{2-}$ with metallic Ag^{110}.

References

1. LINGANE, J.J., *Analytical Chemistry of Selected Metallic Elements*, Reinhold, New York and London, 39 (1966)
2. CHALMERS, R.A., in *Comprehensive Analytical Chemistry* (Ed. C.L. and D.W. Wilson), Vol. 1C, Elsevier, Amsterdam and London, 581 (1962)
3. OLSEN, E.D. and FOREBACK, C.C., *Encyclopedia of Industrial Chemical Analysis* (Ed. F.D. Snell and L.S. Ettre), Vol. 9, Interscience, New York and London, 632 (1970)
4. WEINHARDT, A.E. and HIXSON, A.E., *Ind. Engng Chem.*, **43**, 1676 (1951)
5. FELDMAN, F.J., KNOBLOCK, E.C. and PURDY, W.C., *Analytica chim. Acta*, **38**, 489 (1967)
6. TUCK, D. G., *Analytica chim. Acta*, **27**, 296 (1962)
7. SCHEVCHUK, I.A. and SIMONOVA, T.N., *Ukr. khim. Zh.*, **30**, 983 (1964); *Analyt. Abstr.*, **13**, 141 (1966)
8. TSERKOVNITSKAYA, I.A., IL'INSKAYA, G.I. and BELYAEV, V.P., *Zh. analit. Khim.*, **24**, 1357 (1969); *Analyt. Abstr.*, **20**, 1605 (1971)
9. ADAM, J. and PRIBIL, R., *Talanta*, **18**, 91 (1971)
10. SHINDE, V.M. and KHOPKAR, S.M., *Z. analyt. Chem.*, **249**, 239 (1970); *Analyt. Abstr.*, **20**, 2428 (1971)
11. DE, A.K., KHOPKAR, S.M. and CHALMERS, R.A., *Solvent Extraction of Metals*, Van Nostrand Reinhold, London and New York (1970)
12. DE, A.K. and SEN, A.K., *Talanta*, **13**, 1313 (1966)
13. MULOKOZI, A.M., *Analyst*, **97**, 820 (1972)
14. SUBBOTINA, A.I., ARKHANGEL'SKAYA, E.A. and PETROV, A.M., *Trudy. Khim. i. Khim. Teknol* [*Gor'kii*] 118 (1963); *Analyt. Abstr.*, **12**, 1149 (1965)
15. GALATEANU, I., *J. Chromat.*, **19**, 208 (1965)
16. LEDERER, M. and POLCARO, C., *J. Chromat.*, **84**, 379 (1973)
17. KAWANABE, K., TAKITANI, S., MIYZAKI, M. and TAMURA, Z., *Japan Analyst*, **13**, 976 (1964); *Analyt. Abstr.*, **13**, 5385 (1966)
18. CANIC, V. D., TURCIC, M. N., BUGARSKI-VOJINOVIC, M. B. and PERISIC, N. U., *Z. analyt. Chem.*, **229**, 93 (1967); *Analyt. Abstr.*, **15**, 5211 (1968)
19. BATASHOVA, V.V., BABESHKIN, A.M. and NESMEYANOV, A.N., *Vest. mosk. gos. Univ. Ser. Khim.*, **11**, 361 (1970); *Analyt. Abstr.*, **20**, 2429 (1971)
20. PLOTNIKOV, V.I. and KOCHETKOV, V.L., *Zh. analit. Khim.*, **23**, 377 (1968); *Analyt. Abstr.*, **17**, 2564 (1969)
21. GORDON, L. and FIRSCHING, F.H., *Analyt. Chem.*, **26**, 759 (1954)
22. BELCHER, R., REES, D.I. and STEPHEN, W.I., *Chim. Analit.*, 397 (1959)
23. BELCHER, R., BRAZIER, J.N. and STEPHEN, W.I., *Talanta*, **12**, 778 (1965)
24. BELCHER, R., BRAZIER, J.N. and STEPHEN, W.I., *Talanta*, **12**, 963 (1965)
25. LAITINEN, H.A., *Chemical Analysis*, McGraw-Hill, New York and London, 441 (1960)
26. WESTHEIMER, F.H., *Chem. Rev.*, **45**, 419 (1949)
27. BELCHER, R., CHAKRABARTI, C.L. and STEPHEN, W.I., *Analyst*, **94**, 20 (1969)
28. SPIRAMAM, K., *Talanta*, **19**, 1085 (1972)

29. *British Standards Handbook* No. 19, Chromium Method 2, British Standards Institute, London (1970)
30. KEILY, H.J., ELDRIDGE, A. and HIBBITS, J.O., *Analytica chim. Acta,* **21**, 135 (1959)
31. RAO, G.G. and MURALIKRISHNA, U., *Analytica chim. Acta,* **13**, 8 (1955)
32. HAHN, F.L., *J. Am. chem. Soc.,* **57**, 614 (1935)
33. KOLTHOFF, I. M. and BELCHER, R., *Volumetric Analysis, III*, Interscience, New York, 237, 332 (1957).
34. PRIBIL, R. and SYKORA, J., *Chemiké Listy*, **45**, 105 (1951)
35. ISAGAI, K. and TATESHITA, N., *Japan Analyst,* **4**, 222 (1955)
36. DE SOUSA, A., *Chemist Analyst*, **50**, 9 (1961)
37. AIKENS, D.A. and REILLEY, C.N., *Analyt. Chem.,* **34**, 1707 (1962)
38. DE SOUSA, A., *Talanta,* **20**, 1039 (1973)
39. FLASCHKA, H. and HUDITZ, F., *Z. analyt. Chem.,* **137**, 104 (1952)
40. KRESHKOV, A.P., KUZNETSOV, V.V. and MEZHLUMYAN, P.G., *Zh. analit. Khim.,* **29**, 1349 (1974); *Analyt. Abstr.*, **29**, 3B, 138 (1975)
41. ERDEY, L. and KASA, I., *Talanta,* **10**, 1273 (1963)
42. SALTZMAN, B.E., *Analyt. Chem.,* **24**, 1016 (1952)
43. ALLEN, T.L., *Analyt. Chem.,* **30**, 447 (1958)
44. SANDELL, E.B., *Colorimetric Determination of Traces of Metals*, 3rd edn, Interscience, New York (1959)
45. KOLTHOFF, I. M., SANDELL, E. B., MEEHAN, E. J. and BRUCKENSTEIN, S., *Quantitative Chemical Analysis*, 4th edn, Macmillan, London, 1053 (1969)
46. RAMANAUSKAS, E. I., BUNIKIENE, L. V., SAPRAGONENE, M. S., SHULYUNENE, A. K. and ZHILENAITE, M.V., *Zh. analit. Khim.,* **24**, 244 (1969); *Analyt. Abstr.,* **19**, 1022 (1970)
47. CHENG, K.L., *Chemist Analyst,* **52**, 73 (1963)
48. BARNES, L., *Analyt. Chem.,* **38**, 1083 (1966)
49. YANAGISAWA, M., SUZUKI, M. and TAKEUCHI, T., *Mikrochim. Acta*, 475 (1973)
50. CRESSER, M. S. and MARGRITT, R. *Analytica chim. Acta,* **81**, 196 (1976)
51. L'VOV, B.V., *Spectrochim. Acta,* **17**, 761 (1961)
52. *British Standards Handbook* No. 19, Chromium Method 2, British Standards Institute, London (1970)
53. JACKSON, K.W., WEST, T.S. and BALCHIN, L., *Analytica chim. Acta,* **64**, 363 (1973)
54. HABA, F.R. and WILSON, C.L., *Talanta,* **9**, 841 (1962)
55. VESELAGO, L. I., *Zh. analit. Khim.,* **23**, 384 (1968); *Analyt. Abstr.,* **17**, 2565 (1969)
56. ERDEY, L., SVEHLA, G. and WEBER, O., *Z. analyt. Chem.,* **240**, 91 (1968); *Analyt. Abstr.,* **18**, 12 (1970)
57. KISS-EROSS, K., BUZAS, I. and ERDEY, L., *Z. analyt. Chem.,* **255**, 273 (1971); *Analyt. Abstr.,* **22**, 3117 (1972)
58. RUZICKA, E., *Chemicke Zvesti,* **26**, 516 (1972); *Analyt. Abstr.,* **24**, 2789 (1973)
59. SONGINA, O.A., ZAKHAROV, V.A., BEKTUROVA, G.B. and SMIRNOVA, L.I., *Zh. analit. Khim.,* **29**, 1594 (1974); *Analyt. Abstr.,* **29**, 3B14 (1975)
60. ZHDANOV, A.K., KONDRATOVA, V.F. and AKENT'EVA, N.A., *Uzbek. khim. Zh.,* 13 (1969); *Analyt. Abstr.,* **18**, 2380 (1970)
61. MARINENKO, G. and TAYLOR, J.K., *J. Res. natn Bur. Stand., A,* **67A**, 453 (1963)
62. CHRISTIAN, G.D. and FELDMAN, F.J., *Analytica chim. Acta,* **34**, 115 (1966)
63. COOPER, F.A. and QUALE, J.C., *Analytica chim. Acta,* **91**, 363 (1963)
64. KNOECK, J. and DIEHL, H., *Talanta,* **16**, 181 (1969)
65. FLEET, B. and HO, A.Y.W., *Analyt. Chem.,* **44**, 2156 (1972)
66. LINGANE, J.J. and KOLTHOFF, I.M., *J. Am. chem. Soc.,* **62**, 852 (1940)
67. VON STACKELBERG, M., KLINGER, P., KOCH, W. and KRATH, E., *Tech. Mitt. Krupp Forsch.,* **2**, 59 (1939)
68. JASINSKIENE, E.I. AND BILIDIENE, E.B., *Zh. analit. Khim.,* **23**, 143 (1968); *Analyt. Abstr.,* **17**, 2084 (1969)
69. JASINSKIENE, E.I. and BILIDIENE, E.B., *Zh. analit. Khim.,* **22**, 741 (1967); *Analyt. Abstr.,* **16**, 124 (1969)
70. HADJIIOANNOU, T.P., *Talanta,* **15**, 535 (1968)
71. KREINGOL'D, S.U., BOZHEVOL'NOV, E.A., SUPIN, G.S., ANTONOV, V.N. and PANTELEIMONOVA, A.A., *Zh. analit. Khim.,* **24**, 853 (1969); *Analyt. Abstr.,* **19**, 4848 (1970)
72. WEISZ, H. and GOENNER, M., *Analytica chim. Acta,* **43**, 235 (1968)
73. RICHTER, H.G. and GILLESPIE, A.S., *Analyt. Chem.,* **37**, 1146 (1965)

Citrate

Separations

1. TLC

Citric acid may be separated from other carboxylic acids by thin-layer chromatography. Using cellulose, development (ascending) is effected by using a three-solvent system.[1] The relevant data is given in *Table 6*.

Table 6 Three-solvent system for the separation of carboxylic acids

Acid	*Weight* (μg)	*Solvent system*		
		I	II	III
		R_f	R_f	R_f
Formic	1.3			0.21 ± 0.00
Acetic	1.0	—	—	0.21 ± 0.00
Oxalic	1.0	0.58 ± 0.02	0.62 ± 0.04	0.04 ± 0.01
Tartaric	1.0	0.35 ± 0.02	0.45 ± 0.03	0.03 ± 0.01
Citric	0.5	0.42 ± 0.03	0.57 ± 0.04	0.01 ± 0.01

Solvent I: 40:40:2 Amyl alcohol–formic acid–water
Solvent II: 60:10:20 *n*-butanol–formic acid–water
Solvent III: 80:20 2-butanol–2M NH_4OH.

2. Ion-exchange

Strongly basic carbonate- or hydroxide-form resin will isolate citric acid (together with malic, succinic, ascorbic, etc.). The separation has been applied to plant liquors[2]. Seki[3] has described the separation of citric, malic and tartaric acids using Amberlite CG-120 (200–300 mesh; H^+ form) with acetone–dichloromethane–water, 160:100:9 as eluent.

3. Solvent extraction

Citrate may be 97–99% extracted by means of the triphenylstannonium ion, (Ph_3Sn^+), in the pH range 1.6–3.1. Oxalate and acetate are almost quantitatively extracted in a similar pH range (1.0–2.3 and 1.0–2.4 respectively) but tartrate and formate are not extracted[4]. Solvent extraction using butanol may be used to separate non-volatile carboxylic acids dissolved in water[5].

Determination

A short but useful review of current methods for the determination of citric acid has been given by Witty[6]. Many of the procedures are based on initial conversion of citric acid to pentabromoacetone by the following sequence of reactions:

$$
\begin{array}{lclclcl}
H_2C{\cdot}COOH & & HC{\cdot}COOH & & CH_3 & & CHBr_2 \\
\quad | & & \quad \| & & \ | & & \ | \\
HOC{\cdot}COOH & \rightarrow & HOC & \rightarrow & CO & \rightarrow & CO \\
\quad | & & \quad | & & \ | & & \ | \\
H_2C{\cdot}COOH & & H_2C{\cdot}COOH & & CH_3 & & CBr_3
\end{array}
$$

The determination may be completed gravimetrically, titrimetrically, or by spectrophotometry, depending on the amount of citric acid in the sample. Details of the methods will be given below.

Gravimetric as pentabromoacetone

When amounts greater than 50 mg are present, the most accurate method is the gravimetric one. This is now the official method of the Association of Official Analytical Chemists for determination of citric acid in fruit and fruit products[7]. An abridged version is given below.

Gravimetric determination of citric acid as pentabromoacetone

Reagents

Potassium permanganate: 5% w/v.

Ferrous sulphate: 40% w/v, $FeSO_4{\cdot}7H_2O$ containing 5 mℓ concentrated H_2SO_4 for each 500 mℓ.

Procedure

To the solution of citric acid in 40–45 mℓ solution, add 2 g KBr and 5 mℓ concentrated H_2SO_4. Heat to 50 °C and allow to stand for 5 min. Add 20 mℓ $KMnO_4$ slowly (1–2 mℓ portions), swirling the flask for a few seconds after each addition. Allow to stand for 5 min. Cool to 15 °C then add the $FeSO_4$ slowly and with constant agitation until the mixture starts to clear. Shake for 1 min, continue adding the $FeSO_4$ until the MnO_2 has dissolved, and add a few mℓ excess.

Add 20 g anhydrous Na_2SO_4 with swirling to ensure solution (if Na_2SO_4 remains substantially undissolved, repeat the determination). Cool to 15 °C and shake vigorously for 5 min. Filter immediately through a gooch crucible containing asbestos, washing the residual precipitate from the vessel with portions of the filtrate. Finally wash the precipitate with 50 mℓ cold water, allowing it to remain under suction for a few minutes.

Dry the crucible overnight in a desiccator containing H_2SO_4, or place the crucible in a drying train and aerate until the loss in weight does not exceed 0.2 mg, making the first weighing after 20 min.

Remove the pentabromoacetone from the crucible with alcohol followed by ether, filling the crucible 3 times with each solvent. Dry the crucible for 10 min at 100 °C, cool in a desiccator and weigh. The difference in the two weights gives the weight of pentabromoacetone.

To calculate the weight of anhydrous citric acid, multiply the weight of precipitate by 0.424 which is the theoretical factor. An empirical factor may be used based on the exact procedure used. This would take into account loss by solubility and volatility. The standard deviation of the method is 0.33 per cent.

Titrimetric methods

1. Acid–base titration

Though unselective, citric acid may be determined by titration in aqueous solution with standard NaOH using phenolphthalein as indicator[8]. The dissociation constants are as follows:

$$k_1 = 7.4 \times 10^{-4}$$

$$k_2 = 1.74 \times 10^{-5}$$

$$k_3 = 4.0 \times 10^{-7}$$

The titration may be carried out potentiometrically, in which case three breaks are observed. If azo violet is used as indicator, the amount of NaOH consumed corresponds to two equivalents of acid.

2. Iodimetric titration

Some carboxylic acids may be determined by a direct iodimetric procedure involving liberation of iodine from an iodate–iodide mixture.

$$IO_3^- + 5I^- + 6H^+ \rightarrow 3I_2 + H_2O$$

Under normal conditions citric acid cannot be determined directly but Kolthoff[9] obtained good results by adding an excess of standard thiosulphate to a solution of the acid containing KIO_3 and KI, followed by titration of the liberated I_2 after an interval of time.

Solutions of Ca, Ba, Mg or Zn react with citric acid (and some other carboxylic acids) to give complexes which behave as strong acids. Under these conditions a direct iodimetric titration of citric acid is possible[10]. As in the acid–base titration, the iodimetric method is unselective, and there appears to be little evidence of widespread use.

3. Based on pentabromoacetone

Methods based on pentabromoacetone are far more selective for citrate, and are capable of extension into the sub-milligram region where application may be made to chromatographic fractions. The principle of one variant of the method[11] is as follows. Oxidation and bromination of citric acid converts it to pentabromoacetone by the steps indicated earlier. This is extracted and treated with sodium sulphide liberating bromide. This in turn reacts with silver iodate giving iodate which liberates iodine from potassium iodide. The latter is determined using standard thiosulphate. We can represent the reactions thus:

$$Br^- + AgIO_3 = AgBr + IO_3^-$$

$$IO_3^- + 5I^- + 6H^+ = 3I_2 + 3H_2O$$

$$I_2 + 2S_2O_3^{--} = S_4O_6^{--} + 2I^-$$

Until the work by Hargreaves, Abrahams and Vickery[11] the yield of pentabromoacetone from citric acid was subject to vigorous control of conditions, including time and acid strength. These investigators found that the inclusion of metaphosphoric acid allowed considerable latitude in these conditions; the improved method now finds considerable use. The procedure described below is based on this work.

Titrimetric determination of citric acid via pentabromoacetone

Reagents

Potassium bromide: 1M.
Potassium permanganate: 0.3M.
Sodium sulphide: 4% w/v solution of the monohydrate. Keep in a refrigerator when not in use. Solution is stable for several weeks.
Metaphosphoric acid: 20% w/v. Prepare at room temperature and keep in a refrigerator.
Petroleum ether: B.pt. 30–60 °C.
Potassium chloride: 12.5 mmol ℓ^{-1}. 0.9319 g dried salt made up to 1 ℓ with 0.085M phosphoric acid.
Hydrogen peroxide: 3%.
Sodium thiosulphate: 0.01M (prepared from 0.1M thiosulphate).

Procedure

To the citric acid solution add 18 mℓ M H_2SO_4, 1 mℓ 20% metaphosphoric acid, and dilute with water to 35 mℓ. With the temperature not exceeding 22 °C add 2 mℓ KBr solution and 5 mℓ $KMnO_4$. After about 10 min, without stirring, cool the solution to 10 °C and discharge the colour by the rapid dropwise addition of ice-cold H_2O_2 with stirring.

Transfer the solution to a 125-mℓ pear-shaped separating funnel using about 25 mℓ of petroleum ether in small portions to rinse out the beaker. Shake vigorously, allow the aqueous phase to run off, and wash the ether layer with four 3-mℓ portions of water to remove all halide ions.

Decompose the pentabromoacetone by shaking the ether briefly with two successive 3-mℓ portions of Na_2S solution, the coloured solution being drained each time into a 25-mℓ volumetric flask. Wash the ether with 2-mℓ portions of water until no further colour is removed. Two washings are usually sufficient. Drain these into the same flask, add 2 mℓ 2.0M phosphoric acid and boil gently on a hot-plate for 5–6 min. The addition of a few pieces of quartz, previously extracted with acid and thoroughly washed, just before heating the solution, is recommended.

Cool. Add exactly 5.00 mℓ of the KCl solution, make up to volume, and mix. Pour, without rinsing, into a glass-stoppered 50-mℓ conical flask containing 0.25 g dry $AgIO_3$. Stopper, shake for 5 min and pour through a dry chloride-free filter paper in a funnel.

Titrate suitable aliquots (2 or 5 mℓ) with 0.01 M thiosulphate after adding 2 drops of 0.085M phosphoric acid and 1 mℓ 10% NaI or KI, and allowing to stand for 5 min. Carry out a blank determination to obtain the net titration value for thiosulphate.

In calculating the result, for which the equations given earlier are required, an empirical factor of 0.980 is used for the conversion of citric acid into pentabromoacetone. This is based on 42 determinations carried out by Hargreaves, Abrahams and Vickery[11].

---

4. Compleximetric titration
Crisan and Krausz[12] precipitate organic acids (citric, oxalic, tartaric) with lead, and determine the excess lead with EDTA. The method is rapid and applicable to 8–25 mg citric acid.

5. Redox titration
Citric acid (4–5 mg) may be determined by redox titrimetry[13] using $KMnO_4$. Back titration is made with quinol after a period of $1\frac{1}{2}$ h.

Colorimetric methods

1. Based on pentabromoacetone
Pentabromoacetone reacts with alkaline pyridine producing a red colour which may be used as the basis of a method for determination of citrate[14]. The method is relatively simple, selective, and applicable to citric acid at the 2 μg level. Further modifications have been described[15,16] and the method has been recommended by the Association of Official Analytical Chemists[17]. The standard deviation[6] for the method is 3.7 per cent.

2. Based on pyridine–acetic anhydride
A simple colorimet ic method based on the reaction of citric acid with pyridine and acetic anhydride in the presence of trichloroacetic acid was proposed by Saffran and Denstedt[18] in 1948. In the original work the absorbance was measured using an Evelyn filter with maximum wavelength of 400 nm. A recent assessment of the method[19] indicates that reproducible results may be obtained, but the final concentration of trichloroacetic acid is critical and the method lacks specificity. A modification of the method has been described by Marier and Boulet[20] which may be adapted to the Auto-Analyzer, and which may be used to determine 25 ppm citric acid in solution. White and Davies[21] have made a critical comparison of methods for determination of citric acid in milk. A procedure by Marier, Boulet and Rose[22] with trichloroacetic acid as precipitant, is recommended.

Where the determination of citric acid in protein-containing samples is required, the pyridine–acetic anhydride method may be used[23].

3. Miscellaneous colorimetric methods
Citric acid (as well as oxalic, malonic, malic, ascorbic, and tartaric acids) causes a decrease in the absorbance of the iron(III)-5-nitrosalicylate complex in aqueous or acetate medium at 492 nm. This has been used in a colorimetric procedure[24]. Copper(II) and nitrite cause serious interference.

Another method depends on the change in colour of cerium(IV) in the presence of ferroin during the oxidation of various organic substances[25]. Again the method lacks specificity, applying also to ascorbic, lactic, oxalic and tartaric acids. The absorbance of the residual cerium(IV) in the presence of ferroin is measured at 426 nm.

What is claimed to be a specific method for citrate has been described by Moellering and Gruber[26]. Based on the cleavage of citrate with citrate lyase (citrate oxaloacetate lyase) in the presence of zinc, it may be applied to animal tissues or fruit juices. As little as 0.02 µmol citric acid, equivalent to 0.004 mg citric acid may be determined with a 5 per cent error.

Miscellaneous methods

In order to develop an extremely sensitive method Guyon and Marks[27] have utilized the quenching effect of citrate on the fluorescence at 450 nm of the 1:1 tungstate–flavanol complex. Presumably this is due to tungstate and citrate forming a more stable complex. The method functions satisfactorily at the 0.2 µg citrate level. Determination of citrate is possible in the 0–200 ppb(10^9) range; with slight modification this can be extended to 0–5 ppm.

No interference is caused by iodate, chlorate, bromate, sulphate, sulphite, bromide, chloride, or nitrate. Small amounts of thiocyanate and fluoride may be tolerated. Tartrate, oxalate and iodide interfere even at low levels.

A radiochemical variant of the pentabromoacetone method has been described[28]. Br^{82} is incorporated in the bromination reagent. Results for citrate in serum agree with those obtained from photometric methods.

References

1. DITTMAN, J., *J. Chromat.*, **34**, 407 (1968)
2. GOODBAM, A.E. and STARK, J.B., *Analyt. Chem.*, **29**, 283 (1957)
3. SEKI, T., *J. Chromat.*, **22**, 498 (1966)
4. BOCK, R., NIEDERAUER, H-T. and BEHRENDS, K., *Z. analyt. Chem.*, **190**, 33 (1962)
5. KHOMENKO, A.N. and GONCHAROVA, I.A., *Gidrokhim. Mater.*, **48**, 77 (1968); *Analyt. Abstr.*, **18**, 2830 (1970)
6. WITTY, A.R., *Proc. Soc. analyt. Chem.*, **3**, 183 (1966)
7. *Official Methods of Analysis of the Association of Official Analytical Chemists*, Association of Official Analytical Chemists, Washington, U.S.A., 10th edn, 317 (1965)
8. *Pharmacopeia of the U.S.*, 17th edn, Mack Printing Co., 135 (1965)
9. KOLTHOFF, I.M., *Chem. Weekbl.*, **23**, 260 (1926)
10. KOLTHOFF, I.M., *Pharm. Weekbl.*, **57**, 63 (1920)
11. HARGREAVES, C.A., ABRAHAMS, M.D. and VICKERY, H.B., *Analyt. Chem.*, **23**, 467 (1951)
12. CRISAN, I.A. and KRAUSZ, R., *Studia. Univ. Babes-Bulyai, Ser. Chem.*, **12**, 19 (1967); *Analyt. Abstr.*, **15**, 6720 (1968)
13. BERKA, A. and HILGARD, S., *Mikrochim. Acta*, 174 (1966)
14. ETTINGER, R.H., GDDBAUM, L.R. and SMITH, L.H., *J. biol. Chem.*, **199**, 531 (1952)
15. SAFRONOV, A.P., *Biokhimiya*, **24**, 123 (1959); *Analyt. Abstr.*, **6**, 4514 (1959)
16. JONES, G.B., *Analyt. Biochem.*, **21**, 286 (1967)
17. PRO, M.J. and NELSON, R.A., *J. Ass. off. analyt. Chem.* **39**, 952 (1956)
18. SAFFAN, M. and DENSTEDT, O.F., *J. biol. Chem.*, **175**, 849 (1948)
19. LOWENSTEIN, J.M., *Meth. Enzym.*, **13**, 513 (1969); *Analyt. Abstr.*, **19**, 5044 (1970)
20. MARIER, J.R. and BOULET, M., *J. Dairy Sci.*, **41**, 1683 (1958)
21. WHITE, J.C.D. and DAVIES, D.T., *J. Dairy Res.*, **30**, 171 (1963)
22. MARIER, J.R., BOULET, M. and ROSE, D., *J. Dairy Res.*, **44**, 359 (1961)
23. CHOY, T.K., QUATTRONE, J.J. and ELEFANT, M., *Analytica chim. Acta*, **29**, 114 (1963)
24. LEE, K.S., LEE, D.W. and HWANG, J.Y., *Analyt. Chem.*, **40**, 2049 (1968)
25. MA, T.S. and NAZIMOWITZ, W.L., *Mikrochim. Acta*, 345 (1969)
26. MOELLERING, H. and GRUBER, W., *Analyt. Biochem.*, **17**, 369 (1966)
27. GUYON, J.C. and MARKS, J.Y., *Mikrochim. Acta*, 731 (1969)
28. JACOBS, S.L., *J. nucl. Med.*, **5**, 297 (1964); *Analyt. Abstr.*, **12**, 4069 (1965)

Cyanate

The determination of cyanate (OCN^-) is important industrially, for example in the analysis of plating wastes.

In neutral solution the ion decomposes slowly; in acidic solution hydrolysis is rapid. Even in basic solutions the ion is not completely stable. For this reason reference solutions should be replaced after about one week.

Determination of cyanate as ammonia after first converting it to that form, has been a standard procedure for many years. An important problem therefore is its separation from ammonia when both are present together. Because of its relative instability, such operations as boiling are not feasible. The only suitable procedure is ion-exchange. Strongly acidic resins cannot be used directly because they decompose the cyanate; cation resins in sodium form are generally recommended[1,2].

The commercial product KOCN may be used as a reference standard. The synthesis and purification of KOCN has been described[10].

Determination

Gravimetric methods

Cyanate is precipitated by $AgNO_3$ solution from a dilute nitric acid or neutral solution[3].

$$KOCN + AgNO_3 \rightarrow AgOCN + KNO_3$$

The precipitate can be dried at 100 °C and then weighed. Duval[4] reports that AgOCN maintains its weight up to 138 °C but the evolution of cyanogen becomes significant beyond 240 °C.

Spectrophotometric methods

One approach[2] is to separate cyanate from any ammonia present by ion-exchange, convert it into the ammonium ion by dilute sulphuric acid, and determine this using Nessler's reagent.

$$OCN^- + 2H^+ + 2H_2O \rightarrow NH_4^+ + H_2CO_3$$

No interference is given by urea, ammonium ions, common cations or anions. The conversion of cyanate to ammonium ions in 0.05M H_2SO_4 is complete in less than 10 min. The range of cyanate applicable is given as 40–200 μM.

Kruse and Mellon[1] also employ an ion-exchange separation but use chloramine-T to catalyse the hydrolysis of cyanate to ammonia. The subsequent determination of ammonia is based on the purple colour formed with pyridine-pyrazolone reagent, which is extracted into carbon tetrachloride before measurement. This procedure is more sensitive and selective than the previous one using Nessler's reagent. The range for cyanate is 0.1–10 ppm. Of the common anions, only cyanide and thiocyanate interfere. A composite reagent is used, this being prepared from bis-(3-methyl-1-phenylpyrazol-5-one), pyridine, and 3-methyl-1-phenyl-5-pyrazolone.

When cyanate is added to a dilute solution of a copper salt to which pyridine has been added, a lilac-blue precipitate of $[Cu(C_5H_5N)_2(OCN)_2]$ is formed which dissolves in chloroform giving a sapphire blue colour. This forms the basis of the copper(II)–pyridine method which, until the introduction of methods based on conversion of cyanate to ammonia, was the most sensitive of the cyanate spectrophotometric methods[5]. Recent work[6] indicates that if the absorbance is measured at 315 nm, the sensitivity is improved by a factor of about 30 over procedures using 680 or 700 nm[7, 8].

Amperometric method

The successive amperometric titration of CN^-, Cl^- and OCN^- with Ag^+ as titrant, has been described by Musha and Ikeda[9]. Based on the differences in solubility of AgCN, AgCl, and AgOCN, it enables 0.5–2 μmol of OCN^- to be determined. Platinum and saturated calomel electrodes are employed.

If carbonate is present, it is first precipitated with a barium nitrate solution. The error is $\pm \sim 2$ per cent when almost equal concentrations of the anions are present.

Spectrophotometric determination of cyanate by the copper(II)-pyridine method[7]

Reagents

Potassium cyanate, stock solution:
 0.0193 g KOCN $m\ell^{-1}$ in 0.04M NaOH.

Copper nitrate–pyridine reagent:
 1.38×10^{-4} mol $m\ell^{-1}$ of $Cu(NO_3)_2 \cdot 3H_2O$ and 2.1×10^{-3} mol $m\ell^{-1}$ of pyridine in water.

Procedure

To 10 mℓ of the copper nitrate–pyridine reagent at 25 °C, add 5 mℓ of the aqueous cyanate solution. Mix and adjust the pH to 8.00 using NaOH solution and a pH meter. Allow to stand in a bath at 25 °C for 10 min then transfer to a 50 mℓ separating funnel and extract with 20 mℓ of chloroform in 4 portions. Filter (a No. 202 Reeve-Angel filter paper was used in the original work). Dilute the combined extracts to 25 mℓ by volume and measure the absorbance at 680 nm.

Note

The range for OCN^- is 0.5–5.0 mg. Cyanide does not interfere when present at twice the level of cyanate.

References

1. KRUSE, J.M. and MELLON, M.G., *Analyt. Chem.*, **25**, 1188 (1953)
2. SHAW, W.H.R. and BORDEAUX, J.J., *Analyt. Chem.*, **27**, 136 (1955)

3. DUVAL, C., *Analytica chim. Acta*, **5**, 506 (1951)
4. DUVAL, C., *Inorganic Thermogravimetric Analysis*, 2nd edn, Elsevier, London (1963)
5. WERNER, E.A., *J. chem. Soc.*, **123**, 2577 (1923)
6. WRIGLEY, C.W., *J. Chromat.*, **66**, 189 (1972)
7. MARTIN, E. L. and MCCLELLAND, J., *Analyt. Chem.*, **23**, 1519 (1951)
8. MARIER, J.R. and ROSE, D., *Analyt. Biochem.*, **7**, 304 (1964)
9. MUSHA, S. and IKEDA, S., *Japan Analyst*, **14**, 795 (1965); *Analyt. Abstr.*, **14**, 3028 (1967)
10. FERNELIUS, W.C. (Editor-in-Chief), *Inorganic Synthesis*, McGraw-Hill, New York and London, 87 (1946)

Cyanide

Hydrogen cyanide is used in the manufacture of acrylic fibres, nylon-66 and methyl methacrylate. Sodium cyanide is used in the industrial extraction of silver and gold, electroplating, case hardening of steel, and as an intermediate in the chemical industry.

The extreme toxic hazards of cyanides are well known. In the case of HCN the maximum permissible exposure level over an 8-h working day is 10 ppm. Determination of trace quantities of cyanide in air and industrial effluents is important. In aqueous effluents cyanides may be present as HCN, as the cyanide ion CN^-, and as a variety of ions of the type $M(CN)_x$ in which cyanide ions form complexes with metal ions. The sum of these forms is referred to as 'Total' cyanide. In the examination of industrial waters 'cyanide' includes all CN groups in cyanide compounds present that can be determined as cyanide ion CN^-.

Modern evidence indicates that the toxicity of cyanide solutions depends on free HCN, the CN^- ion being important only because of the HCN in equilibrium with it[1].

$$CN^- + H_2O \rightleftharpoons HCN + OH^-$$

Determination of cyanide has been reviewed by Roberts[2] and Bark and Higson[3], the latter review being restricted to detection and determination of small amounts. Recent developments in the determination of cyanide are included in a general review of analytical methods for anions by Boltz[4].

Cyanide is masked by formaldehyde.

$$CN^- + HCHO + H_2O \rightarrow CN{\cdot}CH_2{\cdot}OH + OH^-$$

This features in several aspects of cyanide analysis, for example where cyanide is determined in the presence of halide ions using the Volhard method. Standard solutions cannot be prepared by accurately weighing out NaCN or KCN. The general procedure used is to prepare a solution of approximate strength from the solid and then standardize it titrimetrically using $AgNO_3$.

In view of the extreme toxicity of cyanides, extreme care must be taken in handling them. In titrimetric work burettes or safety pipettes only should be used to measure samples known or thought to contain cyanides. All procedures in which HCN is likely to be evolved should be conducted in a fume cupboard.

Separations

Hydrogen cyanide can be separated from several other gases by bubbling the gas stream through a NaOH solution.

1. Distillation

Distillation as HCN is a standard method for macro and trace amounts of cyanide. The process has been discussed at length by Ludzack, Moore and Ruchhoft[5]. A NaOH solution is generally used as absorbent. Hydrogen cyanide is liberated from cyanide solutions at pH values below 9. If acidified with tartaric acid, it can be distilled or displaced with a current of air. When complexing agents are present, recovery is more difficult, requiring stronger acids such as phosphoric acid. The degree of activity of cyanides on distillation varies according to the form present. Simple cyanides such as alkali cyanides are readily converted to HCN during distillation. Several metal cyanides, for example those of Cd, Cu, Ni and Zn, react almost as readily. Cyanide complexes of iron show resistance to decomposition under the same conditions. Cobalticyanides decompose very slowly. Conversion of metal cyanides to HCN is facilitated by the presence of magnesium and mercury salts. A useful form of distillation developed by Serfass *et al.*[6] used magnesium(II) and mercury(II) chlorides with H_2SO_4 to decompose complex cyanides. These reduce hexacyanoferrate(II) and hexacyanoferrate(III) to magnesium(II) and mercury(II) simple cyanides.

Cyanides and complex cyanides are distilled from solutions containing copper(I) and HCl. This method is recommended for separation of cyanide from industrial effluents[7]. The procedure is given below. It has been reported that when hydrogen cyanide is distilled under reduced pressure in the presence of zinc acetate, no decomposition occurs of any hexacyanoferrate(II) present[8]. Distillation under reduced pressure from a solution buffered at pH 5.2–5.8 and containing a zinc salt, has been recommended for separation of cyanide in the presence of hexacyanoferrate(II) and hexacyanoferrate(III)[9]. The inclusion of a lead salt is effective in suppressing interference from sulphide and volatile sulphur compounds. Another recent investigation reports the separation by steam distillation of free and total cyanide from industrial samples under different conditions[10]. The distillation procedure is applicable to a wide range of samples including biological materials[11].

Separation of total cyanide by distillation[7]

Reagents

Acid copper(I) chloride solution:
Dissolve 2 g of copper(I) chloride in 100 mℓ of 5M HCl. Prepare daily as required.

Sodium hydroxide: 0.5M.

Apparatus

A 500-mℓ flask fitted with a splash head and water-cooled vertical condenser dipping into a suitable receiver.

Procedure

Place into the distillation flask a volume of sample or diluted sample containing not more than about 50 mg of total cyanide, and make up to

200 mℓ with water if necessary. Add 5 mℓ of acid copper(I) chloride solution and some fragments of porous pot. Assemble the apparatus immediately to avoid possible loss of HCN. Place 20 mℓ of 0.5M NaOH into the receiver with the delivery tube dipping into the solution. Distil, collecting a total volume of about 90 mℓ in the receiver, which should be removed before stopping the distillation.

---

2. Microdiffusion

Separation of hydrogen cyanide using Conway microdiffusion cells is a simple procedure requiring the minimum of manipulation. Furthermore, it can serve to concentrate the free cyanide in the final solution from the original sample levels. It is absorbed in NaOH solution for evaluation by titrimetric or spectrophotometric procedures. The technique enables free cyanide to be separated from hexacyanoferrate(II) and hexacyanoferrate-(III)[12]. Baar[13] has used a modified Cavett flask as an alternative to the Conway cell. This is shown in *Figure 14*.

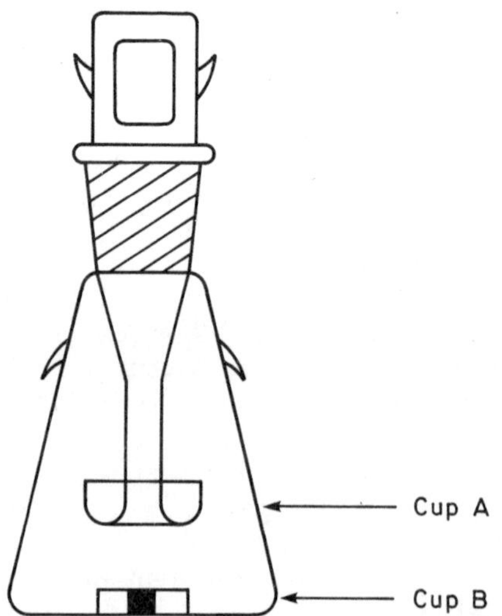

Figure 14 Modified flask for microdiffusion work. (After Baar[13])

The application was to analysis of whole blood, using samples of 2 mℓ containing 0.2 µg of cyanide. Cup A contains the absorbing NaOH solution; Cup B contains a H_2SO_4 solution. The sample is added to the floor of the flask and the reaction started by tilting. A 2-h period is required for complete separation.

A recent gas-chromatographic method for determination of cyanide in biological materials includes microdiffusion as an initial separation step[14].

3. Solvent extraction
Hydrogen cyanide in the range 0–2 mg ℓ$^{-1}$ can be extracted from aqueous solutions using 1,1,1-trichloroethane[1]. This enables it to be separated both from free cyanide and complex cyanides. When the concentration of hydrogen cyanide falls below 4 per cent it becomes necessary to carry out extractions from synthetic samples to construct a calibration curve. The final determination is made spectrophotometrically.

Iron(II)-1,10 phenanthroline has been used to extract less than 200 μg of cyanide into $CHCl_3$ at pH 8.5–10. Iodide, IO_4^-, S^{2-}, SCN^-, Co(II), Cu(II), Fe(II) and Ni(II) interfere[15].

4. Chromatography
Thin-layer chromatography has been applied to cyanide separation by several investigators. Canic and co-workers[16] use starch with acetone-3M NH_4OH (1:4) as solvent. Separation from 12 anions is possible, these including SCN^-, AsO_3^{3-}, AsO_4^{3-} and PO_4^{3-}.

Gagliardi and Pokorny[17] employ silica gel with various solvent systems. Here separation is made from F^-, Cl^-, Br^-, I^-, N_3^-, SCN^-, $[Fe(CN)_6]^{3-}$ and $[Fe(CN)_6]^{4-}$. More recently Thielemann[18] used aluminium foil coated with silica gel and $FeCl_3$ solution for TLC separation of CN^-, SCN^-, $[Fe(CN)_6]^{3-}$ and $[Fe(CN)_6]^{4-}$.

Gas-chromatographic methods have been reported. These are discussed at the end of the section.

Determination

Gravimetric methods

Cyanide can be determined as AgCN after precipitation in the cold with excess of Ag^+, and drying the precipitate at 100 °C. There appears to be little evidence that the method finds any current use.

Titrimetric methods

1. Using $AgNO_3$
The well-known Liebig–Dénigès titration consists of titrating cyanide with standard $AgNO_3$ in ammoniacal solution and in the presence of KI. When $AgNO_3$ is added to cyanide in neutral solution, a soluble complex $K[Ag(CN)_2]$ is formed provided cyanide is in excess.

$$Ag^+ + 2CN^- \leftrightharpoons Ag(CN)_2^-$$

When all the cyanide has reacted, further addition of Ag^+ gives the sparingly soluble silver dicyanoargentate.

$$Ag^+ + Ag(CN)_2^- \leftrightharpoons Ag[Ag(CN)_2]$$

This imparts a turbidity to the solution denoting the end-point, and was the original method proposed by Liebig[19]. Although the titration would be theoretically satisfactory, the precipitation occurring only slightly before the equivalence point, in practice AgCN is precipitated locally and is very slow in redissolving. Dénigès[20] modified the method by using an ammoniacal solution and including KI. In this modification the end-point is indicated by a turbidity due to AgI.

$$Ag[Ag(CN)_2] + 2NH_3 \rightarrow Ag(NH_3)_2^+ + Ag(CN)_2^-$$

$$Ag(NH_3)_2^+ + I^- \rightarrow AgI \downarrow + 2NH_3$$

It is beyond the scope of the present treatment to examine the theoretical aspects of the method. These are discussed in standard texts[21, 22]. The method is recommended by British Standards[23] for determination of cyanide in KCN and NaCN.

Titrimetric determination of cyanide using $AgNO_3$

Procedure

Add 15–20 mℓ of 2M ammonia to the cyanide sample solution and dilute to about 100 mℓ with water. Add 0.2 g of KI. Swirl to dissolve. Titrate with 0.1M $AgNO_3$ solution until a turbidity appears. This is best viewed against a black background. From the above equations it will be seen that $Ag^+ \equiv 2CN^-$.

The Volhard method is applicable to cyanide. In this, an excess of standard $AgNO_3$ is added to cyanide and the solution slightly acidified. A portion is filtered and the filtrate titrated with standard ammonium thiocyanate using ferric alum as indicator. A combination of the Liebig and Volhard methods is useful for analysis of CN^-/SCN^- mixtures. Cyanide alone is given by the Liebig method; the sum of both anions is given by the Volhard method.

Several indicators have been proposed for the argentimetric titration of cyanide. Ryan and Culshaw[24] used *p*-dimethylaminobenzylidine rhodanine

```
H
N——CO
|    |
SC   C=CH—⟨◯⟩—N(CH2)2
  \S/
```

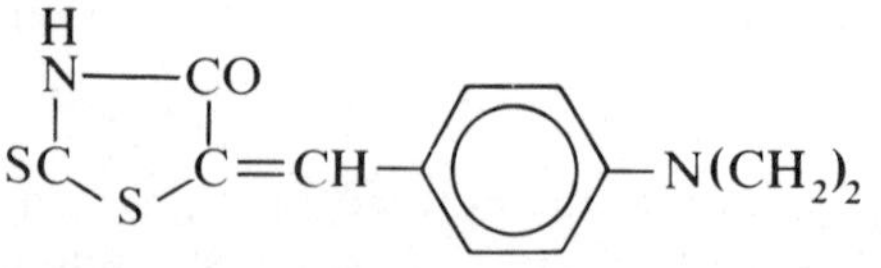

Structure 10 p-Dimethylaminobenzylidine rhodanine

(*Structure 10*). A method employing this is recommended for determination of cyanide in industrial effluents[7]. The colour change is from yellow to pink. Rhodizonic acid in the form of its sodium salt has been proposed by Mehlig[25]. Archer[26] has developed a useful method using a water–alcohol medium and dithizone as indicator. At the end-point, when free silver ions are present, there is a sharp colour change from yellow-orange to deep red-purple. The sensitivity of the method is about ten times as great as that of the Liebig method.

Titration of cyanide using $AgNO_3$ and dithizone as indicator[26]

Reagents

$AgNO_3$:

0.01M prepared by quantitatively diluting an accurately prepared 0.1M solution

Dithizone: 0.01% in acetone.

Procedure

To the cyanide sample solution containing up to 4.0 mg of CN^-, add 50 mℓ of 95% ethanol, 1 mℓ of M NaOH solution, and 2.0 mℓ of dithizone indicator. Titrate with 0.01M $AgNO_3$ to a deep red-purple colour. Carry out a blank determination omitting the sample. Correct the titre accordingly.

Notes

1. At the end-point there should be not more than 20 mℓ of water present including the volume of titrant. Excessive water diminishes the end-point sharpness.
2. Archer states that dithizone gives greater changes both in colour and intensity than *p*-dimethylaminobenzylidine rhodanine, and that it can be applied to initially highly coloured solutions to which the latter indicator is inapplicable.

Another indicator giving a sharp end-point in the $AgNO_3$ titration of cyanide is 1,10-phenanthroline-bromopyrogallol red[27]. This stems from earlier work by the authors on the ternary system $[(\text{phen-Ag-phen})^+]_2\text{BPR}^{2-}$, which provided an extremely sensitive spectrophotometric method for silver ($\varepsilon = 5.1 \times 10^4$). Titrimetric procedures using the indicator can be applied on the macro or micro scale. Thiosulphate, SCN^-, I^-, Fe^{3+}, Co^{2+}, Cu^{2+} and Hg^{2+} interfere in equimolar amounts. Copper does not interfere at one tenth the equimolar amount, and neither do Fe^{3+}, Co^{2+} and Hg^{2+} if present at 1% of the equimolar amount. An indirect spectrophotometric method for cyanide has been based on the same system. This is discussed later in the section.

2. *Mercurimetric*

Mercuric cyanide is much less dissociated than mercuric thiocyanate, and does not affect the titration of Hg^{2+} with thiocyanate.

$$Hg^{2+} + 2CN^- \rightleftharpoons Hg(CN)_2$$

The method consists of adding cyanide to an excess of standard Hg^{2+} and titrating the excess mercuric ions with standard thiocyanate. Various indicators have been proposed, for example sodium nitroprusside and diphenylcarbazone. Variamine blue has been recommended by Gregorowicz and Buhl[28]. The end-point is marked by a persistent violet colour.

3. *Iodimetric*

An older titrimetric method based on bromine cyanide has found considerable use[29]. Bromine reacts quantitatively with weakly alkaline solutions of cyanide (and thiocyanate) to form bromine cyanide.

$$HCN + Br_2 \rightarrow BrCN + H^+ + Br^-$$

This is stable in weakly acid solutions. As it is unaffected by phenol, this can be used to destroy excess bromine. The bromine cyanide reacts with iodide giving iodine which can be titrated with standard thiosulphate.

$$BrCN + 2I^- \rightarrow CN^- + I_2 + Br^-$$

The method enables cyanide to be determined in the presence of Cl^-, Br^-, S^{2-} and $S_2O_3{}^{2-}$. Another application[30] has been to the micro-determination of cyanide when accompanied by $NH_4{}^+$, $NO_2{}^-$ and $NO_3{}^-$.

4. EDTA

Several compleximetric procedures have been developed, mainly by Nomura or de Sousa.

De Sousa utilizes the reaction of cyanide with ammonium nickel sulphate to give the stable ionic tetracyanonickelate(II) anion complex $[Ni(CN)_4]^{2-}$. If a known excess of ammonium nickel sulphate is used and the excess Ni^{2+} ions titrated with standard EDTA, the cyanide content can be evaluated. De Sousa[31–33] has applied the principle to analysis of CN^-/Cl^- mixtures, CN^-/SCN^- mixtures and to determination of CN^- in the presence of Cl^- and SCN^-.

Nomura and co-workers base their methods on mixed-ligand formation. In one indirect procedure suitable for 0.025–2 mg CN^-, titration is made with the 1:1 mercury(II)-EDTA complex. At pH 4–8 the mixed-ligand $[HgY(CN)]^{3-}$ is formed. This reacts with another mole of cyanide to give $Hg(CN)_2$ and EDTA. The latter is titrated[34] with standard $CuSO_4$. Sulphide, V(V), Cu(II), Co(II), Ni(II), Hg(II) and Ag(I) interfere.

A novel method for sequential titration of cyanide and thiocyanate utilizes the fact that the CN^-–Hg(II)–EDTA complex does not absorb at 240 nm, whereas the corresponding thiocyanate complex does. Furthermore the cyanide reaction is much faster than the thiocyanate reaction. In the titration, 5–100 μg CN^- and 10–100 μg SCN^- are titrated with standard $Hg(NO_3)_2$ in a pH 7 buffer and in the presence of EDTA. The end-point for cyanide is denoted by the onset of absorption at 240 nm; that for thiocyanate is indicated by the attainment of constant absorption[35]. A further application provides a method for $CN^-/SCN^-/I^-$ mixtures[36].

Spectroscopic methods

1. Colorimetric and spectrophotometric methods

One of the reviews[3] cited earlier includes a critical account of spectrophotometric methods for cyanide up to 1962. The methods are conveniently classified into three categories, those based on the Konig synthesis, those involving metal complexes, and a group of miscellaneous methods.

The first group depends on the reaction between cyanogen bromide, a suitable aromatic amine, and pyridine. Cyanogen bromide oxidizes pyridine to glutaconic aldehyde which condenses with the aromatic amine to give an intensely coloured system Ar—N=CH—CH=CH—CH=CH—CH—Ar.

The sensitivity depends on the particular amine used. Aldridge[37,38] developed a satisfactory procedure by reacting the CN^- with excess bromine to give cyanogen bromide, removing the excess with arsenic(III) and then reacting the cyanogen bromide with a pyridine–benzidine reagent. Several modifications have been made since its introduction. Nusbaum and Skupeko[39] extracted the dye into *n*-hexanol, thus extending the sensitivity to 0.02–0.5 ppm. Murty and Viswanathan[99] replaced benzidine with barbituric acid. A drawback with this procedure is rapid fading of the colour after reaching the maximum absorbance. Owing to the known carcinogenic properties of benzidine, other compounds were examined as alternatives. None was found to have marked advantages, but *p*-phenylenediamine was found to be the most favourable by Bark and Higson[40]. The range was 0.1–2 μg of CN^-. A second method[41] involving a distillation to separate SCN^-, Fe^{2+}, Ni^{2+}, Cu^{2+} and cyano complexes of Zn and Cu is suitable for 0.005–100 ppm of CN^-. This is now recommended as a method for CN^- in industrial effluents[42]. In the original work the reagent is said to be stable for six weeks; a recent publication[43] has disputed this, claiming that it must be prepared immediately before use.

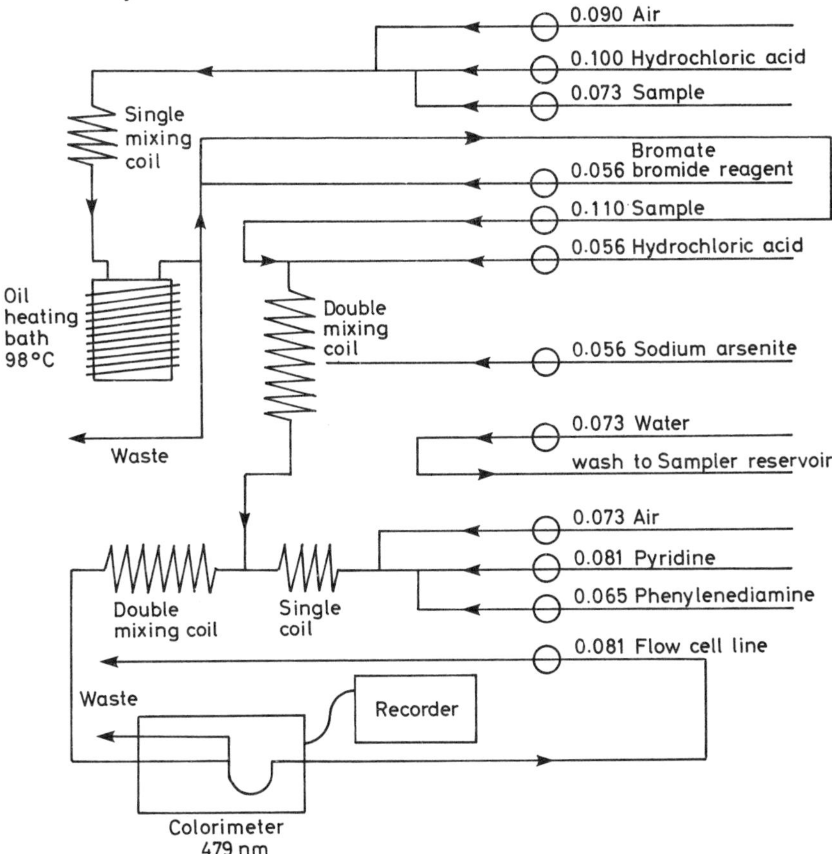

Figure 15 *Flow diagram showing automatic determination of cyanide.* (After Casapieri, Scott and Simpson[44])

The method has appeared in automated form, the AutoAnalyzer including a distillation stage[44]. The design eliminates the need to remove particulate matter by filtration, and can handle 40 samples/h. *Figure 15* shows the general arrangement.

More recently another automated spectrophotometric procedure has appeared utilizing pyridine–benzidine[45].

The pyridine–pyrazolone method proposed by Epstein[46] has found considerable use, particularly since the carcinogenic nature of benzidine became known. Here cyanide is oxidized with chloramine T and the resulting cyanogen chloride allowed to react with pyridine containing 3-methyl-1-phenyl-5-pyrazolone and a small quantity of bis-(3-methyl-1-phenyl-5-pyrazolone). The blue dye is evaluated at 630 nm. The method is sensitive, and can be made more sensitive by extracting into *n*-butanol. A disadvantage is instability of the reagent which must be prepared daily. The method is recommended for water analysis by the American Public Health Association[47]. A preliminary distillation removes or reduces the effects of interferences. Further applications[12, 13] have been made to determination of free cyanide in the presence of $[Fe(CN)_6]^{3-}$ and $[Fe(CN)_6]^{4-}$ and cyanide in blood. Each has been referred to earlier in connection with separation of cyanide. Nagashima[43] finds that a relatively stable violet-blue product is formed when γ-picoline-barbituric acid reagent is added to a cyanide sample which has been treated with chloramine T. The resulting method is applicable to water samples containing 0–0.5 μg mℓ$^{-1}$ of CN^-. No interference is given by Cl^-, NO_2^-, NO_3^-, SO_4^{2-}, CH_3COO^- and CNO^- in concentrations of 1000 μg of their sodium or potassium salts per 10 mℓ, on the determination of 2.0 μg of CN^- in 10 mℓ. Iron(III), $[Fe(CN)_6]^{3-}$, and $[Fe(CN)_6]^{4-}$ have little effect on the same amount of cyanide when present as 100 μg of their potassium salts in 10 mℓ. However, thiocyanate causes a significant positive error. The γ-picoline-barbituric reagent is stable for at least 3 weeks if stored at about 10 °C.

The ability of cyanide to form highly stable metal complexes has been exploited in the development of spectrophotometric methods, both direct and indirect. Komatsu and Nomura[48] react cyanide with the mercury(II)–EDTA complex which absorbs at 250 nm. The resulting $[HgY(CN)]^{3-}$ complex does not absorb at this wavelength and the decrease in absorbance of HgY^{2-} at 250 nm is proportional to the cyanide concentration in the range 0.01–1.2 mg per 50 mℓ of solution. Interference is given by SCN^-, S^{2-}, Br^-, I^-, Cu^{2+}, Ni^{2+}, Co^{2+}, $S_2O_3^{2-}$, Hg^{2+}, Cl^-, NH_4^+, etc. A similar method has appeared based on the metalphthalein–mercury(II) 1:1 complex[49]. Here the range is 1–20 μg CN^- per 50 mℓ. Several cations interfere but can be compensated for. Sulphide and iodide must be absent.

An indirect method consists of treating the cyanide sample with $Hg(NO_3)_2$ to form $Hg(CN)_2$. Excess Hg^{2+} is reacted with copper(II) diethyldithiocarbamate in chloroform and the absorbance measured at 440 nm[49]. Up to 50 μg of CN^- can be determined. Interference is given by S^{2-}, $S_2O_3^{2-}$ and I^- (>1 μg), Ag and Co(>60 μg), Ni(>100 μg) and Cu(>190 μg).

The ternary complex formed between cyanide and mercury(II)-methylthymol blue has been used. Here the absorbance is measured at 615 nm. The calibration curve is linear over the range 5–80 μg CN^- in the final solution. Several cations and anions interfere but can be masked[50]. The coloured product resulting from the reaction of copper(II), variamine blue and cyanide enables the latter to be determined[51] without interference from NH_4^+, NO_3^-, SO_4^{2-} or Cl^-.

The tris(1,10 phenanthroline)–iron(II) complex (ferroin) has featured in several spectrophotometric procedures. Schilt[52] extracted the dicyanobis-(1,10 phenanthroline)–iron(II) complex into chloroform for spectrophotometric measurement. The method has been modified recently and its sensitivity and selectivity improved[53]. In its new form no interference is given by up to 1 gℓ^{-1} of Fe or Cu salts, S^{2-}, $Ca(CN)_2$, acrylonitrile, phenol, methanol, formaldehyde, urea, thiourea, caprolactam or hexamine.

Lambert and Manzo[54] use the highly insoluble tris(1,10 phenanthroline)–iron(II)-triiodide. When this is added to cyanide an equivalent amount of tri(1,10 phen) iron(II) is liberated and can be measured spectrophotometrically. Hiiro and Yamamoto[55] convert cyanide to thiocyanate and extract the tris(1,10 phen) iron(II)-SCN ion-association system into nitrobenzene for measurement at 516 nm. Cyanide in concentrations up to 40 μM can be determined using the method.

The use of chloranilates is well established in the spectrophotometric determination of Cl^-, SO_4^{2-} and F^-. Application to cyanide (as well as sulphide and sulphite) has been made by Humphrey and Hinze[56] using mercuric chloranilate. Depending on the wavelength used, two ranges for cyanide are possible, 0.4–4 μg mℓ^{-1} and 20–200 μg mℓ^{-1}.

Mercury(II)-diphenylcarbazone has featured in several cyanide procedures[57,58]. An indirect method has been based on a ternary system previously developed for determination of trace amounts of silver[59]. The complex, which can be represented as $[(\text{phen-Ag-phen})^+]_2\ \text{BPR}^{2-}$, is produced by interaction of silver(I), 1,10-phenanthroline and bromopyrogallol red. Its molar absorptivity is 5.1×10^4 at 635 nm. When cyanide is present, formation of the complex is inhibited. The lower limit for cyanide using the method is 0.2 ppm. Of 17 cations examined only mercury(II) could not be tolerated. A 1000-fold molar excess (over cyanide) of 14 anions can be tolerated. Bromide, iodide and thiocyanate interfere, but addition of $Pb(NO_3)_2$, $(NH_4)_2SO_4$ and $Ba(NO_3)_2$ followed by treatment by centrifuge prevents this.

Cyanide reacts rapidly with Ni^{2+} ions in ammoniacal solution to form the stable ionic tetracyanonickelate(II) anion complex, $[Ni(CN)_4]^{2-}$. This exhibits an absorption at 267 nm with Beer's law holding over the range 5–200 μg CN^- per 10 mℓ of ammoniacal $NiCl_2$ solution. The molar absorptivity is 1.1×10^4 at this wavelength. A big advantage is that ammoniacal nickel chloride solution can be used as absorbent in the separation of cyanide by distillation. Volatile HCN reacts immediately with the solution forming the complex anion which can be evaluated without further treatment. Sulphide and sulphite interfere, but can be eliminated readily. The method is also applicable to determination of nickel.

Consideration will now be given to a group of spectrophotometric methods for cyanide falling outside the previous categories. Humphrey and Hinze[60] utilize the nucleophilic displacement reaction of organic disulphides with cyanide which produces an absorbing thiol anion and an organic thiocyanate.

$$\text{RSSR} + \text{CN}^- \rightarrow \text{RS}^- + \text{RSCN}$$

Several disulphides were examined including 2,2′-dithiopyridine, 4,4′-dithiodipyridine and 5,5′-dithiobis (2-nitrobenzoic acid). The relatively simple procedure is applicable to 0.2–5.0 μg mℓ$^{-1}$ of cyanide. By varying the reactant ratio the upper limit can be extended to 50 μg mℓ$^{-1}$. Mercaptans, sulphide and sulphite interfere, and so do many metallic ions. The latter can be masked by EDTA with the exception of Cu^{2+} and Hg^{2+}. A disadvantage in the original procedure is the slowness of the reaction, particularly at low concentrations of cyanide. An improvement was obtained when dimethylformamide was used[61], this reducing the time from about 2 h to 30 min.

Guilbault and Kramer[62] describe an ultra-sensitive spectrophotometric procedure that appears to be specific for cyanide. This depends on the reaction between cyanide and *p*-nitrobenzaldehyde in alkaline solution to give an active cyanohydrin capable of reducing various compounds to coloured species. The reaction of this cyanohydrin with *o*-dinitrobenzene is as follows:

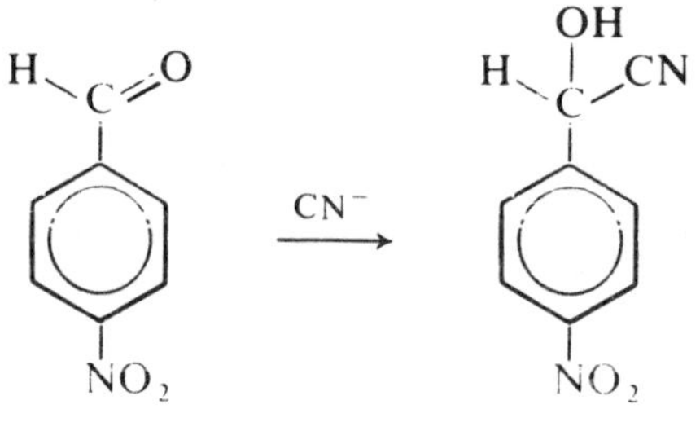

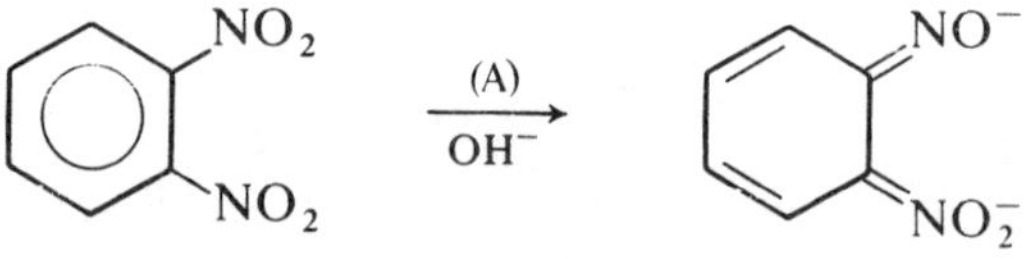

cyanide is regenerated, and a catalytic reaction occurs with increasing sensitivity. The procedure consists of measuring the rate of change in absorbance with time. From calibration plots of $\Delta A/\Delta t$ *v.* CN^- concentration (45–450 ng mℓ$^{-1}$ of solution used) the amount of cyanide present is calculated. Of more than 30 anions tested no interference was found. When 1-benzoyl-1-hydroxyimino-acetone is added as catalyst, as little as 1.3 ng mℓ$^{-1}$ of CN^- can be detected. A further study of the method by Popescu and Dura[63] has been reported. This finds that modification is required if it is to be applied in the presence of $[Fe(CN)_6]^{3-}$ and $[Fe(CN)_6]^{4-}$.

2. *Spectrofluorimetric*

Several quinone derivatives have been shown to be suitable for the spectrofluorimetric determination of cyanide[64,65]. These include *p*-benzoquinone, N-chloro-*p*-benzoquinoneimine and *o*-(*p*-nitrobenzene sulphonyl) quinone monoxime. The first compound reacts with as little as 0.2 μg mℓ$^{-1}$ of CN^- giving a highly fluorescent product. Of a wide range of ions tested none was found to interfere in concentrations up to 0.1M. The reaction is thought to be

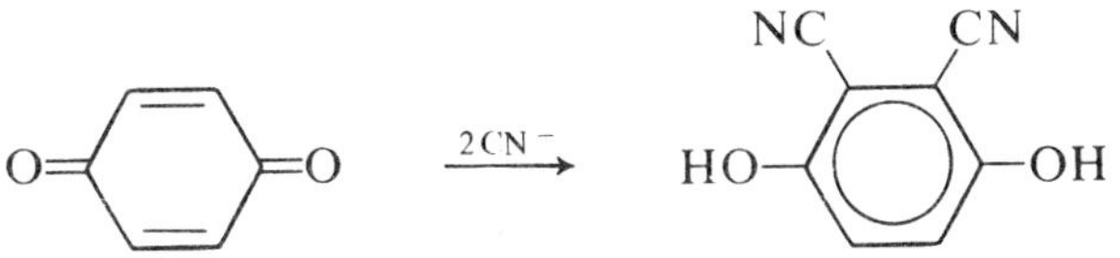

The range for CN^- is 0.2–50 µg.

Takanashi and Tamura[66] use pyridoxal for determination of cyanide in amounts up to 1.3 µg. The method is found to be ten times more sensitive than the CNBr–benzidine spectrophotometric procedure.

When cyanide reacts with 2′,7′-bis(acetoxymercuri) fluorescein (*Structure 11*) the decrease in fluorescence is proportional to the concentration of cyanide.

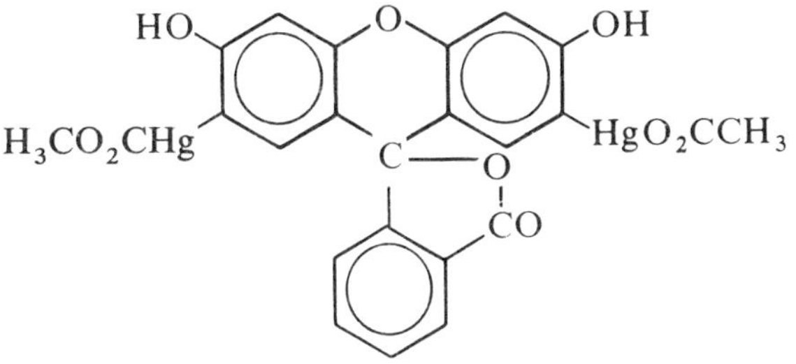

Structure 11 2′7′-bis (acetoxymercuri) fluorescein

This has been developed into a method by Colovos, Haro and Freiser[67] for 3–9 µg of CN^-.

3. Atomic absorption spectroscopy

Indirect methods have appeared for determination of cyanide by AAS. Danchik and Boltz[68] utilize the iron equivalent to cyanide in the dicyano-tris(1,10 phenanthroline)iron(II) complex. A linear response is obtained in the range 0.1–5 ppm CN^-. A more recent method by Manahan and Kunkel[69] for use in sewage analysis, uses the copper associated with cyanide in a 3:1 CN^-–Cu complex. The sensitivity is 2.0×10^{-5}M CN^-.

Electroanalytical methods

1. Potentiometric methods including ion-selective electrodes

The argentimetric titration of cyanide referred to earlier, can be conducted potentiometrically using a silver electrode.

A potentiometric recorder for monitoring HCN in the atmosphere has been described[70]. The gas is passed into an alkaline absorbent after which the potential is measured using silver and calomel electrodes.

Ueno and Tachikawa[71] have investigated the use of several bimetallic electrodes for the titration of cyanide with $AgNO_3$. These include Pt–Ni, Pt–Ag, Pt–W, and Pt–Pd.

The application of ion-selective electrodes (ISE) to cyanide analysis is now well established and there is little doubt that it will become a standard method, for example in the analysis of industrial waters. Commercial electrodes are available, for example the Orion 94–06, and the OP-CN-711 (Radelkis, Hungary). Halide membrane electrodes can be used for determination of cyanide. Of these the iodide electrode (e.g. Orion 94–53, Corning-Eel 47612700) is the most suitable because of its high selectivity. The silver/sulphide electrode (e.g. Orion 94–16) is also applicable. In the case of the Orion 94–06 electrode, the concentration range is 10^{-2}–10^{-6}M CN^-. Common ions such as F^-, NO_3^- and CO_3^{2-} do not interfere, but S^{2-} must be absent. The selectivity constants* for Cl^-, I^- and Br^- are 10^{-6}, 10, and 2×10^{-3} respectively. At high cyanide levels the active life of the electrode is restricted.

In addition to direct measurements the cyanide ISE can be used as an indicator electrode in the argentimetric titration of cyanide. The AgI-based electrode covers the range 10^{-6}–10^{-1}M CN^-. It responds to free cyanide and cyano complexes[72] which are less stable than $Ag(CN)_2^-$. Mascini[73] has investigated the effect on electrode response of the iodide produced in the reaction with AgI at the membrane surface, as a function of pH. Using the Ag/S^{2-} electrode in the 'known addition' technique, Frant, Ross and Riseman[74] are able to determine cyanide down to 0.03 ppm. The error at 1.0 ppm is found to be 2 per cent. In this method, which was applied to wastewater, samples containing Zn^{2+}, Cd^{2+}, Cr^{3+}, Cu^{2+} and Ni^{2+} were effectively treated with EDTA to break down the strong cyanide complexes and release cyanide for measurement.

Conrad[75] has used the Ag/S^{2-} electrode as indicator electrode in the potentiometric titration of CN^-/Cl^- solutions with Ag^+. The response obtained is shown in *Figure 16*.

Due attention has been given to continuous measurements and automatic methods. Fleet and Ho[76] report a method for continuous monitoring of cyanide based on computerized Gran-plot technique. Fleet and von Storp[77] report an evaluation of the cyanide electrode under flow stream conditions. The response was found to be dependent on flow rate and temperature. The same paper indicates that precipitation by cadmium(II) is the best method of removing interfering sulphide.

Application of the cyanide ISE extends into many areas including plant biochemistry. For example, cyanoglycosides are common in many cultivated plants. The glycoside itself, containing bonded cyanide is not toxic, but enzymatic hydrolysis can produce highly toxic HCN. Determination of CN^- in a range of such materials can be made using the cyanide ISE[78]. Further applications appear in the Orion analytical methods guide[79]. A review of ISE for halides and cyanides in chemicals, foods, and pharmaceutical products has been published[80].

2. *Amperometric methods*

An earlier study involving Ag(I) as titrant and a rotating platinum electrode was made by Laitinen, Jennings and Parks[81]. Shinozuka and Stock[82], using a platinum microelectrode, avoid interference of iodide or sulphide by working at a potential of −0.85 V. No interference is given by a 100-fold

* Selectivity constants are discussed on p. 318.

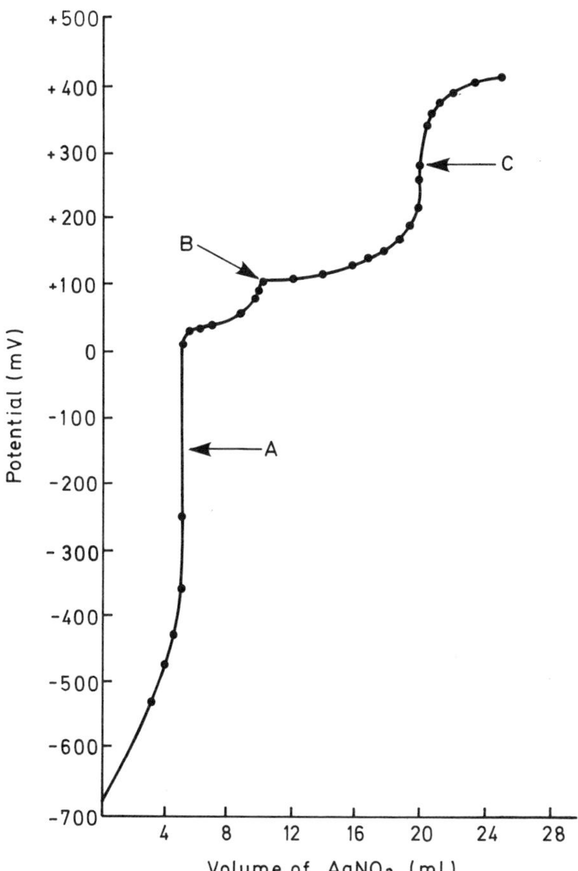

Figure 16 *Potentiometric titration of* CN^-/Cl^- *with 0.1000M* $AgNO_3$ *using Orion 94–16* Ag/S^{2-} *electrode*
A, 1st CN^- *equivalence point representing*

$$Ag^+ + 2CN^- \rightarrow Ag(CN)_2^-$$

B, 2nd equivalence point representing

$$Ag(CN)_2^- + Ag^+ \rightarrow 2AgCN$$

C, End-point Cl^- *representing*

$$Ag^+ + Cl^- \rightarrow AgCl$$

(From Conrad[75])

amount of bromide or chloride. Successive amperometric titration of CN^-, Cl^- and OCN^- in microgram amounts is reported by Musha and Ikeda[83]. The error is about 2 per cent when almost equal amounts of the anions are present.

3. Polarographic methods

Cyanides form stable mercury complexes. The cyanide anodic wave at the dropping mercury electrode which occurs at about −0.4 V in 0.1M NaOH corresponds to the formation of such complexes.

$$Hg + 2CN^- \rightarrow Hg(CN)_2^{2-}$$

This provides a polarographic method suitable for routine purposes. Several developments have been reported. Miller and co-workers[84] using a rapidly rotating gold electrode in a LiOH medium find that the response to cyanide is linear in the range 10^{-6}–10^{-10} g.

Toropova and Averko-Antonovich[86] utilize the catalytic wave which arises in the polarography of the nickel(II)–ethylenediamine complex when cyanide is present. This allows concentrations down to 0.5 μg ℓ$^{-1}$ of CN^- to be determined. A linear response of wave height to concentration is found in the range 0.1–1 μg CN^- ℓ$^{-1}$. A second study involves the nickel(II)–hydroxylamine–cyanide system[86].

Cathode-ray polarography has been applied to cyanide in water at concentrations down to 0.05 μg mℓ$^{-1}$. Large excesses of chloride can be tolerated but free chlorine, bromine and iodine must be absent[87]. An interesting indirect polarographic procedure has been reported by Humphrey and Laird[88]. This is based on the chloranilate ion, well known in connection with spectrophotometric methods for Cl^-, F^-, CN^- and SO_4^{2-}. Humphrey and Laird[88] measure the displaced chloranilate ion by means of a two-electron reduction at the dropping mercury electrode. The resulting reduction current is related to the cyanide concentration .

Catalytic methods

Cyanide inhibits the chemiluminescence of luminol with H_2O_2 in the presence of Cu^{2+}, the induction period increasing with increase in cyanide concentration. Musha and co-workers[89] have based a fixed-concentration method for cyanide on the reaction. Interference is given by Fe^{3+}(>5 ppm), NO_2^- (>0.4 ppm), I^- (>20 ppm) and SO_3^{2-} (>0.5 ppm).

The enzyme β-fructofuranosidease (invertase) is inhibited in its catalysis of the hydrolysis of such substrates as sucrose, by traces of certain metal ions. Small concentrations of anions that form strong complexes with these metals, e.g. CN^-, S^{2-} and I^-, compete with the enzyme for the metals and decrease the inhibitary effect. Mealor and Townshend[90] find that cyanide in concentrations of 10^{-5}–10^{-7} M can be determined using this effect. Optical rotation is used as the measuring technique.

Gas-chromatographic methods

Gas chromatography was applied by Isbell[91] for separating cyanide from mixtures containing O_2, N_2, CH_4, CO_2 and CO, prior to its determination. Two columns were employed, one containing chromosorb P impregnated with 25% glycerol triacetate and the other a molecular sieve. Helium was used as carrier.

A more recent method for both cyanide and thiocyanate first converts them to cyanogen bromide by treatment with bromine and follows this with gas-chromatographic analysis using electron capture detection[92]. As little as

10^{-8} g can be detected; calibration graphs based on peak heights are linear in the 0.0–0.5 ppm CN^- range. Enhancement of sensitivity is possible by extraction in di-isopropyl ether before injection into the column. This allows about 1 ppb (10^9) of CNBr to be detected. No interference by complex cyanides is reported, but these can be determined after conversion to simple cyanides. Determination of cyanide in biological material by gas-chromatography has been reported[14]. Here initial separation is made by microdiffusion into NaOH. This is followed by conversion to cyanogen chloride by chloramine T before gas-chromatography. The column itself consists of 7% Halcomid M-18 on Anakrom ABS (90–110 mesh) at 55 °C with methane–argon (1:19) as carrier gas. Detection is by electron capture. Linear calibration graphs are found for up to about 100 μg CN^- $m\ell^{-1}$.

Radiochemical methods

Radioactive exhange has provided several methods for cyanide. If a Hg^{203}-labelled suspension of $Hg(IO_3)_2$ is added to a cyanide sample, together with KIO_3 to suppress its solubility, un-ionized $^{203}Hg(CN)_2$ is formed. Its activity, measured using a liquid counter, was used by Banyai, Szabadvary and Erdey[93] to determine cyanide.

Bowen[94] has used Γ10-labelled AgI in a similar manner.

$$2CN^- + {}^{110}AgI \rightleftharpoons {}^{110}Ag(CN)_2^- + I^-$$

Here the sample solution is passed through a column of the labelled iodide. The activity of the filtered solution is counted using a well-type NaI crystal focused on the 0.66 MeV γ-ray from ^{110}Ag. The method is rapid and sensitive, and suffers little interference.

Miscellaneous methods

Microgram amounts of cyanide can be determined indirectly[95] using X-ray fluorescence analysis after precipitation with silver(I).

Noshiro and Matsumoto[96] determine several inorganic species, including cyanide, using a commercial CHN analyser. Quantitative paper chromatography offers a method for the estimation of trace amounts of cyanide. This is done[97] by measuring the areas of the white spots formed by 1–6 μg CN^- on Whatman No. 1 paper impregnated with CuS. These are proportional to the amounts of cyanide applied. The boundaries of the spots are enhanced by spraying with 1% methanolic sodium diethyldithiocarbamate. No interference is given by a 100-fold molar excess of SCN^-, Cl^-, Br^-, I^- or OCN^-, or a 24-fold excess of S^{2-}.

Ganchev and Koev[98] use filter paper impregnated with Ag_2CrO_4 (or AgCl or AgBr) for determination of micro amounts of cyanide or dicyanoargentate(I). After applying 0.01 mℓ to the narrow band of filter paper, elution is carried out slowly with water in a special apparatus. The band is dried, treated with H_2S and the white spot cut out and weighed. The procedure permits the determination of 8–80 μg CN^- to within ±1.5%. Application of the method can be made to mixtures of CN^- and $Ag(CN)_2^-$.

References

1. MONTGOMERY, H.A.C., GARDINER, D.K. and GREGORY, J.G.G., *Analyst*, **94**, 284 (1969)
2. ROBERTS, G.L., in *Encyclopedia of Industrial Chemical Analysis* (Ed. F. D. Snell and L. S. Ettre), Vol. 14, Interscience, New York, 403 (1971)
3. BARK, L.S. and HIGSON, H.G., *Analyst*, **88**, 751 (1963)
4. BOLTZ, D.F., *Crit. Rev. analyt. Chem.*, **3**, 147 (1973)
5. LUDZACK, F.J., MOORE, W.A. and RUCHHOFT, C.C., *Analyt. Chem.*, **26**, 1784 (1954)
6. SERFASS, E.J., FREEMAN, R.B., DODGE, B.F. and ZABBAN, W., *Plating*, **39**, 267 (1952)
7. *Official, Standardised and Recommended Methods of Analysis*, Compiled and Edited by N.W. Hanson, 2nd edn, The Society for Analytical Chemistry, London, 455 (1973)
8. ROBERTS, R.F. and JACKSON, B., *Analyst*, **96**, 209 (1971)
9. Ref. 7, 457
10. HILBERT, F. and DARWISH, N.A., *Z. analyt. Chem.*, **255**, 357 (1971); *Analyt. Abstr.*, **22**, 3068 (1972)
11. TOMPSETT, S.L., *Clin. Chem.*, **5**, 587 (1959)
12. KRUSE, J.M. and THIBAULT, L.E., *Analyt. Chem.*, **45**, 2260 (1973)
13. BAAR, S., *Analyst*, **91**, 268 (1966)
14. VALENTOUR, J.C., AGGARWAL, V. and SUNSHINE, I., *Analyt. Chem.*, **46**, 924 (1974)
15. SCHILT, A.A., *Analyt. Chem.*, **30**, 1409 (1958)
16. CANIC, V.D., TURCIC, M.N., BUGARSKI-VOJINOVIC, M.B. and PERISIC, N.U., *Z. analyt. Chem.*, **229**, 93 (1967); *Analyt. Abstr.*, **15**, 5211 (1968)
17. GAGLIARDI, E. and POKORNY, G., *Mikrochim. Acta*, 699 (1965)
18. THIELMANN, H., *Z. analyt. Chem.*, **270**, 128 (1974); *Analyt. Abstr.*, **28**, 2B86 (1975)
19. LIEBIG, J. VON, *Ann. Chem. Liebigs*, **77**, 102 (1851)
20. DÉNIGÈS, G., *Compt. rend.*, **117**, 1078 (1893)
21. LAITINEN, H.A., *Chemical Analysis*, McGraw-Hill, New York, 225 (1960)
22. BUTLER, J.N., *Ionic Equilibria*, Addison-Wesley, Mass., 280 (1964)
23. British Standard 622: (1967) Appendix B, London
24. RYAN, J.A. and CULSHAW, G.W., *Analyst*, **69**, 370 (1944)
25. MEHLIG, J.P., *Chemist Analyst*, **44**, 87 (1955)
26. ARCHER, E.E., *Analyst*, **83**, 571 (1958)
27. DAGNALL, R.M., EL-GHAMRY, M.T. and WEST, T.S., *Talanta*, **13**, 1667 (1966)
28. GREGOROWICZ, Z. and BUHL, F., *Z. analyt. Chem.*, **173**, 115 (1960); *Analyt. Abstr.*, **7**, 4150 (1960)
29. SCHULEK, E., *Z. analyt. Chem.*, **62**, 337 (1923)
30. SCHULEK, E., BURGER, K. and FEHER, M., *Z. analyt. Chem.*, **167**, 429 (1959); *Analyt. Abstr.*, **7**, 451 (1960)
31. DE SOUSA, A., *Inf. Quim. Anal.*, **15**, 61 (1961); *Analyt. Abstr.*, **9**, 127 (1962)
32. DE SOUSA, A., *Inf. Quim. Anal.*, **16**, 126 (1962); *Analyt. Abstr.*, **10**, 2243 (1963)
33. DE SOUSA, A., *Talanta*, **8**, 782 (1961)
34. KOMATSU, S. and NOMURA, T., *J. Chem. Soc. Japan, pure Chem. Sect.*, **87**, 1060 (1966); *Analyt. Abstr.*, **15**, 720 (1968)
35. NOMURA, T., *J. chem. Soc. Japan, pure Chem. Sect.*, **89**, 580 (1968); *Analyt. Abstr.*, **18**, 114 (1970)
36. NOMURA, T., *Bull. chem. Soc. Japan*, **43**, 104 (1970); *Analyt. Abstr.*, **20**, 934 (1971)
37. ALDRIDGE, W.N., *Analyst*, **69**, 262 (1944)
38. ALDRIDGE, W.N., *Analyst*, **70**, 474 (1945)
39. NUSBAUM, I. and SKUPEKO, P., *Analyt. Chem.*, **23**, 875 (1951)
40. BARK, L.S. and HIGSON, H.G., *Talanta*, **11**, 471 (1964)
41. BARK, L.S. and HIGSON, H.G., *Talanta*, **11**, 621 (1964)
42. Ref. 7, 456
43. NAGASHIMA, S., *Analytica chim. Acta*, **91**, 303 (1977)
44. CASAPIERI, P., SCOTT, R. and SIMPSON, E.A., *Analytica chim. Acta*, **49**, 188 (1970)
45. ROYER, J.L., TWICHELL, J.E. and MUIR, S.M., *Analyt. Lett.*, **6**, 619 (1973)
46. EPSTEIN, J., *Analyt. Chem.*, **19**, 272 (1947)
47. American Public Health Association, *Standard Methods for the Examination of Water and Wastewater*, 13th edn, American Public Health Association, New York (1970)
48. KOMATSU, S. and NOMURA, T., *J. chem. Soc. Japan, pure Chem. Sect.*, **87**, 845 (1966); *Analyt. Abstr.*, **14**, 7419 (1967)
49. KOMATSU, S., NOMURA, T. and MOCHIZUKI, F., *J. chem. Soc. Japan, pure Chem. Sect.*, **90**, 944 (1969); *Analyt. Abstr.*, **19**, 3801 (1970)

50. NOMURA, T., *Bull. chem. Soc. Japan*, **41**, 1619 (1968); *Analyt. Abstr.*, **17**, 3378 (1969)
51. GREGOROWICZ, Z. and BUHL, F., *Z. analyt. Chem.*, **187**, 1 (1962); *Analyt. Abstr.*, **9**, 4575 (1962)
52. SCHILT, A.A., *Analyt. Chem.*, **30**, 1409 (1958)
53. KODURA, I. and LADA, Z., *Chemia analit.*, **17**, 871 (1972); *Analyt. Abstr.*, **24**, 3842 (1973)
54. LAMBERT, J.L., and MANZO, D.J., *Analyt. Chem.*, **40**, 1354 (1968)
55. HIIRO, K. and YAMAMOTO, Y., *Analyt. Lett.*, **6**, 761 (1973); *Analyt. Abstr.*, **26**, 2596 (1974)
56. HUMPHREY, R.E. and HINZE, W., *Analyt. Chem.*, **43**, 1100 (1971)
57. OKUTANI, T. and UTSUMI, S., *J. chem. Soc. Japan, pure Chem. Sect.*, **87**, 444 (1966); *Analyt. Abstr.*, **14**, 5341 (1967)
58. OHLWEILER, O.A. and OLIVEIRA, J., *Zh. analit. Khim.*, **14**, 303 (1959); *Analyt. Abstr.*, **7**, 921 (1960)
59. DAGNALL, R.M., EL-GHAMRY, M.T. and WEST, T.S., *Talanta*, **15**, 107 (1968)
60. HUMPHREY, R.E. and HINZE, W., *Talanta*, **18**, 491 (1971)
61. HUMPHREY, R.E. and ALVAREZ, J.J., *Microchem. J.*, **16**, 652 (1971)
62. GUILBAULT, G.G. and KRAMER, D.N., *Analyt. Chem.*, **38**, 834 (1966)
63. POPESCU, G. and DURA, M., *Revta. Chim.*, **21**, 7 (1970); *Analyt. Abstr.*, **20**, 304 (1971)
64. GUILBAULT, G.G. and KRAMER, D.N., *Analyt. Chem.*, **37**, 918 (1965)
65. GUILBAULT, G.G. and KRAMER, D.N., *Analyt. Chem.*, **37**, 1395 (1965)
66. TAKANASHI, S. and TAMURA, Z., *Chem. Pharm. Bull., Tokyo*, **18**, 1633 (1970); *Analyt. Abstr.*, **21**, 118 (1971)
67. COLOVOS, G., HARO, M. and FREISER, H., *Talanta*, **17**, 273 (1970)
68. DANCHIK, R.S. and BOLTZ, D.F., *Analyt. Chem.*, **49**, 567 (1970)
69. MANAHAN, S.E. and KUNKEL, R., *Analyt. Lett.*, **6**, 547 (1973)
70. STRANGE, J.P., *Analyt. Chem.*, **29**, 1878 (1957)
71. UENO, K. and TACHIKAWA, T., *Muroran Kogyo Diagaku Kenku Hokaku*, **2**, 377 (1959); *Chem. Abstr.*, **54**, 1154a (1960)
72. TOTH, K. and PUNGOR, E., *Analytica chim. Acta*, **51**, 221 (1970)
73. MASCINI, M., *Analyt. Chem.*, **45**, 614 (1973)
74. FRANT, M.S., ROSS, J.W. and RISEMAN, J.H., *Analyt. Chem.*, **44**, 2227 (1972)
75. CONRAD, F.J., *Talanta*, **18**, 952 (1971)
76. FLEET, B. and HO, A.Y.W., *Talanta*, **20**, 793 (1973)
77. FLEET, B. and VON STORP, H., *Analyt. Chem.*, **43**, 1575 (1971)
78. GYORGY, B., ANDRÉ, L., STEHLI, L. and PUNGOR, E., *Analytica chim. Acta*, **46**, 318 (1969)
79. *Orion analytical methods guide*, 7th edn, Orion Research Inc., Cambridge, Massachusetts (1975). Available from MSE Scientific Instruments, Crawley, East Sussex, UK
80. PUNGOR, E., *Zh. analit. Khim.*, **25**, 1182 (1970)
81. LAITINEN, H.A., JENNINGS, W.P. and PARKS, T.D., *Ind. Engng Chem. analyt. Edn*, **18**, 574 (1946)
82. SHINOZUKA, F. and STOCK, J.T., *Analyt. Chem.*, **34**, 926 (1962)
83. MUSHA, S. and IKEDA, S., *Japan Analyst*, **14**, 795 (1965); *Analyt. Abstr.*, **14**, 3028 (1967)
84. MILLER, G.W., LONG, L.E., GEORGE, G.M. and SIKES, W.L., *Analyt. Chem.*, **36**, 980 (1964)
85. TOROPOVA, V.F. and AVERKO-ANTONOVICH, A.A., *Zh. analit. Khim.*, **26**, 2437 (1971); *Analyt. Abstr.*, **24**, 3412 (1973)
86. TOROPOVA, V.F. and AVERKO-ANTONOVICH, A.A., *Zh. analit. Khim.*, **27**, 116 (1972)
87. HETMAN, J., *J. appl. Chem.*, **10**, 16 (1960)
88. HUMPHREY, R.E. and LAIRD, C.E., *Analyt. Chem.*, **43**, 1895 (1971)
89. MUSHA, S., ITO, M., YAMAMOTO, Y. and INAMORI, Y., *J. chem. Soc. Japan, pure Chem. Sect.*, **80**, 1285 (1959); *Analyt. Abstr.*, **7**, 4186 (1960)
90. MEALOR, D. and TOWNSHEND, A., *Talanta*, **15**, 1477 (1968)
91. ISBELL, R.E., *Analyt. Chem.*, **35**, 255 (1963)
92. NOTA, G. and PALOMBARI, R., *J. Chromat.*, **84**, 37 (1973)
93. BANYAI, E., SZABADVARY, F. and ERDEY, L., *Talanta*, **10**, (1963)
94. BOWEN, H.J.M., *Analyst*, **97**, 728 (1972)
95. STORK, G. and JUNG, H., *Z. analyt. Chem.*, **249**, 161 (1970); *Analyt. Abstr.*, **20**, 1523 (1971)
96. NOSHIRO, M. and MATSUMOTO, K., *Japan Analyst*, **20**, 1069 (1971); *Analyt. Abstr.*, **25**, 20 (1973)
97. KIELCZEWSKI, W., SCHNEIDER, M. and UCHMAN, W., *Chemia analit.*, **12**, 143 (1967); *Analyt. Abstr.*, **15**, 1932 (1968)
98. GANCHEV, N. and KOEV, K., *Mikrochim. Acta*, 92 (1964)
99. MURTY, G.V.L.N. and VISWANATHAN, T.S., *Analytica chim. Acta*, **25**, 293 (1961)

Fluorosilicate

Fluorosilicate, SiF_6^{2-}, is also known as fluosilicate or hexafluorosilicate and in older literature as silicofluoride. Fluorosilicates find use as fluoridizing agents for water supplies, in the production of synthetic cryolite, and in metal plating. In the separation of fluorine by the traditional Willard and Winter method, the distilled fluorine is partly in the form of fluorosilicic acid.

The analytical literature of the ion is sparse. Earlier methods are discussed by Kolthoff and Stenger[1].

A simple method suitable for assay of fluorosilicic acid consists of adding KNO_3 and ethanol to an ice-cold solution. Potassium fluorosilicate is precipitated and the liberated hydrogen ions titrated with standard alkali using phenolphthalein as indicator. This method has been recently applied to determination of fluorosilicate in chromium plating electrolytes[2]. The precipitated potassium fluorosilicate is washed with 20% KNO_3 or KCl, added to water and the cooled solution neutralized to phenolphthalein. The solution is then heated to 80 °C and titrated with standard alkali to the same end-point.

A spectrophotometric method based on α-molybdosilicic acid enables fluorosilicate to be determined[3] in the presence of hydrofluoric acid, the latter being complexed with $AlCl_3$. Molybdosilicic acid is produced after addition of ammonium molybdate, making strongly acid, and allowing to stand for 3 h. The extinction is measured at 370 nm; Beer's law holds for up to 0.8 mg SiO_2 per 100 mℓ.

Japanese workers have developed a rapid photometric titration method for fluorosilicate in chromium plating baths[4]. Thorium nitrate is used as titrant with iron salicylate as indicator. On adding the indicator the following equilibrium is set up:

$$SiF_6^{2-} + FeR^{2+} + 2H_2O \rightleftharpoons FeF_6^{3-} + R^- + 4H^+ + SiO_2$$

The fluorosilicate is titrated thus:

$$2SiF_6^{2-} + 3Th^{4+} + 4H_2O \rightarrow 3ThF_4 + 8H^+ + 2SiO_2$$

At the end-point FeF_6^{3-} reacts with Th^{4+} to release Fe^{3+} ions which develop a colour by formation of ferric salicylate. At the end-point, the absorbance of ferric salicylate at 510 nm reaches a maximum value, and remains constant on further addition of Th^{4+}. SiO_2 and ThF_4 are maintained in colloidal condition by addition of a surfactant.

Photometric titration of fluorosilicate[4]

Reagents

Chloroacetic acid:	1.5M adjusted to pH 2.8 with NaOH.
Ferric salicylate:	5 mM.
Polyoxyethylene sorbitan laurate:	2%.
Thorium nitrate:	0.25M.

Procedure

Filter a 10 mℓ aliquot (containing 2–12 gℓ$^{-1}$ SiF_6^{2-}), adjust the pH to

3.0 with NaOH and dilute to 100 mℓ in a volumetric flask. To a 10 mℓ aliquot add 5 mℓ of chloroacetic acid solution, 2 mℓ of ferric salicylate and 2 mℓ of polyoxyethylene sorbitan laurate. Titrate the product with 0.25M thorium nitrate solution until the absorbance at 510 nm reaches a maximum value.

Notes

1. There is no interference from Cr^{3+} or Fe at a concentration of less than 10 g$ℓ^{-1}$, or $Cr_2O_7^{2-}$.
2. The error is less than 2 per cent.
3. If iron is present, 1.2 mℓ of 0.03M sodium salicylate may be added in place of ferric salicylate.
4. In the presence of excessive amounts of iron, the extinction of ferric salicylate is decreased with 0.1M EDTA.

References

1. KOLTHOFF, I.M. and STENGER, V.A., *Volumetric Analysis*, Vol. II, Second revised edition, Interscience, New York (1947)
2. VYSOTSKAYA, V.N., *Zav. Lab.*, **37**, 415 (1971); *Analyt. Abstr.*, **22**, 763 (1972)
3. GRAFF, P.R. and LANGMYHR, F.J., *Analytica chim. Acta*, **21**, 429 (1959)
4. MUSHA, S. and HIGASHINO, T., *Japan Analyst*, **7**, 156 (1958); *Chem. Abstr.*, **54**, 1122h (1960)

Formate

Separations

Separation of formate is generally carried out by distillation or chromatography. Thin-layer chromatography on cellulose provides a means of separating formic acid from oxalic, tartaric and citric acids using 80:20 2-butanol–2M ammonia or other solvent mixtures[1]. Further details are given in the sections on citrate and oxalate. In another system, formic is separated from acetic and lactic acids on silica gel G layers using pyridine:petroleum ether 1:2 as solvent[2].

When paper chromatography is used, most simple solvents fail to separate formate and acetate since the R_f values are close. It has been found that phenol saturated with water provides a clear-cut separation[3].

Steam distillation is often used to separate formic acid as a preliminary to its determination, for example, Rientbrock and Hinrichs[4] use it for biological material. The subsequent determination in this instance was by spectrophotometry after reduction of the formate to formaldehyde.

Shelley, Salwin and Horowitz[5] separate formate from foodstuffs by steam distillation, following this with a gas-chromatographic determination of formic, acetic, propionic and butyric acids.

The triphenylstannonium ion, (Ph_3Sn^+), has been investigated as an extractant for organic acids, with benzene as solvent[6]. For formate, the degree of extraction is about 90 per cent at pH 1–2.

Determination

Titrimetric methods

1. Acid–base

A straightforward acid–base titration of formic acid with NaOH and using phenolphthalein as indicator, is possible. The method is non-selective, but it finds application in the assay of formic acid[7]. The equivalence point is at pH 7.88.

2. Redox

Several reagents have been recommended for the redox titration of formic acid. Some offer no special advantage.

Since the extensive study of the permanganate–formate reaction by Stamm[8] in which excess of alkaline $KMnO_4$ was added to formate in the presence of barium ions (to form barium permanganate) and the excess back-titrated, a potentiometric variation has been described[9]. Flaschka and Garrett[20] have attempted to overcome the drawbacks of permanganate by using it only to oxidize the formate. The hydrated manganese(IV) oxide is then removed, reduced with ascorbic acid to manganese(II) and the latter titrated with EDTA. Recently the influence of pH and oxidation time on the reaction has been investigated[10]. The recommended procedure involves dissolving the resulting MnO_2 in aqueous sodium diphosphate, acidified with H_2SO_4 and titrating the Mn^{3+} complex formed with quinol.

Oxidation by potassium manganate has been described by Polak[11]. By selecting conditions, this reagent enables formic, oxalic, and acetic acids to be determined when present together.

Selective oxidation of formic acid in the presence of acetic is also possible using cerium(IV). Oxidation of formic plus acetic can be accomplished using copper(III) thus enabling the acetic acid to be determined[12]. In a later paper Jaiswal and Singh[13] develop a method for formic and oxalic acids. Here, an excess of silver(III) is used to oxidize the formic acid, this being followed by a back-titration. Oxalate is oxidized in the usual way using cerium(IV).

Of the redox methods for formic acid, oxidation by iodine appears to offer some advantages[14]. The method is based on the reaction

$$HCOONa + I_2 \rightarrow NaI + HI + CO_2$$

and is carried out in the presence of potassium hydrogen tartrate. It is not affected by several common organic substances including the calcium salts of butyric, lactic, and gluconic acids, the sodium salts of acetic, benzoic, boric and tartaric acids. There is no interference from benzaldehyde or glucose and none from the sodium salts of phthalic, malic, maleic, fumaric, phenylacetic, aminoacetic, and adipic acids. The interfering substances are sodium oxalate, sodium salicylate, sodium malonate, formaldehyde, acetaldehyde and salicylaldehyde.

Determination of formic acid by oxidation with iodine[14]

Procedure
To 5–20 mℓ of a neutral formate solution containing 25–90 mg formic acid in a 250-mℓ flask, add 1 g solid potassium hydrogen tartrate and a measured excess of standard iodine solution (for X mℓ of 0.1M formate, add $2X$ mℓ of 0.1M iodine solution). Attach a 100 cm water condenser to the flask. Cover the upper end with an inverted 10-mℓ beaker.

Place the flask in boiling water for 25 min. Allow to cool and then wash the condenser thoroughly with 5% KI solution. Titrate the residual iodine with standard 0.1M thiosulphate in the usual way. Carry out a blank determination.

Note
Results published in the paper indicate an accuracy of 0.5 per cent or better for 23–92 mg formate.

Oxidation with mercuric chloride enables formate to be determined without interference from lactic, butyric, acetic, propionic, tartaric, citric or benzoic acids[15]. Other oxidants recommended include chloramine T[16], lead tetra-acetate[17] and alkaline hexacyanoferrate(III)[18].

Gas-chromatography

Reference has been already made to gas-chromatography[5]. Recent work by Omeh[19] indicates that the method can be used to determine formic acid in various aqueous conditions, for example as free acid, or salt in the presence of a mineral or another carboxylic acid. An aqueous solution of formic acid is acidified with HCl and made to react with an appropriate aromatic amine (aniline, *o*-, *m*- or *p*-toluidine, etc.) by boiling under reflux. The products are separated by gas-chromatography and determined.

Spectrophotometric methods

Reduction of formate by magnesium ribbon to formaldehyde followed by condensation of the latter with chromotropic acid (*Structure 12*) enables microgram amounts of formic acid to be determined[4, 21]. 6-amino-1-naphthol-3-sulphonic acid (J acid) (*Structure 13*) or 6-anilino-1-naphthol-3-sulphonic acid (Phenyl J acid) may also be used[22].

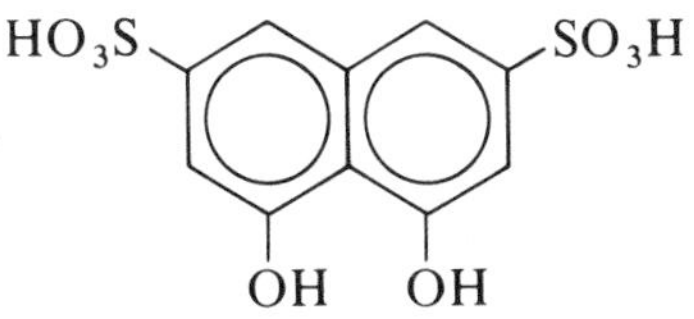

HO_3S SO_3H

OH OH

Structure 12 Chromotropic acid

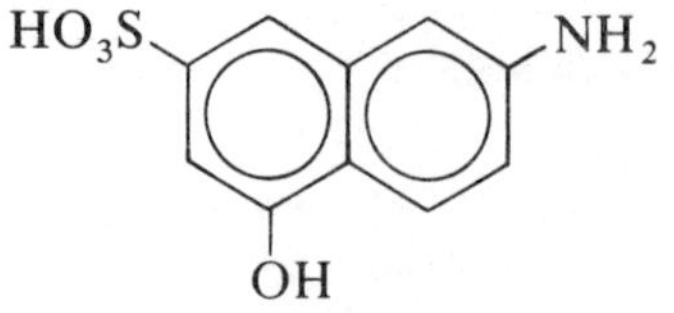

HO_3S ... NH_2 ... OH

Structure 13 6-amino-1-naphthol-3-sulphonic acid (*J acid*)

Stradomskaya and Goncharova[21] apply the method to the determination of formic acid in natural water. Beer's Law is obeyed up to 20 μg; the sensitivity of the method is 1 μg. Phenols in amounts greater than 500 μg ℓ^{-1} do not interfere, neither do organic acids in 10-fold excess. The reduction stage in this procedure has been criticized by Grant[23] who found the yield of formaldehyde to be only 30 per cent. More recently Higgs and Charles[24] found the reproducibility of the method to be not greater than ±30 per cent.

Formaldehyde is the main interference in the indirect spectrophotometric determination of formic acid. It should either be separated or destroyed. The latter can be accomplished using phenylhydrazine[23]. Higgs and Charles[24] developed another method based on the reduction of silver nitrate to silver under slightly acidic buffered conditions.

$$HCOOH + AgNO_3 \rightarrow HCOOAg$$

$$HCOOAg \rightarrow HCOOH + CO_2 + Ag \downarrow$$

In the presence of a protective colloid, for example starch, a clear brown colour is produced, the intensity of which approximates to the Beer–Lambert Law. The accuracy at 95 per cent confidence level is ±4 per cent.

Another recently suggested spectrophotometric method is based on the determination of evolved CO produced when formic acid or formates are heated at 100 °C with concentrated H_2SO_4. The reagent silver sodium *p*-sulphamoylbenzoate is used for the spectrophotometric determination of CO. Oxalate does not interfere with this method.

Miscellaneous methods

The non-selective iodimetric method based on the reaction

$$IO_3^- + 5I^- + 6H^+ \rightarrow 3I_2 + 3H_2O$$

enables direct determination of formate to be made, but 30 min is required for the reaction to proceed to almost completion[25].

Recently, when the need arose to determine a small amount of formic acid in a system capable of generating an additional amount, nuclear magnetic resonance was used[26]. The formyl resonance could be distinguished from background noise down to a concentration of 0.05 per cent.

British Standards[27] have published methods for the analysis of formic acid.

References

1. DITTMAN, J., *J. Chromat.*, **34**, 407 (1968)
2. PREY, V., BERBALK, H. and KAUSZ, M., *Mikrochim. Acta*, 449 (1962)
3. DE JONG, E. and MCCULLOUGH, T., *Chemist Analyst*, **56**, 80 (1967)
4. RIETBROCK, N. and HINRICHS, W-D., *Klin. Wschr.*, **42**, 981 (1964); *Analyt. Abstr.*, **11**, 831 (1966)
5. SHELLEY, R.N., SALWIN, H. and HOROWITZ, W., *J. Ass. off. agric. Chem.*, **46**, 486 (1963)
6. BOCK, R., NIEDERAUER, H-T. and BEHRENDS, K., *Z. analyt. Chem.*, **190**, 33 (1962)
7. British Pharmacopoeia. H.M.S.O. London (1973), A25.
8. STAMM, H., *Angew. Chem.*, **47**, 791 (1934)
9. TATWAWADI, S.V., *Z. analyt. Chem.*, **168**, 15 (1959)
10. BERKA, A. and KONOPASEK, J., *Mikrochim. Acta*, 405 (1968)
11. POLAK, H.L., *Z. analyt. Chem.*, **176**, 34 (1960)
12. JAISWAL, P.K. and CHANDRA, S., *Microchem. J.*, **14**, 289 (1969)
13. JAISWAL, P.K. and SINGH, V.N., *Chim. analyt.*, **53**, 253 (1971)
14. VERMA, R.M. and BOSE, S., *Analytica chim. Acta*, **27**, 176 (1962)
15. VERMA, R.M. and BOSE, S., *J. Ind. Chem. Soc.*, **37**, 47 (1960)
16. SINGH, B. and SOOD, K.C., *Analytica chim. Acta*, **13**, 305 (1955)
17. PERLIN, A.S., *Analyt. Chem.*, **26**, 1053 (1954)
18. DESHMUKH, G.S. and RAO, A.L.J., *Z. analyt.* Chem., **194**, 110 (1963)
19. OMEH, E.O., *J. Chromat.*, **51**, 139 (1970)
20. FLASCHKA, H. and GARRETT, J., *Chemist Analyst*, **52**, 101 (1963)
21. STRADOMSKAYA, A.G. and GONCHAROVA, I.A., *Gidrochim. Mater.*, **43**, 57 (1967); *Analyt. Abstr.*, **15**, 6338 (1968)
22. SAWICKI, E., HAUSER, T.R. and MCPHERSON, S., *Analyt. Chem.*, **34**, 1460 (1962)
23. GRANT, W.H., *Analyt. Chem.*, **20**, 267 (1948)
24. HIGGS, D.G. and CHARLES, A.F., *Analyst*, **96**, 502 (1971)
25. KOLTHOFF, I.M., *Pharm. Weekbl.*, **57**, 63 (1920)
26. BURAKEVICH, J.V. and O'NEILL, J., *Analytica chim. Acta*, **54**, 528 (1971)
27. British Standards 4341: (1968). London. Also addendum No. 1 (1971) to this specification

Hexacyanoferrate(II) and Hexacyanoferrate(III)

Hexacyanoferrate(II) (older name—ferrocyanide) in the form of its sodium or potassium salts, finds application in photography, metal treatment, electroplating, engraving, tanning, dyeing and textile printing. Hexacyanoferrate(III) (older name—ferricyanide) is used in the manufacture of blue pigments. The alkali metal salts find use as anticaking agents and crystal-habit modifiers for commercial sodium chloride. Its potassium salt can be purified to a very high level. In this form it serves as a good reference standard in redox titrimetry[1]. For example a potentiometric method developed by Lingane[2] in which cobalt is titrated with high-purity standard hexacyanoferrate(III) in ammoniacal medium is probably the most accurate method available for determination of cobalt.

The general application of hexacyanoferrate(III) as redox reagent in analysis has been reviewed[3]. Although the determination of hexacyanoferrate(II) and hexacyanoferrate(III) are important no recent review of their analytical chemistry appears to exist.

Separations

1. Precipitation

Quantitative separation of hexacyanoferrate(II) is possible utilizing its sparingly soluble salts, for example those of Ag(I), Pb(II) or Zn(II). It can be both separated from hexacyanoferrate(III), cyanide and thiocyanate, and determined gravimetrically as $(NH_4)_4Fe(CN)_6 \cdot 2MoO_3$. This is discussed more fully in the gravimetric sub-section.

2. Thin-layer chromatography

These separations are shown in *Table 7*.

Table 7 Thin-layer chromatographic separations of hexacyanoferrate(II) and hexacyanoferrate(III)

Support	*Solvent system*	*Ions separated*	*Ref.*
Silica gel containing 5%	Acetone–water 10 : 1	SCN^-, I^-, Br^-, Cl^-, $[Fe(CN)_6]^{3-}$, $[Fe(CN)_6]^{4-}$, ClO_3^-, BrO_3^-, IO_3^-, NO_3^-	4
Silica gel	Various, e.g. butanol–propanol–dibutylamine 9 : 9 : 2	F^-, Cl^-, Br^-, I^-, CN^-, SCN^-, $[Fe(CN)_6]^{3-}$, $[Fe(CN)_6]^{4-}$	5
Silica gel on Al foil	Various, e.g. butanol–ethanol–water 20 : 60 : 20	CN^- $[Fe(CN)_6]^{3-}$ $[Fe(CN)_6]^{4-}$	6

3. Other chromatographic methods

Hexacyanoferrate(II) and hexacyanoferrate(III) can be separated using reverse-phase partition chromatography with Kel-F powder as stationary phase and tributylphosphate as solvent[7].

4. Miscellaneous methods

Under certain conditions cyanide can be distilled without decomposition of any hexacyanoferrate(II) or hexacyanoferrate(III) present, thus effecting a separation. Further information is given in the cyanide section. Serfass *et al.*[8] have used $MgCl_2$ and $HgCl_2$ with H_2SO_4 to decompose complex cyanides. The same treatment reduces hexacyanoferrate(II) and hexacyanoferrate(III) to $Mg(CN)_2$ and $Hg(CN)_2$.

Hexacyanoferrate(III) can be separated and determined at microgram level using a slotted oven technique. The method, developed by Leonard, Shahine and Wilson[9] relies on selective precipitation of hexacyanoferrate(III) as the thorium salt. Quantitative evaluation is based on colorimetric determination of iron using thiocyanate. A description of the oven itself is given in an earlier paper[10].

Determination

Gravimetric methods

Hexacyanoferrate(II) can be determined gravimetrically[11] in the presence of hexacyanoferrate(III), cyanide and thiocyanate. Precipitation is made by adding a solution of ammonium molybdate to an acetate-buffered solution of the sample at pH 3.7. After allowing the precipitate to stand for a few hours it is dried at 120 °C and weighed as $(NH_4)_4Fe(CN)_6 2MoO_3$. The method is applicable to 300 mg of $[Fe(CN)_6]^{4-}$. Accuracy within 1 per cent is reported.

Titrimetric methods

1. Redox

A large number of redox reagents have been proposed for the determination of hexacyanoferrate(III). The monograph by Berka, Vulterin and Zyka[3] lists 17, these including ascorbic acid, hydrazine sulphate, sodium nitrite, stannous chloride and mercurous nitrate. Some appear to be of academic interest only. The present discussion will be restricted to a consideration of ascorbic acid, cerium(IV), titanium(III) and iodimetric procedures.

Hexacyanoferrate(III) reacts with KI in an acidified medium, liberating iodine which can be titrated with standard thiosulphate.

$$2[Fe(CN)_6]^{3-} + 2I^- \rightarrow 2[Fe(CN)_6]^{4-} + I_2$$

The reaction is normally slow but becomes rapid if zinc sulphate is added. Zn^{2+} ions precipitate both hexacyanoferrate(II) and hexacyanoferrate(III), the former precipitate being much less soluble.

Iodimetric determination of hexacyanoferrate(III)

Procedure

To the $[Fe(CN)_6]^{3-}$ solution diluted to about 40 mℓ and contained in a glass-stoppered flask, add 2 g of KI, 2 mℓ of 4M HCl and 10 mℓ of 30% $ZnSO_4$ solution. Stopper the flask, swirl and allow to stand for 1 min. Titrate with standard thiosulphate adding starch near the end-point.

Notes

1. The procedure can be used to standardize thiosulphate if the hexacyanoferrate(III) is prepared from an accurately weighed amount of $K_3Fe(CN)_6$.
2. The iodimetric method is recommended by British Standards[12] for assay of photographic grade hexacyanoferrate(III).

Cerium(IV) is suitable for direct oxidation of hexacyanoferrate(II) in about 1M HCl or H_2SO_4. Cyanide does not interfere.

$$2Ce(SO_4)_2 + 2K_4Fe(CN)_6 \rightarrow 2K_3Fe(CN)_6 + Ce_2(SO_4)_3 + K_2SO_4$$

Ferroin perchlorate is used as indicator; ferroin sulphate can provide poor end-points as a result of containing more than the stoichiometric amount of iron[13]. Rao and Kirshnamurthy[14] use the cerium(IV)–hexacyanoferrate(II) titration as part of a procedure for determination of chloride and hexacyanoferrate(II) in mixtures. First $[Fe(CN)_6]^{4-}$ only is determined using standard cerium(IV). In a second aliquot the sum of $[Fe(CN)_6]^{4-}$ and chloride is determined by $AgNO_3$ titration using chromate as indicator.

The use of ascorbic acid as a standard reductant in quantitative analysis has received considerable attention in recent years largely due to the work of Erdey and co-workers[15,3]. Hexacyanoferrate(III) can be determined either visually or by potentiometric titration.

$$C_6H_8O_6 + 2[Fe(CN)_6]^{3-} \rightarrow C_6H_6O_6 + 2[Fe(CN)_6]^{4-} + 2H^+$$

The determination is made in a solution buffered with sodium acetate or potassium hydrogen carbonate. In the visual titration 2,6-dichlorophenolindophenol is used as indicator, the end-point being marked by the disappearance of blue colour.

Titrimetric determination of hexacyanoferrate(III) using standard ascorbic acid

Reagents

Ascorbic acid, 0.05M approx.:

Dissolve 8.90 g of crystalline ascorbic acid in distilled water, add 0.5 g of EDTA disodium salt and make up to 1 ℓ with water. Store in the dark [Note 1].

2,6-dichlorophenolindophenol:

Prepare a solid dilution in the ratio 2,6-dichlorophenolindophenol-NaCl 1:500. This is stable indefinitely. A 0.1 % solution of the indicator is stable for 3 weeks only.

Procedure

To the neutral solution containing 50–600 mg of $[Fe(CN)_6]^{3-}$ add 1–2 g of solid $KHCO_3$ (or $NaHCO_3$), and about 0.5 g of the indicator mixture. Titrate with 0.05M ascorbic acid until the blue colour which develops, vanishes.

Notes

1. Traces of heavy metals and UV light accelerate the decomposition of ascorbic acid. EDTA masks heavy metals and retards this process.
2. The ascorbic acid solution can be standardized by the above procedure using pure $K_3Fe(CN)_6$ as reference standard.
3. The standard deviation of the method is ± 0.2 per cent.

The hexacyanoferrate(III)–ascorbic acid titration is important as the basis of several indirect determinations. Many oxidizing species, e.g. chromate, react with excess of hexacyanoferrate(II) giving an equivalent amount of hexacyanoferrate(III) which can be titrated as above[17,18]. Hydrogen peroxide can be determined by means of its quantitative reduction of $[Fe(CN)_6]^{3-}$ in alkaline medium. After neutralizing the solution, residual hexacyanoferrate-(III) is determined using ascorbic acid. Many other examples of indirect determinations based on the $[Fe(CN)_6]^{3-}$–ascorbic acid reaction are given in other sections.

A recent study by Ruzicka[20] employs titanium(III) for titration of $[Fe(CN)_6]^{3-}$. The novel feature is use of a titanium chloride solution in glycerol containing formic acid, which is found to be stable in air for four days. Hexacyanoferrate(III) is determined in alkaline medium using a visual or potentiometric end-point.

2. *Precipitation titration*

Hexacyanoferrate(II) can be titrated with $AgNO_3$ at pH 6.5–8.0 using potassium chromate as indicator[21]. The range for $[Fe(CN)_6]^{3-}$ is 15–300 mg and the accuracy ± 0.5 mg. Application of the titration to Cl^-–$[Fe(CN)_6]^{3-}$ mixtures has been referred to already.

Hexacyanoferrate(II) can be titrated with thorium(IV) using alizarin red S, xylenol orange or catechol violet as adsorption indicators[22]. No interference is given by Cl^-, Br^-, I^-, NO_3^- or acetate, but Ag(I), Pb(II), Zn(II), Cd(II), Cu(II), Co(II), Ni(II), $[Fe(CN)_6]^{3-}$, PO_4^{3-}, CrO_4^{2-}, IO_3^- and F^- interfere.

3. *Using EDTA*

A few compleximetric methods have been reported. Vil'borg and Drozdov[23] reduce hexacyanoferrate(III) with KI, precipitate the resulting hexacyanoferrate(II) as $Zn_2Fe(CN)_6$, and then evaluate its zinc content using EDTA.

Krtil[24] has developed a method for insoluble hexacyanoferrate(II) salts. These are dissolved in EDTA which complexes with the cationic constituent present. The excess EDTA is titrated with standard lead(II). Application is made to the hexacyanoferrate(II) salts of Zn, Co, Ni and Cu.

Spectroscopic methods

1. *Spectrophotometric–visible and UV*

The well known colour reaction between hexacyanoferrate(II) and iron(III) in aqueous solution forms the basis of several spectrophotometric procedures. Older forms of the method are insensitive and only applicable to amounts of $[Fe(CN)_6]^{4-}$ in excess of 50 µg. Furthermore, Beer's law is found to apply only if absorbance measurements are made within 1 min of mixing the reagents[25]. A modified method by Marier and Clark[26] with absorbance measurements made at 690 nm increases the sensitivity to 5–80 µg of $[Fe(CN)_6]^{2-}$. A further development by Roberts and Wilson[27] involves preconcentration of the complex on kieselguhr. Although developed specifically for analysis of commerical salt, they find it also applicable to water and effluent samples. The procedure is suitable for as little as 0.10 ppm of $[Fe(CN)_6]^{2-}$, but with modification this can be extended down to 0.013 ppm. No interference is given by metals, cyanide, thiocyanate or nitroprusside in comparable amounts.

Avron and Shavit[28] find that when hexacyanoferrate(II) is reacted with iron(II) in the presence of 4,7 diphenyl 1,10-phenanthroline sulphate, the resulting complex has a molar absorptivity of 20 500 at 535 nm. This enables 0.001 μmol of $[Fe(CN)_6]^{4-}$ to be determined.

Direct spectrophotometric determination of hexacyanoferrate(II) by measuring the absorbance in the UV at 237 nm can be employed[29]. Although not as sensitive as the prussian blue method, it enables 1×10^{-5}M $[Fe(CN)_6]^{4-}$ to be determined in the presence of a 50-fold excess of $[Fe(CN)_6]^{3-}$. Substances that absorb strongly in the UV interfere.

Another approach to the spectrophotometric determination of hexacyanoferrate(II) is to decompose it and determine the resulting iron(II) using 1,10-phenanthroline. Karas-Gasparec and Pinter[30] develop a method suitable for 10^{-5}–10^{-4}M $[Fe(CN)_6]^{4-}$ using this procedure. Presumably the sensitivity could be improved if 4,7-diphenyl 1,10-phenanthroline were used.

Ramanauskas and co-workers[31] have developed a sensitive spectrophotometric method applicable to a number of oxidizing species. Its basis is the decrease in colour intensity of certain triphenylmethane dyes, caused by I^+ or Br^+. In the case of hexacyanoferrate(III), this is reacted with excess iodide in the presence of brilliant green or catechol violet at pH 3–5, and the absorbance measured at 628 and 594 nm respectively. The corresponding ranges for $[Fe(CN)_6]^{3-}$ are 0.021–0.64 μg mℓ$^{-1}$ and 0.02–0.428 μg mℓ$^{-1}$.

2. *Turbidimetric*

Drew and Fitzgerald[32] have reported a turbidimetric method for hexacyanoferrate(III) based on its reaction with potassium tri-oxalato cobaltate(III).

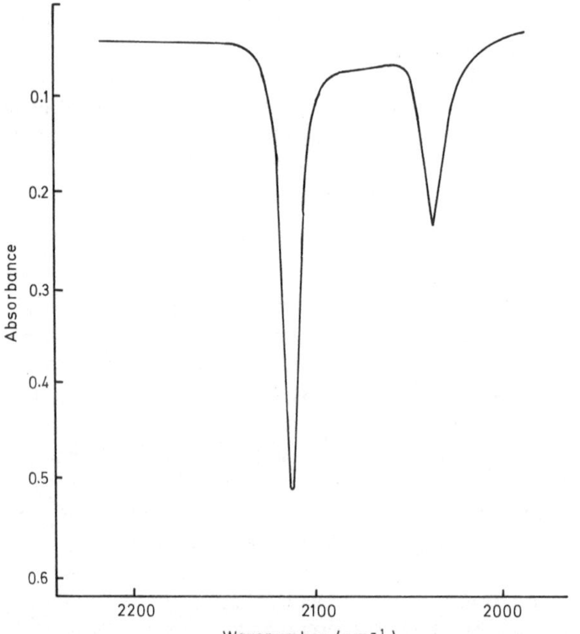

Figure 17 *Infra-red spectrum of 8.0×10^{-2} M potassium hexacyanoferrate (III) and 9.5×10^{-3} M sodium hexacyanoferrate (II) in water.* (From Drew[35])

3. Infra-red

Both hexacyanoferrate(II) and hexacyanoferrate(III) exhibit characteristic infra-red absorption bands[33] in the region between 2100 cm^{-1} and 2000 cm^{-1}. $K_4Fe(CN)_6 \cdot 3H_2O$ produces very strong bands at 2015 and 2040 cm^{-1}; $K_3Fe(CN)_6$ gives strong bands at 2100 and 2115 cm^{-1}. Haba and Wilson[34] use the KBr disc technique for identification and determination of microgram amounts of hexacyanoferrate(II), hexacyanoferrate(III), cobalticyanide, sulphate, chromate and metavanadate in mixtures. For $[Fe(CN)_6]^{3-}$ and $[Fe(CN)_6]^{4-}$ the amounts present should not exceed 20 and 5 μg respectively.

Determination of $[Fe(CN)_6]^{3-}$ and $[Fe(CN_6]^{4-}$ in aqueous solution using infra-red is a more difficult matter. Almost all investigations refer to inherent difficulties such as energy loss, lack of suitable window material and a restricted range of usable absorption frequencies. Drew[35] has overcome the problem of window material by using Irtran transmitting windows. The spectrum obtained from an aqueous solution of $[Fe(CN)_6]^{3-}$ and $[Fe(CN)_6]^{4-}$ is shown in *Figure 17*.

Drew reports that the calibration graphs for solutions of $Na_4Fe(CN)_6$ are linear up to 0.04M with a molar absorptivity of $4.24 \times 10^3 \ell mol^{-1} cm^{-1}$. The useful analytical range for $[Fe(CN)_6]^{4-}$ is 0.03×10^{-2}–4×10^{-2}M.

For $[Fe(CN)_6]^{3-}$ linearity holds for 0.0012M to 0.1M with a molar absorptivity of $1.18 \times 10^3 \ell mol^{-1} cm^{-1}$.

Electroanalytical methods

1. Potentiometric

Furman and Fenton[36] titrate hexacyanoferrate(III) potentiometrically with cerium(III) in a 25–60% K_2CO_3 solution. An inert atmosphere is required. The end-point can be determined amperometrically as well as potentiometrically. The normal potentiometric procedure employs platinum and calomel electrodes; for derivative titrations, two platinum electrodes are used.

Ueno and Tachikawa[37] use platinum as anode and Au, W, Pd, Ag or Ni as cathode for potentiometric titration of hexacyanoferrate(II) with $KMnO_4$ or $Ce(SO_4)_2$. Another reagent proposed for hexacyanoferrate(II) is lead tetra-acetate[38]. A medium of HCl or $HClO_4$ is used, this enabling the reaction to proceed quantitatively in the presence of a relatively high concentration of chloride. Sulphuric acid is unsuitable. Fluoride causes interference but cyanide and $[Fe(CN)_6]^{3-}$ are without effect.

Mercurous perchlorate can be used[39] to titrate $[Fe(CN)_6]^{3-}$ in the presence of a buffer and KSCN.

$$2[Fe(CN)_6]^{3-} + Hg_2^{2+} + 8SCN^- \rightarrow 2[Fe(CN)_6]^{4-} + 2Hg(SCN)_4^{2-}$$

Reference has been made to the hexacyanoferrate(III)–ascorbic acid titration earlier. This can be conducted potentiometrically using platinum and calomel electrodes[16]. An automatic form for use on the micro scale has also been described[40]. This is suitable for 1–10 mg of hexacyanoferrate(III) or hexacyanoferrate(II) after oxidation to hexacyanoferrate(III) by $NaNO_2$.

2. Coulometric

$[Fe(CN)_6]^{4-}$ can be determined coulometrically by oxidation at a platinum electrode in a 0.5M KCl medium[41]. Iodide and thiocyanate interfere; bromide and chloride do not, and neither does cyanide if the determination is made at less than +0.70 V *v*.SCE. The method is applicable to 50–150 mg of $[Fe(CN)_6]^{4-}$ in 100 mℓ.

Another coulometric procedure for hexacyanoferrate(II) employs electro-generated octacyanomolybdate[42].

$$Mo(CN)_8{}^{3-} + [Fe(CN)_6]^{4-} \rightarrow Mo(CN)_8{}^{4-} + [Fe(CN)_6]^{3-}$$

The reaction may be carried out over a wide pH range.

3. Miscellaneous electroanalytical methods

Merrer and Stock[43] have demonstrated that amperometric titration of hexacyanoferrate(III) with mercury(I) perchlorate at a rotating platinum electrode, is accurate. The same authors discuss sources of error at low concentrations of the ion[44]. A further extension of the work has produced a simple bi-amperometric procedure employing two platinum electrodes[45].

Agasyan and Sirakanyan[46] use lead tetra-acetate to titrate hexacyano-ferrate(II) in HCl or H_2SO_4 medium using platinum electrodes. Mixtures of $[Fe(CN)_6]^{3-}$ and $[Fe(CN)_6]^{4-}$ can be analysed by cyclic voltammetry[47]. The peak anodic and cathodic currents at a carbon-paste electrode are found to be proportional to $[Fe(CN)_6]^{4-}$ and $[Fe(CN)_6]^{3-}$ respectively between 10^{-5}M and 10^{-3}M, for ratios of $[Fe(CN)_6]^{3-}$ to $[Fe(CN)_6]^{4-}$ from 0.2 to 5.0.

Miscellaneous methods

Several chromatographic and related methods enable a quantitative estimation of hexacyanoferrate(II) and hexacyanoferrate(III) to be made. Reference has already been made to the slotted oven technique.

Todorova, Getcheva, and Mandova[48] are able to determine $[Fe(CN)_6]^{3-}$ at 3–60 μg levels using paper impregnated with silver chromate. The amount of $[Fe(CN)_6]^{3-}$ is evaluated from the weight of $Ag_3[Fe(CN)_6]$ flecks on the red paper compared with the stain obtained on a standard paper. A precision of ±1 per cent is reported for what is in essence a sub-micro gravimetric method.

Celap and Weisz[49] have applied the ring-oven to semimicro determination of hexacyanoferrate(III). A silver sulphide standard scale is employed in the quantitative evaluation.

A novel amplification method is developed by Weisz and Goenner.[50] The final procedure is titrimetric. A scheme for automating the amplification is included.

References

1. KOLTHOFF, I.M. and BELCHER, R., *Volumetric Analysis*, Vol. III, Interscience, New York (1957)
2. LINGANE, J.J., *Analytica chim. Acta*, **30**, 319 (1964)
3. BERKA, A., VULTERIN, J. and ZYKA, J., *Newer Redox Titrants*, Pergamon Press, Oxford (1965)

4. KAWANABE, K., TAKITANI, S., MIYAZAKI, M. and TAMURA, Z., *Japan Analyst*, **13**, 976 (1964); *Analyt. Abstr.*, **13**, 5385 (1966)
5. GAGLIARDI, E. and POKORNY, G., *Mikrochim. Acta*, 699 (1965)
6. THIELEMANN, H., *Z. analyt. Chem.*, **270**, 128 (1974); *Analyt. Abstr.*, **28**, 2B86 (1975)
7. AKAZA, I., KIBA, T. and TABA, M., *Bull. chem. Soc. Japan*, **42**, 1291 (1969); *Analyt. Abstr.*, **19**, 1289 (1970)
8. SERFASS, E.J., FREEMAN, R.B., DODGE, B.F. and ZABBAN, W., *Plating*, **39**, 267 (1952); *Chem. Abstr.*, **46**, 6514a (1952)
9. LEONARD, M.A., SHAHINE, S.A.E.F. and WILSON, C.L., *Mikrochim. Acta*, 787 (1965)
10. LEONARD, M.A., SHAHINE, S.A.E.F. and WILSON, C.L., *Mikrochim. Acta*, 160 (1965)
11. JIMENO, S.A., *Inf. Quim. Anal.*, **13**, 167 (1959); *Analyt. Abstr.*, **7**, 3253 (1960)
12. British Standard 3752; (1964), London
13. BELCHER, R. and NUTTEN, A.J., *Quantitative Inorganic Analysis*, 3rd edn, Butterworths, London, 239 (1970)
14. RAO, K.B. and KRISHNAMURTHY, C.V., *Ind. J. appl. Chem.*, **31**, 108 (1968); *Analyt. Abstr.*, **19**, 210 (1970)
15. ERDEY, L. and SVEHLA, G., *Chemist Analyst*, **52**, 24 (1963)
16. ERDEY, L. and SVEHLA, G., *Z. analyt. Chem.*, **150**, 407 (1956); *Analyt. Abstr.*, **3**, 3055 (1956)
17. ERDEY, L. and SVEHLA, G., *Z. analyt. Chem.*, **163**, 6 (1958); *Analyt. Abstr.*, **6**, 1620 (1959)
18. ERDEY, L. and SVEHLA, G., *Z. analyt. Chem.*, **167**, 164 (1959); *Analyt. Abstr.*, **7**, 122 (1960)
19. ERDEY, L., SVEHLA, G. and KOLTAI, L., *Analytica chim. Acta*, **27**, 164 (1962)
20. RUZICKA, E., *Chemické Zvesti*, **26**, 516 (1972); *Analyt. Abstr.*, **24**, 2789 (1973)
21. BASHKARA, K., *Recl. Trav. chim. Pays-Bas*, **84**, 69 (1965); *Analyt. Abstr.*, **13**, 2283 (1966)
22. DUBEY, P.S. and TANDON, K.N., *Talanta*, **13**, 765 (1966)
23. VIL'BORG, S.S. and DROZDOV, V.A., *Nauch. Dokl. Vyssh Shkoty Khim. i. Khim. Tekhnol.*, 721 (1958); *Analyt. Abstr.*, **7**, 865 (1960)
24. KRTIL, J., *Colln Czech. chem. Commun. Engl. Edn.*, **39**, 4496 (1967); *Analyt. Abstr.*, **16**, 1870 (1969)
25. LEA, C.H., *Analyst*, **72**, 336 (1947)
26. MARIER, J.R. and CLARK, D.S., *Analyst*, **85**, 574 (1960)
27. ROBERTS, R.F. and WILSON, R.H., *Analyst*, **93**, 237 (1968)
28. AVRON, M. and SHAVIT, N., *Analyt. Biochem.*, **6**, 549 (1963)
29. KIDBY, D.K., *Analyt. Biochem.*, **28**, 230 (1969)
30. KARAS-GASPAREC, V. and PINTER, T., *Croat. Chem. Acta*, **34**, 131 (1962); *Analyt. Abstr.*, **10**, 1804 (1963)
31. RAMANAUSKAS, E.I., BUNIKIENE, L.V., SAPROGONENE, M.S., SHULYUNENE, A.K. and ZHILENAITE, M.V., *Zh. analit. Khim.*, **24**, 244 (1969); *Analyt. Abstr.*, **19**, 1022 (1970)
32. DREW, H.D. and FITZGERALD, J.M., *Analyt. Chem.*, **38**, 778 (1966)
33. MILLER, F.A. and WILKINS, C.H., *Analyt. Chem.*, **24**, 1253 (1952)
34. HABA, F.R. and WILSON, C.L., *Talanta*, **9**, 841 (1962)
35. DREW, D.M., *Analyt. Chem.*, **45**, 2423 (1973)
36. FURMAN, N.H. and FENTON, A.J., *Analyt. Chem.*, **32**, 745 (1960)
37. UENO, K. and TACHIKAWA, T., *J. chem. Soc. Japan, pure Chem. Sect.*, **82**, 577 (1961); *Analyt. Abstr.*, **9**, 4211 (1962)
38. TOLAR, V., SANTRUCEK, J., NEMEC, I. and ZYKA, J., *Zh. analit. Khim.*, **22**, 664 (1967); *Analyt. Abstr.*, **16**, 145 (1969)
39. LUCENA-CONDE, F. and SANCHEZ-BELLIDO, I., *Talanta*, **1**, 305 (1958)
40. ERDEY, L., SVEHLA, G. and WEBER, O., *Z. analyt. Chem.*, **240**, 91 (1968); *Analyt. Abstr.*, **18**, 12 (1970)
41. SIVARAMAIAH, G. and KRISHNAN, V.R., *Z. analyt. Chem.*, **231**, 192 (1967); *Analyt. Abstr.*, **15**, 7261 (1968)
42. HERNANDEZ-MENDEZ, J. and LUCENA-CONDE, F., *Talanta*, **16**, 1114 (1969)
43. MERRER, R.J. and STOCK, J.T., *Analyst*, **92**, 98 (1967)
44. STOCK, J.T. and MERRER, R.J., *Microchem. J.*, **16**, 77 (1971)
45. MERRER, R.J. and STOCK, J.T., *Analytica chim. Acta*, **53**, 233 (1971)
46. AGASYAN, P.K. and SIRAKANYAN, M.A., *Zh. analit. Khim.*, **25**, 1677 (1970); *Analyt. Abstr.*, **22**, 4004 (1972)
47. FARSANG, G. and TOMCSANYI, L., *J. electroanalyt. Chem.*, **13**, 73 (1967)
48. TODOROVA, TZ., GETCHEVA, T. and MANDOVA, B., *Mikrochim. Acta*, 503 (1974)
49. CELAP, M.B. and WEISZ, H., *Mikrochim. Acta*, 24 (1962)
50. WEISZ, H. and GOENNER, M., *Analytica chim. Acta*, **43**, 235 (1968)

Hyponitrite

Separations

1. Anion-exchange

Hyponitrite ($N_2O_2^{2-}$), nitrate, nitrite and N-nitrohydroxylaminate anions can be separated using anion-exchange[1]. The resin is converted to hydroxyl form before use. Elution is made with M Na_2SO_4–0.1 M NaOH.

2. Paper chromatography and paper electrophoresis

Paper chromatography enables hyponitrite to be separated from nitrate, nitrite and hydroxylamine[2]. Whatman No. 1 paper was used and ethanol–H_2O–NaOH (70 mℓ: 30 mℓ: 2 g) as solvent. Veprek-Siska *et al*[3], found that paper electrophoresis could be used to separate hyponitrite, hyponitrate, nitrate, nitrite, HCl, NH_4Cl, hydrazine hydrochloride, and hydroxylamine hydrochloride.

Determination

Titrimetric methods

Moderate concentrations of hyponitrous acid in acidic solution can be determined by a titrimetric method[4] following initial precipitation of silver hyponitrite. The excess of Ag^+ is titrated in the usual way.

Titrimetric determination of hyponitrite[4]

Procedure

To a 25 mℓ aliquot of hyponitrous acid add 25 mℓ of 0.1M $AgNO_3$. Neutralize the solution immediately with 0.1M NaOH until a precipitate of Ag_2O appears. Dissolve this by adding a few drops of 0.1M acetic acid.

Add 5–10 mℓ of an acetate buffer (0.1M acetic acid; 0.1M sodium acetate) and dilute to 100 mℓ in a volumetric flask. The solution now has a pH of 4.5–5.0 at which $Ag_2N_2O_2$ is practically insoluble, but Ag_2O and Ag_2CO_3 soluble.

Filter the solution disregarding the first third or half. Determine the excess Ag^+ in aliquots of the filtrate (Volhard method) and from this evaluate the original hyponitrite concentration.

Spectroscopic methods

Polydoropoulos and Voliotis[5] report that the molar absorptivity of the $N_2O_2^{2-}$ species in acid solution at 232 nm is $6.5(\pm 0.2) \times 10^3$. This is considerably higher than the value of 4.0×10^3 previously reported by Addison, Gamlen and Thompson[6]. Using this wavelength Beer's law was found to hold up to 1.5×10^{-4}M $N_2O_2^{2-}$.

Another approach is conversion of the hyponitrite to nitrite followed by the well known Griess–Ilosvay spectrophotometric method[7]. Hyponitrite is oxidized by $KMnO_4$ in alkaline medium in the presence of Ag^+ or Cu^{2+} ions. Excess MnO_4^- and MnO_4^{2-} are removed by reduction with sodium formate, and the NO_2^- determined spectrophotometrically using 1-naphthylamine. The method can be used for 0.05 µmol of $N_2O_2^{2-}$ with a mean error of ±1.5 per cent.

As an extension of the work they develop methods for $N_2O_2^{2-}$ in the presence of other nitrogen-containing species[8,9]. Hydroxylamine, ammonia and other N-bases are retained on a strongly acidic cation-exchange column at 5 °C. Hyponitrite passes through and may be determined on its own. Further modification allows hyponitrite to be determined in the presence of nitrate, nitrite and nitrohydroxylaminate.

References

1. GUERTLER, O. and HOLZAPFEL, H., *Angew. makromol. Chem.*, **7**, 194 (1969); *Analyt. Abstr.*, **20**, 960 (1971)
2. STEVENS, H.M., *Analytica chim. Acta*, **21**, 456 (1959)
3. VEPREK-SISKA, J., SMIROUS, F., PLISKA, V. and VESELY, F., *Chemikė Listy*, **52**, 410 (1958); *Analyt. Abstr.*, **6**, 115 (1959)
4. POLYDOROPOULOS, C.N. and PIPINIS, M., *Hêm. Hron.*, **28**, 107 (1963); *Chem. Abstr.*, **60**, 4800c (1964)
5. POLYDOROPOULOS, C.N. and VOLIOTIS, S.D., *Analytica chim. Acta*, **40**, 170 (1968)
6. ADDISON, C.C., GAMLEN, G.A. and THOMPSON, R., *J. chem. Soc.*, 338 (1952)
7. HOLZAPFEL, H. and GURTLER, O., *J. prakt. Chem.*, **35**, 59 (1967); *Analyt. Abstr.*, **15**, 3878 (1968)
8. HOLZAPFEL, H. and GURTLER, O., *J. prakt. Chem.*, **35**, 68 (1967); *Analyt. Abstr.*, **15**, 3878 (1968)
9. HOLZAPFEL, H. and GURTLER, O., *J. prakt. Chem.*, **35**, 70 (1967); *Analyt. Abstr.*, **15**, 3878 (1968)

Molybdate

Molybdenum finds extensive use in the ferrous and non-ferrous metallurgical industries where its addition to alloys is beneficial in terms of wear resistance, corrosion resistance and strength. Further industrial applications are to be found in the electronics and missile fields, the latter depending on its use in the manufacture of high-temperature components.

The role of molybdenum as an essential element to higher plants has been established since 1939. Its determination at trace level in plants, animals, waters and geological samples, including soil, has been the subject of widespread study.

Determination of molybdenum has implications in the indirect determination of several other anions at trace level. Phosphate, arsenate and silicate are generally converted to the molybdoheteropoly acids, separated by solvent extraction if necessary, and the molybdenum content of each determined by spectrophotometry or atomic absorption spectroscopy. These methods are discussed in the relevant sections.

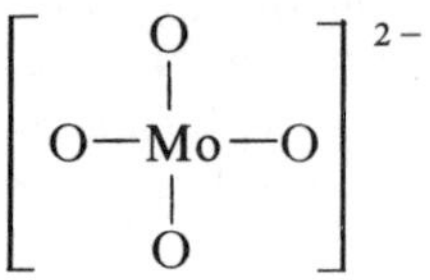

$$\left[\begin{array}{c} O \\ | \\ O{-}Mo{-}O \\ | \\ O \end{array}\right]^{2-}$$

Structure 14 The molybdate ion

Interrelationships between the molybdate ion (*Structure 14*) and other molybdenum ions can be extremely complex. In strongly alkaline media the predominant species are MoO_4^{2-}. In solutions of intermediate pH a number of polyanions are formed by condensation of MoO_4^{2-}. These include dimolybdate $Mo_2O_7^{2-}$ and heptamolybdate $Mo_7O_{24}^{6-}$. The latter is familiar in the form of its ammonium salt $(NH_4)_6Mo_7O_{24}.4H_2O$. The chemistry of molybdenum relevant to its analysis is discussed by Lingane[1].

Molybdenum(VI) is the most important and commonly encountered form of molybdenum in analytical work. Reference standards are usually prepared from sodium molybdate dihydrate, ammonium heptamolybdate tetrahydrate or molybdenum trioxide.

The general analytical chemistry of molybdenum is treated in depth in the monographs by Elwell and Wood[2] and Busev[3]. Other reviews have appeared by Chalmers[4] and Mann[5].

Separations

Most of the end-procedures used in determination of molybdenum are unselective, so that prior separation is necessary in most cases. An excellent account of separation methods is given in the monograph by Korkisch[6], in which solvent extraction, coprecipitation, ion-exchange and other chromatographic methods are discussed at length. More recent work has tended to favour solvent extraction procedures.

1. Precipitation

The solubility of molybdenum(VI) in basic medium can be used to separate it from many species which are precipitated. Repeated precipitation is generally required for complete separation.

In the presence of EDTA and 8-hydroxyquinoline in an acetate buffer, molybdate(VI) is precipitated as the oxine complex due to low stability of the molybdenum(VI)–EDTA complex. Using this[7,8], molybdenum can be separated from Fe(II), Al(III), Be(II), Zn(II), Ni(II), Co(II), Mn(II), Pb(II), Cd(II), Bi(III), Cu(II), Hg(II) and V(IV). Interference is given by Ti, W, V and U.

Benzoin α-oxime precipitates Mo(VI), W(VI), Cr(VI), V(V), Nb(V), Pd(II), and Ta(VI) only, in strong acid solution, this enabling molybdenum(VI) to be separated from a wide selection of other elements[9].

In some cases precipitation can be used to remove interfering species from molybdenum(VI), for example cinchonine precipitates tungsten(VI) leaving molybdenum(VI) in solution.

Yatirajan, Shuja and Kakkar[10] have recommended sulphide as precipitant for separation and determination of molybdenum. They report that precipitation of molybdenum(V) is more complete, and coprecipitation less, than with molybdenum(VI), the form previously used for precipitation in this way. Before treatment, molybdenum(VI) solutions are reduced by boiling with hydrazine sulphate for 3–4 min.

2. *Ion-exchange*

Since molybdenum(VI) in dilute acid, neutral and alkaline solutions is predominantly in anionic form its non-adsorption on strongly acid cation-exchange resins can be used to separate it from a wide range of metals. Because several heavy metal molybdates are insoluble in weakly acid media the inclusion of complexing agents becomes necessary to avoid precipitation.

The adsorption of molybdenum(VI) on anion-exchange resins can be used both for its separation and pre-concentration. Using a diethylaminoethyl (DEAE) cellulose anion-exchanger in thiocyanate medium, molybdenum(VI), rhenium(VII) and tungsten(VI) can be separated. The adsorption order with respect to DEAE is

$$W(VI) > Mo(VI) > Re(VII)$$

and by control of thiocyanate concentration and pH good separation can be achieved[11, 12].

In recent work by Korkisch, Godl and Gross[13] molybdenum at ppM level in fresh water samples is separated and pre-concentrated by anion-exchange. It is subsequently determined by atomic absorption spectroscopy.

Table 8 Selected TLC methods for separation of Mo(VI)

Adsorbent	*Solvent*	*Mo(VI) separated from:*	*Ref.*
Silica gel bound with poly(vinyl) alcohol	M HSCN or 0.5–0.9M malonic acid 1.0–1.8M acetic acid	Binary mixtures with ReO_4^- or WO_4^{2-}	16
Alumina	M–1.16M H_3PO_4	ReO_4^{2-}, VO_3^-, WO_4^{2-}	17
Silica gel	Methanol-3M HCl 7:3 or methanol–MNH_4NO_3 –3M aq NH_3 (14 : 5 : 1)	ReO_4^{2-}, WO_4^{2-}	18
Eastman 'Chroma gram' Silica gel sheets	Methanol–0.6M in HCl and containing 10% water	ReO_4^{2-}, Se(IV)	19

3. *Chromatography*

Other forms of chromatography used in the separation of molybdenum(VI) include paper- and thin-layer chromatography, and electrophoresis. Molybdenum(VI) and tungsten(VI) can be separated using paper chromatography[14]. Molybdenum(VI) and chromium(VI) are separated using paper electrophoresis[15]. Details of some TLC methods are given in *Table 8*.

4. *Solvent extraction*

Solvent extraction is probably the most commonly used method for separating trace amounts of molybdenum(VI) from other species. A more recent trend in such procedures is to determine it directly in the organic phase after extraction. This has the advantages of reduced time, increased selectivity and avoidance of losses which inevitably accompany back-extraction into an aqueous medium. Comprehensive accounts of the solvent extraction of molybdenum are given by Busev and Rodionova[20] and in the monograph by De, Khopkar and Chalmers[21]. While some extraction procedures utilize molybdenum(V) and molybdenum(III) by far the greater number involve molybdenum(VI). The important systems will now be discussed.

Molybdenum is extracted as the intensely red molybdenum(V)–thiocyanate complex. Molybdates therefore require reduction to the pentavalent state before application of this procedure. Many solvents can be used including diethyl ether, amyl acetate, isobutanol, and hexone. Palladium, Rh, Pt, W and Re are co-extracted with Mo(V), but Fe, Al, Ti, Mn, Ni, Co, U and Ta are not. Extraction of tungsten can be prevented by addition of tartrate or citrate. The red colour of the Mo(V)–thiocyanate complex is often used for determination of molybdenum.

More recently interest has centred on evaluating the extracted molybdenum by atomic absorption spectroscopy. In this connection Kim, Owens and Smythe[22] find that extraction with isobutyl methyl ketone leads to an improved method.

The molybdenum(VI)–dithiol (toluene 3,4-dithiol) complex was first reported by Hamence[23]. Extraction into esters such as amyl acetate enables molybdenum to be separated from Co, V, Sn, Pb, Ni, Mn and Al. Small amounts of iron are co-extracted. Tungsten can be masked with citric acid. The extract is suitable for spectrophotometric evaluation. A recent method by Quin and Brooks[24] has applied the system to analysis of biological, geological and steel samples.

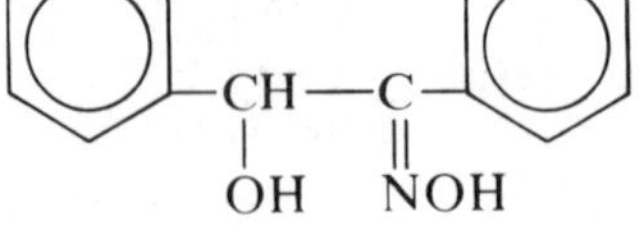

$$C_6H_5-\underset{\underset{OH}{|}}{CH}-\underset{\underset{NOH}{||}}{C}-C_6H_5$$

Structure 15 Benzoin α-oxime

Benzoin α-oxime (*Structure 15*) appears to have high specificity as an extractant for molybdenum(VI). Quantitative extraction[25] occurs into chloroform from 1M HCl. Chromium(VI) oxidizes the reagent and must be first reduced; vanadium(V) must be reduced to vanadium(IV). Tungsten(VI) can be masked with phosphate. The procedure enables molybdenum to be separared from Ta, Nb and W in steel analysis[26].

$N{-}O$, $N{-}O^{\ominus}$ $NH_4^{\oplus}$

Structure 16 Cupferron

Cupferron (*Structure 16*) forms a complex with molybdenum(V) which is completely extracted[27] into chloroform at $pH < 2$. Extraction into isoamyl alcohol[28] is quantitative from 3M H_2SO_4. Iron(III), Ti(IV), V(V), Sn(IV), Cu(II) and W(VI) are also extracted at pH 1.6. The Mo(VI)-cupferron can be used for separation of Mo(VI) and W(VI) by extraction into chloroform at pH 1 from tartrate or citrate media, but the valid pH range is narrow[29].

Molybdenum(VI) is extracted with mesityl oxide from a solution 1M in HCl and 8M in LiCl. Back-extraction is made into 0.5M aqueous ammonia for subsequent determination as the thiocyanate complex[30].

Recently, extraction of 'molybdenum blue' has been proposed for separating molybdenum from Ti, Zr, Cr, Mn, Fe, Co, Ni, U, and Al in a wide variety of samples[31]. The molybdophosphate blue is 99.5% extracted into isobutyl methyl ketone in a single extraction and then back-extracted into the aqueous phase for subsequent evaluation.

5. *Coprecipitation and related techniques*

Coprecipitation using freshly precipitated ferric hydroxide, hydrous manganese dioxide and aluminium hydroxide has been used to separate and preconcentrate molybdenum particularly in seawater[32]. Weiss and Lai[33] have used the coprecipitation of the benzoin α-oxime complex of molybdenum with an excess of the reagent at pH 1.8–5.5. Use of ferric hydroxide as carrier enables molybdenum(VI) to be separated from rhenium(VII) which remains in solution[34].

Kim and Zeitlin[35] have applied the technique of adsorption colloid flotation to separation of molybdenum(VI) from seawater. This technique forms part of a group of separation methods known collectively as adsorptive bubble separation[36]. The relationship of adsorption colloid flotation to other techniques within the group is shown in *Figure 18*. In the case of molybdenum, it consists of introducing the carrier, freshly prepared ferric hydroxide, and a surfactant, and bubbling a stream of air through the solution. Particles of the

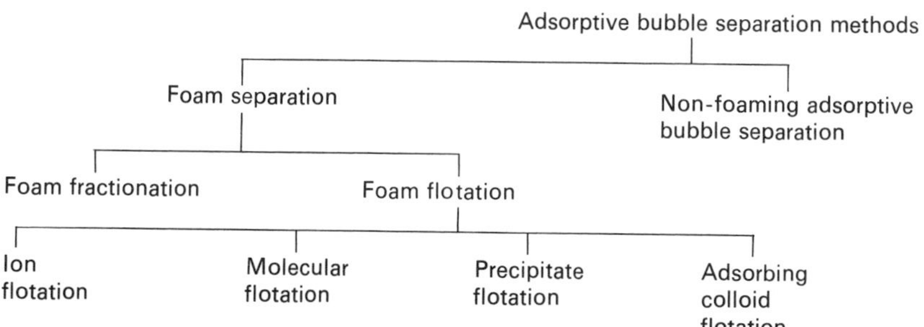

Figure 18 Adsorptive bubble separation methods. (Adapted from Karger *et al.*[36])

hydroxide together with the adsorbed molybdenum(VI) are carried to the surface where they form a well-defined layer. This is physically removed and subsequently analysed. For molybdenum(VI), the thiocyanate spectrophotometric method was used in the original work by Kim and Zeitlin. Using a 500-mℓ sample of seawater the separation is complete in 5 min with a 95% recovery of molybdenum. The general layout of the flotation unit is shown in *Figure 19*.

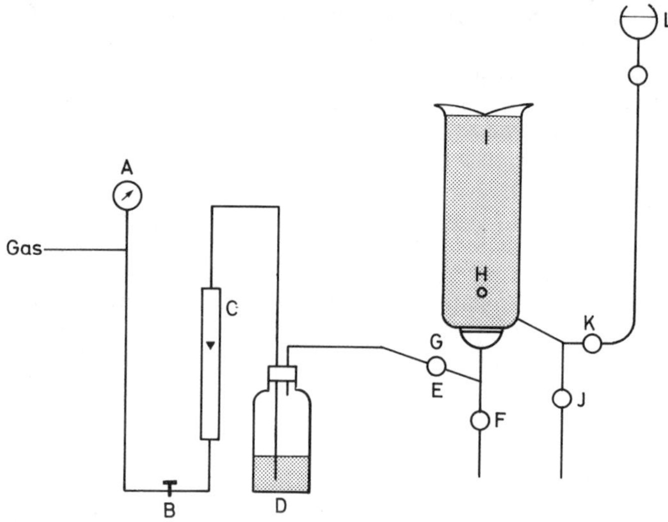

Figure 19 *Flotation unit. A, pressure gauge; B, fine needle valve; C, flow meter; D, gas humidifier; E, gas inlet stop valve; F, pressure releasing valve; G, sintered glass frit; H, rubber serum; I, froth drain; J, waste drain; K, water (push up) inlet; L, water reservoir*
(From Kim and Zeitlin[35])

Determination

Gravimetric methods

Molybdenum(VI) can be precipitated as sulphide or as molybdates of Ca, Ba, Pb, Ag or Hg(I). Alternatively organic precipitants such as 8-hydroxyquinoline or benzoin α-oxime can be used. Ignition to MoO_3 as the final weighing form is often recommended; in other cases such as 8-hydroxyquinoline the complex is weighed after drying at a lower temperature. Thioacetamide has been used to precipitate the sulphide by PFHS[37]. Precipitation of molybdenum(VI) as lead molybdate is generally regarded as a good method. Ignition is carried out at 600–650 °C. This too can be produced by PFHS[38]. The procedure is based on the slow displacement of lead ions from its EDTA complex by chromium(III).

Several organic precipitants for molybdenum(VI) have been investigated. Benzoin α-oxime has already been referred to in connection with separation of molybdenum(VI) by precipitation and solvent extraction. It produces precipitates with several ions including Mo(VI), W(VI), V(V) and UO_2^{2+}.

After filtration the precipitate is ignited at about 600 °C and weighed as MoO_3.

Interference by chromium(VI) and vanadium(V) can be eliminated by reduction to chromium(III) and vanadium(IV). This is conveniently done using sulphur dioxide. Tungsten(VI) can be masked using phosphate.

8-hydroxyquinoline precipitates molybdenum(VI) as $Mo_2(C_9H_6ON)_2$ which may be weighed as such after drying at 200 °C. Several metallic ions interfere. If precipitation is made in the presence of EDTA no interference is given by Fe(III), Al, Be, Zn, Ni, Co, Mn, Pt, Cd, Bi, Cu, and Hg(II) but W(VI), U, V(V) and Ti still interfere[7].

Gravimetric determination of Mo(VI) would normally be used if relatively large amounts required accurate determination. Recent collaborative work on the 8-hydroxyquinoline gravimetric method indicates that it is capable of high accuracy and precision[39]. The method was applied to certificated samples of ferromolybdenum and included inter- and intralaboratory analyses. An examination of the results indicates that while the method does not conform to the highest precision, it is sufficiently high for most purposes. The procedure is simple and rapid, requiring only a single precipitation, and is less tedious than the previously recommended lead molybdate method.

Other gravimetric procedures introduced recently utilize salicylohydroxamic acid[40] and trithiocarbamate[41].

Gravimetric determination of molybdenum (VI) using 8-hydroxyquinoline

Reagents

Acetate buffer:

3 volumes of 50% w/v ammonium acetate +4 volumes of 50% v/v acetic acid.

8-hydroxyquinoline:

Dissolve 3 g of 8-hydroxyquinoline in 8.5 mℓ of acetic acid (Reagent Grade). Dilute to 100 mℓ with water.

Procedure

To a neutral solution of Mo(VI) containing about 0.07 g of molybdenum and in a volume of about 100 mℓ, add 10 mℓ of the acetate buffer. Boil Add 10 mℓ of 3% oxine solution and digest for 2–3 min. Filter the precipitate hot through a sintered glass crucible (porosity 4). Wash with six 15 mℓ-portions of hot water. Dry to constant weight at 200 °C.

Weigh as $MoO_2(C_9H_6ON)_2$. Factor for molybdenum = 0.2304.

Titrimetric methods

1. Redox

Redox method for molybdenum(VI) lack selectivity. The most used method consists of reducing molybdenum(VI) to molybdenum(V) or molybdenum(III) and then re-oxidizing using a standard oxidizing reagent, usually permanganate or ceric sulphate. The main reductants are Hg, Ag, Zn and Cd amalgams, and $SnCl_2$. Others are listed in the review by Chalmers[4].

Reduction with mercury or silver gives molybdenum(V); with zinc or cadmium amalgams molybdenum(III) is produced. In the latter case the familiar Jones reductor can be used. Other elements reduced from higher oxidation states include As, Fe, Ti, Cr, V, U, and W. Nitric acid is also reduced.

If reduction to molybdenum(III) is employed, oxidation by atmospheric oxygen must be avoided. This can be accomplished by running the reduction column effluent into excess of a standard oxidizing reagent and then back-titrating the excess. Masking can sometimes provide selectivity. Speranskaya and Mertsalova[42] determine molybdenum(VI) in the presence of tungsten by masking the latter with fluoride, reducing molybdenum(VI) with a cadmium analgam in H_2SO_4 or HCl, and titrating the resulting molybdenum(III) with $KMnO_4$.

If the reduction is made using Ag, Hg or Sn(II), the degree of reduction is a function of the HCl concentration. Becker and Coetzee[43] have re-investigated the principal methods for molybdenum based on reduction of molybdenum(VI) followed by oxidation. They find that with a silver reductor, reduction to molybdenum(V) is only quantitative if the HCl concentration of the solution is 2.0–2.25M. The same investigation confirms earlier work indicating that when molybdenum(V) is titrated with standard dichromate, a constant negative error of about 1 per cent is produced[44, 45]. The error is attributed to residual traces of copper, which are known to catalyse the atmospheric oxidation of molybdenum(V). Silver reductor columns are often prepared by reducing a silver solution using copper[46]. A modified form of silver reductor has been described in which copper is not used[47]. Becker and Coetzee, in the above study, show that reduction of molybdenum(VI) by mercury is complete in HCl solutions of 2–4M, and that $SnCl_2$ reduction to molybdenum(V) is quantitative if the HCl concentration is greater than 2M. In the Jones reductor the acid concentration is not critical.

2. *Precipitation titrations*

Molybdenum(VI) in macro quantities can be determined by titration with lead or mercury. Titration with $Pb(NO_3)_2$ is probably the best. It can be carried out at pH 4.8–5.5 using dithizone as indicator[48]. Several species interfere. Lassner and Scharf[49] use hexamine as buffer and PAR (4-(2-pyridylazo)-resorcinol) as indicator. When molybdenum(VI) is accompanied by tungsten(VI), both can be titrated by this procedure and molybdenum(VI) determined separately by EDTA titration. Under certain conditions more than 2 mg of sulphate or 3 mg of fluoride interfere[50]. The tungsten(VI) titration can tolerate far more. Cheng and Goydish[51] employ the $Pb(NO_3)_2$ titration to analyse molybdate–perrhenate–fluoride mixtures.

3. *EDTA*

EDTA methods for molybdenum(VI) have evolved through several stages. Earlier work consisted in precipitating molybdenum(VI) with calcium(II) or lead(II) and back-titrating the excess of cation with EDTA.

The molybdenum(V)–EDTA complex, $(MoO_2)_2Y^{2-}$, is more stable than the corresponding molybdenum(VI) complex, and has featured in several procedures. It can be produced by reduction of molybdenum(VI) in strongly acid medium, with hydrazine sulphate in the presence of EDTA. Excess EDTA can be titrated in several ways[52].

A newer approach has been based on the 1:1:1 ternary complex which forms when molybdenum(VI) is boiled with hydroxylamine hydrochloride and EDTA. This is more stable than the molybdenum(VI)–EDTA complex though selectivity is poor. Pribil and Vesely[53] have extended the work using the corresponding ternary complex with DCTA. After formation of the complex, excess DCTA is titrated at pH 5–5.5 with standard zinc using xylenol orange as indicator. The method, which is applicable to 5–40 mg of molybdenum, can be used in the presence of tungsten provided sufficient hydroxylamine chloride (10 g) is added.

Titrimetric determination of molybdate using DCTA[53]

Reagents
Hexamine solution: 10%.
Xylenol orange: 0.5% aqueous.

Procedure
To a nearly neutral solution of Mo(VI) containing 5–40 mg of molybdenum, add 1–2 g of hydroxylamine hydrochloride, dilute to 150–200 mℓ and heat to boiling. The solution becomes yellow or slightly blue-green depending on the molybdenum concentration.

Add excess of standard DCTA and boil the solution for a further 15 min. The solution turns yellow or yellow-green. Cool, add hexamine solution to adjust the pH to 5–5.5, add a few drops of xylenol orange and titrate with 0.05M $ZnCl_2$ to a red-violet colour that persists for 3 min.

Note
If tungsten is present, the titration can be made without interference if 10 g of hydroxylamine hydrochloride is used.

Spectroscopic methods

1. Spectrophotometric
The thiocyanate method is probably the most widely used spectrometric method for molybdenum(VI). It consists of reducing molybdenum(VI) in acid solution, and in the presence of thiocyanate, to orange-red oxypentathiocyanato molybdate(V). This can be extracted into ethers, esters, alcohols, etc., and then evaluated spectrophotometrically.

Despite its extensive use, the method has several inherent disadvantages. The coloured species lacks stability and reproducibility. Strict control of conditions is required if the reduction is to cease at molybdenum(V) only. Under certain conditions reduction to molybdenum(III) is possible; in weakly acid solution there is the possibility of molybdenum blue forming. When Sn(II) chloride is used as reductant small amounts of iron or copper stabilize the colour intensity. Certain organic solvents and oxidizing agents have the same effect. The evidence indicates that the reaction mechanism of the thiocyanate method is complex and still not completely understood[54]. Earlier work on the method is discussed by Sandell[55].

Modern forms usually recommend extraction into *n*-butyl acetate rather than diethyl ether used in earlier work. The wavelength used varies according to the exact procedure, its values ranging from 400 to 550 nm. The molar absorptivity too depends on the procedure. Its value at 475 nm using isoamyl alcohol as solvent[56] is about 1.5×10^4.

Accounts of interference are not in agreement, possibly because certain species only interfere when in relatively large amounts. The following list is only a guide, and the original literature should be consulted for more specific data. Interferences are W(VI), V(V), Ti(III), Cr(VI), U(VI), Co(II), Cu(II), Pb(II), Fe(III), Pt, Rh, Re(VII), Ag, Hg, Au, Se, Te, F^- and NO_3^-. Interference by W(VI) is important in steel analysis. It can be masked using citric, tartaric or oxalic acids, or sufficiently mild reducing conditions[54] used to reduce molybdenum(VI) without affecting tungsten(VI). Application of the method in the general form described above, namely tin(II) reduction followed by extraction into isoamyl alcohol or isoamyl acetate, has found considerable use. It is recommended by the AOAC for molybdenum in plants[57] and by British Standards[58] for molybdenum in steel. Braithwaite and Hobson[59] describe an automatic form of the method suitable for steel analysis.

Newer developments include the use of mixed ligand and ternary complexes. The former depends on the fact that the stability of the molybdenum–thiocyanate complex is enhanced by introducing a second ligand. The mixed complex can be extracted into organic solvents. Tetraphenylarsonium chloride[54, 60], 2-mercaptobenzo-γ-thiopyrone[61], potassium ethyl xanthate[62] and α-anilinobenzylphosphonate[63] have featured in this way. The resulting selectivity and sensitivity is increased, for example in the last reference cited, the molar absorptivity is 5.9×10^3 and relatively high concentrations of Fe, V, and W can be tolerated. In one of the procedures employing tetraphenylarsonium chloride[54] the molybdenum(VI) is reduced using ascorbic acid and titanium(III), thiocyanate added and this extracted with the onium cation. In this case the molar absorptivity is 1.74×10^4 at 470 nm. A 40-fold excess of tungsten over molybdenum can be tolerated.

Moving on to ternary complexes, Gango and Ivanova[64] report such a complex by association of the molybdenum–thiocyanate complex with crystal violet. Another involving rhodamine B has been reported[65]. Here a 1:5:2 complex is formed which may be represented by the equation

$$[MoO(SCN)_5]^{2-} + \underset{\text{pink fluorescent}}{2RhB^+} \rightleftharpoons \underset{\text{blue non-fluorescent}}{Mo(SCN)_5(RhB)_2}$$

The complex absorbs strongly at 600 nm providing a highly selective and sensitive method suitable for molybdenum in soils and plants. A spectrophotometric or fluorescent procedure can be used, the detection limits being 0.1 μg and 0.05 μg Mo respectively.

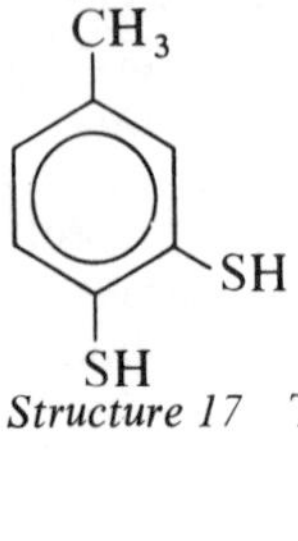

CH_3

SH

SH

Structure 17 Toluene 3,4-dithiol (dithiol)

Toluene 3,4-dithiol (dithiol) (*Structure 17*) forms a dark-green coloured complex product with molybdenum(VI) in mineral acid. Tungsten(VI) and tin(II) also react. The complex is extractable into polar and non-polar organic solvents. Since its introduction by Hamence[66] and Miller and Low[67] it has been widely applied. In benzene the molar absorptivity is 2.86×10^4 at 665 nm. Interference is given by Fe, As, Sb, W, Se, Pt, Re, Sn, Bi, Ti, V, Zr, Th, U, Cu, Pb, Cd, Co, and Ni. Various methods have been devised in order to eliminate these interferences[68, 69].

Solutions of dithiol are notoriously unstable. This has received attention by several investigators. A recent report by De Silva[70] has recommended a method of preparation that gives a product stable for several weeks if stored in a refrigerator. Kobrova[71] finds that both the specificity and sensitivity of the dithiol method is improved if a 0.33% solution of the reagent in 1% NaOH, stabilized with 1% v/v mercaptoacetic acid, is used.

Many of the reported procedures have been developed for specific requirements. De Silva[70] extracts molybdenum(VI) from an HCl medium into tri-*n*-butyl phosphate. Here it is complexed with toluene 3,4-dithiol in a glacial acetic–tri-*n*-butyl phosphate–phosphoric acid medium. The medium suppresses the reaction of dithiol with tungsten(VI), iron(III) and traces of other elements co-extracted with molybdenum. The molar absorptivity in the medium is 1.84×10^4.

Quin and Brooks[72] extract into isoamyl alcohol. The sensitivity is reported as 0.05, 0.5 and 10 ppm for biological, geochemical and steel samples respectively. Ascorbic and citric acids eliminate interference from iron and tungsten; addition of KI gives the method a high tolerance to copper.

The methods discussed so far have been established for some time. Some of the new methods will now be considered.

Bailey *et al.*[73] have discussed the nature and formation mechanism of ternary complexes involving molybdenum. In the same publication they develop a spectrophotometric method based on the ternary complex with catechol violet and cetyltrimethylammonium bromide. Its molar absorptivity is 4.6×10^4 in water at 675 nm, which makes it one of the most sensitive methods for molybdenum. The complex corresponds to a Mo–CV–CTAB ratio of 1:1:2, and obeys Beer's law over the range 9.6–96 ppm. The major interferences arise from elements known to form complexes with catechol violet; the original paper should be consulted for details.

Leong[74] substitutes gallein for catechol violet in the above investigation. The resulting blue water-soluble complex provides a method approximately twice as sensitive as the thiocyanate or dithiol methods. Interference, however, is considerable, and prior separation of molybdenum(VI) is recommended.

Reduction of molybdophosphoric acid to molybdenum blue provides a sensitive method, but it tends to give non-reproducible results. A recent study by Kriss, Rudenko and Yatsimirskii[75] finds that the wavelength of maximum absorbance can vary in the range 680–810 nm depending on the reductant used.

A sensitive method utilizing 2-amino-4-chlorobenzene-thiol ($\varepsilon = 3.6 \times 10^4$ in chloroform) was developed by Kirkbright and Yoe[76]. This has found application in trace determination of phosphate via molybdophosphoric acid.

Twenty five hydroxy and azo compounds have been investigated as potential spectrophotometric reagents for molybdenum(VI) in non-aqueous media[77]. Of these *p*-dimethyl-aminophenyl fluorone showed the greatest sensitivity with $\varepsilon = 4300$. No interference was found for a Mo:W ratio of 2:1.

2. *Fluorimetric*

A fluorimetric method employing the ternary complex between molybdenum, thiocyanate and rhodamine B has been referred to already.

Carminic acid reacts in aqueous solution with both molybdenum(VI) and tungsten(VI) to give complexes suitable for spectrofluorimetry[78]. In the case of molybdenum(VI), the fluorescence is measured at 590 nm with excitation at 560 nm. Some of the interferences that occur can be minimized by appropriate treatment.

3. *Atomic absorption spectroscopy*

Application of AAS to elements that form refractory oxides suffer from low sensitivity and relatively poor detection limits because of the relatively high dissociation energies involved. Earlier studies by David[79] indicated that the sensitivity for molybdenum was inadequate for its direct determination in samples containing less than 100 ppm of molybdenum.

Greater sensitivity is attained using a nitrous oxide-acetylene flame. Ramakrishna, West and Robinson[80] reported a sensitivity of 0.8 ppm for molybdenum using such a flame. In general there is more interference from the matrix under such conditions. Measurements are generally made using the 313.3 nm molybdenum line.

Recent methods tend to employ solvent extraction followed by direct aspiration of the organic phase into the flame. Several systems of this type are listed by Kim, Owens and Smythe[22], who themselves extract the molybdenum–thiocyanate complex into isobutyl methyl ketone before aspiration. Their method was developed for analysis of geological samples, and is applicable in the 1–500 ppm Mo range using 1-g samples. The limit of detection is 0.1 ppm. Another recent method for geological samples is reported by Sutcliffe[81]. More recent work by Kim, Alexander and Smythe[82] employing long-chain alkylamines for preconcentrating traces of Mo, W and Re as thiocyanate complexes, followed by AAS, reduces the detection limit for molybdenum to 0.02 ppm in the final MIBK solution.

Non-flame AAS methods for molybdenum have been reported[83–85]. The first of these employs a graphite cell heated to 2600 °C; the range for molybdenum is 0.1–1 ppm.

Electroanalytical methods

1. *Potentiometric*

Earlier potentiometric procedures for molybdenum(VI) using titanium(III) and chromium(II) were described by Willard[86] and Brintzinger and Oschatz[87]. With chromium(II) the reaction proceeds quantitatively in HCl or H_2SO_4 at 80–100 °C. Two potential jumps are observed corresponding to molybdenum(VI)→molybdenum(V) and molybdenum(V)→molybdenum(III). In recent work Hahn and Moosmueller[88] titrate molybdenum(VI) potentiometrically with $TiCl_3$ in the presence of citric acid.

Mercury(I) perchlorate was used by Tarayan and Ovsepyan[89] who found no interference by tungsten. Dolezal, Moldal and Zyka[90] first reduce molybdenum(VI) to molybdenum(III) using a zinc amalgam, and titrate this potentiometrically with iron(III). They find that sufficient chloride ions must be present if the reduction is to be satisfactory.

Other procedures have been reported by Muralikrishna and Rao[91] who favour the use of strong phosphoric acid media.

2. *Voltammetric and polarographic*

An early study by Uhl[92] indicated that molybdenum(VI) is reduced at the dropping mercury electrode in dilute HNO_3 containing lactic and oxalic acids. Highly sensitive methods for molybdenum(VI) have been reported based on the catalytic reduction wave produced when nitric or perchloric acids are used as supporting electrolytes. Johnson and Robinson[93], using a NO_3^-–H_2SO_4 supporting electrolyte employ the catalytically enhanced wave at about -0.3 V *v.* SCE, this giving a linear response over the concentration range 10^{-5}–10^{-7} M Mo. Subsequent work by Violanda and Cooke[94], again in the presence of nitrate, reported a method having a sensitivity of 0.005 μg Mo mℓ^{-1}. This method has a high tolerance to interference from extraneous ions.

The polarographic reduction of molybdenum(VI) in HCl media has been studied[95]. The wave observed in this medium is considered to be a true reduction wave representing molybdenum(VI)→molybdenum(III), and not a mercuric wave reported in earlier work. In 4M–6M HCl and in the presence of 0.27M–1.08M NH_4F the wave height is proportional to molybdenum concentration in the concentration range 1–6 mM. Tungsten does not interfere.

3. *Miscellaneous electroanalytical*

Amperometric titration of molybdenum(VI) with 8-mercaptoquinoline (thio-oxine) using platinum and mercuric iodide electrodes in various basal solutions has been reported[96]. Vanadium and copper interfere, but a 2-fold excess of Bi, W or Te over Mo does not. The method is applied to ferromolybdenum, steel and other alloys.

Coulometric methods have utilized electrogenerated titanium (III)[97] and iron(II)[98]. In the latter work a bi-amperometric end-point is used. The method can be used for concentrations as small as 7×10^{-5}M Mo(VI). A 30-fold excess of tungsten over molybdenum can be tolerated.

Cupferron can be used in the high-frequency titration of molybdenum-(VI)[99]. Two breaks in the curve correspond to 1:1 and 1:2 molybdenum(VI)–cupferron complexes. Application can be made to molybdenum(VI)/uranium(VI) mixtures.

Catalytic methods

Catalytic methods for molybdenum(VI) are mainly based on its effect on the H_2O_2–KI reaction. Introduced by Yatsimirskii and Afans'eva[100] in 1956, the method has since been investigated by several others. Svehla and Erdey[101] use the reaction for determination of molybdenum in the range 10–100 μg mℓ$^{-1}$.

Weisz, Klockow and Ludwig[102] employ the device of adding iodide at the same rate that it is consumed by the reaction, thus keeping the reaction rate constant. The rate of adding I^- is then proportional to the molybdenum concentration.

The H_2O_2–KI reaction is also catalysed by W, Zr, Ta, and Fe. Babko, Lisetskaya and Tsarenko[103] have investigated the optimum conditions for determination of molybdenum, and of overcoming interference by the above metals.

More recently automatic catalytic methods based on the reaction have appeared[104–106]. In the last method, Bradfield and Strickland[106] overcome interference by iron and tungsten by addition of NH_4F. For the greatest precision and accuracy a preliminary separation of molybdenum using benzoin α-oxime is recommended, a method also used by Babko, Lisetskaya and Tsarenko[103]. The detection limit is 0.003 μg Mo mℓ$^{-1}$ and the method is applied to plant material. A flow diagram of the method by Bradfield and Strickland is shown in *Figure 20*.

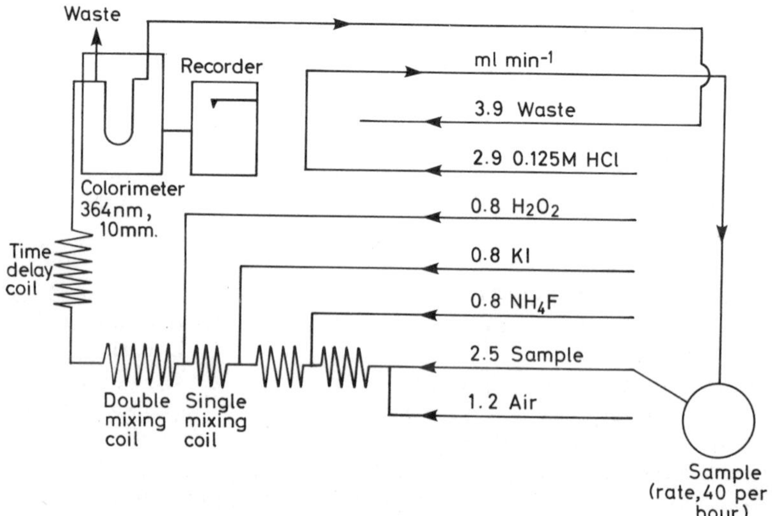

Figure 20 *Catalytic determination of molybdate. Flow diagram for Autoanalyzer.* (After Bradfield and Strickland[104])

Miscellaneous methods

Recent work indicates that molybdenum in seawater can be determined by electron paramagnetic spectrometry[107]. The procedure includes extraction of paramagnetic $Mo(SCN)_5$ into isoamyl alcohol. The detection limit is 0.46 μg Mo ℓ$^{-1}$.

References

1. LINGANE, J.J., *Analytical Chemistry of Selected Metallic Elements*, Reinhold, New York, 85 (1966)
2. ELWELL, W.T. and WOOD, D.F., *Analytical Chemistry of Mo and W*, Pergamon Press, Oxford (1971)
3. BUSEV, A.I., *Analytical Chemistry of Molybdenum*, Israel programme for scientific translations, Oldbourne Press (1964)
4. CHALMERS, R.A., in *Comprehensive Analytical Chemistry* (Ed. C.L. and D.W. Wilson), Vol. IC, Elsevier, Amsterdam, 589 (1962)
5. MANN, J.W., in *Encyclopedia of Industrial Chemical Analysis* (Ed. F.D. Snell and L.S. Ettre), Vol. 16, Interscience, New York, 150 (1972)
6. KORKISCH, J., *Modern Methods for the Separation of Rarer Metal Ions*, Chapter 17, Pergamon Press, Oxford (1969)
7. PRIBIL, R. and MALAT, M., *Colln. Czech. chem. Commun.*, **15**, 120 (1950)
8. MALINEK, M., *Chemiké Listy*, **48**, 30 (1954)
9. YAGODA, H. and FALES, H.A., *J. Am. chem. Soc.*, **60**, 640 (1938)
10. YATIRAJAN, V., SHUJA, U. and KAKKAR, L.R., *Talanta*, **23**, 819 (1976)
11. ISHIDA, K. and KURODA, R., *Analyt. Chem.*, **39**, 212 (1967)
12. KURODA, R. and KAWABUCHI, K., *Z. analyt. Chem.*, **261**, 394 (1972); *Analyt. Abstr.*, **24**, 2809 (1972)
13. KORKISCH, J., GODL, L. and GROSS, H., *Talanta*, **22**, 669 (1975)
14. BLASIUS, E. and CZEKAY, A., *Z. analyt. Chem.*, **156**, 81 (1957); *Analyt. Abstr.*, **4**, 3312 (1957)
15. BLUM, L., *Rev. Chim. Bucharest*, **9**, 28 (1958); *Analyt. Abstr.*, **5**, 3712 (1958)
16. PHIPPS, A.M., *Analyt. Chem.*, **43**, 467 (1971)
17. SHIOBARA, Y., *Japan Analyst*, **17**, 1396 (1968); *Analyt. Abstr.*, **19**, 202 (1970)
18. GAIBAKYAN, D.S., *Uchen. Zap. Erevan. gos. Univ. estestv. Nauk.*, 71 (1971); *Analyt. Abstr.*, **23**, 2293 (1972)
19. KURODA, R., KAWABUCHI, K. and ITO, T., *Talanta*, **15**, 1486 (1968)
20. BUSEV, A.I. and RODIONOVA, T.V., *Zh. analit. Khim.*, **26**, 578 (1971)
21. DE, A.K., KHOPKAR, S.M. and CHALMERS, R.A., *Solvent Extraction of Metals*, Van Nostrand Reinhold Co., London (1970)
22. KIM, C.H., OWENS, C.M. and SMYTHE, L.E., *Talanta*, **21**, 445 (1974)
23. HAMENCE, J.H., *Analyst*, **65**, 152 (1940)
24. QUIN, B.F. and BROOKS, R.R., *Analytica chim. Acta*, **74**, 75 (1975)
25. HOENES, H.J. and STONE, K.G., *Talanta*, **4**, 250 (1960)
26. LUKE, C.L., *Analytica chim. Acta*, **34**, 302 (1966)
27. STARY, J. and SMIZANSKA, J., *Analytica chim. Acta*, **29**, 545 (1963)
28. ALLEN, S.H. and HAMILTON, M.B., *Analytica chim. Acta*, **7**, 483 (1952)
29. PYATNITSKII, I.V. and KRAVTSOVA, L.F., *Ukr. Khim. Zh.*, **35**, 77 (1969); *Analyt. Abstr.*, **18**, 3098 (1970)
30. SHINDE, V.M. and KHOPKAR, S.M., *Ind. J. Chem.*, **7**, 504 (1969); *Analyt. Abstr.*, **19**, 201 (1970)
31. YATIRAJAM, V. and RAM, J., *Talanta*, **20**, 885 (1973)
32. CHAN, K.M. and RILEY, J.P., *Analytica chim. Acta*, **36**, 220 (1966)
33. WEISS, H.V. and LAI, M.G., *Talanta*, **8**, 72 (1961)
34. NOVIKOV, A.I., *Zh. analit. Khim.*, **16**, 588 (1961); *Analyt. Abstr.*, **9**, 1903 (1962)
35. KIM, Y.S. and ZEITLIN, H., *Separation Sci.*, **6**, 505 (1971); *Analyt. Chem.*, **43**, 1390 (1971)
36. KARGER, B.L., GRIEVES, R.B., LEMLICH, R., RUBIN, A.J. and SEBBA, F., *Separation Sci.*, **2**, 401 (1967)
37. BURRIEL-MARTI, F. and MACIERA VIDAN, A., *Analytica chim. Acta*, **26**, 163 (1962)
38. NEWCOMB, G. and MARKHAM, J.J., *Analytica chim. Acta*, **35**, 261 (1966)
39. Methods of Analysis Panel, Glasgow. *Metallurgia*, **83**, 129 (1971)
40. CHAUDHURI, N.K., SARKAR, A.K. and DAS, J., *Z. analyt. Chem.*, **254**, 365 (1971); *Analyt., Abstr.*, **22**, 1561 (1972)
41. JOHRI, K.N., KAUSHIK, N.K. and SINGH, K., *Talanta*, **16**, 432 (1969)
42. SPERANSKAYA, E.F. and MERTSALOVA, V.E., *Khim. khim. Tekhnol. Alma-Ata, Sb*, **2**, 89 (1964); *Chem. Abstr.*, **64**, 1344d (1966)
43. BECKER, J. and COETZEE, C.J., *Analyst*, **92**, 166 (1967)
44. WENIER, R. and BORISS, P., *Z. analyt. Chem.*, **160**, 343 (1958); *Analyt. Abstr.*, **5**, 4086 (1958)
45. GRUBITSCH, H., HALVORSEN, K. and SCHINDLER, G., *Z. analyt. Chem.*, **173**, 414 (1960); *Analyt. Abstr.*, **7**, 4756 (1960)

46. KOLTHOFF, I.M. and BELCHER, R., *Volumetric Analysis III,*, Interscience, New York, 15 (1957)
47. SALAM KHAN, M.A. and STEPHEN, W.I., *Analyst,* **93**, 26 (1968)
48. UEDA, S., YAMAMOTO, Y. and TAKENUCHI, H., *J. chem. Soc. Japan, pure Chem. Sect.,* **88**, 1299 (1967); *Analyt. Abstr.,* **16**, 1857 (1969)
49. LASSNER, E. and SCHARF, R., *Chemist Analyst,* **49**, 68 (1960)
50. LASSNER, E. and SCHEDLE, H., *Talanta,* **13**, 326 (1966)
51. CHENG, K.L. and GOYDISH, B.L., *Microchem. J.,* **13**, 35 (1968)
52. SCHWARZENBACH, G. and FLASCHKA, H., *Complexometric Determinations,* 2nd English edn, Methuen, London, 223 (1969)
53. PRIBIL, R. and VESELY, V., *Talanta,* **17**, 170 (1970)
54. FOGG, A.G., KUMAR, J.L. and BURNS, D.T., *Analyst,* **100**, 311 (1975)
55. SANDELL, E.B., *Colorimetric Determination of Traces of Metals,* 3rd edn, Interscience, New York (1959)
56. CHARLOT, G., *Colorimetric Determination of Elements,* Elsevier, Amsterdam, 301 (1964)
57. *Official Methods of Analysis of the Association of Official Analytical Chemists* (Ed. W. Horowitz), 11th edn, The Association of Official Analytical Chemists, Washington D.C., 42 (1970)
58. *British Standards Handbook* No. 19, British Standards Institute, London (1970)
59. BRAITHWAITE, K. and HOBSON, J.D., *Analyst,* **93**, 633 (1968)
60. TAMHINA, B. and HERAK, M.J., *Mikrochim. Acta,* 553 (1976)
61. SAVARIAR, C.P., ARUNACHALAM, M.K. and HARIHARAN, T.R., *Analytica chim. Acta,* **69**, 305 (1974)
62. ARUNACHALAM, M.K. and KUMARAN, M.K., *Talanta,* **21**, 355 (1974)
63. TAMHINA, B., HERAK, M.J. and JAGODIC, V., *Analytica chim. Acta,* **76**, 417 (1975)
64. GANAGO, L.I. and IVANOVA, I.F., *Zh. analit. Khim.,* **27**, 713 (1972); *Analyt. Abstr.,* **25**, 1555 (1973)
65. HADDAD, P.R., ALEXANDER, P.W. and SMYTHE, L.E., *Talanta,* **22**, 61 (1975)
66. HAMENCE, J.H., *Analyst,* **65**, 152 (1940)
67. MILLER, C.C. and LOW, A.J., *J. chem. Soc.,* 1258 (1940)
68. JEFFREY, P.G., *Analyst,* **81**, 104 (1956)
69. BINGLEY, J.B., *J. agric. Fd Chem.,* **7**, 269 (1959)
70. DE SILVA, M.E.M.S., *Analyst,* **100**, 517 (1975)
71. KOBROVA, M., *Chemiké Listy,* **66**, 768 (1972); *Analyt. Abstr.,* **24**, 778 (1973)
72. QUIN, B.F. and BROOKS, R.R., *Analytica chim. Acta,* **74**, 75 (1975)
73. BAILEY, B.W., CHESTER, J.E., DAGNALL, R.M. and WEST, T.S., *Talanta,* **15**, 1359 (1968)
74. LEONG, C.L., *Analyst,* **95**, 1018 (1970)
75. KRISS, E.E., RUDENKO, V.K. and YATSIMIRSKII, K.B., *Zh. neorg. Khim.,* **16**, 2147 (1971); *Analyt. Abstr.,* **23**, 3141 (1972)
76. KIRKBRIGHT, G.F. and YOE, J.H., *Talanta,* **11**, 415 (1964)
77. PONOMAREV, A.A. and AGRINSKAYA, N.A., *Trudy novocherk. politekh. Inst.,* **266**, 99 (1972); *Analyt. Abstr.,* **24**, 2797 (1973)
78. KIRKBRIGHT, G.F., WEST, T.S. and WOODWARD, C., *Talanta,* **13**, 1637 (1966)
79. DAVID, D.J., *Analyst,* **86**, 730 (1961)
80. RAMAKRISHNA, T.V., WEST, P.W. and ROBINSON, J.W., *Analytica chim. Acta,* **44**, 437 (1969)
81. SUTCLIFFE, P., *Analyst,* **101**, 949 (1976)
82. KIM, C.H., ALEXANDER, P.W. and SMYTHE, L.E., *Talanta,* **22**, 739 (1975)
83. BODROV, M.V. and NIKOLAEV, G.I., *Zh. analit. Khim.,* **24**, 1314 (1969); *Analyt. Abstr.,* **20**, 1644 (1971)
84. MUZZARELLI, R.A.A., *Analytica chim. Acta,* **64**, 371 (1973)
85. JOHNSON, D.J., WEST, T.S. and DAGNALL, R.M., *Analytica chim. Acta,* **65**, 171 (1974)
86. WILLARD, H.H. and FENWICK, F., *J. Am. chem. Soc.,* **45**, 928, 933 (1923)
87. BRINTZINGER, G. and OSCHATZ, F., *Z. analyt. Chem.,* **165**, 221 (1927)
88. HAHN, H. and MOOSMUELLER, A.F., *Z. analyt. Chem.,* **221**, 261 (1966); *Chem. Abstr.,* **66**, 16236e (1967)
89. TARAYAN, V.M. and OVSEPYAN, E.N., *Zav. Lab.,* **17**, 526 (1951)
90. DOLEZAL, J., MOLDAN, B. and ZYKA, J., *Colln Czech. chem. Commun.,* **24**, 3769 (1959); *Analyt. Abstr.,* **7**, 3223 (1960)
91. MURALIKRISHNA, U. and RAO, G.G., *Talanta,* **15**, 143 (1968)
92. UHL, F.A., *Z. analyt. Chem.,* **110**, 102 (1937)
93. JOHNSON, M.G. and ROBINSON, R.J., *Analyt. Chem.,* **24**, 366 (1952)

94. VIOLANDA, A.T. and COOKE, W.D., *Analyt. Chem.*, **36**, 2287 (1964)
95. SPERANSKAYA, E.F. and KOZLOVSKII, M.T., *Zav. Lab.*, **30**, 403 (1964); *Analyt. Abstr.*, **12**, 3857 (1965)
96. PAVLOVA, I.M. and SONGINA, O.A., *Sb. Stat. Aspirantov Soiskatel., Min vyssh. Sved. spets. Obrazov. Kaz SSR, Khim. khim. Tekhnol.*, 218 (1965); *Analyt. Abstr.*, **14**, 3160 (1967)
97. BINDER, E., GOLDSTEIN, G., LAGRANGE, P. and SCHWING, J.P., *Bull. Soc. chim. Fr.*, 2807 (1965); *Analyt. Abstr.*, **14**, 688 (1967)
98. AGASYAN, P.K., TARENOVA, K.K., NIKOLAEVA, E.R. and KATINA, R.M., *Zh. analit. Khim.*, **33**, 547 (1967); *Analyt. Abstr.*, **15**, 4670 (1968)
99. RIOLO, C.B., SOLDI, T.F. and SPINI, G., *Analytica chim. Acta*, **41**, 388 (1968)
100. YATSIMIRSKII, K.B. and AFANS'EVA, L.P., *Zh. analit. Khim.*, **11**, 319 (1956); *Analyt. Abstr.*, **4**, 1194 (1957)
101. SVEHLA, G. and ERDEY, L., *Microchem. J.*, **7**, 206 (1963)
102. WEISZ, H., KLOCKOW, D. and LUDWIG, H., *Talanta*, **16**, 921 (1969)
103. BABKO, A.K., LISETSKAYA, G.S. and TSARENKO, G.F., *Zh. analit. Khim.*, **23**, 1342 (1968); *Analyt. Abstr.*, **18**, 2381 (1970)
104. HADJIIOANNOU, T.P., *Analytica chim. Acta*, **36**, 360 (1966)
105. FUDGE, R., *Analyst*, **95**, 171 (1970)
106. BRADFIELD, E.G. and STRICKLAND, J.F., *Analyst*, **100**, 1 (1975)
107. HANSON, G., SZABO, A. and CHASTEEN, N.D., *Analyt. Chem.*, **49**, 461 (1977)

Nitrate

Nitrate is an anion of major importance particularly in biological areas. Excessive amounts in water supplies indicate pollution from sewage or agricultural effluents. Nitrogen oxides resulting from vehicle exhausts are recognized as important air pollutants. Their determination in air is often made after conversion to nitric acid. The effects of excessive quantities of nitrate in water are well known. Together with phosphate they cause high algal growth followed by decay, this leading to deoxygenation of water with the resulting death of fish and other aquatic animals.

High levels of nitrate in domestic water causes cyanosis in young babies. The relationship between nitrate (and nitrite) and formation of nitrosamines has received considerable attention recently. The matter is reviewed by Wolff and Wasserman[1] and Egan[2]. In the UK, Water Authorities follow WHO standards laid down in 1970. These recommend that NO_3^-–N in drinking water should be less than 11.3 $mg\ell^{-1}$. Values of 11.3–22.6 $mg\ell^{-1}$ are acceptable; those in excess of 22.6 $mg\,\ell^{-1}$ are unacceptable.

The analytical chemistry of nitrate has been reviewed by Clear and Roth[3] and Streuli and Averell[4]. In many ways the analytical chemistry of nitrate is linked to that of nitrite. One standard method for determination of nitrate is reduction to nitrite followed by its determination. In certain areas, for example soil analysis, a knowledge of how much nitrogen is present as ammonium, nitrate and nitrite is important. This will be discussed later in the section. In the case of nitrate and nitrite only, the sum can be determined using methods applicable to both anions. This can be followed by a determination of nitrate only after destruction of nitrite using sulphamic acid or other means.

Separations and pre-concentration

1. Gravimetric

A useful method of separating NO_3^- depends on the fact that both barium and silver nitrates are soluble. Anions whose barium and silver salts are insoluble can therefore be separated by precipitation. If silver sulphate is used, chloride can be separated from nitrate. Dolance and Healy[5] used this procedure for removing interferences in the analysis of plating baths for nitrate. In this work the most effective reagent found was a mixture of perchloric acid, barium perchlorate and silver perchlorate, none of which interfered with the subsequent spectrophotometric determination of nitrate. The reagent is added dropwise until no further precipitation takes place. The precipitate is allowed to stand for not less than one hour, filtered and washed three times with water, the washings being collected with the filtrate for nitrate analysis.

2. Ion-exchange

Both separation and pre-concentration can be achieved using this technique. Westland and Langford[6] concentrate nitrate in water by passing it through an anion-exchange resin in chloride form (Amberlite 1R-4B). Elution is made with a 1% chloride solution, and results in a ten-fold concentration. Ion-exchange has been used[7] to separate nitrate from chloride and bicarbonate. Here two cation-exchange resins are used. The first, in silver form, removes chloride. The second, in hydrogen form, removes the silver displaced from the first. Solutions leaving the second resin are acidic thus eliminating the bicarbonate present.

A cation-exchange column in Pb^{2+} form has been investigated by Ryabinin and Bogatyrev[8] for separation of nitrate and sulphate. In determination of nitrate, its separation from nitrite is an important consideration. An ion-exchange separation method has been developed by Schmit and Henry[9] using a thin film of methacrylate polymer substituted with tetra-alkylammonium groups on a zipax support material.

3. Distillation as ammonia

Reduction to ammonia followed by its distillation is a standard method for separation of nitrate. The separated ammonia can be determined by a selection of spectrophotometric and titrimetric methods for evaluation of the original nitrate. A review of reagents which can be used for the reduction has been published by Niedermaier[10]. Earlier forms of the method were inclined to be tedious and time-consuming. Newer procedures are far more rapid, and can even be automated[11]. One of the oldest and best known methods of reduction utilizes Devarda's alloy, this consisting of Al–Cu–Zn in the proportions 45%, 50% and 5% respectively[12]. The main reduction is produced by the aluminium, which reacts with nitrate as follows.

$$3NO_3^- + 8Al + 5OH^- + 2H_2O \rightarrow 3NH_3 + 8AlO_2$$

The reduction is made under alkaline conditions. A suitable glass assembly for macro-amounts of nitrate is shown in *Figure 21*. When milligram amounts of nitrate are involved, modified apparatus is required. A form of micro-distillation apparatus is described by Bremner and Keeney[14].

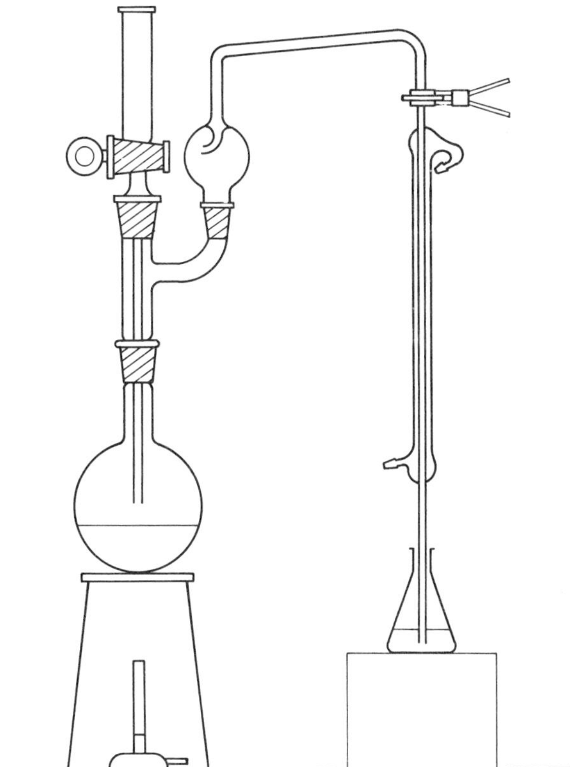

Figure 21 Distillation apparatus for determination of nitrate by distillation using Devarda's alloy

Other reductants recommended for reduction of nitrate include titanium-(III) and chromium(III). Titanium(III) in basic medium undergoes the following reaction.

$$NO_3^- + 8Ti^{3+} + 6OH^- \rightarrow NH_4^+ + 8TiO_2 + H_2O$$

The distillation method not only allows the determination of NH_4^+, NO_3^- and NO_2^- when present together, but enables this to be accomplished without interference from glutamine and other alkali-labile organic nitrogen compounds. This becomes important in the analysis of soil extracts. The topic has been discussed in a comprehensive review by Bremner[13]. Considering the three nitrogen ions NH_4^+, NO_3^- and NO_2^-, steam distillation with magnesium oxide will first produce ammonia equivalent to the ammonium content. When Devarda's alloy is added and the distillation continued, ammonia equivalent to nitrate + nitrite is produced. To discriminate between nitrate and nitrite, use can be made of the fact[14] that sulphamic acid decomposes nitrite rapidly to nitrogen without affecting ammonium or nitrate.

If $Ti(III)SO_4$ is used in place of Devarda's alloy, reduction of nitrate takes place without the corresponding reduction of nitrite[11].

The distillation method can be applied to turbid or coloured solutions without difficulty. A further advantage of the method is that where tracer studies are carried out on ^{15}N-enriched compounds, conversion of the resulting NH_3 to N_2 for mass-spectroscopic assay of nitrogen-15, is easy.

Some comment is required on the familiar Kjeldahl method. At one time the Devarda method was commonly used for total nitrogen, but has now been largely replaced by the Kjeldahl method for this purpose. Before the Kjeldahl method can be applied, however, some treatment of the sample is required. The nitrate is reacted with salicylic acid in the presence of H_2SO_4 to give nitrosalicylic acid, which on reduction by thiosulphate gives aminosalicylic acid. The Kjeldahl method can now be applied[15].

4. Microdiffusion

This approach is related to the distillation method, and has been used on soil extracts. Ferrous sulphate in 0.5M H_2SO_4 and in the presence of Ag_2SO_4 as catalyst will reduce nitrate to ammonia in a Conway-type microdiffusion unit[16]. The method is suitable for up to 200 μg of nitrate in a 5-mℓ aliquot of soil sample.

5. Solvent extraction

Nitrate is extracted by the tetraphenylarsonium chloride system[17]. At pH 1–2 the degree of extraction into chloroform is 95–99 %. Although extraction procedures feature in several nitrate spectrophotometric procedures, they are not of general applicability.

6. Thin-layer chromatography

Nitrate can be separated from 12 other ions using thin-layer chromatography on maize-starch and acetone-3M aq. NH_3 (1:4) as solvent[18]. The ions are NO_2^-, $S_2O_3^{2-}$, CrO_4^{2-}, N_3^-, CN^-, SCN^-, BO_3^{3-}, S^{2-}, AsO_3^{3-}, AsO_4^{3-}, SO_4^{2-} and PO_4^{3-}.

Hatcher and Schall[19] isolate nitrate from organic matter in feeds using TLC on a 0.375 mm layer of Alumina G. The development solvent is 0.05M NaOH–acetone (15:88). After removal of the nitrate zone, a spectrophotometric procedure is applied for its determination down to 10 ppm.

Determination

One of the most important current developments in nitrate determination is the nitrate ion-selective electrode. Already it has shown itself capable of giving comparable results to more laborious but hitherto standard methods. The process of assimilating the electrode will no doubt continue, and accordingly, the relative importance of some other methods will probably decline as a result of this.

Gravimetric methods

Although gravimetric procedures are normally avoided if more convenient and rapid alternatives are available, they still play a role in certain situations.

The quantitative precipitation of nitrate by the strong base nitron(1,4-diphenyl-3,5-endanilo-4,5-dihydro-1,2,4-triazole) was introduced by Busch[20]

```
                     ⊕
              N——————N—C6H5
         ⊖    ||     ||
H5C6—H—C      CH
                \  /
                 N
                 |
                C6H5
```

Structure 18 *Nitron* (1,4-diphenyl-3,5-endanilo-4,5-dihydro-1,2,4-triazole)

in 1905. The compound is believed to exist as the Zwitterion (*Structure 18*). The white crystalline precipitate which contains 16.52% nitrate is dried at 105 °C before weighing. A discussion of the reagent is included in a review of nitrate gravimetric methods by Williams[21]. Of the many drawbacks to the method, the following are the most serious:

1. The relatively high solubility of the precipitate. This becomes tolerable in the presence of excess reagent.
2. Lack of sensitivity.
3. Variation in composition of the precipitate.
4. Interference by a large number of anions which include Br^-, I^-, ClO_3^-, ClO_4^-, CrO_4^{2-}, $[Fe(CN)_6]^{3-}$, $[Fe(CN)_6]^{4-}$, SCN^-, NO_2^-, $C_2O_4^{2-}$, and IO_3^-. Chloride can be tolerated in small amounts only.

It is only possible to use the method, therefore, when the sample is free of many common anions. Addition of lead acetate removes several interfering ions by precipitation. Others can be masked or decomposed using conventional procedures. Thus nitrite can be eliminated by addition of sulphamic acid, bromide is oxidized and removed as bromine, and chromate is reduced using hydrazine sulphate. Perchlorate is not easy to remove simply.

Gravimetric determination of nitrate using nitron

Reagent

Nitron: 10 g in 100 mℓ of 5% acetic acid solution.

Procedure

To a neutral solution of 80–100 mℓ and containing not greater than 0.1 g of nitrate, add 0.5 mℓ of M H_2SO_4 or 1 mℓ of glacial acetic acid. Heat on a water bath until the temperature approaches the boiling point, then add 10–12 mℓ of reagent. Stir, allow to cool and keep at 0 °C for 2 h. Filter through a sintered glass filter and wash with 20–30 mℓ of cold saturated nitron nitrate solution in several small portions. Wash finally with 3 portions of 3 mℓ of ice-cold water. Dry at 105 °C for 1 h. Weigh as $C_{20}H_{16}N_4HNO_3$. The factor for NO_3^- is 0.1652.

Notes

1. The reagent should be stored in a brown bottle.

2. The method is unsuitable for the micro-scale. Attempts to do so gave an 81% recovery of nitrate[22].

Several compounds are known to form sparingly soluble nitrates. Until about 1960 no systematic studies had been made on such compounds to elucidate the factors responsible for this property. Stephen[23] and co-workers have indicated that eight known nitrate-precipitating reagents are structurally dissimilar. The only feature in common appears to be that they are all organic bases of fairly high molecular weight and molecular volume. It would seem that the property of giving sparingly soluble nitrates depends on the whole molecule rather than any specific grouping.

An examination of several reagents has indicated that di-(1-naphthylmethyl)amine (*Structure 19*) first prepared by Rupe and Becherer in 1923,

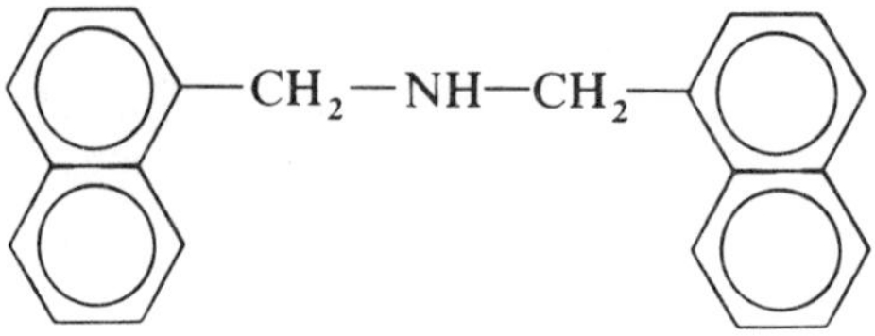

$CH_2—NH—CH_2$

Structure 19 Di-(1-naphthylmethyl) amine

is more sensitive to nitrate than nitron. Further work by Stephen and co-workers[24] on N-substituted 1-naphthylmethylamines has shown that N-(4-chlorobenzyl)-1-naphthylmethylamine is particularly useful for both gravimetric and titrimetric determination of nitrate. This reagent behaves essentially like nitron, but without many of its disadvantages. Determination of 1–50 mg of nitrate using the reagent presents no problem. For practical details the original paper should be consulted.

Other useful reagents found in the same investigation are N-benzyl-1-naphthylmethylamine and N-(4-methylbenzyl)-1-naphthylamine. These reagents give no precipitate with 5 mg mℓ^{-1} concentrations of BrO_3^-, Br^-, Cl^-, IO_3^-, SO_4^{2-}, $H_2PO_4^-$, $HC_4H_4O_6^-$ (hydrogen tartrate) and $S_2O_8^{2-}$ except the 4-chlorobenzyl derivative which gives a slight precipitate with Cl^- and Br^-. The same test gives heavy precipitates in most cases with ClO_3^-, ClO_4^-, $[Fe(CN)_6]^{3-}$, $[Fe(CN)_6]^{4-}$, I^-, NO_2^-, MnO_4^-, SCN^-, WO_3^{2-}, $C_2O_4^{2-}$ and MoO_4^{2-}. An interesting application of N-(4-chlorobenzyl)-1 naphthylmethylamine is in the consecutive determination of perchlorate and nitrate, a problem referred to earlier in connection with nitron. First perchlorate is precipitated with tetraphenylphosphonium perchlorate and evaluated gravimetrically.

$$1\,mg\,(C_6H_5)_4P^+ClO_4^- \equiv 0.2266\,mg\,ClO_4^-$$

Filtrate nitrate is determined either gravimetrically or titrimetrically using N-(4-chlorobenzyl)-1-naphthyl-methylamine[25]. In the gravimetric procedure

$$1\,mg\,(C_{18}H_{17}ClNH_2)^+NO_3^- \equiv 0.1800\,mg\,NO_3^-$$

The method is time-consuming, requiring the precipitate to be set aside for 5–24 h depending on the amount of nitrate present. For amounts in excess of 10 mg filtration can be made in 5 h; smaller amounts require a longer time.

Hartmann and Bathge[26] have used di-cyclo-hexylthallium(III) sulphate as a gravimetric reagent for nitrate. A full discussion of this reagent together with its synthesis is given in the monograph by Belcher and Wilson[27]. Recently the reagent has appeared in a titrimetric procedure in which the end-point is monitored potentiometrically by the normal method or using an ion-selective electrode. This is discussed later in this section.

A novel micro method for both nitrate and nitrite is described in which CO_2 produced in their reduction by formic acid is evaluated gravimetrically[28]. The corresponding reactions are

$$2KNO_3 + 6HCOOH \rightarrow 2HCOOK + N_2O + 4CO_2 + 2H_2O$$

$$7NaNO_2 + 13HCOOH \rightarrow 7HCOONa + 3NO + 6CO_2 + 9H_2O + 2N_2O$$

Since N_2O shows no solubility in alkaline solutions, the gaseous products can be passed into a manometer sealed by an alkaline solution and the N_2O measured gasometrically. Alternatively, the authors recommend gravimetric determination of evolved CO_2 using conventional type adsorption tubes. Results to within ± 0.2 per cent absolute are reported for nitrate and nitrite determined in this way.

Titrimetric methods

Titrimetric methods for nitrate are based on reduction to a lower nitrogen oxidation state. This is followed either by direct titration of the reduced form, for example ammonia, or by back-titration of the excess of reductant used.

Reduction of nitrate to ammonia has been discussed already to some extent in connection with separation of nitrate. A number of reductants can be used including Fe(II), Ti(III), Devarda's alloy, Cr(III) and U(IV). Several of the systems require exclusion of air. Nitrate may be reduced to NH_3, NO, NO_2^- or hydroxylamine.

1. Reduction to nitric oxide—Leithe's method

This method, in which nitrate is reduced by excess iron(II) in acidic solution, is based on earlier work notably by Kolthoff, Sandell and Muskovitz[29]. The excess of iron(II) is back-titrated preferably with standard dichromate.

$$3Fe^{2+} + NO_3^- + 4H^+ \rightarrow 3Fe^{3+} + NO + 2H_2O$$

Kolthoff, Sandell and Muskovitz used molybdenum as catalyst in the original work, and were able to reduce the boiling time to 10 min. However, it was still necessary to employ a CO_2 atmosphere to prevent oxidation of NO and iron(II). The improvement by Leithe[31] consisted of increasing the concentration of H_2SO_4 to 6–8M. This was found to eliminate the need for a catalyst and the CO_2 atmosphere. Furthermore the boiling time was reduced to 3 min.

Latimer and Chambers[30] have reported that while freshly-prepared Leithe reagent gives excellent results, a precipitate appears in 1–2 h and then blank values begin to decrease in an erratic manner. To rectify this, they recommend an improved reagent which is stated to be stable for five or six days. This modification is incorporated in the Leithe procedure described below.

Titrimetric determination of nitrate by modified Leithe procedure

Reagents

$FeSO_4$–HCl solution:

Dissolve 92 g of $FeSO_4 \cdot 7H_2O$ in 200 mℓ of water containing 20 mℓ of concentrated HCl, and dilute to 1 ℓ.

Ferroin indicator (1,10 phenanthroline-ferrous sulphate): 0.0025M.

$K_2Cr_2O_7$: M/60.

Procedure

Pipette 25 mℓ of nitrate sample containing 25–80 mg nitrate into a 250-mℓ conical flask. Add 5 g of NaCl, a 15-mℓ aliquot of the $FeSO_4$–HCl reagent and 20 mℓ of concentrated H_2SO_4. Heat to boiling, then boil gently for 3 min. Cool under a tap, add 50 mℓ of cold water and 1 mℓ of ferroin indicator. Titrate with M/60 $K_2Cr_2O_7$ until the brown colour turns blue-green. Conduct a blank in exactly the same way and correct the amount of ferrous sulphate consumed accordingly.

On the basis of M/60 $K_2Cr_2O_7$

$$1 \text{ m}\ell \text{ M/60} K_2Cr_2O_7 \equiv 2.067 \text{ mg } NO_3^-$$

Notes

1. Heitner-Wirguin and Friedman[32] have observed that chloride interferes with the Leithe procedure, and recommend that the blank should contain a similar amount of chloride to the sample being analysed. Chloride exerts a similar effect on the modified reagent.
2. Nitrite interferes with the procedure but amounts up to about 46 mg can be satisfactorily eliminated using urea.

---

2. Reduction to NH_3

A general titrimetric method for nitrate consists of reducing it to ammonia using Devarda's alloy in alkaline solution, distilling the ammonia evolved into standard acid or boric acid, and then completing the determination with an acid–base titration. If boric acid is used, its function is simply to retain the ammonia. As a weak acid it does not affect the subsequent titration of ammonia with standard acid.

Little comment is required in addition to the previous discussion on separation of nitrate using this procedure. The apparatus shown in *Figure 21* is used. Ammonium ions and nitrite interfere. Methods of dealing with this have been discussed already. About two-thirds of the solution should be distilled over, and a blank determination carried out under the same conditions. Some doubt has been expressed on the effectiveness of the procedure. Erdey, Polos and Gregorowicz[33] state that positive errors occur due to alkali being picked up mechanically by the evolved gas. They attribute the error mainly to apparatus design and recommend another method for evaluation of evolved ammonia. This is to reduce nitrate to ammonia using 'ferrum reductum', i.e. metallic iron, in the presence of $NiSO_4$ as catalyst. The evolved ammonia is precipitated in acidic medium as ammonium tetraphenylboron. This is filtered, washed, dissolved in acetone and titrated with standard $AgNO_3$ using variamine blue acetate as indicator. Accurate results are claimed, even on micro quantities of nitrate.

3. Miscellaneous

An older method, but still useful, is based on titration of nitrate with Fe(II) $(NH_4)_2SO_4$ in strong H_2SO_4 solution[34]. Complete reduction of nitrate to nitric oxide is indicated by the brown or pink colour due to the $FeSO_4$–NO complex. A high concentration of H_2SO_4, greater than 75%, is necessary throughout the titration. The temperature must be kept below 60 °C, and below 40 °C as the end-point is approached. Experimental details are given in some standard texts[35,36].

The Kjeldahl method, if modified as described earlier, is suitable for determination of nitrate. Also, several titrimetric procedures have been developed as alternatives to the gravimetric procedures with organic reagents. Experimental details are given in the sources quoted earlier.

Awad and Hassan have based micro-titrimetric procedures on reduction with iron(II), titanium(III) or mixtures of both[37]. Titanium(III) reduces nitrate in strongly acid, citrate-buffered, and acetate-buffered media with consumption of 3, 6 and 8 equivalents of titanium(III) per nitrate respectively. The reaction depends not only on the reacting media but on the nature of the nitrate samples. In general the reduction can be accomplished in minutes. Using iron(II) the reduction time depends on the concentration of HCl used. If ammonium molybdate is used as catalyst, reduction is complete in as little as 2 min.

Spectroscopic methods

1. Spectrophotometric—visible and UV

Spectroscopic methods occupy a substantial part of the analytical chemistry of nitrate. The methods fall into 4 main divisions:

1. Based on nitration of organic compounds particularly phenolic compounds. This group includes the chromotropic acid, 2,4-xylenol, 2,6-xylenol, phenoldisulphonic acid and 1-aminopyrene methods.
2. Based on oxidation of organic compounds. The brucine method is an example of this type.
3. Based on reduction of nitrate to nitrite or ammonia, followed by their determination. The best known method in this category is reduction to nitrite followed by the Griess–Ilosvay procedure.
4. Based on absorption in the UV.

In addition to methods falling into the above categories, several important methods fall outside; these will be discussed later in the sub-section.

Although sometimes difficult experimentally, procedures based on nitration are the most important. Trace determination is often required in media containing chloride and nitrite. With few exceptions these ions interfere with procedures based on nitration and oxidation. Furthermore, nitrite interferes with reduction-based procedures. Elimination of such interferences can often be achieved by simple means. In addition to interference problems, many nitrate spectrophotometric procedures suffer from other defects such as non-linearity of absorbance curves or excessive analysis time. A recent account of spectrophotometric methods for nitrate has been published[4]. Individual procedures will now be discussed.

West and Sarma[38] introduced a specific and sensitive spot test for nitrate based on its reaction with chromotropic acid (4,5-dihydroxy-2,7-naphthalenedisulphonic acid) in concentrated H_2SO_4. Later, West and Lyles[39] introduced a spectrophotometric method based on the yellow reaction product. The absorption maximum occurs at 410 nm. Chloride was found to produce anomalies, and interference was given by iron(III), chlorine and certain other oxidizing agents. A later study by West and Ramachandran[40] reported that chloride was effectively masked with antimony, which also eliminated potential interference by iron(III). The resulting method is claimed to be free of interference and capable of nitrate determination in the range 0.5–50 μg. Robinson and Hsu[41] have made a study of the reaction itself. Several applications of the method have been made, for example to nitrate in soil[42,43]. Experimental details of the method are given at the end of this sub-section.

An indirect method based on reduction of nitrate to nitrite and followed by the Griess–Ilosvay method, has found considerable use in recent years. As the spectrophotometric procedure concerns nitrite, it is discussed in that section. The present treatment will consider the various methods proposed for reducing nitrate to nitrite. Of the many reductants proposed, zinc and cadmium appear to be the most favoured. Mullin and Riley[44] used hydrazine in a method developed for fresh and saline waters. An important advantage of this method is its high sensitivity and relative freedom from interference. The disadvantage is that reduction must be carried out at a constant temperature for at least 20 h under closely controlled pH conditions. Henriksen[45] was able to reduce the reduction time to 15 min by increasing the temperature to 70 °C, and an automatic form of this procedure was developed.

Zinc dust has been used as reductant by several workers[46–48]. A recent study by Matsunaga and Nishimura[49] finds that zinc in the presence of ammonium chloride is more effective as reductant than cadmium. Cadmium can be used in several ways, for example[50,51] as columns of amalgamated cadmium or metallic cadmium[52–54]. The study by Schall and Hatcher[54] is included as a recommended method for nitrate and nitrite in animal feeds[55]. Reduction by cadmium is also recommended in conjunction with the Griess–Ilosvay procedure for determination of nitrate in metal products and extracts[56].

An improvement in the use of cadmium is reported by Elliott and Porter[57] in an investigation of nitrate determination in bacon and curing brines. This consists of shaking the nitrate solution with spongy cadmium for 5 min. The result is the same as a 40–60 min cadmium column reduction. Copperized cadmium has been investigated by Wood, Armstrong and Richard[58]. An automated form of this procedure has been developed by Henriksen and Selmer-Olsen[59]. Some difficulty was experienced by Lambert and DuBois[60] in obtaining a uniform copperized cadmium. Instead, they used a mixed catalyst of $CuSO_4$, NH_4Cl and dibasic sodium phosphate in conjunction with powdered cadmium, and obtained excellent results.

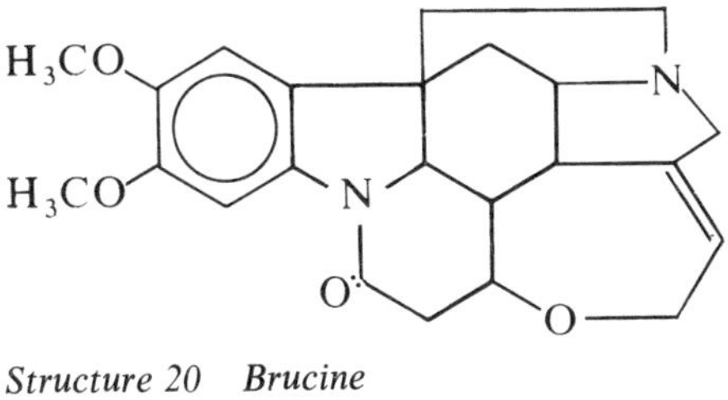

Structure 20 Brucine

Nitrate reacts with the alkaloid brucine, $C_{23}H_{26}N_2O_4$ (*Structure 20*) in H_2SO_4 giving a red colour that quickly changes to yellow. The calibration curve is linear for the wavelength of maximum absorption. For precise work it is necessary to prepare standards covering the whole range. Nitrate plus nitrite can be analysed in one of two ways using brucine. The sum of both can be determined at high acidity, with nitrite only being determined at lower acidity. Alternatively nitrite can be determined using a different method and a suitable correction for this made using the brucine method.

In addition to nitrite, chloride interferes. Despite the above limitations the brucine method is widely used for determination of nitrate in water. Interference by nitrite can be eliminated by treatment with urea. Recent work on determination of nitrate in the 0.05–2.5 ppm range reports that 1 μg of iron produces serious interference, with copper and cadmium (100 ppm) giving negative errors, and the same amount of K, Na and Mn causing slight interference[61]. The same work describes determination of nitrate + nitrite by oxidizing the latter with $KMnO_4$. Excess $KMnO_4$ is destroyed with oxalic acid. Application of the method has been made to determination of nitrate in soil and plant extracts[62].

UV absorption bands due to nitrate ion having maxima at 193.6 nm were observed by Scheibe[63] in 1926. The possibility of using these analytically was first suggested by Hoather[64], and later a rapid method with absorbance measurements at 210 nm was published[65]. Although UV absorbance procedures are rapid and simple, several other species interfere at this wavelength[66]. These include Fe^{3+}, Cu^{2+}, Pb^{2+}, Mo^{6+}, Cr^{6+}, V^{5+}, Ti^{4+}, I^-, SCN^-, NO_2^-, $S_2O_3^{2-}$ and Br^-. In addition, organic matter interferes at this wavelength. By subtracting a multiple of the absorbance at 275 nm from the absorbance at 210 nm, interference by organic matter may be compensated for. Addition of H_2SO_4 to a solution of nitrate containing chloride can cause a change in the absorption spectrum, the maximum being shifted to about 230 nm. Determination of nitrate at this wavelength is easier because absorption by other species is considerably less than at the lower wavelength. Armstrong[67] therefore recommends inclusion of H_2SO_4 in the procedure. The method finds application in water analysis[68] and is a tentative method of the American Public Health Association[69]. The UV method enables direct simultaneous determination of nitrate and nitrite to be made[70].

This is based on the fact that only nitrite absorbs at 355 nm but nitrate and nitrite absorb at 302 nm. The method has lower limits of 0.02 mg $m\ell^{-1}$ for nitrite and 0.09 mg $m\ell^{-1}$ for nitrate using 1 cm cells. Several ions interfere at either one or both wavelengths. These are listed in the original paper. An indirect UV method has appeared recently[73]. In this, nitrate is reduced to ammonia by titanium(III), and displaced by air for evaluation by gas-phase UV absorption at 201 nm. Cobalt, copper, iron(III) and zinc cause a depression in the signal. They do not affect the determination of nitrogen as ammonium-nitrogen by a similar method. The interference is attributed to partial oxidation of titanium(III) or formation of an unstable intermediate complex with these ions, which decomposes with loss of nitrogen in some form other than ammonia.

Phenoldisulphonic acid forms an intense yellow colour with nitrate. Despite its wide usage it suffers from several drawbacks. The method is time-consuming, requiring the nitrate sample to be evaporated to dryness. This is in order that only a small amount of sulphuric acid is required to produce a suitable nitrating mixture. The acid is then neutralized by an excess of alkali hydroxide solution. There are several reports of unreliability[71,72]. Chloride, nitrite and organic matter interfere. The effect of ammonium ions has produced a curious anomaly. Many procedures, including recently published ones, refer to an ammoniacal solution of the reagent despite the report by Hora and Webber[72] that in the presence of ammonium losses of nitrate can be as much as 50%. These workers recommend a preliminary evaporation in the presence of KOH to eliminate ammonium and prevent such loss. Nitrite interference can be eliminated using sulphamic acid, urea or thiourea. Chloride is removed using silver salts.

2,4-xylenol and 2,6-xylenol when nitrated give coloured products. The reaction with 2,4-xylenol produces 6-nitro-2,4-xylenol which can be steam distilled into NaOH giving a coloured product, or extracted into toluene and then reacted with NaOH[74]. Nitrite gives the same reaction but can be destroyed using urea. Norwitz and Gordon[75] have developed an improved method; their paper includes a survey of conditions used by previous investigators of the 2,4 xylenol method. Their procedure consists of heating the sample with H_2SO_4 and 2,4-xylenol to give the nitrated product, then distilling into an ammoniacal water–isopropanol mixture. The intense colour of the ammonium salt of 6-nitro-2,4-xylenol is measured at 455 nm. Nitrite only gives slight interference in this procedure. Reproducibility is said to be excellent.

The method is recommended in a British Standard specification[76] for analysis of industrial waters. The range for this procedure is up to 30 μg of nitrate. Extraction is made into toluene. Chloride, sulphate, iron(III) and copper do not interfere when below 1500, 5000, 500 and 250 μg respectively. An automated form of the 2,4-xylenol method has been developed for fertilizer analysis[77].

The corresponding method employing 2,6-xylenol has been critically studied by Hartley and Asai[78]. Their recommended method is a relatively simple one. A study by Andrews[79] has indicated that it is four times more sensitive than the 2,4-xylenol method.

One of the oldest spectrophotometric methods for nitrate consists of reducing it to ammonium and then determining this. Methods of effecting the reduction have been considered already in connection with separation of nitrate. The present discussion will focus on spectrophotometric end-procedures. An earlier method for determination of the resulting ammonia employs Nessler's reagent, originally reported in 1856. The reactions are

$$2HgI_4^{2-} + 2NH_3 \rightarrow 2NH_3HgI_2 + 4I^-$$
$$2NH_3HgI_2 \rightarrow NH_2Hg_2I_3 \downarrow + I^- + NH_4^+$$

Flocculation of the precipitate is inhibited by gum arabic. The absorbance is measured at 410 nm; the range is 0.2–2.0 ppm (NH_3). Several workers have used the procedure including Allerton[80]. Details are given in the monograph by Charlot[81]. In a more recent form of the method, Harrison[82] employs $CrCl_2$ in the presence of NaOH, as reductant.

Several criticisms can be made of the Nessler procedure itself. The reagent is unstable, and the colour is critically dependent on the time of reaction, temperature, the amount of reagent used, and the presence of cations.

There are several alternatives to Nessler's reagent for determination of ammonia produced in the reduction. Pappenhagen[83] employs $FeSO_4$ in alkaline medium to reduce nitrate, then applies the pyridine–pyrazolone method of Kruse and Mellon[84]. The method is suitable for 0.01–0.1 mg NO_3^-–N. Nitrite and ammonia interfere; ammonia can be removed by ion-exchange. Cyanide, thiocyanate and cyanate interfere forming coloured products with the reagent. Anion-exchange can be employed to remove these.

Ammonia can also be determined using the indophenol blue and indanetrione methods. The former method depends on the blue complex formed when ammonia reacts with alkali phenol and hypochlorite[85,86]. A recent application of the method to automatic determination of ammonium and nitrate in soil extracts has been made by Keay and Menagé[11]. First the sample is steam distilled with MgO to give ammonia equivalent to the ammonium content only. Inclusion of titanium(III) sulphate during the distillation gives ammonia equivalent to ammonium plus nitrate. Nitrite is not reduced by the treatment. The method has been used for fertilizer and water analysis. A recent investigation of the indophenol method itself has been made by Weatherburn[87].

The indanetrione hydrate method developed by Jacobs[88,89] permits as little as 0.56 μg of N to be determined as ammonia. Though principally applied to analysis of proteins, food diets and heterocyclic nitrogen compounds, Jacobs[90] anticipated no difficulties in using it for nitrates.

In addition to methods falling into the four divisions listed earlier, several others have been developed. Japanese workers have produced interesting spectrophotometric methods based on cuproin and neocuproin. Yamamoto, Okamoto and TaO[91] find that if small amounts of certain anions (nitrate, perchlorate, phthalate and tetraphenylborate) are present in aqueous solution, Cu(I) ions are extracted as the cuproin or neocuproin-Cu(I)-anion ion pairs. The colour intensity of the organic phase is found to be proportional to the amounts of these anions present in the aqueous phase. For nitrate, the range of applicability is 10^{-6}–10^{-5}M. Chloride interferes at a molar ratio of 10, but this is eliminated by AgCl precipitation. Nitrite interferes in a ten-fold molar excess; this is eliminated using sulphamic acid. Thiocyanate, cyanide, bromide and iodide interfere even in equimolar amounts. The method lends itself to AAS by means of the copper. This is discussed later in the section.

Another extraction-spectrophotometric development by Yamamoto, Uchikawa and Akabori[92] utilizes crystal violet. Extraction into chlorobenzene is made at pH 6; the absorbance is measured at 595 nm. Phosphate and sulphate do not interfere even in 1000-fold excess. Chloride gives a slight positive error in amounts greater than a 10-fold excess. Beer's law holds over the range 4–20 μM NO_3^-.

Bhatty and Townshend[93] use toluene which undergoes nitration. The product is extracted into toluene giving a molecular complex, and its absorbance measured at 284 nm. Interferences by NO_2^-, Br^-, I^-, SCN^-, SO_3^{2-} and Hg^{2+} are easily eliminated. The range is 1–18 ppm nitrate.

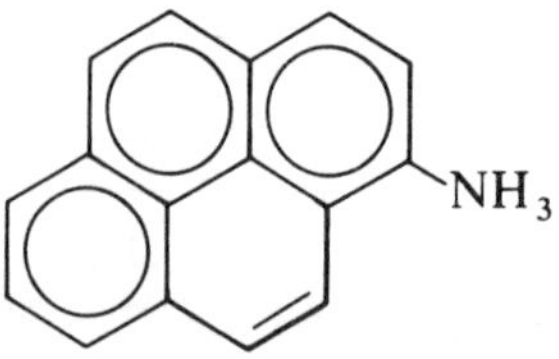

NH_3

Structure 21 Aminopyrene

A new and sensitive spectrophotometric method using aminopyrene (*Structure 21*) was introduced by Sawicki, Johnson and Stanley[94] in 1963. Though it does not conform to Beer's law, its sensitivity is high ($\varepsilon = 94\,000$) making it suitable for air-pollution studies, and the procedure is simple. Nitrite and nitrate can be determined together, and in the presence of a 50-fold excess of bisulphite.

A method based on nitration of tetraphenylphosphonium chloride, followed by extraction of the product into $CHCl_3$ has been found suitable for analysis of potable water[95]. The 200 ppm of chloride tolerated by the method is far in excess of the amounts normally found in such waters.

Studies in air and water pollution, sanitation and public health have demanded more sensitive methods for nitrate than many of the methods so far discussed. Tan[96] has described a spectrophotometric procedure in the μg ℓ^{-1} range based on nitration of 2,6-dimethylphenol. After extraction into toluene its absorbance between 600 and 400 nm is recorded. For the analytical procedure the absorbance is taken as the difference between the absorbance at the 428 nm peak and the plateau absorbance in the 560–520 nm range. Interferences by nitrite and chloride are removed using sulphamic acid and mercury(II) sulphate respectively. A linear relationship is found for absorbance to nitrate concentration in the range 0–900 μg ℓ^{-1}, with the lowest reliable determination at 50 μg ℓ^{-1}. The accuracy is about ±5%.

Data for selected nitrate spectrophotometric procedures are given in *Table 9*.

Spectrophotometric determination of NO_3^- using chromotropic acid[40]

Reagents

Purified chromotropic acid: A saturated solution of disodium salt of 1,8-dihydroxy-3,6-naphthalene disulphonic acid is processed twice using

Table 9 Data on selected spectrophotometric procedures for nitrate[a]

Reagent or technique	*Apparent molar absorptivity*	λ (nm)	*Interfering ions or species*	*Comments*
Brucine	1500	400–410	Cl^-, NO_2^-, ClO_4^-, Fe^{3+}	Obeys Beer's law over narrow range only. Range 0.05–2.5 ppm
Phenol-disulphonic acid	10 000	410	Cl^-, NO_2^-, CO_3^{2-}, Br^-, I^-, Mn^{4+}, Fe^{3+}, NH_4^+, organic matter	Complicated procedure
Chromotropic acid	18 000[b]	357	$Cl^- > NO_2^- > Fe^{3+}$, BrO_3^-, Br^-, Ti^{4+}, HCHO	Deviation from Beer's law above 1 mg ℓ^{-1} NO_3^- Range 0.5–50 µg NO_3^-
Direct UV	9000[c]	210–220	Fe^{3+}, Cu^{2+}, Pb^{2+}, Mo^{6+}, Cr^{6+}, V^{5+}, Ti^{4+}, I^-, SCN^-, NO_2^-, $S_2O_3^{2-}$, Br^-, organic matter	Measurements at 275 nm will correct for organic matter
2,4-xylenol	3300	432	$> Cl^-$, NO_2^-, Fe^{3+}, Cu^{2+}	
2,6-xylenol	7900 (324 nm) ~17 300 (304 nm)	304–324	Cl^-, NO_2^-	Simplest procedure
Toluene	4200	284	Br^-, I^-, NO_2^-, SCN^-, SO_3^{2-}, Hg^{2+}	Range 1–18 ppm

[a] Data should be taken as a general guide owing to their dependence on the particular procedure used.
[b] Assuming 1-cm cell.
[c] Varies according to λ used.

decolorizing charcoal. The purified reagent is crystallized from the filtered solution by addition of H_2SO_4. The product is washed several times with ethanol and dried below 80 °C.
Prepare a 0.1 % solution in concentrated H_2SO_4. This should be colourless if the acid is nitrate-free. The reagent is stable for two weeks.
Sulphite–urea solution: Dissolve 5 g of urea and 4 g of reagent-grade anhydrous Na_2SO_3 in 100 mℓ of distilled water.
Antimony solution: Dissolve 0.5 g of antimony metal in 80 mℓ of concentrated H_2SO_4 by heating. Cool and add 20 mℓ of ice water. Any salt which crystallizes when kept overnight is dissolved by heating.

Procedure

Pipette 2.5 mℓ of the sample solution containing nitrate in the range 0.2–20 mg $ℓ^{-1}$, into a dry 10-mℓ volumetric flask. To each flask add 1 drop of sulphite–urea solution, place the flasks in a tray of cold water (10–20 °C) and add 2 mℓ of the antimony sulphate solution, swirling each flask during the addition. After allowing to stand in the bath for about 4 min, add 1 mℓ of chromotropic acid reagent, swirl the flasks again and then allow to stand in the cooling bath for a further 3 min. Next add concentrated H_2SO_4 to adjust the volume to the 10-mℓ mark, stopper the flasks and mix the contents by inverting them 4 times. Finally allow the solutions to stand for 45 min at room temperature and again adjust the volume to the 10-mℓ mark with concentrated H_2SO_4. The final mixing should be done gently to avoid introducing gas bubbles. Doubly-distilled water is substituted for nitrate solution in running a blank.

Take the absorbance measurement at 410 nm 15 min or more after the last adjustment of volume. Rinse the cell with the solution and then fill it carefully to avoid trapping bubbles. This is conveniently done by tilting the 1-cm cell to a slanting position (30° to horizontal) with the ground side facing upwards, and pouring the solution very carefully down the side of the cell. The measurement is made using water in the reference cell.

Notes

1. The method can be applied directly to water samples without initial evaporation or precipitation. However, appreciable amounts of suspended impurities should be removed by filtration or using a centrifuge.
2. The H_2SO_4 used must be nitrate-free.
3. Amounts of chloride greater than 2000 mg can be tolerated using the above procedure. This can be extended to over 4000 mg by doubling the strength of the antimony solution.

---

2. Fluorimetric

Axelrod, Bonelli and Lodge[97] have described a sensitive fluorimetric method for nitrate based on a one-step direct reaction. The nitrate is reacted with fluorescein in H_2SO_4 to give the di-nitrated dye. The fluorescence is measured at 485 nm with excitation at 435 nm. As little as 0.01 μg $mℓ^{-1}$ of nitrate (in the reacted solution) can be determined. Chloride, bromide and iodide interfere, but the effect of chloride can be eliminated using antimony(III) or by including a 100-fold excess of iron(II). The latter would be affected by any oxidizing agents in the sample. A 10-fold excess of nitrite over nitrate causes no interference, but larger amounts have effect.

Sawicki[98] has used 2,3-diaminonaphthalene in a fluorimetric procedure. Nitrate is first reduced to nitrite, and this reacted with the reagent. The range for nitrate is 0.05–5 μg mℓ^{-1} in aqueous solution; with modification it can be made five times more sensitive.

A recent method by Afghan and Ryan[99] employs 2,2′-dihydroxy-4,4′-dimethoxybenzophenone (*Structure 22*).

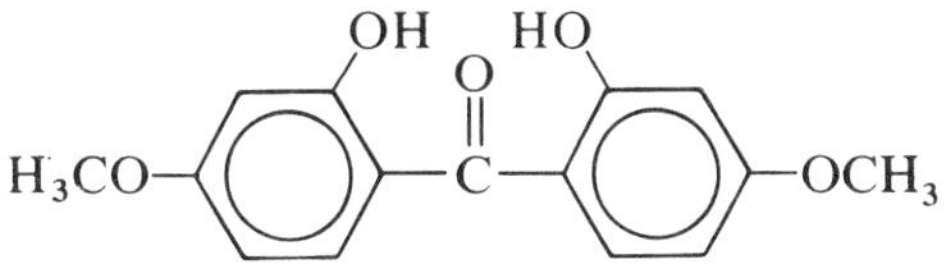

Structure 22 2,2′-dihydroxy-4,4′-dimethoxybenzophenone

The method is an automatic one capable of analysing 20 samples/h. Application is made to water and sediments containing as little as 5 μg ℓ^{-1} of NO_3^-–N. Possible interference from high concentrations of chloride, sulphide and humic acid substances is eliminated.

3. *Infra-red*

Nitron, discussed earlier in this section, has been used for identification of several anions by infra-red spectroscopy. When applied to nitrate, the spectrum of nitron nitrate exhibits characteristic absorption peaks at 1370 and 1337 cm^{-1}. Magee, Shahine and Wilson[100] have developed a quantitative method based on the 1370 cm^{-1} peak. The results at milligram level give a standard deviation of about 5 per cent. No significant effect is given by the presence of NO_2^-, ClO_4^-, BrO_3^-, ClO_3^-, CrO_4^{2-}, IO_4^-, and I^- at twice the NO_3^- level. Wilhite and Ellis[101], and more recently Yang and Low[102] have investigated infra-red internal reflectance spectroscopy for determination of nitrate.

4. *Atomic absorption spectroscopy*

A standard approach to the analysis of anions by AAS is to include the anion in a complex containing a metal atom. The determination is then made indirectly by evaluating the metal using AAS. This has been applied by Japanese workers[103,104] to nitrate analysis using the ion-pair with bis-(2,9-dimethyl-1,10 phenanthroline) copper(I). The ion-pair is extracted into isobutyl methyl ketone and AAS carried out using an air–acetylene flame. A linear response for 10–70 μM NO_3^- is obtained using a wavelength of 325 nm. No interference occurs from 10-fold amounts of sulphite, 100-fold amounts of carbonate or 1000-fold amounts of SO_4^{2-} and PO_4^{3-}, but I^-, SCN^-, ClO_4^- and equal amounts of Cl^- and SiO_3^{2-} interfere.

Houser and Fauth[105] have used a similar system for determination of nitrite and nitrate by AAS. In this method nitrite is oxidized to nitrate using $Ce(SO_4)_2$ or $KMnO_4$.

Electroanalytical methods

1. Potentiometric including ion-selective electrodes

Potentiometric methods for nitrate are mainly concerned with the nitrate ion-selective electrode. The electrode is probably the most important single factor to emerge in trace nitrate determination in recent years. Its effect on other nitrate methods has been considerable, and in many cases it has provided comparable results with those obtained by standard methods.

At least three commercial nitrate electrodes are available, all based on a liquid anion exchanger. The Orion 92–07 electrode incorporates a tris (substituted *o*-phenanthroline) nickel(II) ion exchanger dissolved in an organic solvent. The Corning 476134 electrode exchanger is a tridodecylhexadecylammonium nitrate in *n*-octyl-*o*-nitrophenylether. No information is available on the Beckman 39618 ion exchange material. Davies, Moody and Thomas[106] have provided constructional details of two nitrate electrodes with sensor poly(vinyl chloride) membranes incorporating commercial Corning and Orion nitrate liquid ion exchangers. The nitrate electrode can be used in two principal ways. An empirical calibration curve can be constructed of electrode potential plotted against nitrate concentration; the latter on a logarithmic scale. The linear plot can now be used to determine the concentration of an unknown nitrate solution. A calomel reference is usually used in conjunction with the nitrate electrode.

Alternatively the nitrate electrode can be employed in a potentiometric titration, where its function is simply to locate the equivalence point. Few applications have utilized the latter mode. Comparative data on commercially available nitrate electrodes have been summarized by Davies, Moody and Thomas[106].

The effective concentration range of the electrode is 10^{-6}–10^{-1}M NO_3^-. Common ions such as SO_4^{2-}, Cl^-, PO_4^{3-} and CO_3^{2-} have little effect. Nitrite responds to a certain extent. Methods by which this can be overcome are discussed later. The electrode is insensitive to cations. The principal interferences are I^-, ClO_3^- and ClO_4^-. A word of caution is necessary on inconsistencies in the literature on selectivity data for ion-selective electrodes. These are often presented without reference to the methods used in their derivation. For example selectivities quoted for HCO_3^-, CO_3^{2-} and PO_4^{3-} are unrealistic because these ions hydrolyse in aqueous solution and the resulting hydroxyl ions could also contribute to the measured selectivity. This is discussed in a basic paper[107] on the development and publication of work involving ion-selective electrodes.

The nitrate electrode functions over a wide range of pH, usually from 2 to 12. Materova, Grekovich and Garbuzova[108] have developed a form of nitrate electrode for use with strongly acidic solutions. It contains tetradecylammonium nitrate embedded in a PVC matrix, plasticized with dibutyl phthalate or dioctyl phthalate used as an active component. Nitric acid in the range 10^{-4}–6.2M can be determined using this electrode.

An important aspect of the ion-selective electrode is that it can be easily adapted to automatic use. Several investigators have reported flow-through units for this purpose. One such design by Milham[109] is shown in *Figure 22.*

For anions such as chloride where effective reagents are available for precipitation or complex-formation, potentiometric titration procedures

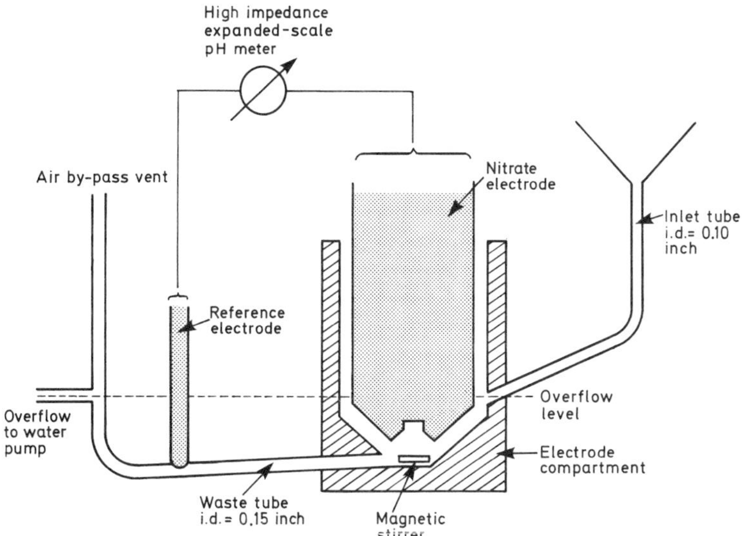

Figure 22 Flow-through unit for use with nitrate ion-selective electrode (From Milham[109])

can be developed in which the appropriate electrode is used to locate the end-point. In this respect the situation for nitrate is far less satisfactory. Nevertheless, such procedures have been developed using diphenylthallium-(III) sulphate[110] and nitron[111]. In the nitron investigation, the acid dissociation constant of nitron is reported as 10.34 and the solubility product of nitron nitrate $1.78 \pm 0.03 \times 10^{-6}$ at 20 °C and in 0.05M K_2SO_4. The optimal concentration of nitrate for the titration is about 0.01M. Application is made to fertilizer analysis. The diphenylthallium(III) sulphate method involves precipitation of $(C_6H_5)_2TlNO_3$, and is applicable to 0.01M to 0.1M NO_3^-. The nitrate electrode performs poorly in solutions more acidic than pH 2. Above pH 4 diphenylthallium(III) hydroxide begins to precipitate giving high results. Nitrite is not precipitated by $(C_6H_5)_2Tl^+$, but in the acidic solution used for the titration, nitrite disproportionates giving nitrate and nitric oxide. It becomes necessary, therefore, to destroy nitrite before the titration. This is conveniently done by adjusting the pH to about 4 and adding hydrazine sulphate. The major drawbacks of the method are interference from halides and the relatively high nitrate range for which the titration is applicable.

Application of the nitrate electrode is now extensive. The examples quoted are intended to illustrate the range of application. A much fuller list is given in Orion literature[112].

Application to water analysis gives comparative results to procedures using brucine[113] and xylenol orange[114]. Bunton and Crosby[115] have compared use of the electrode with five other methods of nitrate trace determination, mainly spectrophotometric. In soil analysis the electrode has given results that agree with steam distillation methods, though the phenoldisulphonic acid method gave slightly lower results. A recent application to soil employs an ultrasonic device that eliminates the need for continuous stirring[117]. In soil analysis, while the actual measurement by electrode is rapid, pre-treatment of the sample, this including shaking and filtration, often takes several hours. Another recent application to soil involves an automatic procedure capable of dealing with 60 samples[118]. Nitrate in plant extracts has been determined by Paul and Carlson[119], whose results compare well with the phenoldisulphonic acid method.

An interesting use of the nitrate ion-selective electrode is in the analysis of nitrate–nitrite mixtures. Morie, Ledford and Glover[120] accomplish this by measuring the potential of a solution containing nitrate and nitrite before and after oxidizing the nitrite to nitrate with $KMnO_4$. The procedure is used for determination of nitrogen oxides in cigarette smoke. One of the most useful applications of the electrode is in the determination of nitrogen oxides as air pollutants resulting from motor vehicle exhausts[121]. Several approaches have been used to this problem. They include the Saltzman–Jacobs–Hochheiser method which utilizes the Griess–Ilosvay reaction. This is described on page 147 of the nitrite section.

The ion-selective electrode approach is based on gas-phase oxidation of N-oxides to HNO_3. This uses O_3 as oxidizing agent.

$$NO + O_3 \leftrightharpoons NO_2 + O_2$$

$$2NO_2 + O_3 \leftrightharpoons N_2O_5 + O_2$$

The nitrogen pentoxide is absorbed and undergoes hydrolysis.

$$N_2O_5 + H_2O \rightarrow 2HNO_3$$

This is monitored using the nitrate electrode[122]. The method enables nitrogen dioxide and nitric oxide in flowing gaseous mixtures to be measured at ppm level.

Not all nitrate potentiometric procedures employ the nitrate electrode. Birum *et al.*[123] pass a nitrate solution through a cation-exchange column, then titrate the resulting HNO_3 potentiometrically in a methanol or ketone medium. For nitrates of Group III and above the titrant is KOH; those of Groups I and II are titrated with tetraethylammonium hydroxide. Nitrites can be titrated similarly using a methanol or ethyl methyl ketone solution of perchloric acid, in a medium of methanol or methanol–acetone. The method can be used for analysis of the nitrates and nitrites of several elements as well as for nitrate–nitrite mixtures.

2. *Voltammetric and amperometric*

Early work on the behaviour of such ions as nitrate and bromate at the dropping mercury electrode indicated peculiarities. Reduction potentials were found to shift to more positive values with increase in charge of cations for the series K^+, Ba^{2+}, La^{3+}. Such ions as La^{3+} are known to catalyse the reduction of nitrate. It is now believed that the catalytic effect is caused by the hydrolysis products of such ions[124]. A useful summary of polarography of the nitrate ion is given in a general review of nitrate analysis quoted at the beginning of this section[4]. As well as La(III), other cations that catalyse the reduction include zirconium(IV) and uranium(VI). Calibration curves can be linear or non-linear over a narrow range of nitrate concentration. The methods of Rand and Heukelekian[125] and Hamm and Withrow[126] give a linear response, but in the former case destruction of nitrate by iron(II) is required in some cases to avoid residual current difficulties.

In discussing spectrophotometric determination of nitrate, reference is made to methods based on nitration of 2,6-xylenol in strong H_2SO_4 medium. Here the NO_3^- ion is converted into the nitronium ion NO_2^+.

$$HNO_3 + H_2SO_4 \rightleftharpoons NO_2^+ + HSO_4^- + H_2O$$

This is followed by the reaction:

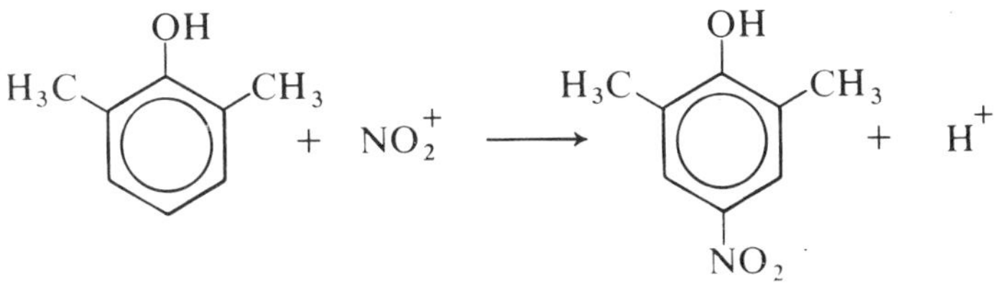

$$\text{2,6-xylenol } (\text{OH}; \text{H}_3\text{C}, \text{CH}_3) + NO_2^+ \longrightarrow \text{4-nitro-2,6-xylenol } (\text{OH}; \text{H}_3\text{C}, \text{CH}_3; \text{NO}_2) + H^+$$

Hartley and Curran[127] have developed a method based on polarographic reduction of 4-nitro-2,6-xylenol. The reduction is reproducible, rapid and nearly quantitative. The diffusion-controlled limiting current is linearly proportional to nitrate concentration over the range 2×10^{-5}–10^{-3}M. Chloride is a serious interference but can be easily removed. Oxygen is a minor interference that can be tolerated in high-nitrate samples.

Gal'pern and Il'ina[128] determine HNO_3 as impurity in H_2SO_4 using a polarographic procedure with 0.5M $CaCl_2$ as supporting electrolyte. The nitrate reduction potential $E_{\frac{1}{2}} = -1.83$ V *v.* the saturated calomel electrode, the wave height being rectilinear from 0.05 mM to 1 mM. Montenegro, Cruz and Matias[129] using mercury as anode and a uranyl acetate supporting electrolyte find $E_{\frac{1}{2}} = -1.0$ V *v.* a mercury pool. The method is slightly more sensitive for nitrate than nitrite. Many ions interfere including Al^{3+}, Fe^{3+}, Pb^{2+}, Ni^{2+} and $H_2PO_4^-$. For analysis of nitrate–nitrite mixtures, both are first evaluated together from the polarogram, and then nitrate on its own after removal of nitrite using methanol. Application is made to waters and fertilizers.

A portable polarographic instrument for determination of nitrate in water samples has been described[130]. The waves are developed in the presence of zirconium(IV) and uranium(VI). A new voltammetric method capable of reaching ppb (10^9) levels has been reported[131]. This employs a pyrolytic graphite electrode. Reduction of nitrate is electrocatalytic and occurs at -1.0 V *v.* a saturated calomel electrode, when copper and cadmium metals have been deposited on the working electrode. Iron, chloride, sulphate and organic matter do not interfere, but nitrite is reduced under the same conditions. A linear calibration holds for 1 μM (62 ppb(10^9)) to 1 mM (62 ppm) of nitrate.

There appears to be little widespread use of polarography for the determination of nitrate, though it has been listed as a tentative method in water analysis[132].

3. *Coulometric*

When nitrate and nitrite are dissolved in cooled concentrated H_2SO_4, they behave as NO_2^+ and NO^+ respectively. NO_2^+ can be titrated with electrogenerated Fe^{2+} using platinum and Hg/Hg_2SO_4 electrodes[133]. As little as 12 μmol of nitrate can be determined in the presence of a 70-fold excess of nitrite.

Karlsson and Torstensson[134] have based a coulometric method on iodimetric titration of nitrite resulting from reduction of nitrate using a copperized cadmium reductor. Between pH 5 and 10 the main reaction for reduction of nitrate can be written

$$Cd + NO_3^- + 2NH_3 + 2NH_4^+ \rightarrow Cd(NH_3)_4^{2+} + NO_2^- + H_2O$$

Nitrite is determined by a coulometric method previously developed by the same authors[135]. This involves reduction of nitrite by iodide followed by coulometric reduction of the resulting iodine. The nitrate method is applicable in the range 0.01–100 μg mℓ$^{-1}$. An analysis, including the reduction step, can be completed in less than 10 min. A particular advantage of the method is its ability to deal with coloured samples, for which conventional spectrophotometric methods often fail. It has been applied to coloured fruit juices, meat samples, and waste water. From the details given it will be clear that it can be used for nitrate–nitrite mixtures.

Miscellaneous methods

Several gasometric methods for nitrate have been published. Awad and Hassan[136] base their micro method on reduction of nitrate to nitric oxide in acid medium. Mercury, iron(II), titanium(III) or hydroquinone can be used as reductants. With hydroquinone, molybdenum(VI) catalyses the reaction according to the proposed scheme

$$C_6H_4(OH)_2 + 2Mo(VI) \rightarrow C_6H_4O_2 + 2Mo(V) + 2H^+$$

$$NO_3^- + 4H^+ + 3Mo(V) \rightarrow NO + 2H_2O + 3Mo(V)$$

A specially designed simple glass apparatus is used. Hassan[137] has extended the method, reducing with iodide or iodine in the presence of halogen acids. The reactions are

$$2NO_3^- + 3I^- + 6Cl^- \rightarrow 2NO + 4H_2O + 3ICl_2^-$$

$$2NO_3^- + 3I_2 + 8H^+ + 12Cl^- \rightarrow 2NO + 4H_2O + 6ICl_2^-$$

The nitric oxide is collected in a nitrometer and its volume measured. Calculation of nitrate content is made using the expression

$$NO_3^-\% = \frac{(V - v)(P - p) \times 273 \times 14.01}{(273 + t) \times W \times 224 \times 760}$$

where V = volume of NO in mℓ; v = blank in mℓ; P = atmospheric pressure, mm Hg; p = water vapour pressure, mm Hg at room temperature t; t = room temperature; W = weight sample in mg.

The best results are obtained when 20% $SnCl_2$ is used as absorption solution for the iodine. Organic nitrates as well as inorganic nitrates may be determined.

Van Slyke and Lo Monte[138] describe a similar method based on nitric oxide evolved on reacting nitrate with mercury and H_2SO_4. The method is extended to accommodate nitrate–nitrite mixtures by utilizing the nitrite–sulphamic acid reaction to give nitrogen.

An enzymatic method for nitrate has been based on the specific reduction of nitrate to nitrite by a dissimilatory nitrate reductase from Escherichia coli [strain B] and formate[139]. The assay involves a 4-h incubation at 45 °C followed by diazotization and coupling in a Griess–Ilosvay type reaction. The determination is specific, with a sensitivity of 0.1 μg N (as nitrate) in a final volume of 10 mℓ.

The Weisz ring-oven has been used for determination of nitrate and nitrite in nanogram amounts both singly and when present together[140]. Using a segment technique, a stable standard scale is not required. The nitrate is reduced to nitrite using zinc; colour development is by the Griess–Ilosvay reaction. Antimony, arsenic and lead in 10-fold amounts do not interfere in the determination of nitrate.

References

1. WOLFF, I.A. and WASSERMAN, A.E., *Science*, **177**, 15 (1972)
2. EGAN, H., *Fd Cosmet. Toxic.*, **9**, 81 (1971)
3. CLEAR, A.J. and ROTH, M., in *Treatise on Analytical Chemistry* (Ed. I.M. Kolthoff and P.J. Elving), Part II, Vol. 5, Interscience, New York, 268 (1961)
4. STREULI, C.A. and AVERELL, P.A., *Analytical Chemistry of Nitrogen and its Compounds*, Chapter 4, Wiley-Interscience, New York (1970)
5. DOLANCE, A. and HEALY, P.W., *Ind. Engng Chem. analyt. Edn*, **17**, 718 (1945)
6. WESTLAND, A.D. and LANGFORD, R.R., *Analyt. Chem.*, **28**, 1996 (1956)
7. PAUL, J.L. and CARLSON, R.M., *J. agric. Fd Chem.*, **16**, 766 (1968)
8. RYABININ, A.I. and BOGATYREV, V.L., *Zh. analit. Khim.*, **23**, 894 (1968); *Analyt. Abstr.*, **18**, 875 (1970)
9. SCHMIT, J.A. and HENRY, R.A., *Chromatographia*, **3**, 497 (1970); *Analyt. Abstr.*, **21**, 2242 (1971)
10. NIEDERMAIER, T., *Z. analyt. Chem.*, **223**, 336 (1966)
11. KEAY, J. and MENAGÉ, P.M.A., *Analyst*, **95**, 379 (1970)
12. DEVARDA, A., *Chemiker-zeitung*, **16**, 1952 (1892)
13. BREMNER, J.M., in *Methods of Soil Analysis* (Ed. C.A. Black), Part II: *Chemical and Microbiological Properties*, Agronomy No. 9, American Society of Agronomy, Madison, Wisconsin (1965)
14. BREMNER, J.M. and KEENEY, D.R., *Analytica chim. Acta*, **32**, 485 (1965)
15. DICKINSON, W.E., *Analyt. Chem.*, **26**, 777 (1954)
16. PREMI, P.R. and CORNFIELD, A.H., *Analyst*, **92**, 196 (1967)
17. BOCK, R. and BEILSTEIN, G.M., *Z. analyt. Chem.*, **192**, 44 (1963)
18. CANIC, V.D., TURCIC, M.N., BUGARSKI-VOJINOVIC, M.B. and PERISIC, N.U., *Z. analyt. Chem.*, **229**, 93 (1967); *Analyt. Abstr.*, **15**, 5211 (1968)
19. HATCHER, D.W. and SCHALL, E.D., *J. Ass. off. agric. Chem.*, **48**, 648 (1965)
20. BUSCH, M., *Ber.*, **38**, 861 (1905)
21. WILLIAMS, M., *Ind. Chemist*, 594 (1954)
22. AWAD, W.I., HASSAN, S.S.M. and ZAKI, M.T.M., *Talanta*, **18**, 219 (1971)
23. STEPHEN, W.I., *Feigl Anniversary Symposium, Birmingham 1962* (Ed. P.W. West, A.M.G. Macdonald and T.S. West), Elsevier, London, 156 (1963)
24. HUTTON, R.C., SALAM, S.A. and STEPHEN, W.I., *J. chem. Soc.*, 1573(A) (1966)
25. HUTTON, R.C. and STEPHEN, W.I., *Analyst*, **92**, 501 (1967)
26. HARTMANN, H. and BATHGE, G., *Angew. Chem.*, **65**, 107 (1953)
27. BELCHER, R. and WILSON, C.L., *New Methods in Analytical Chemistry*, Chapman and Hall, London, 69 (1955)

28. AWAD, W.I., HASSAN, S.S.M. and ZAKI, M.T.M., *Talanta*, **18**, 219 (1971)
29. KOLTHOFF, I.M., SANDELL, E.B. and MUSKOVITZ, B., *J. Am. chem. Soc.*, **55**, 1454 (1933)
30. LATIMER, G.W. and CHAMBERS, O.K., *Talanta*, **12**, 417 (1965)
31. LEITHE, W., *Mikrochemie*, **33**, 48 (1947); *Analyt. Chem.*, **20**, 1082 (1948)
32. HEITNER-WIRGUIN, C. and FRIEDMAN, D., *Talanta*, **9**, 121 (1960)
33. ERDEY, L., POLOS, L. and GREGOROWICZ, Z., *Talanta*, **3**, 6 (1959)
34. BOWMAN, F.C. and SCOTT, W.W., *J. Ind. Engng Chem.*, **7**, 766 (1915)
35. KOLTHOFF, I.M. and BELCHER, R., *Volumetric Analysis*, Vol. III, Interscience, New York, 609 (1957)
36. WILLIAMS, A.F., in *Comprehensive Analytical Chemistry* (Ed. C.L. and D.W. Wilson), Vol. 1C, Elsevier, Amsterdam, 207 (1962)
37. AWAD, W.I. and HASSAN, S.S.M., *Talanta*, **16**, 1383 (1969)
38. WEST, P.W. and SARMA, P., *Mikrochim. Acta*, 506 (1957)
39. WEST, P.W. and LYLES, G.L., *Analytica chim. Acta*, **23**, 227 (1960)
40. WEST, P.W. and RAMACHANDRAN, T.P., *Analytica chim. Acta*, **35**, 317 (1966)
41. ROBINSON, J.W. and HSU, C.J., *Analytica chim. Acta*, **44**, 51 (1969)
42. CLARKE, A. L. and JENNINGS, A. C., *J. agric. Fd Chem.*, **13**, 174 (1965)
43. BASARGIN, N.N. and CHERNOVA, E.A., *Zh. analit. Khim.*, **23**, 102 (1968); *Analyt. Abstr.*, **17**, 2417 (1969)
44. MULLIN, J.B. and RILEY, J.P., *Analytica chim. Acta*, **12**, 464 (1955)
45. HENRIKSEN, A., *Analyst*, **90**, 83 (1965)
46. AKISADA, T., *Japan Analyst*, **12**, 614 (1963); *Analyt. Abstr.*, **12**, 621 (1965)
47. KOMATSU, S. and HAGINO, K., *J. chem. Soc. Japan, pure Chem. Sect.*, **88**, 1157 (1967); *Analyt. Abstr.*, **16**, 1202 (1969)
48. MORIMOTO, M., HIRAKOBA, A. and ISHIBASHI, R., *Japan Analyst*, **16**, 1335 (1967); *Analyt. Abstr.*, **16**, 1203 (1969)
49. MATSUNAGA, K. and HISHIMURA, M., *Analytica chim. Acta*, **45**, 350 (1969)
50. MORRIS, A.W. and RILEY, J.P., *Analytica chim. Acta*, **29**, 272 (1963)
51. ISAEVA, A.B. and BOGOYAVLENSKII, A.N., *Okeanologiya*, **8**, 539 (1968); *Analyt. Abstr.*, **17**, 1210 (1969)
52. KAMM, L., MCKEOWN, G.G. and SMITH, D.M., *J. Ass. off. agric. Chem.*, **48**, 892 (1965)
53. KAMM, L., BRAY, D.F. and COFFIN, D.E., *J. Ass. off. analyt. Chem.*, **51**, 140 (1968)
54. SCHALL, E.D. and HATCHER, D.W., *J. Ass. off. analyt. Chem.*, **51**, 763 (1968)
55. *Official Methods of Analysis of the Association of Official Analytical Chemistry* (Ed. W. Horowitz), 11th edn, AOAC, Washington, D.C., 126 (1970)
56. *Official, Standardised and Recommended Methods of Analysis* (Compiled and Edited by N.W. Hanson), 2nd edn, The Chemical Society, London (1973)
57. ELLIOTT, R.J. and PORTER, A.G., *Analyst*, **96**, 523 (1971)
58. WOOD, E.D., ARMSTRONG, F.J.A. and RICHARD, F.A., *J. mar. Biol. Ass. UK*, **47**, 23 (1967)
59. HENRIKSEN, A. and SELMER-OLSEN, A.R., *Analyst*, **95**, 514 (1970)
60. LAMBERT, R.S. and DUBOIS, R.J., *Analyt. Chem.*, **43**, 955 (1971)
61. SAITO, G., SUGIMOTO, K. and HAGINO, K., *Japan Analyst*, **20**, 542 (1971); *Analyt. Abstr.*, **23**, 2415 (1972)
62. BAKER, A.S., *J. agric. Fd Chem.*, **15**, 802 (1967)
63. SCHEIBE, G., *Ber.*, **59**, 1321 (1926)
64. HOATHER, R.C., *Proc. Soc. Wat. Treat. Exam.*, **2**, 9 (1953)
65. HOATHER, R.C. and RACKHAM, R.F., *Analyst*, **84**, 548 (1959)
66. BASTIAN, R., WEBERLING, R. and PALILLA, F., *Analyt. Chem.*, **29**, 1795 (1957)
67. ARMSTRONG, F.A.J., *Analyt. Chem.*, **35**, 1292 (1963)
68. NAVONE, R., *J. Am. Wat. Wks Ass.*, **56**, 781 (1964)
69. American Public Health Association, *Standard Methods for the Examination of Water and Wastewater*, 13th edn, American Public Health Association, Washington, D.C. (1971)
70. WETTERS, J.H. and UGLUM, K.L., *Analyt. Chem.*, **42**, 335 (1970)
71. GOLDMAN, E. and JACOBS, R., *J. Am. Wat. Wks Ass.*, **53**, 187 (1961)
72. HORA, F.B. and WEBBER, P.J., *Analyst*, **85**, 567 (1960)
73. CRESSER, M.S., *Analyst*, **102**, 99 (1977)
74. BARNES, H., *Analyst*, **75**, 388 (1950)
75. NORWITZ, G. and GORDON, H., *Analytica chim. Acta*, **89**, 177 (1977)
76. British Standard 2690: Part 7 (1968), London
77. DOCHERTY, A.C., *Lab. Pract.*, **18**, 47 (1969)
78. HARTLEY, A.M. and ASAI, R.I., *Analyt. Chem.*, **35**, 1207 (1963)

79. ANDREWS, D. W. W., *Analyst*, **89**, 730 (1964)
80. ALLERTON, F.W., *Analyst*, **72**, 349 (1947)
81. CHARLOT, G., *Colorimetric Determination of Elements*, Elsevier, Amsterdam, 320 (1964)
82. HARRISON, G.A.F., *Talanta*, **9**, 533 (1962)
83. PAPPENHAGEN, J.M., *Analyt. Chem.*, **30**, 282 (1958)
84. KRUSE, J.M. and MELLON, M.G., *Analyt. Chem.*, **25**, 1188 (1953)
85. RUSELL, J.A., *J. biol. Chem.*, **156**, 457 (1944)
86. Ref. 81, 321
87. WEATHERBURN, M.W., *Analyt. Chem.*, **39**, 971 (1967)
88. JACOBS, S., *Nature, Lond.*, **183**, 262 (1959)
89. JACOBS, S., *Analyst*, **87**, 53 (1962)
90. JACOBS, S., *Feigl Anniversary Symposium, Birmingham 1962* (Ed. P.W. West, A.M.G. Macdonald, and T.S. West), Elsevier, London, 200 (1963)
91. YAMAMOTO, Y., OKAMOTO, N. and TAO, E., *Analytica chim. Acta*, **47**, 127 (1969)
92. YAMAMOTO, Y., UCHIKAWA, S. and AKABORI, K., *Bull. chem. Soc. Japan*, **37**, 1718 (1964); *Analyt. Abstr.*, **13**, 1233 (1966)
93. BHATTY, M.K. and TOWNSHEND, A., *Analytica chim. Acta*, **56**, 55 (1971)
94. SAWICKI, E., JOHNSON, H. and STANLEY, T.W., *Analyt. Chem.*, **35**, 1934 (1963)
95. BURNS, D.T., FOGG, A.G. and WILLCOX, A., *Mikrochim. Acta*, 205 (1971)
96. TAN, Y.L., *Analytica chim. Acta*, **91**, 373 (1977)
97. AXELROD, H.D., BONELLI, J.E. and LODGE, J.P., *Analytica chim. Acta*, **51**, 21 (1970)
98. SAWICKI, C.R., *Analyt. Lett.*, **4**, 761 (1971)
99. AFGHAN, B.K. and RYAN, J.F., *Analyt. Chem.*, **47**, 2347 (1975)
100. MAGEE, R.J., SHAHINE, S.A.E.F. and WILSON, C.L., *Mikrochim. Acta*, 1019 (1964)
101. WILHITE, R.N. and ELLIS, R.F., *Appl. Spectroscopy*, **17**, 168 (1963)
102. YANG, R.T. and LOW, M.J.D., *Analyt. Chem.*, **45**, 2014 (1973)
103. KUMAMARU, T., TAO, E., OKAMOTO, N. and YAMAMOTO, Y., *Bull. chem. Soc. Japan.*, **38**, 2204 (1965); *Analyt. Abstr.*, **14**, 1934 (1967)
104. YAMAMOTO, Y., KUMAMARU, T., HAYASHI, Y. and OTANI, Y., *Japan Analyst*, **18**, 359 (1969); *Analyt. Abstr.*, **22**, 105 (1972)
105. HOUSER, M.E. and FAUTH, M.I., *Microchem. J.*, **15**, 399 (1970)
106. DAVIES, J.E.W., MOODY, G.J. and THOMAS, J.D.R., *Analyst*, **97**, 87 (1972)
107. MOODY, G.J. and THOMAS, J.D.R., *Talanta*, **19**, 623 (1972)
108. MATEROVA, E.A., GREKOVICH, A.L. and GARBUZOVA, N.V., *Zh. analit. Khim.*, **29**, 1900 (1974)
109. MILHAM, P.J., *Analyst*, **95**, 758 (1970)
110. DIGREGORIO, J.S. and MORRIS, M.D., *Analyt. Chem.*, **42**, 94 (1970)
111. HULANICKI, A. and MAJ, M., *Talanta*, **22**, 767 (1975)
112. *Orion Research Analytical Methods Guide*, 7th edn, MSE Scientific Instruments, Manor Royal, Crawley, Sussex, UK
113. LANGMUIR, D. and JACOBSON, R.L., *Environ. Sci. Technol.*, **4**, 834 (1970)
114. SMITH, G.R., *Analyt. Lett.*, **8**, 503 (1975)
115. BUNTON, N.A. and CROSBY, N.T., *Water Treat. Exam.*, **18**, 338 (1969)
116. MAHENDRAPPA, M.K., *Soil Sci.*, 132 (1969)
117. SIMEONOV, V., ASENOV, I. and DIADOV, V., *Talanta*, **24**, 199 (1976)
118. GOODMAN, D., *Analyst*, **101**, 943 (1976)
119. PAUL, J.L. and CARLSON, R.M., *J. agric. Fd Chem.*, **16**, 766 (1968)
120. MORIE, G.P., LEDFORD, C.J. and GLOVER, C.A., *Analytica chim. Acta*, **60**, 397 (1972)
121. MCFARLAND, J.H. and BENTON, C.S., *J. Chem. Educ.*, **49**, 21 (1972)
122. DI MARTINI, R., *Analyt. Chem.*, **42**, 1102 (1970)
123. BIRUM, A.M., KOMAROVA, K.A., KRESHKOVA, E.K. and YAROVENKO, A.N., *Isv. vyssh ucheb. zaved Khim. khim. Tekhol.*, **9**, 546 (1966); *Analyt. Abstr.*, **14**, 6065 (1967)
124. *Progress in Polarography* (Ed. P. Zuman), Interscience, New York, 225 (1962)
125. RAND, M.C. and HEUKELEKIAN, H., *Analyt. Chem.*, **25**, 878 (1953)
126. HAMM, R.E. and WITHROW, C.D., *Analyt. Chem.*, **27**, 1913 (1955)
127. HARTLEY, A.M. and CURRAN, D.J., *Analyt. Chem.*, **35**, 686 (1963)
128. GAL'PERN, G.M. and IL'INA, V.A., *Zav. Lab.*, **36**, 1046 (1970); *Analyt. Abstr.*, **21**, 165 (1971)
129. MONTENEGRO, M.I., CRUZ, M.J. and MATIAS, M.L., *Revta. port Quim*, **13**, 217 (1971); *Analyt. Abstr.*, **24**, 103 (1973)
130. YOUNG, R.L., EVERETT SPELL, J., SIU, H.M., PHILIP, R.H. and JONES, E.R., *Environ. Sci. Technol.*, **9**, 1075 (1975)
131. BODINI, M.E. and SAWYER, D.T., *Analyt. Chem.*, **49**, 485 (1977)

132. American Public Health Association, *Standard Methods for the Examination of Water and Wastewater*, 12th edn, American Public Health Association, Washington D.C. (1965)
133. GIUFFRE, L., LOSIO, E. and FONTANI LAMMA, F., *Annali Chim.*, **57**, 1450 (1967); *Analyt. Abstr.*, **16**, 1831 (1969)
134. KARLSSON, R. and TORSTENSSON, L-G., *Talanta*, **22**, 27 (1975)
135. KARLSSON, R. and TORSTENSSON, L-G., *Talanta*, **21**, 945 (1974)
136. AWAD, W.I. and HASSAN, S.S.M., *Talanta*, **16**, 1393 (1969)
137. HASSAN, S.S.M., *Analyst*, **96**, 59 (1971)
138. VAN SLYKE, D.D. and LO MONTE, A.F., *Microchem. J.*, **14**, 608 (1969)
139. MCNAMARA, A.L., MEEKER, G.B. and SHAW, P.D., *J. agric. Fd Chem.*, **19**, 229 (1971)
140. WEISZ, H. and HANIF, M., *Analytica chim. Acta*, **81**, 179 (1976)

Nitrite

Sodium and potassium nitrites find extensive use as preservatives and in the fixation of colour in food products. Nitrite is an intermediate state in the nitrogen cycle. As such it is found in soils, waters and effluents. Industrially it is used to inhibit corrosion in industrial water.

The toxic effects of nitrite can occur by several mechanisms. It combines with blood pigment to produce methaemoglobin in which oxygen is no longer available to the tissues. Recently, concern has been expressed that it may combine in the stomach with amines and amides to produce highly carcinogenic nitrosamines[1–2]. The amount of nitrate permitted in certain foodstuffs is governed by legislation. Thus preserves in Food Regulations (1962) are allowed a maximum of 500 ppm of nitrite as $NaNO_2$.

Another important aspect of nitrite analytical chemistry concerns air pollution. Nitrogen oxides from motor vehicle exhausts and industrial processes are now recognized as serious air pollutants. The Jacobs–Hochheiser[4] modification of the well-known Saltzman method for determination of NO_2 in air involves passing the air sample through an alkaline solution and then analysing for nitrite.

The determination of nitrite is linked in several ways with that of nitrate. A standard method for determination of nitrate involves reduction to nitrite followed by determination of the latter. Conversely nitrite can be oxidized to nitrate by such oxidants as manganese(VII) or cerium(IV) and then determined indirectly in that form. Determination of nitrate and nitrite when present together is an important analysis particularly for soil samples. One approach here is determination of nitrate plus nitrite using a method common to both anions. This is followed by a second determination after destruction of nitrite using sulphanilamide, urea, sulphamic acid or hydrazine sulphate. The reactions for sulphamic acid and urea are given below.

$$HOSO_2 \cdot NH_2 + HNO_2 \rightarrow N_2 + H_2SO_4 + H_2O$$

$$CO(NH_2)_2 + 2HNO_2 \rightarrow 2N_2 + CO_2 + 3H_2O$$

The analytical chemistry of nitrites is included in several reviews[5–8].

Separations

Few separation methods appear to exist for nitrite.

1. Thin-layer chromatography
Canic *et al.*[9] separate nitrite from several other anions using TLC on starch with acetone–3M aqueous NH_3 (1:4) as solvent. Kawanabe *et al.*[10], also using TLC separate NO_2^- from F^-, $S_2O_3^{2-}$, SO_4^{2-}, CrO_4^{2-}, PO_4^{3-}, AsO_4^{3-} and AsO_3^{3-}, on silica gel with methanol–butanol–water (3:1:1) as solvent.

2. Solvent extraction
The triphenylstannonium system has been used to extract nitrite using benzene as solvent. An extraction of 97% is reported[11] in the pH range 1.0–2.2.

Determination

Titrimetric methods

1. Acidimetric
This is based on titration of the ammonia produced when nitrite (and nitrate) are reduced using Devarda's alloy. A modern form of the method is used by Bremner and Keeney[12] for determination of nitrite and nitrate in soil or plant extracts. The method is conducted on samples containing up to 2 mg of inorganic nitrogen. In one aliquot both anions are converted to ammonium ion and ammonia steam distilled into dilute boric acid for titration with standard acid. In a second aliquot nitrite is destroyed with sulphamic acid before the above procedure is applied.

2. Redox
Almost all titrimetric methods for nitrite employ redox reactions. Hypohalites, Ce(IV), chlorate, chloramine-T, lead tetra-acetate, $KMnO_4$, Mn(III), Co(III), hexacyanoferrate(III) and other oxidizing species have been used. Details of earlier work are given in standard texts[13,14]. In most instances the direct titration is slow and unsatisfactory. This can be overcome by adding excess of the reagent and conducting a back-titration. Another problem is decomposition and air-oxidation of HNO_2 during the titration. This can occur when $KMnO_4$ is used as titrant. Lack of suitable indicators is another problem, for example when hypochlorite is used. This has been overcome by employing a potentiometric or amperometric end-point. An alternative solution is to use an iodimetric end-procedure by adding KI to excess of the oxidant.

Direct iodimetry requires strict control of experimental conditions.

$$2HNO_2 + 2I^- + 2H^+ \rightarrow 2NO + I_2 + 2H_2O$$

The presence of NO prevents direct titration of liberated iodine because it reacts with oxygen and causes more iodine to be produced. Absence of oxygen is therefore required during the titration. This complicates the procedure.

Alkaline hexacyanoferrate(III) has been used for redox determination of several reducing substances, often with osmic acid as catalyst. Sant[15] observed that while hexacyanoferrate(III) is unable to oxidize nitrite even in the presence of osmic acid, the reaction proceeds quantitatively in the presence of zinc sulphate.

$$2[Fe(CN)_6]^{3-} + NO_2^- + 2OH^- \rightarrow 2[Fe(CN)_6]^{4-} + NO_3^- + H_2O$$

$$2K_4[Fe(CN)_6] + 3ZnSO_4 \rightarrow K_2Zn_3[Fe(CN)_6]_2 + 3K_2SO_4$$

The method is simple. To a known volume of hexacyanoferrate(III), 2 or 3 g of $ZnSO_4$ are added, and the mixture heated to boiling. Nitrite solution is now run in from a burette until the solution is completely decolorized. The presence of large amounts of nitrate cause no interference. In the original investigation quantities of nitrite from 2 to 45 mg were determined.

Chloramine-T, a reagent used in many redox procedures for nitrite, has been re-investigated by Agderdenbos[16] who found that a modified older method gave satisfactory results[17].

$$CH_3 \cdot C_6H_4 \cdot SO_2NClNa + NaNO_2 + H_2O \rightarrow NaNO_3 + CH_3C_6H_4SO_2NH_2 + NaCl$$

$$CH_3 \cdot C_6H_4SO_2NClNa + 2KI + 2HCl \rightarrow CH_3C_6H_4SO_2NH_2 + I_2 + NaCl + 2KCl$$

The procedure, given below, is indirect and employs an iodimetric end-point.

Titrimetric determination of nitrite using hexacyanoferrate (III)[16]

Reagents

Chloramine-T:

Approximately 0.05M. Dissolve about 25 g of the reagent (sodium salt of *p*-toluene sulphochloramide, $CH_3C_6H_4SO_2NClNa \cdot 3H_2O$ in water. Filter into a 2-ℓ volumetric flask. Dilute to mark. Keep in an amber bottle.

Procedure

Pipette 25 mℓ of chloramine-T (or 50 mℓ if more than 30 mg of nitrite present) solution into a 500-mℓ stoppered conical flask. Add the nitrite sample and dilute to about 150 mℓ. Add 10 mℓ of 9M acetic acid and after 2 min add 10 mℓ of 10% KI. Place in the dark for 5 min then titrate with standard thiosulphate using starch to detect the end-point.

Carry out a blank determination in the same way. The amount of nitrite is calculated from the quantity of thiosulphate consumed.

1 mℓ 0.1M thiosulphate ≡ 2.30 mg nitrite

Notes

1. Chloramine-T solutions are not particularly stable. Blank checks should therefore be carried out regularly.
2. The maximum permitted amounts of interfering ions (those giving 0.3% error when 25 mg of NO_2^- is present) are as follows:
   <1 mg S^{2-}, NH_4^+, SCN^-
   1 mg $[Fe(CN)_6]^{4-}$

5 mg Cu(II)
50 mg I^-
125 mg (or more) Br^-, $[Fe(CN)_6]^{3-}$, Hg(II), Pb(II), ClO_3^-.

3. The interfering effects of Cu^{2+} and NH_4^+ may be eliminated by prior cation-exchange.

Spectroscopic methods

1. Spectrophotometric—visible and UV

A large number of spectrophotometric methods have been developed for nitrite. Many are variations of the well-established Griess–Ilosvay method. Sawicki *et al.*[18] have made a critical comparison of 52 nitrite spectrophotometric methods.

An important group is based on diazotization followed by coupling reactions to give azo-dyes. In the original Griess–Ilosvay method, sulphanilic acid and 1-naphthylamine were used[19, 20].

1-naphthylamine is now known to be carcinogenic[21] and has been replaced by several other compounds notably 1-naphthylamine-7-sulphonic acid (Cleve's acid), N-1-naphthylethylenediamine, and dimethyl-1-naphthylamine.

Sulphanilamide is often used in place of sulphanilic acid. In general, all the variations are referred to as the 'Griess–Ilosvay method'. The reaction has been extensively studied over a number of decades. A major investigation by Rider and Mellon[22] clarified the fundamental conditions governing successful application of the method. This has formed the basis of modern forms of the method. Diazotization should be carried out in strongly acid solutions and at as low a temperature as possible. The coupling, which should only be carried out when diazotization is complete, should be made at the lowest acidity possible.

Bunton, Crosby and Patterson[23] have investigated the variation of the method utilizing Cleve's acid, and established optimum conditions. While its sensitivity is not as high as the form using N-1-naphthylethylenediamine, the same colour is produced and solutions of the reagent are more stable[24]. Sawicki, Stanley and Elbert[25] were able to produce the azo-dye by employing one reagent, *p*-phenylazoaniline, which functions both as diazotizing and coupling reagent[25]. The molar absorptivity in this form of the method is 67000 at 959 nm compared with 50000 at 550 nm using sulphanilic acid and N-1-naphthylethylenediamine. Kieruczenkowa[26], using Schäffer acid (6-hydroxynaphthalene-2-sulphonic acid) as coupling agent in conjunction with sulphanilic acid, obtained a much lower sensitivity ($\varepsilon = 12000$).

Automatic forms of the method for application to water and soil extracts have been reported[27–29]. The flow diagram used by Henriksen and Selmer-Olsen is shown in *Figure 23*.

A Technicon AutoAnalyzer is employed. This incorporates a column containing copperized cadmium for reduction of nitrate to nitrite, the method giving the sum of nitrate plus nitrite. Nitrite, if present, is determined without using the reductor. Nitrate is evaluated by difference.

The need for increased sensitivity has produced two extensions of the

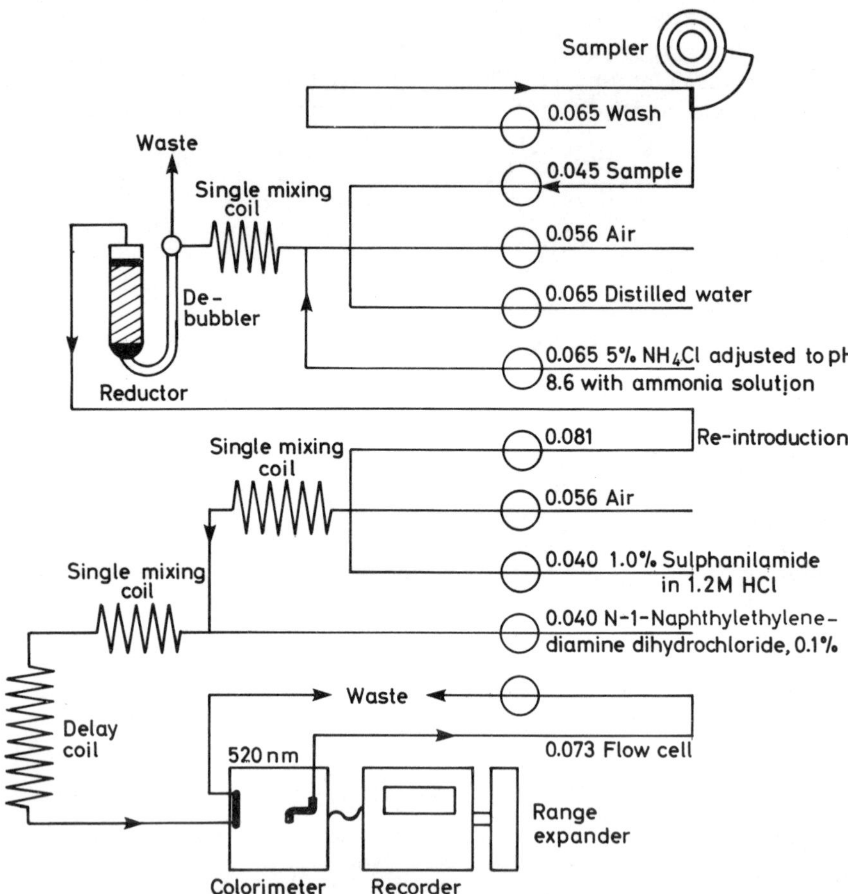

Figure 23 Flow diagram showing automatic determination of nitrate and nitrite in water.
(After Henriksen and Silmer-Olsen[29])

Griess–Ilosvay method. One is solvent-extraction of the dye; the other is concentration of the dye on an anion-exchange resin. Extraction of the positively charged dye is reported by Foris and Sweet[30]. In this work a single reagent is used for diazotization and coupling (8-aminoquinoline), and extraction made into *n*-heptanol. A sensitivity of 0.0038 ppm is achieved based on an absorbance of 0.010 at 465 nm and using a 40 mℓ sample. The method is suitable for NO_2^- in the range 0.5–16 μg. Recently, Japanese workers added *n*-dodecylbenzenesulphonate to the dye, the negatively charged ion coupling with the positively charged dye[31]. The product is extracted into carbon tetrachloride, back-extracted into hydrochloric acid and the absorbance measured at 543 nm. The back-extraction was found to be necessary due to turbidity in the organic phase. The sensitivity of the procedure is reported as 0.0007 μg-at NO_2^--N ℓ^{-1}* against 0.02 μg-at

* The original nomenclature has been retained here. The meaning of 0.0007 μg-atom of nitrogen nitrite ℓ^{-1} will be clear by analogy with gm-mole ℓ^{-1}, a unit now obsolete according to SI units.

NO_2^--N ℓ^{-1} for the normal procedure. Application of the method was made to nitrite in seawater.

Another method based on extraction is reported by Toei and Kiyose[62]. In this, *p*-aminoacetophenone is used to diazotize and *m*-phenylenediamine as coupling reagent. Extraction is made into toluene at pH 9 and the absorbance measured at 450 nm. The molar absorptivity is reported as about 2.3×10^4. Nitrite in the range 1–30 ppb (10^9) can be determined. Thiosulphate, copper(II), and iron(III) interfere but the effect of iron(III) can be eliminated by phosphate. The authors find that EDTA cannot be used as masking agent due to its interference.

Concentration of the dye on an anion-exchange column has been developed by Wada and Hattori[32]. The dye is collected on a Dowex-X8 resin and eluted with 60% acetic acid. A sensitivity of 1 ng-at N ℓ^{-1} is achieved, the range being 0.001–0.1 μg-at NO_2^--N ℓ^{-1} using 5000–1000 mℓ samples.

It will be apparent from the above discussion that it is not possible to assign one value for the sensitivity of modern forms of the Griess–Ilosvay method. This will vary according to the reagents used and the conditions. Using sulphanilic acid and N-1-naphthylethylenediamine, the molar absorptivity is about 50 000. To a certain extent the same applies to interferences. Many of the interfering species quoted in the literature apply to the procedure employing 1-naphthylamine which can no longer be recommended. Furthermore, while some sources quote a particular species as interfering, others quote the maximum amount that can be tolerated. An example of the latter is the British Standards method[33] for determination of nitrite (1–15 μg NO_2^--N) in industrial water. This method employs sulphanilic acid and 1-naphthylamine-7-sulphonic acid (Cleve's acid). The following do not interfere when below the levels stated.

Cl^-	5000 μg	Fe^{2+}	1000 μg
SO_4^{2-}	5000 μg	Fe^{3+}	500 μg
Ca^{2+}	2500 μg	Meta-phosphate	500 μg
Cu^{2+}	1000 μg	(expressed as P_2O_5)	
Mg^{2+}	1000 μg	NH_4^+	2000 μg

The following have been quoted as interfering in the procedure using 1-naphthylamine: Cl_2, NCl_3, Fe(III), Hg(I), Hg(II), Ag(I), Bi(III), Sb(III), Pb(II), Au(III), Cu(II), chloroplatinate, metavanadate, urea, aliphatic amines, and strong oxidizing and reducing agents.

Of the spectrophotometric methods for nitrite, modifications of the Griess–Ilosvay are the most extensively used. In addition to examples already quoted, application has been made to nitrite in NH_4NO_3[34], meat[35], air-pollution[4], blood[37], feeding stuffs[38] and baby foods[39].

Methods other than the Griess–Ilosvay will now be discussed. Sawicki *et al.*[36] have developed extremely sensitive methods based on free-radical

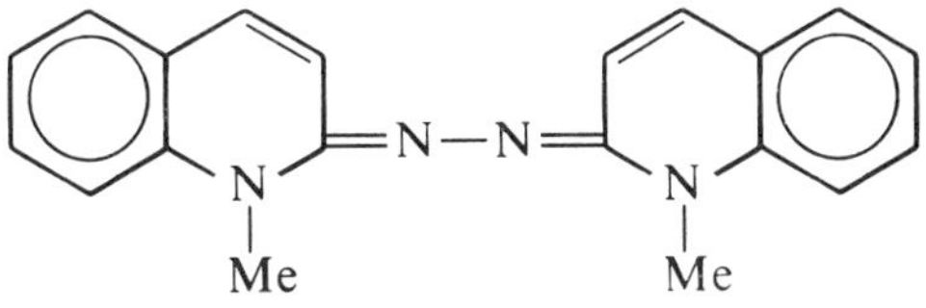

Structure 23 1-methyl-2-quinolone azine

chromogens. Several give molar absorptivities in excess of 200 000; 1-methyl-2-quinoline azine (*Structure 23*) gives the extraordinary value of 1 270 000. Beer's law is not obeyed. In addition to sensitivity, a special advantage is that sulphite, which interferes in the azo-dye method, is without effect.

Determination of nitrite using brucine has been the subject of several investigations[40–42]. Saito, Sugimoto and Hagino[42] find that nitrite gives rectilinear graphs in H_2SO_4–$HClO_4$ mixtures but not in H_2SO_4 alone. The absorbance is measured at 430 nm. Of the interferences iron is the most serious.

Hartley and Asai[43] find that 2,6-xylenol has some advantage over the Griess–Ilosvay method in that both nitrate and nitrite can be determined individually in the same sample using one reagent. Apart from halides which reduce nitrite, no other common ions are found to interfere. High concentrations of nitrite cannot be determined by the diazotization and coupling method due to the slight solubilities of the azo dyes. Lin and Cheng[44] react NO_2^- with certain aromatic ortho diamines and extract the product into *n*-butanol or isoamyl alcohol. Beer's law holds for 2–10 μmol NO_2^- in a 50 mℓ volume. Of the compounds examined, 3,3′-diaminobenzidine gives a molar absorptivity of 3500 at 350 nm. Most common ions do not interfere but oxidizing agents must be excluded. Molybdenum(VI), Cr(III), Cu, Ni and Fe(III) interfere but are eliminated with EDTA or tartrate. Silver and selenium interfere. The method is suitable for nitrate after reduction. Nitrite reacts with resorcinol in acid medium. The resulting nitroso compound forms a pale yellow chelate with the zirconyl ion, having a molar absorptivity of 2.67×10^4 at 347 nm[63]. The colour is stable for 24 h and selectivity is good. The range is from a few parts per 100 million to 1 ppm of nitrite. Of ions that normally occur in water, only phosphate and Fe^{3+} give serious interference, but both can be eliminated.

Spectrophotometric determination of nitrite by a modified Griess–Ilosvay method[23]

The method has a range of 1–10 μg NO_2^-—N.

Reagents

Sulphanilic acid:

Dissolve 0.5 g of analytical grade sulphanilic acid in a solution containing 30 mℓ of analytical grade glacial acetic acid and 120 mℓ of water. Store in a brown bottle

Cleve's acid:

Dissolve 0.5 g of Cleve's acid in 120 mℓ of water, warming on a water bath. Filter the solution, cool, and add 30 mℓ of glacial acetic acid. Store in a brown bottle.

Standard nitrite solution:

Dissolve 0.493 g of analytical grade sodium nitrite in water. Dilute to 1 ℓ in a volumetric flask. Immediately before use dilute 10 mℓ of this solution to 1 ℓ. Then 1 mℓ of solution ≡ 1 μg NO_2^-—N.

Procedure
Pipette an aliquot of nitrate solution into a 50-mℓ volumetric flask and adjust the volume to 40 mℓ. Add 2 mℓ of sulphanilic acid and leave for 10 min for diazotization. Then add 2 mℓ of Cleve's acid solution and allow 20 min for coupling. Read the absorbance at 525 nm in a 1-cm cell against water in a reference cell.

Although the nitrite ion absorbs in the UV, the molar absorptivity is so low (~23 at 355 nm) that it is generally converted to species having a much greater value for trace determination. Wetters and Uglum[45] have developed a direct method for simultaneous determination of nitrite and nitrate in the UV. This depends on the fact that only nitrite absorbs at 355 nm but both absorb at 302 nm. The lower limits for each are 0.02 mg $m\ell^{-1}$ for nitrite and 0.09 mg $m\ell^{-1}$ for nitrate.

Weiss and Boltz[46] give a brief summary of previous UV work on the determination of nitrite, and apply antipyrine to its determination in the range 0.1–12 ppm. The molar absorptivity is 7.61×10^3 ℓ mol^{-1} cm^{-1} at 343 nm. No interference occurs with Cu(II), Mn(II), Hg(II), Mg, Ni, Ca, Br^-, Cl^-, F^-, NO_3^-, PO_4^{3-}, ClO_4^- or oxalate. For a fuller list the original work should be consulted.

2. Fluorimetric
A fluorimetric method has been based on naphthol [2,3-d]-triazole after the diazotization of naphthalene-2,3 diamine[47]. Nitrite in the range 0–850 ng can be determined without interference from NH_4^+ or NO_3^-, but serious interference is given by Cu(II), Al, Bi, Ni, Cr(III), Sn(II), Se(IV) and Fe(III).

A very sensitive fluorimetric method has been based on diazotization with *p*-chloraniline and coupling with 2,6-diaminopyridine. The resulting azo product reacts with $CuSO_4$ to give a highly fluorescent triazole. Maximum fluorescence is exhibited at 430 nm with excitation at 360 nm. The lower limit is 2 ng $m\ell^{-1}$ nitrite using a 10-mℓ sample[48].

3. Atomic absorption spectroscopy
Japanese workers[49,50] determine NO_3^- by extracting its ion-pair with (2,9-dimethyl-1,10-phenanthroline) copper(I) into isobutyl methyl ketone, followed by AAS based on the copper. Houser and Fauth[51] have extended the method to nitrite by prior oxidation using cerium(IV).

Electroanalytical methods

1. Potentiometric including ion-selective electrodes
Morales and Zyka[52] find that nitrite can be titrated with lead tetra-acetate in a chloride solution (to remove Pb^{2+} produced) using saturated calomel-Pt electrodes. The end-point inflection is about 250 mV for 0.01 mℓ and the error within 0.17% for 2–35 mg nitrite. In later work Co(III) was used as titrant[53].

As in many other areas of analysis, the ion-selective electrode has found application. Previous work[54] on the nitrate ISE had indicated some response to nitrite. Morie, Ledford and Glover[55] use the nitrate ISE for analysis of nitrate–nitrite mixtures. First the potential of the mixture is determined. Nitrite is then oxidized by $KMnO_4$ and the potential re-determined. An equation is developed enabling each to be evaluated. Application is made to cigarette smoke after dissolving it in a basic solution.

2. Miscellaneous electroanalytical methods

Constant potential coulometry is used by Harrar[56], in which nitrite is directly oxidized to nitrate at a platinum electrode. Though the accuracy is good, the electrolysis time exceeds 20 min.

Karlsson and Torstensson[57] find that the Griess–Ilosvay method gives poor precision when applied to meat analysis, and have developed instead a constant potential coulometric method. The basis is reduction of nitrite by iodide to give iodine.

$$2HNO_2 + I^- + 2H^+ \rightarrow I_2 + 2NO + 2H_2O$$

From 0.005 to 5 mg nitrite is determined in less than 5 min with an error of ±0.1%. Anodic amperometric titration of low concentrations of nitrite with sulphamic acid or cerium(IV) has been reported by Stock and Bjork[58].

Miscellaneous methods

A novel method based on measuring the CO_2 and N_2O liberated on adding anhydrous formic acid to nitrite, has been described[59]. The reaction is

$$7NaNO_2 + 13HCOOH \rightarrow 7HCOONa + 6CO_2 + 9H_2O + 3NO + 2N_2O$$

The nitrous oxide is measured gasometrically; CO_2 is determined gravimetrically. Van Slyke and Lo Monte[60] develop a similar method which can be extended to nitrite–nitrate mixtures.

The Weisz ring-oven has been used for determination of nitrite and nitrate in nanogram amounts, when present singly or together[61].

References

1. WOLFF, I.A. and WASSERMAN, A.E., *Science*, **177**, 15 (1972)
2. EGAN, H., *Fd Cosmet. Toxic.*, **9**, 81 (1971)
3. Anon., *Nature, Lond.*, **239**, 63 (1972)
4. JACOBS, M.B. and HOCHHEISER, S., *Analyt. Chem.*, **30**, 426 (1958)
5. CLEAR, A.J., in *Treatise on Analytical Chemistry* (Ed. I.M. Kolthoff and P.J. Elving), Part II, Vol. 5, Interscience, New York, 275 (1961)
6. STREULI, C.A. and AVERELL, P.A., *Analytical Chemistry of Nitrogen and its Compounds*, Chapter 4, Wiley-Interscience, New York (1970)
7. SAWICKI, E., PFAFF, J. and STANLEY, T. W., *Rev. Univ. Ind. Santander, Columbia*, **5**, 337 (1963)
8. BARK, L.S., *Ind. Chemist*, 608 (1961)
9. CANIC, V.D., TURCIC, M.N., BUGARSKI-VOJINOVIC, M.B. and PERISIC, N.U., *Z. analyt. Chem.*, **229**, 93 (1967); *Analyt. Abstr.*, **15**, 5211 (1968)
10. KAWANABE, K., TAKITANI, S., MIYAZAKI, M. and TAMURA, Z., *Japan Analyst*, **13**, 976 (1964); *Analyt. Abstr.*, **13**, 5385 (1966)
11. BOCK, R. and NIEDERAUER, H-T., *Z. analyt. Chem.*, **190**, 33 (1962)

12. BREMNER, J.M. and KEENEY, D.R., *Analytica chim. Acta,* **32**, 485 (1965)
13. KOLTHOFF, I.M. and BELCHER, R., *Volumetric Analysis,* Vol. III, Interscience, New York (1957)
14. BERKA, A., VULTERIN, J. and ZYKA, J., *Newer Redox Titrants,* Pergamon Press, Oxford (1965)
15. SANT, B.R., *Analytica chim. Acta,* **19**, 523 (1958)
16. AGDERDENBOS, J., *Talanta,* **17**, 238 (1970)
17. MITCHELL, A. D. and WARD, A. M., *Modern Methods in Quantitative Chemical Analysis,* Longmans Green, London, 150 (1932)
18. SAWICKI, E., STANLEY, T.W., PFAFF, J. and D'AMICO, A., *Talanta,* **10**, 641 (1963)
19. GRIESS, P., *Ber.*, **12**, 427 (1879)
20. ILOSVAY, M.L., *Bull. Soc. chim.,* **2**, 317 (1889)
21. *Precautions for Laboratory Workers Who Handle Aromatic Amines,* Chester Beatty Research Institute, London (1965)
22. RIDER, B.F. and MELLON, M.G., *Ind. Engng Chem. analyt. Edn,* **18**, 96 (1946)
23. BUNTON, N.G., CROSBY, N.T. and PATTERSON, S.J., *Analyst,* **94**, 585 (1969)
24. Personal communication, N.T. Crosby
25. SAWICKI, E., STANLEY, T. W. and ELBERT, W.C., *Analyt. Chem.,* **34**, 297 (1962)
26. KIERUCZENKOWA, A., *Chemia analit.,* **12**, 1031 (1967); *Analyt. Abstr.,* **15**, 7231 (1968)
27. KAMPHAKE, L.J., HANNAH, S.A. and COHEN, J.M., *Wat. Res.,* **1**, 205 (1967); *Analyt. Abstr.,* **15**, 3627 (1968)
28. HENRIKSEN, A., *Analyst,* **90**, 83 (1965)
29. HENRIKSEN, A. and SELMER-OLSEN, A.R., *Analyst,* **95**, 514 (1970)
30. FORIS, A. and SWEET, T.R., *Analyt. Chem.,* **37**, 701 (1965)
31. MATSUNAGA, K., OYAMA, T. and NISHIMURA, M., *Analytica chim. Acta,* **58**, 228 (1972)
32. WADA, E. and HATTORI, A., *Analytica chim. Acta,* **56**, 233 (1971)
33. British Standard 2690: Part 7 (1968) London
34. British Standard 4267: (1968) London
35. *Official, Standardised and Recommended Methods of Analysis,* 2nd edn (Edited and compiled by N.W. Hanson), The Chemical Society, London (1973)
36. SAWICKI, E., STANLEY, T.W., PFAFF, J. and JOHNSON, H. *Analyt. Chem.,* **35**, 2183 (1963)
37. SCHECHTER, H., GRUENER, N. and SHUVAL, H.I., *Analytica chim. Acta,* **60**, 93 (1972)
38. SCHALL, E.D. and HATCHER, D.W., *J. Ass. off. analyt. Chem.,* **51**, 763 (1968)
39. KAMM, L., BRAY, D.F. and COFFIN, D.F., *J. Ass. off. analyt. Chem.,* **51**, 40 (1968)
40. FISHER, F.L., IBERT, E.R. and BECKMAN, H.F., *Analyt. Chem.,* **30**, 1972 (1958)
41. FABRUS, H. and MALY, J., *Cesk. Hug.,* **13**, 300 (1968); *Chem. Abstr.,* **69**, 61437 (1968)
42. SAITO, G., SUGIMOTO, K. and HAGINO, K., *Japan Analyst,* **20**, 542 (1971); *Analyt. Abstr.,* **23**, 2415 (1972)
43. HARTLEY, A.M. and ASAI, R. I., *Analyt. Chem.,* **35**, 1214 (1963)
44. LIN, E. and CHENG, K.L., *Mikrochim. Acta,* 652 (1970)
45. WETTERS, J.H. and UGLUM, K.L., *Analyt. Chem.,* **42**, 335 (1970)
46. WEISS, K.G. and BOLTZ, D.F., *Analytica chim. Acta,* **55**, 77 (1971)
47. WIERSMA, J.H., *Analyt. Lett.,* **3**, 123 (1970)
48. DOMBROWSKI, L.J. and PRATT, E.J., *Analyt. Chem.,* **44**, 2268 (1972)
49. KUMAMARU, T., TAO E. and YAMAMOTO, Y., *Bull. chem. Soc. Japan,* **38**, 2204 (1965); *Analyt. Abstr.,* **14**, 1934 (1967)
50. YAMAMOTO, Y., KUMAMARU, T., HAYASHI, Y. and OTANI, Y., *Japan Analyst,* **18**, 359 (1969); *Analyt. Abstr.,* **22**, 105 (1972)
51. HOUSER, M.E. and FAUTH, M.I., *Microchem. J.,* **15**, 399 (1970)
52. MORALES, A. and ZYKA, J., *Colln Czech. chem. Commun.,* **27**, 1029 (1962); *Analyt. Abstr.,* **9**, 4637 (1962)
53. HANIF, M., DOLEZAL, J. and ZYKA, J., *Microchem. J.,* **16**, 291 (1971)
54. DIGREGORIO, J.S. and MORRIS, M.D., *Analyt. Chem.,* **42**, 94 (1970)
55. MORIE, G.P., LEDFORD, C.J. and GLOVER, C.A., *Analytica chim. Acta,* **60**, 397 (1972)
56. HARRAR, J.E., *Analyt. Chem.,* **43**, 143 (1971)
57. KARLSSON, R. and TORSTENSSON, L-G., *Talanta,* **21**, 945 (1974)
58. STOCK, J.T. and BJORK, R.G., *Talanta,* **11**, 315 (1964)
59. AWAD, W.I., HASSAN, S.S.M. and ZAKI, M.T.M., *Talanta,* **18**, 219 (1971)
60. VAN SLYKE, D.D. and LO MONTE, A.F., *Microchem. J.,* **14**, 608 (1969)
61. WEISZ, H. and HANIF, M., *Analytica chim. Acta,* **81**, 179 (1976)
62. TOEI, K. and KIYOSE, T., *Analytica chim. Acta,* **88**, 125 (1977)
63. GABBAY, J., ALMOG, Y., DAVIDSON, M. and DONAGI, A.E., *Analyst,* **102**, 371 (1977)

Oxalate

Separations

Separation of oxalate may be accomplished using several methods.

1. Thin layer chromatography
TLC on cellulose enables oxalate to be separated from other carboxylic acid salts[1].

The relevant data is given in *Table 10*.

Table 10 Separation of oxalic acid from other carboxylic acids[1]

Acid	*Weight* (μg)	*Solvent system* I	II	III
		R_f	R_f	R_f
Formic	1.3			0.21 ± 0.0
Acetic	1.0			0.21 ± 0.0
Oxalic	1.0	0.58 ± 0.02	0.62 ± 0.04	0.04 ± 0.0
Tartaric	1.0	0.35 ± 0.02	0.45 ± 0.03	0.03 ± 0.0
Citric	0.5	0.42 ± 0.03	0.57 ± 0.04	0.01 ± 0.0

Solvent I 40:40:2 Amyl alcohol–formic acid–water.
Solvent II 60:10:20 *n*-butanol–formic acid–water.
Solvent III 80:20 2-butanol–2M NH_4OH.

2. Gas-chromatography
This may be used to separate oxalate as well as borate, carbonate, phosphate, sulphate, arsenite, arsenate, phosphite, and vanadate by means of their trimethylsilyl derivatives[2]. These are prepared by reaction of the ammonium salts with trifluorobis(trimethylsilyl)acetamide in dimethylformamide. A unique peak is obtained for each anion.

3. Solvent extraction
Oxalate is 99 per cent extracted[3] by the triphenyl-stannonium ion, Ph_3Sn^+, at pH 1–2.3.

Determination

The determination of oxalate in biological materials has been reviewed[4].

Gravimetric methods

Sarudi[5,6] has described methods for gravimetric determination of oxalate as thorium oxalate and more recently as calcium oxalate[7].

The thorium salt can be weighed as the dihydrate after drying at 105–110 °C or as the monohydrate at 200–220 °C. There is no interference from malic, citric, tartaric or succinic acids.

The calcium salt also provides a separation from the same anions if re-precipitation is carried out. Tartaric and citric acids cause the most interference and succinic the least. Sodium chloride causes slight interference, but errors of 5 per cent can be caused by the presence of magnesium.

Titrimetric methods

Many titrimetric procedures are described in the literature, based on acid–base, redox, iodimetric, or compleximetric principles. It is probable that the older iodimetric procedures are little used at the present time.

1. Acid–base

Oxalic acid is sufficiently strong ($pK_{a_1} = 1.25$; $pK_{a_2} = 4.28$) for direct titration with sodium hydroxide.

Improved results are obtained if chemiluminescent indicators are used.

In alkaline medium, lucigenin (dimethyldiacridylium dinitrate) exhibits a green fluorescent light in the presence of H_2O_2. This chemiluminescence is enhanced by the presence of fluorescein.

A mixed indicator containing both compounds has been recommended for the titration of oxalate with sodium hydroxide, an excellent response being obtained when the titration is begun at about 60 °C. Acetic, tartaric, and citric acids interfere[8].

2. Redox

Titrations with $KMnO_4$, Ce(IV), Co(III), $KBrO_3$ and KIO_3 have been described.

The reaction between oxalate and permanganate is complex and is discussed in detail in several sources, for example Kolthoff and Belcher[15]. Accurate results are only obtainable under controlled conditions[16]. These include addition of about 90 per cent of the required permanganate at a rapid rate, waiting for the permanganate to decolorize, heating to 55–60 °C and completing the titration slowly to a faint permanent (30 s) pink. The high accuracy obtainable appears to be due to cancellation of errors.

Earlier studies on the titration of oxalate with cerium(IV) indicated several difficulties. For example, if the titration is made in a perchlorate medium, the titrant is unstable. A detailed study of the reaction by Rao and Rao[9] enabled some of the discrepancies to be explained and eliminated. The important features are:

1. At low concentrations of reactants, the reaction rate is high at all concentrations of HCl between 0.2M and 6.0M.
2. At high concentrations, the reaction rate is at first rapid but then slows down.
3. Sulphate retards the reaction; ICl speeds it up.

It was concluded that removal of sulphate was essential if the reaction was to proceed without using a high temperature or a catalyst. This was done by precipitation as the barium salt.

In a later paper[10] potentiometric titration of oxalate with ammonium hexanitratocerate(IV) in HCl or HNO_3 with small amounts of KI and KIO_3 present to ensure rapid attainment of steady potentials, was recommended. Under these conditions the reaction is very rapid even at room temperature. The error was reported as ± 0.1 per cent for 0.05M Ce(IV) solution and ± 0.4 per cent for 0.01M solutions.

The cerium(IV)–oxalate reaction has been studied recently in connection with the high-precision standardization of cerium(IV) solutions[11]. A potentiometric procedure is recommended for accurate results. An alternative visual procedure involves addition of excess standard cerium(IV) to an oxalate solution, this being followed by a back-titration with iron(II).

Titrimetric determination of oxalate

Procedure[11]

To the oxalate solution in 1M H_2SO_4 and heated to about 60 °C, add an excess of 0.1M Ce(IV) rather rapidly. Allow to stand for a few minutes, cool and titrate with 0.1M Fe^{++} using ferroin as indicator.

---

3. Compleximetric

When a species of interest undergoes a redox reaction quantitatively, and produces a metal ion capable of forming a stable EDTA complex, the possibility exists of developing a compleximetric procedure for the species.

This general approach has been applied to oxalate by several workers. Earlier methods were based on reduction of $KMnO_4$ under highly alkaline conditions, separation of manganese(IV) oxide, reduction by ascorbic acid and finally titration of manganese(II) with EDTA. More recent work has entailed reduction under acid conditions followed by titration of manganese-(II) with EDTA in alkaline solution after addition of ascorbic acid[12].

Another approach has been the precipitation of oxalate with excess lead followed by the EDTA titration of the lead using catechol violet as indicator[13]. The method is rapid and suitable for the range 3–10 mg oxalic acid.

Determination of oxalate using EDTA[12]

Reagents

EDTA, 0.05M.

Methylthymol blue: KNO_3 1:100 solid dilution.

Procedure

To 5–25 mℓ of a weakly alkaline solution containing 40–220 mg oxalate, add 10 mℓ of 20 per cent H_2SO_4 and dilute to 30–40 mℓ with water. Warm to 80 °C and add dropwise freshly filtered (glass filter) 0.02M $KMnO_4$ until the solution turns slightly violet.

Cool, add 1 drop of 5 % aqueous sodium sulphite solution to discharge the colour, and 0.5 g of ascorbic acid. Now add 15 mℓ of 0.880 ammonia and a few drops of the methylthymol blue indicator. Titrate the manganese(II) with 0.0500M EDTA.

---

4. Iodimetric

Oxalic acid is one of the carboxylic acids capable of being determined by a direct iodimetric procedure involving liberation of iodine from an iodate–iodide mixture, provided that the calcium or magnesium salt of a strong acid is present.

$$IO_3^- + 5I^- + 6H^+ \rightarrow 3I_2 + H_2O$$

Spectroscopic methods

Several spectrophotometric methods for oxalate are indirect in that the oxalate is first converted to some other species. For example one approach entails reduction to glycollic acid and subsequent determination of the latter using chromotropic acid[14].

A very sensitive indirect method based on the diminution in absorbance caused by oxalate on the red U(IV)–4-(2-pyridylazo)resorcinol(PAR) complex, has appeared recently[17]. This is one of the few oxalate methods available in the parts per million region. The diminution in absorbance at 515 nm is linear in the range 0–3 ppm. The method is relatively simple in operation. A detailed study of interferences is given in the original paper; an abbreviated list is given in *Table 11.*

Table 11 Effects of foreign ions on the determination of oxalate using U(IV)-4-(2-pyridylazo) resorcinol (PAR) complex[17]

Foreign ion	*Amount permitted* (ppm)[a]	*Foreign ion*	*Amount permitted* (ppm)[a]
Fe^{3+}	9	Cl^-	200
NH_4^+	107	$EDTA^{2-}$	21
F^-	8	NO_3^-	200
Br^-	114	NO_2^-	45
I^-	200	Acetate	138
SO_3^{2-}	200	Tartrate	47
SO_4^{2-}	200	Citrate	32
		PO_4^{3-}	18

[a] Amounts of ions (ppm) producing greater than 2 per cent relative error on 4.00 ppm oxalate.

One direct method depends on oxalate reacting with indole under suitable conditions to give a red or pink compound[18]. Though not very sensitive (0.05–1.00 mg oxalate per mℓ), there is no interference from acetic, propionic, tartaric, citric, benzoic, or uric acids. Large amounts of chloride and phosphate interfere.

Decrease in absorbance of the ferric-5-nitrosalicylate complex at 492 nm on addition of oxalate provides the basis for a recently introduced method[19].

Solution spectrofluorimetry is another approach to trace determination of oxalate. This has the basic advantage of considerably greater sensitivity than absorption spectrophotometry. Several chemical systems have been used. One indirect method depends on the fact that cerium(III) exhibits fluoresence whereas cerium(IV) does not[20]. The range for oxalate is 8.8–44 μg with excitation maximum at 260 nm and fluorescence emission maximum at 350 nm. Arsenic(III) or iodide may be determined as well as oxalate by their reduction of cerium(IV).

A more recent method[21] has as its basis the quenching by oxalate of the fluorescence of the Zr-3-hydroxyflavone chelate in dilute H_2SO_4. The method is very selective, simple, and sensitive (1–10 μg oxalate). Interfering ions are shown in *Table 12*.

Table 12 Interfering ions for 5 μg oxalate in 100 mℓ sample[21]

Ion	*Amount permitted* (μg)	*Ion*	*Amount permitted* (μg)
UO_2^{2+}	6000	$Cr_2O_7^{2-}$	200
BrO_3^-	5000	Fe^{3+}	100
SiO_3^{2-}	4000	WO_4^{2-}	80
IO_3^-	1000	MoO_4^{2-}	20
Al^{3+}	500	IO_4^-	20
NO^{2-}	400	Citrate	20
PO_4^{3-}	200	F^-	1

Electrochemical methods

Amperometric methods have been described for the determination of oxalate[22, 23]. One potentiometric method has already been referred to[10]. In another, electrochemically generated lanthanum(III) ions are used to titrate oxalate at pH 4.6. A precision of about 2 per cent is found for the range 0.5–2.6 mg oxalate[24].

Recently, ion-selective electrodes have found application. Mukherji[25] uses a calcium(II) electrode to titrate oxalate at pH 7 to 11, and in the range 8.3–33 mg oxalate. Selig[26] has based his method on the lead electrode. This enables the end-point to be detected in the potentiometric titration of 1–25 mg of oxalic acid (in 40 per cent *p*-dioxane) with lead perchlorate. Citrate and other strong lead complexing agents cause interference, and so do anions forming insoluble lead compounds.

Miscellaneous methods

Enzymatic methods have been developed and are particularly suited to samples of biological origin. Crawhall and Watts[27] use the specific enzyme oxalate decarboxylase to determine oxalic acid in human plasma. The acid is decarboxylated by the enzyme, producing carbon dioxide.

$$(COOH)_2 \rightarrow CO_2 + H \cdot COOH$$

The same principle is used by Knowles and Hodgkinson[28] who greatly increase the sensitivity by employing a modified Technicon AutoAnalyzer for the measurement of the carbon dioxide. The minimum detectable concentration of oxalic acid is about 5 μg per 100 mℓ. Phosphate and sulphate inhibit the enzymatic activity, but this effect can be allowed for by adding appropriate concentrations of these ions when calibrating the equipment.

References

1. DITTMAN, J., *J. Chromat.*, **34**, 407 (1968)
2. BUTTS, W.C. and RAINEY, W.T., *Analyt. Chem.*, **43**, 538 (1971)
3. BOCK, R., NIEDERAUER, H-T. and BEHRENDS, K., *Z. analyt. Chem.*, **190**, 33 (1962)
4. HODGKINSON, A., *Clin. Chem.*, **16**, 547 (1970)
5. SARUDI, I., *Z. analyt. Chem.*, **203**, 106 (1964)
6. SARUDI, I., *Z. analyt. Chem.*, **211**, 281 (1965)
7. SARUDI, I., *Pharm. Zentralhalle Dtl.*, **106**, 217 (1967); *Analyt. Abstr.*, **15**, 2984 (1968)
8. ERDEY, L., PICKERING, W.F. and WILSON, C.L., *Talanta*, **9**, 371 (1962)
9. RAO, V.P. and RAO, G.G., *Talanta*, **2**, 370 (1959)
10. RAO, G.G., MURTY, K.S. and RAO, P.V.K., *Talanta*, **10**, 657 (1963)
11. ZIELEN, A.J., *Analyt. Chem.*, **40**, 139 (1968)
12. SZEKERES, L., KARDOS, E. and SZEKERES, G.L., *Chemist Analyst*, **54**, 116 (1965)
13. CRISAN, I.A. and KRAUSZ, R., *Studia. Univ. Babes-Bolyai, Ser. Chem.*, **12**, 19 (1967); *Analyt. Abstr.*, **15**, 6720 (1968)
14. HODGKINSON, A. and ZAREMBSKI, P.M., *Analyst*, **86**, 16 (1961)
15. KOLTHOFF, I.M. and BELCHER, R., *Volumetric Analysis*, Vol. III, Interscience, London, 48 (1957)
16. LAITINEN, H.A., *Chemical Analysis*, McGraw-Hill, London, 363 (1960)
17. NEAS, R.E. and GUYON, J.C., *Analyt. Chem.*, **44**, 799 (1972)
18. BERGERMAN, J. and ELLIOT, J.S., *Analyt. Chem.*, **27**, 1014 (1955)
19. LEE, K.S., LEE, D.W. and HWANG, J.Y., *Analyt. Chem.*, **40**, 2049 (1968)
20. KIRKBRIGHT, G.F., WEST, T.S. and WOODWARD, C., *Analytica chim. Acta*, **36**, 298 (1966)
21. BRITTON, D.A. and GUYON, J.C., *Analytica chim. Acta*, **44**, 397 (1969)
22. BORK, V.A. and SAI'NIKOVA, K.S., *Zh. analit. Khim.*, **23**, 901 (1968); *Analyt. Abstr.*, **18**, 756 (1970)
23. SILVERMAN, N.P. and SKOOK, D.A., *Analyt. Chem.*, **35**, 131 (1963)
24. CURRAN, D.J. and FLETCHER, K.S., *Analyt. Chem.*, **41**, 267 (1969)
25. MUKHERJI, A.K., *Analytica chim. Acta*, **40**, 354 (1968)
26. SELIG, W., *Microchem. J.*, **15**, 452 (1970)
27. CRAWHALL, J.C. and WATTS, R.W.E., *Clin. Sci.*, **41**, 213 (1971)
28. KNOWLES, C.F. and HODGKINSON, A., *Analyst*. **97**, 474 (1972)

Permanganate

Permanganate finds several important industrial uses, for example as an oxidant in the organic chemical industry, and in cleaning preparations for the metallurgical industry.

Its use in analysis has been long established. Despite the introduction of newer oxidizing reagents, potassium permanganate still features in many recommended analytical procedures. One such procedure concerns the extent of pollution in waters. This is measured by estimating the amount of oxygen used up in oxidizing the sample. A standard method employs permanganate, the result obtained being referred to as the permanganate value of chemical oxygen demand. The procedure consists of reacting the sample with an acidified standard $KMnO_4$ solution, usually at 27 °C, and then measuring titrimetrically the excess and hence the amount consumed[1,2].

Separations

Few separation methods appear to exist for permanganate, and those are mainly centred on large organic cations of the tetraphenylarsonium type, $(C_6H_5)_4As^+$. Permanganate belongs to a group of anions that form insoluble ion-pairs with such cations. Tribalat[3] has investigated the extraction of such ion-pairs into chloroform. Studies by others indicate that permanganate is 100 per cent extracted into chloroform in the pH range 1–12 by the tetraphenylarsonium system[4]. Complete extraction into chloroform is also reported using the tetraphenylphosphonium system[5], $(C_6H_5)_4P^+$ and the triphenylsulphonium system[6], $(C_6H_5)_3S^+$, both over a wide pH range.

Several amines have been examined as possible extractants for permanganate[7]. Only didecylamine and dihexylamine in benzene were found to be effective. The absorption maximum of the violet extract was found to be at 340 nm and remained unchanged though the extract ultimately turned brown.

Japanese workers[8,9] have reported coprecipitation of permanganate on $PbSO_4$ and $BaSO_4$.

Determination

Analytical methods for permanganate are almost exclusively redox.

Titrimetric methods

1. Redox

When on its own, determination of permanganate presents little problem. Accurate standardization of permanganate solutions is a regular and well established part of many analytical determinations, and is discussed at length in standard texts[10–12]. Direct titration by adding standard reductant to permanganate is not possible because coloured reaction products mask the end-point. Direct titration is possible if the sample solution (containing permanganate) is delivered from the burette into a known volume of standard reductant. Alternatively a known excess of suitable reductant such as oxalic acid can be added to the permanganate sample and a back-titration performed with standard $KMnO_4$.

If accepted procedures for standardizing $KMnO_4$ solutions for analytical purposes are used for determination of permanganate, the matter of accuracy should be considered. The procedures were developed for an accuracy of

± 0.1 per cent or better, and may not be justified for routine work where lower accuracy might be acceptable. This is relevant to the known tendency for permanganate to change in concentration due to decomposition.

Individual reagents and procedures will now be briefly discussed. The background theory falls outside the scope of the present treatment, and will be found in the standard texts cited earlier.

Arsenic trioxide is obtainable in a very high state of purity and is probably the best reference standard for highly accurate determination of permanganate. Under correct conditions the reaction of arsenic(III) with permanganate proceeds smoothly and without side reactions.

$$4MnO_4^- + 5As_2O_3 + 12H^+ \rightarrow 5As_2O_5 + 4Mn^{2+} + 6H_2O$$

The use of I^-, IO_3^- or ICl as catalyst is necessary. Both visual and potentiometric titrations are possible. In the usual form permanganate functions as its own indicator. Alternatively *o*-phenanthroline-ferrous sulphate (ferroin) can be used. A procedure often used is one developed by Lang[13]. The method is not selective. Many other oxidants interfere. Experimental details are given later is this sub-section.

Sodium oxalate is a commonly used reagent for accurate standardization of permanganate.

$$5C_2O_4^{2-} + 2MnO_4^- + 16H^+ \rightarrow 10CO_2 + 2Mn^{2+} + 8H_2O$$

Owing to its uncertain water of crystallization the acid itself is unsuitable for accurate work. The reaction is complex, requiring a rigorous procedure for precise results. Several other oxidants interfere if present with permanganate. The procedure generally recommended was developed by Fowler and Bright[14]. Experimental details are given later.

Permanganate can be determined using a standard Fe(II) solution.

$$10Fe^{2+} + 2MnO_4^- + 16H^+ \rightarrow 10Fe^{3+} + 2Mn^{2+} + 8H_2O$$

If the acid used is HCl, the presence of iron(II) can induce its oxidation to Cl_2 and hypochlorous acid. This effect is inhibited by the presence of Mn(II). Furthermore, the yellow colour of ferric chloride formed in the reaction masks the end-point. This effect is prevented by addition of orthophosphoric acid to form the colourless ferric phosphate complex. Both manganese(II) and phosphate are conveniently combined in one reagent known as the Zimmermann–Reinhardt solution after the two principal investigators.

Where iron(II) is to be used to determine permanganate, the stable compound ferrous ethylenediamine sulphate, $[C_2H_4(NH_2)_2H_2SO_4 \cdot FeSO_4 4H_2O]$, is a good reference standard[15]. It can be prepared in high purity and is stable in the solid state over long periods of time. Ferrous ammonium sulphate is unsuitable for accurate work due to the spontaneous oxidation of its iron content on storage.

Several oxidizing species are reduced by iron(II), so that this method like the previous ones is subject to considerable interference. Determination of permanganate by iron(II) reduction has been adapted to a compleximetric finish[16]. This is accomplished by titrating the resulting iron(III) with standard EDTA using salicylic acid as indicator. The same method is applicable to bromate and persulphate.

The redox methods already discussed have been restricted to the main reagents. A large number of other reducing reagents have been proposed including Cu(I), Sn(II), W(III), U(IV) and V(IV) compounds[17]. Advantages are not always apparent; many of the reagents are of academic interest only. Often relatively simple redox procedures can be used, for example an aliquot of permanganate sample can be added to acidified KI and the liberated iodine titrated with standard thiosulphate. Selectivity can often be achieved by masking. Thus in the above procedure permanganate (or chromate) can be determined in the presence of iron(III) if the latter is masked with sodium hexametaphosphate[18]. For 13–65 mg of Mn as MnO_4^- in the presence of 10–340 mg of Fe^{3+}, the error is ± 0.3 per cent.

Erdey, Buzas and Vigh[19] have developed redox methods for permanganate (and other oxidizing species) based on ascorbic acid. One method involves adding excess of standard iron(II) to the permanganate sample and titrating the resulting iron(III) with ascorbic acid. Others employ a potentiometric end-point and will be discussed under that heading.

An interesting redox procedure introduced by Berka[20] utilizes quinol. This offers some selectivity enabling 10–130 mg of permanganate to be determined in the presence of other oxidizing agents such as dichromate, hexacyanoferrate(III), and chloramine T. With 13–130 mg of $KMnO_4$ in the presence of 20–2000 mg of another oxidizing agent, the relative error is less than 1.8 per cent. An exception is vanadium(V) which causes a much greater error. The method is not rapid. First the permanganate is reduced to manganese dioxide using sodium formate in an alkaline solution. The precipitate of hydrated manganese dioxide is filtered off, washed, dissolved in $Na_2H_2P_2O_7$ and manganese(III) pyrophosphate titrated with a standard quinol solution.

Titrimetric determination of permanganate

Procedure I—using As_2O_3 (Lang[13])

Weigh out accurately 0.2–0.25 g of As_2O_3 previously dried for 1–2 h at 105–110 °C (Note 1). Dissolve in 15 mℓ of 2M NaOH solution, add about 50 mℓ of water, 15 mℓ of 1:1 HCl and 1 drop of 0.002M KIO_3 or KI. Titrate with the permanganate solution until a pale pink colour persists for 30 s.

Notes

1. The weight range of As_2O_3 given assumes that the permanganate is about 0.1N (0.02M). Stronger solutions can be quantitatively diluted before analysis. If weaker permanganate solutions are involved, the amount of As_2O_3 taken can be correspondingly reduced. When this is done by diluting a stronger arsenic(III) solution, a rubber suction bulb should be employed. Arsenic solutions should not be pipetted by mouth. An acid concentration of 0.5–1M HCl is suitable at the start of the titration.

Procedure II—using sodium oxalate[14]

To about 0.3 g of accurately weighed sodium oxalate (previously dried at 105–110 °C for 2 h) add 250 mℓ of dilute H_2SO_4 15 mℓ conc. acid added to 285 mℓ of water, boiled for 10–15 min and cooled) and stir (Note 2). Adjust the temperature to 27 ± 3 °C. Add nine-tenths of the permanganate solution at a rate of 25–35 mℓ min^{-1} with stirring. Allow to stand until the pink colour goes. Heat the solution to 55–60 °C, then complete the titration to a pale pink that persists for 30 s.

Notes

2. The same comment applies to sodium oxalate as to the arsenious oxide in Note 1.
3. As with Procedure I, Procedure II is capable of high accuracy.

Procedure III—using ferrous ethylenediamine sulphate[15]
To an appropriate amount of the compound, accurately weighed, add sufficient H_2SO_4 to make about 1M. Titrate with the permanganate solution to a faint permanent pink.

Notes

4. Synthesis of the reagent is given in the text by Belcher and Wilson[21].

Procedure IV—indirect iodimetric[22]
To about 0.1 g of permanganate in about 40 mℓ of water, add 3 g of KI dissolved in 10 mℓ of water and sufficient H_2SO_4 to make the solution 0.03–0.1 M in acid. Allow to stand for 10 min then titrate the liberated iodine with standard thiosulphate.

$$2MnO_4^- + 10I^- + 16H^+ \rightarrow 2Mn^{2+} + 5I_2 + 8H_2O$$

$$MnO_4^- \equiv 5S_2O_3^{2-}$$

Spectroscopic methods

1. Spectrophotometric
A standard method for determination of trace amounts of manganese involves periodate oxidation to manganese(VII) followed by spectrophotometric evaluation of the permanganate. The absorption spectra of permanganate and dichromate, each at 10^{-3}M, and in 1M H_2SO_4, 0.7M H_3PO_4, are given in *Figure 24*. The absorption peaks for permanganate occur at 520 and 545 nm. If chromium(VI) is present, a situation often found in steel analysis, evaluation of the permanganate is preferably made at 545 nm because the absorption by chromium(VI) is lower at this wavelength. Interference by chromium(VI) can be removed by dropwise addition of potassium nitrite solution.

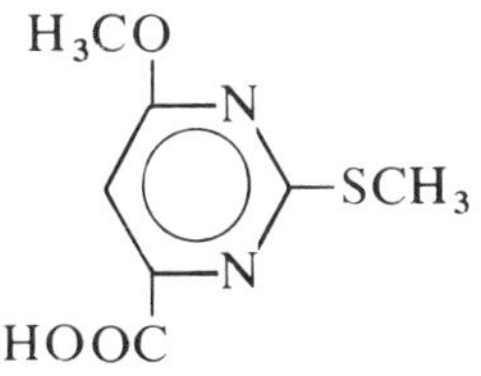

H_3CO — N — SCH_3 — N — HOOC

Structure 24 6-methoxy-2-methyl-thiopyrimidine-4 carboxylic acid

Chung and Meloan[23] reduce permanganate with 6-methoxy-2-methyl-thiopyrimidine-4 carboxylic acid (*Structure 24*) in strong alkaline solution, and measure the absorbance at 580 nm. When permanganate is added to the

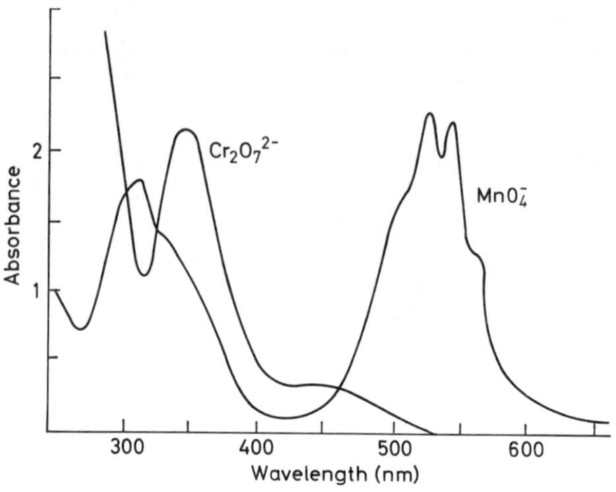

Figure 24 *Absorption spectra for permanganate and dichromate ions, each 000.1 M in 1 M H_2SO_4 and 0.7 M H_3PO_4*

reagent, a dark navy-blue colour is produced in very alkaline solution. This changes to bright green in a few seconds. The authors attribute this to the manganate ion, the navy-blue colour being a mixture of the purple permanganate and the bright green manganate ion. It is suggested that the reaction sequence is as follows:

H$_3$CS, N, OCH$_3$, N, COOH $+ 2MnO_4^- + H_2O \xrightarrow{NaOH}$ H$_3$CS(=O), N, OCH$_3$, N, COO$^-$ $+ 2MnO_4^{2-}$

Beer's law holds over the range 3.3×10^{-5}–1×10^{-3}M. The molar absorptivity is 1.47×10^3 at 580 nm. Of 59 ions tested, none formed a colour or precipitate, but several formed hydroxides or hydrated oxides in the strongly basic solution used.

Ramanauskas *et al.*[24] have developed an interesting group of spectrophotometric methods for oxidizing agents, including permanganate, based on triphenylmethane dyes. This is based on the reaction of iodide or bromide,

$(C_2H_5)_2N$ ... C ... $=N(C_2H_5)_2Cl$

Structure 25 *Brilliant green*

with certain triphenylmethane dyes in the presence of chloramine B, chloramine T or sodium hypochlorite. It is established that the resulting I^+ or Br^+ causes a decrease in colour intensity of the dye[25,26]. The extension of this reaction to oxidizing species is by virtue of their reaction with KI. The excess of iodide reacts in the above manner thus forming the basis of a method. Brilliant green (*Structure 25*) and crystal violet (*Structure 26*)

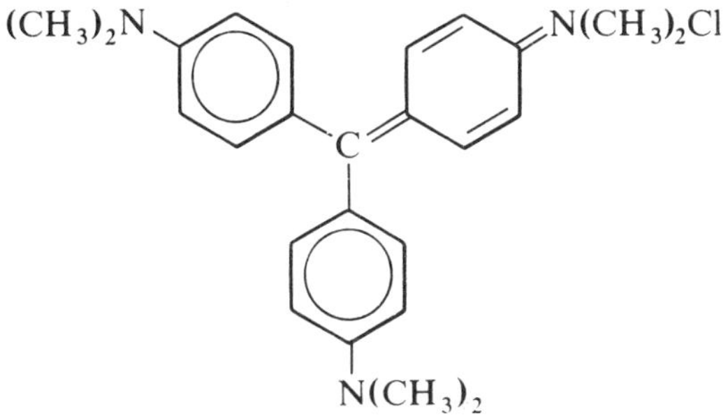

$(CH_3)_2N$ — $N(CH_3)_2Cl$ — $N(CH_3)_2$

Structure 26 *Crystal violet*

in the presence of chloramine B are suitable. The reaction is conducted at pH 3–5. Sensitivities are generally better than 0.01 μg mℓ$^{-1}$ of the oxidizing species.

2. Fluorimetric

Babko, Dubovenko and Mikhailova[27] have based a method for determination of manganese on first oxidizing it to permanganate then reacting this with siloxene, with which it develops fluorescence. The sensitivity is 0.1–1 μg Mn as permanganate.

Electroanalytical methods

1. Potentiometric

Reference has been made earlier to redox methods for permanganate based on ascorbic acid. Erdey, Svehla and Weber[28] have developed an indirect potentiometric method for permanganate (and dichromate) based on the hexacyanoferrate(III)–ascorbic acid reaction. First the permanganate is treated with a known excess of standard hexacyanoferrate(II). The resulting hexacyanoferrate(III) is titrated with standard ascorbic acid using an automatic potentiometric titrator with platinum and calomel electrodes. The range for permanganate is 0.1–1 mg and the coefficient of variation less than 2 per cent. A direct automatic micro-potentiometric method for permanganate using hexacyanoferrate(II) is also reported [29]. This enables the sequential titration of permanganate and vanadyl to be performed by adjusting the acidity of the medium.

2. Amperometric

Manganese(VII), chromium(VI) and vanadium(V) can be determined sequentially using an amperometric method[30]. Potassium iodide is used as titrant. Permanganate is titrated in a medium of 0.1M H_2SO_4 saturated with K_2SO_4, using a graphite indicator electrode maintained at 0.6 V *v.* a saturated calomel electrode. The method is applicable to as little as 10 μg of MnO_4^- in 20 mℓ. A 50-fold excess of chromium or a 100-fold excess of vanadium relative to manganese does not affect the determination of manganese. Application is made to steel analysis.

3. Coulometric

Russian workers[31] have developed a coulometric method for permanganate based on electrogenerated Fe^{2+}. The procedure is an adaption of earlier work by Hanselman and Rogers[32] based on ion-exchange membranes as a means of extending the number of reagents available for coulometry. Continuous coulometric titration of permanganate has been reported[33]. This again is based on electrogeneration of iron(II) at a platinum electrode.

An important advance in the automated determination of permanganate (and dichromate) utilizes a porous catalytic oxygen electrode[34]. A form of this type of electrode has been described recently[35]. The basis of the method is reaction of permanganate with H_2O_2, in which oxygen is produced.

$$2MnO_4^- + 5H_2O_2 + 5H^+ \rightarrow 2Mn^{2+} + 8H_2O + 5O_2$$

This produces an electrode response with a coulometric efficiency approaching 100 per cent. The method is relevant to determination of oxygen demand, and offers an attractive alternative to existing automated permanganate (and dichromate) methods based on spectrophotometry.

4. Voltammetric

Permanganate in the range 0.17–8.7 mg can be determined by voltammetric reduction at a rotating gold electrode in 1–3M $HClO_4$ or HNO_3 at 0.80 V*v.* a saturated calomel electrode. A standard addition procedure is necessary due to instability of the electrode[36]. Polarography has been used for simultaneous determination of permanganate and manganate in alkali liquors[37].

References

1. American Public Health Association, *Standard Methods for the Examination of Water and Wastewater*, 13th edn, American Public Health Association, New York (1970)
2. *Official, Standardised and Recommended Methods of Analysis*, 2nd edn (Compiled and Edited by N.W. Hanson), The Society for Analytical Chemistry, London (1973)
3. TRIBALAT, S., *Analytica chim. Acta*, **3**, 113 (1949)
4. BOCK, R. and BEILSTEIN, G.M., *Z. analyt. Chem.*, **192**, 44 (1963)
5. NEEB, R., *Z. analyt. Chem.*, **154**, 17 (1957)
6. BOCK, R. and HUMMEL, C., *Z. analyt. Chem.*, **198**, 176 (1963)
7. SHEVCHUK, I.A., NIKOL'SKAYA, N.N. and SIMONOVA, T.N., *Ukr. khim. Zh.*, **32**, 635 (1966); *Analyt. Abstr.*, **14**, 6112 (1967)
8. HAYASHI, K. and UZUMASA, Y., *J. chem. Soc. Japan, pure Chem. Sect.*, **81**, 906 (1960); *Analyt. Abstr.*, **8**, 2862 (1961)
9. TANIGAWA, Y., WAKI, S. and TAKIYAMA, K., *Japan Analyst*, **14**, 315 (1965); *Analyt. Abstr.*, **13**, 6844 (1966)
10. KOLTHOFF, I.M., SANDELL, E.B., MEEHAN, E.J. and BRUCKENSTEIN, S., *Quantitative Chemical Analysis*, 4th edn, MacMillan, London (1969)
11. KOLTHOFF, I.M. and BELCHER, R., *Volumetric Analysis*, Vol. III, Interscience, New York (1957)
12. LAITINEN, H.A., *Chemical Analysis*, McGraw-Hill, New York (1960)
13. LANG, R., *Z. anorg. Chem.*, **152**, 197 (1926)

14. FOWLER, R.M. and BRIGHT, H.A., *J. Res. Nat. Bur. Stand.*, **15**, 493 (1935)
15. CARAWAY, K.P. and OESPER, R.E., *J. Chem. Educ.*, **24**, 235 (1947)
16. KELLNER, A. and SZEKERES, L., *Chemist Analyst*, **54**, 75 (1965)
17. BERKA, A., VULTERIN, J. and ZYKA, J., *Newer Redox Titrants*, Pergamon Press, Oxford (1965)
18. RIPAN, R. and STANISAV, C., *Studia. Univ. Babes-Bolyai*, **9**, 77 (1964); *Analyt. Abstr.*, **13**, 6193 (1966)
19. ERDEY, L., BUZAS, I. and VIGH, K., *Periodica polytech.*, **3**, 1 (1959); *Analyt. Abstr.*, **6**, 4262 (1959)
20. BERKA, A., *Z. analyt. Chem.*, **246**, 322 (1969); *Analyt. Abstr.*, **19**, 3033 (1970)
21. BELCHER, R. and WILSON, C.L., *New Methods in Analytical Chemistry*, Chapman and Hall, London, 249 (1955)
22. CHARLOT, G. and BÉZIER, D., *Quantitative Inorganic Analysis*, Methuen, London, 58 (1957)
23. CHUNG, O.K. and MELOAN, C.E., *Analyt. Chem.*, **39**, 525 (1967)
24. RAMANAUSKAS, E.I., BUNIKIENE, L.V., SAPROGONENE, M.S., SHULYUNENE, A.K., ZHILENAITE, M.V., *Zh. analit. Khim.*, **24**, 244 (1969); *Analyt. Abstr.*, **19**, 1022 (1970)
25. BUNIKIENE, L.V. and RAMANAUSKAS, E.I., *Zh. analit. Khim.*, **23**, 1364 (1968); *Analyt. Abstr.*, **18**, 2396 (1970)
26. RAMANAUSKAS, E.I., BUNIKIENE, L.V. and ZHILENAITE, M., *Nauch. Trudy Vyssh. Ucheb. Zaved. Lit. SSR, Khim, khim. Tekhnol.*, 29 (1968); *Analyt. Abstr.*, **18**, 3962 (1970)
27. BABKO, A.K., DUBOVENKO, L.I. and MIKHAILOVA, L.S., *Ukr. khim. Zh.*, **32**, 614 (1966); *Analyt. Abstr.*, **14**, 6111 (1967)
28. ERDEY, L., SVEHLA, G. and WEBER, O., *Z. analyt. Chem.*, **240**, 91 (1968); *Analyt. Abstr.*, **18**, 12 (1970)
29. KISS-EROSS, K., BUZAS, I. and ERDEY, L., *Z. analyt. Chem.*, **255**, 271 (1971); *Analyt. Abstr.*, **22**, 3139 (1972)
30. SONGINA, O.A., ZAKHAROV, V.A., BEKTUROVA, G.B. and SMIRNOVA, L.I., *Zh. analit. Khim.*, **29**, 1594 (1974); *Analyt. Abstr.*, **29**, 3B14 (1975)
31. BARIKOV, V.G., SONGINA, O.A. and SEREDA, T.G., *Zav. Lab.*, **38**, 641 (1972); *Analyt. Abstr.*, **24**, 133 (1973)
32. HANSELMAN, R.B. and ROGERS, L.B., *Analyt. Chem.*, **32**, 1240 (1960)
33. TAKAHASHI, T. and SUKURAI, H., *Talanta*, **10**, 971 (1963)
34. FLEET, B., HO, A.Y.W. and TENYGL, J., *Analyt. Chem.*, **44**, 2156 (1972)
35. TENYGL, J. and FLEET, B., *Colln Czech. chem. Commun.*, **38**, 1714 (1973); *Analyt. Abstr.*, **26**, 112 (1974)
36. HUBER, C.O., *Analyt. Chem.*, **36**, 1873 (1964)
37. LANDSBERG, R. and THIELE, R., *Chem. Tech. Berlin*, **15**, 627 (1963); *Analyt. Abstr.*, **12**, 1174 (1965)

Perrhenate and Pertechnetate

Rhenium exhibits oxidation states from +1 to +7. The +4, +6 and +7 states, particularly the last one, are the most stable. Perrhenate (ReO_4^-) is the end-product of almost all oxidative reactions involving rhenium and its compounds in solution, and is the form in which it is usually determined. It is stable over a very wide range of pH. Potassium perrhenate is generally used as reference standard in rhenium analysis.

Unlike permanganate, perrhenate is not a strong oxidizing agent. This being so, it is not easily reduced. The general analytical chemistry of rhenium, and technetium which is similar, is reviewed in several sources[1–4].

Pertechnetate is more strongly oxidizing than perrhenate and is the usual form of technetium in aqueous solution. Like perrhenate it is stable over a wide range of pH.

From an analytical standpoint an important aspect is determination of perrhenate in the presence of molybdate, due to the association of these elements in nature.

Separations

1. Distillation

Distillation of the heptoxides, Re_2O_7 and Tc_2O_7 from combinations of HBr, HCl, H_2SO_4, $HClO_4$ and H_3PO_4 provides a separation from many elements. A common method is steam distillation from a H_2SO_4 solution at 260–270 °C. As(III), Se(IV), Se(VI), Te(IV), Sb(III), Sb(V), and Hg are not separated, and the method does not enable rhenium and technetium to be separated.

2. Precipitation

Rhenium and technetium in all oxidation states, including +7, are precipitated as the sulphides, which may be re-oxidized to the +7 state.

Tetraphenylarsonium chloride (TPAC) precipitates tetraphenylarsonium perrhenate (Ph_4AsReO_4), from acid solutions[5]. Technetium is precipitated in the same manner. The method is subject to several interferences which are somewhat tedious to remove. These will be discussed more fully when gravimetric determination of perrhenate and pertechnetate in this form is dealt with.

3. Coprecipitation

Microgram amounts of perrhenate and pertechnetate are coprecipitated with tetraphenylarsonium perchlorate as carrier, in acid, neutral, or alkaline solutions[6]. Furthermore, although rhenium(VII) is not precipitated by NH_4OH it is coprecipitated by hydroxide precipitates in slightly basic solutions.

4. Paper and TLC

Several separation procedures based on this have appeared recently. Some are given in *Table 13*.

Table 13 Paper and TLC separations for ReO_4^-

Technique	*Solvent*	*Separation*	*Ref.*
TLC (alumina)	1M–1.16M H_3PO_4	ReO_4^-, MoO_4^{2-}, VO_3^-, WO_4^{2-}	7
TLC (silica gel bound with poly-(vinyl) alcohol)	M HSCN or 0.5–0.9M Malonic acid or 1.0–1.8 M acetic acid or 1.0–1.8M NH_4SCN	ReO_4^-, MoO_4^{2-}, WO_4^{2-}	8
TLC (silica gel sheets)	Acidic aq. methanol mixtures	ReO_4^-, MoO_4^{2-}, SeO_3^{2-}	9

Table 13 continued

Technique	*Solvent*	*Separation*	*Ref.*
TLC (silica gel 'G')	*n*-butanol–6M HCl (5:2) v/v	ReO_4^-, MoO_4^{2-}, WO_4^{2-}	10
Paper (Whatman DE-20[a])	4M HCl	ReO_4^-, Re(V), Re(IV), Sn^{4+}	11
Strongly basic anion-exchange paper (and others)	2M HCl	ReO_4^-, $ReCl_6^{2-}$	11

[a] At 0°C to inhibit decomposition of Re(V) during development.

5. *Ion-exchange chromatography*

Perrhenate and pertechnetate may be separated from interfering cations using ion-exchange chromatography[6]. Anion-exchange is useful particularly in the separation of molybdate(VI). Ishida and Kuroda[12] use a weakly basic cellulose ion-exchanger[13] for this separation. Anion-exchange using a nitric acid–methanol solvent has enabled perrhenate and pertechnetate to be separated[14].

6. *Solvent extraction*

A considerable amount of work has been carried out on the solvent extraction of both rhenium and technetium. For the reason given earlier, separation of perrhenate and molybdate has received particular attention. The monograph by Colton[1] contains a detailed account of methods up to 1961.

Solvent extraction of tetraphenylarsonium perrhenate enables small amounts of rhenium to be separated from large quantities of molybdenum. Extraction is made at pH 8–9 into chloroform, dichloroethane, etc[5].

Tetraphenylarsonium pertechnetate may be extracted into chloroform from alkaline solutions. Extraction of perrhenate into pyridine from alkaline solutions[13] enables 10–100 μg Re to be separated from 100 mg Mo. A very rapid method (20 s) for separation of technetium from a molybdenum matrix containing ruthenium, by extraction into pyridine, has been published[14].

More recent methods include complex formation and extraction of perrhenate with Victoria blue 4R (C.I. Basic Blue 8) into benzene[15]. Here I^-, SCN^-, ClO_4^- and ClO_3^- should be absent. The method is applicable to molybdenum ores. In another method, reduction in 1M H_2SO_4 with liquid zinc amalgam followed by extraction into isopentanol from 3M H_2SO_4 enables rhenium to be separated from almost all important interferences[16].

Determination

The most important analytical methods for rhenium and technetium have been gravimetric and spectrophotometric. Recently, new approaches have included atomic absorption spectroscopy and ion-selective electrodes.

Gravimetric methods

Older gravimetric methods based on precipitation of nitron perrhenate or thallous perrhenate are less effective than precipitation of the sparingly soluble tetraphenylarsonium perrhenate (Ph_4AsReO_4), or tetraphenylarsonium pertechnetate[5]. The presence of sodium chloride produces a granular precipitate. After being allowed to stand overnight, the precipitate is dried at 110 °C. Interference in this procedure consists of other ions precipitated by the Ph_4As^+ cation, and ions forming insoluble chlorides. These include MnO_4^-, ClO_4^-, SCN^-, I^-, Br^-, F^-, Hg^{2+}, Bi^{3+}, Pb^{2+}, Ag^+ and Sn^{4+}. Nitrate concentration must be low. Separation of the above ions is therefore necessary, and this detracts from the usefulness of the method. The reagent has been used as the basis of an infra-red method for perrhenate and pertechnetate. This will be discussed later.

Spectroscopic methods

Many spectrophotometric methods have been reported for perrhenate and pertechnetate, some of which include extraction of the coloured species into an organic solvent. Some are listed in *Table 14*.

The possibility of dilute perrhenate solutions ($\sim 5\,\mu g\,m\ell^{-1}$ Re(VII) changing strength on storage has been investigated by Al-Sibaai and Fogg[23]. Absorbance measurements on the ion-association complex with brilliant green[21] indicated no loss after two months when stored in soda-glass or rigid polyethylene bottles.

Coprecipitation of perrhenate and pertechnetate by tetraphenylarsonium perchlorate as carrier has been developed into an infra-red method[24]. The precipitate is washed, dried and 2 mg mixed with 300 mg of KBr. This is pressed to give a clear disc for infra-red spectroscopy. The perrhenate and pertechnetate peaks at 10.94 μm and 11.09 μm respectively, are measured. A base-line technique is used for evaluation of the absorbance and this corrected to a 300 mg basis. A great advantage of the method is that while SCN^-, $S_2O_8^{2-}$, ClO_3^-, ClO_4^- and IO_4^- all form precipitates with TPAC under the same conditions, no strong absorbance bands are produced at 11 μm and no interference occurs.

Atomic absorption methods have been published for determination of rhenium. Biechler and Long[25] use the 3460 Å line and a nitrous oxide–acetylene mixture. More recently Bailey and Rankin[26] prefer the resonance lines at 2274.62, 2287.51, and 2294.49, claiming enhanced sensitivity. In the case of technetium details are available for the preparation of a technetium hollow-cathode lamp. The 2614.23–2615.87 Å doublet is used in measurements. A sensitivity of 3.0 μg mℓ$^{-1}$ Tc is obtained using a fuel-rich acetylene–air flame[27].

Miscellaneous methods

A liquid ion-exchange membrane electrode sensitive to perrhenate and thiocyanate has been described. It produces a Nernstian response over several orders of magnitude with a detection limit of 10^{-6}M perrhenate[28].

Table 14 Spectrophotometric methods for perrhenate and pertechnetate

Reagent	*Wavelength* (nm)	*Molar absorptivity* (ε)	*Interferences*	*Comments*	*Ref.*
Thiocyanate	430(ReO_4^-)	45 300	Mo, but may be eliminated	$SnCl_2$ red.	17
	513(TcO_4^-)	52 200		$SnCl_2$ red. not required	
α-Furildioxime	532(ReO_4^-)	41 300	Mo, but may be eliminated		18
	530(TcO_4^-)	3330	NO_3^-, F^-		
Methyl violet	595(TcO_4^-)[a]				19
Potassium hexacyanoferrate(II)	680(TcO_4^-)	~10 800		Applicable to Tc in pres. Re without sep.	20
Sulphosalicylic acid	460(TcO_4^-)			Suitable for Tc in fairly large amounts of Re, Mn, Mo and Fe^{3+}	20
α-Picolinic acid	~470–480 (TcO_4^-)	~4400[b]	Mo		20
Brilliant green	640(ReO_4^-)[c]	100 000[d]			21 22

[a] Extracted into chlorobenzene.
[b] When reduced with ascorbic acid.
[c] Extracted into benzene.
[d] Figure based on 100 per cent extraction of ReO_4^-.

For perrhenate and pertechnetate, polarographic waves are irreversible. A study by Lingane[29] on perrhenate indicates a three-electron reduction in 4M $HClO_4$ or HCl. Corresponding studies[30,31] have appeared on pertechnetate.

Perrhenate catalyses the reduction of sodium tellurate by stannous chloride and this has been used as the basis of a catalytic method in which the resulting tellurium is determined spectrophotometrically[32].

In the absence of other radioactive species, technetium may be detected in microgram amounts by its radioactivity. The β-emission has very low energy, and self-absorption in the specimen is a problem. The method is unsuitable for quantitative work, but neutron activation analysis has been used[33] for small amounts of technetium.

References

1. COLTON, R., *The Chemistry of Rhenium and Technetium,* Chapter 2, Wiley, London (1965)
2. PEACOCK, R.D., *The Chemistry of Technetium and Rhenium,* Chapter 11, Elsevier, London (1966)
3. LOWENHEIM, F.A., *Encyclopedia of Industrial Chemical Analysis* (Ed. F.D. Snell and L.S. Ettre), Vol. 17, Interscience, New York, 515 (1973)
4. MAGEE, R.J., *Comprehensive Analytical Chemistry* (Ed. C.L. Wilson and D.W. Wilson), Vol. 1C, Elsevier, London, 626 (1962)
5. TRIBALAT, S., *Analytica chim. Acta,* 3, 113 (1949)
6. KORKISH, J., *Modern Methods for the Separation of the Rarer Metal Ions,* Pergamon Press, New York, 504 (1969)
7. GAIBAKYAN, D.S., *Uchen. Zap. Erevan. gos. univ., estestv. Nauk,* 71 (1971); *Analyt. Abstr.,* **23**, 2293 (1972)
8. SHIOBARA, Y., *Japan Analyst,* **17**, 1396 (1968); *Analyt. Abstr.,* **19**, 202 (1970)
9. PHIPPS, A.M., *Analyt. Chem.,* **43**, 467 (1971)
10. JOHRI, K.N. and MEHRA, H.C., *Mikrochim. Acta,* 317 (1971)
11. PAVLOVA, M., *J. Chromat.,* **51**, 346 (1970)
12. ISHIDA, K. and KURODA, R., *Analyt. Chem.,* **39**, 212 (1967)
13. MESHRI, D.T. and HALDAR, B.C., *J. Sci. Ind. Res., India,* **20B**, 551 (1961); *Analyt. Abstr.,* **9**, 1902 (1962)
14. NEIRINCKX, R.D. and DE JESUS, A.S.M., *Analytica chim. Acta,* **59**, 324 (1972)
15. PILIPENKO, A.T., KISH, P.P. and ZHELTVAI, I.I., *Ukr. khim. Zh.,* **37**, 477 (1971); *Analyt. Abstr.,* **22**, 1571 (1972)
16. YATIRAJAM, V. and KAKKAR, L.R., *Talanta,* **17**, 759 (1970)
17. CROUTHAMEL, C.E., *Analyt. Chem.,* **29**, 1756 (1957)
18. MELOCHE, V.W., MARTIN, R.L. and WEBB, W.H., *Analyt. Chem.,* **29**, 527 (1957)
19. FUJINAGA, T., KOYAMA, M., KANCHIKU, Y. and TSURUBO, S., *Bull. chem. Soc. Japan,* **40**, 817 (1967); *Analyt. Abstr.,* **15**, 4685 (1968)
20. AL-KAYSSI, M., MAGEE, R.J. and WILSON, C.L., *Talanta,* **9**, 125 (1962)
21. FOGG, A.G., BURGESS, C. and BURNS, D.T., *Analyst,* **95**, 1012 (1970)
22. OKUBO, T. and KOJIMA, M., *Japan Analyst,* **14**, 843 (1965); *Chem. Abstr.,* **63**, 17138 (1965)
23. AL-SIBAAI, A.A. and FOGG, A.G., *Analyst,* **98**, 732 (1973)
24. MAGEE, R.J. and AL-KAYSSI, M., *Analytica chim. Acta,* **27**, 469 (1962)
25. BIECHLER, D.G. and LONG, C.H., *Atom. Abs. Newsl.,* **8**, 56 (1969)
26. BAILEY, B.W. and RANKIN, J.M., *Analyt. Chem.,* **43**, 936 (1971)
27. HARELAND, W.A., EBERSOLE, E.R. and RAMACHANDRAN, T.P., *Analyt. Chem.,* **44**, 520 (1972)
28. HIRSCH, R.F. and PORTOCK, J.D., *Analyt. Letters,* **2**, 295 (1969)
29. LINGANE, J.J., *J. Am. chem. Soc.,* **64**, 1001 (1942)
30. COLTON, R., DALZIEL, J., GRIFFITH, W.P. and WILKINSON, G., *J. chem. Soc.,* 71 (1960)
31. SALARIA, G.B.S., RULFS, C.L. and ELVING, P.J., *J. chem. Soc.,* 2479 (1963)
32. POLVEKTOV, N.S. and KONONENKO, L.I., *Zav. Lab.,* **25**, 548 (1959); *Analyt. Abstr.,* **7**, 998 (1960)
33. BOYD, G.E. and LARSON, Q.V., *J. phys. Chem.,* **60**, 707 (1956)

Perruthenate

When ruthenium is dissolved in 2M NaOH and treated with $K_2S_2O_8$, ruthenate (RuO_4^{2-}) is formed. Dilution of this to 0.25M in NaOH and oxidation with hypochlorite produces perruthenate (RuO_4^-).

Aqueous solutions of potassium perruthenate are unstable, decomposing to give oxygen and the orange ruthenate. In acid solution important oxidation states are +3 and +4. Oxidation of the +4 state under strongly oxidizing conditions, for example with $K_2S_2O_8$, produces the +8 tetroxide (RuO_4), with unstable intermediates +6 and +7. RuO_4 is formed by distillation from either acid or alkaline solutions under strongly oxidizing conditions. When distilled into alkali, ruthenium tetroxide initially forms a green solution of perruthenate which then reduces to the orange ruthenate. Ruthenate and perruthenate are much more stable in alkaline solution. Distillation of RuO_4 into HCl yields chloro-complexes of the metal.

A potential diagram for ruthenium oxygen species in alkaline solution is given in *Figure 25*[1, 2].

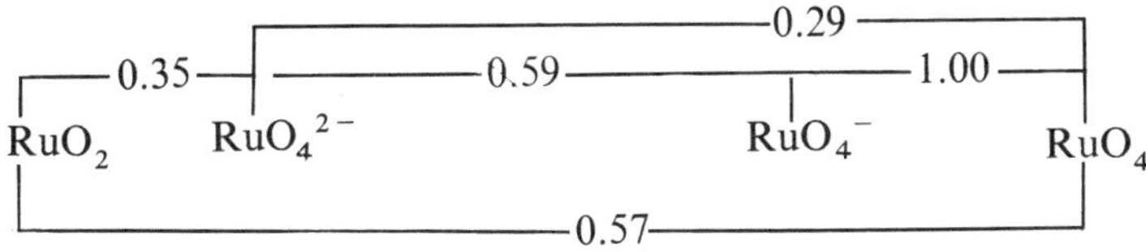

Figure 25 Potentials for ruthenium–oxygen species in alkaline solution

Larsen and Ross[3] state that stable solutions of perruthenate are obtained only when the tetroxide is distilled into 1M NaOH containing hypochlorite, and that at higher hydroxide concentrations (~6M) the perruthenate is rapidly reduced by water to ruthenate even in the presence of hypochlorite. Cotton and Woolf[4] obtain perruthenate solutions of adequate stability for analysis by collecting the tetroxide in 0.5–1.0M Na_2CO_3 solutions containing hypochlorite, and then utilize the most sensitive perruthenate absorbance peak at 315 nm without interference from the broad hypochlorite maximum around 296 nm. Spectra of various ruthenium species in 1M NaOH are shown[3] in *Figure 26*.

Separation

The above discussion will have emphasized the importance of distillation for separation of ruthenium. Distillation from H_2SO_4 containing sodium bismuthate, into sodium carbonate solution containing hypochlorite enables perruthenate to be determined spectrophotometrically without interference from a wide range of elements.

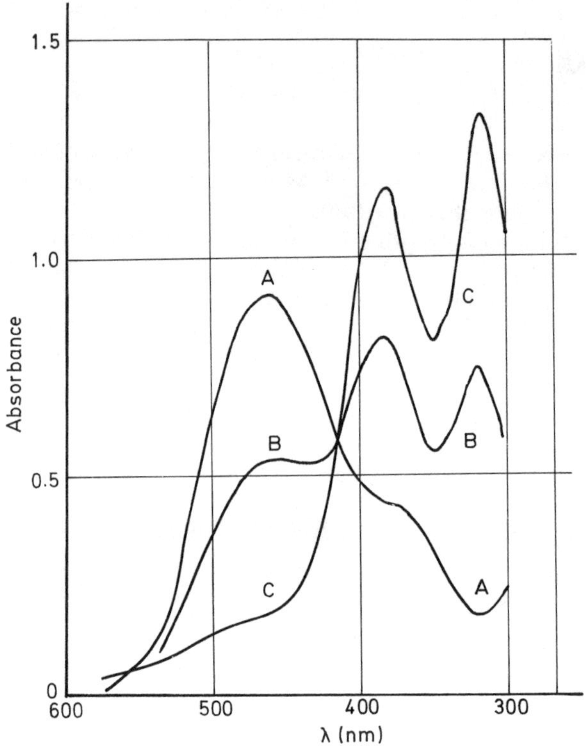

Figure 26 *Spectrum of (A) ruthenium (VI), (B) ruthenium (VI and VII) and (C) ruthenium (VII) in 1M NaOH.*
(From Larsen and Ross[3])

Determination

The analytical chemistry of ruthenium has been reviewed[5].

Larsen and Ross[3] investigated the conditions for spectrophotometric determination of ruthenium as perruthenate. Ruthenium species were converted by oxidation in H_2SO_4 containing sodium bismuthate and the resulting tetroxide distilled into NaOH containing hypochlorite. The perruthenate absorbance was measured at 385 nm. For 200–400 μg of ruthenium, a ± 2 per cent error was found at the 95 per cent confidence limit. The molar absorptivity at 385 nm was found to be 2150. Cotton and Woolf[4] use 315 nm at which value the molar absorptivity is 2600.

More recent work on perruthenate and ruthenate by Nowogrocki and Tridot[6] find the extinction maxima for the ions to be 385 nm ($\varepsilon = 2275$ for RuO_4^-; 905 for RuO_4^{2-}) and 465 nm ($\varepsilon = 275$ for RuO_4^-; 1960 for RuO_4^{2-}) respectively. From a measurement at these two wavelengths, the proportion in each ionic form may be evaluated.

Flame AAS is not particularly sensitive for ruthenium, the lower limit being 10 μg mℓ^{-1}. In contrast, carbon rod AAS is much more sensitive and relatively free from interferences[7,8].

References

1. CONNICK, R.E. and HURLEY, C.R., *J. Am. chem. Soc.*, **74**, 5012 (1952)
2. SILVERMAN, M.D. and LEVY, H.A., *J. Am. chem. Soc.*, **76**, 3319 (1954)
3. LARSEN, R.F. and ROSS, L.E., *Analyt. Chem.*, **31**, 176 (1959)
4. COTTON, T.M. and WOOLF, A.A., *Analyt. Chem.*, **34**, 1385 (1962)
5. AVTOKRATOVA, T.D., *Analytical Chemistry of Ruthenium*, Israel Programme for Scientific Translations, Jerusalem (Oldbourne Press, London) (1963)
6. NOWOGROCKI, G. and TRIDOT, G., *Bull. Soc. chim. Fr.*, 684 (1965)
7. EVERETT, G.L., *Analyst*, **101**, 348 (1976)
8. MEGARRITY, R.G. and SIEBERT, B.D., *Analyst*, **102**, 95 (1977)

Selenate and Selenite

Selenium is used in the electronics industry for the manufacture of rectifiers and photoconductivity cells. More recently it has found application in xerography. A less important use occurs in the manufacture of glass and ceramics including enamels.

Selenium is a cumulative toxic substance which can cause a serious health hazard when present in food or water. However, at very low levels it appears to be an essential trace element in animal nutrition.

In aqueous solutions selenium exists as selenate(+6) or selenite(+4). Both states are useful analytically. Heating in hydrochloric acid solution causes reduction to selenium(IV). Many reductants, for example ascorbic acid, sulphur dioxide, and hydrazine reduce selenium to the elemental form. This finds application both in separation and determination of selenium.

An important study by Shendrikar and West[1] has provided information on the rate of loss of selenium from aqueous solutions stored in containers of various materials. The Se^{75} isotope was utilized in this work, with containers of pyrex glass, flint glass and polyethylene. The selenium solution contained 100 ppm of selenium as selenium(VI). Solutions in nitric acid showed good stability, with losses of only 1% or less in 15 days. At pH 7 the loss was approximately twice as much. In general, flint glass beakers gave the same response as pyrex. Polyethylene, probably the most commonly used material for sample storage, showed a loss in excess of 8% in 15 days, a much greater loss than from either pyrex or flint glass.

Selenium analytical chemistry has been the subject of several reviews, some of them recent[2–6]. The last reference, a review by Olson, Palmer and Whitehead[6] is specifically directed to determination of selenium in biological materials, an important aspect of selenium analysis. Sample preparation, storage and destruction of organic matter are also included. Recovery of selenium from food and biological samples presents a difficult problem when fatty materials are present. This has caused some analysts to employ neutron activation analysis, in which initial digestion is not required.

An important aspect of selenium analysis is its determination in the presence of tellurium. This will be discussed where appropriate.

Selenium(IV) reference standards can be prepared from sodium selenite.

An approximate weight is dissolved in dilute HCl and the solution standardized iodimetrically. A better method is to dissolve an accurately weighed amount of pure selenium shot in the minimum amount of concentrated HCl containing a few millilitres of concentrated HNO_3. The mixture is warmed to assist dissolution and then heated to expel brown fumes. After cooling it is made up to volume with distilled water, first adding sufficient HCl to make the final solution approximately 1M. Selenium(VI) solutions are generally prepared from selenic acid or sodium selenate decahydrate, by weighing out the requisite amount.

Separations

Separation of selenium (and tellurium) is discussed at length in the monograph by Korkisch[7].

1. Distillation

Selenium can be separated from many elements by distillation from HCl or preferably HBr solution. Both selenium and tellurium are reduced to the +4 state and distilled as the halides and oxyhalides. The acid concentration should be in excess of 6M and the temperature above 100 °C. Various acid combinations have been used including HCl/H_2SO_4, HBr/H_2SO_4 and $HClO_4/HBr$. When biological materials are involved, distillation from a Br_2/HBr mixture is often employed. Here the function of bromine is to oxidize selenium to at least the +4 state. Excess bromine distils at a lower temperature. The presence of HBr ensures that selenium(VI) is reduced to selenium(IV) for distillation. The selenium tetrabromide produced in the distillation is usually absorbed in water. Distillation is applicable[8] to trace quantities of selenium.

Certain elements are distilled either completely or partially with selenium. Using Br_2/HBr, As, Sn, Ge, Sb and Te are distilled at least in part. Distillation from H_2SO_4/HCl is less selective, selenium being accompanied by Ge, Sb, Sn, Te, Mo, Re and Hg. A study of the various distillation procedures has been made by Fogg and Wilkinson[9], who conclude that a $HBr/Br_2/H_2SO_4$ mixture is best.

Contradictory statements appear in the literature on the distillation of selenium/tellurium mixtures. Some sources indicate that these elements can be separated from each other using HCl/H_2SO_4, H_2SO_4/HBr or $HClO_4/HBr$ mixtures; others state that distilled selenium is accompanied by tellurium. A suitable distillation apparatus is shown in *Figure 27*. Experimental details of the distillation applied to plant material is given in Official Methods of Analysis of the AOAC[10]. After distillation from HBr, selenium can be reduced to elemental form with ascorbic acid. This both separates selenium from any elements carried over in the distillation, and allows its determination to be made gravimetrically.

It has been reported[11] that HBr distillations can introduce a fluorescence which subsequently interferes with fluorimetric procedures applied to the distillate.

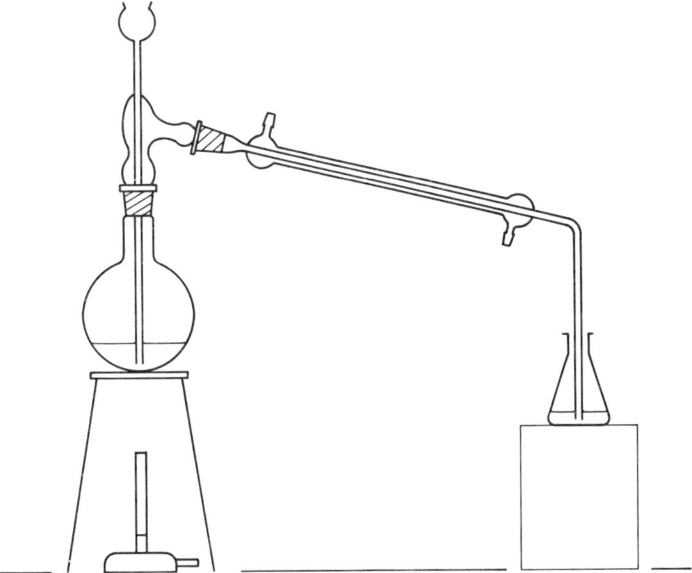

Figure 27 Distillation apparatus for selenium.
(After A.O.A.C[10])

2. *Ion-exchange*

Selenium(IV) is not adsorbed on strongly acid resins from HCl solutions of concentration 0.1–12M. Cation-exchange can therefore be used [12] to remove interfering metals before determination of selenium. In the case of plant material one group of workers[13] has found the technique unsatisfactory. Under certain conditions selenium(IV) is retained on cation-exchangers, and this has been utilized by Yamamoto and Sakai[14] in separating microgram amounts of selenium from sulphate and iron(III).

In contrast to selenium(IV), tellurium(IV) is relatively strongly adsorbed on cation-exchangers at low acid concentrations. A method for separating the two elements can be based on this.

Selenium(IV) is not adsorbed on strongly basic resins at low concentrations of HCl (below 4M) but some retention occurs at higher acidities. This permits separation of selenium and tellurium. Selenium(IV) is eluted with HCl of concentration less than 4M. Tellurium(IV) remains on the column and is subsequently eluted using 0.1–1M HCl.

Neither selenium(VI) nor tellurium(VI) are adsorbed on anion exchangers from HCl, irrespective of its concentration. This has value analytically, for example it allows large quantities of selenium(VI) to be separated from traces of sulphate[15]. The procedure was used for determination of traces of sulphur in high-purity selenium. Iguchi[16] has separated selenium(VI) and tellurium(VI) from sulphite by the same means.

Ion-exchange paper has been used to separate selenium(IV) from tellurium-(IV)[17] and selenium(VI) from selenium(IV)[18]. In the latter work an SB-2 anion-exchange paper in chloride form was employed, with M HCl as the developing solution.

3. Solvent extraction

The past decade has seen marked activity in the development of solvent-extraction procedures for both selenium and tellurium, and the topic now has an extensive literature, In many instances the extracted species can be used for direct spectrophotometric determination of the elements. *Table 15*

Table 15 Selected solvent extraction systems for selenium(IV)

System		*Comments*	*Ref.*
Reagent	*Solvent*		
Toluene-3,4-dithiol	Ethylene chloride	Acidity must be not less than 10M (HCl). Only Pd(II), Te(IV), Au, W(VI) and Re(VII) are precipitated at this acidity	20
Toluene-3,4-dithiol	Ethylene chloride–CCl_4 (1:1)	Acidity 6–8M HCl	11
Diethyldithiocarbamate	Tributyl phosphate	Se(IV) extracted; Se(VI) not extracted. Back-extraction of Se(IV) into 10% $HClO_4$–H_2O_2 (20:1) possible	21
Diethyldithiophosphoric acid	Carbon tetrachloride	Se(VI) not extracted. Acidity 0.1–10M HCl or 0.5–7.5M H_2SO_4	22
3,3′-diamino benzidine	Benzene, toluene, or xylene	Extraction at pH 6–7. EDTA and F^- used for masking. Complex formation depends on several factors	23
2-theonyltrifluoracetone	Xylene	Extraction at pH 0.5–4.5. Se can be determined directly in extract with 3,3′-diaminobenzidine	24
Dithizone	Carbon tetrachloride	Extraction from 6M HCl. Probably most sensitive spectrophotometric procedure. $\varepsilon_{420} = 7–8 \times 10^4$. [See note below]	25 26 27 28
1,2-diaminobenzene	Toluene	More selective than 3,3′-diaminobenzidine because extraction occurs at lower pH	29
2,3-diaminonaphthalene	Cyclohexane	Same comment as for 1,2-diaminobenzene, but to a greater extent	30

Note: The dithizone system has been subject to some controversy. Ramakrishna and Irving state that selenium(IV)dithizonate is not extracted, only its oxidation product, and that it can be collected as a red solid from the aqueous phase. Stary *et al.* believe that a 1:4 Se(IV)dithizonate is extracted.

lists some of the extraction procedures for separation of selenium from other species, and in some cases selenium(IV) from selenium(VI). Other extraction methods are discussed in the reviews already cited, and in the monograph by De, Khopkar and Chalmers[19].

4. Precipitation

Selenium is reduced and precipitated in elemental form from a concentrated HCl solution by SO_2 and other reducing agents. This provides a separation from most elements including tellurium, the latter being precipitated in the 2–4M HCl range. For quantitative separation of selenium precipitation[30] should be made from concentrated HCl but not less than 9M HCl.

The resulting precipitate can be dried at 105 °C and used for gravimetric determination of the selenium. This is discussed later in this section. When selenium and tellurium are together in aqueous solution evaporation to dryness is required in order to obtain a solution in concentrated HCl. Owing to the volatility of the chlorides, this operation cannot be done from HCl solution. No loss of selenium occurs if solutions of selenium(IV) in H_2SO_4 are evaporated to white fumes. Similarly, boiling with HNO_3 causes no loss. To avoid a lengthy evaporation selenium and tellurium can be precipitated by an appropriate method, the washed precipitates dissolved in the minimum quantity of a nitric acid solution, and evaporation to dryness carried out on a waterbath[31].

Reduction to elementary selenium can be made on selenium distillates, this providing a separation from the few elements carried over. Ascorbic acid has been used for this purpose.

Reduction by SO_2 can be made in other media as well as HCl. Williams and Haskett[43] have made a comparative study in which the precipitated selenium is dried and evaluated gravimetrically in each case. The results indicate that the reduction is quantitative in 6M HCl, 1.5M H_2SO_4 or 3M $HClO_4$. Perchloric acid was found to give the most consistent results.

Selenium and tellurium can be separated using tetraphenylarsonium chloride, which precipitates tellurium only in 5M HCl[32]. Several species interfere by precipitating with the reagent. These include Br^-, I^-, F^-, NO_3^-, Mo(VI) and W(VI).

5. Coprecipitation

Small amounts of selenium are coprecipitated with arsenic. The procedure was applied to copper and lead alloys by Luke[33], and was later applied to biological materials after initial decomposition using the oxygen flask technique. Stanton and McDonald[34] use a slightly modified form of Luke's method for determination of selenium in soils and sediments. After separation, in the 0.1–500 ppm range, the 3,3′-diaminobenzidine spectrophotometric method was used. More recently applications have been made to food analysis[35] and geological and biological samples[36]. In the latter work the precipitate is dissolved in a small volume of HNO_3 and the selenium determined by AAS.

Japanese workers[37] have investigated coprecipitation of selenium(IV) on freshly precipitated ferric hydroxide. The procedure is carried out in an acetate buffer at below pH 7. Coprecipitation decreases with increasing pH, being only 10 per cent at pH 10.

6. Paper and thin-layer chromatography

For small amounts of selenium paper and thin-layer chromatography offers a range of separations. Data on some of the methods are given in *Table 16.*

Table 16 Separation of selenium(IV) using paper and thin-layer chromatography

Technique	*Solvent system*	Se(IV) *separated from*	*Ref.*
Paper	Pyridine–propanol–H_2O (1:2:1)	Se(VI)	38
Paper (circular)	Acetone–'acids'–H_2O (7:2:1)	Te(IV)	39
Paper (reverse phase ascending)	Tributyl phosphate (stationary phase) M–2M HBr or 8M NaBr as mobile phase	Te(IV), Cu(II), Ni, Zn, Pb, Fe(III), Co, As(III), Ti(IV), Th	40
Paper and TLC (silica gel sheets. Silica gel on glass)	Various including methanol–0.6M HCl–10% H_2O	RuO_4^-, Mo(VI)	41
TLC (silica gel)	Amyl acetate in conc. HCl	Te(IV)	42

Determination

Gravimetric methods

Reduction to the elemental form followed by gravimetric determination is only suitable when appreciable amounts of selenium are present. If the solution contains selenium(VI), initial reduction to selenium(IV) is conveniently done by warming in the presence of dilute HCl. Reduction by SO_2 in the cold produces the element in the red form; warming the suspension produces a black amorphous variety that tends to occlude impurities. The precipitate is washed, dried at about 105 °C and weighed.

Sulphur dioxide can be used in gaseous form or added in the form of an aqueous or methanolic solution. Other reductants include hydroxylamine, hydrazine, ascorbic acid, 1,2,3-trimethyl-3-pyrazoline-5-thione and *m*-(mercaptoacetamido)phenol. Several aspects of the reduction of selenium(IV) by SO_2 have been investigated by Williams and Haskett[43] who find that selenium(VI) is not reduced by SO_2. Furthermore if the reduction by SO_2 is made in a perchloric acid medium, selenium(IV) can be determined without interference from selenium(VI).

Reduction using 1,2,3-trimethyl-3-pyrazoline-5-thione brings additional selectivity to the method[44]. From 20 to 550 mg of selenium(IV) in a citric acid–HCl medium, is treated with the reagent. Reduction is complete in 1 h on a water bath. Interference by Te(IV), Pb(II), Hg(II), Sn, Sb(III) and Ca can be prevented. Silver is precipitated, and copper inhibits the precipitation of selenium.

In addition to reduction to the elemental form, other gravimetric procedures have been described. One[45] utilizes 2,3-diaminonaphthalene, a reagent also used for spectrophotometric and fluorimetric determination of selenium. The range for the gravimetric determination is 10–50 mg; the factor for selenium is 0.3385.

Gravimetric determination of selenium by sulphur dioxide reduction[43]

Procedure

To the selenium(IV) solution, add 100 mℓ of 3M $HClO_4$. Slowly add 1.0 g of Na_2SO_3, stir, cover the beaker and allow to stand at room temperature for 15 min.

Digest on a hot plate at about 96 °C for 30 min to convert the red form of selenium to the black. Filter through a tared glass filter crucible, wash several times with distilled water and finally with acetone. Dry at 110 °C to constant weight.

Titrimetric methods

Earlier titrimetric methods for selenium(IV) were based on its reduction to selenium by potassium iodide and titrating liberated iodine with standard thiosulphate, or reduction of selenium(IV) with excess standard thiosulphate followed by a back-titration using standard iodine.

$$SeO_3^{2-} + 4I^- + 6H^+ \rightarrow Se + 2I_2 + 3H_2O$$

$$4Na_2S_2O_3 + H_2SeO_3 + 4HCl \rightarrow Na_2SeS_4O_6 + Na_2S_4O_6 + 4NaCl + 3H_2O$$

Each is discussed in the monograph by Kolthoff and Belcher[46].

A standard method[47] for selenium(IV) consists of adding an excess of standard $KMnO_4$ followed by a back-titration with standard iron(II). As tellurium(IV) undergoes the same reaction the $KMnO_4$ consumed is equivalent to the sum total of both if tellurium(IV) is also present. The analogous method using standard dichromate and iron(II) oxidizes tellurium(IV) only[48]. Thus two aliquots of a tellurium(IV)/selenium(IV) mixture, analysed by each method, enables the composition to be determined. Naidu and Rao[49] have recently described a method in which only one aliquot is required. Selenium(IV) and tellurium(IV) are oxidized by $KMnO_4$ in condensed phosphoric acid medium. Tellurium(VI) is then selectively reduced using arsenic(III) with osmium tetroxide as catalyst. The method is simple and rapid with no critical conditions. No interference is given by Fe(III), As(V), Ag, Tl(III), Se(VI), U(VI), Cu(II), Ni, K, Na, Al or Mg.

Selenium(IV) and tellurium(IV) can be quantitatively oxidized by periodate in the presence of borax[50]. The authors suggest that by combination with the dichromate–iron(II) method described above, application could be made to selenium(IV)/tellurium(IV) mixtures.

Saxena[51] has used glucose and D-fructose for reduction of selenium(IV) to elementary selenium. This is treated with ferric chloride in 4M HCl and the resulting Fe^{2+} titrated with cerium(IV). Several species interfere including Ag(I), Tl(I), Cu(II), Hg(II), Zn(II), Pd(II), Au(III), Bi(III), Te(IV), Zr(IV) and Th(IV).

An alternative titrimetric method for analysis of selenium(IV)/tellurium(IV) mixtures has been based on iodimetry[52]. In this, KI is added to the acidic mixture. Elementary selenium and tellurium are formed plus an equivalent amount of iodine which is titrated with thiosulphate. In a second aliquot the solution is neutralized with sodium bicarbonate before the titration. Now tellurium reacts with an equivalent amount of iodine, and the remaining iodine equivalent to selenium is titrated with hydrazine amperometrically.

Other titrimetric methods for selenium have been reported by Solymosi[53] and Schulek[54], the latter being for micro amounts.

Titrimetric determination of selenium(IV) or selenium(IV) and tellurium(IV) in admixture[49]

Reagents

$KMnO_4$: 0.01M (0.05N)

As(III): 0.0125M (0.05N) molarity is on the basis As_2O_3.

Osmic acid: 0.1 %.

Condensed phosphoric acid:

100 mℓ of orthophosphoric acid (85–90 %) is heated in a 250-mℓ beaker with 3–4 mℓ of HNO_3 (1 + 1) until brown fumes of nitrogen dioxide are no longer evolved. The acid is stored in a brown bottle.

Procedure

To an aliquot containing selenium(IV) and tellurium(IV) add 1–5 mℓ of condensed phosphoric acid and dilute to 25 mℓ with water. Add a known excess of standard $KMnO_4$. After 3–5 min, titrate with a standard iron(II) solution using ferroin as indicator. If the indicator becomes sluggish 2–3 mℓ of 10M H_2SO_4 should be added. The amount of standard $KMnO_4$ consumed gives the amount of selenium(IV) plus tellurium(IV), or selenium(IV) if tellurium(IV) is absent.

To the solution, add a known excess of arsenic(III) solution. Add 0.4 mℓ of 0.1 % osmic acid and titrate the unreacted arsenic(III) with standard $KMnO_4$. The arsenic(III) consumed is equivalent to tellurium(IV) present.

$$2KMnO_4 + 5H_2SeO_3 + 3H_2SO_4 \rightarrow 5H_2SeO_4 + 2MnSO_4 + 3H_2O + K_2SO_4$$

Spectroscopic methods

1. Colorimetric and spectrophotometric methods

Reduction of selenium(IV) to the elemental state in the form of a stable sol has been used in several colorimetric procedures. The reduction is carried out using the reagents previously listed. One procedure, which employs hydrazine or ascorbic acid, is now recommended as a standard method[55]. The procedure avoids the use of known carcinogenic reagents and the need for distillation. It finds use in the 10–100 μg Se range.

The Weisz ring-oven has been used for separation and semi-quantitative determination of selenium. Application has been made by West and Cimerman[56] to air pollution studies.

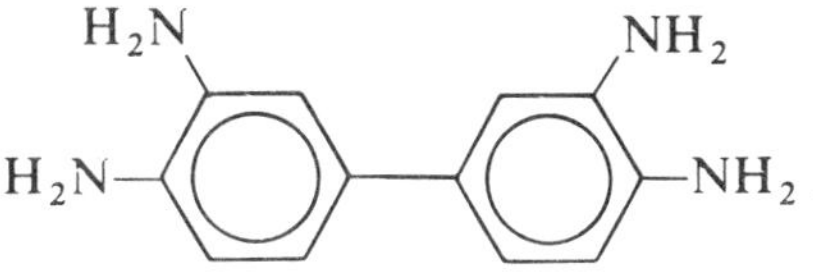

Structure 27 3,3′ diaminobenzidine

The most successful spectrophotometric methods for selenium appear to be those based on reaction of selenium(IV) with *o*-diamines to give piazselenols. Of these 3,3′-diaminobenzidine (DAB) (*Structure 27*) was introduced by Hoste and Gillis[57] in 1955. The intense yellow complex with selenium(IV) which forms in acid media below pH 4 has absorption maxima at 340 and 420 nm in aqueous solution. The reaction has been shown to proceed as follows[58]:

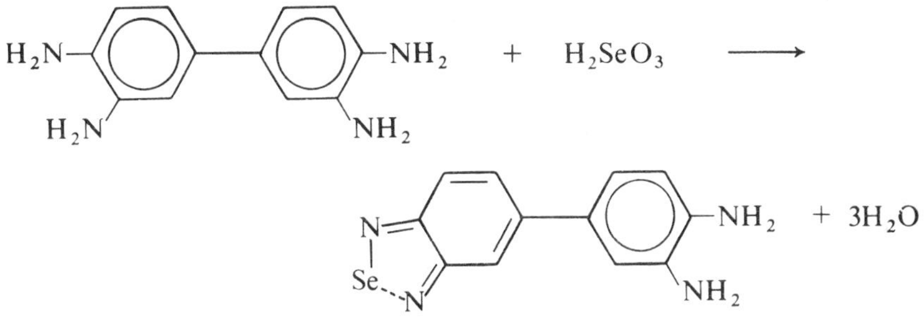

$$\text{DAB} + H_2SeO_3 \longrightarrow \text{piazselenol} + 3H_2O$$

Cheng[59] introduced two improvements. EDTA was used to mask interfering ions, and the complex was extracted into toluene. In this form of the method no interference is given by Fe, Cu, Mo(VI), Ti, Cr(III), Ni(II), Co(II), Te(IV) or As, but strong oxidizing or reducing species must be absent. The sensitivity limit is stated to be 50 ppb (10^9) using 1-cm cells. The molar absorptivity is about 2.89×10^4 at 340 nm. Several applications of this form of the method appear. Cummins, Martin and Maag[60], and Cummins *et al.*[61] have modified and improved it for use on biological samples. The lower limit for this form of the method is 1.0 μg Se. A serious defect in the method is the known carcinogenic nature of DAB. Its use in the fluorimetric determination of selenium is discussed later.

Another important reagent in the *o*-diamine category is 2,3-diaminonaphthalene (DAN) which is more sensitive than DAB[62, 45]. Here the absorbance is measured at 380 nm. Beer's law holds for 0–20 μg Se when extraction is made into toluene. Although DAN is twice as sensitive as DAB, it is more susceptible to interference. The paper by Lott *et al.*[45] should be consulted for a complete account of interfering ions. Oxidizing substances such as hypochlorite oxidize the reagent itself; reducing substances such as tin(II) reduce selenium(IV) to the elemental form. The reagent is more important as a fluorimetric reagent for selenium where the sensitivity is ten times greater than in the spectrophotometric procedure. It is not known for certain whether DAN is carcinogenic, but its similarity to DAB makes this possible.

Other *o*-diamines have been investigated as spectrophotometric reagents, particularly 1,2-diaminobenzene[63, 64] and 4-substituted *o*-phenylenediamines. Tanaka and Kawashima[65] have conducted a critical study of 4-methyl-4-chloro- and 4-nitro-*o*-phenylenediamine. Of these, 4-methyl-*o*-phenylenediamine has been further investigated by Kawashima and Ueno[66] and appears to have advantages over the others. These workers apply the method to traces of selenium in iron and steel. Full colour development requires about 2 h at 25 °C but is attained in 5 min at 70 °C. Iron(III) is extracted in capric acid in chloroform. Several metals, e.g. Mo(VI), W(VI) and V(V) are extracted as oxinates into chloroform. Finally the 5-methylpiazselenol formed between the reagent and selenium(IV) is extracted into toluene and the absorbance measured at 337 nm. Beer's law is found to hold over the range 1–40 μg selenium(IV) per 10 mℓ of toluene. For the determination of 19.7 μg of selenium the amounts of various ions that can be tolerated (in mg) are as follows:

Al(III)	200	Co(II)	200
As(V)	5	Mg(II)	400
Ba(II)	500	Mn(II)	400
Ca(II)	400	Ni(II)	200
Cd(II)	200	Cr(III)	100
		V(V)	2

Oxidizing species such as iron(III) and chromium(VI) interfere by forming coloured products. Iron(III) is removed by extraction with caprate or using EDTA. Chromium(VI) can be reduced with hydrogen peroxide. The resulting chromium(III) does not interfere in amounts up to 100 mg. 10 mg of copper(II) and 2 mg of vanadium(V) do not interfere if the toluene is washed with 0.1 M HCl.

Several other reagents form piazselenols with selenium(IV). Although the reactions are fairly sensitive, solutions of the reagents tend to be unstable, and the methods are subject to considerable interference, particularly from oxidizing agents.

A second group of spectrophotometric methods for selenium(IV) involves formation of complexes in which the selenium bonds either partially or completely to sulphur ligands. Reagents in this category include thioglycollic acid[67], 2-mercaptobenzoic acid[68], and bismuthiol II[69]. A useful summary of methods in the group is given by Cresser and West[68]. This lists sensitivities, molar absorptivities and interferences. The 2-mercaptobenzoic acid method given in the same paper, extracts the complex into ethyl acetate. The molar absorptivity is 1.56×10^4 and the sensitivity 0.005 μg of selenium making it the most sensitive method of the group. Interference is given by Hg, Te, Cu, Ni, Co, Ag, Li and Zr, but ion-exchange, masking and pre-extraction techniques are able to deal with all except mercury(II). The range for the method is 0.008–1.5 ppm.

Some important selenium spectrophotometric methods fall outside the two categories discussed above. Those based on catalytic activity of selenium(IV) are dealt with later in the section. Some methods involve reacting selenium(IV) with a reagent to produce an intermediate which in turn is reacted with a colour-producing reagent. Such a method is one developed by Osburn, Shendrikar and West[70] for air-pollution studies. Based on a spot test by Feigl and Demant[71], in which hydroxylamine hydrochloride is oxidized to nitrous acid by selenous acid under strongly acid conditions, the resulting nitrite is converted by a Griess–Ilosvay type reaction into an azo-dye. The range for selenium is from 0.01 to 0.20 mg ℓ^{-1}; the method is extremely sensitive ($\varepsilon_{544\,nm} = 1.93 \times 10^5$). A period of 90 min is required for colour development. The effects of common ions that interfere can be eliminated.

Ramanauskas, Bunikiene and co-workers have developed several new spectrophotometric methods for anions based on triphenylmethane dyes. The basis of these is the reaction of iodide or bromide with the dyes in the presence of chloramine B, chloramine T or hypochlorite. They establish that the resulting I^+ or Br^+ causes a decrease in colour intensity of the dye. In the case of selenium(IV), it is allowed to react with a known excess of KI, and residual iodide is evaluated in the above manner[72]. The sensitivity is 8 and 7 ng Se mℓ^{-1} for brilliant green and malachite green respectively. A tenfold excess of Sb(III), Hg(II), Hg(I), Ag, Fe(III), Bi(III), Cu(II) or S^{2-} over Se(IV), or a 100-fold excess of Pb(II) and Sn(II), interfere.

2. *Fluorimetric*

The fluorescence exhibited by piazselenols formed by reacting selenium(IV) with *o*-diamines provide extremely sensitive methods for selenium. This has led to extensive application in analysis of biochemical samples containing sub-microgram amounts of selenium.

2,3-diaminonaphthalene (DAN) is more sensitive than 3,3′-diaminobenzidine (DAB), but subject to greater interference[62]. Extraction systems have been incorporated. Parker and Harvey[62] extracted the complex into toluene but found the extract unstable. Cyclohexane was found to be good though its high volatility is a disadvantage. The sensitivity is greater in fluorimetric procedures than spectrophotometric ones using the same reagent. Furthermore for biological samples the technique can be applied after wet oxidation[73] but without prior separation of selenium. However, wet-oxidation procedures applied to selenium-containing materials are known to present problems. This is discussed by Hall and Gupta[74] who developed a fluorimetric procedure based on 2,3-diaminonaphthalene for plant material at levels as low as 0.005 ppm of selenium in dried material. Other studies on the method utilizing DAN include those of Nazarenko *et al.*[75,76] and Hemsted, Sina and Cekicer[77] who present a simplified procedure suitable for soils. Olson[78] has made a comparative study of the method with 5 other trace methods for selenium, including neutron activation. The reagent DAN is commercially available. Details of its purification and storage are given by Hall and Gupta[74]. The fluorimetric method using DAN, as well as the corresponding spectrophotometric method, are recommended by the Society for Analytical Chemistry[79] where full experimental details are given. An automatic fluorimetric method using DAN has recently appeared[88].

3. Nephelometric and turbidimetric

Smith and Lott[80] use DAN for the nephelometric determination of selenium. It is applied in the range between the maximum for the spectrophotometric method and the minimum for the gravimetric. The small solid particles formed lend themselves to nephelometry with the advantage of applicability to coloured solutions and high selectivity. A turbidimetric method suitable for use after ion-exchange separation of selenium, has been described for the 10–100 μg Se range[55].

4. Atomic absorption and atomic fluorescence spectroscopy

Selenium can be determined by conventional AAS but the methods suffer from several drawbacks. The most sensitive absorption line is at 196 nm resulting in much of the source energy being absorbed by the flame. As a result the signal-to-noise ratio is low, and the sensitivity is limited to about 1 ppm.

An indirect method in which the Se(IV)–DAN complex is extracted, further reacted with palladium chloride and the palladium measured by AAS, has been developed[81]. This brings about an improvement in sensitivity, but two other approaches appear to be superior. One is to use a hydride generation technique in which selenium is converted into the hydride and then swept into an argon–hydrogen flame[82]. Siemer and Hagemann[83] describe an improved hydride generator for use in determination of selenium in feed and forage samples. This is illustrated in *Figure 28*. A sensitivity of 6×10^{-10} g of selenium is attained with a relative standard deviation of 5–8 per cent. Another recent study by Thompson and Thomerson[84] reports a detection limit of 0.0018 μg Se mℓ$^{-1}$. The same work indicates that selenium(VI) solutions give a negligible response compared with selenium(IV). In contrast to tellurium where reduction of tellurium(VI) to tellurium(IV) is quantitative

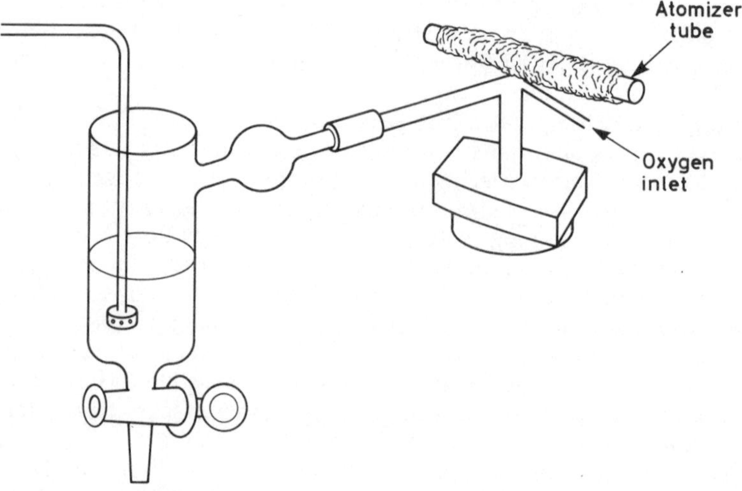

Figure 28 *Hydride generator for determination of selenium by AAS. The atomizer tube is wrapped with quartz wool to reduce temperature fluctuations.* (After Siemer and Hagemann[83])

using HCl, similar reduction of selenium(VI) solutions produces less than 50% of selenium(IV). Smith[85] has investigated interference effects on the determination of several elements by AAS using the hydride technique. The results reveal that the technique is not as simple as previously thought.

The second approach, namely flameless AAS, has several advantages[86]. Its range is 1.0–50 μg ℓ^{-1} Se. Interfering metal cations are removed by ion-exchange, and molybdenum can be added to enhance sensitivity and suppress interference by anions.

Determination of selenium by AFS using the volatile hydride technique has been reported[87]. The detection limit (twice the noise level at the base line) is about 0.0001 μg Se.

5. *Molecular emission cavity analysis (MECA)*

Both selenium and tellurium can be determined using this technique[89]. An account of the technique itself is given on p. 580.

Electroanalytical methods

1. *Potentiometric*

Malone and Christian[90] have prepared a selenium(IV)-ion-selective electrode by replacing the liquid ion-exchanger in a conventional lead ion-selective electrode with a saturated solution of 3,3′-diaminobenzidine in hexane. A rectilinear response is found over the range 0.1–1 mM at pH 2.5. The selectivity appears to be good.

Potentiometric (and amperometric) procedures for selenium and tellurium based on ascorbic acid enable milligram amounts to be determined individually or when present together[91].

2. *Coulometric*

The few coulometric methods are recent in origin. Patriarche[92] reduces selenium(IV) to the elemental state with iodide being oxidized to free iodine. This is evaluated by addition of excess standard thiosulphate followed by a back-titration with electrogenerated iodine. Microamounts of selenium(IV) and tellurium(IV) can be titrated with electrogenerated hypobromite[93]. Electrogenerated iron(II) has been used, again for tellurium(IV) as well as selenium(IV)[94]. Here oxidation is made with a four-fold excess of standard $KMnO_4$ and the back-titration made with iron(II).

3. *Polarographic*

The first polarographic method for selenium was published in 1935. Of the the more recent work, an important series of investigations by Christian, Knoblock and Purdy[95,96] has clarified earlier work and described the polarographic characteristics of selenium(IV) in a number of electrolytes. As many as three polarographic reduction waves for selenium(IV) are found, depending on the pH. The authors recommend polarographic determination of selenium(IV) in a buffered electrolyte at pH 2.0–2.5. Copper interferes but can be removed by dithizone extraction into chloroform.

As in several other trace methods for selenium, application of polarography to biological materials is fraught with difficulties. If less than 4 μg of selenium is present, separation before applying polarography is recommended.

Catalytic methods

Kawashima and Tanaka[97] find that submicrogram amounts of selenium(IV) can be determined by utilizing its catalytic effect on the reduction of 1,4,6,11-tetraazonaphthacene:

$$\text{(1,4,6,11-tetraazonaphthacene)} + 2H^+ \xrightarrow[\text{glyoxal}]{H_3PO_2} \text{(dihydro product, two N–H)}$$

Selenium(VI) does not interfere but barium(II) and iron(III) interfere at the 1 mg level, vanadium(V) and tungsten(VI) at 0.1 mg and manganese(II) and copper(II) at 0.01 mg. Bismuth(III), tin(II), tellurium(IV) and iodide interfere at all levels. Interference by antimony(III) is masked with tartaric acid. The procedure is relative simple, involving a spectrophotometric end-procedure. A more recent catalytic method by Kawashima, Kai and Takashima[98] is based on the selenium(IV)-catalysed oxidation of *p*-hydrazinobenzenesulphonic acid to the *p*-diazobenzenediazonium ion. The latter is coupled with *m*-phenylenediamine to give a yellow azo-dye which is measured spectrophotometrically. Selenium(IV) at 10^{-7}M can be determined giving an effective molar absorptivity of 1.2×10^6. With extraction this is increased to 2.4×10^6. The absorbance is measured in a 1-cm cell. Copper(II), cerium(IV), molybdenum(VI) and iodide interfere at the 100 μg level. Iron(III), vanadium(V) and chromium(VI) interfere at 10 μg. Some interferences can be prevented, but not tellurium(IV).

Bognar and Sarosi[99] make use of the selenium(IV)-catalysed $KClO_3$-hydrazinium sulphate reaction. The sensitivity of this catalytic method is 4 ng Se mℓ^{-1}. West and Ramakrishna[100] base their method on the reduction of methylene blue by sodium sulphite, again catalysed by selenium(IV). Determinations can be made in the range 0.1–1.0 μg selenium. Of many ions tested only copper interfered when in excess of 10 μg.

Radiochemical methods

In recent years neutron activation has gained in importance as a means of trace selenium determination particularly for biological samples. The main reason for this has already been referred to, namely the difficulties in quantitative recovery of selenium using conventional pre-treatment techniques. The review by Olson, Palmer and Whitehead[6] cited earlier contains an excellent discussion of neutron activation analysis applied to selenium in biological samples.

Application of the technique has been made to air-pollution particulates[101] and soils[102]. In the latter study the sample is irradiated for 2 days using a neutron flux of 1.5×10^3 n cm^2 s^{-1}. The resulting γ-activity is measured using a 35 cm^2 germanium (lithium) detector connected to a multi-channel analyser. The 265-keV peak of 120-day selenium-75 was used as the basis of analysis. Using the method 0.18–1.6 ppm of selenium can be determined.

Gas-chromatographic methods

A marked trend in recent methods of sub-micro inorganic analysis has been the application of gas chromatography. The Se(IV)–2,3-diaminonaphthalene (DAN) complex can be extracted into hexane and an aliquot of the extract analysed using the technique[103]. Detection is made using electron capture. The method has been applied to human blood, urine and river water. A complete analysis takes about 3 h, this including digestion and 2 h for complete complex formation. The study confirms earlier work indicating that elements normally present in biological material that interfere with the Se(IV)–DAN reaction can be eliminated by using EDTA as masking agent. Electron capture appears to be extremely sensitive to the complex. A linear response is obtained over the range 0.01–0.1 µg Se, the smallest amount of selenium actually injected into the gas-chromatograph being only 0.0005 µg.

Shimoishi[104] and Akiba, Shimoishi and Toei[105] have used 1,2-diamino-4-nitrobenzene in a gas-chromatographic procedure. Selenium(IV) reacts with the reagent to form 5-nitropiazselenol which is detected by means of a gas-chromatograph equipped with an electron-capture detector.

The first paper concerns analysis of milk, milk-products and albumin. An interesting feature of the method is its ability to determine selenium(VI) and total selenium. Selenium occurs in biological materials in both states. Of these selenium(VI) is the more difficult to determine. Shimoishi first determines selenium(IV), for which the method is specific. Then total selenium is determined after reduction of selenium(VI) to selenium(IV), and selenium(VI) evaluated by difference. The amount of selenium(VI) in milk was found to be about 60% of the total selenium content. The practical detection limit of the method is 0.005 µg Se.

The second paper is concerned with selenium content of highly purified arsenic or arsenic(III) oxide used in the manufacture of semiconductors.

References

1. SHENDRIKAR, A.D. and WEST, P.W., *Analytica chim. Acta,* **74**, 189 (1975)
2. NAZARENKO, I.I. and ERMOKOV, A.N., *The Analytical Chemistry of Selenium and Tellurium* (Trans. R. Kondor), Halstead Press–John Wiley, New York (1972)
3. GREEN, T.E. and TURLEY, M., in *Treatise on Analytical Chemistry* (Ed. I.M. Kolthoff and P.J. Elving), Part II, Vol. 7, John Wiley, New York, 137 (1961)
4. LOWENHEIM, F.A., in *An Encyclopedia of Industrial Chemical Analysis* (Ed. F.D. Snell and L.S. Ettre), Vol. 17, Interscience, New York, 580 (1973)
5. ELWELL, W.T. and SAINT, H.C.J., in *Comprehensive Analytical Chemistry* (Ed. C.L. and D.W. Wilson), Vol. 1C, Elsevier, Amsterdam, 296 (1962)
6. OLSON, O.E., PALMER, I.S. and WHITEHEAD, E.I., in *Methods of Biochemical Analysis* (Ed. D. Glick), Vol. 21, John Wiley, London, 39 (1973)
7. KORKISCH, J., *Modern Methods for the Separation of Rarer Metal Ions,* Pergamon Press, Oxford, 357 (1969)

8. BARCZA, L., *Z. analyt. Chem.*, **199**, 10 (1963)
9. FOGG, D.N. and WILKINSON, N.T., *Analyst*, **81**, 525 (1956)
10. *Official Methods of Analysis of the AOAC*, Association of Official Agricultural Chemists, 10th edn, Washington, D.C., 109 (1965)
11. WATKINSON, J.H., *Analyt. Chem.*, **32**, 981 (1960)
12. SCHUMANN, H. AND KOELLING, W., *Z. Chem.*, **1**, 371 (1961); *Chem. Abstr.*, **57**, 3076c (1962)
13. CUKOR, P., WALZYCK, J. and LOTT, P.F., *Analytica chim. Acta*, **30**, 473 (1964)
14. YAMAMOTO, M. and SAKAI, H., *Analytica chim. Acta*, **32**, 370 (1965)
15. MIYAMOTO, M., *Japan Analyst*, **10**, 211 (1961); *Analyt. Abstr.*, **10**, 2245 (1963)
16. IGUCHI, A., *Bull. chem. Soc. Japan*, **31**, 748 (1958); *Analyt. Abstr.*, **6**, 2567 (1959)
17. LEDERER, M. and KERTES, S., *Analytica chim. Acta*, **15**, 226 (1956)
18. BAROOSHIAN, A.V., LAUTENSCHLEGER, M.J. and HARRIS, W.G., *Atomlight*, **71**, 5 (1970); *Analyt. Abstr.*, **20**, 3014 (1971)
19. DE, A.K., KHOPKAR, S.M. and CHALMERS, R.A., *Solvent Extraction of Metals*, Van Nostrand Reinhold, London and New York (1970)
20. CLARK, R.E.D., *Analyst*, **83**, 396 (1958)
21. INARIDA, M., *Bull. chem. Soc. Japan*, **39**, 403 (1966); *Analyt. Abstr.*, **14**, 3148 (1967)
22. BODE, H. and ARNSWALD, W., *Z. analyt. Chem.*, **185**, 179 (1962)
23. PATROVSKY, V., *Chemiké Listy*, **64**, 715 (1970)
24. AKKI, S.B. and KHOPKAR, S.M., *Separation Sci.*, **6**, 455 (1971)
25. RAMAKRISHNA, R.S. and IRVING, H.M.N.H., *Chem. Commun.*, 1356 (1969)
26. RAMAKRISHNA, R.S. and IRVING, H.M.N.H., *Analytica chim. Acta*, **49**, 9 (1970)
27. STARY, J., MAREK, J., KRATZER, K. and SEBESTA, F., *Analytica chim. Acta*, **57**, 393 (1971)
28. KASTERKA, B. and DOBROVOLSKI, J., *Chemia Analit.*, **15**, 303 (1970); *Analyt. Abstr.*, **20**, 2424 (1971)
29. KUNTE, N.S., and RANADE, S.N., *Ind. J. Chem.*, **8**, 370 (1970)
30. HILLEBRAND, W.F., LUNDELL, G.E.F., BRIGHT, H.A. and HOFFMAN, J.I., *Applied Inorganic Analysis*, 2nd edn, John Wiley, New York (1953)
31. Ref. 4, 590
32. BODE, H., *Z. analyt. Chem.*, **134**, 100 (1951)
33. LUKE, C.L., *Analyt. Chem.*, **31**, 572 (1959)
34. STANTON, R.E. and MCDONALD, A.J., *Analyst*, **90**, 497 (1965)
35. EWAN, R.C., BAUMANN, C.A. and POPE, A.L., *J. agric. Fd Chem.*, **16**, 212 (1968)
36. SEVERNE, B.C. and BROOKS, R.R., *Analytica chim. Acta*, **58**, 216 (1972)
37. ISHIBASHI, M., FUJINAGA, T., KUWAMOTO, T. and MURAI, S., *J. chem. Soc. Japan, pure Chem. Sect.*, **88**, 76 (1967); *Analyt. Abstr.*, **15**, 3636 (1968)
38. KEMPE, G. and DENN, W., *Z. analyt. Chem.*, **217**, 169 (1966); *Analyt. Abstr.*, **14**, 3952 (1967)
39. MAO CHIH-HSIANG, *Acta chim. Sinica*, **31**, 432 (1965); *Chem. Abstr.*, **64**, 8909f (1966)
40. HU ZHI-TEI, *Acta chim. Sinica*, **30**, 426 (1964); *Analyt. Abstr.*, **12**, 5758 (1965)
41. PHIPPS, A.M., *Analyt. Chem.*, **43**, 467 (1971)
42. RAI, J. and KUKREJA, V.P., *Chromatographia*, **2**, 18 (1969); *Analyt. Abstr.*, **18**, 3093 (1970)
43. WILLIAMS, L.R. and HASKETT, P.R., *Analyt. Chem.*, **41**, 1138 (1969)
44. TANAKA, T., KATAGIHARA, H. and IRITANI, N., *Japan Analyst*, **20**, 163 (1971); *Analyt. Abstr.*, **23**, 236 (1972)
45. LOTT, P.F., CUKOR, P., MORIBER, G. and SOLGA, J., *Analyt. Chem.*, **35**, 1159 (1963)
46. KOLTHOFF, I.M. and BELCHER, R., *Volumetric Analysis*, Vol. III. Interscience, New York, 327 (1957)
47. SCHRENK, W.T. and BROWNING, B.L., *J. Am. chem. Soc.*, **48**, 139 (1926)
48. LENHER, V. and WAKEFIELD, H.F., *J. Am. Chem. Soc.*, **45**, 1423 (1923)
49. NAIDU, P.P. and RAO, G.G., *Talanta*, **18**, 112 (1971)
50. KAUSHIK, R,L. and PROSAD, R., *J. Ind. chem. Soc.*, **46**, 921 (1969)
51. SAXENA, O.C., *J. appl. Chem.*, **32**, 89 (1969)
52. ZAKHAROV, V.A., SONGINA, O.A. and KLYUEVA, R.I., *Zav. Lab.*, **38**, 1066 (1972); *Analyt Abstr.*, **24**, 2164 (1973)
53. SOLYMOSI, F., *Chemist Analyst*, **52**, 42 (1963)
54. SCHULEK, E. and BARCZA, L., *Talanta*, **3**, 27, 31 (1959)
55. *Official, Standardised and Recommended Methods of Analysis*, 2nd edn (Compiled and Edited by N.W. Hanson), The Society for Analytical Chemistry, London, 440 (1973)
56. WEST, P.W. and CIMERMAN, C., *Analyt. Chem.*, **36**, 2013 (1964)
57. HOSTE, J. and GILLIS, J., *Analytica chim. Acta*, **12**, 158 (1955)
58. PARKER, C.A. and HARVEY, L.G., *Analyst*, **86**, 54 (1961)

59. CHENG, K.L., *Analyt. Chem.*, **28**, 1738 (1956)
60. CUMMINS, L.M., MARTIN, J.L. and MAAG, D.D., *Analyt. Chem.*, **37**, 430 (1965)
61. CUMMINS, L.M., MARTIN, J.L., MAAG, G.W. and MAAG, D.D., *Analyt. Chem.*, **36**, 382 (1964)
62. PARKER, C.A. and HARVEY, L.G., *Analyst*, **87**, 558 (1962)
63. THROOP, L.J., *Analyt. Chem.*, **32**, 1807 (1960)
64. ARIOSHI, H., KINIWA, M. and TOEI, K., *Talanta*, **5**, 112 (1960)
65. TANAKA, M. and KAWASHIMA, T., *Talanta*, **12**, 211 (1965)
66. KAWASHIMA, T. and UENO, A., *Analytica chim. Acta*, **58**, 219 (1972)
67. KIRKBRIGHT, G.F. and NG, W.K., *Analytica chim. Acta*, **35**, 116 (1966)
68. CRESSER, M.S. and WEST, T.S., *Analyst*, **93**, 595 (1968)
69. YOSHIDA, H., TAGA, M. and HIKIME, S., *Japan Analyst*, **14**, 4670 (1967)
70. OSBURN, R.L., SHENDRIKAR, A.D. and WEST, P.W., *Analyt. Chem.*, **43**, 594 (1971)
71. FEIGL, F. and DEMANT, V., *Mikrochim. Acta*, **1**, 134 (1937)
72. RAMANAUSKAS, E.I. and SHULYUNENE, A.K., *Zh. analit. Khim.*, **23**, 1589 (1968); *Analyt. Abstr.*, **18**, 3932 (1970)
73. WATKINSON, J.H., *Analyt. Chem.*, **38**, 92 (1966)
74. HALL, R.J. and GUPTA, P.L., *Analyst*, **94**, 292 (1969)
75. NAZARENKO, I.I., KISLOV, A.M., KISLOVA, I.V. and MALEVSKII, A.YU., *Zh. analit. Khim.*, **25**, 1135 (1970); *Analyt. Abstr.*, **21**, 3363 (1971)
76. NAZARENKO, I.I., KISLOVA, I.V., GUSEINOV, T.M., MKRTCHYAN, M.A. and KISLOV, A.M., *Zh. analit. Khim.*, **30**, 733 (1975)
77. HEMSTED, W.R.T., SINA, M. and CEKICER, S., *Analyst*, **97**, 383 (1972)
78. OLSON, O.E., *J. Ass. off. analyt. Chem.*, **52**, 627 (1969)
79. Ref. 55, 288
80. SMITH, R.E. and LOTT, P.F., *Microchem. J.*, **20**, 519 (1975)
81. LAU, H.K.Y. and LOTT, P.F., *Talanta*, **18**, 303 (1971)
82. MANNING, D.C., *Atom. Abs. Newsl.*, **10**, 123 (1971)
83. SIEMER, D.D. and HAGEMANN, L., *Analyt. Lett.*, **8**, 323 (1975)
84. THOMPSON, K.C. and THOMERSON, D.R., *Analyst*, **99**, 595 (1974)
85. SMITH, A.E., *Analyst*, **100**, 300 (1975)
86. HENN, E.L., *Analyt. Chem.*, **47**, 428 (1975)
87. THOMPSON, K.C., *Analyst*, **100**, 307 (1975)
88. BROWN, M.W. and WATKINSON, J.H., *Analytica chim. Acta*, **89**, 29 (1977)
89. BELCHER, R., KOUIMTZIS, T. AND TOWNSHEND, A., *Analytica chim. Acta*, **68**, 297 (1974)
90. MALONE, T.L. and CHRISTIAN, G.D., *Analyt. Lett.*, **7**, 33 (1974)
91. IVANOVA, Z.I., IGNATENKO, E.G. and TARASOVA, V.A., *Zh. analit. Khim.*, **28**, 1980 (1973); *Analyt. Abstr.*, **28**, 6B 163 (1975)
92. PATRIARCHE, G.J., *Analyt. Lett.*, **5**, 45 (1972)
93. AGASAYAN, L.B., NIKOLAEVA, E.R. and AGASAYAN, P.K., *Vest. mosk. gos. Univ. Ser. Khim.*, **21**, 96 (1966); *Analyt. Abstr.*, **14**, 7456 (1967)
94. AGASAYAN, P.K., DENISOVA, A.N., AGASAYAN, L.B. and NIKOLAEVA, E.R., *Zav. Lab.*, **34**, 129 (1968); *Analyt. Abstr.*, **16**, 2442 (1969)
95. CHRISTIAN, G.D., KNOBLOCK, E.C. and PURDY, W.C., *Analyt. Chem.*, **35**, 1128 (1963)
96. CHRISTIAN, G.D., KNOBLOCK, E.C. and PURDY, W.C., *Analyt. Chem.*, **37**, 425 (1965)
97. KAWASHIMA, T. and TANAKA, M., *Analytica chim. Acta*, **40**, 137 (1968)
98. KAWASHIMA, T., KAI, S. and TAKASHIMA, S., *Analytica chim. Acta*, **89**, 65 (1977)
99. BOGNAR, J. and SAROSI, S., *Mikrochim. Acta*, 361 (1969)
100. WEST, P.W. and RAMAKRISHNA, T.V., *Analyt. Chem.*, **40**, 966 (1968)
101. DAMS, R., ROBBINS, J.A., RAHN, K.A. and WINCHESTER, J.W., *Analyt. Chem.*, **42**, 861 (1970)
102. KRONBORG, O.J. and STEINNES, E., *Analyst*, **100**, 835 (1975)
103. YOUNG, J.W. and CHRISTIAN, G.D., *Analytica chim. Acta*, **65**, 127 (1973)
104. SHIMOISHI, Y., *Analyst*, **101**, 298 (1976)
105. AKIBA, M., SHIMOISHI, Y. and TOEI, K., *Analyst*, **101**, 644 (1976)

Selenocyanate

Separations

1. Distillation

Selenocyanate ($SeCN^-$), is conveniently separated by treatment with bromine which converts it to cyanogen bromide.

$$SeCN^- + 4Br_2 + 4H_2O \rightarrow CNBr + 7Br^- + SeO_4^{2-} + 8H^+$$

This can be distilled and then determined by the methods given below.

2. Ion-exchange

Selenocyanate and thiocyanate can be separated using anion-exchange paper SB2 and 6M $LiNO_3$ as solvent[1].

Determination

Titrimetric methods

1. Iodimetric

This is based on the above reaction. Selenocyanate is converted to cyanogen bromide by bromine, the excess of which is destroyed with phenol. The cyanogen bromide is then reacted with KI liberating iodine which is titrated with standard thiosulphate[2]. In a later study of the method Schulek and Barcza[3] note that while sulphate, chloride and perchlorate do not interfere with the method, bromide does, possibly by affecting the equilibrium of the following reaction and causing it to move to the left-hand side.

$$H_2SeO_3 + Br_2 + H_2O \rightleftharpoons HSeO_4^- + 3H^+ + 2Br^-$$

The interference can be prevented either by carrying out a BrCN distillation or by treatment with sodium tungstate.

Iodimetric determination of selenocyanate[2]

Reagents

p-Ethoxychrysoidine, 0.2% in ethanol.
Phenol, 5%.
Sodium thiosulphate, 0.1M.
Hydrochloric acid, 20%.

Procedure

To 5 mℓ of the sample solution add 75 mℓ of water and 1 g of boric acid. Boil for 10 min, cool, and transfer to a 200-mℓ Erlenmeyer flask.

Add 80 mℓ of water and neutralize with 0.1M HCl using 1 drop of *p*-ethoxychrysoidine solution. Add saturated bromine water until the solution is yellow. After a few minutes add 3–5 mℓ of phenol, then 2–3 mℓ of 20% HCl and 0.2 g of KI after a five-minute interval. Titrate the liberated iodine with standard thiosulphate using starch near the end-point.

1 mℓ 0.1M thiosulphate ≡ 0.5249 mg $SeCN^-$

Spectroscopic methods

1. Spectrophotometric

Vasuki, Shankaranarayana and Majumder[6] have recently described a method for determination of micro quantities of selenocyanate based on the reaction of cyanogen bromide with pyridine–benzidine. The reaction, which gives an intense orange to red coloured solution, was previously used by Aldridge[4, 5] for the determination of cyanide and thiocyanate.

The absorbance is measured at 518 nm. Beer's law holds for up to 0.5 μg $SeCN^-$ $m\ell^{-1}$.

References

1. LEDERER, M. and MARTINI-BETTOLO, R., *J. Chromatog.*, **35**, 213 (1968)
2. SCHULEK, E. and KOROS, E., *Z. analyt. Chem.*, **139**, 20 (1953); *Analyt. Abstr.*, **1**, 75 (1954)
3. SCHULEK, E. and BARCZA, L., *Talanta*, **3**, 23 (1959)
4. ALDRIDGE, W.N., *Analyst*, **69**, 262 (1944)
5. ALDRIDGE, W.N., *Analyst*, **70**, 474 (1945)
6. VASUKI, K., SHANKARANARAYANA, M.L. and MAJUMDER, S.K., *Analytica chim. Acta*, **45**, 353 (1969)

Silicate

The determination of silicate in solution is an important aspect of silicon analysis, the general procedure being conversion of other forms of silicon into soluble silicate as a preliminary step. Thus rocks, glasses, etc., are usually decomposed by fusion with NaOH and the melt dissolved to produce a silicate solution for evaluation.

The importance of silicate analysis extends to semiconductors, metallurgical products, glass, rocks and industrial waters. Medical aspects are important in connection with silicosis caused by continuous inhalation of siliceous or quartz dusts.

Determination of silicate in the presence of phosphorus, arsenic and germanium presents special problems. This aspect will be discussed at several points in the section. The general analytical chemistry of silicon has been reviewed by Shell[1] and Thomas[2]. Recently, Bennett[3] has produced an extensive and authoritative review of silicate analysis in the context of ceramics and geochemistry. This includes a discussion of the determination of silicon itself. As stated in the preface, decomposition methods are not included in the scope of this book, and accordingly, the present section will assume that the silicate is already in soluble form. Decomposition of samples is a particularly important aspect of silicate analysis. A discussion of the present situation is included in the above review by Bennett. Decomposition methods for inorganic materials generally are treated at length in the monograph by Dolezal, Povondra and Sulcek[4].

It should be emphasized that in analytical work involving low levels of silicate, polythene ware should be used in place of glass to avoid contamination. This is particularly so in the case of reference standard silicate solutions.

Standard solutions of silicate Fuse an accurately weighed amount of pure silica with approximately ten times its weight of anhdyrous sodium carbonate in a platinum crucible. Cool and dissolve the melt in water contained in a polythene beaker. Make up to volume in a volumetric flask. Store in a polythene bottle.

Separation and pre-concentration

1. Precipitation

Silicate can be separated from phosphate by precipitating the latter as ammonium molybdophosphate[5]. The method is applicable to 0.2–2 mg of each anion and was developed for use in organic microanalysis.

2. Solvent extraction

This has proved to be particularly useful for separations within the groups of heteropolyacid-forming elements P, As, Si and Ge. The subject is discussed on p. 447. Several of the proposed schemes are given in *Table 45* in the orthophosphate section. An examination of this table indicates that in several instances the other ions are extracted leaving silicate in the aqueous phase. In other procedures molybdosilicic acid is extracted into 2-ethylhexanol[6], isobutyl methyl ketone-citrate[8], tri-iso-octylamine nitrate in 1,2 dichloroethane[9] and diethylether-pentanol[10,7]. These extractions refer to the heteropolyacid itself and not its reduced form. Reduced molybdophosphoric acid is readily extracted into organic solvents; in contrast reduced molybdosilicic acid is not. Kakita and Goto[11] have reported extraction of reduced molybdosilicic acid into isoamyl alcohol if the acid concentration of the aqueous phase is increased. A spectrophotometric procedure has been based on this. Another extraction procedure based on reduced molybdosilicic acid is reported by Trudell and Boltz[12]. Here, extraction into chloroform is facilitated by the presence of propane-1,2-diol carbonate. The separation is followed by a spectrophotometric end-procedure.

3. Chromatographic

Several forms of chromatography find application in silicate separation. Pilson and Fragala[13] separate silicate and phosphate using thin-layer chromatography on S and S Ecteola cellulose, with isopropanol–H_2O–anhydrous acetic acid (20:5:2) as developing solvent. The method is applicable to amounts of silicate as little as 1 μℓ of 10^{-4}M silicate solution.

A gas-chromatographic separation based on trimethylsilyl derivatives has appeared[14]. Ion-exchange can be used in several ways. Interfering ions can be removed before the spectrophotometric determination of silicate[15]. Silicic acid is separated from several accompanying elements, including iron, aluminium and uranium, by first passing through a cation-exchange column and then a weakly basic anion column[16]. The α-form of the acid is not retained by either, but conversion of β- and γ-forms of silicic acid to the α-form is required before application of the procedure. Ion-exchange has also been used for pre-concentration of silicate. In this work, Wickbold[17] found that the effectiveness of the separation was enhanced by the presence of HF, the resulting fluorosilicate being retained more strongly by the anion exchanger. It was subsequently eluted with boric acid.

4. Distillation

Separation of silicic acid by distillation is claimed to be effective in the analysis of silicates, including Portland cement. The H_2SiF_6 is steam distilled using a glycerol bath[18] which is gradually raised to about 135 °C.

5. Suppression of unwanted species

Though not strictly in the category of separation, this approach has enabled selectivity to be attained within the group of heteropolyacid-forming elements P, As and Si. A fuller account of the approach is given in the orthophosphate section on p. 467. The important principles are:

1. Citric, tartaric and oxalic acids destroy molybdophosphoric acid but not molybdosilicic acid. Citric acid also destroys molybdoarsenic acid.
2. If perchloric acid is added before ammonium molybdate, molybdosilicic acid is not formed, but the corresponding acids of phosphorus and arsenic are.

Based on these principles, a spectrophotometric method for silicate applicable in the presence of phosphate and arsenate, has been developed. This is discussed later in the present section.

Determination

Gravimetric methods

The classical method for determination of soluble silicates consists of dehydration of silicic acid by evaporating an acid solution, and finally evaluating the silica gravimetrically. To obtain silicon in soluble form, samples are either decomposed by acids or fused with sodium carbonate and the resulting melt treated with acid, usually hydrochloric. Perchloric acid is often recommended as an alternative to HCl or H_2SO_4, having the advantage that almost all perchlorates are soluble in dilute perchloric acid or water. When perchloric acid is used, preliminary treatment with nitric acid should be undertaken if strong reductants are likely to be present. Sulphuric acid suffers from the disadvantage of producing several insoluble sulphates, or anhydrous sulphates that dissolve slowly. Contamination of the silica can result in each instance.

The overall dehydration of orthosilicic acid can be represented as:

$$H_4SiO_4 \rightarrow SiO_2 + 2H_2O$$

The procedure, including the colloidal behaviour of silica, is complex; the present treatment is not meant to be comprehensive but seeks to outline the main features. A fuller treatment is given in references cited earlier[1,2], as well as in the standard text by Kolthoff *et al*[19].

Although extremely laborious and time-consuming, the classical method is capable of giving accurate results if certain procedural refinements are made. The method is old, having been used by Klaproth who employed repeated evaporation with HCl to separate silica[20]. Newer methods, particularly the gravimetric or titrimetric procedures based on quinoline molybdosilicate have been recommended in its place, but it probably still finds some application.

In the procedure itself the acid solution is evaporated to dryness and the dry residue heated at about 110 °C for a further period of about 1 h. The residue is digested for not longer than 15 min in 10% HCl, which brings into solution soluble salts, but dissolves up least silica. The silica is filtered off and washed with hot 5% HCl. A second evaporation is carried out on the filtrate and the resulting silica washed with cold 1% HCl. The two silica precipitates are ignited together in a platinum dish for gravimetric evaluation. Some silicate still remains in solution even after the second dehydration.

For accurate analysis this can be determined spectrophotometrically and a correction applied for total silicate. Ignition of the precipitated and washed silica is carried out at 1200 °C. The product is impure, but the weight of pure silica can be determined by treatment with HF and H_2SO_4, and eliminating silicon as H_2SiF_6 or SiF_4. From the weights of the original impure precipitate and the residue, the weight of pure silica can be calculated. The treatment consists of adding to the impure silica a few drops of water, a few drops of concentrated H_2SO_4, and about 5 mℓ of 60% HF. Evaporation to dryness followed by ignition at 1200 °C results in expulsion of silicon as well as decomposition of any sulphates formed by metallic impurities. The procedure can be repeated if thought necessary.

It has been mentioned that the method is remarkably free from interferences. Fluoride causes low results due to volatilization of H_2SiF_6 or SiF_4. This can be prevented by adding boric acid, the excess of which can be removed as methyl borate before the dehydration procedure. If tin(IV) is present H_2SO_4 should be used in preference to another acid, in order to keep the tin(IV) in solution.

Several gravimetric procedures have been based on precipitation of molybdosilicic acid with organic bases, these including 2,4-dimethylquinoline[21], 8-hydroxyquinoline[22–24], and quinoline[25,21,26]. Recently Harzdorf[27] has made a study of 54 organic bases as potential precipitants for molybdosilicic acid. This work indicates that pyridine is the best for amounts of silica down to 0.1 mg.

2,4-dimethylquinoline recommended by Miller and Chalmers[21] produces a precipitate with low solubility but hygroscopic in nature. For this reason ignition at 500–600 °C to molybdosilicic anhydride is necessary. 8-hydroxyquinoline, first recommended by Volynets[22], produces a precipitate of composition $(C_9H_7ON)_4H_4[SiO_4 \cdot 12MoO_3]$. Precise conditions for its use have been prescribed by Merz[28]. Recent investigations by Ohlweiler *et al.*[24] describe its use for analysis of silicates containing P, Ti and Zr. In this work, preliminary operations include use of boron trioxide and lithium carbonate as flux and EDTA in conjunction with ion-exchange to remove cations and anions produced from the sample. The precipitate is dried at 140 °C; the factor for SiO_2 in the precipitate is 0.02510.

Quinoline was first recommended for precipitation of molybdosilicate by Wilson[29] as part of a titrimetric method analogous to that for phosphorus. This is treated in more detail in the discussion of titrimetric methods later in the section. Miller and Chalmers[21] developed a gravimetric form in which the precipitate was dried at 120–150 °C. An extensive investigation by Armand and Berthoux[26] elucidated the conditions under which the α and β forms of molybdosilicic acid were produced. In addition, the same study stipulated the conditions necessary for complete precipitation and minimum solubility of quinoline molybdosilicate. Earlier work on the α and β forms of molybdosilicic acid had been reported by Strickland[30]. The precipitate, which has the composition $(C_9H_7N)_4H_4[SiO_4 \cdot 12MoO_3]$ is easy to filter and can be adequately dried in an hour at 150 °C.

More recently the gravimetric determination of silicate as quinoline molybdosilicate has been used after preliminary separation of phosphate as ammonium molybdophosphate[5]. The method, applicable to 0.2–2 mg of each anion, was developed for use in elemental organic microanalysis. In another application to analysis of organosilicon compounds on the milligram scale, the sample is decomposed with sodium peroxide in a nickel bomb and the resulting silicate determined gravimetrically as quinoline molybdosilicate[31]. As to which is the best organic base for gravimetric determination of silicate, the choice almost certainly lies between quinoline and 8-hydroxyquinoline.

In addition to the above methods silicate can also be determined gravimetrically as K_2SiF_6. The method was recommended by Hollander and Rieman[32] in 1947 and is useful in the presence of fluoride.

Titrimetric methods

1. Acid–base titration of organic molybdosilicates

Determination of silicate by alkalimetric titration of quinoline molybdosilicate was introduced by Wilson[29] in 1949 and is generally regarded as one of the better, if not the best method for silicate on the macro- and micro-scale. Originally an attempt was made to develop the gravimetric 8-hydroxyquinoline procedure of Brabson, Duncan and Murphy[25] into titrimetric form by dissolving the precipitate in standard NaOH and back-titrating the excess with standard acid. This was unsuccessful, but replacing the organic base with quinoline produced an effective method. The sequence of reactions can be represented as follows:

$$Na_2SiO_3 + H_2O + 2HCl \rightarrow H_4SiO_4 + 2NaCl$$

$$H_4SiO_4 + 12(NH_4)_2MoO_4 + 24HCl \rightarrow H_4[SiO_4 \cdot 12MoO_3] + 24NH_4Cl + 12H_2O$$

$$4C_9H_7NHCl + H_4[SiO_4\cdot 12MoO_3] \rightarrow (C_9H_7N)_4H_4[SiO_4\cdot 12MoO_3] + 4HCl$$

$$(C_9H_7N)_4H_4[SiO_4\cdot 12MoO_4] + 24NaOH \rightarrow 4C_9H_7N + SiO_2 + 14H_2O + 12Na_2MoO_4$$

The method is rapid, applicable to silicate equivalent to 60 mg of silica, and gives results of greater precision than the classical method involving dehydration of silica. Application has been made to analysis of organosilicon compounds following fusion with KOH and to soluble silicates[33].

Titrimetric determination of silicate via quinoline molybdosilicate[29]

Reagents

Quinoline solution:
2%. The quinoline should be pure. Purify if necessary by distillation, retaining the 230–240 °C fraction. Add 20 mℓ of pure quinoline to about 800 mℓ of hot water containing 25 mℓ of concentrated HCl, with constant stirring. Cool, add paper pulp and again stir vigorously. When the pulp has settled filter through a pulp pad and make up to 1 ℓ.

Ammonium molybdate:
10% w/v. Filter after 24 h and use within 1 week.

Thymol blue indicator:
Dissolve 0.4 g of thymol blue in 200 mℓ of ethanol, add 8.6 mℓ of 0.1 M NaOH and dilute to 1 ℓ with water.

Cresol red–thymol blue indicator solution:
Grind 0.1 g of cresol red with 5.3 mℓ of 0.1 M NaOH until dissolved. Dilute to 100 mℓ with water. Dissolve 0.1 g of thymol blue in 20 mℓ of ethanol, add 2.1 mℓ of 0.1M NaOH and dilute to 100 mℓ with water. Mix the two solutions.

Acetic acid, dilute:
Dilute 33 mℓ of glacial acetic acid to 100 mℓ with water.

HCl: 1:1, 1:9, and 0.5M.

NaOH: 1M, free of CO_2.

Procedure

To the silicate solution, containing not more than 76 mg silicate (SiO_3^{2-}) and contained in a stoppered flask, add 8 drops of thymol blue indicator, then concentrated HCl dropwise until the colour changes to red. Add 8 mℓ of dilute HCl (1:9), 5 mℓ of dilute acetic acid and then 30 mℓ of 10% molybdate solution, mixing well by swirling during the addition and for 1 min after the last addition. Immerse the flask in a boiling water-bath for 10–12 min so that its temperature reaches 80–90 °C.

Remove from the bath, add 40 mℓ of diluted HCl (1:1) and immediately precipitate the silicon by running in 65 mℓ of quinoline solution from a fast-flowing burette while swirling the solution. Replace on the water-bath and again raise the temperature to 80–90 °C for a further 5 min with occasional swirling. Cool rapidly to 15 °C or less and allow the precipitate to settle. Decant the supernatant liquor through a paper pulp pad contained in a 3-inch funnel, and suck dry before starting to wash the precipitate. Wash twice by decantation with 25–30 mℓ of cold water before transferring the precipitate to the pad. After transfer, wash the precipitate thoroughly with six 30 mℓ-portions of cold (15 °C) water, sucking dry after each wash.

Carefully transfer the precipitate and pad to the original flask and dissolve in 30.00 mℓ of 1M NaOH. It is recommended that this is done by running the NaOH solution down the sides of the funnel into the flask, thus removing small traces of precipitate adhering to the glass. Finally, wash down the funnel thoroughly with water using the minimum volume necessary.

Stopper the flask and shake until the precipitate has completely dissolved. Add a few drops of the cresol red–thymol blue indicator and back-titrate with 0.5M HCl to a yellow colour.

A blank determination should be made. Its value, usually about 0.6 mℓ, is attributed to the NaOH.

$$1\ \text{m}\ell\ \text{M NaOH} \equiv 3.182\ \text{mg}\ SiO_3^{2-} \equiv 2.513\ \text{mg}\ SiO_2.$$

Note

No systematic investigation of interferences was made in the original work except to show that phosphate interferes. The analogous method for phosphate on pp. 456 and 460 provides additional information on interferences.

---

2. *Acid–base titration after precipitation as potassium fluorosilicate*

Titrimetric determination of silicate based on initial precipitation as potassium fluorosilicate is often regarded as equivalent to, if not superior to the classical gravimetric method, and the titrimetric form of the organic base molybdosilicate methods. Its introduction is sometimes attributed to Kordon[34] who used it in metallurgical analysis. Earlier work was reported by Tananaeff and Babko[35] who applied it to glass analysis, and Travers[36] who appears to have suggested the method.

Precipitation is effected by adding excess of potassium chloride to a strongly acid solution of the silicate containing HF.

$$H_2SiO_3 + 6HF + 2KCl \leftrightharpoons K_2SiF_6 + 3H_2O + 2HCl$$

The solubility of the precipitate is reduced to tolerable levels by the presence of a large excess of KCl. It is washed with a KCl solution, transferred to boiling water and the liberated HF titrated with standard NaOH using phenolphthalein or a bromothymol blue–phenol red mixture, as indicator. The overall reaction can be represented as:

$$K_2SiF_6 + 4NaOH \leftrightharpoons SiO_2 + 4NaF + 2KF + 2H_2O$$

The method is rapid in relation to the classical method, requiring about 2 h. As it is frequently used for the analysis of alloy steels and other metallurgical products, possible interference by a wide range of metallic ions becomes an important consideration. Ca, Mg and Fe have no significant effect[37]. In alloy steels, Mn, Cr, Ni and W up to 20%, Co up to 10%, and Mo, V and Cu up to 5% have no effect[38]. Titanium and Zr interfere but the effect of titanium can be repressed by addition of Ca^{2+} ions. Reports on the effect of aluminium are conflicting. In the study by Morris[37], aluminium in the range 15–30 mg causes no effect on the determination of silicate in solutions containing the equivalent of 125 mg of silica. Other reports indicate that interference by coprecipitation, as in the case of titanium, can occur. Addition of calcium chloride has been recommended to prevent this[39,40]. Non-interference by fluoride is an important feature of the method.

A careful investigation using modern statistical techniques has been carried out by Morris[37]. Over the range 60–190 mg SiO_2 the standard deviation was found to be 0.29 mg with a coefficient of variation of 0.15% at the 190 mg level and 0.48% at 60 mg. The same investigation indicates that the only effects of statistical significance are the temperature at which the fluorosilicate is precipitated and the volume of wash water used. Application of the method has been widespread, extending to slags[41,37], cement[42], iron-ore[43,37], alloys[44,45,37] and rocks and minerals[40,37].

Titrimetric determination of silicate after precipitation[40] as K_2SiF_6

Reagents

Calcium chloride solution: 20%.
Potassium chloride solution: 70 g KCl in 1 ℓ of 1:1 ethanol–water.
NaOH; 0.15M.
Phenolphthalein: 1%.

Procedure

To the sample solution in a volume not exceeding 50 mℓ and containing silicate equivalent to 40–100 mg SiO_2, add 10 mℓ of concentrated HCl and 10 mℓ of concentrated HNO_3. Boil the solution for 1 min. Cool the beaker and solution in a water trough to 30–40 °C, then transfer the solution to a 200-mℓ plastic beaker using the minimum amount of distilled water to wash the glass beaker. Add about 5 mℓ of 20% $CaCl_2$ solution and about 1 g of NaF. Stir with a magnetic stirrer until all the NaF dissolves, then add solid KCl until an excess of 2–3 g over saturation point is present (about 25 g) and continue stirring for 2–3 min.

Filter the precipitate on a Buchner funnel using a No. 42 filter paper, and wash thoroughly with a solution of 70 g of KCl in 1 ℓ of 1:1 ethanol–water. Wash six to ten times with about 10-mℓ portions of solution in order to ensure complete removal of all excess acid.

Transfer the washed precipitate, filter paper and stirring bar to a 1 ℓ beaker containing 500 mℓ of boiled and still very hot distilled water. Wash the Buchner funnel with hot distilled water to remove any adhering precipitate and add this to the beaker.

Titrate with 0.15M NaOH using 1% phenolphthalein as indicator. Determine blanks with each fresh batch of reagents used.

1 mℓ 0.15M NaOH ≡ 2.252 mg SiO_2

Note

In the above method, which was applied to analysis of rocks and minerals, the sample was initially fused with Na_2O_2 in a nickel crucible. Full details are given in the original paper.

---

3. Using EDTA

Jenik[46] has proposed precipitation of silicic acid or alkaline silicates as $CoSi_4O_9$ by adding cobalt nitrate solution to an alkaline solution of the silicate containing acetone. The precipitate is centrifuged, washed, dissolved in ammoniacal EDTA and the cobalt content determined by back-titration of excess EDTA using magnesium(II).

More recently a method has been developed based on molybdosilicic acid[47]. In this the heteropoly acid is extracted into isoamyl alcohol, back-extracted into the aqueous phase and the molybdate reduced by hydrazine hydrochloride. Excess standard EDTA is added and a back-titration made with zinc(II). For 40–60% Si in prepared samples, the error was found to be below 0.6%. Phosphorus, arsenic and germanium interfere.

Spectroscopic methods

1. Spectrophotometric methods

These are invariably based on heteropoly acid formation, and may be grouped according to the species on which absorbance measurements are made. They are:

1. The molybdosilicic acid complex itself, $H_4SiMo_{12}O_{40}$.
2. Its blue reduction product.
3. Other molybdate complexes formed after breakdown of the initially formed heteropoly acid.
4. Ion-association complexes formed with molybdosilicic acid, particularly the rhodamine B ion-association complex.

An important factor is the existence of α and β isomers of molybdosilicic acid and the implication of this on analytical procedures[30]. At low acidity the α-form is stable. The β-form, which develops at high acidity, reverts slowly to the α-form. Both forms produce the familiar molybdenum blue species when reduced. Each form has a different molar absorptivity. It is important, therefore, to know the range of conditions under which each form is relatively stable, and to use one form exclusively. On reduction the α-heteropoly acid produces a greenish blue colour; the β-form a deep blue colour[48]. Both the α and β forms have featured in analytical procedures. The β-form has about twice the molar absorptivity of the α-form but the conditions of high acidity necessary for its formation are rigorous.

A recent study by Pungor and co-workers[49–51] has provided more information on the interplay between the α and β modifications. Furthermore, the differences in molar absorptivity and other irregularities found in the various spectrophotometric procedures are attributed not to the heteropoly acids, but to the isopolymolybdates formed with them. This work will be referred to again later.

A detailed account of earlier work on the spectrophotometric determination of silicon is given in the monograph by Boltz (see Potter[52]). The various forms of the method will now be considered in more detail.

(a) In general the silicate solution is acidified, ammonium molybdate solution added and allowed to stand to ensure complete formation of molybdosilicic acid. Ringbom, Ahlers and Siitonen[48] employ the α-form, measuring the absorbance at 390 nm. More recently Kollar, Plichon and Saulnier[9] used an extraction procedure to separate the heteropoly acid from excess molybdate. The α-heteropoly acid in aqueous solution is extracted by triiso-octylamine nitrate in dichloro-1,2-ethane according to an equilibrium which involves dissociation of the extracted species in the organic phase.

$$\alpha_{aq} + 4(R_3NHNO_3)_s \leftrightharpoons [\alpha(R_3NH)_3]_{s^-} + (R_3NH)_{s^+} + 4(NO_3^-)_{aq} + xH^+$$

where s = dichloro-1,2-ethane

Determination of the heteropoly acid in the organic phase gives a molar absorptivity of 2.8×10^{-4} ℓ cm^{-1} $mole^{-1}$ at 300 nm which is considerably higher than the value generally found for this form of the method.

Several ions interfere in the determination as the heteropoly acid. Fluoride interferes by formation of the fluorosilicate complex. This may be overcome by addition of boric acid. Zirconium(IV), Ti (IV), Sn(IV), and W(VI) interfere by precipitation. They can be complexed by addition of fluoride followed by a calculated amount of boric acid to destroy the silicon complex but not the complexes of Zr(IV), Ti(IV), Sn(IV) and W(VI). Vanadate interferes by producing a molybdovanadate complex. This can be extracted. Several common anions interfere by complexing with the molybdenum in the heteropoly acid, which is not very stable. These include chloride and citrate. The main interference, however, is caused by P(V), As(V) and Ge(IV) which themselves form heteropoly acids. This problem has attracted much attention in recent years not only in connection with determination of silicate but in the determination of P(V), As(V) and Ge(IV). This is discussed in more detail below.

The β-form of molybdosilicic acid exhibits a much greater absorbance in the UV ($\varepsilon_{300\,nm} \sim 2.0 \times 10^4$) but many species cause interference in this range.

Chalmers and Sinclair[53,54] use β-molybdosilicic acid as the basis of a method with its more advantageous molar absorptivity. This is accomplished by stabilizing the β-form with acetone. In order to derive selectivity in the presence of phosphorus(V) use is made of a device briefly referred to earlier, namely the suppression of unwanted species. The basis of this is that mannitol as well as citric, tartaric and oxalic acids destroy molybdophosphoric acid but not molybdosilicic acid. Citric acid also destroys molybdoarsenic acid. Furthermore, if perchloric acid is added before ammonium molybdate, molybdosilicic acid is not formed but the corresponding acids of phosphorus and arsenic are.

An explanation of these reactions in terms of the kinetics and thermodynamics of formation of the corresponding acids is given in the phosphate section on p. 467 and will not be repeated here. In practice, these principles coupled with the enhanced stability of molybdosilicic acid in the presence of acetone enables silicate to be determined in the presence of phosphate. Mannitol appears to be the most effective over a wide range of phosphate concentration and was finally selected in the above mentioned work. The resulting method for up to 500 μg SiO_2 in the presence of phosphate, is rapid and sensitive, the absorbance being measured at 370 nm.

The alternative approach to selectivity within the group Si(IV), P(V), As(V) and Ge(IV) is solvent extraction. Some examples are given in *Table 45* in the phosphate section. This includes one procedure in which silicate is determined in the aqueous phase after extraction of molybdophosphoric acid[55]. Further examples are given in *Table 17* which also provides data on

Table 17 Spectrophotometric methods for silicate following selective extraction of molybdosilicic acid

Extraction system for silicate	*Final procedure*	*Comments*	*Ref.*
Si-HPA extracted into 2-ethylhexanol at pH < 0.4	Back-extraction into H_2O. Spectrophotometric determination as HPB at 690 nm	No int. As. Spectrophotometric determination As(V) in aq. phase. Range 10–80 μg Si	56
Si-HPA extracted into diethylether–pentanol (5:1) 2M in HCl	Spectric. via Mo(VI) in UV	Range 0.1–0.4 ppm Si. No int. by P. P in aq. phase determined via Mo(VI), UV, or AAS	57
Si-HPA extracted into diethylether–pentanol (5:1)	Back extraction into H_2O. MoO_4^{2-} converted to peroxomolybdic acid for spectrophotometric determination	Range 0.25–2.5 ppm Si. Int. by > 25 ppm AsO_4^{3-}, NO_3^- or VO_3^-, > 50 ppm $Cr_2O_7^{2-}$ or F^-	10
Si-HPB extracted into isoamyl alcohol	Spectric. on HPB $\varepsilon = 1.85 \times 10^4$	Range 0.3–40 μg Si. Tolerance limits include 5 mg As, 0.3 mg P, and 0.0001 mg Ge for 4 μg Si	11
Si-HPB extracted into $CHCl_3$ in presence of propane–1,2-diol carbonate	Spectric. on HPB $\varepsilon_{775\ nm} = 2.02 \times 10^4$	Range 0.1–1.4 ppm Si. Limited amounts AsO_4^{3-} and PO_4^{3-} tolerated. No int. MoO_4^{2-}, NO_3^-, Br^-, Cl^-, SO_4^{2-}, acetate, etc.	12

HPA = heteropoly acid.
HPB = heteropoly blue.

extraction–spectrophotometric procedures for silicate. Studies by Pungor and co-workers[49–51] on Si(IV), P(V), As(V) and Ge(IV) when present together, indicate that a complete analysis utilizing heteropoly acid formation is possible without recourse to separation or reduction. The basis here is that despite many similarities in the four heteropoly acids, sufficient differences exist to allow the specific determination of each. To accomplish this, judicious variation of acid concentration, molybdate concentration, wavelength, α and β modifications and medium is necessary. The original work should be consulted for details.

(b) Molybdosilicic acid like the corresponding heteropoly acids of phosphorus and arsenic is easily reduced, the anion being known as molybdenum blue. Spectrophotometric methods based on the blue species are more sensitive than those employing the unreduced form, and their application has been more widespread. The maximum absorbance is at 800–820 nm. In order to find the most effective method of reduction, a wide selection of compounds has been examined[58,59]. These include stannous chloride, metol (*p*-methylaminophenol sulphate), ferrous iron, 2,4-diaminophenol, 1-amino-2-naphthol-4-sulphonic acid and sodium sulphite. Mullin and Riley[59] recommend metol. Duce and Yamamura[60] find that 1-amino-2-naphthol-4-sulphonic acid mixed with sodium hydrogen sulphite and sodium hydroxide is the most reliable in terms of stability of the reduced species, stability of the reducing reagent (the shelf life is at least one month) and colour reproducibility.

Solvent extraction of unreduced molybdosilicic acid is now established as a means of enhancing sensitivity. The heteropoly acid can be back-extracted into an aqueous phase and then reduced to molybdenum blue. This is illustrated in *Table 17*. Solvent extraction is particularly useful for determination of silicate in the presence of arsenate and phosphate. Reduced molybdosilicic acid is not extracted as readily into organic solvents. Kakita and Goto[11] find that extraction of molybdenum blue into isoamyl alcohol is possible if the acid concentration of the aqueous layer is sufficiently high. In addition to the tolerance limits of some ions in *Table 17*, other values are: Sb and Te, 5 mg; Pb and Ti, 10 mg; Sn, Ce, V, Bi, Nb, Ta, Ca, Hg and Ag, 25 mg; W, 50 mg; Cr, 75 mg; and Al, Mn, Mg, Zn, Cu, Co, Ni, Cd, and Be, 125 mg. Tungsten which is precipitated as WO_3 is re-dissolved by HF. The method is applicable to high-purity metal analysis.

Published molybdenum blue methods for silicate vary considerably in the conditions employed to develop and measure the reduced species. The variables include pH of the solution, the quantity and composition of the molybdenum reagent, the nature and quantity of the complexing reagent sometimes added to mask residual molybdate and destroy molybdenum complexes, the reducing reagent and the absorbance wavelength. Furthermore, a wide selection of pre-treatment procedures has been used before application of the spectrophotometric procedure itself. Duce and Yamamura[60] describe a versatile spectrophotometric method that combines the desirable features of previous molybdenum blue methods with three pre-treatment procedures capable of dealing with a wide range of silicon-containing samples. The spectrophotometric procedure is given below, together with data on interferences.

Spectrophotometric determination of microgram amounts of silicate (5–100 μg Si) as molybdenum blue[60]

Reagents

Ammonium molybdate reagent:
Dissolve 50 g of ammonium heptamolybdate tetrahydrate in water, filter the solution through a 0.45-μm membrane filter, then dilute to 500 mℓ.

Oxalic acid–tartaric acid complexing reagent:
0.75M in each component.

Reducing agent:
Dissolve 27 g of $NaHSO_3$, 2 g of NaOH, and 0.50 g of 1-amino-2-naphthol-4-sulphonic acid in 225 mℓ of water, filter, and dilute to 250 mℓ.

Procedure

Place the sample aliquot of 75 mℓ or less, containing 5–100 μg of reactive silicon, into a 100-mℓ polyethylene beaker. Adjust the pH to 1.1 ± 0.1 with 3M H_2SO_4 or 6M HNO_3, then add 10 mℓ of ammonium molybdate reagent. Adjust the pH to 1.3 ± 0.1 with either 3M H_2SO_4 or 6M ammonia, and allow to stand for 10 min. Add 10 mℓ of the complexing reagent, mix, and after 30 s but within 1 min of the addition of the complexing reagent, add 2 mℓ of the reducing solution. Wait 20 min for colour development, then dilute the solution to 100 mℓ with water in a volumetric flask. Measure the absorbance against water at 815 nm (infra-red source and detector) or at 795 nm (visible source and detector) in 1 or 5 cm cells.

Notes

1. The organic complexing reagent is introduced to mask residual molybdate and destroy other molybdate complexes. It also slowly decomposes the molybdosilicic acid complex, so the time interval (30–60 s) between adding the complexing solution and the reducing reagent must be adhered to.
2. Fluoride, tin(II), citrate, oxalate and tartrate must be absent (except the oxalic and tartaric acids contained in the complexing reagent). The following species can be tolerated in the molar ratios to silicon indicated.

   Al: at least 950.

   Co, Cr(III), Cr(VI), Fe,* lanthanides†, Mn, Ni and Zn: at least 185.
   Cu: 20 (samples containing much Cu should be analysed by another procedure given in the same paper. Copper(II) absorbs at 810 nm).

   If alkaline earths are present HNO_3 should be used in place of H_2SO_4 for pH adjustment.
   Up to 10 mmol of Cl^-, ClO_4^-, NO_3^-, and SO_4^{2-}, and 0.005 mmol of PO_4^{3-} per sample aliquot do not interfere.
3. The procedure given is the first of five developed in the original study.

* Samples containing iron are best analysed by another procedure given in the same paper.
† Lanthanide oxalates are insoluble, so the sample solution must be centrifuged or filtered.

The other procedures can be applied in various situations, for example procedure V is suitable for determination of total silicon in metal salt solutions containing fluoride.

(c) An indirect near-infra-red spectrophotometric method for silicate has been based on measuring the absorbance of the chloroform extract of a green complex formed between molybdenum and 2-amino-4-chlorobenzenethiol hydrochloride[61]. The method consists of first producing molybdosilicic acid, which is extracted and its molybdenum content stripped in dilute NH_4OH before forming the complex with 2-amino-4-chlorobenzenethiol hydrochloride. After extracting this complex into chloroform, its absorbance is measured at 715 nm. The limit of detection is 0.034 μg silicon per mℓ of the aqueous heteropoly acid solution. Permissible amounts of various ions in the determination of 4.0 μg of silicon per 50 ml of aqueous heteropoly acid are (in ppm)

NO_2^-	0
$Cr_2O_7^{2-}$, Fe^{3+}, VO_3^-	1
F^-	5
PO_4^{3-}, AsO_4^{3-}	10
AsO_3^{3-}, Pb^{2+}	25
Al^{3+}, Zn^{2+}	50

(d) Golkowska[62,63] has utilized the ion-association complex formed between molybdosilicic acid and rhodamine B in a spectrophotometric procedure. The range is 5–50 ng Si $m\ell^{-1}$ with absorbance measurements being made at 590 nm or 550 nm. No interference is given by 100-fold molar ratios of arsenic or phosphorus to silicon. The complex itself has a molar ratio rhodamine B:Si of 4:1, which remains the same in aqueous or organic media. The molar absorptivity at 550 nm is 5×10^5 ℓ $mole^{-1}$ cm^{-1}.

2. *Atomic absorption spectroscopy*

The introduction of the N_2O–acetylene flame into AAS extended its range to include such elements as silicon. Much of the published material in the past decade on direct determination of silicon by AAS has centred on two problems, decomposition techniques and inter-element interference. Some discussion of decomposition techniques for silicates is included in a paper by Boar and Ingram[64] who apply AAS to analysis of coal ash and silicate rocks. Using the N_2O–acetylene flame and the 251.6 nm resonance line, the practical sensitivity is about 3 μg $m\ell^{-1}$ of silicon, with the optimum range at about 100–1000 μg $m\ell^{-1}$.

Several media have been used, for example HCl and HF–boric acid. The sensitivity does not appear to be greatly affected by this.

Inter-element interference is a more important problem, and has been the subject of many investigations[65–67]. One of the first detailed studies was made by Price and Roos[65] who found that Al, Ca, Fe, Na and V enhance the Si response, but PO_4^{3-} suppresses it. It was found that in some cases the interference could be compensated for by adding measured amounts of the cation concerned. Other workers have reported interference resulting partly from the media used. The recent investigation by Musil and Nehasilova[67] has attempted to establish which ions interfere in 10 mg $m\ell^{-1}$ amounts in the determination of 50 μg $m\ell^{-1}$ of silicon by AAS. Sulphuric acid shows a depressive effect. The study confirms that alkali metals exert an enhancing effect, but this does not reach a plateau with increasing amounts indicating that they must be kept strictly constant for reproducible results. Most elements are found to enhance silicon absorption with only nickel and acids exerting a depressive effect. The effects of copper and zinc are shown to be negligible.

A much more sensitive method is derived from using indirect AAS based on the molybdenum content of molybdosilicic acid. This is largely due to the 12:1 ratio of Mo to Si in the heteropoly acid.

Selective extraction of molybdosilicic acid (or the corresponding acids of phosphorus and arsenic) enables silicate to be determined in the presence of phosphate or asenate. Hurford and Boltz[7] extract molybdosilicic acid with a diethylether–pentanol mixture. The extract is washed to remove excess molybdate, back-extracted into an aqueous phase and decomposed before the AAS stage. The range is 0.1–1.2 ppm Si. Kirkbright, Smith and West[68] extract β-molybdosilicic acid into butanol and then use the extract directly for AAS. In this method the range is 0.08–1.2 ppm silicon. No interference is given by phosphate, but arsenic(V) and germanium(IV) interfere giving high results. One hundred fold amounts of the following species do not interfere with the determination of silicate:

> Al(III), Au(III), Bi(III), Ca(II), Cd(II), Co(II), Cr(III), Cu(II), Fe(III), Ni(II), Pb(II), Mg(II), Mn(II), Se(IV), Te(IV), Zn(II), V(V), W(VI), F^-, EDTA, NO_3^-, and SO_4^{2-}.

Ramakrishna, Robinson and West[69] have extended the general approach to determination of silicon in the presence of arsenic as well as phosphorus. Silicate, in the range 1–10 μg, is extracted into isobutyl methyl ketone and the organic extract used directly for AAS. Germanium interferes.

An interesting offshoot of AAS is atomic absorption inhibition titration[70, 71]. This involves titrating the anion with a metal cation solution (Mg^{2+} was used) while monitoring the atomic absorption signal for the metal. The end-point is indicated by a distinct increase in the Mg^{2+} signal. The method, which functions down to 1 μg ml^{-1} of silica was used for simultaneous determination of silicate, phosphate and sulphate in water samples. Evaluation of the anions was made using a set of linear equations.

3. *Atomic fluorescence spectroscopy*

An AFS method utilizing an electrodeless discharge tube source has been developed for determination of silicon[72].

Electroanalytical methods

Few electroanalytical methods have been described for silicate. Ackerman[73] has titrated silicate potentiometrically with 1 M KF using a titanium indicator electrode. In another method, both α and β forms of molybdosilicic acid are titrated potentiometrically with Sn(II) oxalate or 4-amino-3-hydroxy-naphthalene-1-sulphonic acid. In all instances the volume of titrant is proportional to the silicate concentration, but with 4-amino-3-hydroxy naphthalene-1-sulphonic acid the reaction is non-stoichiometric[74].

Kinetic methods

The rate of formation of molybdosilicic acid has provided the basis of a kinetic method for silicate. Hargis[75] found that the rate of formation of the β-isomer is

$$\frac{d[\beta\text{-isomer}]}{dt} = \frac{k_1 k_2[Si(OH)_4][HMo_2{}^+]^6}{k_{-1}[H^+]^7 + k_2[HMo_2{}^+]^5}$$

where $HMo_2{}^+$ represents an assumed molybdate dimer. At low acidity $k_{-1}[H^+]^7 \ll [HMo_2{}^+]^5$ so that the rate equation simplifies to

$$\frac{d[\beta\text{-isomer}]}{dt} = k_1[Si(OH)_4][HMo_2{}^+]$$

An analytical procedure based on this is described in another paper by Hargis[76]. Where initial concentrations of molybdate are the same for a series of samples, the initial rate of change of absorbance is proportional to the silicate concentration. The heteropoly acid is monitored by means of its absorbance. A calibration curve is made of initial reaction rate against silicate concentration. Apart from good precision and sensitivity, a further advantage claimed is that absorbance measurements made at carefully selected times to compensate for spontaneous conversion of the β to the α isomer are unnecessary. The method only requires 10–30 s of reaction time.

For 3.36 ppm of silicon, other anions are tolerated in the following amounts (ppm).

$PO_4{}^{3-}$	10	$C_2H_3O_2{}^-$	> 4000
$AsO_4{}^{3-}$	25	$NO_3{}^-$	> 4000
$SO_4{}^{2-}$	2000	$ClO_4{}^-$	> 4000
Br^-	2400		
Cl^-	3000		
F^-	50		

For cations generally, the tolerances are over 3000 ppm with the exception of iron(III) which interferes above 50 ppm.

Ingle and Crouch[77] develop a differential kinetic method by which silicate and phosphate are determined in mixtures. Again based on β-molybdosilicic acid, 1–10 ppm of silicon can be determined in the presence of up to 10 ppm of phosphorus with an accuracy better than 3 per cent. The basis here is that the molybdophosphoric acid forms much more rapidly than the corresponding silicon heteropoly acid. The rate of formation of the molybdosilicic acid is therefore measurable after phosphate has reacted. An automatic reaction rate system is employed enabling the analysis to be completed in less than 5 min.

Miscellaneous methods

A thermometric method based on adding a mixed HF–urea reagent to a silicate sample has been reported[78]. The rise in temperature due to formation of H_2SiF_6 and K_2SiF_6, and precipitation of the latter, is measured. Application is made to analysis of sodium silicate and metal silicates.

References

1. SHELL, H.R., in *Treatise on Analytical Chemistry* (Ed. I.M. Kolthoff and P.J. Elving), Part II, Vol. 2, Interscience, New York, 107 (1962)
2. THOMAS, H., in *Comprehensive Analytical Chemistry* (Ed. C.L. and D.W. Wilson), Vol. 1C, Elsevier, Amsterdam, 149 (1962)
3. BENNETT, H., *Analyst*, **102**, 153 (1977)
4. DOLEZAL, J., POVONDRA, P. and SULCEK, Z., *Decomposition Techniques in Inorganic Analysis*, Iliffe, London (1966)
5. MACDONALD, A.M.G. and VAN DER VOORT, F.H., *Analyst*, **93**, 65 (1968)
6. PAUL, J., *Analytica chim. Acta*, **35**, 200 (1966)
7. HURFORD, T.R. and BOLTZ, D.F., *Analyt. Chem.*, **40**, 379 (1968)
8. RAMAKRISHNA, T.V., ROBINSON, J.W. and WEST, P.W., *Analytica chim. Acta*, **45**, 43 (1969)
9. KOLLAR, R., PLICHON, V. and SAULNIER, J., *Analytica chim. Acta*, **50**, 457 (1970)
10. TRUDELL, L.A. and BOLTZ, D.F., *Analyt. Lett.*, **3**, 465 (1970)
11. KAKITA, Y. and GOTO, H., *Talanta*, **14**, 543 (1967)
12. TRUDELL, L.A. and BOLTZ, D.F., *Analytica chim. Acta*, **52**, 343 (1970)
13. PILSON, M.E.Q. and FRAGALA, R.J., *Analytica chim. Acta*, **52**, 553 (1970)
14. WU, F.F.H., GOTZ, J., JAMIESON, W.D. and MASSON, C., *J. Chromat.*, **48**, 515 (1970)
15. SUSSMAN, S. and PORTNOY, I.L., *Analyt. Chem.*, **24**, 1644 (1952)
16. NEMODRUK, A.A., PALEI, P.N. and BEZROGOVA, E.V., *Zh. analit. Khim.*, **25**, 319 (1970); *Analyt. Abstr.*, **21**, 1005 (1971)
17. WICKBOLD, R., *Z. analyt. Chem.*, **171**, 81 (1959); *Analyt. Abstr.*, **7**, 2662 (1960)
18. GEYER, R. and MUECKE, H., *Z. Chemie. Lpz.*, **8**, 388 (1968); *Analyt. Abstr.*, **18**, 1567 (1970)
19. KOLTHOFF, I.M., SANDELL, E.B., MEEHAN, E.J. and BRUCKENSTEIN, S., *Quantitative Chemical Analysis*, 4th edn, Chapter 31, MacMillan, London (1969)
20. SZABADVARY, F., *History of Analytical Chemistry*, Pergamon Press, London, 123 (1966)
21. MILLER, C.C. and CHALMERS, R.A., *Analyst*, **78**, 24 (1953)
22. VOLYNETS, M.I., *Zav. Lab.*, **5**, 162 (1936)
23. BRABSON, J.A., MATTRAW, H.C., MAXWELL, G.E., DARROW, A. and NEEDHARM, M.F., *Analyt. Chem.*, **20**, 504 (1948)
24. OHLWEILER, O.A., MEDITSCH, J.O., SILVEIRA, C.L.P. and SILVA, S., *Analytica chim. Acta*, **61**, 57 (1972)
25. BRABSON, J.A., DUNCAN, R.D. and MURPHY, I.J., *Analyt. Chem.*, **35**, 1102 (1963)
26. ARMAND, M. and BERTHOUX, J., *Analytica chim. Acta*, **8**, 510 (1953)
27. HARZDORF, C., *Z. analyt. Chem.*, **227**, 96 (1967)
28. MERZ, J.A., *Svensk. kem. Tidskr.*, **53**, 374 (1941)
29. WILSON, H.N., *Analyst*, **74**, 243 (1949)
30. STRICKLAND, J.D.H., *J. Am. chem. Soc.*, **74**, 862 (1952)
31. CHRISTOPHER, A.J. and FENNELL, T.R.F.W., *Talanta*, **12**, 1003 (1965)
32. HOLLANDER, M. and RIEMAN, W., *Ceram. Age*, **50**, 168 (1947)
33. KLIMOVA, V.A. and VITALINA, M.D., *Trudy Komiss. Anal. Khim. Akad. Nauk. SSR*, **13**, 7 (1963); *Analyt. Abstr.*, **11**, 5539 (1964)
34. KORDON, F., *Arch. Eisenhütt Wes.*, **18**, 139 (1945)
35. TANANAEFF, N.A. and BABKO, A.K., *Z. analyt. Chem.*, **82**, 145 (1930)
36. TRAVERS, A., *Compt. Rend.*, **173**, 714 (1921)
37. MORRIS, A.G.C., *Analyst*, **90**, 325 (1965)
38. Ref. 2, 155
39. LOUVRIER, J. and VOINOVITCH, I.A., *Ind. Ceram.*, 243 (1959); *Analyt. Abstr.*, **7**, 2661 (1960)
40. MCLAUGHLIN, R.J.W. and BISKUPSKI, V.S., *Analytica chim. Acta*, **32**, 165 (1965)
41. BIEBER, B. and VECERA, Z., *Hutn Listy*, **15**, 397 (1960); *Analyt. Abstr.*, **8**, 70 (1961)
42. CALLEJA, J. and BADE, B., *Rev. Cienc. Apl.*, **15**, 39 (1961); *Analyt. Abstr.*, **9**, 161 (1962)
43. GLASO, O. and PATZAUER, G., *Analytica chim. Acta*, **25**, 189 (1961)
44. VELKEN, S., *J. Iron. Steel Inst.*, 119 (1958)
45. WAGNER, F., *Z. analyt Chem.*, **178**, 34 (1960)
46. JENIK, J., *Chem. Prumysl.*, **11**, 189 (1961); *Analyt. Abstr.*, **8**, 4548 (1961)
47. VASIL'EVA, M.G. and BESHIKDASH'YAN, M.T., *Zh. analit. Khim.*, **25**, 1592 (1970); *Analyt. Abstr.*, **22**, 707 (1972)
48. RINGBOM, A., AHLERS, P.E. and SIITONEN, S., *Analytica chim. Acta*, **20**, 78 (1959)
49. HALASZ, A. and PUNGOR, E., *Talanta*, **18**, 557 (1971)

50. HALASZ, A. and PUNGOR, E., *Talanta,* **18**, 569 (1971)
51. HALASZ, A., PUNGOR, E. and POLYAK, K., *Talanta,* **18**, 577 (1971)
52. POTTER, G.V., in *Colorimetric Determination of Non-Metals* (Ed. D.F. Boltz), Interscience, New York (1958)
53. CHALMERS, R.A. and SINCLAIR, A.G., *Analytica chim. Acta,* **33**, 384 (1965)
54. CHALMERS, R.A. and SINCLAIR, A.G., *Analytica chim. Acta,* **34**, 412 (1966)
55. PAUL, J., *Mikrochim. Acta,* 836 (1965)
56. PAUL, J., *Analytica chim. Acta,* **35**, 200 (1966)
57. HURFORD, T.R. and BOLTZ, D.F., *Analyt. Chem.,* **40**, 379 (1968)
58. JEAN, M., *Chim. Anal.,* **38**, 37 (1956)
59. MULLIN, J.B. and RILEY, J.P., *Analytica chim. Acta,* **12**, 162 (1955)
60. DUCE, F.A. and YAMAMURA, S.S., *Talanta,* **17**, 143 (1970)
61. TRUDELL, L.A. and BOLTZ, D.F., *Talanta,* **19**, 37 (1972)
62. GOLKOWSKA, A., *Chemia analit.,* **15**, 59 (1970)
63. GOLKOWSKA, A. and PSZONICKI, L., *Talanta,* **20**, 749 (1973)
64. BOAR, P.L. and INGRAM, L.K., *Analyst,* **95**, 124 (1970)
65. PRICE, W.J. and ROOS, J.T.H., *Analyst,* **93**, 709 (1968)
66. GUEST, R.J. and MACPHERSON, D.R., *Analytica chim. Acta,* **71**, 233 (1974)
67. MUSIL, J. and NEHASILOVA, M., *Talanta,* **23**, 729 (1976)
68. KIRKBRIGHT, G.F., SMITH, A.M. and WEST, T.S., *Analyst,* **92**, 411 (1967)
69. RAMAKRISHNA, R.V., ROBINSON, J.W. and WEST, P.W., *Analytica chim. Acta,* **45**, 43 (1969)
70. LOOYENGA, R.W. and HUBER, C.O., *Analyt. Chem.,* **43**, 498 (1971)
71. LIU, C.I. and HUBER, C.O., *Analyt. Chem.,* **44**, 2200 (1972)
72. KIRKBRIGHT, G.F., RAO, A.P. and WEST, T.S., *Analyt. Lett.,* **2**, 465 (1969)
73. ACKERMAN, G., *Talanta,* **17**, 693, 701 (1971)
74. DOROKHOVA, E.N. and OPARINA, L.I., *Zh. analit. Khim.,* **25**, 544 (1970); *Analyt. Abstr.,* **21**, 999 (1971)
75. HARGIS, L.G., *Analyt. Chem.,* **42**, 1497 (1970)
76. HARGIS, L.G., *Analytica chim. Acta,* **52**, 1 (1970)
77. INGLE, J.D. and CROUCH, S.R., *Analyt. Chem.,* **43**, 7 (1971)
78. STRAUSS, H. and RUTKOWSKI, R., *Plaste Kautsch,* **19**, 665 (1972); *Analyt. Abstr.,* **24**, 2760 (1973)

Tartrate

Separation

Tartaric acid may be separated from other carboxylic acids by TLC on cellulose[1]. The relevant data is given in the section on citrate. Paper impregnated with nickel hydroxide has been used for the chromatographic separation of 2–30 μg tartrate[2]. The subsequent determination was performed by revealing the nickel tartrate spot with dithio-oxamide, cutting it out, weighing it, and comparing this with standards.

Ion-exchange methods of separation have been developed. Seki[3] has described separation of tartaric, citric and malic acids on Amberlite CG-120 (200–300 mesh; H^+ form) with acetone–dichloromethane–water 160:100:9 as eluant. Application of ion-exchange separation of tartrate to wines has been described[4].

Determination

Titrimetric methods

These are based on acid–base, iodimetric, or redox principles. The older iodimetric method probably finds little current use.

1. Acid–base

A mixture of fluorescein and lucigenin (dimethyldiacridylium dinitrate) has been recommended as a chemiluminescent indicator for the alkalimetric titration of tartaric acid as well as oxalic and acetic acids[5]. This is based on the green fluorescence exhibited by lucigenin in alkaline solution and in the presence of hydrogen peroxide. The chemiluminescence is markedly increased by the presence of fluorescein. In the procedure the titration is begun at a temperature of about 60 °C.

The standard quantitative determination of tartaric acid is by precipitation of the acid potassium salt with excess of potassium acetate and acetic acid in the presence of a high concentration of alcohol. The precipitate is subsequently titrated with standard alkali[6]. This method is often applied to the analysis of baking powder[7].

2. Redox

Several reagents have been recommended including potassium manganate, potassium permanganate, cerium(IV) sulphate, ammonium hexanitratocerate(IV), and lead(IV) acetate.

When K_2MnO_4 is used it has been recommended that the sample is partly oxidized in weakly acidic $KMnO_4$ solution before final oxidation with alkaline manganate[8]. Berka and Hilgard[9] describe a method for the determination of about 6 mg of tartaric acid using an excess of $KMnO_4$ followed by a back titration with quinol. Diphenylamine is used as indicator; a period of 4 h is required for the oxidation at room temperature but this may be reduced to 1 h at 40 °C. Berka[10] has also used lead(IV) acetate as oxidant. Here, the excess of lead acetate is titrated potentiometrically with hydroquinone after 30 min.

Cerium(IV) has been widely used for the determination of organic acids including tartaric, and much effort has been directed to finding conditions under which a fixed stoichiometry is obtained for the reaction. Rao, Subrahmanyam and Rao[11] find that ammonium hexanitratocerate(IV) in nitric acid medium gives a fixed stoichiometry over a wide range of temperature and time, with 6 mole of cerium(IV) being consumed per mole of tartaric acid, the products being carbon dioxide and formic acid. The main drawback is the lack of specificity and interference by such species as chloride when an excess of oxidant is used.

Determination of tartaric acid[9] using $KMnO_4$

Reagents

$KMnO_4$, 0.02M(0.1N)
Buffer pH 4.0 (acetate).
$MnSO_4$, 0.5M

H_2SO_4, 2M
Disodium hydrogen pyrophosphate—saturated solution.
0.05M(0.1N) quinol:

Dissolve 5.50 g of the pure sublimed substance in about 500 mℓ of warm water, adding acid so that the final concentration will be about 1% in HCl, Cool and dilute to exactly 1 litre with water.

Diphenylamine in 96% H_2SO_4—3% solution.

Procedure

To a solution containing about 6 mg of tartaric acid, add 1 mℓ of 2M acetate buffer and 5 mℓ of 0.1N $KMnO_4$. Set aside for 4 h at room temperature or 1 h at 40 °C.

Add 10 mℓ 0.5M $MnSO_4$ solution, 4 mℓ of 2M H_2SO_4 and 30 mℓ of saturated aqueous $Na_2H_2P_2O_7$ solution. Dilute to 70–100 mℓ. Titrate with 0.1N quinol to a pale pink colour, add 3 drops of diphenylamine indicator, then continue the titration until the deep violet colour changes to pale yellow. Carry out a blank determination.

---

3. *EDTA*

Published procedures are centred on the compleximetric titration of lead. In one such procedure tartaric acid is precipitated as its lead salt and this is titrated with EDTA using catechol violet as indicator[12]. The range for tartaric acid is given as 6–18 mg. A method by Berka[13] involves lead(IV) acetate. Excess of the reagent is used to oxidize the tartaric acid in the presence of acetic acid and potassium acetate, the excess being hydrolysed with boiling water. The resulting suspension is filtered and the filtrate lead determined by an indirect compleximetric procedure. Both the above procedures are subject to interference by a variety of substances.

Spectroscopic methods

Spectrophotometric methods for the determination of small amounts of tartrate are often unreliable and highly empirical, with little or no understanding of the basic chemistry involved. Johnson[14] has developed a differential spectrophotometric method based on chloranilic acid. When applied to tartrate in baking powder similar results were obtained to the official A.O.A.C. method referred to earlier, but in less time.

Nisli and Townshend[20] have based their method, which may be used in the presence or absence of citrate, on the two consecutive reactions given below.

$$\mathrm{HOOC{-}\underset{\displaystyle OH}{\underset{|}{CH}}{-}\underset{\displaystyle OH}{\underset{|}{CH}}{-}COOH + IO_4^- \rightarrow 2HOOC{-}CHO + IO_3^-} \qquad (1)$$

$$\mathrm{HOOC{-}CHO + IO_4^- \rightarrow CO_2 + HCOOH + IO_3^-} \qquad (2)$$

The resulting iodate is determined spectrophotometrically as tri-iodide after reaction with iodide. The excess of periodate is masked with molybdate at pH 3. For tartrate on its own, oxidation conditions are 1 h at 45–50 °C. The concentration of tartrate is one third of the iodate concentration. The range of tartrate for the method is 5–30 μg. When citrate is present, oxidizing conditions are modified by carrying out the reaction at 0 °C. At this temperature oxidation ceases at the aldehyde stage, i.e. only reaction (1) occurs. Accordingly, the tartrate concentration in this instance is equal to that of the iodate formed. Citrate does not interfere in amounts of 6 mg for a tartrate range of 15–60 μg.

Other recent spectrophotometric methods for tartrate include oxidation by ceric sulphate followed by a measurement of the absorbance of the residual cerium(IV) in the presence of ferroin[15], the decrease in absorbance of Fe(III)-5-nitrosalicylate[16], and reaction of tartaric acid with β-naphthol[17]. The optical activity of tartrate has featured in analytical methods. Kirsten and Nilsson[18] have evaluated the optimum conditions for its determination in the presence of other optically active compounds. More recently Pearson and Kirschner[19] have developed a photometric titrimetric method.

References

1. DITTMAN, J., *J. Chromat.*, **34**, 407 (1968)
2. TSVETANA, T., *Trudy Vyssh. Inst. Narod. Stopanst. Varna*, **1**, 187 (1961); *Analyt. Abstr.*, **9**, 4754 (1962)
3. SEKI, T., *J. Chromat.*, **22**, 498 (1966)
4. FALKOVICH, J.E., *Pischevaya Techn.*, 158 (1960); *Chem. Abstr.*, **55**, 7756b (1961)
5. ERDEY, L., PICKERING, W.F. and WILSON, C.L., *Talanta*, **9**, 371 (1962)
6. *Official Methods of Analysis of the Association of Official Agricultural Chemists*, 11th edn (1970)
7. PEARSON, D., *The Chemical Analysis of Foods*, 6th edn, J. and A. Churchill, London (1970)
8. POLAK, H.L., PRONK, H.F. and DEN BOEF, G., *Z. analyt. Chem.*, **190**, 377 (1962)
9. BERKA, A. and HILGARD, S., *Mikrochim. Acta*, 164 (1966)
10. BERKA, A., *Analytica chim. Acta*, **24**, 171 (1961)
11. RAO, G.G., SUBRAHMANYAM, I. and RAO, B.M., *Talanta*, **19**, 1083 (1972)
12. CRISAN, I.A. and KRAUSZ, R., *Studia Univ. Babes-Bolyai, Ser. Chem.*, **12**, 19 (1967); *Analyt. Abstr.*, **15**, 6720 (1968)
13. BERKA, A., *Z. analyt. Chem.*, **195**, 263 (1963)
14. JOHNSON, A.R., *Analytica chim. Acta*, **33**, 397 (1965)
15. MA, T.S. and NAZIMOWITZ, W.L., *Mikrochim. Acta*, 345 (1969)
16. LEE, K.S., *Analyt. Chem.*, **40**, 2049 (1968)
17. CHRISTIAN, G.D., *Talanta*, **16**, 255 (1969)
18. KIRSTEN, W.J. and NILSSON, S.K., *Analytica chim. Acta*, **27**, 345 (1962)
19. PEARSON, K.H. and KIRSCHNER, S., *Analytica chim. Acta*, **48**, 339 (1969)
20. NISLI, G. and TOWNSHEND, A., *Talanta*, **15**, 1480 (1968)

Tellurate and Tellurite

Tellurium finds use in the metallurgical industry as an alloy constituent, for example it improves the acid-resistance of lead used in batteries. Other uses include the manufacture of heat and abrasive resistance rubber. It appears as a by-product in the electrolytic refining of copper where its determination in the presence of several other elements is important. In the semiconductor industry its determination in tellurium-doped single crystals is often required at ultra-trace levels.

Chemically it resembles selenium. The analytical chemistry of both elements is usually presented together. In aqueous solution tellurium occurs in the +4 and +6 states. As with selenium, reduction to the elemental form can be brought about by several reductants including SO_2, $SnCl_2$ and hydrazine.

The selenium section contains many references to analytical procedures common to both elements as well as their separation, and analysis when present in admixture. This should be consulted in conjunction with the present account of tellurium analysis.

Reference standard solutions of tellurium(IV) are generally prepared from the pure metal. This is dissolved in concentrated HCl containing a small amount of concentrated HNO_3. Slight heating is required to dissolve the metal. The solution is then heated to expel brown fumes, cooled, and made up to volume adding sufficient HCl to make the final acidity about 1M.

Tellurium(VI) solutions can be prepared from pure sodium tellurate. Its exact strength is determined by analysis.

Several reviews[1–4] cover the analytical chemistry of tellurium.

Separations

Bock and Tschopel[5] have reviewed the separation and determination of small amounts of tellurium. Separation of tellurium (and selenium) is discussed at length in the monograph by Korkish[6]. Individual methods will now be discussed.

1. Distillation

In contrast to selenium, tellurium is not readily volatile from concentrated HCl solutions at below 100 °C. Distillation from H_2SO_4/HBr is said to give a distillate containing selenium relatively free from tellurium. With the large number of newer alternative methods, particularly those based on solvent extraction, one can assume that the more time-consuming distillation methods will become less important.

2. Ion-exchange

In contrast to selenium(IV) which is not adsorbed on cation-exchange resins at any concentration of HCl, tellurium(IV) is relatively strongly adsorbed at low acid concentrations. Methods for separating tellurium(IV) and selenium-(IV) have been based on this. Tellurium(VI) is not adsorbed under any acidic conditions. Some ion-exchange procedures involving tellurium are given in the selenium section. Tellurium can be separated from Cu, Ni, Fe and Pb by cation-exchange[7]. Separation of tellurium from the chloride complexes of the platinum metals is described in the same paper.

Tellurium(IV) is separated from iodide, iodate and iodine by a cation-exchanger in tin(II) form[8]. The tellurium is reduced to elemental form and retained on the resin. The iodine species pass through.

In contrast to selenium(IV), tellurium(IV) is more strongly retained on an anion-exchange column, and this increases up to about 8M in HCl. This enables selenium and tellurium to be separated, the selenium(IV) being eluted with HCl of concentration below 4M. Adsorbed tellurium is subsequently eluted with dilute (0.1–1M) HCl. Anion-exchange has been used to separate tellurium(IV) and selenium(IV) from heavy metals[9]. For this purpose lithium chloride is used as a complexing reagent. With suitable concentrations of lithium chloride, tellurium(IV) can be separated from binary mixtures with Bi(III), Pb(II), Sb(III), Au(III), Fe(III) or Se(IV). Separation from certain multicomponent mixtures containing Ag(I), Ni(II) and Al(III) is also possible.

An anion-exchange separation of tellurium(IV) and tellurium(VI) has been reported[10].

3. Solvent extraction

Solvent extraction has been an active area in the analytical chemistry of tellurium, and an extensive literature exists. A critical review of the subject up to the end of 1973 has been published by Havezov and Jordanov[11]. The present treatment will be restricted to a discussion of a few important systems. Methods include extraction of neutral non-polar compounds, chelate compounds, ion-association compounds as well as extraction by solvation.

Tellurium(VI) is strongly oxidizing, and will oxidize a large number of organic solvents as well as many inorganic ions. Extraction systems are often used in spectrophotometric procedures.

Of the dithiocarbamates, the chelate formed between tellurium(IV) and diethyldithiocarbamate can be extracted with a high distribution coefficient into polar and non-polar solvents[12, 13]. In the presence of EDTA or cyanide at pH 8.5–8.8, only Bi, Sb(III) and Tl(III) are extracted with Te(IV). If the extracted species are to be subjected to AAS for determination of tellurium, extraction is made into amyl acetate[14] or isobutyl methyl ketone[15].

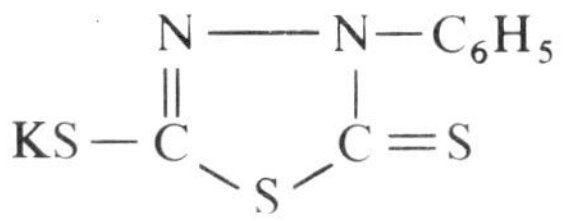

```
       N ——— N—C6H5
       ||     |
KS — C        C = S
        \   /
          S
```

Structure 28 Bismuthiol II

At pH 3 Bismuthiol II (Bismuthon II) (*Structure 28*) forms a co-ordination compound with tellurium(IV). This can be extracted into non-polar solvents. If chloroform is used a high molar absorptivity is attained[16] ($\varepsilon_{335} = 3.5 \times 10^4$). The selectivity is improved if a preliminary extraction is made with isobutyl methyl ketone from HCl. Then tellurium(VI) remains in the acid phase and tellurium(IV) is quantitatively extracted.

Of the ion-association systems, extraction of tellurium(IV) from 4–6M HCl using long-chain amines LA-1 or Amberlite LA-2 enables tellurium to be separated from selenium(IV)[17]. This separation is based on the great difference in stability of the chloro-complexes of the two elements. Another extraction in the same category utilizes Victoria Blue 4R (*Structure 29*), which also provides a spectrophotometric procedure. Extraction is made into a nitrobenzene–chloroform mixture from an aqueous solution of about 4.5M in H_2SO_4 and 0.7M in KBr. The method is sensitive ($\varepsilon_{602\,nm} = 8 \times 10^4$) but not very selective[18]. Small amounts of tellurium(IV) can be extracted into isobutyl methyl ketone from 4–7M HCl. This provides a separation from Zn(II), Cu(II), Pb(II), Cd(II) and Se(IV)[19].

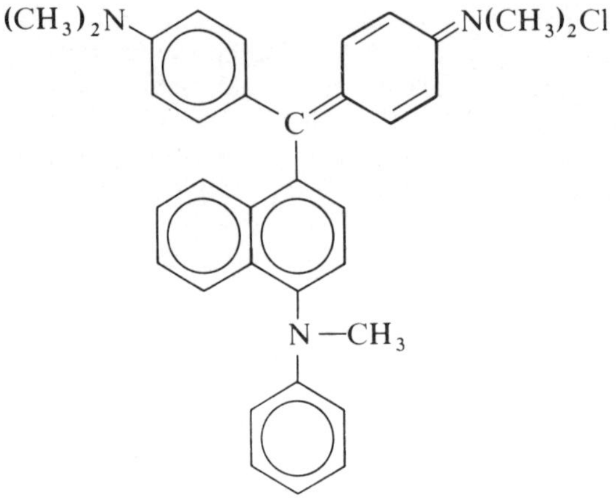

$(CH_3)_2N$ $N(CH_3)_2Cl$

C

$N-CH_3$

Structure 29 Victoria Blue 4R

4. Precipitation

Both tellurium(IV) and selenium(IV) are reduced to elemental form by SO_2 in acidic solution. This enables both to be separated from other elements and determined gravimetrically. By carrying out the reduction at different acidities, tellurium can be separated from selenium. Further details of this and their gravimetric separation using tetraphenylarsonium chloride are given in the selenium section.

5. Coprecipitation

Tellurium(IV) and tellurium(VI) are completely coprecipitated with $Fe(OH)_3$ from ammoniacal solutions of pH 9.4–9.7. Only about 1 % of any selenium(VI) present is coprecipitated under the same conditions[20].

6. Paper and thin-layer chromatography

Some chromatographic separations are included in *Table 16* in the selenium section. Moghissi[21] has separated TeO_3^{2-}, I^- and IO_3^- using TLC. Silica gel, kieselguhr or lanthanum oxide were used as supports and acetone–1M NH_4OH (1:1) as developing solvent.

Determination

Gravimetric methods

One of the earliest analytical methods for tellurium was gravimetric determination in the elemental form after reduction by SO_2 in an acidified solution. Other reductants include hydrazine and $SnCl_2$. Precipitation is generally made from HCl solutions of concentration 1.5–5M. Under the conditions, any selenium(IV) present will also be reduced. This can be prevented by precipitation of selenium(IV) from concentrated HCl, in which case tellurium(IV) does not precipitate at all. On filtering it remains in the filtrate and can then be precipitated after diluting the solution. Coagulation of the tellurium precipitate is achieved by boiling the solution. An important source of error is oxidation of the finely divided particles. This is minimized by washing with ethanol or isopropanol after first washing it free of chloride. Drying is carried out at 90 °C. The procedure is fully discussed in one of the reviews cited earlier[4].

A new gravimetric method based on Bismuthiol II has been reported by Wang and Cheng[22]. Tellurium(IV) is quantitatively precipitated by the reagent at a pH of about 2. The precipitate decomposes on heating but is satisfactorily air-dried and weighed as $Te(C_6H_5N_2C_2S_3)_4$, the gravimetric factor being 0.1140. An accuracy of ±0.5 per cent or better is quoted on 20 mg amounts of tellurium. Precipitation may be carried out in the presence of EDTA.

Titrimetric methods

These methods are essentially redox and have utilized a wide selection of oxidants. A standard, though older method[23], consists of oxidizing tellurium(IV) with excess standard $KMnO_4$ followed by a back-titration with standard iron(II). If selenium(IV) is also present, this too will be oxidized. To determine tellurium(IV) in the presence of selenium(IV), the analogous method[24] using standard dichromate can be used.

$$3H_2TeO_3 + K_2Cr_2O_7 + 8HCl \rightarrow 3H_2TeO_4 + 2CrCl_3 + 2KCl + 4H_2O$$

Using both methods and two sample aliquots, tellurium(IV)/selenium(IV) mixtures can be analysed. The same result can be obtained using one aliquot[25]. The procedure for this method, by Naidu and RaO[25], is given in the selenium section. Another recent method[26] for titrimetric determination of tellurium(IV) uses periodate.

$$TeO_3^{2-} + IO_4^- \rightarrow TeO_4^{2-} + IO_3^-$$

Oxidation by excess dichromate followed by back-titration using iron(II) has been adapted to the micro range for determination of tellurium in organotellurium compounds[27]. An alternative end-procedure is spectrophotometric determination of unconsumed dichromate.

One disadvantage with many of the redox methods for tellurium(IV) is that heating or standing for prolonged periods is required. For example, in the procedure of Lenher and Wakefield[24] 30 min is required before the excess dichromate can be titrated. Using a silver(I)–manganese(II) perchlorate catalyst in the cerimetric titration of tellurium, the reaction time is reduced to 3–7 min[28]. The back-titration is made with iron(II) using ferroin as indicator. For 10–105 mg of tellurium the standard deviation is ±0.21 per cent.

Iodimetric methods have been reported for both tellurium and selenium. A recent method by Zakharov *et al.* enables tellurium(IV)/selenium(IV) mixtures to be analysed. Details are given in the selenium section.

Methods already discussed have been concerned with tellurium in the +4 state. Two recent iodimetric procedures utilized the quantitative reduction of tellurium(VI). Beyak and Jaselskis[29] reduce tellurium(VI) with KI in a citric acid-buffered solution at pH 2–3.

$$H_6TeO_6 + 3I^- + 3H^+ \rightarrow TeOOH^+ + I_3^- + 4H_2O$$

After heating at 80 °C for 30 min in a securely stoppered flask the iodine is titrated with standard thiosulphate. The method, which is applicable to 4–80 mg of tellurium can be carried out in the presence of tellurium(IV) and selenium(VI) but selenium(IV) is reduced by KI and must be absent. Tolstikov and Epik[30] treat the tellurium(VI) sample solution, buffered at pH 5, with sodium arsenite and KI. After heating and allowing to cool the solution is made alkaline and excess arsenic(III) titrated with standard iodine. The range is 1–30 mg of tellurium. Tellurium(IV) may be determined similarly after prior oxidation to tellurium(VI) using hydrogen peroxide.

A direct photometric titration of tellurium(IV) has been reported[31]. The determination is made with dichromate, the chromium(VI) absorption peak at 380–430 nm being used to monitor the reaction. Tellurium(IV) and (VI) do not absorb in this range. Selenium(IV) and (VI) do not interfere, neither do chloride and phosphate in concentrations of 0.05M and 0.2M respectively. The titration is made in a HNO_3 or $HClO_4$ medium in which the dichromate–tellurium(IV) reaction is fast. The method is applicable to 3–30 mg of tellurium.

Spectroscopic methods

1. Spectrophotometric—visible and UV

Earlier colorimetric methods were based on reduction of tellurium solutions by $SnCl_2$ or hypophosphorous acid. The absorbance can be measured in the visible region at 420 nm or in the UV at 240–290 nm[32]. Selenium can be determined in the same way. Several species interfere including oxidizing agents, Fe(III), Cu(II), I^- and $S_2O_3^{2-}$.

The absorption spectrum of iodotellurite forms the basis of another method[33,34]. The absorption spectrum of the complex shows a sharp maximum at 285 nm. Absorbance measurements can be made also on a short plateau at 335 nm. Application of the method has been made to determination of tellurium in gallium arsenide[35].

Most spectrophotometric reagents for tellurium involve sulphur-containing ligands, these including thiourea, thioglycollic acid, sodium diethyldithiocarbamate and mercaptoacetic acid. In many of the more recent methods the coloured species are extracted. Diethyldithiocarbamate has been extensively studied by Bode. Thioglycollic acid (*Structure 30*) is also suitable for selenium(IV). The method is relatively insensitive ($\varepsilon_{260} = 3330$), the optimum range being 8–27 ppm. It is however convenient, and useful for milligram

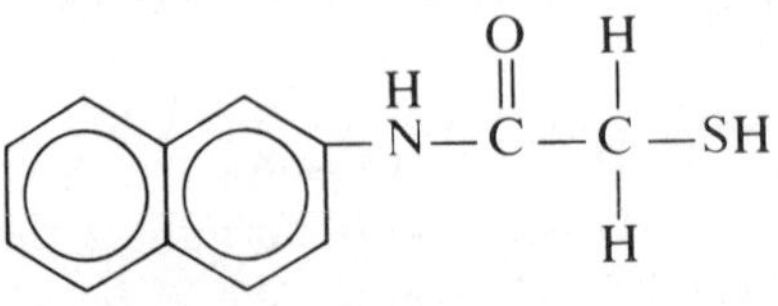

Structure 30 Thioglycollic acid

Table 18 Data for selected extractive-spectrophotometric procedures for tellurium(IV)

Reagent	*Comments*	*Molar absorptivity*	*Ref.*
Diethyldithiocarbamate	Extracted into CCl_4. EDTA and KCN used for masking. Only Bi(III), Tl(III), Hg(II), Ag(I) and > Ca(II) interfere	3.6×10^3(428 nm)	13 36
Bismuthiol II	Extracted in $CHCl_3$. Selectivity improved with preliminary extraction into MIBK from HCl solution	3.5×10^4(335 nm)	16 37
Victoria Blue R	Extracted into benzene–nitrobenzene from 4.5–5.0M H_2SO_4. In and Hg interfere	8.0×10^4(602 nm)	18
1-pyrrolidine-carbodithioate	Extracted into $CHCl_3$. Cd(II), Co(II), Cu(II), Fe(III), Pb(II), Mn(II), Hg(II), Ni(II), Tl(I) and Zn(II) interfere. Certain other cations are tolerated in limited amounts	8.12×10^4(257 nm)	38
5-mercapto-3-(2 naphthyl)-1,3,4-thiadiazole-2-thione (derivative of Bismuthiol II)	Extracted into $CHCl_3$, C_6H_6, or cyclohexane. Beer's law holds 1–50 μg Te ml^{-1} No interference from 200-fold Se	3.0×10^4(328 nm)	39
1,4-diphenylthiosemicarbazide (in presence of Br^-)	Extracted into C_6H_6. Beer's law holds for 10–120 μg Te in 5 mℓ benzene. Interference by Fe(III), Bi(III), Nb, Zr, Ga, Cr(VI), Cu(II) and V(V). Equal amounts of Se tolerated	$\sim 10^4$ (480 nm or 380–390 nm)	40

amounts of both elements either singly or in mixtures. 5-mercapto-3-(2-naphthyl)-1,3,4-thiadiazole-2-thione, a derivative of Bismuthiol II, is useful for determination of tellurium in the presence of large amounts of selenium. Details of the above methods and the following methods are given in *Table 18*.

Tellurium(IV) forms coloured halide complexes, for example $TeBr_6^{2-}$, in strongly acid media. These have been developed into spectrophotometric procedures. The complexes can often form ion-association systems with dyestuffs such as Rhodamine 4G or Victoria Blue R and extraction made into suitable organic solvents. Mel'chekova and Murashova[40] find that the tellurium(IV)–bromide complex reacts with 1,4-diphenylthiosemicarbazide giving a system capable of greater sensitivity.

Several other extractive-spectrophotometric methods have appeared for tellurium(IV). The review by Havezov and Jordanov[11] cited earlier contains information on several of these.

Spectrophotometric determination of tellurium(IV) using diethyldithiocarbamate[13]

Reagents

Cupferron: 2% aqueous solution.
Sodium diethyldithiocarbamate: 0.5% aqueous solution.
Buffer pH 8.6:
5 g of boric acid, 1 g of EDTA and 1 g of potassium dihydrogen phosphate in 100 mℓ. Adjust pH to 8.6.

Procedure

The sample solution should contain 10–15 μg tellurium(IV) in 20 mℓ. Adjust the pH to 1–2, then add 10 mℓ of cupferron solution. Extract with successive portions of chloroform until a colourless extract is obtained. Chloroform removes excess cupferron in addition to interfering metal cupferrates.

To the aqueous solution add 5 mℓ of the buffer followed by solid KCN. Adjust the pH to 8.5–8.8. Add 1 mℓ of 0.5% aqueous sodium diethyldithiocarbamate solution and extract with 3 successive portions of carbon tetrachloride. Measure the absorbance of the organic phase at 428 nm.

---

2. Fluorimetric

Tellurium(IV) exhibits a red fluorescence[41] in a glass of about 9M HCl at −196 °C. This has been utilized for its spectrophotometric determination in the range 0.02–0.64 ppm. The fluorescence is measured[42] at 586 nm using an exciting wavelength of 380 nm. Transparent silica tubes of length 200 mm, bore 3 mm and 1 mm walls are employed, a sample of 0.5 mℓ being sufficient for analysis. Such tubes can be placed directly into liquid nitrogen and brought back to room temperature after measurement, without fracture.

Of 50 foreign ions examined at 50-fold excess over Te(IV), only Fe(III), Sn(II) and I^- were found to interfere. Tin(II) can be eliminated by prior oxidation; iron(III) is removed using a solvent extraction procedure. A similar fluorimetric method has been reported by Kelyi and Kushnirenko[43].

3. AAS and AFS

In a study of the three tellurium lines at 214.3, 225.9 and 238.6 nm Chakrabarti[44] found the 214.3 nm line to be the most sensitive. Using a 5-pass optical system a sensitivity of 0.23 ppm was reported and a detection limit of 0.076 ppm.

Most atomic absorption methods for tellurium involve a preliminary extraction. In such cases the choice of a suitable solvent is important. Marcek, Kinson and Belcher[14] in applying the tellurium(IV)-diethyldithiocarbamate extraction procedure of Bode, extract into amyl acetate before atomic absorption. The method is used for tellurium in steel in the 0.0005–0.03 % range. The sensitivity is reported as 1.3 ppm in aqueous solutions and 0.3 ppm in amyl acetate.

In recent years the continued improvement in instrument and lamp design has enabled direct determination of tellurium to be made in acidic solutions, and without extraction[45].

A recent trend in both AAS and AFS has been conversion of certain elements into volatile hydrides for introduction into the flame. The technique has been applied to tellurium and selenium. Thompson and Thomerson[46] use the technique for tellurium and report a detection limit of 0.0015 μg mℓ^{-1}. The design of one hydride generator is shown in *Figure 28* in the selenium section. The hydride is generated by adding the acidified solution to a dilute solution of sodium borohydride. The above investigation indicates that tellurium(VI) solutions are quantitatively reduced to tellurium(IV) by HCl in contrast to selenium(VI) where only about 50 % is reduced.

Greenland and Campbell[47] report a rapid atomic absorption method using hydride generation, for tellurium in silicate rocks. As little as 5 ng g^{-1} of tellurium can be determined using a 0.25 g sample.

Application of hydride generation has also been made to determination of tellurium by AFS. Here the detection limit is 0.0001 μg or less[48]. Some reservations have been expressed on the technique[49].

4. Molecular emission cavity analysis (MECA)

MECA is a relatively new technique. Its basis, and a brief account of the equipment is given on p. 580. Successful application has been made to both tellurium and selenium. For tellurium the emission at 780 °C permits determination of as little as 1 μg if the background emission of the cavity is taken into account[50].

Electroanalytical methods

Relatively few electroanalytical methods exist for tellurium(IV) and tellurium(VI). Cornwell[51] has used a potentiometric procedure in the analysis of tellurium(IV)–tellurium(VI) compounds for total tellurium. Its basis is the classical method of Schrenk and Browning[23] referred to earlier. After oxidation with excess of standard dichromate, the back-titration is made potentiometrically with standard iron(II). In the same investigation tellurium-(VI) is determined amperometrically using the following reaction:

$$TeO_4^{2-} + 2HCl \xrightarrow[\text{distil}]{\text{boil}} TeO_3^{2-} + H_2O + Cl_2$$

The chlorine is swept by a stream of nitrogen into KI and the resulting iodine titrated amperometrically with thiosulphate.

Tulyupa, Barkalov and Usatenko[52] titrate tellurium(IV) and selenium(IV) amperometrically with N-hexyl- and N-cyclopentyl-dithiocarbamate as reagents. For 0.1–0.2 mg amounts of tellurium or selenium the error is less than 2 per cent. Copper, mercury and thallium(III) interfere. Tellurium(IV)/selenium(IV) mixtures can be analysed by conducting the titration at different pH values. Ascorbic acid has featured in potentiometric and amperometric procedures for determination of milligram amounts of tellurium and selenium, individually and in admixture[53].

Tellurium(IV) and selenium(IV) can be determined coulometrically using electrogenerated hypobromite[54].

Detailed investigations into the polarographic reduction of tellurite have been carried out by Lingane and Niedrach[55] and Schmidt and von Stackelberg[56]. These and other studies have been largely confined to alkaline solutions. At a pH of 7–11 tellurium(IV) is reduced to the element. At the dropping mercury electrode this remains on the electrode. Above pH 11 reduction proceeds to the telluride ion Te^{2-}. Jamieson and Perone[57] have recently carried out a polarographic, coulometric and stationary electrode study of tellurium(IV) reduction in alkaline solutions.

Determination of tellurium(IV) in the range 8–20 μM has been made using oscillopolarography[58].

Miscellaneous methods

Neutron activation analysis has an estimated sensitivity of about 5×10^{-9} g for tellurium. Application has been made to tellurium in gallium arsenide[59] and rocks[60].

Tellurate can be determined by polarimetry[61]. The method is applicable to 0.15–1.5 mg $m\ell^{-1}$ of tellurium(VI). Large amounts of Te(IV), Se(IV) and Se(VI), and moderate amounts of As(V) do not interfere. Interference by Pb, Cd and Sn can be masked, but NO_3^- must be absent.

References

1. NAZARENKO, I.I. and ERMOKOV, A.N., *The Analytical Chemistry of Selenium and Tellurium* (Trans. R. Kondor), Halstead Press–John Wiley, New York (1972)
2. GREEN, T.E. and TURLEY, M., in *Treatise on Analytical Chemistry* (Ed. I.M. Kolthoff and P.J. Elving), Part II, Vol. 7, John Wiley, New York, 137 (1961)
3. LOWENHEIM, F.A., in *An Encyclopedia of Industrial Chemical Analysis* (Ed. F.D. Snell and L.S. Ettre), Vol. 17, Interscience, New York, 580 (1973)
4. LYLE, S.J., in *Comprehensive Analytical Chemistry* (Ed. C.L. and D.W. Wilson), Vol. 1C, Elsevier, Amsterdam, 305 (1962)
5. BOCK, R. and TSCHOPEL, P., *Z. analyt. Chem.*, **246**, 81 (1969)
6. KORKISH, J., *Modern Methods for the Separation of Rarer Metal Ions*, Pergamon Press, Oxford, 357 (1969)
7. STREL'NIKOVA, N.P. and LYSTSOVA, G.G., *Zav. Lab.*, **26**, 142 (1960); *Analyt. Abstr.*, **7**, 4240 (1960)
8. MUNZE, R., *J. prakt. Chem.*, **7**, 262 (1959)

9. BUSEV, A.I., BAGBANLY, I.L., BAGBANLY, S.I., GUSEINOV, I.K. and RUSTAMOV, N.KH., *Zh. analit. Khim.*, **25**, 1374 (1970); *Analyt. Abstr.*, **21**, 4075 (1971)
10. KIMURA, K., IKEDA, N. and INARIDA, M., *Japan Analyst*, **7**, 174 (1958); *Analyt. Abstr.*, **6**, 140 (1959)
11. HAVEZOV, I. and JORDANOV, N., *Talanta*, **21**, 1013 (1974)
12. BODE, H., *Z. analyt. Chem.*, **143**, 182 (1954)
13. BODE, H., *Z. analyt. Chem.*, **144**, 90 (1955)
14. MARCEK, M.V., KINSON, K. and BELCHER, C.B., *Analytica chim. Acta*, **41**, 447 (1968)
15. CHAKRABARTI, C.L., *Analytica chim. Acta*, **39**, 293 (1967)
16. KAWAMURA, K., ITO, H. and TANABE, T., *Japan Analyst*, **19**, 824 (1970); *Analyt. Abstr.*, **21**, 4107 (1971)
17. NAKAGAWA, G., *J. chem. Soc. Japan, pure Chem. Sect.*, **81**, 1258 (1960); *Analyt. Abstr.*, **9**, 4073 (1962)
18. KISH, P.P. and KREMENEVA, S.G., *Zh. analit. Khim.*, **25**, 2200 (1970); *Analyt. Abstr.*, **23**, 3137 (1972)
19. JORDANOV, N. and HAVEZOV, I., *Z. analyt. Chem.*, **248**, 296 (1969); *Analyt. Abstr.*, **20**, 174 (1971)
20. PLOTNIKOV, V.I., *Zh. analit. Khim.*, **14**, 595 (1959); *Analyt. Abstr.*, **7**, 2706 (1960)
21. MOGHISSI, A., *J. Chromat.*, **13**, 542 (1964)
22. WANG, J. and CHENG, K.W., *International Symposium on Analytical Chemistry*, Birmingham (1969)
23. SCHRENK, W.T. and BROWNING, B.L., *J. Am. chem. Soc.*, **48**, 139 (1926)
24. LENHER, V. and WAKEFIELD, H.F., *J. Am. chem. Soc.*, **45**, 1423 (1923)
25. NAIDU, P.P. and RAO, G.G., *Talanta*, **18**, 112 (1971)
26. KAUSHIK, R.L. and PROSAD, R., *J. Ind. Chem. Soc.*, **46**, 921 (1969)
27. MA, T.S. and ZOELLNER, W.G., *Mikrochim. Acta*, 329 (1971)
28. GUILBAULT, G.G. and MCCURDY, W.H., *Analytica chim. Acta*, **24**, 214 (1961)
29. BEYAK, R. and JASELSKIS, B., *Analyt. Chem.*, **42**, 518 (1970)
30. TOLSTIKOV, V.P. and EPIK, P.A., *Ukr. khim. Zh.*, **35**, 1219 (1969); *Analyt. Abstr.*, **19**, 4845 (1970)
31. DIKSHITULA, L.S.A. and SATYANARAYANA, D., *Talanta*, **22**, 313 (1975)
32. JOHNSON, R.A., *Colorimetric Determination of non-Metals* (Ed. D.F. Boltz), Interscience, New York, 315 (1958)
33. JOHNSON, R.A. and KWAN, F.P., *Analyt. Chem.*, **23**, 651 (1951)
34. Ref. 32, 323
35. ROBERTS, J.A., WINWOOD, J. and MILLETT, E.J., *Proceedings of the Society for Analytical Chemistry Conference at Nottingham* (1965), Heffer and Sons Ltd., Cambridge, 528 (1965)
36. LUKE, C.L., *Analyt. Chem.*, **31**, 572 (1959)
37. NAVRATIL, O. and SORFA, J., *Colln Czech. chem. Commun.*, **34**, 975 (1969); *Analyt. Abstr.*, **19**, 196 (1970)
38. LOOYENGA, R.W. and BOLTZ, D.F., *Mikrochim. Acta*, 507 (1971)
39. BUSEV, A.I. and SIMONOVA, L.N., *Zh. analit. Khim.*, **22**, 1850 (1967); *Analyt. Abstr.*, **17**, 832 (1969)
40. MEL'CHEKOVA, Z.E. and MURASHOVA, V.I., *Zh. analit. Khim.*, **25**, 556 (1970); *Analyt. Abstr.*, **21**, 1066 (1971)
41. KIRKBRIGHT, G.F., SAW, C.G. and WEST, T.S., *Talanta*, **16**, 65 (1969)
42. KIRKBRIGHT, G.F., SAW, C.G. and WEST, T.S., *Analyst*, **94**, 457 (1969)
43. KELYI, M.U. and KUSHNIRENKO, I.YA., *Zh. prikl. Spektrosk.*, **10**, 810 (1969); *Analyt. Abstr.*, **19**, 2044 (1970)
44. CHAKRABARTI, C.L., *Analytica chim. Acta*, **39**, 293 (1967)
45. COBB, W.D., FOSTER, W.W. and HARRISON, T.S., *Analyst*, **101**, 39 (1976)
46. THOMPSON, K.C. and THOMERSON, D.R., *Analyst*, **99**, 595 (1974)
47. GREENLAND, L.P. and CAMPBELL, E.Y., *Analytica chim. Acta*, **87**, 323 (1976)
48. THOMPSON, K.C., *Analyst*, **100**, 307 (1975)
49. SMITH, A.E., *Analyst*, **100**, 300 (1975)
50. BELCHER, R., KOUIMTZIS, T. and TOWNSHEND, A., *Analytica chim. Acta*, **68**, 297 (1974)
51. CORNWELL, J.C., *Analytica chim. Acta*, **53**, 325 (1971)
52. TULYUPA, F.M., BARKALOV, V.S. and USATENKO, YU.I., *Zh. analit. Khim.*, **22**, 399 (1967); *Analyt. Abstr.*, **16**, 122 (1969)
53. IVANOVA, Z.I., IGNATENKO, E.G. and TARASOVA, V.A., *Zh. analit. Khim.*, **28**, 1980 (1973); *Analyt. Abstr.*, **28**, 6B, 163 (1975)

54. AGASYAN, R.K., DENISOVA, A.N., AGASYAN, L.B. and NIKOLAEVA, E.R., *Zav. Lab.*, **34**, 129 (1968); *Analyt. Abstr.*, **16**, 2442 (1969)
55. LINGANE, J.J. and NIEDRACH, L.W., *J. Am. chem. Soc.*, **71**, 196 (1949)
56. SCHMIDT, H. and VON STACKELBERG, M., *J. Polarog. Soc.*, **8**, 49 (1962)
57. JAMIESON, R.A. and PERONE, S.P., *J. electroanalyt. Chem.*, **23**, 441 (1969)
58. CHIKRYZOVA, E.G. and KOPANSKAYA, L.S., *Zh. analit. Khim.*, **23**, 394 (1968); *Analyt. Abstr.*, **17**, 2707 (1969)
59. LLOYD, K.W., Ref. 35, 180
60. LAVI, N., *Analytica chim. Acta*, **70**, 199 (1974)
61. LANESE, J.G. and JASELSKIS, B., *Analyt. Chem.*, **35**, 1880 (1963)

Tetrafluoroborate

Fluoroborates (or tetrafluoroborates) find application mainly in the metal processing industries, for example in tin and lead plating. As good solvents for metal oxides they are particuarly useful in fluxing operations, electropolishing, and in cleaning metal surfaces prior to electroplating.

Separations

From an analytical standpoint they may be separated by precipitation with nitron or tetraphenylarsonium chloride (TPAC), although these methods, and particularly the first, suffer certain disadvantages. A much better method is to employ solvent extraction.

Pasztor and Bode[1] have carried out a systematic study of thionin derivatives for extraction and direct photometric determination of boron (which was converted to BF_4^-). Over 30 organic solvents, mainly chlorinated or brominated were included. Polyuektov, Kononenko and Lauer[2] use methyl violet at pH 3.4, extracting into benzene. More recently Behrends[3] employed tetraphenylarsonium chloride. At pH 7–12 this forms a water-insoluble complex with tetrafluoroborate which may be extracted into dichloromethane. After extraction it was used as the basis of a partition titrimetric method. Tetraphenylarsonium chloride was also used by Coursier, Hure and Platzer[4] who extracted into chloroform.

An extraction method based on ferroin, tris(1,10-phenanthroline) iron(II) sulphate has been developed by Archer, Doolittle and Young[5]. Here the ion-association complex with tetrafluoroborate is extracted at pH 2–10 into *n*-butyronitrile. The spectrophotometric method used following the extraction will be discussed below.

Determination

Gravimetric methods

Gravimetric determination of tetrafluoroborate as nitron fluoroborate, $C_{20}H_{16}N_4HBF_4$, has several drawbacks, particularly the relatively high solubility of the precipitate, which necessitates using an empirical factor. Use of tetraphenylarsonium chloride overcomes some of the disadvantages. It is more stable than nitron, the precipitate is purer, and it can be applied to smaller quantities of fluoroborate[6]. The precipitate is dried at 105 °C after 'controlled washing', details of which appear in the procedure given below.

Gravimetric determination of fluoroborate using tetraphenylarsonium chloride[6]

Reagents
Ammonium hydroxide (NH_4OH): 15M and 1M.
TPAC: 0.07M.
Tetraphenylarsonium tetrafluoroborate:
250 mℓ of a saturated solution to which is added 10 mℓ of 0.880 ammonia.

Procedure
To 10 mℓ of solution containing approximately 0.03 g NH_4BF_4, add 5 mℓ of 15M NH_4OH and 5 mℓ of water immediately before precipitation with TPAC. A volume of 0.07M TPAC sufficient to give a final concentration of 0.018M is added slowly, with stirring. Allow to stand in an ice bath for 1 h. Filter through a sintered glass filter of medium porosity. Wash with 3 mℓ cold dilute NH_4OH, then 30–40 mℓ of the tetraphenylarsonium tetrafluoroborate solution. When transfer of the precipitate is complete wash with 5 mℓ of cold dilute NH_4OH.

Dry to constant weight at 105 °C.

Spectrophotometric methods

In addition to the gravimetric method based on TPAC, and described above, the same workers developed an indirect spectrophotometric method using the same reagent. TPAC is added to precipitate the tetrafluoroborate. Excess of the reagent is determined spectrophotometrically in the UV at 220 nm.

Spectrophotometric determination of fluoroborate[6]

Procedure
To 5 mℓ of solution containing 0.02–0.04 g NH_4BF_4 in a 25-mℓ volumetric flask, add 5 mℓ of 0.880 ammonia and 10.00 mℓ of standard TPAC (0.06689M used in original work). Dilute to 25 mℓ and allow to stand for 1 h with occasional shaking. Pipette 5 mℓ, using a pipette with a filter paper wrapped lightly around the tip, and held by a rubber band. Dilute to 2ℓ, and measure the absorbance at 220 nm against a reference made by diluting 1 mℓ of 0.880 ammonia to 2ℓ.

Archer, Doolittle and Young[5] use ferroin for direct spectrophotometric determination of tetrafluoroborate. The ion-association complex is selectively extracted, in the presence of ferroin, into *n*-butyronitrile, and the absorbance measured at 520 nm. 74 per cent of the tetrafluoroborate is extracted in a single extraction; Beer's law holds over a wide concentration range. KNO_2, KBr, KNO_3, KSCN and $KHC_8H_4O_4$ cause strong interference, NH_4Cl causes moderate interference, while Na_2SO_4, $Na_2C_2O_4$, NaH_2PO_4, Na_3PO_4, $NaKC_4H_4O_6 \cdot 4H_2O$, $K_2Cr_2O_7$ and Na_2SO_3 cause slight interference.

Miscellaneous methods

A titrimetric method based on initial precipitation of fluoroborate as cetyltrimethylammonium tetrafluoroborate, $C_{19}H_{42}NBF_4$, has been described[7]. The precipitate solubility is less than one-tenth of that of nitron tetrafluoroborate and the method may be used in the presence of hydrofluoric and boric acids. The need for three standard solutions of three different reagents detracts from the usefulness of the method.

Mention has been made of extraction of the water-insoluble TPA-tetrafluoroborate complex into dichloromethane[3]. This was developed into a partition titration method in which the excess of TPAC in the aqueous phase was determined amperometrically, or photometrically at 220 nm. Neither fluoride nor borate interferes in the method. Several anions which react with TPAC, for example chlorate, perchlorate and nitrate, must be absent.

Ion-selective electrodes have found application in the determination of fluoroborate. In one method titration of tetrafluoroborate with TPAC at 2 °C is monitored by a perchlorate liquid ion-exchange electrode (Orion Research, Inc.), also sensitive to tetrafluoroborate. Amounts as low as 0.25 mmol may be determined to within 1 per cent[8]. Another method for determination of boron via tetrafluoroborate employs the same electrode. Nitrate and iodide were found to cause greatest interference[9].

References

1. PASZTOR, L. and BODE, J.D., *Analytica chim. Acta*, **24**, 467 (1961)
2. POLUEKTOV, B.S., KONONENKO, L.I. and LAUER, R.S., *Zh. analit. Khim.*, **13**, 396 (1958)
3. BEHRENDS, K., *Z. analyt. Chem.*, **216**, 13 (1966); *Analyt. Abstr.*, **14**, 4643 (1967)
4. COURSIER, J., HURE, J. and PLATZER, R., *Analytica chim. Acta.*, **13**, 379 (1955)
5. ARCHER, V.S., DOOLITTLE, F.G. and YOUNG, L.M., *Talanta*, **15**, 864 (1968)
6. AFFSPRUNG, H.E. and ARCHER, V.S., *Analyt. Chem.*, **36**, 2512 (1964)
7. SCHAACK, H.J. and WAGNER, W., *Z. analyt. Chem.*, **146**, 326 (1955); *Analyt. Abstr.*, **2**, 2996 (1955)
8. SMITH, M.J. and MANAHAN, S.E., *Analytica chim. Acta*, **48**, 315 (1969)
9. CARLSON, R.M. and PAUL, J.L., *Analyt. Chem.*, **40**, 1292 (1968)

Tetraphenylborate

The tetraphenylborate anion (Ph_4B^-) is unique in that the salts with K, Rb, Cs and NH_4^+ are insoluble. Precipitation using sodium tetraphenylborate is a familiar method for determination of these elements.

Separation

Precipitation as the insoluble alkali salts provides a separation of tetraphenylborate from almost all other anions. Another method is solvent extraction. Yamamoto, Okamoto and Tao[1] extract the ion-pair formed between copper(I) chelate cations (cuproine- or neocuproine-) and tetraphenylborate, [Cu-(cuproine)$_2^+$][Ph_4B^-] into chloroform or chlorobenzene.

Determination

Spectrophotometric methods

In the extraction of tetraphenylborate by the coloured copper(I) cations referred to above, a spectrophotometric determination is possible on the extract. After shaking the extract with anhydrous sodium sulphate to remove traces of water, the absorbance is measured at 550 nm.

Tetraphenylborates separated as the insoluble alkali salts may be decomposed by strong acids and the resulting boric acid determined. Raber and Likussar[7] used 1,1′-dianthrimide in this method, measuring the absorbance at 620 nm.

Electroanalytical methods

Potassium tetraphenylborate is soluble in acetone–water mixtures but the silver salt is insoluble[2]. This has been used as the basis of analytical procedures. Patriarche and Lingane[3] claim that coulometric titration of the tetraphenylborate ion with silver(I) in an aqueous–acetone medium is stoichiometrically exact although doubts had been cast on this in earlier work[4]. The method serves as an accurate finish to determination of small amounts (0.3–10 mg) of K^+, Rb^+, or Cs^+ following precipitation as the tetraphenylborates. Sodium nitrate is used as a supporting electrolyte in a neutral medium containing 35–50 % acetone[3].

Heyrovsky[5] has used both potentiometric and amperometric end-points in titrating tetraphenylborate with $Hg(NO_3)_2$ or $Hg(ClO_4)_2$. The potentiometric circuit involved a mercury coated platinum electrode and saturated calomel electrode joined by an agar bridge, the amperometric circuit a dropping mercury electrode and saturated calomel electrode.

Another amperometric method has been described in which tetraphenylborate precipitated as the potassium salt is dissolved in acetonitrile–water mixtures and titrated with aqueous silver nitrate[6]. This method utilizes a dropping mercury electrode as indicator with a mercury pool as a non-polarized reference electrode. A high degree of precision is claimed.

References

1. YAMAMOTO, Y., OKAMOTO, N. and TAO, E., *Analytica chim. Acta,* **47**, 127 (1969)
2. RUDORFF, W. and ZANNIER, H., *Z. analyt. Chem.*, **137**, 1 (1952)
3. PATRIARCHE, G.J. and LINGANE, J.J., *Analyt. Chem.*, **39**, 168 (1967)
4. CRANE, F.E., *Analytica chim. Acta,* **16**, 370 (1957)
5. HEYROVSKY, A., *Z. analyt. Chem.*, **173**, 301 (1960); *Analyt. Abstr.*, **7**, 4853 (1960)
6. FINDEIS, A.F. and VRIES, T. DE, *Analyt. Chem.,* **28**, 1899 (1956)
7. RABER, H. and LIKUSSAR, W., *Mikrochim. Acta,* 92 (1972)

Thiocyanate

Ammonium and alkali thiocyanates find application in several fields including photography, catalysis, agricultural chemicals (notably in weedkillers), dyeing and printing of textiles, and rust inhibition (hence in paints). Ammonium thiocyanate is an important starting material in the manufacture of thiourea. Though not as toxic as cyanide, thiocyanate is harmful to aquatic life. Its determination at low levels in water and effluents is therefore important.

Reviews of its analytical chemistry have been published[1–3], though it appears to have been overlooked in recent reviews covering sulphur compounds. The most useful review is that by Hanley and Czech[2] which includes an account of separation methods as well as a comprehensive treatment of methods for determination of thiocyanate.

Separation

In many cases separation of thiocyanate is not required, selectivity being achieved by other means, for example by masking. Thus for thiocyanate/cyanide mixtures, cyanide can be masked by formaldehyde, and the thiocyanate titration carried out without interference, by the Volhard method.

1. Precipitation

Thiocyanate can be precipitated as silver thiocyanate from a dilute nitric acid solution. If the precipitate is treated with hydrogen sulphide, insoluble silver sulphide is formed and thiocyanate passes back into solution. The method is applicable to trace quantities of thiocyanate as well as macro amounts[4].

Sparingly soluble cuprous thiocyanate can be used for separation. Precipitation is made by adding cupric sulphate and bisulphite to the thiocyanate solution. Both the above insoluble forms can be used for gravimetric determination of thiocyanate.

Precipitation as the light green copper pyridine thiocyanate $Cu(C_{10}H_6NO_2)_2H_2O$ was described by Spacu[5]. Several metallic ions interfere if the reaction is used for separation of thiocyanate.

2. Solvent extraction

The triphenylarsonium ion $(C_6H_5)_4As^+$ and related onium cations can be used for separating thiocyanate from other sulphur anions by solvent extraction. Thiocyanate is 97% extracted into chloroform at pH 1–2 whereas thiosulphate, sulphite and sulphate are little extracted[6]. Using tetraphenylphosphonium chloride, thiocyanate is completely extracted into chloroform at pH 2–12. Again, $S_2O_3^{2-}$, SO_3^{2-} and SO_4^{2-} are little extracted[7].

Other extraction systems are cited in the monograph by De, Khopkar and Chalmers[8].

3. Paper and thin-layer chromatography

These methods are important for separation of thiocyanate at trace levels. Details of some of the methods are given in *Table 19*. Several additional references are given in the review by Hanley and Czech[2].

4. Gas chromatography

This is discussed in the miscellaneous group of methods for determination of thiocyanate.

Determination

Bromine will oxidize thiocyanate quantitatively to sulphate.

$$SCN^- + 4Br_2 + 4H_2O \rightarrow SO_4^{2-} + 7Br^- + BrCN + 8H^+$$

It may be determined in that form after removing excess bromine.

Gravimetric methods

In view of the alternative methods available, it is doubtful whether the gravimetric determination of thiocyanate finds current usage.

Silver thiocyanate is precipitated in dilute HNO_3 and can be weighed after drying at 115 °C. Halides and cyanide must be absent. Gravimetric determination as cuprous thiocyanate, has been known for a considerable time. The method is better known[15] for determination of copper. Precipitation is made from neutral or slightly acid solution by saturating the solution with sulphur dioxide in the cold (or adding as a saturated solution) followed by addition of cupric sulphate. The precipitate is weighed after drying at 110–120 °C. Thiocyanate can be determined as $BaSO_4$ after adding bromine water and heating on a water bath for 1 h. Precipitation as copper pyridine thiocyanate has been referred to earlier.

Table 19 Paper and thin-layer chromatographic methods for separation of thiocyanate

Technique	*Solvent*	SCN^- *separated from:*	*Ref.*
Paper (Whatman No. 1)	Butanol–acetone–aq. NH_3 (3:13:4) or butanol–dimethyl formamide–aq. NH_3 (3:1:1)	Cl^-, Br^-, I^-	9
TLC (silica gel)	Several including butanol–propanol–dibutylamine (9 : 9 : 2)	F^-, Cl^-, Br^-, I^-, CN^- $[Fe(CN)_6]^{3-}$, $[Fe(CN)_6]^{4-}$	10
TLC (maize starch)	Acetone–3M aq. NH_3 (1 : 4)	NO_2^-, $S_2O_3^{2-}$, CrO_4^{2-}, N_3^- CN^-, BO_3^{3-}, S^{2-}, AsO_3^{3-} NO_3^-, SO_4^{2-}, PO_4^{3-}, AsO_4^{3-}	11
TLC silica gel + 5% soluble starch	Acetone–H_2O (10 : 1)	Cl^-, Br^-, I^-, $[Fe(CN)_6]^{3-}$ $[Fe(CN)_6]^{4-}$, ClO_3^-, BrO_3^- IO_3^-, NO_3^-	12
TLC Gelman SA and SG	Several including butanol–pyridine–acetic acid–H_2O (15 : 10 : 3 : 12)	SO_4^{2-}, $S_2O_3^{2-}$, $S_3O_6^{2-}$, $S_4O_6^{2-}$	13
TLC silica gel on Al foil	$FeCl_3$ solution	CN^-, $[Fe(CN)_6]^{3-}$, $[Fe(CN)_6]^{4-}$	14

Titrimetric methods

2. Iodimetric methods

One of the most widely used methods[16,18] for thiocyanate is based on its reaction with bromine in weakly acid conditions to form cyanogen bromide.

$$SCN^- + 4Br_2 + 4H_2O \rightarrow CNBr + SO_4^{2-} + 7Br^- + 8H^+$$

Excess bromine is removed by adding phenol, hydrazine, etc., without affecting the cyanogen bromide which can then be evaluated iodimetrically by addition of KI and titrating the liberated iodine with thiosulphate.

$$BrCN + 2I^- \rightarrow CN^- + I_2 + Br^-$$

Chloride, bromide, sulphide, sulphites and thiosulphates do not interfere. Cyanide interferes and must be removed or masked. Experimental details are given below.

Another iodimetric procedure employs excess standard iodine to oxidize thiocyanate in a bicarbonate medium[17,19].

$$SCN^- + 4I_2 + 4H_2O \rightarrow SO_4^{2-} + 7I^- + ICN + 8H^+$$

Excess iodine is back-titrated with standard thiosulphate. Cyanogen iodide is not affected by thiosulphate, but reacts with starch, so that detection of the end-point must be based on disappearance of the yellow iodine colour.

A useful modification of the method has been developed by Sant[20]. In this the oxidation is made in a borate–boric acid buffer at pH 9–10, and excess iodine is titrated with arsenic(III). The presence of the buffer causes the reaction to go to completion.

$$2I_2 + As_2O_3 + 2H_2O \leftrightarrows 4HI + As_2O_5$$

Iodimetric determination of thiocyanate[16]

Procedure

To 0.3–90 mg of thiocyanate in an iodine flask, add 5 mℓ of 20% orthophosphoric acid followed by bromine-water until a deep yellow colour persists. Shake and allow to stand for a few minutes. Add 2 mℓ of 5% phenol solution and shake until the bromine colour disappears.

Add 0.5 g KI, shake to dissolve, and allow to stand for a few minutes. Titrate with standard thiosulphate using starch as indicator. From the equations given above it will be seen that

$$SCN^- \equiv 2S_2O_3^{2-}$$

Note

If cyanide is present, removal by distillation can be carried out. This is discussed in the cyanide section.

---

3. Argentimetric

The Volhard method for chloride can be applied in exactly the same form to thiocyanate. An excess of standard Ag^+ is added, and back-titration made with standard thiocyanate using ferric alum as indicator. The end-point is indicated by the intense red colour of $Fe(SCN)^{++}$. The titration can be performed in a relatively strong acidic solution. Some acid is essential to prevent hydrolysis of iron(III). Interference is given by cyanide and halides. When thiocyanate is accompanied by cyanide, the following procedure can be employed. Cyanide is masked using formaldehyde and the Volhard method applied to the thiocyanate without interference. Alternatively, the sum of cyanide and thiocyanate can be determined by the Volhard method, and cyanide determined alone in a second aliquot using the Liebig titration. Thiocyanate is evaluated by difference.

Thiocyanate can also be titrated directly with $AgNO_3$ using adsorption indicators. The method suffers from the same defects as the corresponding method for halides, in particular the indistinct end-point when moderate amounts of electrolytes are present. Dichlorofluorescein is probably the best indicator. Eosin (tetrabromofluorescein) is good. Being a much stronger acid than fluorescein it can be used in solutions as acidic as pH 2.

Titrimetric determination of thiocyanate using $AgNO_3$ and eosin as indicator

Indicator

0.1 % eosin in 70 % ethanol.

Procedure

Acidify the thiocyanate aliquot with few mℓ of 6M acetic acid. Add 10 drops of indicator and titrate with a standard $AgNO_3$ solution until the precipitate suddenly becomes intensely red.

---

3. Using mercuric nitrate

This method again is similar to the corresponding method for chloride in which diphenylcarbazone is used as indicator.

The titration forms part of a method by Deshmukh (see Ref. 21) for determination of cerium(IV). In this, excess of standard potassium thiocyanate is added, and back-titration made with standard $Hg(NO_3)_2$.

Sodium nitroprusside can be used as an alternative indicator.

4. Miscellaneous

The literature indicates that a wide range of oxidants have been proposed for determination of thiocyanate, these including bromate, hypobromite, hypochlorite, permanganate, iodate, chloramine, N-bromosuccinimide, hexacyanoferrate(III) and Ce(IV). Details of most appear in well-known sources on redox titrimetry[21,22]. No obvious advantages are apparent in many of these reagents, and it becomes a matter of personal preference as to which one is used.

Cerium(IV) has been investigated by several workers, this resulting in a multiplicity of recommended procedures. Singh and Siefker[23] have attempted to rationalize the situation. Using cerium(IV) in conjunction with iodine monochloride as pre-oxidant, they find that accurate and reproducible results are obtained in the presence of HCl in the pH range 1.7–4.5M. Low results obtained at high acidity reported by previous workers are explained in terms of loss of H_2S and SO_2, this being supported by infra-red evidence.

Of the new methods proposed, one employing N-bromosuccinimide (*Structure 31*) appears to have several advantages[24]. The reagent itself can

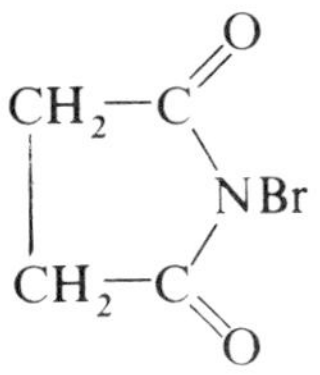

$$\begin{array}{l} CH_2-C(=O) \\ \quad | \qquad \backslash \\ \quad | \qquad NBr \\ \quad | \qquad / \\ CH_2-C(=O) \end{array}$$

Structure 31 N-bromosuccinimide

be used as a reference standard, and is stable. The titration is direct and relatively simple to carry out. Bordeaux red is used as indicator. An account of earlier work using the reagent is given in a standard text[21].

De Sousa[25–27] has developed novel compleximetric methods for determination of thiocyanate in mixtures. In $SCN^-/CN^-/Cl^-$ mixtures use is made of the fact that AgCl is insoluble in hot HNO_3 while AgCN and AgSCN are decomposed and dissolved, the AgSCN being oxidized to sulphate. The AgCl is filtered off, washed, dissolved in a solution of potassium tetracyanonickelate and the liberated Ni^{2+} titrated with EDTA.

$$2AgCl + [Ni(CN)_4]^{2-} \rightarrow 2[Ag(CN)_2]^- + Ni^{2+} + 2Cl^-$$

Filtrate sulphate resulting from thiocyanate is precipitated as $BaSO_4$ and this evaluated titrimetrically using EDTA. Cyanide is determined in a separate aliquot by adding a known excess of standard $NiSO_4$ to form nickel tetracyanide, and titrating the excess Ni^{2+} with EDTA.

Nomura[28] uses a different approach for SCN^-/CN^- and $SCN^-/CN^-/I^-$ mixtures[29]. Titration is made with $Hg(II)NO_3$ in the presence of EDTA. The end-point is detected photometrically. Mixed ligand complexes are formed but while the cyanide–Hg(II)–EDTA does not absorb at 240 nm, the thiocyanate–Hg(II)–EDTA does. The reaction rate of cyanide with mercury(II)–EDTA is much faster than the corresponding rate with thiocyanate. A sequential titration can therefore be performed, in which the end-point for cyanide is marked by the appearance of an absorption at 240 nm. The corresponding end-point for thiocyanate is indicated by the attainment of a constant absorption. Iodide and sulphide interfere with both titrations. Bromide, Ag^+ and NH_4^+ interfere with the thiocyanate titration only.

The $CN^-/SCN^-/I^-$ determination is also based on the formation of 1:1 complexes with mercury(II)–EDTA, but employs methylthymol blue or cresolphthalein as visual indicators.

Spectroscopic methods

1. Colorimetric and spectrophotometric methods

Thiocyanate reacts with iron(III) to give intensely red-coloured complexes. At relatively low thiocyanate concentrations the coloured species are predominantly $Fe(SCN)^{2+}$. The reaction has found extensive use[29] both in the determination of thiocyanate and iron. Fluoride, metaphosphates, pyrophosphates, oxalate, salicylate, keto acids, phenols and tannins interfere. Appreciable amounts of SO_4^{2-}, PO_4^{3-} and Mn interfere. Mercury(I) and silver(I) form insoluble thiocyanates. Mercury(II), Cd, Zn and Sb(III) form complexes with thiocyanate with consequent reduction in the $Fe(SCN)^{2+}$ colour. Copper, Bi, Ti, U, Mo, Ru, Ir and Os interfere by forming thiocyanate complexes. Iodide interferes by affecting the stability of the complex. Non-interference by cyanide is an important feature of the method.

The method has several advantages, for example, the reagent is readily available and the procedure is straightforward. The main disadvantages are colour instability and interference by a wide range of species. As far as the colour instability is concerned, this is a function of several factors including the type and concentration of acid used, and temperature. In an investigation of thiocyanate determination in various effluents and polluted waters, Whiston and Cherry[30] remove phenolic compounds using De-Acidite E anion-exchange resin (in chloride form) before applying the method. The method is recommended for determination of thiocyanate in industrial effluents[31]. This source contains a table giving maximum permissible levels of interfering ions for the procedure given.

The benzidine–pyridine method introduced by Aldridge[32, 33] suffers from the disadvantage that benzidine is carcinogenic.

Thiocyanate reacts with the copper–pyridine system to give the dipyridine cupric thiocyanate complex $Cu(C_5H_5N)_2(SCN)_2$. This was developed into a spectrophotometric method by Kruse and Mellon[34]. Though not as sensitive as the pyridine–pyrazolone method, it is highly specific and the procedure simple and rapid. The complex can be extracted into chloroform and the absorbance measured at 410 nm. The original range in the Kruse and Mellon procedure was 0.5–20 ppm. Interferences are shown in *Table 20.*

Table 20 Interferences in the copper–pyridine spectrophotometric method for thiocyanate

Ion	*Interfering level* (ppm)
CN^-, $[Fe(CN)_6]^{3-}$ (See note)	5
Cyanate (See note)	50
Br^-	100
BrO_3^-	200
Acetate, oxalate, tartrate	300
Citrate, NO_3^-	500
Cl^-, CrO_4^{2-}, F^-, IO_3^-, PO_4^{3-}	1000
SO_4^{2-}	10 000

Note: Cyanides, complex cyanides and cyanate can be decomposed by boiling with acids. Iodide interferes, but can be oxidized to iodine and extracted into carbon tetrachloride. Mercury and nickel are the only cations to give serious interference.

The pyridine–pyrazolone method is based on conversion of thiocyanate to cyanogen chloride by chloramine-T using Fe(III) as catalyst, and then reacting the cyanogen chloride with pyridine containing 3-methyl-1-phenyl-2-pyrazolin-5-one to give a blue dye[35,33]. Beer's law holds over the range 0.4–2.5 μg of thiocyanate. Extraction into *n*-butanol enhances the sensitivity. Absorbance measurements are made at 620 nm in water or 630 nm when extracted into *n*-butanol. The reagent is relatively unstable and requires lengthy preparation. Phenolic substances interfere. Reducing species can be tolerated in small amounts only. Further details of the method are given in the monograph by Sandell[29].

The methods already described have been in use for a considerable time. Attention will now be given to newer methods. Neas and Guyon[36] find that thiocyanate reacts with a mixed oxidation state rhenium(III)–rhenium(V) species to give a complex showing maximum absorbance at 390 nm. It is established that the complex is a 1:2 rhenium–thiocyanate type. Beer's law holds over the range 0–5 ppm. For a complete list of levels at which foreign ions can be tolerated, the original paper should be consulted. Iodate and bromate interfere at all levels. The most serious interferences are the oxidizing species Ce(IV), $Cr_2O_7^{2-}$, VO_3^-, ClO_3^-, IO_4^-, NO_3^-, and NO_2^- which interfere at 3 ppm or below for 9.5 ppm of thiocyanate present.

Einaga, Ishi and Iwasaki[37] find that thiocyanate forms a mixed-ligand complex with mercury(II) in the presence of quinoline. The resulting complex bisthiocyanatobisquinoline mercury(II) is extracted into $CHCl_3$ in the pH range 5.1–6.5, and its absorbance measured at 498 nm. Beer's law holds from about 20 to 50 μg thiocyanate. Chloride, Br^-, I^-, CN^- and large amounts of NH_4^+ and Cu(II) interfere.

Yamamoto, Tarumoto and Hanamoto[38] utilize the ternary chelate formed between thiocyanate and tris(1,10 phenanthroline)Fe(II). This is extracted into nitrobenzene and the decrease in absorbance of the aqueous phase measured at 516 nm. The range is 2–40 μM thiocyanate. Some interfering cations can be masked with EDTA. Interfering anions must be removed.

Tsubouchi[39] employs neutral red in an extractive-spectrophotometric procedure. It was found that when small amounts of certain anions such as thiocyanate, perchlorate, iodide or bromomercurate(II), were present in the aqueous phase, neutral red cations were extracted into an organic solvent as ion-pairs. The colour intensity of the organic phase was found to be proportional to the amount of the particular anion present in the aqueous phase. In the case of thiocyanate, continuous variation measurements indicate that it is extracted as (neutral red)$^+$ SCN. The absorbance maximum is at 552 nm. Nitrobenzene is used as solvent, the colour of the extract remaining constant for 2 h. Interferences are given in *Table 21*.

The *p*-phenylenediamine method described for cyanide can be applied to thiocyanate in effluents in the absence of cyanide and complex cyanides[40]. The distillation procedure may be omitted. Conversion of the cyanide calibration curve for use with thiocyanate is made by multiplying by 2.23.

Methylene blue and thiocyanate form a 1:1 complex extractable into dichloroethane. Koh and Iwasaki[41] have based a method on the system. The decrease in absorbance at 657 nm is measured. Iodide and perchlorate interfere when present in amounts comparable with thiocyanate. The range is 0.2 μM–10 μM thiocyanate.

Table 21 Effects of foreign ions on extractive-spectrophotometric determination of thiocyanate using neutral red[39]

Ion[a]	*Mole ratio*	*Recovery of SCN (%)*[b]	*Ion*[a]	*Mole ratio*	*Recovery of SCN (%)*[b]
Ca^{2+}	50	101	SiO_3^{2-}	100	100
Mg^{2+}	50	100	Cl^-	200	102
Al^{3+}	50	100	Br^-	200	103
Fe^{3+}	3	82	CN^-	500	97
	30	99[c]	HCO_3^-	500	98
NH_4^+	500	101	NO_3^-	5	106
$H_2PO_4^-$	500	99	F^-	500	98
SO_4^{2-}	500	101	CH_3COO^-	300	103

[a] Cations were added as their sulphates; anions were added as their sodium or potassium salts.
[b] SCN^- taken: 8×10^{-6}M as KSCN.
[c] EDTA added: 10^{-3}M.

2. Atomic absorption spectroscopy

An indirect AAS method has been based on the copper content of the dithiocyanate–dipyridine–Cu(II) complex[42]. The range is 0.5–2.0 ppm SCN^-.

3. Molecular emission cavity analysis (MECA)

MECA for sulphur-containing compounds is based on measuring the S_2 emission at 384 nm. The method is sensitive allowing ng amounts to be determined in samples of a few μℓ. Potassium thiocyanate gives a broad multipeak response when present alone; addition of perchloric acid gives a single, enhanced and more rapid response. Phosphoric acid enhances the peak still more[43] giving the greatest intensity per ng sulphur for a range of sulphur anions including thiocyanate. The reference quoted includes an account of the technique itself. A brief description of the technique is given in the sulphide section on p. 580.

Electroanalytical methods

1. Potentiometric methods including ion-selective electrodes

Thiocyanate can be titrated potentiometrically with Ag^+ using a silver electrode and with $Ba(NO_3)_2$ present to reduce adsorption errors. Scheibitz[44] has used the Ag^+ potentiometric titration in gelatin for the sequential titration of bromide and thiocyanate. In aqueous solution these ions cannot be discriminated by potentiometric titration. In the presence of gelatin the specific surface of AgBr becomes relatively larger, and bromide more strongly adsorbed than thiocyanate.

The mercurimetric titration of thiocyanate can be carried out potentiometrically using a silver wire indicator electrode, but the accuracy appears to be low[45].

Differential electrolytic potentiometry has been applied by Bishop and Dhaneshwar[46] to argentimetric titrations including that of thiocyanate. A brief account of the technique is given on p. 316.

Hirsch and Portock[47] report that the Orion perchlorate electrode (liquid ion-exchange type 92-81) is also sensitive to thiocyanate and perrhenate. Potentiometric titration of thiocyanate with Ag^+ and Hg^{2+} using the electrode was found to be satisfactory. Ross and Durst[48] report a solid-state thiocyanate electrode, consisting of AgS and AgSCN in finely divided state, mixed and pressed in the form of a polycrystalline membrane. The analytical behaviour of an electrode of AgSCN mixed with thermoplastic polymer has been investigated by Mascini[49]. It was found to be sensitive to Ag^+ and thiocyanate, giving a response of 59 mV per decade of concentration change. In the concentration range 0.1 M–10 µM, changes in pH from 1 to 13 had no effect. Behaviour in non-aqueous solvents was also studied. Here the response was almost Nernstian in the 0.1 M–0.1 mM range.

A solid-state thiocyanate ion selective electrode is now commercially available[50], the Orion 94–58. Its concentration range is given as 10^0–5×10^{-6} M. Bromide, NH_3, $S_2O_3{}^{2-}$, CN^-, I^- and S^{2-} interfere seriously, but Cl^- can be tolerated in quantities up to 20 times the amount of thiocyanate present.

2. *Coulometric methods*

The Ag^+ ion can be electrogenerated with 100% current efficiency at a silver anode, and has been used in coulometric procedures for thiocyanate. Both constant potential and constant current forms of the method have been developed[51].

3. *Polarography*

A good account of the development of polarographic methods for thiocyanate is contained in one of the sources quoted earlier[2]. Plowman and Wilson[52] applied the technique to analysis of acidic solutions containing HCN, H_2O_2 and $SO_4{}^{2-}$ as well as SCN^-. Their investigation confirmed the well-formed anodic wave due to reversible depolarization of a dropping mercury electrode. Perchloric acid (0.1M) was found to be a satisfactory supporting electrolyte. Nyman and Alberts[53] studied the anodic polarographic oxidation of mercury in solutions of thiocyanate. An interpretation is made in terms of complex ions of the type

$$[Hg(SCN)_j]^{(2-j)} \qquad \text{where } j = 2, 3 \text{ and } 4.$$

The appropriate stepwise formation constants are evaluated.

Miscellaneous methods

The catalytic effect of SCN^-, $S_2O_3{}^-$ and S^{2-} on the iodine–azide reaction has been known for some time[54].

$$2N_3{}^- + I_2 \rightarrow 2I^- + N_2$$

Michalski and Wtorkowska[55] report that amounts of thiocyanate down to 8×10^{-11} g mℓ$^{-1}$ can be determined using this effect. The kinetic measurements are carried out amperometrically.

Both thiocyanate and cyanide have been determined using gas-chromatography[56]. Treatment with bromine converts each to cyanogen bromide which is determined gas-chromatographically using electron capture detection. As little as 10^{-8} g of the anions can be determined. For thiocyanate the calibration graphs are linear over the range 0.0–1.2 ppm. An improvement in sensitivity is obtained if the cyanogen bromide is extracted into diisopropyl ether before injection into the column. The detection limit then is 1 ppb(10^9) of cyanogen bromide. Complex cyanides do not interfere but can be determined after conversion to simple cyanides. Thiocyanate in thiocyanate/cyanide mixtures can be determined by masking cyanide with formaldehyde.

Microgram to milligram amounts of thiocyanate (as well as Cl^-, CN^- and PO_4^{3-}) can be determined indirectly by X-ray fluorescence[57]. Thiocyanate in the range 6 µg–1 mg is precipitated by $AgNO_3$, with Br^- or I^- being used as reference standards. The mixed precipitates are analysed directly on the filter paper.

Celap and Weisz[58] employ ring spot colorimetry for determination of SCN^- as well as Cl^-, Br^-, I^-, AsO_4^{3-}, $Cr_2O_7^{2-}$ and $[Fe(CN)_6]^{3-}$. Quantitative evaluation is made by comparison with standard silver sulphide rings. The anions are washed into the ring zone and fixed there as the insoluble silver salts. These are converted to silver sulphide for comparison. The method is applicable to milligram quantities of thiocyanate.

Another micro quantitative method on paper has been described by Ganchev and Koev[59]. Here a small known volume containing 10–150 µg of thiocyanate is placed in the centre of a paper strip evenly impregnated with silver chromate. Migration of thiocyanate is effected by slow introduction of water through a second filter paper arranged vertically below the strip. The thiocyanate reacts with silver chromate forming white spots of silver thiocyanate. These are subsequently dried, cut out, and weighed. Thiocyanate can be determined alone or in mixtures with chloride and iodide. The simple glass apparatus employed is described in the paper.

Thiocyanate and iodide in mixtures can be analysed by thermometric titration using $AgNO_3$ as titrant[60]. A differential titration apparatus was employed in the original work. This gave sharp end-points which enabled each constituent to be determined when present in 0.01 M solution.

References

1. HEINRICH, B.J., in *Treatise on Analytical Chemistry* (Ed. I.M. Kolthoff and P.J. Elving), Part II, Vol. 7, Interscience, New York, 87 (1961)
2. HANLEY, A.V. and CZECH, F.W., in *The Analytical Chemistry of Sulphur and its Compounds* (Ed. J.H. Karchmer), Part I, Wiley-Interscience, New York and London, 379 (1970)
3. LOWENHEIM, F.A., in *Encyclopedia of Industrial Chemical Analysis* (Ed. F.D. Snell and L.S. Ettre), Vol. 18, Interscience, New York, 433 (1973)
4. CHARLOT, G. and BEZIER, D., *Quantitative Inorganic Analysis,* Methuen, London, 382 (1957)
5. SPACU, G., *Bul. Soc. Sti. Cluj*, **1**, 284 (1922); *J. chem. Soc.* **ii**, 40 (1923)
6. BOCK, R. and BEILSTEIN, G.M., *Z. analyt. Chem.*, **192**, 44 (1963)
7. BOCK, R. and JAINZ, J., *Z. analyt. Chem.*, **198**, 315 (1963)
8. DE, A.K., KHOPKAR, S.M. and CHALMERS, R.A., *Solvent Extraction of Metals,* Van Nostrand, New York (1970)
9. MAO, C-H., *Acta chim. Sinica,* **30**, 496 (1964); *Analyt. Abstr.*, **13**, 533 (1966)
10. GAGLIARDI, E. and POKORNY, G., *Mikrochim. Acta,* 699 (1965)
11. CANIC, V.D., TURCIC, M.N., BUGARSKI-VOJINOVIC, M.B. and PERISIC, N.U., *Z. analyt. Chem.*, **229**, 93 (1967); *Analyt. Abstr.*, **15**, 5211 (1968)

12. KAWANABE, K., TAKITANI, S., MIYAZAKI, M. and TAMURA, Z., *Japan Analyst*, **13**, 976 (1964); *Analyt. Abstr.*, **13**, 976 (1964)
13. KELLY, D.P., *J. Chromat.*, **51**, 343 (1970)
14. THIELEMANN, H., *Z. analyt. Chem.*, **270**, 128 (1974)
15. NEWMAN, E.J., *Analyst*, **88**, 500 (1963)
16. SCHULEK, E., *Z. analyt. Chem.*, **62**, 337 (1923); *Chem. Abstr.*, **17**, 3465 (1923)
17. RUPP, E. and SCHIED, A., *Ber.*, **35**, 2191 (1902)
18. KOLTHOFF, I.M. and BELCHER, R., *Volumetric Analysis III*, Interscience, New York, 303 (1957)
19. Ref. 18, 305
20. SANT, B.R., *Ber.*, **88**, 581 (1955); *Analyt. Abstr.*, **2**, 2375 (1955)
21. BERKA, A., VULTERIN, J. and ZYKA, J., *Newer Redox Titrants*, Pergamon Press, Oxford (1965)
22. KOLTHOFF, I.M. and BELCHER, R., *Volumetric Analysis III*, Interscience, New York (1957)
23. SINGH, S. and SIEFKER, J.R., *Analytica chim. Acta*, **27**, 489 (1962)
24. SARWAR, M., WAHEED, H.A., CHOWDHRI, A. and THIBERT, R.J., *Mikrochim. Acta*, 683 (1973)
25. DE SOUSA, A., *Talanta*, **8**, 782 (1961)
26. DE SOUSA, A., *Inf. Quim. Anal.*, **16**, 126 (1962); *Analyt. Abstr.*, **10**, 2243 (1963)
27. DE SOUSA, A., *Inf. Quim. Anal.*, **14**, 130 (1963); *Analyt. Abstr.*, **11**, 5446 (1964)
28. NOMURA, T., *J. chem. Soc. Japan, pure Chem. Sect.*, **89**, 580 (1968); *Analyt. Abstr.*, **18**, 114 (1970)
29. SANDELL, E.B., *Colorimetric Determination of Trace Metals*, 3rd edn, Interscience, New York (1959)
30. WHISTON, T.G. and CHERRY, G.W., *Analyst*, **87**, 819 (1962)
31. *Official, Standardised and Recommended Methods of Analysis*, 2nd edn (Compiled and Edited by N.W. Hanson), The Society for Analytical Chemistry, London, 452 (1973)
32. ALDRIDGE, W.N., *Analyst*, **69**, 262 (1944)
33. ALDRIDGE, W.N., *Analyst*, **70**, 474 (1945)
34. KRUSE, J.M. and MELLON, M.G., *Analyt. Chem.*, **25**, 446 (1953)
35. EPSTEIN, J., *Analyt. Chem.*, **19**, 272 (1947)
36. NEAS, R.E. and GUYON, J.C., *Analyt. Chem.*, **41**, 1470 (1969)
37. EINAGA, H., ISHI, H. and IWASAKI, I., *Talanta*, **20**, 1017 (1973)
38. YAMAMOTO, Y., TARUMOTO, T. and HANAMOTO, Y., *Bull. chem. Soc. Japan*, **42**, 268 (1969); *Analyt. Abstr.*, **18**, 3050 (1970)
39. TSUBOUCHI, M., *Analytica chim. Acta*, **54**, 143 (1971)
40. Ref. 31, 454
41. KOH, T. and IWASAKI, I., *Bull. chem. Soc. Japan*, **40**, 569 (1967); *Analyt. Abstr.*, **15**, 3866 (1968)
42. DANCHIK, R.S. and BOLTZ, D.F., *Analyt. Chem.*, **40**, 2215 (1968)
43. BELCHER, R., BOGDANSKI, S.L., KNOWLES, D.J. and TOWNSHEND, A., *Analytica chim. Acta*, **77**, 53 (1975)
44. SCHEIBITZ, M., *Z. wiss. Photogr.*, **54**, 46 (1960); *Analyt. Abstr.*, **8**, 4631 (1961)
45. KOLTHOFF, I.M. and LINGANE, J.J., *J. Am. chem. Soc.*, **57**, 2377 (1935)
46. BISHOP, E. and DHANESHWAR, R.G., *Analyst*, **87**, 207 (1962)
47. HIRSCH, R.F. and PORTOCK, J.D., *Analyt. Lett.*, **2**, 295 (1969)
48. ROSS, J.W. and DURST, R.A., in *Ion Selective Electrodes*, Special Publication No. 314 NBS, Washington, D.C., 79 (1969)
49. MASCINI, M., *Analytica chim. Acta*, **62**, 29 (1972)
50. Orion Research Incorporated, Cambridge, Mass., U.S. Available from MSE-Fisons, Manor Royal, Crawley, West Sussex, U.K.
51. LINGANE, J.J., *Electroanalytical Chemistry*, 2nd edn, Interscience, New York, 514, 599 (1958)
52. PLOWMAN, R.A. and WILSON, I.R., *Analyst*, **85**, 222 (1960)
53. NYMAN, C.J. and ALBERTS, G.S., *Analyt. Chem.*, **32**, 207 (1960)
54. GOTO, H. and SHISHIOKAWA, T., *J. chem. Soc. Japan, pure Chem. Sect.*, **65**, 673 (1944); *Chem. Abstr.*, **41**, 3392c (1947)
55. MICKALSKI, E. and WTORKOWSKA, A., *Chemia analit.*, **6**, 365 (1961); *Analyt. Abstr.*, **9**, 74 (1962)
56. NOTA, G. and PALOMBARI, R., *J. Chromat.*, **84**, 37 (1973)
57. STORK, G. and JUNG, H., *Z. analyt. Chem.*, **249**, 161 (1970); *Analyt. Abstr.*, **20**, 1523 (1971)
58. CELAP, M.B. and WEISZ, H., *Mikrochim. Acta*, 24 (1962)
59. GANCHEV, N. and KOEV, K., *Mikrochim. Acta*, 87 (1964)
60. TAKEUCHI, T. and YAMAZAKI, M., *J. chem. Soc. Japan, pure Chem. Sect.*, **72**, 1263 (1969); *Chem. Abstr.*, **72**, 18094e (1970)

Tungstate

The extensive use of tungsten in the manufacture of alloy steels is well known. Other uses include the manufacture of tungsten carbide, wear-resistance components and filaments for lamps and vacuum tubes.

Compounds of tungsten are known in oxidation states from +2 to +6. The +6 state is stable and the most familiar, particularly in analytical work. In dilute acid, neutral or alkaline solutions, tungsten(VI) is predominantly in anionic form. Its solution chemistry is complicated, largely due to its tendency to form polyacids. In solutions above pH 8, WO_4^{2-} are the main species; from pH 6 to 4 anions of hexatungstic acid appear to predominate. In HCl solutions stronger than 4M, tungsten(VI) forms chloride complexes.

Lingane[1] has discussed the chemistry of tungsten related to its analytical methods. Reference standards for tungsten(VI) are generally prepared from sodium tungstate ($Na_2WO_4{\cdot}2H_2O$) or pure tungsten trioxide.

Several reviews of the analytical chemistry of tungsten have been published[2–4]. Reviews of specific aspects of tungsten determination will be referred to at the appropriate places in the text.

Separations

Separation of tungsten(VI) can be accomplished using precipitation, ion-exchange, solvent extraction, paper and thin-layer chromatography, paper electrophoresis and coprecipitation. Korkisch[5] has presented a comprehensive review of the principal methods.

In recent years solvent extraction has been extensively investigated for separation of trace amounts of tungsten, and the technique is now incorporated into many analytical procedures.

1. Precipitation

The alkaloid base cinchonine (*Structure 32*) precipitates tungstate in mineral acid solutions. Arsenic(V) and phosphorus(V) interfere by forming complexes.

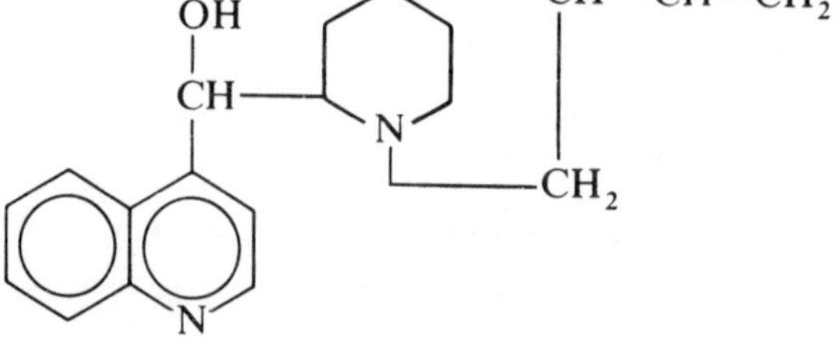

CH—CH=CH_2
OH
CH
N
CH_2
N

Structure 32 Cinchonine

Silica is also precipitated. The method is useful for separating macro amounts of tungsten, and enables the element to be separated from molybdenum(VI).

A modern application of the separation is included in British Standards method[6] for tungsten in steel. The separation is made by hydrolysis, with cinchonine being used as auxiliary precipitant.

Alternative precipitants have been recommended, for example benzoin α-oxime, but in this case the precipitate is generally extracted into an organic solvent to achieve separation from other elements also precipitated by the reagent.

2. *Ion-exchange*

Both cation- and anion-exchange find use in separation of tungsten(VI). As in the case of molybdenum(VI), non-adsorption of tungsten(VI) on strongly acid cation exchangers enables it to be separated from metals that would otherwise interfere in analytical methods. These metals are retained on the column; tungsten(VI) passes into the effluent[7].

Bottei and Trusk[8] use cation-exchange to separate tungsten from several interfering elements before its fluorimetric determination.

With anion-exchange resins, tungsten(VI) is retained both in the absence and presence of complexing agents such as thioglycollic acid. Ishida and Kuroda[9] separate tungsten(VI), rhenium(VII) and molybdenum(VI) using a weakly basic anion-exchanger diethylaminoethyl cellulose in thiocyanate medium. Application is subsequently made to determination of molybdenum and tungsten in rhenium metal[10].

3. *Solvent-extraction*

Several extraction systems are important. Dithiol (toluene 3,4-dithiol) was used by Hamence[11] for separation of both molybdenum and tungsten. In 10M HCl and in the presence of a reductant, tungsten forms a highly coloured complex which can be extracted into esters such as amyl acetate. Tungsten(VI) is separated from Co, V, Sn, Pb, Ni, Mn and Al, but small amounts of iron are co-extracted, and molybdenum is completely extracted with tungsten. The separation can be extended into the spectrophotometric determination of tungsten(VI), for example Stonhill[12] utilizes it in the analysis of titanium dioxide pigments for traces of molybdenum and tungsten.

Another important extraction system employs benzoin α-oxime. Tungsten-(VI) together with molybdenum(VI) is precipitated by the reagent, and this extracted into chloroform[13,14]. For complete recovery of tungsten several extractions are usually required. Vanadium and chromium are also extracted, but with appropriate masking tungsten and molybdenum can be separated from these. Like molybdenum, tungsten is extracted from acid solutions in the presence of a reducing agent and thiocyanate. The separation is not as satisfactory in the case of tungsten.

Yatirajam and Dhamija[15] have used the procedure recently for separation of tungsten prior to its gravimetric determination with tetraphenylarsonium chloride. Instead of using the usual reductant, stannous chloride, they employ mercury, and extract into a solution of tribenzylamine in chloroform. Back-extraction is made into a slightly alkaline aqueous solution containing hydrogen peroxide to destroy excess thiocyanate and oxidize tungsten back to the +6 oxidation state. The separation is applicable to amounts of tungsten up to 50 mg so that it is not restricted to trace amounts usually associated with solvent extraction procedures.

In addition to the extraction systems discussed, others based on mesityl oxide[16], 8-hydroxyquinoline[17] and benzohydroxamic acid[18] have been reported. Extractive separation of tungsten as phosphotungstate is reported in a recent investigation[26]. Extraction is made into isobutyl methyl ketone from 0.1–1M HCl. From 10 to 100 mg of tungsten can be separated from Fe, Ni, Co, Cr, Mn, Cu, Ca, U, Th, As, Sb, Bi and Si. The extraction of smaller amounts is dependent on the tungsten-phosphorus ratio.

Table 22 Paper and TLC procedures for separating tungsten(VI)

Technique	*Solvent system*	*W(VI) separated from*	*Ref.*
Paper	Various. Most effective: 70% HNO_3–*n*-butanol (6:4)	Numerous elements including Mo, Ti, Th, Mg, UO_2^{2+}, V, Co, Ni, Zn, Al, Fe. Also NH_4^+	19
Paper	Ethanol–$CHCl_3$–10% aq. oxalic acid (7:2:1)	MoO_4^{2-}	20
TLC (alumina)	1–1.16M H_3PO_4	ReO_4^-, MoO_4^{2-}, VO_3^-	21
TLC (silica gel with binder)	1–1.8M NH_4SCN	ReO_4^- or MoO_4^{2-}	22
TLC (silica gel)	Methanol–3M HCl (7:3) or methanol–M NH_4NO_3–3M aq.NH_3 (14:5:1)	ReO_4^- or MoO_4^{2-}	23
TLC	Acidic solutions of butyl and amyl alcohols	MoO_4^{2-} VO_3^-	24

Note: The study in reference 20 also involved paper electrophoresis. This technique was also employed by Blum[25] to separate tungsten(VI) and chromium(VI).

4. *Paper and thin-layer chromatography*

Table 22 gives details of the more important separations.

5. *Coprecipitation*

Like molybdenum(VI), tungsten(VI) is coprecipitated[27] on ferric hydroxide. This occurs in the pH range 5–8 and can be used to separate tungstate and perrhenate. The procedure has been applied to analysis of seawater[28].

Other carriers have been recommended, including metastannic acid[29] and molybdophosphate[30].

Determination

Gravimetric methods

In recent years the use of gravimetric methods generally has declined except in cases where high precision is required, or where no satisfactory alternatives exist. Determination of tungsten is one such example, the difficulty being that titrimetric methods for its determination are generally unreliable.

The use of cinchonine for precipitating tungsten has been referred to already in connection with separation methods. In its use as a gravimetric reagent for W, As(V), P(V) and Si interfere, but Mo(VI) is without effect. Ignition is carried out at 700–850 °C for weighing as WO_3, the complex itself being hydroscopic. A British Standards Method[6] has been based on the procedure.

Tungsten(VI) in a nitric acid medium forms a peroxytungstate with hydrogen peroxide. On heating, this decomposes precipitating tungstic acid which is filtered, ignited at 700–850 °C to WO_3 and weighed[31]. The procedure recommends heating the solution to 60 °C to effect precipitation. Subsequent work by Crossland and Fennell[32] found that heating at 80 °C is more effective in bringing about complete precipitation.

Miller and Thow[33] examined the effectiveness of several organic bases for precipitating tungsten(VI) as phosphotungstate. Of these, tributylamine showed certain advantages and was accordingly recommended. The procedure consists of adding the tungsten(VI) solution to a phosphate–HCl solution at pH 2 and then adding tri-*n*-butylamine chloride solution. The precipitate is easy to filter, does not adhere to glassware; the reagent is relatively less expensive than other compounds examined. If the precipitate, $[(C_4H_9)_3NH]PW_{12}O_{40}$, is dried at 105 °C, the results are not precise. Better results are obtained in the range 195–220 °C. Nitric or sulphuric acids can be substituted for the HCl originally recommended. Sulphuric acid tends to hinder precipitation. If used, the precipitate should be left overnight before filtration. Perchloric acid must be absent, and this also applies to molybdenum and vanadium. Considerable amounts of Ca, Co, Cu, Mn and Ni (chlorides), lead nitrate, and large amounts of NaCl, $NaNO_3$ and Na_2SO_4 can be tolerated. The method is applicable in the range 10–200 mg tungsten as tungsten(VI). The procedure is given later in this sub-section.

Tungstate can be determined gravimetrically as silver tungstate using the technique of precipitation from homogeneous solution[34]. Lutz and Conroy[35] analyse alkali metal tungstates using the novel procedure of converting them completely to alkali metal chlorides in a stream of HCl at 500 °C. The tungstate is evaluated from the initial and final weights. Other gravimetric procedures involve 8-hydroxyquinoline[56], variamine blue[37], and tetraphenylarsonium chloride[15]. The last procedure includes a preliminary extraction step using tribenzylamine and may be modified to prevent interference by vanadium and titanium. Suitable for 5–60 mg of tungsten, the method was applied to a range of industrial samples, mainly alloys. Chloride and acetate decrease the extraction very slightly, and so do SO_4^{2-}, PO_4^{3-}, citrate, tartrate and oxalate with increasing effect in that order.

Several other gravimetric methods for tungsten(VI) are given in the reviews cited earlier[2, 3].

Crossland and Fennell[32] have carried out a comparative study of three gravimetric and one titrimetric method for determination of macro amounts of tungsten(VI). *Table 23* gives a summary of the gravimetric results.

Table 23 Comparison of three gravimetric methods for determination of tungsten(VI)[32]

Method	*Recovery tungstate (%)*	*Standard deviation*	*Comments*
Tri-*n*-butylamine[33]	100.24	0.055	Recovery is mean of 4 analyses
Decomposition of peroxotungstate[31] (modified)	99.52	0.093	Recovery is mean of 6 analyses
Benzidine	99.96	0.070	Recovery is mean of 5 analyses

Notes:
1. The reference standard used was specpure tungsten nitrate. This was assumed to be 100% pure.
2. Application of the methods were made in the 50–100 mg tungsten range.
3. The standard deviations quoted are pooled values that include additional determinations.

It is unfortunate that the only method having no bias involves benzidine which is known to be carcinogenic. Of the three methods, only the one based on decomposition of peroxotungstate is not affected by small amounts of molybdenum.

Gravimetric determination of tungstate using tri-n-butylamine[33,32]

Reagents

Tributylamine:
Purify by distillation at a pressure of 3 mm Hg, collecting the 56.5–60 °C fraction.

Tributylamine chloride reagent:
Before use, shake 1 ml of the purified material with 40 mℓ of 0.25M HCl to give a 2% w/v solution. Prepare daily.

Tributylamine chloride wash solution:
Dilute the above solution 20 times to give a 0.1% w/v solution. Prepare daily.

Procedure

To about 50 ml of solution containing 10–200 mg of tungsten as tungsten-(VI) add at least 85 mg of phosphate as disodium hydrogen orthophosphate and stir to dissolve. Gradually add 1:1 HCl with stirring until the pH is about 2, and add about 4 ml in excess. Dilute to 100 ml with water.

Heat the solution almost to the boiling point, add 10 ml of the prepared tributylamine chloride solution dropwise with stirring, and continue to heat until the solution has coagulated. Cool, and allow to stand overnight. Filter through a fine-pore sintered glass filter and wash with the minimum amount of cold tributylamine chloride wash solution followed by a little cold water.

Heat the precipitate for 2 h at 210 °C, cool in a desiccator and weigh. The gravimetric factor is 0.6424.

Titrimetric methods

It has been pointed out already that titrimetric procedures for tungstate are generally unsatisfactory. In one of the recent reviews of tungsten analytical chemistry, the discussion of titrimetric procedure is curtailed for this reason[4]. The procedures are based on precipitation or complex formation.

1. Precipitation titration

Precipitation titrations using lead salts have been reported. Lassner and Scharf[38] were able to determine tungsten(VI) and molybdenum(VI) by first titrating both with Pb^{2+} in a hexamine buffer and with PAR (4-(2-pyridylazo)-resorcinol) (*Structure 33*) as indicator. Molybdenum(VI) was then determined

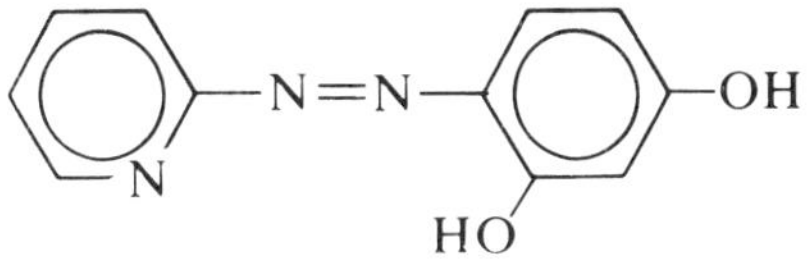

Structure 33 4-(2-pyridylazo)-resorcinol (PAR)

separately using EDTA. Up to 50 mg of sulphate and 200 mg of fluoride can be tolerated in the tungsten(VI) titration[39]. An alternative to PAR has been recommended by Brantner[40].

Cheng and Goydish[41] have attempted to improve the Lassner and Scharf procedure by employing xylenol orange as indicator, working at a different pH value, and adding molybdenum(VI) to make the molybdenum(VI)–tungsten(VI) ratio >1.

A mercurimetric method in which the end-point is detected by fluorescence, has been published[42].

2. EDTA

Direct titration of tungsten(VI) by EDTA is not possible. Kinnune and Wennerstrand[43] add excess EDTA to a strongly acidic solution of tungsten-(VI), buffer with acetate to pH 5 and titrate the excess EDTA with Tl(III) using xylenol orange as indicator. The end-point is not satisfactory[44].

Indirect methods have been based on precipitation of tungsten(VI) with lead or calcium ions. Thus de Sousa[45] determines the calcium content of precipitated $CaWO_4$. Popova and Seraya[46] precipitate tungsten(VI) using lead acetate. Unconsumed lead is titrated with EDTA using xylenol orange[46]. A similar method is described by Bourvet, Lecuire and Weis[47].

3. *Miscellaneous titrimetric methods*

Redox procedures have not featured a great deal in the titrimetric determination of tungstate. Geyer and Henze[48] found that tungsten(VI) is quantitatively reduced to tungsten(V) in strong HCl solutions by chromium(II) and vanadium(II). The tungsten(V) is formed by reaction of tungsten(VI) and tungsten(III) probably through tungsten(IV). There is no potentiometric indication of this when tungsten(VI) is titrated with tungsten(III), but a blue colour characteristic of tungsten(IV) appears and disappears. The above reactions with chromium(II) and vanadium(II) allow tungsten(VI) to be determined. Orthophosphoric acid interferes.

A study by Nemodruk and Bezrogova[49] indicates that tungsten(VI) can be reduced to tungsten(V) by the radiation from a mercury-quartz lamp for 30 min. The resulting tungsten(V) is determined either photometrically with thiocyanate or by titration with NH_4VO_3 using phenylanthranilic acid as indicator. For 7.5–10 mg of tungsten the error is within ± 2 per cent.

A titrimetric procedure[50] for tungsten(VI), chromium(VI) and molybdenum(VI) has been based on formation of ion-pairs with Ba^{2+}. Nitchromazo is used as indicator. In the case of tungstate, $Ba(HWO_4)_2$ is formed. The reaction is quantitative in 80–90% acetone when the pH of the original aqueous solution is 4.0–5.5. The range is 10^{-3}–10^{-5} moleℓ^{-1} of tungsten.

Spectroscopic methods

1. *Spectrophotometric methods*

The most commonly used spectrophotometric method for tungsten(VI) is the thiocyanate method. This originates from studies published in 1932 by Feigl and Krumholz[51] in which a weakly alkaline tungstate solution was observed to give a yellow complex with thiocyanate in the presence of tin(II) chloride. Molybdenum(VI) was found to interfere. In the intervening years the method has been the subject of extensive investigations aimed at improving its precision and selectivity. A survey of these investigations has been given by Fogg, Marriott and Burns[52].

There were several indications that the method was unreliable. Earlier workers concluded that in order to obtain precise results the thiocyanate must be added after reduction of tungsten(VI) to tungsten(V) to avoid being reduced itself. Furthermore there was indication that more than one tungsten(V)–thiocyanate complex could be formed, and that each had a different molar absorptivity. One of the detailed investigations of the method was made by Crouthamel and Johnson[54], who drew attention to the essential conditions required for more reliable results.

Examination of published procedures shows that three forms of the method are used. The tungsten(V)–thiocyanate complex can be evaluated in aqueous or aqueous–acetone solution. It can be extracted and determined as the free acid. It can be extracted and determined as the tetraphenylarsonium or other onium salts. Extraction of the onium salts rather than the free acids appears[53] to have improved the determination of several metals with thiocyanate.

Affsprung and Murphy[55] extract the water-insoluble tetraphenylarsonium salt of the tungsten(V)–thiocyanate complex into chloroform. This has been further developed by Fogg, Marriott and Burns[56]. The essential feature of their method is reduction by $SnCl_2$ and titanium(III) to the tungsten(V) state followed by extraction of the TPAC salt into chloroform containing quinol, the latter to prevent oxidation in the solvent phase. This form of the method has a molar absorptivity of 1.47×10^4. Application was made to determination of tungsten in steel. The amount of molybdenum tolerated was found to be dependent on the iron content of the solution.

A recent form of the method by Yatirajam and Dhamija[57] employs mercury as reductant and a 2% solution of tribenzylamine in chloroform as solvent for the extraction. Uranium, Ti, V, Cr, Fe, Co, Ni, Mn, Al, Pb, Sn, Bi, Pd, Sb and Cu are without effect but Pt and Mo in equal amounts to W cause interference.

In the thiocyanate method generally, various devices have been used to overcome interference. Peng and Sandell[58] extract both tungsten and molybdenum with benzoin α-oxime. Luke[59] removes iron by extraction with isobutyl methyl ketone, and other metals with cupferron.

Despite its defects application of the thiocyanate method has been widespread and particularly in metallurgical analysis.

Toluene 3,4-dithiol ('dithiol') gives a sparingly soluble bluish-green complex with tungsten(VI)[60]. Molybdenum(VI) reacts similarly. Dithiol forms coloured complexes with several metals including Cu, Sn and Bi, but solvent-extraction can be used to eliminate interference from these. A general disadvantage of dithiol is its instability. De Silva[61] has recently described the preparation of a more stable form which can be kept for several weeks if stored in a refrigerator.

When tungstate is to be determined in the presence of molybdenum, use can be made of masking tungsten(VI) with citric acid and allowing removal of the molybdenum complex by extraction. After demasking, tungsten(VI) can then be determined on its own[13].

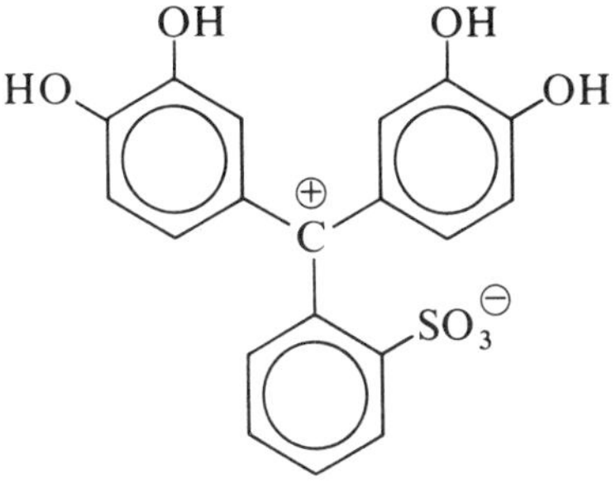

Structure 34 Catechol violet

Catechol violet (*Structure 34*) has received attention as a spectrophotometric reagent for tungsten(VI) particularly from Russian workers. Busev and Sokolova[62] used the reagent in the presence of EDTA to selectively determine tungsten in the presence of molybdenum. Another investigation[63] applies the reagent to tungsten in steel and other alloys, the range being 0.02–0.25 mg tungsten in a final volume of 50 ml. A more recent procedure[64] is able to determine tungsten(VI) in the presence of large amounts of molybdenum(VI) and claims greater reliability than the thiocyanate method.

2. *Fluorimetric methods*

The red fluorescent complex formed between tungsten(VI) and carminic acid has been used[65] for determination of tungsten in the range 0.04–0.36 ppm. Maximum fluorescence is given at 585 nm with excitation at 515 nm. Many ions interfere; several can be prevented from doing so by addition of ascorbic acid. Residual interferences have to be eliminated by separation.

Flavanol gives a blue fluorescence with tungsten(VI) at pH 2.5–5.5. This can be used for its determination in the range 6–42 μg tungsten per 100 mℓ of solution[66]. Vanadium, iron and chromium interfere even in small amounts, but larger amounts of nickel, manganese and copper can be tolerated. In a later publication the same authors describe ion-exchange separation of tungsten prior to its determination using the method[8].

3. *Atomic absorption spectroscopy*

Direct AAS of tungsten is of limited sensitivity only. The most sensitive lines are 255.1, 268.1 and 294.4 nm but the 400.9 nm line is generally recommended because of the favorable signal-to-noise ratio.

An indirect method by Chong and Boltz[67] consists of precipitating lead(II) tungstate by an excess of lead(II), followed by measurement of the excess by AAS. This is applicable to 3–30 ppm tungsten. For determination of 8 ppm of tungsten, Al^{3+}, VO_3^-, CrO_4^{2-} and MoO_4^{2-} must be absent; Fe^{2+} and Mn^{2+} can be tolerated at the 10 ppm level.

Atomic absorption has been used in conjunction with solvent extraction of the tungsten(V)–thiocyanate complex[68]. Interferences were found to be negligible for cations and anions. Application was made to geological samples.

Electroanalytical methods

1. *Potentiometric methods*

Silver nitrate has been used in the potentiometric titration of tungsten(VI). Shivahare[69], using a silver indicator electrode *v.* SCE observed an inflection in the curve corresponding to Ag_2WO_4. More recently Lal[70] has employed a dithizone-impregnated membrane electrode in the titration of standard $AgNO_3$ with Na_2WO_4. The reverse titration, by adding $AgNO_3$ to Na_2WO_4 was found not to be possible.

Sinclair[71] has reported that Na_2WO_4 containing mannitol can be titrated potentiometrically with 0.05M H_2SO_4. A sharp drop in potential occurs when one proton per tungstate ion has been added.

Potentiometric (as well as conductimetric and amperometric) titration of tungsten(VI) with lead(II) has been reported[72]. In this work a tungsten electrode is employed, and control of pH within the range 6.5–7.5 is essential. Tungsten at levels as low as 10^{-4}M can be determined. Cations forming insoluble tungstates, for example Ag(I), Cd(II), Th(IV) and Hg(II), interfere and so do anions reacting with Pb(II). High concentrations of neutral salts and complex-forming ions such as acetate, tartrate, oxalate, citrate and phosphate must be absent.

2. *Amperometric methods*

Amperometric titration of tungsten and molybdenum in a single sample can be made using $Pb(NO_3)_2$ in an acetate buffer at pH 4.5. The tungsten is first separated by acid hydrolysis in the presence of gelatin. Platinum and saturated calomel electrodes are employed[73].

3. *Polarography*

Earlier work on tungsten(VI) using polarography is discussed in the monograph by Kolthoff and Lingane[74]. In 12M HCl tungsten(VI) undergoes stepwise reduction to tungsten(V) and tungsten(III)[75]. The half-wave potential of the 2nd wave is -0.56 V *v.* SCE. This becomes slightly more negative as the concentration of HCl is decreased.

Issa, Abd-el-Nabey and Hendawey[76] have examined the behaviour of tungsten(VI) at the dropping mercury electrode in the presence of various acids. Determination of up to mM tungstate is possible in HCl; in H_3PO_4 the polarographic current is linear up to 4 mM in highly acidic solutions.

Polotebnova and Danilina[77] use polarography after a preliminary separation of tungsten(VI) as the phosphotungstovanado complex. The half-wave potential (*v.* SCE) is -0.52 V in H_2SO_4 media. A sensitivity of 0.04 mg tungsten $m\ell^{-1}$ in the final solution is reported.

O'Shea and Parker[78] determine tungstate by utilizing the kinetic polarographic wave produced in the H_2O_2–oxalic acid system. The polarogram at the dropping mercury electrode shows a kinetic peak at $+0.233$ V. Two linear portions cover 5–20 μM WO_4^{2-} and 0.04–0.25 μM WO_4^{2-}. A defect in the method is interference by Cr(VI), Fe(III), Mo(VI), Ti(IV) and V(V).

Miscellaneous methods

Catalytic methods for tungsten(VI) have been based on several reactions. Hadjiioannou and Valkana[79] use a fixed-concentration method for the effect of tungsten on the H_2O_2–I^- reaction. Omarova, Speranskaya and Kozlovskii[80] utilize the reduction of basic blue by titanium(III), which is catalysed by tungsten(VI). In this procedure the reaction rate is followed spectrophotometrically at 445 nm.

Neutron activation and isotope dilution analysis are used by Baishya and Heslop[81] for the determination of tungsten in high-speed steel and aluminium. The isotope dilution method is based on extraction of tungsten into chloroform using a sub-stoichiometric amount of toluene 3,4-dithiol. In the neutron activation method the sample is irradiated with a neutron flux of about 3.6×10^{12} n$cm^{-2}s^{-1}$ for 4 h after which the γ-emissions due to W-185 and W-187 are counted.

References

1. LINGANE, J.J., *Analytical Chemistry of Selected Metallic Elements*, Reinholt, New York and London, 113 (1966)
2. CHALMERS, R.A., in *Comprehensive Analytical Chemistry* (Ed. C. L. and D. W. Wilson), Vol. 1C, Elsevier, Amsterdam, 598 (1962)

3. ELWELL, W.T. and WOOD, D.F., *Analytical Chemistry of Molybdenum and Tungsten,* Pergamon Press, Oxford (1971)
4. LOWENHEIM, F.A., in *Encyclopedia of Industrial Chemical Analysis* (Ed. F. D. Snell and L. S. Ettre), Vol. 19, Interscience, New York and London, 190 (1974)
5. KORKISCH, J., *Modern Methods for the Separation of Rarer Metal Ions.* Pergamon Press, Oxford, 476 (1969)
6. *British Standards Handbook No. 19,* Method 1 for tungsten in steel, British Standards Institute, London (1970)
7. GOTTSCHALK, G., *Z. analyt. Chem.,* **187**, 164 (1962); *Analyt. Abstr.,* **9**, 4173 (1962)
8. BOTTEI, R.S. and TRUSK, B.A., *Analytica chim. Acta,* **37**, 409 (1967); **41**, 374 (1968)
9. ISHIDA, K. and KURODA, R., *Analyt. Chem.,* **39**, 212 (1964)
10. KURODA, R. and KASUAKI, K., *Z. analyt. Chem.,* **261**, 394 (1972); *Analyt. Abstr.,* **24**, 2809 (1973)
11. HAMENCE, J.H., *Analyst,* **65**, 152 (1940)
12. STONHILL, L.G., *Chemist Analyst,* **47**, 68 (1958)
13. JEFFREY, P.C., *Analyst,* **81**, 104 (1956)
14. PFEIFER, V. and HECHT, F., *Z. analyt. Chem.,* **177**, 175 (1960)
15. YATIRAJAM, V. and DHAMIJA, S., *Talanta,* **23**, 599 (1976)
16. SHINDE, V.M. and KHOPKAR, S.M., *Talanta,* **16**, 525 (1969)
17. EBERLE, A.R., *Analyt. Chem.,* **35**, 669 (1963)
18. POLUEKTOVA, E.N. and NAZARENKO, V.A., *Zh. analit. Khim.,* **22**, 746 (1967); *Analyt. Abstr.,* **16**, 130 (1969)
19. QUERSHI, M. and KHAN, F., *J. Chromat.,* **34**, 222 (1968)
20. BLASIUS, E. and CZEKAY, A., *Z. analyt. Chem.,* **156**, 81 (1957); *Analyt. Abstr.,* **4**, 3312 (1957)
21. GAIBAKYAN, D. S., *Uchen. Zap. Erevan. gas. Univ. estestv. Nauk,* 71 (1971); *Analyt. Abstr.,* **23**, 2293 (1972)
22. SHIOBARA, Y., *Japan Analyst.* **17**, 1396 (1968); *Analyt. Abstr.,* **19**, 202 (1970)
23. KURODA, R., KAWABUCHI, K. and ITO, T., *Talanta,* **15**, 1486 (1968)
24. GAIBAKYAN, D.S., *Armyan. khim. Zh.,* **22**, 13 (1969); *Analyt. Abstr.,* **18**, 2975 (1970)
25. BLUM, D., *Rev. Chim. Bucharest,* **9**, 28 (1958); *Analyt. Abstr.,* **5**, 3712 (1958)
26. YATIRAJAM, V. and DHAMIJA, S., *Talanta,* **24**, 52 (1977)
27. NOVIKOV, A.I., *Zh. analit. Khim.,* **15**, 742 (1960); *Analyt. Abstr.,* **9**, 1903 (1962)
28. ISHIBASHI, M., FUJINAGA, T., KUWAMOTO, T., KOYAMA, M. and SUGBAYASHI, S., *Japan Analyst,* **81**, 392 (1960)
29. NISHIDA, H., *Japan Analyst,* **13**, 760 (1964); *Analyt. Abstr.,* **13**, 4131 (1966)
30. TARASEVICH, N.I., KHLYSTOVA, A.D. and PAK, E.A., *Zav. Lab.,* **25**, 955 (1959); *Analyt. Abstr.,* **7**, 2205 (1960)
31. DAMS, R. and HOSTE, J., *Talanta,* **8**, 664 (1961)
32. CROSSLAND, B. and FENNELL, T.R.F.W., *Analyst,* **94**, 989 (1969)
33. MILLER, C.C. and THOW, D.H., *Analyst,* **84**, 440 (1959)
34. VARUGHESE, K. and RAO, K.S., *Analytica chim. Acta,* **57**, 219 (1971)
35. LUTZ, C.W. and CONROY, L.E., *Analyt. Chem.,* **38**, 139 (1966)
36. VINOGRADOV, A.V. and DRONOVA, M.I., *Zh. analit. Khim.,* **23**, 696 (1968); *Analyt. Abstr.,* **18**, 176 (1970)
37. ERDEY, L., BUZAS, I. and VIGH, K., *Talanta,* **14**, 515 (1967)
38. LASSNER, E. and SCHARF, R., *Chemist Analyst,* **49**, 68 (1960)
39. LASSNER, E. and SCHEDLE, H., *Talanta,* **13**, 326 (1966)
40. BRANTNER, H., *Mikrochim. Acta,* 125 (1962)
41. CHENG, K.L. and GOYDISH, B.L., *Microchem. J.,* **13**, 35 (1968)
42. ANDRUSHKO, G.S., MAKSMYCHEVA, Z.T. and TALIPOV. SH.T., *Dokl. Akad. Nauk. uzbek. SSR,* 26 (1970); *Analyt. Abstr.,* **21**, 173 (1971)
43. KINNUNEN, J. and WENNERSTRAND, B., *Chemist Analyst,* **47**, 38 (1958)
44. SCHWARZENBACH, G. and FLASCHKA, H., *Complexometric Titrations,* 2nd English edn, Methuen, London, 226 (1969)
45. DE SOUSA, A., *Analytica chim. Acta,* **9**, 309 (1953)
46. POPOVA, O.I. and SERAYA, O.G., *Zh. analit. Khim.,* **23**, 791 (1968); *Analyt. Abstr.,* **18**, 177 (1970)
47. BOURVET, P., LECUIRE, J-M. and WEIS, C., *Chim. analyt.,* **52**, 1114 (1970); *Analyt. Abstr.,* **21**, 1807 (1971)
48. GEYER, R. and HENZE, G., *Wiss. techn. Hochsch. Chem. Leuna-Merseburg,* **3**, 261 (1960/1); *Chem. Abstr.,* **57**, 1542 (1961)

49. NEMODRUK, A.A. and BEZROGOVA, E.V., *Zh. analit. Khim.*, **24**, 404 (1969); *Analyt. Abstr.*, **19**, 2221 (1970)
50. KRESHKOV, A.P., KUZNETSOV, V.V. and MEZHLUMYAN, P.G., *Zh. analit. Khim.*, **29**, 1349 (1974); *Analyt. Abstr.*, **29**, 3B, 138 (1975)
51. FEIGL, F. and KRUMHOLZ, P., *Angew. Chem.*, **45**, 674 (1932); *Chem. Abstr.*, **27**, 243 (1933)
52. FOGG, A.G., MARRIOTT, D.R. and BURNS, D.T., *Analyst*, **95**, 848 (1970)
53. BOWD, A.J., BURNS, D.T. and FOGG, A.G., *Talanta*, **16**, 719 (1969)
54. CROUTHAMEL, C.E. and JOHNSON, C.E., *Analyt. Chem.*, **26**, 1284 (1954)
55. AFFSPRUNG, H.E. and MURPHY, J.W., *Analytica chim. Acta*, **30**, 501 (1964)
56. FOGG, A.G., MARRIOTT, D.R. and BURNS, D.T., *Analyst*, **95**, 854 (1970)
57. YATIRAJAM, V. and DHAMIJA, S., *Talanta*, **22**, 760 (1975)
58. PENG, P.Y. and SANDELL, E.B., *Analytica chim. Acta*, **29**, 325 (1963)
59. LUKE, C.L., *Analyt. Chem.*, **36**, 1327 (1964)
60. SANDELL, E.B., *Colorimetric Determination of Traces of Metals*, 3rd edn, Interscience, New York (1959)
61. DE SILVA, M.E.M.S., *Analyst*, **100**, 517 (1975)
62. BUSEV, A.I. and SOKOLOVA, T.A., *Zh. analit. Khim.*, **23**, 1348 (1968); *Analyt. Abstr.*, **18**, 2382 (1970)
63. PASHCHENKO, E.N. and MAL'TSEV, V.F., *Zav. Lab.*, **34**, 12 (1968)
64. LEBEDEVA, L.I., GOLUBTSOVA, Z.G. and YANKLOVICH, N.G., *Zh. analit. Khim.*, **26**, 1962 (1971); *Analyt. Abstr.*, **24**, 1548 (1973)
65. KIRKBRIGHT, G.F., WEST, T.S. and WOODWARD, C., *Talanta*, **13**, 1637 (1966)
66. BOTTEI, R.S. and TRUSK, BR.A., *Analyt. Chem.*, **35**, 1910 (1963)
67. CHONG, R.W. and BOLTZ, D.F., *Analyt. Lett.*, **8**, 721 (1975)
68. KIM, C.H., ALEXANDER, P.W. and SMYTHE, L.E., *Talanta*, **23**, 573 (1976)
69. SHIVAHARE, G.C., *Naturwissenschaften*, **52**, 157 (1965); *Analyt. Abstr.*, **13**, 4132 (1966)
70. LAL, S., *Z. analyt. Chem.*, **255**, 210 (1971); *Analyt. Abstr.*, **22**, 3121 (1972)
71. SINCLAIR, A.G., *Talanta*, **16**, 459 (1969)
72. GUPTA, C.M., *J. Proc. Inst. Chem. India*, **38**, 211 (1966); *Analyt. Abstr.*, **15**, 156 (1968)
73. BOGOVINA, V.I., NOVAK, V.P. and MAL'TSEV, V.F., *Zh. analit. Khim.*, **20**, 951 (1965); *Analyt. Abstr.*, **14**, 2559 (1967)
74. KOLTHOFF, I.M. and LINGANE, J.J., *Polarography*, 2nd edn, Vol. II, Interscience, New York and London, 461 (1965)
75. LINGANE, J.J. and SMALL, L.A., *J. Am. chem. Soc.*, **71**, 973 (1949)
76. ISSA, R.M., ABD-EL-NABEY, and HENDAWEY, A.M., *Z. analyt. Chem.*, **240**, 9 (1968); *Analyt. Abstr.*, **18**, 178 (1970)
77. POLOTEBNOVA, N.A. and DANILINA, L.M., *Zav. Lab.*, **36**, 261 (1970)
78. O'SHEA, T.A. and PARKER, G.A., *Analyt. Chem.*, **44**, 184 (1972)
79. HADJIIOANNOU, T.P. and VALKANA, C.G., *Hĕm. Hron.*, **32**, 89 (1967)
80. OMAROVA, E.S., SPERANSKAYA, E.F. and KOZLOVSKII, M.T., *Zh. analit. Khim.*, **23**, 1826 (1968); *Analyt. Abstr.*, **18**, 3947 (1970)
81. BAISHYA, N.K. and HESLOP, R.B., *Analytica chim. Acta*, **53**, 87 (1971)

Vanadate

Much of the analytical chemistry of vanadium is concerned with its use in ferrous and non-ferrous metallurgy. It also finds application in catalysis and in the paint and ceramic industries.

Vanadium solutions generally contain several species in a complicated series of equilibria. In not very acid solutions polynuclear complexes predominate. Pervanadyl ion (VO_2^+) becomes a major species in strongly acidic solutions. Vanadium(V) is an oxidant comparable with dichromate.

Alkaline vanadate solutions contain another series of polynuclear complexes as the predominant species. In strongly alkaline solutions the main species present is VO_4^{3-}. A valuable discussion of the fundamental chemistry of vanadium(V) related to its analysis is given by Lingane[1].

The analytical chemistry of vanadium has been reviewed[2–5]. Vanadium(V) solutions can be prepared from ammonium metavanadate (NH_4VO_3), V_2O_5, or sodium vanadate. For more accurate work solutions prepared from sodium vanadate are generally standardized using cupferron.

Separations

A full discussion of separation methods for vanadium is given in the monograph by Korkisch[6].

1. Precipitation

Precipitation of vanadium(V) with cupferron from strongly acid solutions enables a separation to be made from U(VI), Cr(III), Mn(II), Al(III), Ni(II), Zn(II) and P. Several elements are precipitated under the same conditons, notably Fe, Mo, W and Ti.

Use can be made of the solubility of vanadium(V) in strongly alkaline media. Under these conditions Fe, Co, Ni, Ti, Zr, etc., can be removed in insoluble form. Uranium, Mo, Cr(VI) and Al remain in solution with vanadium(V).

8-hydroxyquinoline precipitates vanadium(V) but not chromium(VI).

2. Ion-exchange

Separations involving vanadium(V) can be made using both cation and anion exchangers. Vanadium(V) is separated from Fe(III), Co, Ni, lanthanides, Al, Zn, Bi, etc., on Dowex-50 cation-exchange resin using 0.1 M H_2SO_4 or $HClO_4$ containing H_2O_2 as eluent. The peroxide forms a complex with vanadium(V) which is not retained on the column; the other elements are retained[7].

Other separations are based on adsorption of vanadium with other species being eluted. This is best accomplished by using SO_2 to reduce vanadium(V) to vanadium(IV), the latter being more strongly retained on cation-exchange resins. Separation from large amounts of orthophosphate is possible in this way[8].

Federov, Andreev and Lide[9] use an anion-exchange resin in NO_3^- form to separate V(V) from Mg, Ca, Zn, Cd, Co, and Ni.

3. Other chromatographic methods

Vanadium(V) is separated from Mo(VI), W(VI) and Fe(III) using an Al_2O_3 column and potassium hydrogen carbonate solution containing H_2O_2 as eluant. The other species are retained on the column[10]. Tserkovnitskaya and Luginin[11] find that vanadium(V) and vanadium(IV) can be separated using a column of PTFE particles supporting a saturated solution of benzohydroxamic acid in tributyl phosphate as stationary phase. Unadsorbed vanadium(IV) is removed with 5M H_3PO_4. Vanadium(V) is eluted with concentrated H_3PO_4.

Thin-layer chromatography on alumina enables VO_3^-, ReO_4^-, MoO_4^{2-}

and WO_4^{2-} to be separated[12]. The eluant is 1M–1.16M H_3PO_4. Gas-chromatography has found application. More details are given at the end of the section.

4. Solvent extraction

Solvent extraction is probably the most important method for separating vanadium(V) in current use. Both chelate and ion-association systems are involved. The technique often forms part of a spectrophotometric or atomic absorption method.

Extraction systems for vanadium(V) include the use of 8-hydroxyquinoline, cupferron, dithiocarbamates, N-benzoylphenylhydroxylamine (*Structure 35*), 4-(2-pyridylazo)-resorcinol (PAR), and benzoin α-oxime. The present discussion will concern itself with some of the more important systems in current use. A detailed account of vanadium extraction methods is given in the monograph by Korkisch[6] cited earlier.

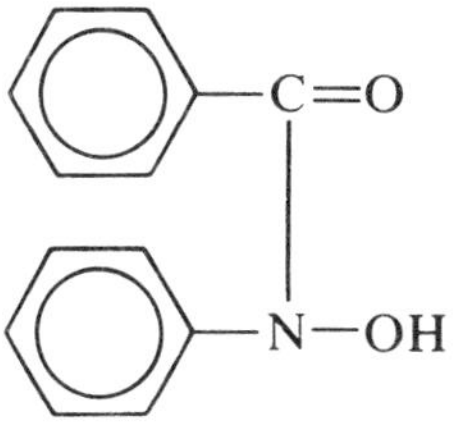

C=O

N—OH

Structure 35 N-benzoylphenylhydroxylamine

Extraction of the 8-hydroxyquinoline complex at pH 4–5 into chloroform enables vanadium(V) to be separated from chromium(VI). A separation from molybdenum(VI) in soil analysis is made by extracting the oxine complex at pH 3.5–4.0 into chloroform[13]. Cupferron was found to be an effective reagent by Bock and Gorbach[14]. A later investigation by Crump-Wiesner and Purdy[15] concluded that cupferron is the best of eight chelating reagents in terms of working pH, range and freedom from interference. Vanadium(V) is completely extracted into isobutyl methyl ketone from 1M HCl solutions, this solvent being the best if the subsequent determination of vanadium is to be made by AAS. Essentially no interference was found for all metals examined at concentrations 1000 times greater than the vanadium.

The yellow benzoin α-oxime complex with vanadium(V) can be extracted into chloroform at pH 2.2 and used for spectrophotometric determination[16] of vanadium. Luke[17] has employed the system for determination of vanadium in the presence of chromium, in steel samples. First $Na_2S_2O_5$ is used to reduce Cr(VI) to Cr(III) and V(V) to V(IV). The V(IV) is selectively oxidized to V(V) with $KMnO_4$, retaining chromium in the tervalent form. Finally vanadium(V) is extracted into chloroform as the benzoin α-oxime complex and evaluated. Inglot and Panz[18] use essentially the same method except that a polarographic finish is employed. In a method for vanadium in copper ore, Kozlicka and Wojtowicz[19] extract vanadium(V) using benzoin α-oxime, then complete the determination spectrophotometrically using PAR.

5. Coprecipitation
Vanadium(V) together with Cr(III), Mo(VI), Ti and Sn are coprecipitated on $Fe(OH)_3$. Other collectors[6] include the hydroxides of Al, Zn and Mg. An investigation of the coprecipitation of vanadium(V) with ammonium molybdophosphate indicates that 80–90% is separated from a HCl solution[20].

6. Miscellaneous
Vanadium(V) remains in solution when subjected to mercury cathode electrolysis.

Determination

Gravimetric methods

Vanadate can be determined gravimetrically using both inorganic and organic precipitants. Silver(I), Hg(I) and Pb(II) have been used, though not without difficulties, these including uncertainty in composition of the precipitates, and interference from numerous ions. For example, when Hg(I) is used, halides, MoO_4^{2-}, WO_4^{2-} and CrO_4^{2-} are also precipitated.

Of the organic precipitants oxine and cupferron are generally regarded as the best. Using oxine, precipitation is made at pH 5–6. Many elements interfere including Fe, Ti, Mo, W, Co and Ni. All but tungsten and molybdenum can be masked[21] using EDTA. The cupferron method also suffers extensive interference. Here the precipitate is ignited to V_2O_5 for gravimetric evaluation. A discussion of gravimetric methods for vanadium(V) is given by Chalmers[4]. The same source provides experimental procedures.

Titrimetric methods

1. Redox including iodimetric
Reduction of vanadium(V) to vanadium(IV) followed by re-oxidation using a standard oxidizing reagent provides the basis of one group of methods. Reduction can be accomplished in several ways. Sulphur dioxide at boiling temperature and in H_2SO_4 medium, is effective. Excess SO_2 is removed by passing a stream of CO_2 through the solution. Molybdenum(VI) is not reduced by SO_2, this enabling vanadium(V) to be determined in the presence of molybdenum(VI). Bismuth amalgams can also be used. Here again reduction terminates at the vanadium(IV) stage.

Oxidation of vanadium(IV) is generally carried out using standard $KMnO_4$. The reaction is slow at room temperature, and is best done in hot solution.

$$5VO^{2+} + MnO_4^- + H_2O \rightarrow 5VO_2^+ + Mn^{2+} + 2H^+$$

An alternative method is to titrate vanadium(V) directly using a standard reductant. Iron(II) is generally used, the reduction being quantitative below pH 1.5. Suitable indicators are diphenylamine derivatives or N-phenylanthranilic acid.

$$VO_2^+ + Fe^{2+} + 2H^+ \rightarrow VO^{2+} + Fe^{3+} + H_2O$$

Titration with iron(II) forms part of a British Standards method[22] for vanadium in iron, steel or ferro-vanadium. Oxidation is made with excess $KMnO_4$ to ensure that vanadium is entirely in the +5 state. Excess $KMnO_4$ is destroyed with sodium nitrite, residual nitrite being removed with sulphamic acid. Finally the solution is titrated with standard iron(II).

Several other redox methods have been published involving ascorbic acid, chromium(II), copper(I), hydrazine, etc. An account of these is given in monograph by Berka, Vulterin and Zyka[23]. In several cases potentiometric end-points are employed.

An iodimetric method has been based on reduction of vanadium(V) by KI in strongly acid HCl solutions.

$$2VO_4^{3-} + 2I^- + 12H^+ \rightarrow 2VO^{2+} + I_2 + 6H_2O$$

The liberated iodine is titrated with standard thiosulphate[24].

Titration of vanadium (V) with iron(II)[25]

Reagents

Ammonium ferrous sulphate: 0.1M in 0.5M H_2SO_4.
Barium diphenylamine sulphonate: 0.5% aqueous.

Procedure

Add 5M H_2SO_4 to the vanadium(V) solution until it is 1.5M in acid, and then 15 mℓ of concentrated H_3PO_4 per 100 mℓ of solution. Add 4–5 drops of the indicator and titrate with the standard iron(II) solution until the violet colour of the indicator is discharged.

---

2. Compleximetric

Procedures have been based on initial reduction of vanadium(V) to vanadium(IV). Thus Flaschka and Abdine[26] first reduce vanadium(V) with ascorbic acid then determine vanadium(IV) directly using a Cu/PAN indicator system. No interference is given by tungsten but molybdenum must be absent. Kinnunen and Wennerstrand[27] employ a back-titration with thorium nitrate using xylenol orange as indicator.

Khalifa and El-Sirafy[28] and Gardels and Cornwell[29] employ potentiometric end-point detection. In the former work vanadium(V) is first reduced to VO^{2+} with SO_3^{2-}, excess EDTA added and a back-titration made with Hg^{2+} potentiometrically. Since vanadium(V) does not react in the same way, the method can be used for analysis of binary mixtures with Cd, Co, Ni, Ca, Mg, Sr, In and Hg. This is accomplished by first analysing the unreduced solution to find the concentration of the additional metal. Vanadium is determined by difference after analysing the reduced solution.

A new direct compleximetric method for vanadium(V) has been developed by Tanaka and Ishida[30]. This results from a theoretical consideration of the effect of iron(II) on the vanadium(V)–EDTA reaction. The titration, in which variamine blue is used as indicator, gives a sharp end-point at pH 1.7–2.0. Less than 10 mg of vanadium can be determined with an error of ±0.01 mg.

Copper and silver interfere. Phosphoric, citric and tartaric acids produce a sluggish end-point. Other species can be tolerated in amounts specified in the original paper.

Other compleximetric methods are described in the monograph by Schwarzenbach and Flaschka[31].

3. Miscellaneous

Titrimetric procedures based on Ag^+ and Pb^{2+} have been published and are discussed by Chalmers[4].

Spectroscopic methods

1. Colorimetric and spectrophotometric

Vanadium(V) can be determined spectrophotometrically using hydrogen peroxide, oxine, xylenol orange, PAR(4-(2-pyridylazo)-resorcinol), 3,3′-dimethylnaphthidine, PAN(1-(2-pyridylazo)-2-naphthol) (*Structure 36*), or the phosphotungstovanadic acid complex. Both in terms of sensitivity and selectivity the method using PAR appears to have distinct advantages.

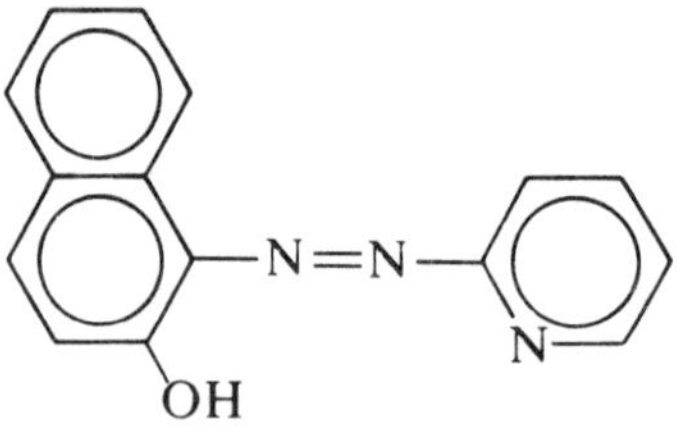

Structure 36 1-(2-pyridylazo)-2-naphthol (PAN)

The yellow phosphotungstovanadic acid complex ($\varepsilon_{400} = 2.0 \times 10^3$) suffers considerable interference mainly from elements forming slightly soluble phosphates. Non-interference by aluminium and chromium gives the method some advantage in specific cases.

Vanadium(V) forms a red-brown complex with H_2O_2 with a molar absorptivity of 300 at 450 nm. Interferences include Ti, Mo(VI), Fe(III), I^-, and Br^-. Iron(III) can be successfully masked with phosphate or fluoride[32].

Xylenol orange forms two complexes with vanadium(V) in slightly acid solution, depending on its ratio to vanadium. The molar absorptivities are $\varepsilon_{590} = 2.0 \times 10^4$ and $\varepsilon_{320} = 1.3 \times 10^4$. In the presence of DCTA (diaminocyclohexanetetra-acetic acid) the method suffers very little interference.

PAR is one of the most sensitive reagents for vanadium(V). The violet complex has maximum absorbance at about 550 nm in the pH range 5–7. Complete colour development requires about 30 min after which it remains stable for 2 h. The molar absorptivity is 3.6×10^4 at 550 nm. Several sources describe the complex as a 1:1 type[33–35]; one investigation describes it as a 2:1 PAR:V type[36]. Beer's law is followed over the range 0.04–1 $\mu g\ m\ell^{-1}$ vanadium, this permitting the determination of 1–5 μg vanadium in 25 mℓ of solution. PAR reacts with many metal ions including Co, Pb, Th, Sc, In, Ga,

Pd, and U. Titanium (IV), Nb(V) and Zr also interfere. The colour formation is hindered by tartrate, oxalate, NaF and EDTA. Moderate amounts of Cr(VI), Mo(VI), W(VI) and NO_3^- are without effect. DCTA (diaminocyclohexanetetra-acetic acid) does not affect the vanadium(V)–PAR complex and may be used to mask several metals but Ti, Nb, U and Zr continue to interfere[33]. Kawahata *et al.*[34] report that common anions do not interfere. More recent work on the method has utilized the vanadium(V)–PAR complex as the anionic component of an ion-pair. Siroki and Djordjevic[37] extract the vanadium(V)–PAR complex with tetraphenylphosphonium- or tetraphenylarsonium chloride into chloroform or similar solvents and measure the absorbance at 560 nm. The resulting method has enhanced sensitivity ($\varepsilon_{560} = 3.9 \times 10^4$). Only Co and Ga interfere.

Minczewski, Chwastowska and Pham Thi Hong Mai[38] use crystal violet as the cationic component. The resulting 1:1:1 ion-association complex is assumed to have *Structure 37*. After extraction into benzene–isobutyl methyl

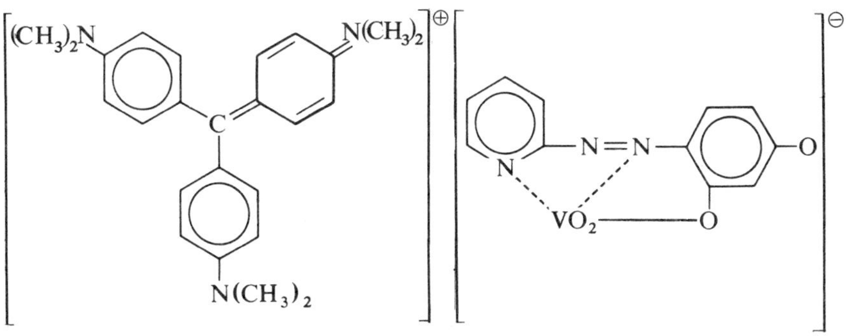

Structure 37 *Assumed structure of ion-association complex formed between anion complex of vanadium with PAR* (4-(2-pyridylazo) resorcinol) *and crystal violet*

ketone (3 + 2) the absorbance is measured at 585 nm. Beer's law holds for 0.05–0.5 µg mℓ^{-1} vanadium, with $\varepsilon = 1.1 \times 10^5$. The method, which was applied to trace vanadium in plant material after wet ashing, suffers interference from several anions. Only sulphate and acetate do not interfere, but Cl^-, F^-, oxalate, citrate and tartrate can be tolerated at concentrations less than 100 times the vanadium concentration.

Mal'tseva, Shalamova and Gusev[39] use hydroxylamine in 0.2M H_2SO_4 to produce a 1:1:1 V–PAR–NH_2OH complex at pH 5–6. This provides a highly sensitive method ($\varepsilon = 3.5 \times 10^4$) but selectivity is low. Increasing the acidity improves the selectivity but this causes a decrease in sensitivity. No interference is given by Re, Th, U, Mo, Mn, Zr and other elements.

Of the newer spectrophotometric methods introduced for vanadium(V) one based on tropolone is claimed to be almost specific[40]. The blue coloured complex formed in highly acidic medium is extracted into chloroform giving a molar absorptivity of 4.63×10^3 at 590 nm. Most anions do not interfere. Of 37 cations examined only Tl(III), Ru(III), Pt(IV), Ir(IV), Mn(II), Ta(V), and Ce(III) interfere and this can be prevented by masking with EDTA.

The use of 3,3′-dimethylnaphthidine has been re-assessed by Bannard and Burton[41]. Earlier reports on this reagent had produced conflicting evidence on suitable conditions for the analysis, and colour stability. The above investigation described a simple procedure for vanadium in the range 0.08–2 ppm. Interference was only found with Cr(VI), Fe(II), Fe(III), Ce(III) and Ce(IV).

2. *Atomic absorption spectroscopy*

Atomic absorption spectroscopy is suitable for determination of vanadium. Generally the 318 nm wavelength is used in conjunction with an air–acetylene flame.

A sensitive form of the technique employing a carbon filament atom reservoir has been developed by Jackson, West and Balchin[42] and applied to determination of vanadium in titanium dioxide. A detection limit of 3.3×10^{-10} g of vanadium is reported using a sample of 1 μℓ and the 318.4 nm line. Flash atomization is made at 2500 °C.

3. *Miscellaneous spectroscopic methods*

Metavanadate in amounts over 5 μg can be identified and determined in mixtures with hexacyanoferrate(II), hexacyanoferrate(III), cobalticyanide, sulphate and chromate, using infra-red spectroscopy[43]. The procedure involves preparing KBr discs containing the sample and can be completed in about 20 min.

Electroanalytical methods

1. *Potentiometric methods*

Some potentiometric procedures have been referred to earlier in the section.

Using mild reducing conditions vanadium(V) can be titrated potentiometrically in the presence of Cr(III), U(VI), Mo(V), W(VI) and Ti(IV). When stronger reductants are used, mixtures of V(V) with Fe, U, Cr and Ti can often be analysed from a single potentiometric titration. Thiosulphate reacts slowly with vanadium(V), but the rate can be increased using copper(II) as catalyst[44]. RaO and Sharma[45] have based a potentiometric titration on this which enables vanadium(V) to be determined in the presence of Fe, Mn, Cr, Mo and U. Uranium(VI) and molybdenum(VI) do, in fact, react slowly with thiosulphate, but only after the reduction of any vanadium or iron present. Iron(III) is reduced giving a second break in the potentiometric curve, but does not interfere if in amounts less than 10 times that of vanadium.

RaO and Dikshitulu[46] use stronger reduction conditions in the form of iron(II) in a strong H_3PO_4 medium. The method allows the sequential titration of vanadium(V) and uranium(VI) or vanadium(V) and molybdenum(VI). Two breaks appear in the potentiometric curve, the first representing vanadium(V) → vanadium(IV), the second representing vanadium(IV) → vanadium(III) and uranium(VI) → uranium(IV) or molybdenum(VI) → molybdenum(V). Manganese(II) and tungsten(VI) do not interfere. The authors claim that the method is superior to those employing Ti(III), Sn(II) or Cr(II).

A related method by Muralikrishna and RaO[47] consists of reducing vanadium(V) with excess iron(II) followed by oxidation using standard dichromate, again in a strong H_3PO_4 medium. This allows the sequential titration of molybdenum(VI) and vanadium(V). Reduction to vanadium(III) and molybdenum(V) is produced by addition of excess iron(II). On titrating with dichromate the first potential break represents oxidation of excess iron(II). A second corresponds to vanadium(III)→vanadium(IV) and molybdenum(V)→molybdenum(VI). A further break represents vanadium-(IV)→vanadium(V).

Hexacyanoferrate(II) has been used for microdetermination of vanadium(V) and permanganate by automatic potentiometric titration[48].

2. *Polarographic methods*

In dilute acid media vanadium(V) is reduced polarographically to vanadium-(IV) and vanadium(II). Because the potential of the vanadium(V)/vanadium-(IV) couple is more positive than the oxidation potential of mercury, the first diffusion current starts from zero applied e.m.f. The half-wave potential of the second wave (representing vanadium(IV)→vanadium(II)) is −0.98 V *v.* SCE.

A double wave is also produced when vanadate ion is reduced in ammoniacal medium, corresponding to vanadium(IV) and vanadium(II).

Polarography of vanadium chelates with catechol and pyrogallol has been studied by Zelinka, Bartusek and Okac[49]. When conducted in an acetate or pyridine buffer at pH 5.3 and containing catechol, $E_{\frac{1}{2}} = -0.53$ V and the wave height is independent of catechol concentration. Under these conditions vanadium(V) reduced to vanadium(IV), and vanadium(III) is oxidized by air to vanadium(IV). Pyrogallol is less suitable than catechol.

Oscillopolarography has been used by Morales, Gonzales and Dias[50] for determination of vanadium in the range 0.5–6 μg mℓ^{-1}. Potential interference by Zr, Th, Bi and Cu(II) can be prevented. Application is made to analysis of ores.

3. *Miscellaneous electroanalytical methods*

An amperometric method[51] has been based on the precipitation titration of vanadium(V) with $AgNO_3$. The dropping mercury indicator electrode is set at −0.3 V *v.* SCE and sodium nitrate used as basal electrolyte.

Songina *et al.*[52] use KI as titrant in the sequential determination of Mn, Cr and V. The titration is made in 6M H_2SO_4 using a graphite-disc indicator electrode maintained at 0.6 V *v.* SCE. The lower limit for the determination is 130 μg vanadium in 20 mℓ of solution.

Numerous constant current coulometric methods have been described. These have employed electrogenerated Ag, Fe, Sn and Ti. Bard and Lingane[53] used tin(II) for the determination of milligram quantities of vanadium. The end-point was detected both potentiometrically and spectrophotometrically.

A recent investigation by Bishop and Hitchcock[54] applies potentiostatic coulometry to determination of vanadium(V). Current integration is made by a high quality integrating capacitor manufactured from polystyrene. Vanadium(V) is determined at −0.128 V in acetate buffer or at +0.247 V in 2.0M H_2SO_4.

Catalytic methods

Many catalytic methods for vanadium(V) are based on Landolt-type reactions[55]. Thompson and Svehla[56] use the bromate–iodide reaction with ascorbic acid present as delaying agent. A fixed-concentration procedure is employed. Interference by Cu, Fe, Mo and Ti is prevented by using a citric acid–sodium citrate buffer at pH 2.2. The range is 0–10 μg V mℓ$^{-1}$.

Bognar and Jellinek[57] utilize the same reaction. In earlier work[58,59] the same investigators used the reaction between chlorate and chloride with stannous chloride, and chlorate and chloride with hydrazine sulphate as delaying agents.

An extremely sensitive catalytic method by Fuller and Ottaway[60] is based on oxidation of Bordeaux by bromate in acid medium. Based on a fixed-concentration procedure, the range is 0.005–0.2 μg vanadium mℓ$^{-1}$. Of 37 ions examined about 10 were found to interfere. The most serious are SCN^-, NO_2^-, I^-, Rh and Cu.

An automatic catalytic method[61] has been developed based on oxidation of iodide by hydrogen peroxide. The range is 0.6–12 μg vanadium with relative errors of about 2 per cent. A determination can be completed in 15–20 s.

Gas chromatographic methods

Butts and Rainey[62,63] have reported the formation of trimethylsilyl derivatives of several anions, including vanadate, and have developed gas-chromatographic methods utilizing these. As well as vanadate, the procedure enables phosphite, carbonate, oxalate, sulphate, phosphate, arsenate and sulphamate to be determined. A gas chromatogram illustrating the method is given on p. 563.

References

1. LINGANE, J.J., *Analytical Chemistry of Selected Metallic Elements*, Reinhold, New York, 123 (1966)
2. GRADY, H.R., in *Treatise on Analytical Chemistry* (Ed. I. M. Kolthoff and P. J. Elving), Part II, Vol. 8, Interscience, New York, 177 (1963)
3. LOWENHEIM, F.A., in *Encyclopedia of Industrial Chemical Analysis* (Ed. F. D. Snell and L. S. Ettre), Vol. 19, Interscience, New York, 320 (1974)
4. CHALMERS, R.A., in *Comprehensive Analytical Chemistry* (Ed. C. L. and D. W. Wilson), Vol. 1C, Elsevier, Amsterdam, 542 (1962)
5. SVEHLA, G. and TOLG, G., *Talanta*, **23**, 755 (1976)
6. KORKISCH, J., *Modern Methods for the Separation of Rarer Metal Ions*, Pergamon Press, Oxford, 435 (1969)
7. FRITZ, J.S. and ABBINK, J.E., *Analyt. Chem.*, **34**, 1080 (1962)
8. HARTMANN, S., *Z. analyt. Chem.*, **151**, 332 (1956); *Analyt. Abstr.*, **3**, 3314 (1956)
9. FEDEROV, P.I., ANDREEV, V.K. and LIDE, T.V., *Zh. analit. Khim.*, **30**, 379 (1975); *Analyt. Abstr.*, **30**, 3B 115 (1976)
10. RYAZANOV, I.P. and CHISTOTA, L.M., *Sb. Nauch. Trud. Magnitogrsk. Gorno Metallurg. Inst.*, 154 (1958): *Analyt. Abstr.*, **6**, 1746 (1959)
11. TSERKOVNITSKAYA, I.A. and LUGININ, V.A., *Vest. leningr. gos. Univ., Ser. Fiz. Khim.*, 162 (1969); *Analyt. Abstr.*, **18**, 3085 (1970)
12. GAIBAKYAN, D.S., *Uchen. Zap. Erevan. gos. Univ., estetv. Nauk*, **71** (1971); *Analyt. Abstr.*, **23**, 2293 (1972)
13. LYUBIMOVA, I.N., *Vest. Mosk. Univ. Biol. Pochvoved.*, **25**, 73 (1970); *Chem. Abstr.*, **74**, 106835 (1971)

14. BOCK, R. and GORBACH, S., *Mikrochim. Acta,* 593 (1958)
15. CRUMP-WIESNER, H.J. and PURDY, W.C., *Talanta,* **16**, 124 (1969)
16. PENG, P.Y. and SANDELL, E.B., *Analytica chim. Acta,* **29**, 325 (1963)
17. LUKE, C.L., *Analytica chim. Acta,* **37**, 267 (1967)
18. INGLOT, J. and PANZ, M., *Chemia analit.,* **15**, 965 (1970); *Analyt. Abstr.,* **21**, 1115 (1971)
19. KOZLICKA, M. and WOJTOWICZ, M., *Z. analyt. Chem.,* **257**, 191 (1971); *Analyt. Abstr.,* **22**, 3007 (1972)
20. TSYGANOK, L.P., CHUIKO, V.T. and REZNIK, B.E., *Zh. analit. Khim.,* **27**, 2180 (1972)
21. PRIBIL, R. and SEDLAR, V., *Colln Czech. chem. Commun.,* **16**, 69 (1951)
22. *British Standards Handbook* No. 19, British Standards Institute, London (1970)
23. BERKA, A., VULTERIN, J. and ZYKA, J., *Newer Redox Titrants,* Pergamon Press, Oxford (1965)
24. VOGEL, A.I., *A Textbook of Quantitative Inorganic Analysis,* 3rd edn, Longmans, London, 381 (1961)
25. CHARLOT, G. and BEZIER, D., *Quantitative Inorganic Analysis,* Methuen, London, 623 (1957)
26. FLASCHKA, H. and ABDINE, H., *Chemist Analyst,* **45**, 58 (1956)
27. KINNUNEN, J. and WENNERSTRAND, B., *Chemist Analyst,* **46**, 92 (1957)
28. KHALIFA, H. and EL-SIRAFY, A., *Z. analyt. Chem.,* **227**, 109 (1967); *Analyt. Abstr.,* **15**, 3294 (1968)
29. GARDELS, M.C. and CORNWELL, J.C., *Analyt. Chem.,* **38**, 774 (1966)
30. TANAKA, M. and ISHIDA, A., *Analytica chim. Acta,* **36**, 515 (1966)
31. SCHWARZENBACH, G. and FLASCHKA, H., *Compleximetric Titrations,* 2nd English edn, Methuen, London, 213 (1969)
32. SANDELL, E.B., *Colorimetric Determination of Traces of Metals,* 3rd edn, Interscience, New York, 923 (1959)
33. BUDEVSKI, O. and DZHONOVA, L., *Talanta,* **12**, 291 (1965)
34. KAWAHATA, M., MOCHIZUKI, H., KAJIYAMA, R. and ICHIHASHI, K., *Japan Analyst,* **14**, 348 (1965); *Analyt. Abstr.,* **13**, 6821 (1966)
35. AGARWALA, B.V. and DEY, A.K., *Current Sci., India,* **36**, 544 (1967)
36. GEARY, W.J. and LARSSON, C.N., *Proceedings of the SAC conference, Nottingham 1965,* Heffer and Sons Ltd, Cambridge, 455 (1965)
37. SIROKI, M. and DJORDJEVIC, C., *Analytica chim. Acta,* **57**, 301 (1971)
38. MINCZEWSKI, J., CHWASTOWSKA, J. and PHAM THI HONG MAI, *Analyst,* **100**, 708 (1975)
39. MAL'TSEVA, L.S., SHALAMOVA, G.G. and GUSEV, S.I., *Zh. analit. Khim.,* **29**, 2053 (1974); *Analyt. Abstr.,* **29**, 5B 118 (1975)
40. RIZVI, G.H. and SINGH, R.P., *Talanta,* **19**, 1198 (1972)
41. BANNARD, L.G. and BURTON, J.D., *Analyst,* **93**, 142 (1968)
42. JACKSON, K.W., WEST, T.S. and BALCHIN, L., *Analyt. Chem.,* **45**, 240 (1973)
43. HABA, F.R. and WILSON, C.L., *Talanta,* **9**, 841 (1962)
44. OBERHELMANN, G., *Am. J. Sci.,* **39**, 530 (1915)
45. RAO, N.P.R. and SHARMA, B.V.S., *Chemist Analyst,* **54**, 107 (1965)
46. RAO, G.G. and DIKSHITULU, S.A., *Talanta,* **10**, 1023 (1963)
47. MURALIKRISHNA, U. and RAO, G.G., *Talanta,* **15**, 143 (1968)
48. KISS-EROSS, K., BUZAS, I. and ERDEY, L., *Z. analyt. Chem.,* **255**, 271 (1971); *Analyt. Abstr.,* **22**, 3139 (1972)
49. ZELINKA, J., BARTUSEK, M. and OKAC, A., *Colln Czech. chem. Commun.,* **39**, 83 (1974); *Analyt. Abstr.,* **27**, 676 (1974)
50. MORALES, A., GONZALES, B.F. and DIAZ, C., *Chemist Analyst,* **56**, 89 (1967)
51. SAXENA, R.S. and SHARMA, O.P., *Indian J. Chem.,* **2**, 502 (1964)
52. SONGINA, O.A., ZAKHAROV, V.A., BEKTUROVA, G.B. and SMIRNOVA, L.I., *Zh. analit. Khim.,* **29**, 1594 (1974); *Analyt. Abstr.,* **29**, 3B 14 (1975)
53. BARD, A.J. and LINGANE, J.J., *Analytica chim. Acta,* **20**, 581 (1959)
54. BISHOP, E. and HITCHCOCK, P.H., *Analyst,* **98**, 572 (1973)
55. SVEHLA, G., *Analyst,* **94**, 513 (1969)
56. THOMPSON, H. and SVEHLA, G., *Microchem. J.,* **13**, 576 (1968)
57. BOGNAR, J. and JELLINEK, O., *Mikrochim. Acta,* 366 (1969)
58. BOGNAR, J. and SAROSI, S., *Mikrochim. Acta,* 813 (1967)
59. BOGNAR, J. and JELLINEK, O., *Mikrochim. Acta,* 193 (1967)
60. FULLER, C.W. and OTTAWAY, J.M., *Analyst,* **95**, 41 (1970)
61. HADJIIOANNU, T.P. and SISKOS, P.A., *Mikrochim. Acta,* 51 (1975)
62. BUTTS, W.C., *Analyt. Lett.,* **3**, 29 (1970)
63. BUTTS, W.C. and RAINEY, W.T., *Analyt. Chem.,* **43**, 538 (1971)

Part 2

Halogen Anions

Bromate

Potassium bromate finds considerable industrial application as a bleaching agent.

Separations

Bromate, chlorate and iodate in millimolar amounts, can be separated by anion-exchange[1]. Bromate can be separated from chlorate, iodate, chlorite, bromite, perchlorate, fluoride, bromide, chloride and iodide by TLC and paper chromatography. Details are given in *Table 25* in the chlorate section. In addition, bromate can be separated[2] from iodate, periodate and chromate by TLC and Al_2O_3.

Determination

Analytical methods for bromate are almost entirely based on its oxidizing properties. Bromate belongs to a group of oxidizing anions capable of being reduced by SO_2. It can be subsequently determined as bromide. A convenient method of carrying out the reduction is to add a 1% solution of potassium bisulphite and boil off the excess SO_2. This procedure is useful in the analysis of bromate–bromide mixtures. Further reference will be made to it when discussing EDTA and amperometric methods.

Titrimetric methods

Titrimetric methods are essentially redox. Potassium bromate is well known as a strong oxidizing reagent in quantitative analysis.

$$BrO_3^- + 6H^+ + 6e \rightleftharpoons Br^- + 3H_2O$$

The salt is readily purified by recrystallization and standard solutions prepared from accurately weighed amounts. Arsenic(III), iodide and several other species can be determined by direct titration with bromate. In the context of bromate determination, the same reactions can be employed using standard reductants, for example arsenic(III).

1. Iodimetric methods

The bromate–iodide reaction takes place in dilute mineral acid. It is relatively slow, compared for example with the iodate–iodide reaction. Furthermore it does not proceed directly according to the stoichiometric equation

$$BrO_3^- + 6I^- + 6H^+ \rightarrow Br^- + 3I_2 + 3H_2O$$

but involves an intermediate step. An account of earlier work on the reaction has been reviewed[3]. HCl is regarded as being more effective than H_2SO_4. In either case, the concentration must be not less than 0.5M if the reaction is to take place reasonably quickly and with exact stoichiometry. Ammonium molybdate may be used as catalyst. This is generally employed if the acidity is lower than the above value.

The relatively slow reactions of bromate and chlorate with iodide have been used to advantage for determination of iodate in their presence. In a pH 5 phthalate-buffered solution, iodate reacts immediately producing iodine which is titrated with standard thiosulphate. A second titration after 3 min represents iodine resulting from bromate, chlorate or both. Szekeres[4–6] has developed procedures for analysing mixtures of various anions containing bromate. These include BrO_3^-–IO_4^-, IO_3^-–IO_4^-–BrO_3^-–ClO_3^- and CrO_4^{2-}–AsO_4^{3-}–IO_4^-–IO_3^-–BrO_3^-–ClO_3^-. The iodimetric titration of bromate is featured in each case.

The iodimetric method is recommended for determination of bromate in flour by the Association of Official Analytical Chemists[7]. From the above discussion it will be clear that the method is not selective.

Iodimetric titration of bromate (for about 50 mg of bromate)

Procedure

To 25 mℓ of bromate solution add 1 g of KI and 5 mℓ of 4M HCl (or the equivalent of H_2SO_4). Swirl the solution well. Titrate the iodine with standard 0.1M thiosulphate using freshly prepared starch indicator near the end-point.

---

2. Using arsenic(III)

The reaction can be represented by the equation

$$BrO_3^- + 3As(III) + 6H^+ \rightarrow Br^- + 3As(V) + 3H_2O$$

The reaction, which is normally slow, is catalysed by chlorine, bromine, and particularly iodine. A potentiometric form of the method by Norkus and Stul'gene[24] employs OsO_4 as catalyst. This is discussed later in this section.

In the titration, when the reaction is complete, the first excess of bromate reacts with bromide to form free bromine. This destroys certain indicators causing irreversible colour changes.

$$BrO_3^- + 5Br^- + 6H^+ \rightarrow 3Br_2 + 3H_2O$$

Several indicators have been proposed. Methyl orange and naphthol blue-black function as irreversible indicators, the latter being the better. Of the reversible indicators *p*-ethoxychrysoidine introduced by Schulek and Rozsa[8] appears to be the best. The experimental procedure is essentially the one given in the arsenic section for its determination using standard bromate. A standard arsenic(III) solution is used with the bromate being added from the burette. The limits of HCl concentration for which the bromate–arsenite reaction is quantitative have been elucidated for both the visual titration using rosaniline hydrochloride as indicator, and the potentiometric titration[9].

3. Ascorbimetric methods

Halogenates, XO_3^-, in the presence of catalysts, react in acid medium with ascorbic acid to form dehydro ascorbic acid and halide ion.

$$XO_3^- + 3C_6H_8O_6 \rightarrow X^- + 3C_6H_6O_6 + 3H_2O$$

Reduction of bromate is relatively more difficult than iodate, requiring higher acidity and a catalyst. Selenious acid is generally used for this purpose, in the presence of manganese(II) sulphate with mercury(II) chloride as indicator[10]. The method allows 10–100 mg of bromate to be determined. An alternative procedure employing the well-established hexacyanoferrate(III)–ascorbic acid titration, has been proposed.

$$2[Fe(CN)_6]^{3-} + C_6H_8O_6 \rightarrow 2[Fe(CN)_6]^{4-} + C_6H_6O_6 + 2H^+$$

The bromate is reacted with hexacyanoferrate(II).

$$BrO_3^- + 6[Fe(CN)_6]^{4-} + 6H^+ \rightarrow Br^- + 6[Fe(CN)_6]^{3-} + 3H_2O$$

and the resulting hexacyanoferrate(III) titrated with standard ascorbic acid using 2,6-dichlorophenolindophenol as indicator[11]. The method is applicable to halogens, hypohalites, halites and other halates. Later work by Erdey and co-workers[12] employed the 2-hydroxy derivative of variamine blue, 2-hydroxy-4-amino-4′-methoxy diphenylamine as indicator in the hexacyanoferrate(III)–ascorbic acid titration. The indicator can be used in the form of a solid dilution with NaCl. More recently an automatic potentiometric form of the titration has been used for determination of bromate[13].

Ascorbimetric methods are capable of giving good results, but they appear to have little advantage over iodimetric and arsenic(III) methods for bromate.

4. Miscellaneous methods

Leonard, Shahine and Wilson[14] find that micro amounts of bromate (and iodate) can be titrated directly with chromium(II) using the vanadium(II)–1,10 phenanthroline complex as redox indicator. The indicator has a deep blue-violet reduction form and an almost colourless oxidation form.

EDTA has been applied to determination of bromate. Bromate–bromide mixtures can be analysed by precipitating bromide as silver bromide, reacting this with $K_2Ni(CN)_4$, and titrating the liberated nickel ions with standard EDTA. A second aliquot is treated with arsenic(III), this reducing bromate to bromide. The first procedure is then repeated[15]. Chlorides, iodides and heavy metals interfere.

Kellner and Szekeres[16] determine bromate, as well as several other oxidizing species, by first reacting with excess Fe^{2+}, followed by titration of the resulting Fe^{3+} with EDTA using salicylic acid as indicator. The method is applicable to 10–270 mg of bromate. Neither of the EDTA procedures is selective.

Spectrophotometric methods

Few spectrophotometric methods have been reported for bromate. Most are based on redox properties and are unselective.

Bromate in trace amounts gives colour reactions with strychnine, methyl orange, indigo carmine and several other compounds. MacDonald and Yoe[17] have developed a method based on the reddish-brown colour produced between bromate and *o*-arsinilic acid. Beer's law holds for up to 50 ppm with the absorbance being measured at 463 nm. For 20 ppm of bromate, interference is given by bromide, iodide, iodate, nitrite, Au^{3+}, Ce^{4+} and Fe^{3+} at the 1 ppm level. The absorbance depends on acidity, time, temperature, the presence of redox ions, reagent concentration and bromate,concentration. The absorbance maximum holds for 2 min only. Sensitivity is 0.05 µg BrO_3^- mℓ^{-1}. Later workers have reported instability in the colour formation[18].

Hashmi, Ahmad and Rashid[19] use *o*-aminobenzoic acid for the range 20–30 µg BrO_3^-. As little as 3 ppm can be determined. No interference is given by iodate, chlorate or organic compounds.

In another method the same workers[20] use an equimolar mixture of isoniazid and 2,3,5-triphenyltetrazonium chloride in dilute HCl. Here a pink colour is produced with iodate at 33 °C, but with bromate, only at 60 °C. Mixtures can be analysed for amounts of 10–300 µg per 50 mℓ of each ion.

Odler[21] has developed a method suitable for bromate or nitrite based on 1,2,3-tris(2-diethylaminoethoxy)benzene hydrochloride. In acid solutions of pH less than 1, bromate produces a yellow colour, and nitrite brown. The colour increases to a maximum, then decreases, so the procedure involves a fixed waiting time before measuring the absorbance at 400 nm. The range is $0.5–5.0 \times 10^{-3}$M. Interferences are reported to be small.

A simple spectrophotometric method by Meditsch and Santos[22] employs fuschine. Bromate in the range 0.5–2.5 ppm can be determined with no interference from traces of chlorate and iodate.

When antipyrine, perchloric acid, and sodium nitrite are added to bromate, a red complex is produced with absorbance maximum at 525 nm and a molar absorptivity of 2×10^3 mole^{-1} cm$^{-1}\ell$. Beer's law holds for 25.0–140 ppm. Interference is reported for arsenic(III), cerium(IV), iron(III), chromate, dichromate and chloride[18].

Electroanalytical methods

1. Potentiometric

Bromate can be titrated potentiometrically with ferrous ammonium sulphate in an orthophosphoric acid solution[23]. When the concentration of the latter is less than 8M reduction goes directly to bromide, but results are inaccurate due to loss of bromine. At higher concentrations of H_3PO_4 two inflections are observed due to reduction to bromine and bromide respectively. Under these conditions the slight loss of bromine at the first inflection has little effect. In both titrations chloride, iodide, chlorate, iodate, nitrate and periodate interfere.

Reference has been made to the potentiometric determination of bromate by Norkus and Stul'gene[24] using arsenic(III). The method allows complete analysis of BrO^-–BrO_2^-–BrO_3^-–Br^- mixtures using one sample. The oxidizing species are titrated using standard arsenic(III), and the bromide with standard $AgNO_3$.

In essence the method is analogous to one developed for the corresponding chlorine anions, the main steps being:

1. Hypobromite is titrated with standard arsenic(III) in strongly alkaline solution using platinum and calomel electrodes.
2. OsO_4 is added to the same solution and bromite titrated similarly.
3. Bromate is titrated either directly or indirectly. In the direct titration, the solution is made 0.25–0.5M in H_2SO_4 and titrated with arsenic (III). Alternatively a known excess of arsenic(III) is added to the solution which is made more than 0.5M in H_2SO_4, and back-titration made with $KMnO_4$. The back-titration procedure is more suitable when significant amounts of bromide are present. The $KMnO_4$–As(III) reaction is also catalysed by OsO_4.
4. For bromide determination, the platinum electrode is replaced with a silver electrode and the same solution titrated with standard $AgNO_3$.

The procedure is given below.

Successive potentiometric determination[24] of BrO^-–BrO_2^-–BrO_3^-–Br^-

Reagents

Arsenic(III): 0.025M (0.1N). Molarity stated assumes use of As_2O_3. For preparation of As(III) see p. 9.

OsO_4 catalyst: 0.1 per cent solution in 0.3M NaOH

$AgNO_3$: 0.1M (0.1N)

$KMnO_4$: 0.02M (0.1N)

Outline procedure

Determination of hypobromite

To an aliquot of the sample solution, add 0.5–2 mℓ of 10M NaOH.

Insert the platinum and calomel electrodes and titrate slowly with arsenic-(III) while vigorously stirring using a magnetic stirrer.

Determination of bromite

Add to the same solution 3 or 4 drops of the OsO_4 catalyst and titrate with arsenic(III) as above.

Determination of bromate

Direct

Neutralize the solution by addition of 5M H_2SO_4, and acidify with the same acid until its concentration is 0.25–0.5M. Add arsenic(III) until the yellow colour which appears is discharged, then continue the titration to the potential jump.

Back-titration

Add a known excess of 0.025M arsenic(III) to the alkaline solution, then acidify with 5M H_2SO_4 until it is greater than 0.5M in H_2SO_4. Back titrate with 0.02M $KMnO_4$ to a potential jump.

Determination of bromide

Carefully remove the platinum electrode (with rinsing) and replace with a silver electrode. Titrate in the same H_2SO_4 medium with 0.1M $AgNO_3$ to a potential jump.

Note

In the calculation it is assumed that 1 mℓ of exactly 0.025M As(III) corresponds to 4.795 mg of hypobromite, 2.798 mg of bromite, and 2.132 mg of bromate. The corresponding figure for bromide using 0.1M $AgNO_3$ is 7.991 mg.

$$BrO^- + AsO_3^{3-} \rightarrow Br^- + AsO_4^{3-}$$

$$BrO_2^- + 2AsO_3^{3-} \rightarrow Br^- + 2AsO_4^{3-}$$

$$BrO_3^- + 3AsO_3^{3-} \rightarrow Br^- + 3AsO_4^{3-}$$

2. Amperometric

Bromate–bromide mixtures can be analysed using an amperometric procedure[25]. First bromide is titrated amperometrically with standard $AgNO_3$ in a medium of 0.1M KNO_3 containing 0.02% gelatin. The electrodes used are a rotating platinum wire and saturated calomel. Bromate is then reduced to bromide using aqueous H_2SO_3 and the titration repeated. Errors of less than 0.4 per cent are reported.

3. Polarographic

Both bromate and iodate are reduced at the dropping mercury electrode, but chlorate and periodate are not. In alkaline medium reduction of bromate occurs as a 6-electron step:

$$BrO_3^- + 6e + 3H_2O \rightarrow Br^- + 6OH^-$$

Because of its greater overvoltage, the reduction potential for bromate is much greater than for iodate. This enables determination[26] of bromate to be made without interference from iodate.

Miscellaneous methods

Pennington[27] has determined oxidizing species by gas-chromatographic evaluation of the iodine liberated from KI. Although bromate is not specifically mentioned in this work, the method presumably applies. Samples of oxidizing agents as low as 5 mg can be analysed within 5 min.

References

1. SKLOSS, J.L., HUDSON, J.A. and CUMMISKEY, C.L., *Analyt. Chem.*, **37**, 1240 (1965)
2. LEDERER, M. and POLCARO, C., *J. Chromat.*, **84**, 379 (1973)
3. KOLTHOFF, I.M. and BELCHER, R., *Volumetric Analysis*, Vol. III, Interscience, New York, 269 (1957)
4. SZEKERES, L., *Z. analyt. Chem.*, **165**, 32 (1959); *Analyt. Abstr.*, **6**, 3502 (1959)
5. SZEKERES, L., *Z. analyt. Chem.*, **172**, 256 (1960); *Analyt. Abstr.*, **7**, 3739 (1960)
6. SZEKERES, L., *Annali. Chim.*, **51**, 200 (1961); *Analyt. Abstr.*, **8**, 4932 (1961)
7. *Official Methods of Analysis*, 11th edn, Association of Official Analytical Chemists, Washington, D.C. (1970)
8. SCHULEK, E. and ROZSA, P., *Z. analyt. Chem.*, **115**, 185 (1939)
9. OTTAWAY, J.M. and BISHOP, E., *Analytica chim Acta*, **33**, 153 (1965)
10. ERDEY, L., BODOR, E. and BUZAS, H., *Z. analyt. Chem.*, **134**, 412 (1952); *Chem. Abstr.*, **46**, 3457e (1952)
11. ERDEY, L. and SVEHLA, G., *Z. analyt. Chem.*, **167**, 164 (1959); *Analyt. Abstr.*, **7**, 122 (1960)
12. ERDEY, L. and KASA, I., *Talanta*, **10**, 1273 (1963)
13. ERDEY, L., SVEHLA, G. and WEBER, O., *Z. analyt. Chem.*, **240**, 91 (1968); *Analyt. Abstr.*, **18**, 12 (1970)
14. LEONARD, M.A., SHAHINE, S.A.E.F. and WILSON, C.L., *Talanta*, **16**, 470 (1969)
15. DE SOUSA, A., *Z. analyt. Chem.*, **174**, 337 (1960); *Analyt. Abstr.*, **8**, 125 (1961)
16. KELLNER, A. and SZEKERES, L., *Chemist Analyst*, **54**, 75 (1965)
17. MACDONALD, J.C. and YOE, J.H., *Analytica chim. Acta*, **28**, 383 (1963)
18. QURESHI, M., QURESHI, S.Z. and ZEHRA, N., *Mikrochim. Acta*, 831 (1970)
19. HASHMI, M.H., AHMAD, H. and RASHID, A., *Analyt. Chem.*, **36**, 2028 (1964)
20. HASHMI, M.H., AHMAD, H., RASHID, A. and AZAM, F., *Analyt. Chem.*, **36**, 2471 (1964)
21. ODLER, I., *Analyt. Chem.*, **41**, 1116 (1964)
22. MEDITSCH, J.O. and SANTOS, S.E. DE A., *Reuta Quim. Ind., Rio de J.*, **40**, 14 (1971); *Analyt. Abstr.*, **23**, 3853 (1972)
23. VUTERIN, J., *Colln Czech. chem. Commun. Engl. Edn*, **32**, 3349 (1967); *Analyt. Abstr.*, **15**, 7255 (1969)
24. NORKUS, P. and STUL'GENE, S., *Zh. analit. Khim.*, **24**, 1565 (1969); *Analyt. Abstr.*, **20**, 3029 (1971)
25. IKEDA, S. and SATAKE, H., *Japan Analyst*, **20**, 721 (1971); *Analyt. Abstr.*, **23**, 2453 (1972)
26. HEMALA, M., *Chemické Listy*, **47**, 1323 (1953)
27. PENNINGTON, S.N., *J. Chromat.*, **36**, 400 (1968)

Bromide

The close similarity between the analytical chemistry of chloride and bromide is indicated in the chloride section which contains the essential details of the principal methods for separation and determination of halides. To avoid needless repetition of detail, these methods will be simply referred to in the present section unless special comment is necessary. Emphasis will be given to methods relating to the determination of bromide itself.

Separations

Bromide can be separated using a range of chromatographic techniques including ion-exchange. These are discussed in the chloride section. Foti[1] has investigated the concentration of bromide in sea-water by ion-exchange, using a radiotracer technique. Separation by distillation is applicable to bromide separation. Free bromide may be liberated from acid bromide solutions using very strong oxidizing conditions. Another method is distillation as cyanogen bromide which can be collected in NaOH. Winefordner and Maung Tin[2] have separated 5–20 ppm bromide from about 1000 ppm chloride by such a method. The subsequent determination was by null-point potentiometry. The total time required for sample preparation, separation and determination is 15 min; the method is precise to 0.1 ppm and accurate to 0.5 ppm.

Determination

Bromide can be determined gravimetrically as silver bromide under the same conditions described for the analogous chloride method, and is subject to the same interferences. A procedure involving precipitation from homogeneous solution has been described by Firsching[3]. This allows chloride, bromide and iodide to be determined gravimetrically by successive precipitation of each at decreasing pH values. This is achieved by volatilization of ammonia from the solution.

Titrimetric methods

1. Argentimetric methods

All three principal argentimetric methods, namely the Volhard, Mohr and adsorption indicator (Fajans) methods are suitable for determination of bromide. If the Volhard or Mohr methods are used the procedure given for chloride can be used without modification. In the case of the adsorption indicator method eosin (tetrabromofluorescein) is probably the best indicator, with fluorescein also being suitable. Eosin, being a much stronger acid than fluorescein can be used for titration of bromide in solutions of higher acidity ($pH < 2$). Addition of acetic acid was recommended by Kolthoff and Berk[4] to enhance the colour change. In a recent study, Kapel, Fry and Shelton[5] have studied the effect of adding various surface-active substances in the titration. Of these hydroxypropylmethylcellulose was found to give the best end-point, and was superior to agar in this respect. The same investigation confirms that eosin is the best indicator for bromide, and fluorescein for the mixed halides (chloride, bromide, iodide). It was not found possible to determine each individually in such mixtures.

Titrimetric determination of bromide using the adsorption indicator method

Reagents

$AgNO_3$: 0.1M.

Indicator: 0.1 % aqueous solution of eosin (sodium salt).

Procedure

To the neutral bromide solution in 50–100 mℓ and not more concentrated than 0.05M, add 10 drops of the indicator and 2–3 mℓ of 6M acetic acid. Titrate with 0.1M $AgNO_3$ with constant swirling and in diffuse light. The AgBr flocculates just before the equivalence point at which the precipitate assumes an intense red colour. It should be noted that dextrin, which is recommended as a protective colloid in the titration of chloride is not suitable for bromide or iodide.

Two other indicators have been recommended for the argentimetric titration of bromide. Mehlig[6] finds that potassium rhodizonate is suitable. In this case the solution turns from yellow to salmon-pink at the end-point while the precipitate becomes heliotrope. Pribil and Markova[7] use xylenol orange, which is suitable for chloride and iodide as well as bromide.

2. Mercurimetric methods

Bromide can be titrated mercurimetrically using nitroprusside, diphenylcarbazide, or diphenylcarbazone as indicators. The Cheng modification is applicable and provides an excellent method for low concentrations of bromide. Details of these methods appear in the chloride section.

It should be pointed out that the mercurimetric method cannot be extended to iodide. Neither is it suitable for mixed halides.

3. Using EDTA

Indirect compleximetric methods for bromide have been published. Gusev and Kozhevnikova[8] first precipitated bromide quantitatively with 2-(2-hydroxy-1-naphthylmethylene amino) pyridine in the presence of lead, the precipitate having the composition $(C_{16}H_{12}ON_2)_2PbBr_2$. Its lead content is titrated with standard EDTA using xylenol orange as indicator, and the bromide evaluated from this. Synthesis of the reagent is described in the analogous chloride method, details of which are given in that section.

De Sousa[9] has developed several EDTA methods for halides. Where bromide and iodide are to be determined together, one aliquot is treated with $AgNO_3$ and the precipitate oxidized with chromic acid. Iodide is oxidized to iodate; liberated bromine is removed in a current of air. The iodate is reduced to iodide and again precipitated as silver iodide for evaluation. In a second aliquot the combined silver halides are dissolved in nickel tetracyanide and the displaced nickel(II) ions titrated with standard EDTA, this giving the sum of bromide plus iodide. Bromide is found by difference.

In another method bromide, chloride and iodide are determined. Again the nickel tetracyanide complex is involved for total halides. The method does not appear to be suitable for routine work[10]. Compleximetric determination of bromide and bromate when present together can also be made using the nickel tetracyanide reaction. In this case bromate in a second aliquot is reduced to bromide with arsenic(III) and the total bromide determined as above[11].

4. Redox methods

Of the many redox titrimetric procedures developed for bromide, those based on oxidation to bromate by hypochlorite have found the most extensive use. They are often referred to as Kolthoff–Yutzy or Kolthoff–Yutzy–Van der Meulen procedures. Suitable for micro as well as macro analysis because of the six-fold amplification involved, they have found considerable use in determination of bromide resulting from oxygen-flask combustion of organic samples[12]. The oxidation is made using hot alkaline sodium hypochlorite in the presence of a sodium dihydrogen phosphate buffer. Excess hypochlorite is destroyed with sodium formate and the determination completed iodimetrically using molybdate to catalyse the otherwise slow bromate–iodide reaction. The oxidation probably occurs in two distinct steps, the overall reaction being

$$Br^- + 3ClO^- \rightarrow BrO_3^- + 3Cl^-$$

The subsequent steps are

$$BrO_3^- + 6I^- + 6H^+ \rightarrow 3I_2 + Br^- + 3H_2O$$

$$2S_2O_3^{2-} + I_2 \rightarrow S_4O_6^{2-} + 2I^-$$

from which it can be seen that

$$Br^- \equiv 6S_2O_3^{2-}$$

An important feature of the method is that it enables bromide to be determined in the presence of a large excess of chloride. Iodide will react similarly to bromide if present. It can be removed by boiling the original solution with sodium nitrite and sulphuric acid to drive off the liberated iodine. The hypochlorite method has a long history of development much of which has been concerned with the type of buffer and the pH for which the oxidation is quantitative[13, 14]. A recent application of the method has been made to bromide residues in foods[15]. Here the method is used after decomposition of the samples using the oxygen-flask technique. An alternative procedure based on a spectrophotometric end-point is included.

Redox titrimetric procedures for bromide depend on oxidation to bromine or bromate. In the first category several oxidants have been proposed. The resulting bromine can either be distilled or extracted. Its subsequent determination is usually iodimetric. An alternative approach is to measure the quantity of oxidizing titrant consumed. Here the end-point is generally detected potentiometrically.

A relatively simple titration based on oxidation of bromide to bromine has been described by Summersgill[16]. Manganic sulphate is used as selective oxidant.

$$2Mn^{3+} + 2Br^- \rightarrow 2Mn^{2+} + Br_2$$

The resulting bromine is extracted into CCl_4 and reacted with KI to liberate an equivalent amount of iodine. This is titrated with standard thiosulphate.

$$Br_2 + 2KI \rightarrow I_2 + 2KBr$$

The manganic sulphate, which is easily prepared, can decompose after 5 h but this disadvantage is offset by several advantages. No pH adjustments or heating are required, the method is rapid, requiring only 10 min for each determination, and chloride is unaffected by the reagent. The results are reproducible to at least one part in 200. Experimental details are given later in this sub-section.

Bromide can also be determined using cerium(IV) or lead tetra-acetate. These employ a potentiometric end-point and will be discussed later.

Titrimetric determination of bromide based on hypochlorite oxidation

Reagents

Sodium hypochlorite solution:

Bromide-free commercial NaOCl is convenient and suitable[17]; earlier workers synthesized it[14]. It should be about 0.5M (1N).

Procedure

To the bromide sample in not more than 25 mℓ, add 1 g of $NaH_2PO_4 \cdot 2H_2O$, 10 g of NaCl, and 5 mℓ of 0.5M NaOCl solution. Heat the solution just to boiling, and then add 5 mℓ of 50 % sodium formate. Allow to cool, dilute to 150 mℓ and add 1 g of KI, 25 mℓ of 3M H_2SO_4 and 1 drop of 0.5N ammonium molybdate. Titrate the iodine immediately with standard thiosulphate adding starch near the end-point. Carry out a blank determination under identical conditions, substituting an equal volume of water for the bromide solution.

Notes

1. The addition of a large amount of NaCl specified in a precursor to the above method can be omitted if the amount of bromide is less than 2 mg.
2. Chloride does not interfere, but iodide does, the results then giving $Br^- + I^-$.
3. Large amounts of calcium or magnesium cause slightly lower results.
4. It is known that the starch–iodine end-point is much less distinct in a high salt concentration. Meditsch[18] has investigated several dyes containing the quaternary ammonium group, as alternatives to starch. Malachite green is found to be the most effective with methylene blue also giving a good response. As these indicators are unaffected by a high salt concentration they should provide good alternatives.

Titrimetric determination of bromide based on manganese(III) oxidation[16]

Reagents

Manganic sulphate reagent:

Prepare a mixed H_2SO_4–H_3PO_4 solution by adding 30 mℓ of concentrated H_2SO_4 and 10 mℓ of syrupy H_3PO_4 to 110 mℓ of water. To 20 mℓ of this solution, to which 1–2 g of $MnSO_4 \cdot 4H_2O$ has been added, run in slowly 20–25 mℓ of approximately 0.02M (0.1N) $KMnO_4$ solution.

Procedure

Pipette the Br^-–Cl^- sample (10 or 20 mℓ) into a separating funnel and add 20 mℓ of CCl_4. Add the prepared Mn(III) sulphate reagent (40–45 mℓ). Replace the stopper and shake. Run out the lower brown layer under excess of a 10 % KI solution. Add further portions of CCl_4 and extract until no traces of yellow colour are seen in the lower layer. Three or four extractions are generally sufficient. Titrate the liberated iodine with standard thiosulphate using starch as indicator, or until the pink colour of iodine is just discharged from the CCl_4 layer.

Notes
1. Solutions of bromide from 0.1M to 0.005M can be determined without modification to the method.
2. The CCl_4 is easily recovered by:
   (a) Shaking the residues with dilute thiosulphate solutions to remove any traces of iodine.
   (b) Shaking with portions of distilled water until the washings give no precipitate with $AgNO_3$.
3. If iodide is present, iodine will be liberated and the final result will represent the sum of Br^- plus I^-.
4. No common ions are known to interfere. Ions such as sulphite, nitrite and peroxide are immediately oxidized by the excess Mn(III) sulphate.

---

5. Miscellaneous titrimetric procedures
The Vieböck mercuric oxycyanide method described in the chloride section is applicable to bromide, though for its determination alone the mercurimetric method as modified by Cheng is probably better.

Spectroscopic methods

1. Spectrophotometric, visible and UV methods
Many of the spectrophotometric methods described for chloride are suitable for bromide and in some cases iodide. They are:

1. The mercuric thiocyanate method. A related method[19] based on silver thiocyanate is suitable for bromide and iodide in the presence of chloride.
2. The mercuric diphenylcarbazone/-ide method.
3. The iron(III)-bromide complexes method. Here the presence of bromide causes the appearance of a band at 420 nm.
4. The method based on displacement of HCN from $Hg(CN)_2$ by a halide.
5. The method based on phenylmercury(II) halides and their reactions with sodium diethyldithiocarbamate.

Further details as well as references are given in the chloride section.

Several bromide spectrophotometric methods depend on initial oxidation to bromine. Such methods generally lack specificity. Under certain conditions chloride is not oxidized. Furthermore, iodide may be oxidized by iron(III) to iodine and this removed by boiling thus providing a method for bromide in the presence of iodide. Chloramine-T (*Structure 38*) is often used for oxidizing

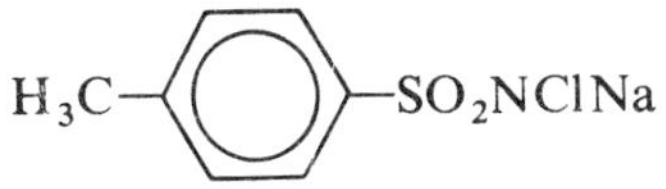

H_3C—C_6H_4—SO_2NClNa

Structure 38 Chloramine-T

bromide to bromine. After oxidation the resulting bromine can be determined by several methods. It reacts with methyl orange giving a colourless product. The same reaction occurs with chlorine. Phenol red (*Structure 39*) was proposed by Stenger and Kolthoff[20].

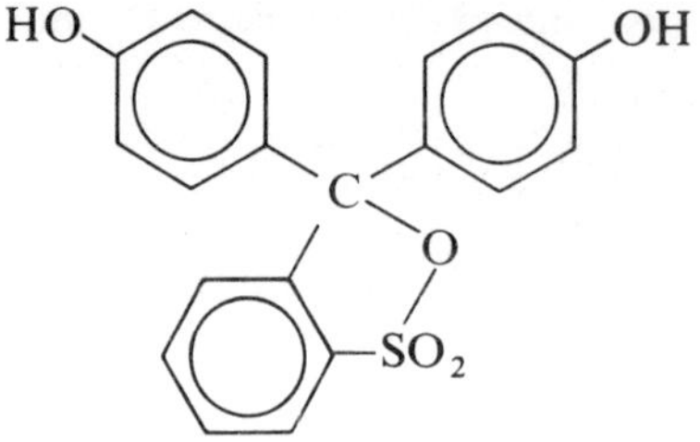

Structure 39 *Phenol red*

This reacts with bromine in alkaline solution but a close control on conditions is required. Initial oxidation[21] can be made by hypochlorite or chloramine-T. Beer's law is not obeyed. A modification of the method by Golman and Byles is now a standard method[22] for water analysis. The minimum detectable concentration is reported as 100 $\mu g\,\ell^{-1}$ Br^-. Cresol red (*o*-cresol sulphonaphthalein) a phenol-red type dye is reported to be more sensitive than phenol red itself. Another compound used is fluorescein, which is oxidized to eosin. Again iodine interferes but traces of chlorine can be tolerated[23]. Elbeih and El-Sirafy[24] oxidize bromide to bromine by warming with an anhydrous acetic acid–30% H_2O_2 (10:1) mixture. Chloride is not oxidized by the reagent. The bromine is determined spectrophotometrically using chromotrope 2B. The range is 30–70 μg Br^- and application to natural water samples is found to be satisfactory.

Several newer reagents have been investigated recently including triphenylmethane dyes. Likussar[25] uses the oxazine dyestuff Nile blue and extracts into $CHCl_3$ before measuring the absorbance at 625 nm. Iodide as well as bromide can be determined. Beer's law holds for 1–6 ppm Br^- and 0.5–3 ppm I^-.

Bunikiene, Ramanauskas and co-workers have examined a wide range of triphenylmethane (TPM) dyes. Iodide and bromide react with some TPM dyes in the presence of chloramine B, chloramine T or NaClO. It is established that the resulting I^+ or Br^+ causes a decrease in colour intensity of the dye. Eleven dyes were examined for determination of bromide of which brilliant green and acid violet S were found to be best[26]. The sensitivity was reported as about 0.01 $\mu g\,m\ell^{-1}$. Further work indicated that crystal violet in the presence of chloramine B or NaClO was also suitable for bromide and iodide[27]. The absorbance measurements are made at 590 nm for bromide and 582 nm for iodide. Copper, Mn, Ca, K, Na, chloride and sulphate do not interfere but carbonate, bicarbonate, and nitrate do. In a subsequent publication the same investigators find that malachite green is suitable for determination of both bromide and iodide[28]. Optimum conditions are established for the determination using brilliant green and malachite green.

A spectrophotometric method for bromide can be based on the Kolthoff–Yutzy oxidation of bromide to bromate. The latter is reacted with acidified

KI and the resulting iodine determined spectrophotometrically at 350 nm. Application is made to bromide in food[15].

Both bromide and iodide form complexes with mercury(II)–EDTA at pH 3.5–7.7 and 5.0–8.3 respectively. Measurement of the absorbance at 250 nm enables bromide in the range 0.05–1.6 mg to be determined. For iodide the corresponding range is 0.05–2.0 mg with the absorbance being measured at 260 nm. The presence of cyanide, thiocyanate, sulphide and cobalt(II) interferes in each case. In addition, NH_4^+ and Ag^+ interfere with the iodide method[29].

Bromide reacts with palladous sulphate in aqueous solution producing characteristic spectra in the UV. This enables bromide in the range 0.5–7.0 μg mℓ$^{-1}$ to be determined. Absorbance measurements are made at 230 nm; the same reaction is given[30] by chloride and iodide.

2. *Molecular emission*

In the presence of indium, bromide (as well as chloride and iodide) produces strong molecular emissions in a cool diffusion flame. This enables each halide to be determined in the presence of the other two[31]. The method is discussed more fully in the chloride section.

Electroanalytical methods

1. *Potentiometric methods including ion-selective electrodes*

The potentiometric methods described for chloride are largely applicable to bromide. In the zero-current classical titration using standard $AgNO_3$ as titrant, the curve is well defined. Considerable application of the method has been made to microanalysis of organobromine compounds following oxygen-flask combustion. In this application the conversion factor is less favourable than for chloride, that is, for a given weight of sample the $AgNO_3$ titre is less owing to the higher molecular weight of the bromo-compound. To some extent this is compensated for by an increase in potential change at the equivalence point. Where bromide is accompanied by chloride and iodide, the titration of total halides presents little problem. However, determination of individual members is difficult due to mixed halide precipitation. In the evaluation of potentiometric curves from mixed halides, Martin[32] has indicated how end-points may be obtained from the intersection of straight lines, and how corrections can be applied when the mole ratio of halides is greater than 21:1. The problem of mixed halides can be overcome by elimination of bromide in a second aliquot and then titrating chloride on its own[33].

Differential electrolytic potentiometry (DEP) is applicable to bromide. In the form of the method employing constant current coulometry, 10^{-11} mol of bromide can be determined using a 0.5 mℓ cell and in a medium of 0.01M HNO_3 in 80:20 methal–water[34].

Bromide in the presence of chloride, iodide and fluoride can be titrated potentiometrically using a mixed $AgNO_3$–$Th(NO_3)_4$ titrant[35]. Other potentiometric procedures, for example using mercury(II) are applicable to bromide in addition to chloride. These are discussed in the chloride section.

Attention will now be given to potentiometric procedures developed for bromide itself. Wharton[36] reports that bromide at macro- and semi-micro levels (1–200 mg in 25–100 mℓ) can be titrated with ammonium hexanitrato-cerate(IV) in 2M perchloric acid. The potential break is about 300 mV using platinum and saturated calomel electrodes. Iodide up to at least 0.02M does not interfere and neither does sulphate up to 0.005M. Chloride depresses the end-point potential break, but is still permissible up to 0.04M.

Ogienko[37] uses hypochlorite as titrant for bromide. Sulphate does not interfere though the potential break becomes less in its presence. Chloride at levels up to 15 g ℓ$^{-1}$ does not interfere; further amounts cause displacement in the position of the potential break.

Pflaum, Frohliger and Berge[38] describe direct potentiometric determination of bromide in the 10^{-1}–10^{-4}M range, using an Ag–AgBr indicator electrode and calomel reference electrode. Acetate, chloride, nitrate, perchlorate and sulphate have no effect at the 2000 ppm level, but cyanide, dichromate, iodide, permanganate and thiosulphate interfere at 10 ppm. In general, anions that oxidize bromide to bromine, or react with Ag^+ giving salts more insoluble than AgBr, or which form silver complexes, will interfere and must be removed.

When bromide is accompanied by hypobromite, bromite and bromate, potentiometric titration with arsenic(III) in alkaline medium provides a solution[39]. Titration in the absence and presence of OsO_4 enables hypobromite and bromite to be determined. Bromate is determined using the same titrant but in a H_2SO_4 solution. Finally bromide is determined with $AgNO_3$ using a silver indicator electrode instead of the platinum electrode used for the previous anions. A complete determination of all four anions takes about 15 min.

Other redox titrants recommended for potentiometric bromide include lead tetra-acetate[40], cobalt(III)[41] and cerium(IV)[42].

The use of ion-selective electrodes in the determination of bromide closely follows that for chloride and little further will be added to the discussion in that section. The solid-state Orion 94-17 AgCl electrode is itself more selective to bromide than chloride as indicated by the selectivity ratio of 3×10^2 for bromide. The corresponding bromide electrode, Orion 94-35, has a concentration range[43] of 10^0–5×10^{-6}M. Interferences for this electrode are given in *Table 24*.

Table 24 Interferences for bromide electrode Orion 94-35

Ion	*Selectivity ratio*
S^{2-}	Very high
CN^-	1.2×10^4
I^-	5×10^3
NH_3	0.5
Cl^-	2.5×10^{-3}
OH^-	3×10^{-5}

No interference is given by nitrate, fluoride, bicarbonate, sulphate or phosphate. It will be seen that the electrode is far more sensitive to iodide than bromide, so that iodide can be present only in very small amounts if it is not to interfere with determination of bromide. As with chloride, the Ag^+/S^{2-} solid-state electrode, for example the Orion 94-16, is suitable for determination of bromide. Here the maximum permissible ratio of chloride to bromide is given by

$$\frac{[Cl^-]}{[Br^-]} = \frac{K_{sp}(AgCl)}{K_{sp}(AgBr)} \cong 20$$

where K_{sp} is the solubility product, indicating that a chloride concentration of 20 times the bromide concentration will cause error in the bromide determination[44]. Several applications of the bromide ion-selective electrode have been reported, including organic microanalysis[45] of organo-bromine compounds, serum[46], plasma[47], soft drinks[48] and atmospheric water[49].

2. *Coulometric methods*

Bromide as well as chloride and iodide can be determined using coulometric analysis. A commonly used form of the method utilizes the electrogenerated argentous ion. Halide mixtures are analysed by successive electrolysis at appropriate potentials. For example Cadersky[50] determines 5–100 μg Br^- in samples containing chloride. A more detailed discussion is given in the chloride section.

3. *Amperometric methods*

Amperometric procedures for bromide have been recorded. Like chloride, bromide can be determined using $Cd(NO_3)_2$ as titrant in an anhydrous acetic acid medium. The method[51], which is based on precipitation of $CdBr_2$, can also be applied to thiocyanate. Ikeda and Musha[52] determine bromide, chloride and iodide in the presence of cyanide and cyanate. Details are given in the iodide section. More recently Ikeda and Satake[53] report an amperometric method for bromide and bromate when present together. In this work a rotating platinum electrode is employed with $AgNO_3$ as titrant. The bromate content is found by treating an aliquot with H_2SO_3 and then titrating the total bromide.

4. *Voltammetry*

Bromide can be determined by polarography. Calzolari, Gabrielli and Marletta[54] use a rapid form of the method for determination of chloride, bromide and iodide in algae after initial combustion. For chloride and iodide the anodic waves are recorded; for bromide the cathodic wave of the bromate ion is recorded, this being produced by quantitative oxidation of bromide under controlled conditions.

Gorokhovskii and Ismagilova[55] use a silver electrode of new design for the oscillopolarographic determination of bromide as well as chloride and iodide. The method is applicable to 10^{-3}–10^{-6}M concentrations of halides. A voltammetric determination of bromide and iodide using a rotating pyrolytic-graphite electrode has been published[56]. A cathode-ray polarographic method by Rooney[57] enables chloride, bromide and iodide as well as several other anions to be determined.

Catalytic methods

Ammonia is oxidized to trichloramine by hypochlorite according to the following reaction:

$$NH_3 + 3ClO^- + 3H^+ \rightarrow NCl_3 + 3H_2O$$

In the presence of bromide ions, hypochlorite is converted to hypobromite which oxidizes ammonia to nitrogen.

$$ClO^- + Br^- \rightarrow BrO^- + Cl^-$$

$$3BrO^- + 2NH_3 \rightarrow N_2 + 3H_2O + 3Br^-$$

Thus bromide inhibits the chlorination of ammonia to form trichloramine. This has been used[58] as the basis of a catalytic-spectrophotometric method for 0.02–1.20 ppm of bromide. The basis of another method is the catalytic effect of bromide on the oxidation of iodine to iodate by Ce(IV) in the presence of $K_2Cr_2O_7$ and in a HNO_3 medium[59]. Application is made to bromide in the range 0.01–0.1 ppm in natural waters. Chloride in excess of 1 ppm interferes, but can be determined using the mercuric thiocyanate method and allowed for. The method is similar to another by Fishaman and Skovgstad[60] in which bromide catalyses the oxidation of iodine to iodate by $KMnO_4$ in a H_2SO_4 medium. The range here is 0.001–0.1 ppm Br^-. Free chlorine must be absent.

An initial report[66] has been recently published of a kinetic method for bromide based on its inhibition of the rate of destruction of methyl orange by bromate. It is capable of application at the 5×10^{-9}M Br^- level.

Radiochemical methods

Both bromide and chloride can be determined by adding $^{203}Hg(IO_3)_2$ and measuring the activity of the resulting $HgCl_2$ or $HgBr_2$ complexes[61]. The $HgBr_2$ complex can be extracted into diethyl ether and the γ-activity of the aqueous phase measured[62]. Neutron activation has been used for both bromide and chloride. Separation of radioiodine and radiobromine in irradiated samples has been carried out by solvent extraction and anion-exchange. Ohno[63] has developed a method for both halides for which the limit of detection is about 0.01 μg for iodide and 0.1 μg for bromide. Neutron activation analysis has been applied to determination of bromide in cigarettes and other materials[64].

Gas-chromatographic methods

Gas-chromatography has provided a rapid method for separation and determination of small amounts of halides. Details of some of the methods are given in the chloride section.

A method for bromide in blood has been developed by Archer[65] in which the bromide in a protein-free filtrate is oxidized to bromine by $KMnO_4$ in acid solution. The bromine is extracted into cyclohexane containing cyclohexene to give 1,2-dibromohexene. This is determined by gas-chromatography using 1,6-dibromohexene as internal standard. The method is applicable to 0.1–1.0 mg Br^- $m\ell^{-1}$. Gas-chromatography is recommended for determination of bromide in grain by the Committee for Analytical Methods for Residues of Pesticides and Veterinary Products in Foodstuffs[67]. The method is based on an investigation by Heuser and Scudamore[68]. Peaks due to 2-bromoethanol are measured by an electron capture detector. Nitrogen is used as carrier; the column of stainless steel is packed with 15% m/m polypropylene glycol on 60–80 mesh Chromosorb W, and operated at not greater than 120 °C.

Miscellaneous methods

Several methods fall outside the preceding categories. In some cases they apply to chloride as well as bromide. They include semi-quantitative use of the ring-oven[69] and circular TLC[70].

Radcliffe[71] has developed a rapid method for traces of bromide in natural waters using X-ray fluorescence. The bromide is collected on a filter-disc containing an anion-exchange resin. The fluorescence of the $BrK_{\alpha 1}$ line is subsequently measured using a tungsten X-ray tube. All intensities are compared with a 100 ppm bromide standard. The detection limit is 0.05 ppm and the error about 5 per cent.

References

1. FOTI, S.C., *Rep. Congr. atom. Energy Commn U.S.*, AD 734383 (1971); *Analyt. Abstr.*, **24**, 511 (1973)
2. WINEFORDNER, J.D. and MAUNG TIN, *Analyt. Chem.*, **35**, 382 (1963)
3. FIRSCHING, F.H., *Analyt. Chem.*, **32**, 1876 (1960)
4. KOLTHOFF, I.M. and BERK, L.H., *Z. analyt. Chem.*, **70**, 369 (1927)
5. KAPEL, M., FRY, J.C. and SHELTON, D.R., *Analyst*, **100**, 570 (1975)
6. MEHLIG, J.D., *Chemist Analyst*, **44**, 87 (1955)
7. PRIBIL, R. and MARKOVA, V., *Chemické Listy*, **60**, 89 (1966); *Analyt. Abstr.*, **14**, 2544 (1967)
8. GUSEV, S.I. and KOZHEVNIKOVA, I.A., *Zh. analit. Khim.*, **18**, 366 (1963); *Analyt. Abstr.*, **11**, 968 (1964)
9. DE SOUSA, A., *Analytica chim. Acta*, **22**, 520 (1960)
10. DE SOUSA, A., *Inf. Quim. Anal.*, **17**, 127 (1963); *Analyt. Abstr.*, **11**, 5476 (1964)
11. DE SOUSA, A., *Z. analyt. Chem.*, **174**, 337 (1960); *Analyt. Abstr.*, **8**, 125 (1961)
12. FILDES, J.E. and MACDONALD, A.M.G., *Analytica chim. Acta*, **24**, 121 (1961)
13. KOLTHOFF, I.M. and BELCHER, R., *Volumetric Analysis*, Vol III, Interscience, New York, 254 (1957)
14. BELCHER, R. and WILSON, C.L., *New Methods in Analytical Chemistry*, Chapman and Hall, London, 201 (1955)
15. DOW, M.L., *J. Ass. off. analyt. Chem.*, **53**, 1040 (1970)
16. SUMMERSGILL, N., *Chemy Ind.*, 782 (1961)
17. HASLAM, J. and MOSES, G., *Analyst*, **75**, 343 (1950)
18. MEDITSCH, J.O., *Analytica chim. Acta*, **31**, 286 (1964)
19. UTSUMI, S., *J. chem. Soc. Japan*, **74**, 35 (1953); *Chem. Abstr.*, **47**, 6815f (1953)
20. STENGER, V.A. and KOLTHOFF, I.M., *J. Am. chem. Soc.*, **57**, 831 (1935)
21. HOUGHTON, G.U., *J. Soc. chem. Ind., Lond.*, **65**, 277 (1946)
22. American Public Health Association, American Waterworks Association and Water Pollution Control Federation, *Standard Methods for the Examination of Water and Wastewater*, 13th edn, American Public Health Association, New York (1970)

23. POHL, F.A., *Z. analyt. Chem.*, **149**, 68 (1956); *Analyt. Abstr.*, **3**, 2081 (1956)
24. ELBEIH, I.I.M. and EL-SIRAFY, A.A., *Chemist Analyst*, **54**, 8 (1965)
25. LIKUSSAR, W., *Analytica chim. Acta*, **49**, 97 (1970)
26. BUNIKIENE, L.V. and RAMANAUSKAS, E.I., *Zh. analit. Khim.*, **23**, 1364 (1968); *Analyt. Abstr.*, **18**, 2396 (1970)
27. RAMANAUSKAS, E.I., BUNIKIENE, L.V. and ZHILENAIT, M., *Nauch. Trud. vyssh. Ucheb. Zaved. Lit. SSR, Khim. khim. Tekhnol.*, 29(1968); *Analyt. Abstr.*, **18**, 3962 (1970)
28. BUNIKIENE, L., RAMANAUSKAS, E.I. and TAMULYAVICHUTE, M., *Nauch. Trud. vyssh. Ucheb. Zaved. Lit. SSR, Khim. khim. Tekhnol.*, 41 (1970); *Analyt. Abstr.*, **22**, 1568 (1972)
29. KOMATSU, S. and NORMURA, T., *J. chem. Soc. Japan, Pure Chem. Sect.*, **88**, 63 (1967); *Analyt. Abstr.*, **15**, 3316 (1968)
30. CHAPMAN, F.W. and SHERWOOD, R.M., *Analyt. Chem.*, **29**, 172 (1957)
31. DAGNALL, R.M., THOMPSON, K.C. and WEST, T.S., *Analyst*, **94**, 643 (1969)
32. MARTIN, A.J., *Analyt. Chem.*, **30**, 233 (1958)
33. PROKOPOV, T.S., *Analyt. Chem.*, **42**, 1096 (1970)
34. BISHOP, E. and DHANESHWAR, R.G., *Analyt. Chem.*, **36**, 726 (1964)
35. CHOU, D.H. and SAMS, L.C., *Microchem. J.*, **14**, 507 (1969)
36. WHARTON, H.W., *Talanta*, **13**, 919 (1966)
37. OGIENKO, V.S., *Zh. prikl, Khim., Leningr.*, **33**, 2486 (1960); *Analyt. Abstr.*, **9**, 128 (1962)
38. PFLAUM, R.T., FROHLIGER, J.O. and BERGE, D.G., *Analyt. Chem.*, **34**, 1812 (1962)
39. NORKUS, P. and STULGIENE, S., *Zh. analit. Khim.*, **24**, 1565 (1969); *Analyt. Abstr.*, **20**, 3029 (1971)
40. BUZKOVÁ, V., MULDAN, B. and ZYKA, J., *Colln. Czech. chem. Commun. Engl. Edn*, **30**, 28 (1965); *Analyt. Abstr.*, **13**, 2341 (1966)
41. SRAMKOVA, B., ZYKA, J. and DOLEZAL, J., *J. electroanal. Chem.*, **30**, 177 (1971)
42. MATHUR, N.K., RAO, S.P. and GAUR, J.N., *J. scient. ind. Res.*, **20**, 552 (1961); *Analyt. Abstr.*, **9**, 1896 (1962)
43. Orion Technical Information
44. BAZZELLE, W.E., *Analytica chim. Acta*, **54**, 29 (1971)
45. POTMAN, W. and DAHMEN, E.A.M.F., *Mikrochim. Acta*, 303 (1972)
46. CARTER, R.A., *Proc. Ass. clin. Biochem.*, **5**, 67 (1968)
47. DEGENHART, H.J., ABEIN, G., BEVAART, B. and BAKS, J., *Clinica Chim. Acta*, **38**, 217 (1972)
48. TURNER, D.L., *J. Food Sci.*, **37**, 791 (1972)
49. HARRIS, R.C. and WILLIAMS, H.H., *J. appl. Met.*, **8**, 229 (1969)
50. CADERSKY, I., *Mikrochim. Acta*, 401 (1966)
51. KRESHKOV, A.P., BORK, V.A., SHVYRKOVA, L.A. and APARSHEVA, M.I., *Zh. analit. Khim.*, **20**, 704 (1965); *Analyt. Abstr.*, **14**, 573 (1967)
52. IKEDA, S. and MUSHA, S., *Japan Analyst.*, **16**, 445 (1967); *Analyt. Abstr.*, **15**, 6633 (1968)
53. IKEDA, S. and SATAKE, H., *Japan Analyst*, **20**, 721 (1971); *Analyt. Abstr.*, **23**, 2453 (1972)
54. CALZOLARI, C., GABRIELLI, L.F. and MARLETTA, G.P., *Analyst*, **94**, 774 (1969)
55. GOROKHOVSKII, V.M. and ISMAGILOVA, F.K., *Zh. analit. Khim.*, **21**, 87 (1966); *Analyt. Abstr.*, **14**, 5393 (1967)
56. DRYHURST, G. and ELVING, P.J., *J. electroanal. Chem.*, **12**, 416 (1966)
57. ROONEY, R.C., *J. polarogr. Soc.*, **10**, 49 (1964)
58. ZITOMER, F. and LAMBERT, J.L., *Analyt. Chem.*, **35**, 1731 (1963)
59. YONEHARA, N., UTSUMI, S. and IWASAKI, I., *Bull. chem. Soc. Japan*, **38**, 1887 (1965); *Analyt. Abstr.*, **14**, 5067 (1967)
60. FISHAMAN, M.J. and SKOVGSTAD, M.W., *Analyt. Chem.*, **35**, 146 (1963)
61. BANYAI, E., SZABADVARY, F. and ERDEY, L., *Mikrochim. Acta*, 427 (1962)
62. BANYAI, E. and SZABADVARY, F., *Mikrochim. Acta*, 729 (1968)
63. OHNO, S., *Analyst*, **96**, 423 (1971)
64. JANKINS, R.W., NEWMAN, R.H., IKEDA, R.M. and CARPENTER, R.D., *Anal. Lett.*, **4**, 451 (1970)
65. ARCHER, A.W., *Analyst*, **97**, 428 (1972)
66. HASTY, R.A., LIMA, E.J. and OTTAWAY, J.M., *Analyst*, **102**, 313 (1977)
67. *Committee for Analytical Methods for Residues of Pesticides and Veterinary Products in Foodstuffs, Analyst*, **101**, 386 (1976)
68. HEUSER, S.G. and SCUDAMORE, K.A., *Pestic. Sci.*, **1**, 244 (1970)
69. CELAP, M.B. and WEISZ, H., *Microchim. Acta*, 24 (1962)
70. HASHMI, M.H. and CHUGHTAI, N.A., *Mikrochim. Acta*, 1040 (1968)
71. RADCLIFFE, D., *Anal. Lett.*, **3**, 573 (1970)

Bromite

Bromite and hypobromite are very similar and reference will be made to methods given in the section on hypobromite, which should be read in conjunction with the present account. In several instances methods will be applicable to either ion.

Solutions of hypobromite often contain bromite and bromate. Where bromite and hypobromite need to be determined in mixtures, selectivity for bromite is achieved by difference in reaction rates or elimination of hypobromite by reaction with phenol or ammonium ions (though some investigators have contested the value of this).

Separations

Bromite is separated from perchlorate, chlorate, chlorite, bromate and iodate by thin-layer chromatography[1]. The absorbent used is Aluminium oxide G–Kieselgur G (1:1) and the solvent butanol–acetone–aq. NH_3–H_2O (8:10:2:1).

Determination

Titrimetric methods

1. Iodimetric

Together with other species such as hypobromite and bromate, bromite is reduced by an acidified solution of KI, liberating iodine which may be titrated with standard thiosulphate[2].

$$BrO_2^- + 4I^- + 4H^+ \rightarrow 2I_2 + Br^- + 2H_2O$$

Standard arsenic(III) may be used[3] for titration of the iodine.

$$I_2 + AsO_3^{3-} + H_2O \rightarrow AsO_4^{3-} + 2I^- + 2H^+$$

In its normal use the iodimetric method is not selective for bromite. When accompanied by hypobromite, destruction of the latter by phenol and $(NH_4)_2SO_4$ have been reported[4,2].

$$4BrO^- + 2NH_4^+ \rightarrow 4Br^- + N_2 + 4H_2O$$

According to later workers[3] neither is effective if the bromite concentration is appreciable, due to phenol and ammonium salts reacting with bromite as well as hypobromite. Furthermore, phenol is reported to react with iodine causing interference. Details of the above procedures are given in the section on hypobromite.

2. Using arsenic(III)

A direct titration of bromite using arsenic(III) with tartrazine as indicator, has been described[5]. If bromite is accompanied by hypobromite, reduction of bromite only begins when the reduction of hypobromite has been completed. This method requires a prior titration using the indicator externally.

An alternative procedure is to add excess standard arsenic(III) and back-titrate with standard iodine. This is included as part of a method by Hashmi and Ayaz[2] for the determination of hypobromite, bromite and bromate. Addition of excess arsenic(III) followed by back-titration with iodine gives hypobromite plus bromite only. The same procedure following destruction of hypobromite with ammonium ions gives bromite alone. An iodimetric titration gives the sum of all three anions. Experimental details are given below.

Velghe and Claeys[3] propose a method for the same three anions using one arsenic(III) standard solution only. A full discussion of the method together with the experimental procedure is given in the hypobromite section.

Titrimetric determination of bromite, hypobromite and bromate in mixtures[2]

Reagent

Arsenic(III) solution 0.03M (0.12N):

Dissolve the approximate weight of As_2O_3 in 10% NaOH. Make acid to phenolphthalein, then add 10 g solid $NaHCO_3$. Dilute to 1ℓ and standardize with iodine. For weight of As_2O_3 required see p. 9.

Procedure

1. To a 5-mℓ aliquot add 3 or 4 g of solid KI followed by 10 mℓ of 2M H_2SO_4. Dilute to twice its volume. Titrate the liberated I_2 with standard thiosulphate using starch. The titre represents the sum of all three anions.

$$BrO^- + 2I^- + 2H^+ \rightarrow I_2 + Br^- + H_2O$$

$$BrO_2^- + 4I^- + 4H^+ \rightarrow 2I_2 + Br^- + 2H_2O$$

$$BrO_3^- + 6I^- + 6H^+ \rightarrow 3I_2 + Br^- + 3H_2O$$

2. Add a 5-mℓ aliquot to excess $(NH_4)_2SO_4$ and about 1 g of $NaHCO_3$. After 10 min add 3 or 4 g of solid KI and 10 mℓ of 2M H_2SO_4. Allow the solution to stand for 5 min. Dilute to twice its volume and titrate with standard thiosulphate. The titre represents bromite plus bromate.

$$4BrO^- + 2NH_4^+ \xrightarrow{\text{pH } 8\text{–}9} 4Br^- + N_2 + 4H_2O$$

$$BrO_2^- + 4I^- + 4H^+ \longrightarrow 2I_2 + Br^- + 2H_2O$$

$$BrO_3^- + 6I^- + 6H^+ \longrightarrow 3I_2 + Br^- + 3H_2O$$

3. To a 5-mℓ aliquot add a known excess of arsenic(III). After 5 min add 4 or 5 g of $NaHCO_3$ followed by dilute acetic acid to neutralize the NaOH (note: The original solution containing hypobromite, bromite and bromate is alkaline with NaOH) until each drop of acetic gives a free effervescence. Titrate the solution with standard I_2 using starch as indicator. The titre represents hypobromite plus bromite.

$$BrO^- + AsO_3^{3-} \rightarrow AsO_4^{3-} + Br^-$$

$$BrO_2^- + 2AsO_3^{3-} \rightarrow 2AsO_4^{3-} + Br^-$$

BrO_3^-: No reaction.

4. Add a 5-mℓ aliquot to an excess of solid $(NH_4)_2SO_4$ and about 1 g of $NaHCO_3$. After 10 min add a known excess of standard As(III), allow to stand for 5 min, then titrate with standard iodine.
The titre gives bromite only.

$$BrO_2^- + 2AsO_3^{3-} \rightarrow 2AsO_4^{3-} + Br^-.$$

Calculation: Titre (1) – (2) = BrO^-

$$(2) - [(1) - (3)] = BrO_2^- = (4)$$

$$(1) - (3) = BrO_3^-$$

Electroanalytical methods

Anderson and Madsen[6] have developed two potentiometric methods for determination of bromite and hypobromite. One of these, in which bromite is titrated with arsenic(III) in the presence of OsO_4 as catalyst, is also suitable for bromite alone or in the presence of bromate and bromide. Full details are given in the section on hypobromite. An extension of the method which includes the determination of bromate and bromide in addition to hypobromite and bromite, has been reported by Norkus and Stulg'ene[7]. Experimental details are given in the bromate section.

Fuchs and Landsberg[8] find that bromite and hypobromite can be determined simultaneously using chronopotentiometry with a gold electrode or by conventional polarography. The presence of calcium or barium interferes with the method.

Krivis and Supp[9] have investigated the polarographic behaviour of bromite. A reduction wave is found at about –0.88 V this being well separated from the hypobromite (0.0 V) and bromate (–1.7 V) waves. The diffusion current is found to vary linearly with bromite concentration up to about 2 mg per 10 mℓ. The investigators note a reaction between sodium bromite and mercury, and recommend that the dropping mercury electrode is inserted into the cell immediately before analysis. The electrode reaction over the pH range 7–10 appears to be

$$BrO_2^- + 4H^+ + 4e \rightarrow Br^- + 2H_2O$$

References

1. PESCHKE, W., *J. Chromat.*, **20**, 573 (1965)
2. HASHMI, M.H. and AYAZ, A.A., *Analyt. Chem.*, **35**, 908 (1963)
3. VELGHE, N. and CLAEYS, A., *Analytica chim. Acta*, **60**, 377 (1972)
4. CHAPIN, R., *J. Am. chem. Soc.*, **56**, 2211 (1934)
5. HASHMI, M.H. and AYAZ, A.A., *Analyst*, **89**, 147 (1964)
6. ANDERSEN, T. and MADSEN, H.E.L., *Analyt. Chem.*, **37**, 49 (1965)
7. NORKUS, P.K. and STULG'ENE, S.P., *Zh. analit. Khim.*, **24**, 1565 (1969); *Analyt. Abstr.*, **20**, 3029 (1971)
8. FUCHS, H. and LANDSBERG, R., *Analytica chim. Acta*, **45**, 505 (1969)
9. KRIVIS, A.F. and SUPP, G.R., *Analyt. Chem.*, **40**, 2063 (1968)

Chlorate

Sodium chlorate is manufactured on a large scale industrially. A major use is in the manufacture of chlorine dioxide for the pulp and paper industry. It also finds use as a defoliant and weedkiller, in ore processing, in dye manufacture and in the production of perchlorates and various chemical intermediates. Potassium chlorate finds use in match manufacture and in pyrotechnics generally.

Separations

1. Ion-exchange

Chlorate, iodate and bromate in millimolar amounts can be separated[1] using either a Dowex 21K (trimethylbenzylammonium) anion resin, or a Dowex 2 (dimethylethanolbenzylammonium) anion resin, both in nitrate form. Elution in each case is by sodium nitrate, the order of elution being the reverse of that for simple halides, namely iodate, bromate followed by chlorate.

2. Paper and thin-layer chromatography

Data on several of these are summarized in *Table 25*.

3. Solvent extraction

Chlorate can be solvent extracted using tetraphenylarsonium chloride and related compounds. The unsolvated ion-pairs are extracted in chloroform.

With tetraphenylarsonium chloride itself[9], chlorate is 100 per cent extracted into $CHCl_3$ at pH 2–12. Iodate and periodate are little extracted by the system. With triphenylsulphonium chloride, chlorate and perchlorate are 100 per cent extracted[10] into $CHCl_3$ at pH 2–12. Bromate is 28 per cent extracted, and iodate and periodate hardly at all. Much the same applies in the case of tetraphenylphosphonium chloride. Again chlorate and perchlorate are 100 per cent extracted in $CHCl_3$ at pH 2–11 with bromate only 32 per cent extracted[11].

Determination

Analytical methods for chlorate are essentially redox. Selectivity within groups of other oxidizing anions is often achieved by utilizing differences in reaction rates. For example the reaction between chlorate and iodide is slower than the corresponding reaction between bromate or iodate with iodide. Another useful analytical feature of chlorate is that it can be easily reduced to chloride and then determined in that form. Suitable reductants include SO_2 in gaseous form or as bisulphite, or nitrite.

Table 25 Paper and thin-layer chromatographic methods for separation of chlorate

Technique	*Solvent*	*Ions separated*	*Ref.*
Paper and TLC (TLC: Silufol UV 254 plates)	Butanol–pyridine–aq. NH_3 (0.880) (2 : 2 : 1)	ClO_3^-–ClO^-–ClO_2^-–ClO_4^-	2
Paper	Isopropanol–H_2O–pyridine–aq. NH_3 (0.880) (15 : 2 : 2 : 2)	ClO_3^-–ClO_2^-–Cl^-–ClO_4^-	3
TLC	Isopropanol–tetrahydrofuran–aq. NH_3 (0.880) (50 : 30 : 20)	ClO_3^-–ClO_2^-–Cl^-–ClO_4^-	4
Circular paper	Butanol–dimethylformamide–aq. NH_3 (0.880) (3 : 1 : 1) or butanol–acetone–aq. NH_3 (1 : 3 : 1)	ClO_3^-–BrO_3^-–IO_3^-	5
TLC (Al_2O_3 + Kieselguhr G 1:1)	Butanol–acetone–aq. NH_3(0.880) –H_2O (8 : 10 : 2 : 1)	ClO_3^-–ClO_2^-–BrO_3^-–IO_3^-–ClO_4^-	6
TLC (Corn Starch)	Acetone–3M aq. NH_3 (7 : 3)	ClO_3^-–BrO_3^-–IO_3^-–ClO_4^-–F^-–Br^-–Cl^-–I^-	7
TLC (Silica gel)	Acetone–ethylmethylketone–14% aq. NH_3 (6 : 4 : 1)	ClO_3^-–BrO_2^-–IO_3^-–F^-–Br^-–Cl^-–I^-	8

Titrimetric methods

1. Iodimetric methods

As stated above, the reaction between chlorate and acidified iodide is relatively slow.

$$ClO_3^- + 6I^- + 6H^+ \rightarrow 3I_2 + Cl^- + 3H_2O$$

If the concentration of HCl is increased, the reaction rate increases, but a high concentration causes air-oxidation of iodide. Several species such as iron(II) and molybdenum(VI) catalyse the reaction. Molybdenum(IV) also catalyses the air-oxidation of iodide. Several procedures have been recommended to improve the titration[12]. Despite the above difficulties the iodimetric method has remained an important one. It features in a method for analysis of chlorine dioxide, chlorous acid, chlorite, chlorate and chloride when present together[13]. Roth[14] describes a simple form of the titration suitable for determination of chlorate in defoliants and weedkillers.

It is possible to react ClO_3^- with acidified KBr instead of KI. The resulting bromine reacts with KI liberating iodine which is then titrated in the usual way with standard thiosulphate. This form of the method is incorporated in a British Standards method[15] for assay of sodium chlorate.

A variation of the method utilizes the hydrazine–iodine reaction. Hydrazine is well known as a reductimetric titrant[16, 17].

$$N_2H_4 \rightarrow N_2 + 4H^+ + 4e$$

Its reaction with iodine is slow in acid solutions but rapid in bicarbonate-buffered solutions of pH 7–7.4. Panwar, Mathur and RaO[19] used it in the following way. The chlorate sample is reacted with KBr in strong HCl solution. The resulting bromine liberates iodine from KI, and is titrated with standard hydrazine hydrochloride in a bicarbonate buffer.

$$ClO_3^- + 6Br^- + 6H^+ \rightarrow 3Br_2 + Cl^- + 3H_2O$$

$$Br_2 + 2KI \rightarrow 2KBr + I_2$$

$$N_2H_4 + 2I_2 \rightarrow N_2 + 4I^- + 4H^+$$

The procedure is given below.

The relatively slow reduction of chlorate by iodide or bromide can be turned to advantage analytically. Szekeres[18], in a titrimetric method for IO_4^-–IO_3^-–BrO_3^-–ClO_3^- mixtures, first determines all four anions iodimetrically by KBr–KI reduction in a HCl medium. In a second aliquot the titration is conducted in a dilute sulphuric acid medium, and after a shorter waiting time. In this case the iodine liberated is equivalent to periodate, iodate and bromate only. Further titrations enable all four anions to be determined.

Titrimetric determination of chlorate using hydrazine hydrochloride[19]

Reagents

Hydrazine hydrochloride:

The hydrochloride ($N_2H_4 \cdot 2HCl$) is used because of its greater solubility. It can be purified by recrystallization from water. To prepare a 0.025M solution, dissolve 2.6237 g of the pure salt in water and make up to exactly 1 ℓ. It can be standardized against iodine which has itself been standardized using sodium arsenite.

Procedure
To 10.0 mℓ of the chlorate solution add 1 g of KBr and 20 mℓ of concentrated HCl (the final concentration of HCl should be 8M). Stopper the flask and allow to stand for 5 min. Add 10 mℓ of 10% KI and sufficient sodium bicarbonate to give a slight excess (pH 7–7.4). Titrate with the standard hydrazine using starch or sodium starch glycollate near the end-point.

Note
1. Addition of excessive bicarbonate should be avoided to prevent the decomposition of hydrazine.
2. The pertinent equations have been given earlier in this section.

---

2. Reduction by arsenic(III)
Chlorate is reduced on boiling with arsenic(III) in a HCl medium. Excess arsenic(III) is titrated with standard $KBrO_3$. The reduction is catalysed[20] by OsO_4. Alternatively the well known arsenic(III)-cerium(IV) reaction can be utilized. This was done by Smith and Veraguth[21] for determination of chlorate in the presence of perchlorate. The chlorate is reduced by excess arsenic(III) or iron(II). Back titration is with standard cerium(IV) using ferroin as redox indicator and osmic acid as catalyst. Perchlorate is not reduced under these conditions.

The induced reduction of chlorate by arsenic(III) has also been investigated by Csanyi and Szabo[22] who find that it is catalysed by Ag^+ ions. Chlorate, hypochlorite, chlorite and chloride can be determined in one aliquot by potentiometric titration with arsenic(III) and using OsO_4 as catalyst[23]. Experimental details are given later in this section.

3. Miscellaneous reduction methods
Chlorate is quantitatively reduced by ascorbic acid in 2M H_2SO_4.

$$ClO_3^- + 3C_6H_8O_6 \rightarrow Cl^- + 3C_6H_6O_6 + 3H_2O$$

The titration is done in hot solution with selenious acid and manganese(II) sulphate as catalysts[24]. The end-point is indicated by the orange colour of colloidal selenium. Mercury(II) chloride can be used as an alternative indicator. An interesting feature of the method is that it is a direct titration in contrast to other redox methods for chlorate.

It has been already noted that chlorate can be reduced with SO_2 and the excess removed by boiling. This is an important difference between chlorate and perchlorate. Perchlorate remains unaffected but may be subsequently reduced on boiling with titanium(III). In a recent method Coetzee[25] reduced chlorate to chloride using sodium nitrite or sodium bisulphate. The resulting chloride is determined by titration with silver nitrate. Leonard, Shahine and Wilson[26] have determined a number of oxidizing species, including chlorate, by treatment with excess standard chromium(II) followed by back-titration with standard iron(III). The indicator used is vanadium(II)-1,10-phenanthroline complex.

4. Using EDTA

Compleximetric methods have been described[27,28] for ClO_3^-–ClO_4^- and Cl^-–ClO_3^-–ClO_4^- mixtures. Each is based on selective reduction to chloride followed by its evaluation by precipitation as silver chloride, treatment with ammoniacal nickel tetracyanide and titration of the liberated Ni^{2+} ions with EDTA.

Spectroscopic methods

1. Spectrophotometric methods

Few spectrophotometric methods for chlorate have been published.

Chlorate reacts with *o*-tolidine in strong HCl solution, giving a yellow colour. A method based on the reaction allows 0.05–10 ppm of chlorate to be determined[29,30]. Nitrite interferes and so does iron(III) but in the latter instance the effect is additive and a correction can be applied. Chloride and nitrate do not interfere. Benzidine was used in the same manner but this compound is now known to be carcinogenic.

Jordanov and Daiev[31] find that N,N,N′,N′-tetramethyl-*o*-tolidine (tetron) (*Structure 40*) is more sensitive than *o*-tolidine itself.

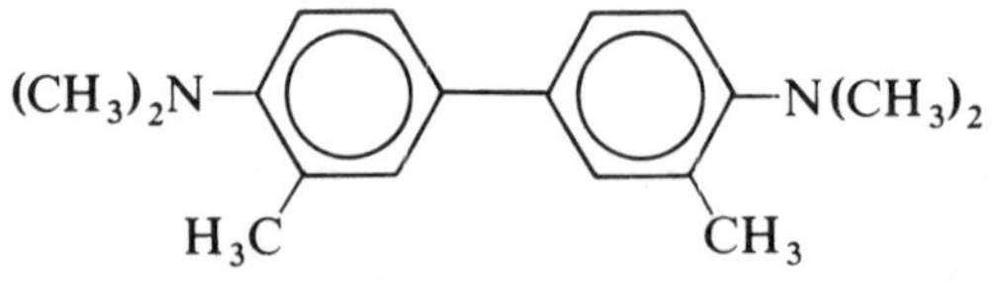

$(CH_3)_2N$–[benzene ring]–[benzene ring]–$N(CH_3)_2$, with H_3C and CH_3 substituents

Structure 40 NNN′N′ tetramethyl-*o*-tolidine (*tetron*)

The same reaction is given by a number of oxidizing species including bromate, iodate and permanganate.

Chlorate reacts with brucine in H_2SO_4 medium giving a coloured species with maximum absorbance at 435 nm. The method based on this is applicable in the presence of perchlorate and can therefore be applied to analysis of explosives and pyrotechnic mixtures containing it[32].

The interference by chlorate with formation of the coloured rhenium–α furildioxime complex forms the basis of a newer spectrophotometric method[33] for chlorate. Up to 5 ppm of chlorate can be determined.

2. Infra-red

Small amounts of chlorate in the range 0.1–1.0 mg can be determined in the presence of perchlorate, bromate, iodate, periodate, etc., by means of its infra-red spectrum[34]. The potassium bromide disc technique used involves a freeze-drying operation. Absorbance measurements are carried out[34] at 490.2 cm^{-1}.

Electroanalytical methods

1. Potentiometric methods including use of ion-selective electrodes
Chlorate can be titrated potentiometrically with arsenic(III) using OsO_4 as catalyst[23]. By choosing the appropriate conditions, successive determination of hypochlorite, chlorite, chlorate and chloride is possible, using arsenic-(III) for the first three and either $AgNO_3$ or $Hg(NO_3)_2$ for the chloride. The basic steps are as follows:

1. First hypochlorite is determined. If no chlorite is present this can be titrated potentiometrically at a pH above 8 in a bicarbonate medium. If chlorite is present the titration is made at above pH 12.
2. Chlorite is titrated in weakly alkaline solution at pH 8–12 and in the the presence of OsO_4.
3. Chlorate is titrated directly with arsenic(III) in a H_2SO_4 medium, again with OsO_4 as catalyst.
4. Chloride is determined potentiometrically by argentimetric or mercurimetric titration. The procedure is given below.

Successive potentiometric titration of hypochlorite, chlorite, chlorate and chloride[23]

Reagents

As(III)	: 0.025M (0.1N). Molarity assumes use of As_2O_3. For preparation of As(III) solutions see p. 9.
OsO_4	: 0.1% in 3M NaOH.
$AgNO_3$	: 0.1M (0.1N)
$Hg(NO_3)_2$	: 0.05M (0.1N)

Outline procedure

Determination of hypochlorite
To the mixture containing 0.25–1.5 mmol hypochlorite, add NaOH, insert platinum and calomel electrodes, and titrate with arsenic(III) with vigorous stirring until a large potential change occurs (Note 1).

Determination of chlorite
After the hypochlorite has been titrated, add 5 mℓ of saturated $NaHCO_3$ and a few drops of 0.1% aqueous alizarin yellow P. Add 5M H_2SO_4 dropwise until the colour changes from red-lilac to yellow. Add 4–5 drops of the OsO_4 catalyst and titrate as above.

Determination of chlorate
After the chlorite titration, add 5M H_2SO_4 dropwise until no further CO_2 is evolved, then further amounts until the H_2SO_4 concentration is 1–2M. Add an additional 1–3 drops of OsO_4 then titrate slowly with arsenic(III) as above.

Determination of chloride
After the chlorate titration, remove the platinum electrode with rinsing and replace with a silver electrode. Titrate with 0.1M $AgNO_3$ while stirring vigorously.

Notes

1. If no chlorite is present, the NaOH can be replaced with 235 mℓ of saturated $NaHCO_3$.
2. Calculations are made on the basis that 1 mℓ of exactly 0.025M arsenic(III) solution corresponds to 2.573 mg ClO^-, 1.686 mg ClO_2^- and 1.391 mg ClO_3^-.

A recent investigation by Hiiro, Moody and Thomas[37] has shown that the nitrate ion-selective electrode can be adapted for use with chlorate. This was accomplished by converting the nitrate liquid ion-exchanger in a Corning No. 477316 electrode, into chlorate form. The limit of detection of the resulting electrode was found to be 3×10^{-5}M, this being lower than the detection limit for the nitrate electrode which is itself sensitive to chlorate. The study includes a determination of selectivity coefficients for the electrode towards other ions.

2. Polarographic methods

Chlorate is not reduced at the dropping mercury electrode from alkaline, neutral or moderately acid solutions. In view of the extremely positive value of the standard potential for the reaction:

$$ClO_3^- + 6H^+ + 6e \rightleftharpoons Cl^- + 3H_2O \qquad E^0 = +1.47V$$

this suggests a very slow step in the reduction process. Attempts to overcome this difficulty have included use of catalysts, a strongly acid supporting electrolyte, and conversion of chlorate to some other species capable of giving a reduction wave. Meites and Hofsass[35] use the rapid stoichiometric reaction between chlorate and excess iron(II) in 3M HCl. No interference is given by ClO_4^- or Cl^-. Strong oxidizing agents, for example hypochlorite and chlorine, interfere and must be removed. This is conveniently done in a prior controlled-potential electrolysis from a weakly acidic solution.

3. Miscellaneous electroanalytical methods

An amperometric method using a rotating platinum electrode enables chlorate–chloride mixtures to be analysed[36]. The titrant is 0.1M $AgNO_3$. After initial determination of chloride, the chlorate is reduced by boiling the solution with 0.6% aqueous SO_2 for 5 min and the titration repeated for total chloride. The analysis is carried out in a medium of 0.1M KNO_3 containing 4 mℓ of 0.5% gelatin.

References

1. SKLOSS, J.L., HUDSON, J.A. and CUMMISKEY, C.L., *Analyt. Chem.*, **37**, 1240 (1965)
2. THIELEMANN, H., *Mikrochim. Acta,* 746 (1971)
3. HARRISON, B.L. and ROSENBLATT, D.L., *J. Chromat.*, **13**, 271 (1964)
4. SEILER, H. and SEILER, M., *Helv. chim. Acta,* **50**, 2477 (1967)

5. MAO, C-H., *Acta chim. sin.*, **30**, 412 (1964); *Analyt. Abstr.*, **12**, 5786 (1965)
6. PESCHKE, W., *J. Chromat.*, **20**, 573 (1965)
7. PETROVIC, S.M. and CANIC, V.D., *Z. analyt. Chem.*, **228**, 339 (1967); *Analyt. Abstr.*, **15**, 4674 (1968)
8. TAKEUCHI, T. and TSUNODA, Y., *J. chem. Soc. Japan, pure Chem. Sect.*, **87**, 251 (1966); *Analyt. Abstr.*, **14**, 4682 (1967)
9. BOCK, R. and BEILSTEIN, G.M., *Z. analyt. Chem.*, **192**, 44 (1963)
10. BOCK, R. and HUMMEL, C., *Z. analyt. Chem.*, **198**, 176 (1963)
11. BOCK, R. and JAINZ, J., *Z. analyt. Chem.*, **198**, 315 (1963)
12. KOLTHOFF, I.M. and BELCHER, R., *Volumetric Analysis*, Vol. III, Interscience, New York, 271 (1957)
13. HONG, C.C. and RAPSON, W.H., *Can. J. Chem.*, **46**, 2061 (1968)
14. ROTH, F.J., *J. Ass. off. analyt. Chem.*, **52**, 1294 (1969)
15. British Standard 4122: (1967), London
16. BELCHER, R. and WILSON, C.L., *New Methods of Analytical Chemistry*, 2nd edn, Chapman and Hall, London, 93 (1964)
17. BERKA, A., VULTERIN, J. and ZYKA, J., *Newer Redox Titrants*, Pergamon Press, Oxford, 180 (1965)
18. SZEKERES, L., *Z. analyt. Chem.*, **172**, 256 (1960); *Analyt. Abstr.*, **7**, 3739 (1960)
19. PANWAR, K.S., MATHUR, N.K. and RAO, S.P., *Analytica chim. Acta*, **24**, 541 (1961)
20. VAN DER MEULEN, J.H., *Chem. Weekbl.*, **28**, 238 (1931)
21. SMITH, G.F. and VERAGUTH, A.J., *Analytica chim. Acta*, **17**, 386 (1957)
22. CSANYI, L.J. and SZABO, M., *Talanta*, **1**, 359 (1958)
23. NORKUS, P.K. and STUL'GENE, S.L., *Zh. analit. Khim.*, **24**, 884 (1969); *Analyt. Abstr.*, **19**, 4862 (1970)
24. ERDEY, L. and BODOR, E., *Z. analyt. Chem.*, **133**, 265 (1951)
25. COETZEE, C.J., *Z. analyt. Chem.*, **234**, 245 (1968); *Analyt. Abstr.*, **16**, 3009 (1969)
26. LEONARD, M.A., SHAHINE, S.A.E.F., and WILSON, C.L., *Talanta*, **16**, 470 (1969)
27. DE SOUSA, A., *Chemist Analyst*, **49**, 18 (1960)
28. DE SOUSA, A., *Analytica chim. Acta*, **24**, 424 (1961)
29. WILLIAMS, D. and HAINES, G.S., *Ind. Engng Chem. analyt. Edn*, **17**, 538 (1945)
30. URONE, P. and BONDE, E., *Analyt. Chem.*, **32**, 1666 (1960)
31. JORDANOV, N. and DAIEV, CH., *Talanta*, **10**, 163 (1963)
32. EGERS, C., *Analyt. Chem.*, **27**, 1199 (1955)
33. TRAUTWEIN, N.L. and GUYON, J.C., *Analytica chim. Acta*, **41**, 275 (1968)
34. MILLER, M.W. and PHILP, R.H., *Talanta*, **10**, 763 (1963)
35. MEITES, L. and HOFSASS, H., *Analyt. Chem.*, **31**, 119 (1959)
36. MUSHA, S. and IKEDA, S., *J. chem. Soc. Japan, pure Chem. Sect.*, **90**, 180 (1969); *Analyt. Abstr.*, **19**, 213 (1970)
37. HIIRO, K., MOODY, G.J. and THOMAS, J.D.R., *Talanta*, **22**, 918 (1975)

Chloride

The importance of chloride determination extends into all the major scientific and technological areas including pure chemistry, industrial chemistry, agriculture, geology, biochemistry including clinical biochemistry, and environmental chemistry. In some instances it represents the final stage in the determination of other species. Thus in elemental organic analysis of chlorine-containing materials, the sample can be decomposed by oxygen-flask combustion and the resulting chloride evaluated. Several chlorine-containing anions such as hypochlorite can be determined as chloride after reduction to that form.

Chloride determination is important at all concentration levels from macro-determination in high-purity chlorides to ppb (10^9) in steam-generating feed waters.

Separations

Although many of the new methods for chloride are selective, separation is still an important aspect of chloride analysis. A wide range of methods is to be found in the literature. For separation of chloride, bromide and iodide, some are of doubtful value if accurate results are required.

1. Gravimetric methods

Precipitation of chloride as silver chloride will separate it from many elements. Species precipitated by the reagent, silver nitrate, will interfere. These include bromide, iodide, cyanide and thiocyanate.

Precipitation from homogeneous solution (PFHS) allows the successive formation of AgI, AgBr and AgCl at certain pH ranges, this being achieved by volatilization of ammonia which causes a slow decrease in the pH. Gravimetric evaluation of the precipitates enables all three halides to be determined[1].

2. Coprecipitation

Rodabaugh and Upperman[2] have coprecipitated traces of chloride on lead phosphate. This is subsequently dissolved in an iron(III) solution and the chloride determined by the mercury(II)–thiocyanate method. Application of the method is made to analysis of high-purity water.

Chwastowska, Marczenko and Stolarczyk[3] coprecipitate AgCl in amounts below 20 μg on $BaSO_4$ as carrier. This is followed by turbidimetric determination of the chloride after dissolving up the precipitate.

3. Ion-exchange

Several ion-exchange methods have been described, particularly for separating chloride from other halides. Cation-exchange can be used to separate chloride from heavy metals. Where separation of halides is required, anion-exchange methods are available. De Geiso, Reeman and Lindenbaum[4] separate mixtures of chloride, bromide and iodide containing not more than 2.6 mmol of each, but 3 h is required for complete separation. Holzapfel and Gurtler[5] have separated fluoride, chloride, bromide and iodide in amounts up to 3 mmol of each on a 150-cm column of Wolfatit SBW. The ions are eluted in the order given. A total of 2.6ℓ of M $NaNO_3$ solution is used as eluant though elution with sodium oxalate and $NaNO_3$ respectively is found to be more effective for certain halide pairs.

Separation of all four halides has been investigated by Zaievskaya and Starobinets[6] who find the best results using Dowex 1-X4 resin and 0.045M KOH as eluant. In later work the method is extended to include thiocyanate. This is achieved using a 40-cm column of A-25 anionite in hydroxyl form and NaOH as eluant[7].

Liquid ion-exchange has been applied[8] to separation of chloride, bromide, iodide and fluoride. The method was found to be suitable for separation of up

Table 26 Paper and thin-layer chromatographic methods for separation of chloride

Technique	*Solvent system*	*Ions separated*	*Ref.*
Paper	Isopropanol–H_2O–pyridine–NH_3 (0.880) (15:2:2:2)	Cl^-, ClO_2^-, ClO_3^-, ClO_4^-	11
Paper (Whatman No. 1)	Butanol–acetone–aq. NH_3 (3:13:4) or Butanol–dimethylformamide–aq. NH_3 (1.5–15M)[a] (3:1:1)	Cl^-, Br^-, I^-, SCN^-	12
TLC cellulose and paper	Acetone–water (various mixtures)	Cl^-, Br^-, I^-, F^-	13
TLC	Isopropanol–tetrahydrofuran–NH_3 (0.880) (50:30:20)	Cl^-, ClO_2^-, ClO_3^-, ClO_4^-	14
TLC silica gel	Butanol–propanol–dibutylamine (9:9:2) and other solvents	Cl^-, Br^-, I^-, F^-, CN^-, SCN^- $[Fe(CN)_6]^{3-}$, $[Fe(CN)_6]^{4-}$	15
TLC	Acetone–*n*-butanol–NH_3 (0.880)–H_2O (65:20:10:5)	Cl^-, Br^-, I^-, F^-	16
TLC Corn starch	Acetone–3M aq. NH_3 (7:3)	Cl^-, Br^-, I^-, F^-, ClO_4^-, ClO_3^-, BrO_3^-, IO_3^-	17
TLC Silica gel	Acetone–ethyl methyl ketone–14% aq. NH_3 (6:4:1)	Cl^-, Br^-, I^-, F^-, IO_3^-, BrO_3^-, ClO_3^-	18
TLC Silica gel	Satd. aq. isobutyl alcohol–40% aq. ammonium acetate (4:1)	Cl^-, Br^-, I^-, PO_4^{3-}	19
TLC Silica gel + 5% corn starch	Acetone–H_2O (10:1)	Cl^-, Br^-, I^-, SCN^-, $[Fe(CN)_6]^{3-}$	20

[a] Concentration does not affect R_f values.

to a total of 100 μmol of halides. Separation of fluoride and chloride was found to be the most difficult.

4. Column, thin-layer and paper chromatography

Column chromatography using hydrous zirconium oxide has enabled iodide, bromide and chloride to be separated[9]. Elution was made with 0.15M, 0.25M and M KNO_3 respectively. The same investigator has studied the separation of halides on aluminium oxide columns, layers and coated paper. In using the column technique iodide, bromide and chloride were eluted[10] in that order using 0.2M KNO_3.

Paper chromatographic methods have now been generally superseded by thin-layer chromatography. *Table 26* contains details of the more important paper and thin-layer methods.

5. Gas-chromatographic methods

This technique has been applied recently to separation and determination of halides. It is discussed more fully later in this section.

6. Distillation

Though not a general method for separation of chloride, distillation has provided a method. Elsheimer, Johnson and Kochen[21] separate trace amounts of Cl^- from aqueous solutions containing plutonium and uranium by cerium(IV) oxidation to chlorine followed by its distillation. For amounts of chloride up to 50 μg a recovery of 80% is reported.

Determination

In looking for a suitable method for determination of chloride, the analyst is faced with a bewildering choice. The final selection will depend on the level of chloride in the sample, the precision and accuracy sought, the number of samples, nature of other species present and the equipment available.

Where circumstances are not antagonistic, titration with silver nitrate or mercuric nitrate are suitable for milligram quantities. The mercuric thiocyanate spectrophotometric method is suitable where high sensitivity is required. As in several other areas of analysis the ion-selective electrode is still being assimilated. Its obvious advantages such as speed and ability to be automated make it attractive particularly where large numbers of samples are involved. The methods cited are discussed more fully later in the section.

There appears to be no recent general review of chloride determination. The review by Armstrong, Gill and Rolf[22] is a valuable survey of the situation up to the time of its publication. Other more specialized reviews will be given where appropriate in the text.

Gravimetric methods

Soluble chloride is determined gravimetrically as AgCl by addition of excess silver nitrate solution. The precipitation is carried out in the presence of dilute HNO_3. After filtration and washing it is dried at 100–200 °C before weighing.

$$Cl^- + Ag^+ \rightarrow AgCl$$

Like the classical gravimetric determination of sulphate as $BaSO_4$, the method has a voluminous literature and strict adherence to a prescribed technique is essential if high accuracy is to be attained. That the method is capable of high accuracy has long been recognized, and with the possible exception of modern coulometric methods it must remain the ultimate method for direct assay of high purity chlorides. Its principles are discussed in the standard text by Kolthoff *et al.*[23]. The important factors are as follows:

1. The presence of dilute HNO_3 is required to prevent precipitation of carbonate, phosphate, etc., as insoluble silver salts. Nitric acid also assists coagulation of the precipitate.
2. After formation of the precipitate a waiting period of some hours is required to complete the process of coagulation, and to allow aging to occur.
3. Washing the precipitate with water causes peptization. This is prevented by using a dilute HNO_3 solution.
4. Exposure to light causes slow decomposition of the precipitate into silver and chlorine which can be serious. Where there is strong sunlight the operation should be carried out in subdued light.
5. The solubility of the precipitate is reduced to negligible values when a slight excess of the reagent is present. The solubility is increased by alkali and ammonium salts. The same applies in the presence of electrolytes not having a common ion with the precipitate.
6. Coprecipitation is of little significance analytically (in contrast to the $BaSO_4$ method for sulphate) if the procedure is carried out properly.
7. The precipitate is not collected on a filter paper to avoid the possibility of subsequent reduction. A sintered glass filter is used instead.

Interferences are numerous, consisting of ions giving low solubility silver salts, e.g. thiocyanate and cyanide, species giving precipitates in boiling HNO_3, e.g. bismuth(III), antimony(III), tin(IV) and antimony(V), species complexing with halides, e.g. mercury(II), cadmium(II), tin(IV), and chromium(III), species capable of reducing silver(I) and finally iron(III). Bromide and iodide are best removed by oxidation and volatilization in elemental form.

Gravimetric determination of chloride

Procedure

Dilute the sample, containing about 0.1 g of chloride, to about 150 mℓ, and add 1 mℓ of 1:1 nitric acid. To the cold solution add slowly and with stirring, a slight excess of 0.1M $AgNO_3$ solution (an excess of 5–10 mℓ of the $AgNO_3$ solution based on the chloride content).

Heat the solution nearly to the boil, stirring occasionally, then remove from the heat. When the precipitate has settled, test for complete precipitation by adding a few drops of the $AgNO_3$ solution. Allow to stand for 1–2 h.

Filter through a weighed sintered glass filter and wash the precipitate two or three times with cold dilute (1:1000) HNO_3 by decanting before transferring it to the glass filter. Ensure that complete transfer of the precipitate has been made, if necessary using a 'policeman'. Wash the precipitate with further small portions of dilute HNO_3 until the washings produce no turbidity with dilute HCl. Dry the precipitate for 1 h at 110–200 °C. The factor for chloride in the precipitate is 0.24736.

Notes

1. The analysis should be carried out in subdued light.
2. After use the sintered filters are best cleaned with an ammoniacal solution followed by dilute HNO_3 and then distilled water.

The AgCl gravimetric method is capable of very high accuracy provided adequate precautions are taken. Little[24] has presented a reliable yet reasonably simple procedure in full detail. Using it, a single sample in triplicate requires 10–12 h of actual working time in a total time of 65 h. *Table 27* gives an indication of both the accuracy and precision of Little's procedure in relation to a similar method adopted by Imperial Chemical Industries[25].

Table 27 Comparison of molarity of a hydrochloric acid solution

ICI 'Ultimate silver standard'[25]	*Little*[24] *procedure*
0.099422	0.099401
	0.099394
	0.099398
	0.099399
	0.099398
	mean: 0.099398
	SD of mean: 0.000001

Titrimetric methods

1. Argentimetric methods

Although argentimetric methods have their origins well back into the 19th century they still feature prominently in the determination of halides and are often quoted as recommended methods.

Direct titrimetric methods are generally based on the slight excess of Ag^+ ions after complete precipitation of chloride. This can react giving coloured silver complexes, for example with chromate. Alternatively adsorption indicators can be used. The well known Volhard method depends on addition of an excess of standard silver nitrate followed by titration of this excess with standard thiocyanate.

A large number of indicators have been proposed for argentimetric titrations. Those introduced up to 1967 have been reviewed by Desai, Desai and Gandhi[26]. This review includes indicators for all applications of argentimetric titrations including anions other than halides.

Determination of chloride and the other halides using $AgNO_3$ has a voluminous literature in which attention to theory in terms of ionic-equilibrium concepts plays a prominent part. Though fundamentally important, it is outside the scope of the present treatment to deal with this and the reader is referred to standard texts which discuss it in some detail[27–29, 32]. The potentiometric determination of chloride using $AgNO_3$ is important and is discussed in the sub-section on electroanalytical methods below.

Mohr titration

This direct method was introduced in 1856 and consists of titrating a chloride solution with standard $AgNO_3$ using K_2CrO_4 as indicator. A slight excess of Ag^+ produces a reddish-brown precipitate of silver chromate (Ag_2CrO_4). This is far more soluble than AgCl and accordingly does not form until precipitation of AgCl is complete. The titration functions in a limited pH range only, pH 6.5–10.3, with the optimum value of pH 7. At values below 6.5 the solubility of Ag_2CrO_4 becomes excessive. Above pH 10.5 precipitation of AgOH begins. The pH is adjusted by saturating the solution with $NaHCO_3$ or $Ca(HCO_3)_2$.

A study by Belcher, Macdonald and Parry[30] has clarified and improved several features of the method. An important recommendation in this investigation is the use of a neutralized indicator which also exerts a buffering effect adjusting the pH to 7 ± 0.1 (if the original pH was in the range 5.5–10.0). An earlier alternative to neutralizing the indicator with nitric acid was to employ a K_2CrO_4–$K_2Cr_2O_7$ solution[31].

The accuracy of the Mohr method is slightly less than the Volhard method. Interferences are given in *Table 28*.

Table 28 Interferences in Mohr method for chloride

Interfering species	*Comments*
Br^-, I^-	
Fe(III), Bi(III), Sn(IV)	Precipitated as basic salts. Int. by Fe(III) partially removed by addition of F^-
Ni(II), Co(II), Cu(II)	Mask colour
Pb(II), Ba(II)	Precipitated as chromates. Int. removed by addition of SO_4^{2-}
$S_2O_3^{2-}$	
SO_3^{2-}, S^{2-}, CO_3^{2-}, $C_2O_4^{2-}$	Int. by formation of low solubility Ag salts in neutral solution. $C_2O_4^{2-}$ can be precipitated as calcium oxalate
NH_4^+	pH adjustment will overcome int. Optimum pH is 5.8

Notes

1. Attempts to overcome interference of cations by EDTA have been unsuccessful[30].
2. In moderate or large amounts, phosphorus(V) and arsenic(V) interfere slightly.
3. The Mohr method can tolerate a higher concentration of electrolytes than the adsorption indicator method described later.

Interference by ammonium requires comment. Presence of this ion causes the end-point to occur too late. A value of pH 7.2 has been quoted as the upper limit to prevent this. Block and Waters[33] found that in the presence of 100 mg of ammonium, interference occurred even at pH 6.5–7.2. Later, a communication by Wanninen[34] noted that the errors due to ammonium can be calculated using conditional constants. A further comment on the situation is made by Anfaelt and Jagner[35] who investigate the ionic-equilibria by computer. They confirm the errors detected by Block and Waters and find that the optimum pH value for avoiding an error due to ammonium ions is 5.8.

In general the Mohr method may be used satisfactorily for amounts of chloride down to about 0.1 mg. The method is recommended by one organization as a standard method for water analysis[36].

Titration of chloride by Mohr method

Reagents

$AgNO_3$:0.1M.

Weigh out the appropriate amount of pure $AgNO_3$ previously dried for 1–2 h at 110°C.

Neutralized indicator: 4.2 g K_2CrO_4 and 0.7 g $K_2Cr_2O_7$ per 100 mℓ water.

Procedure

To 25 mℓ of the chloride solution add 1 mℓ of the indicator (see Note). Titrate with 0.1M $AgNO_3$ solution. The end-point is indicated by a colour change from yellow to a permanent reddish-brown due to the formation of Ag_2CrO_4.

Note

Before titration and addition of the indicator, the solution should be in the pH range 5.5–10.0. If more acid than pH 5.5 it is conveniently neutralized by adding chloride-free borax, $NaHCO_3$ or $CaCO_3$.

Volhard titration

This is an indirect method. An excess of standard $AgNO_3$ is added to the chloride solution and the excess back-titrated with standard potassium thiocyanate to give the very slightly soluble silver thiocyanate.

$$Cl^- + Ag^+ \rightleftharpoons AgCl$$

$$Ag^+ + SCN^- \rightleftharpoons AgSCN$$

Iron(III) is used as indicator, this reacting with the first excess of thiocyanate ions to give the intensely coloured ferric thiocyanate complex $[FeSCN]^{++}$. The titration can be conducted in a fairly strongly acid solution. In fact the solution needs to be acidic to prevent hydrolysis of the iron(III) indicator. The Volhard method is subject to less interference than the other two principal argentimetric methods for halides. It is very sensitive, rather more sensitive than the Mohr method. It will be noted that the end-point colour is produced by a soluble species rather than a precipitate as in the Mohr method.

The need to use two standard solutions in contrast to the one used in the direct argentimetric methods is offset by the wider applicability and sensitivity.

Silver thiocyanate is less soluble than AgCl, so that after the excess silver has been titrated, an excess of thiocyanate may react with the AgCl.

$$SCN^- + AgCl \rightleftharpoons AgSCN + Cl^-$$

The effect of this would be end-point fading and consumption of too much thiocyanate. One solution to the problem is filtration of the AgCl before back-titration. If this is done, sufficient time must be allowed before filtration to allow coagulation of the precipitate to take place, and for removal of any adsorbed Ag^+ ions from the precipitate surface. Schulek, Pungor and Kethelyi[37] have recommended addition of KNO_3 followed by 3 min boiling, as an effective method for bringing about coagulation. Another method of overcoming any thiocyanate–AgCl interaction is introduction of immiscible liquids, for example nitrobenzene, to form a protective coating around the AgCl particles[38].

Interferences in the method are as follows. Cyanide forms a precipitate with Ag^+ in acid solution. Species oxidizing thiocyanate interfere but may be removed by treatment with iron(II). Lower nitrogen oxides (generally derived from HNO_3) interact with thiocyanate giving a coloured complex. These are removed by boiling the solution before analysis. Palladium, mercury and copper(I) also react with thiocyanate. Interference by copper(I) is overcome by prior oxidation to copper(II).

Various reducing agents will affect the iron(III) indicator. Ions complexing with chloride, e.g. mercury(II), chromium(III), and thallium(III) must be removed. Finally, ions imparting strong colours, for example Co^{2+} and Ni^{2+} should be absent. Non-interference by phosphate is important as this ion causes interference in the Mohr method when present in amounts in excess of 25 mg ℓ^{-1}.

Despite the introduction of newer chloride methods, the Volhard method finds extensive use, and is listed as a recommended method by various institutions. These include chloride in meat[39], cement[40] and concrete[41].

Titrimetric determination of chloride by the Volhard method
(0.05–0.1 g Cl^-).

Reagents

$AgNO_3$: 0.1M.

Use $AgNO_3$ as reference standard as in the Mohr method. Dry pure $AgNO_3$ for 1–2 h at 110°C then weigh out the appropriate amount and make up to volume.

KSCN: 0.1M.

Prepare a solution containing approximately 9.8 g of KSCN per litre. Standardize as below.

Indicator:

A saturated solution of ammonium ferric sulphate containing a few drops of 6M HNO_3 per 25 mℓ.

Procedure

Standardization of KSCN: Dilute a 25.0 mℓ aliquot of the standard $AgNO_3$ solution to about 100 mℓ and add 2 mℓ of freshly boiled concentrated HNO_3 and 1 mℓ of the ferric indicator. Titrate with the KSCN solution until the first permament red-brown colour is produced.

Titration of chloride

Procedure A (involving filtration)

Transfer a 25 mℓ aliquot of chloride solution to a beaker, add 5 mℓ of 6M HNO_3 and a small measured excess of 0.1M $AgNO_3$. Stir well at intervals over a 5 min period. Filter the precipitate collecting the filtrate in a conical flask. Wash the precipitate well with dilute (1 %) HNO_3.

Add 1 mℓ of the indicator to the filtrate plus washings, and titrate with standard KSCN until the first permanent red-brown colour is produced.

Procedure B (involving nitrobenzene)

Transfer a 25 mℓ aliquot of chloride solution to a conical flask, add 5 mℓ of 6M HNO_3 and a small measured excess of 0.1M $AgNO_3$. Add 2–3 mℓ of pure nitrobenzene (Note 2) and 1 mℓ of the indicator. Shake well to coagulate the precipitate. Titrate with 0.1M KSCN to the first permanent red-brown colour.

Notes

1. Indicator error can be ignored when decimolar solutions are employed.
2. Care is required in handling nitrobenzene. Prolonged breathing of the vapour can be dangerous. Furthermore the liquid is absorbed through the skin.

Adsorption indicator titrations

The name Fajans is often used to describe this method in recognition of his contribution. The indicator action can be seen from a consideration of a silver chloride precipitate just before and just after complete precipitation of chloride using $AgNO_3$. What happens is the consequence of the well-known tendency of precipitates to adsorb common ions. Before complete precipitation and in a medium containing free chloride ions (as well as other ions) there will be a tendency to adsorb chloride ions as shown in *Figure 29*(a).

When all the chloride ions have reacted to give AgCl, some of the excess $AgNO_3$ will be adsorbed as shown in *Figure 29*(b). Fluorescein is strongly adsorbed as the anion on a positively charged silver surface, displacing the nitrate and forming with silver the red silver fluoresceinate. This is in contrast to the behaviour of fluorescein in a $AgNO_3$ solution, where no interaction takes place. The indicator therefore acts essentially as an indicator for adsorbed lattice ions.

The precipitate surface is not always of the same charge. Fluorescein is adsorbed as the anion on a positively charged AgCl surface. Rhodamine 6G used for bromide determination is adsorbed as the cation on a negatively charged AgBr surface.

Several indicators have been proposed for determination of chloride, of which dichlorofluorescein is probably the best. A disadvantage, and this applies equally to the determination of bromide and iodide using adsorption indicators, is that the silver halide precipitate is sensitized to the effect of light by the layer of adsorbed dye. For this reason the titration should be conducted with the minimum exposure to light.

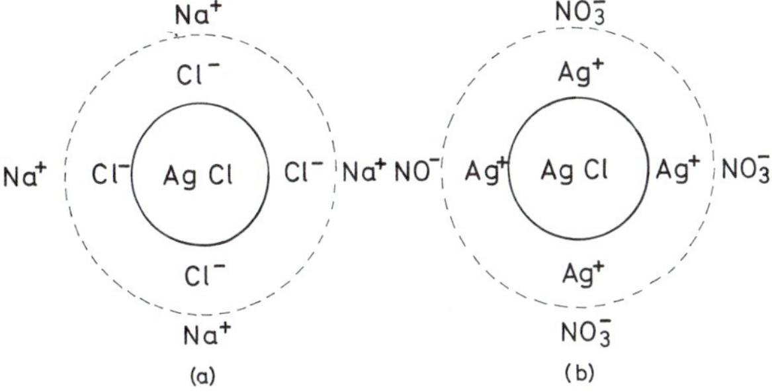

Figure 29 *Silver chloride precipitate:*
(a) in presence of excess Cl^- *ions;*
(b) in presence of excess Ag^+ *ions*

The pH range for which the titration is valid will depend on the ionization constant of the indicator; dichlorofluorescein is a stronger acid than fluorescein. This enables it to be used between pH 4 and 10.5 in comparison with pH 6.5 to 10.5 for fluorescein. The indicator mechanism outlined above has certain implications for the precipitate itself. In order to possess a large surface, it should remain partially at least, dispersed as a sol. The precipitate tends to flocculate shortly before the end-point, particularly if the halide concentration is high and if large amounts of neutral salts are present. Protective colloids, for example dextrin and gum arabic may be added to maintain part of the precipitate in colloidal suspension. Kapal, Fry and Shelton[42] have recently conducted an investigation of surface-active substances for use in the titration. They find that hydroxypropylmethylcellulose gives a good end-point and is better than agar in this respect. It is suitable for use in determination of chloride, bromide or iodide, in which case fluorescein may be used as indicator. Determination of all three halides in admixture was not found to be possible.

Titration of chloride (or bromide and iodide) fails when the halide concentration is low. This is due to the amount of precipitate being too small for effective judgement of the colour change. For chloride, the lower limit which can be satisfactorily determined is about 0.005M, that is about 0.2 mg Cl^- in a 25 mℓ aliquot.

Titrimetric determination of chloride using an adsorption indicator

Reagents

$AgNO_3$: 0.1M.

Prepared as described in the previous argentimetric procedures.

Indicators

Fluorescein or dichlorofluorescein; 0.2 g in 100 mℓ of 70 % ethanol, or 2.0 g of the sodium salts in 100 mℓ water.

Procedure

Pipette 25 mℓ of the chloride solution into a conical flask and dilute to 50 mℓ. The pH should be adjusted if necessary to be within the range 7–10 for fluorescein or 4–10 for dichlorofluorescein. Add 5–10 drops of the indicator and titrate with 0.1M $AgNO_3$. Very near the equivalence point the precipitate flocculates. Continue the titration carefully with vigorous shaking to a reddish end-point.

Note

The titration should be made in diffuse light.

At this point it may be pertinent to summarize the principal features of the three main argentimetric methods for chloride. The Volhard method is subject to the least interference, has the widest applicability and gives the highest accuracy. It requires two standard solutions and is rather less convenient being an indirect procedure. The Mohr is direct, slightly less accurate but subject to greater interference. Furthermore, electrolytes have an effect on the titration. The adsorption indicator method enables titrations to be made at lower pH values than allowed by the Mohr method, but again electrolytes have a marked effect.

Miscellaneous argentimetric procedures

Potassium rhodizonate has been found[43,44] to be more sensitive than chromate or ferric alum in the titration of halides, thiocyanate and cyanide. For chloride the end-point change is from yellow to reddish violet due to the formation of silver rhodizonate. Like chromate the indicator cannot be used in acid solution. The range of interference remains the same as in the original method. A comparative study produced results within 0.07 % of those obtained using the Mohr and Volhard methods. The back-titration of Ag^+ with chloride is not possible because the indicator colour remains unchanged in the presence of excess halide.

Archer[45] has extended earlier work by Karabash[46] and has demonstrated that dithizone is an effective indicator for both halides and cyanide. The titration is made in a high concentration of acetone, and is applicable to microgram amounts of chloride if 0.004M $AgNO_3$ is used as titrant.

2. Mercurimetric

Direct titration of chloride with mercury(II) depends on the formation of undissociated mercuric chloride complexes. The slight excess of mercuric ions at the end-point can be detected using suitable indicators. Sodium nitroprusside was originally used, this forming the slightly soluble compound $HgFe(CN)_5NO$ with Hg^{2+} and imparting a white turbidity. Later work indicated that diphenylcarbazide and diphenylcarbazone are more effective. The blue-violet complex formed between Hg^{2+} and diphenylcarbazone is shown in *Structure 41*.

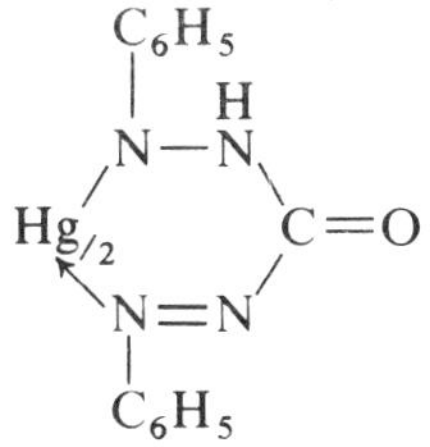

```
   C6H5
   |   H
   N—N
  /     \
Hg/2     C=O
 ↖      /
   N=N
   |
   C6H5
```

Structure 41 Hg(II)-diphenylcarbazone complex

Mercuric nitrate or perchlorate is used as titrant. An important advantage of the method is its ability to be carried out in acidic solution. The reaction itself is more complex than it might first appear. Several complexes such as $HgCl_4^{2-}$ and $HgCl^+$ are formed of which $HgCl_2$ is the most stable. The reaction is certainly non-stoichiometric, and requires strict control of conditions for accurate results. It is subject to a small indicator error which can be determined experimentally. An account of earlier work on the method has been given by Macdonald[47].

When dilute solutions are used the titration in aqueous medium is unsatisfactory. Several attempts have been made to develop a satisfactory titration in ethanol–water mixtures, of which the work by Cheng[48] has been impressive. Most modern procedures are based on this modification. Cheng recommended carrying out the titration in an 80% alcoholic solution at an apparent pH of 3.5. A marked improvement in the end-point is produced when compared with a similar titration in purely aqueous solutions. Furthermore the titration conforms to a stricter stoichiometry. The remainder of the present discussion will refer to this form of the method.

White[49], in an examination of the method and its application to organic micro-elemental analysis, found that the optimum pH is 3.6. In a subsequent publication White[50] applied the method to simultaneous determination of sulphur and chlorine in organic compounds. Variation of the pH from the optimum value produces two sources of error. At higher pH values a pink colour begins to appear before the true end-point and results are low. At lower pH values the intensity of colour with excess mercury(II) is diminished and becomes marked below pH 3. In this case results are high. The pH adjustment is made using dilute HNO_3.

Interferences are as follows. Alkali metals, alkaline earths and moderate amounts of copper or iron(II) have no effect. Iron(III), chromate, phosphate, sulphide, bromide and iodide are the most serious interferences. Phosphate interferes by exerting a buffering effect on the pH. Sulphate inhibits the formation of the indicator colour, probably due to the low solubility of mercury(II) sulphate in the alcohol–water medium. It is conveniently removed by addition of $Ba(NO_3)_2$ just before the pH adjustment. Cyanide and thiocyanate form little-ionized compounds with mercury(II). Interference by fluoride and phosphate has been investigated by Colson[51] in connection with the analysis of organic materials by oxygen-flask combustion. Addition of thorium nitrate was found to be effective, the precipitates of thorium phosphate and thorium fluoride being filtered off before the titration.

At the lower end of the range the method extends into the sub-micro region. Belcher, Gouverneur and Macdonald[52] applied it to sub-micro organic analysis where the optimum amount of sample contained 20–25 μg of chlorine. The analysis was preceded by oxygen-flask combustion of the sample. In the method developed by White[49] described above, samples of 1–1.5 mg of chloride were employed. In the same investigation it is stated that a 20 mℓ aliquot of aqueous solution containing as little as 15 μg of chlorine per mℓ can be titrated with an accuracy of 1–2%. The standard deviation deteriorates rapidly with decreasing amounts of chloride. Another source quotes a standard deviation of ±40 ng Cl^- for 1 μg Cl^- $mℓ^{-1}$. The method is said to be applicable to as little as 5 μg of chloride.

An obvious application of the method is to analysis of waters. Here it is far superior to the Mohr, Volhard or Viebock methods, and is recommended by several authorities[36,53]. Recently, the method has been subjected to a collaborative study by Steyermark, Lalancette and Contreras[54]. In general their results are good and the method is recommended for use after oxygen-flask combustion of samples.

Titrimetric determination of Cl^- (1–1.5 mg) using mercuric nitrate[49]

Reagents

Mercuric nitrate: Approx. 0.005M.
Dissolve 3.4 g of $Hg(NO_3)_2$ H_2O in 570 mℓ of 0.01M NHO_3. Allow to stand for 48 h then filter and make up to 2ℓ. Standardize as described below.

Sodium chloride: 0.01M.
Prepare by weighing out an appropriate amount and making up to a known volume.

Bromophenol blue: 0.1 % in ethanol.
Diphenylcarbazone: 0.1 % in ethanol.
Nitric acid: 0.1M, 0.01M.

Standardization of mercuric nitrate

Pipette 5 mℓ of the standard NaCl solution into a flask and add 10 mℓ of distilled water and 2 drops of bromophenol blue indicator. Neutralize to the yellow colour. Add 0.5 mℓ of 0.1M HNO_3 followed by 100 mℓ of 95% ethanol and titrate as described in procedure. Determine the indicator blank on 15 mℓ of distilled water (about 0.035 mℓ of 0.005M $Hg(NO_3)_2$).

Procedure for chloride

To the solution containing about 1–1.5 mg of chloride add 2 drops of bromophenol blue indicator. Add 0.1M HNO_3 until the yellow colour appears then add a further 0.5 mℓ of 0.1M HNO_3 followed by 100 mℓ of 95% ethanol. The pH of the solution should now be 3.6. Add 0.5 mℓ of the diphenylcarbazone indicator, then titrate with mercuric nitrate with constant swirling until the first appearance of violet in the colourless solution.

---

3. *Using EDTA*

Indirect determination of chloride using EDTA is possible by interaction of precipitated AgCl with $K_2Ni(CN)_4$.

$$2AgCl + Ni(CN)_4^{2-} \rightarrow 2Ag(CN)_2^{-} + Ni^{2+} + 2Cl^{-}$$

The Ni^{2+} ions are titrated with standard EDTA using murexide as indicator[55]. Isolation of the precipitate is an obvious disadvantage and this also applies to another method by Gusev, Sokolova and Kozhevnikova[56]. In this, chloride reacts with Pb^{2+} and 2-(2-hydroxy-1-naphthylmethylene amino)-pyridine to give a compound, $RPbCl_2$ where R is the organic ligand. The precipitate is filtered, dissolved in HNO_3 and the lead ions titrated with standard EDTA using xylenol orange as indicator. A similar method exists for bromide.

De Sousa has developed several methods in which chloride can be determined in the presence of the other ions. They include chloride in the presence of bromide and iodide[57], iodide[58], cyanate and thiocyanate[59], and chlorate and perchlorate[60]. Compleximetric methods for chloride appear to have found little use, probably due to their inconvenient procedures.

4. *Redox methods*

Although redox methods are not used in the determination of chloride alone, they have some importance in the analysis of halide mixtures. Iodide is the most easily oxidized as the redox potentials indicate.

	E°
$Cl_2 + 2e \leftrightharpoons 2Cl^-$	+1.359
$Br_2 + 2e \leftrightharpoons 2Br^-$	+1.066
$I_2 + 2e \leftrightharpoons 2I^-$	+0.6197

Oxidation of iodide is readily accomplished without effect on any chloride or bromide present. Determination of chloride and bromide when present together is more difficult as their redox potentials are closer together. Selective oxidation of bromide may be achieved using various reagents, though the accuracy of such procedures is not high. These and other titrimetric methods for the sequential determination of chloride, bromide and iodide are discussed later in this section.

5. *Miscellaneous titrimetric methods*

The Vieböck method for halides employs mercuric oxycyanide.

$$2HgOHCN + 2NaX \rightarrow Hg(CN)_2 + 2NaOH$$

$$X = Cl^-, Br^- \text{ or } I^-$$

The NaOH produced is titrated with standard acid[61]. Its main application has been in the micro-titration of halides following oxygen-flask combustion of organic samples. Its advantages in this respect are high accuracy and specificity, this enabling the determination[62] to be made in the presence of nitrogen or sulphur. The mercurimetric method described earlier in this section is probably more effective for individual determination of chloride or bromide.

Titrimetric determination of halide mixtures (*chloride, bromide and iodide*)
It is pertinent at this point to look at the classical titrimetric methods available for analysis of halide mixtures without prior separation.

The total halides can be determined using the Volhard method. The Vieböck method described above can also be used. A form of this method has been described by Belcher, Macdonald and Nutten[63]. It should be noted that certain methods previously described for chloride are not suitable for mixtures of halides. The mercurimetric method falls into this category.

Having determined the total halides, bromide or iodide can be determined by selective redox methods and the chloride evaluated by difference. If iodide is present, this is conveniently determined in the presence of chloride and bromide using the Leipert method. This is based on oxidation of iodide to iodate using bromine water, followed by destruction of excess bromine and an iodimetric finish involving thiosulphate.

$$I^- + 3Br_2 + 3H_2O \rightarrow IO_3^- + 6Br^- + 6H^+$$

$$IO_3^- + 5I^- + 6H^+ \rightarrow 3I_2 + 3H_2O$$

Details of the method are given in the iodide section. Bromide and chloride in relatively large amounts do not interfere. The method has been recommended for analysis of halide mixtures resulting from halogen-containing organic samples.

Analysis of chloride and bromide mixtures by classical titrimetry and without prior separation, presents difficulties. Several methods have been recommended but no simple effective method has emerged. Selective oxidation of bromide to bromate or bromine has been the general approach employed. Many such methods are discussed in the monograph by Kolthoff and Belcher[64]. Bromide is selectively oxidized by hypochlorite. The method, associated with the names of Kolthoff and Yutzy, and van der Meulen, is discussed in the bromide section.

Oxidation of bromide to bromine has been used as the basis of a selective method by Summersgill[65]. The oxidant used is manganic sulphate.

$$2Mn^{3+} + 2Br^- \rightarrow 2Mn^{2+} + Br_2$$

The bromine formed reacts with excess KI and the liberated iodine titrated with standard thiosulphate. Chloride does not interfere. If iodide is present the final result will give the total of bromide plus iodide. Experimental details are given in the bromide section. EDTA methods have been described tor halide mixtures. The lengthy procedures involved make them unattractive.

The present discussion concerns classical methods only. As will be seen later in this section, the problem can be satisfactorily solved using physical methods.

Spectroscopic methods

1. Spectrophotometric methods—visible and UV

The mercury thiocyanate method introduced by Japanese workers[66,67] in 1952 is now firmly established as one of the best methods for determination of trace amounts of chloride. It depends on the reaction of chloride with mercuric thiocyanate to form the sparingly ionized mercuric chloride complex. An equivalent amount of thiocyanate is liberated and reacts with iron(III) to give the intense red complex $Fe(SCN)^{2+}$. The reaction may be represented by the equations

$$2Cl^- + Hg(SCN)_2 \rightarrow HgCl_2 + 2SCN^-$$

$$SCN^- + Fe^{3+} \rightarrow Fe(SCN)^{2+}$$

The method is reliable, and applicable in the lower ppb (10^9) range. No strict control of experimental conditions is required. Absorbance measurements are made at 460 nm. As the reaction is conducted in an acidic solution interferences tend to be small. Nitric acid or perchloric acid can be used, the sensitivity being similar in each case, but H_2SO_4 gives a much lower sensitivity. Perchloric acid is favoured by Florence and Farrar[68] on the grounds of lower blanks and more consistent results. These workers found that HNO_3 sometimes gives low and erratic results. This was traced to the presence of nitrogen peroxide. The same investigators found the limit of detection for the method to be 15 ppb (10^9) at the 95 per cent confidence level. Rodabaugh and Upperman[2], also involved with determination of chloride at the ppb (10^9) level, pre-concentrate it in a 250 mℓ sample by coprecipitation on lead phosphate. With careful technique, they claim a detection limit of 1 ppb (10^9) of chloride in the original sample. Though the method is capable of operating in the ppb region, it can be used at much higher concentrations, for example in the 0.1–50 ppm range.

Earlier studies on the method suggested that the final coloured species could be contaminated by extraneous chloride in the laboratory atmosphere, and that errors could be introduced in this way[69]. Elsheimer and Kochen[70] have shown that this is unlikely during the period of measurement. Automatic forms of the method have been described[71,72].

The acid conditions of the method result in little interference. Moderate amounts of fluoride, nitrate, nitrite, sulphate and phosphate can be tolerated. Larger amounts of sulphate and phosphate interfere. Not unexpectedly bromide and iodide interfere. When used for determination of 100 ppb (10^9) of chloride, ammonia has no effect up to 85 ppm. Hydrazine does not interfere at the 1 ppm level, but causes an error of +13 per cent at 5 ppm. High concentrations of ethanol, isopropanol, tartaric acid and acetone impart a yellow colour to the ferric thiocyanate. A useful list showing the effects of various species on the determination of 20 ppb (10^9) of chloride is included in the study by Rodabaugh and Upperman[2] cited earlier.

Application of the method is extensive and includes chloride in high purity water[2], boiler feed water[68], industrial water[73] and biological material[74].

A modified form of the method has been reported in which the liberated thiocyanate is extracted into nitrobenzene as tris(1,10-phenanthroline)iron(II)thiocyanate and determined spectrophotometrically[75]. Beer's law holds over the concentration range 0.8–5.6 × 10^{-5} M Cl^-. The colour stability and apparent sensitivity are claimed to be superior to those for the mercury(II)–iron(III)-thiocyanate method. Large amounts of sulphate, phosphate, fluoride, carbonate, K^+, Na^+, NH_4^+ and acetate have negligible effect, but bromide, iodide, cyanide, sulphide and thiocyanate interfere.

Spectrophotometric determination of chloride using the mercury(II)thiocyanate method[76]

Reagents

Mercury(II)thiocyanate:
A saturated solution in water, 0.07%.

Iron(III) perchlorate:
Dissolve 6 g in 100 mℓ of 4M $HClO_4$.
It may also be prepared by dissolving 14.0 g of pure iron wire in dilute HNO_3. When dissolved, add 120 mℓ of 60% $HClO_4$ and heat the solution until it fumes. Continue heating until the solution turns purple, then cool and dilute to 1ℓ.

Procedure

Pipette 10 mℓ of the sample into a 50-mℓ volumetric flask and add 5 mℓ of 60% $HClO_4$, 1 mℓ of mercuric thiocyanate and then 2 mℓ of $Fe(ClO_4)_3$. Make up to volume and mix well. Stand for 10 min then measure the absorbance at 460 nm.

Notes

1. The range is 0.05–5 ppm.
2. In the procedure given, the $HClO_4$ concentration is about 1.5M. This gives the most sensitive response but blanks are rather high. Lower blanks are obtained in about 1.0M $HClO_4$, but, then the sensitivity is lower and deviation from Beer's law is greater.

Excess mercuric ions after reaction with chloride, may be determined by means of the violet-coloured complex with diphenylcarbazone (*Structure 42*) or diphenylcarbazide (*Structure 43*).

$$C_6H_5\text{—N=N—CO—NH—NH—}C_6H_5$$

Structure 42 Diphenylcarbazone

Gerlach and Frazier[77] preferred the former, but found it necessary to purify the compound to prevent fading of the coloured complex. The reagent solution requires preparation daily. Interference is given by copper, iron(III),

$$C_6H_5\text{—NH—NH—CO—NH—NH—}C_6H_5$$

Structure 43 Diphenylcarbazide

bromide, iodide, thiocyanate, acetate and smaller amounts of oxalate and dichromate. Though the method is sensitive ($\varepsilon = 19000$ at 520 nm) the disadvantages cited detract from its usefulness.

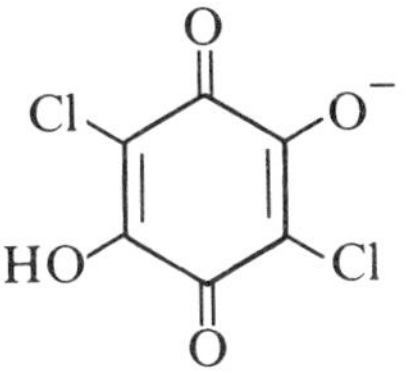

Structure 44 *Chloranilate ion*

Mercuric chloranilate reacts with chloride forming slightly dissociated mercuric chloride and an equivalent amount of the reddish-purple acid chloranilate ion (*Structure 44*).

$$HgC_6Cl_2O_4 + 2Cl^- + H^+ \rightarrow HgCl_2 + HC_6Cl_2O_4^-$$

This was developed into a spectrophotometric method for chloride by Barney and Bertolacini[78, 79] and represents the first application of chloranilates to analytical work. In the original investigation addition of 0.5N acid was found to be necessary since the absorption bands for chloranilic acid are pH-dependent. The optimum wavelength for absorbance measurements was found to be 530 nm at which the molar absorptivity is 0.18×10^3. Fluoride, bromide, iodide, bromate, phosphate and thiocyanate interfere. Beer's law holds over the range 0–100 mg $Cl^- \ell^{-1}$. Bode, Eggeling and Steinbrecht[80] have determined the dissociation constants of chloranilic acid in various media and discuss the implication on the determination of several anions including chloride. A recent investigation by Hammer and Craig[81] recommends that 0.05M $HClO_4$ is used in place of 0.05M HNO_3, the latter having considerable absorption bands in the 300 nm region where the absorbance can also be measured. The same workers find an improvement if a 40% ethanol medium is used and the absorbance measured at 305.5 nm after removal of excess mercuric chloranilate using a centrifuge and pressure filtration.

Spectrophotometric determination of chloride using mercuric chloranilate[78]

Procedure

Pass the chloride solution through a 15 cm × 1.5 cm cation exchange column (20–50 mesh in H^+ form). If the pH of the effluent is below 2 or above 12, it is adjusted to 7 with dilute HNO_3 or NH_4OH. To an aliquot containing not more than 1 mg of chloride in less than 45 mℓ of water in a 100 mℓ volumetric flask, add 5 mℓ of M pure HNO_3 and 50 mℓ of methyl cellosolve. Dilute to volume with distilled water, add 0.2 g of mercuric chloranilate and shake intermittently for 15 min. Remove excess mercuric chloranilate by filtration then measure the absorbance at 530 nm against a blank prepared in the same manner.

Iron(III) chloride complexes, for example $FeCl^{2+}$, absorb in the visible region of the spectrum but to a much greater extent in the UV. West and Coll[82] have developed a direct spectrophotometric method which is both simple and reliable, and suitable for routine use in the range 0–12.5 mg $Cl^- \ell^{-1}$. Two procedures are given, each having advantages in certain circumstances. Bromide and iodide interfere but may be corrected for.

Other spectrophotometric methods have been based on oxidation of chloride to chlorine followed by its determination. A reagent formerly used for this was *o*-tolidine. This is now controlled by the Carcinogenic Substances Regulations. Scheubeck and Ernst[84] use $KMnO_4$ at different acidities to selectively oxidize bromide and chloride. This is followed by treatment with *o*-tolidine. The range is 1–10 μg for chloride and 10–100 μg for bromide. Application was made to water and corrosion products. Both chlorine and bromine oxidize methyl orange (*Structure 45*) removing the azo-group to

$$NaO_3S-C_6H_4-N{=}N-C_6H_4-N(CH_3)_2$$

Structure 45 Methyl orange

give the colourless *p*-halodimethylaniline and phenyl *p*-sulphonic acid, and may be determined in this way[83]. Another method is based on the exchange reaction between chloride and silver iodate. The resulting iodine is determined spectrophotometrically.

$$AgIO_3 + Cl^- \rightarrow AgCl\downarrow + IO_3^-$$

$$IO_3^- + 6H^+ + 5I^- \rightarrow 3I_2 + 3H_2O$$

Bhatty and Uden[85] base an indirect method on the displacement of hydrogen cyanide from mercury(II) cyanide.

$$Hg(CN)_2 + 2X^- + 2H^+ \rightarrow HgX_2 + 2HCN$$

$$X^- = Cl^-, Br^-, I^- \text{ or } SCN^-$$

The hydrogen cyanide is distilled into KOH and evaluated. When this is done by iodimetric titration a linear response to chloride is obtained but the stoichiometry is unexpected. An alternative procedure used was conversion of the cyanide to a dye using the pyridine–pyrazolone reagent. This is suitable for determination of chloride in the range 0.014–0.43 μg $m\ell^{-1}$.

In another procedure chloride is converted to phenylmercury(II) chloride which, after extraction into $CHCl_3$, reacts with sodium diethyldithiocarbamate. The resulting complex, phenylmercury(II)diethyldithiocarbamate has adsorption maxima at 257 and 297 nm, either of which can be used analytically. The corresponding molar absorptivities are 21.3×10^3 and 6.5×10^3. Chloride in the range 0.04–0.32 ppm can be determined in 250 mℓ aqueous samples with an average relative mean error of 12 per cent. Interfering species are restricted to Ag(I), Hg(I), Hg(II), bromide, iodide, thiocyanate, cyanide and nitrite. The method is also applicable to bromide and iodide, and is claimed to be as effective as the mercury(II) thiocyanate method[86].

2. *Nephelometric and turbidimetric methods*

The nephelometric method is the oldest of the photometric methods for chloride. In a suspension of AgCl in 50% methanol a concentration of 4-300 × 10^{-6}M Cl^- can be determined[87] with an average deviation of 3-4 per cent. Johnson[88] has provided experimental details required for the highest precision using nephelometry. Substances giving insoluble salts in dilute HNO_3 interfere, for example bromide and iodide. Practical details are given in the monograph by Boltz[89].

Turbidimetric methods normally show a lower reproducibility than spectrophotometric methods, being more vulnerable to such factors as temperature, time, order of addition of reagents, and acidity. Chwastowska, Marczenko and Stolarczyk[3] have used the method for determination of trace chloride in reagents after separation by coprecipitation of AgCl on a $BaSO_4$ carrier. Less than 20 µg of chloride may be determined in samples ranging from 0.5 to 5.0 g.

Recently an automatic turbidimetric method for discrete sample analysis of chloride in water has appeared[90]. Chlorides are precipitated as AgCl and the measurements carried out on the suspensions at 600 nm. Up to 30 samples, plus blanks and standards, can be analysed in 48 min. The method described is applicable in the 5–250 ppm Cl^- range, but adaption to higher or lower ranges is possible.

3. *Indirect atomic absorption spectroscopy*

Indirect methods involving AAS have been published in which chloride is precipitated with Ag^+ and either the excess of Ag^+ in solution determined, or that in the dissolved precipitate[91,92].

An alternative approach has been based on AAS determination of mercury in phenyl mercury(II) chloride[93]. The complex is extracted into $CHCl_3$, the latter evaporated off and the residue dissolved in ethyl acetate. Mercury is determined by means of its 253.65 nm line using an air–acetylene flame. As little as 0.015 ppm of chloride can be determined in a 250 mℓ sample. Interference is given by Ag(I), Hg(I), Hg(II), Br^-, I^-, SCN^- and CN^-.

4. *Molecular emission*

Like sulphur and phosphorus, chlorine, bromine and iodine have their principal atomic resonance lines in the vacuum UV. Conventional methods for determination of halides by flame methods involve indirect procedures such as addition of known amounts of Ag^+ ions to the halide solution, filtration and measurements of excess Ag^+ in the filtrate either by FES or AAS. Such procedures do not discriminate between chloride, bromide and iodide.

Following their investigation of molecular emissions from sulphur, phosphorus and tin using cool nitrogen–hydrogen flames, Dagnall, Thompson and West[94] have applied the technique to determination of halides. Indium was found to be the most suitable element for producing strong halide emissions. The InCl and InBr emissions lie in the near UV and are not clearly visible; the InI emission is visible as a dark blue colour in the central region of the flame. It is assumed that the emission is caused by a chemiluminescent reduction reaction of an indium(III) species leading to an excited indium(I) halide molecule. The spectrum for InCl is shown in *Figure 30*.

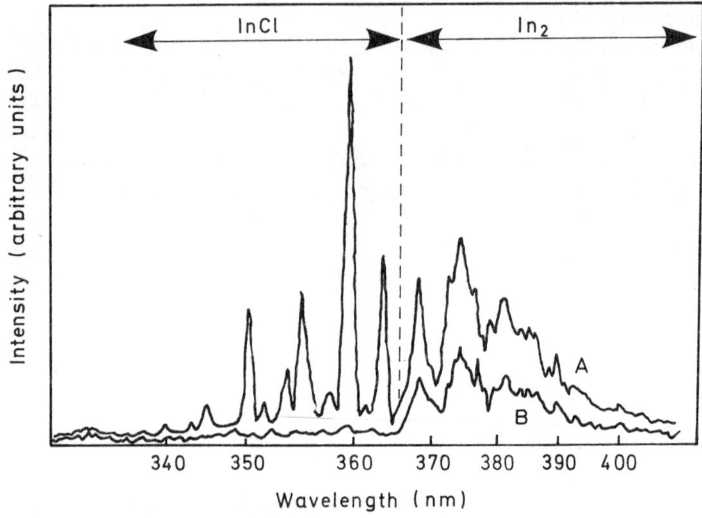

Figure 30 *Emission spectrum of InCl.*
A, *sample with indium* 2.94×10^{-3} *M, chloride* 1×10^{-2} *M and nitrate* 7×10^{-2} *M;* B, *blank with indium* 2.94×10^{-3} *M and nitrate* 7×10^{-2} *M.*
(After Dagnall, Thompson and West[94])

The equipment used is a standard flame-emission atomic-absorption spectrophotometer (Unicam SP 900 A), fitted with the standard air–acetylene (rectangular) burner head, and a non-standard burner head which is described in the original paper. Data on the determination of chloride, bromide and iodide are given in *Table 29*.

Table 29 Determination of halides by molecular emission[94]

Halide	*Optimum* (nm)	*Range*
Cl^-	360	2×10^{-4}–4×10^{-3}M (7.1–142 ppm)
Br^-	376	5×10^{-5}–10^{-3}M (1.8–35.5 ppm)
I^-	410	4×10^{-5}–8×10^{-4}M (5.1–102 ppm)

Chloride and bromide can be determined individually in the presence of a large excess of the other two halides. Iodide can be determined in a large excess of chloride. The original paper should be consulted for further details.

Electroanalytical methods

1. Potentiometric including ion-selective electrodes

Chloride can be determined by several potentiometric procedures ranging from zero-current (classical) potentiometry to the more recent ones employing ion-selective electrodes. The widespread application of the chloride ion-selective electrode suggests that for certain ranges of chloride concentration it will displace other chloride methods.

In zero-current potentiometry the general arrangement is a silver indicator electrode and calomel reference electrode, the latter connected through a salt bridge. The titrant is generally $AgNO_3$ though some chloride potentiometric methods utilize mercury(II). An alcoholic medium is preferred, this enhancing the potential jump at the equivalence point. The indicator electrode potential is related, through the Nernst equation, to the chloride (or other halide) being titrated. A standard form of the method is described by Shiner and Smith[95] who found the error for chloride to be less than 0.1 per cent. When applied to halide mixtures the determination of total halide presents no problems, but determination of individual halides in a mixture is more difficult. The problem is largely due to mixed halide precipitation. The general form of the potentiometric curve for mixed halides is shown in *Figure 31*.

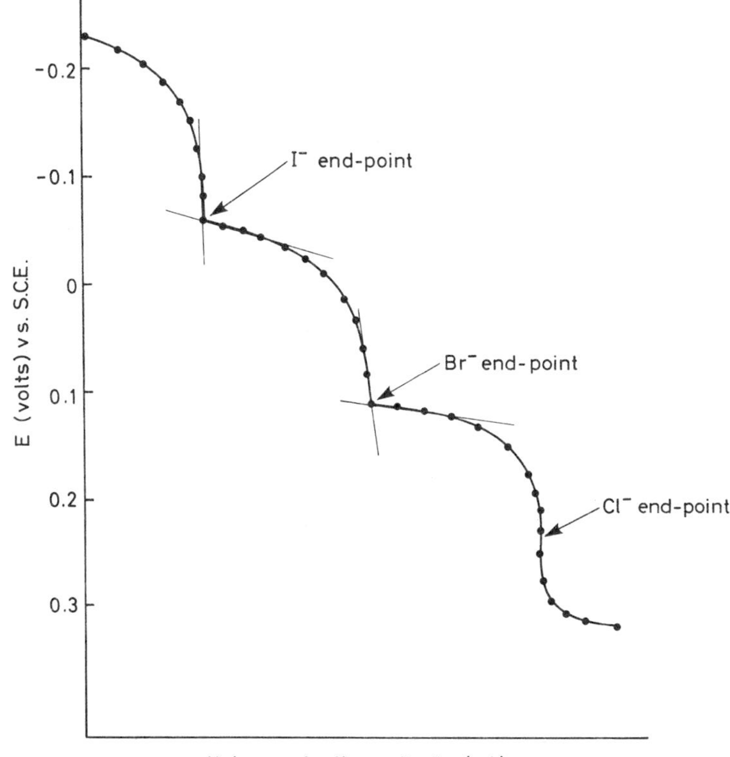

Figure 31 Potentiometric curve (idealized) for titration of halide mixtures

Matrin[96] has shown that in such curves, iodide and bromide end-points may be obtained by intersection of two straight lines, and that corrections may be applied when the mole-ratio of halides is greater than 20:1. Titration of chloride in chloride–bromide mixtures is susceptible to errors for the reason given above, namely that silver halides readily form mixed crystals or solid solutions. This can result in appreciable amounts of chloride being precipitated before its position in the titration sequence, i.e. when bromide is being titrated. Prokopov[97] has tackled this by first obtaining the bromide plus chloride titre, and then treating a second aliquot with hydrogen peroxide to oxidize bromide to bromine. This is eliminated by reaction with oxine, allowing chloride to be titrated without interference.

$$H_2O_2 + 2Br^- + 2H^+ \rightarrow Br_2 + 2H_2O$$

$$C_9H_7ON + 2Br_2 \rightarrow C_9H_5Br_2ON + 2HBr$$

The bromide formed in the reaction is repeatedly oxidized until all is consumed by oxine. Iodide reacts similarly so that the procedure can be applied to iodide–bromide–chloride mixtures.

In the potentiometric titration of halide mixtures, errors can be caused by adsorption of common ions on the precipitate surface. This is so when a silver electrode is used and when a silver halide ion-selective electrode is used. Kuttel *et al.*[98] find that addition of $NaNO_3$ to a concentration in excess of 1M is effective in reducing this error.

Potentiometric titration of chloride has found considerable application in elemental organic microanalysis. This is discussed at length by Dixon[99]. To avoid contamination of the test solution with chloride ions from the calomel electrode, she employs a modified form containing two nitrate bridges. Chloride is titrated in an isopropanol–water medium with 0.002M $AgNO_3$.

The calomel electrode may be replaced by another reference electrode including the metallic type. Another variant of the potentiometric method is constant-current potentiometry. Freeman[100] has used this for determination of chloride using a circuit based on earlier work by Reilley, Cooke and Furman[101]. The system employs two polarizable electrodes. Direct potentiometric titration of chloride using $AgNO_3$ is capable of dealing with concentrations as low as 5×10^{-5}M.

Furman and Low[102] applied the concentration-cell technique to determination of trace chloride. They used a carefully matched pair of electrodes prepared by electrodepositing silver on to Pt gauze and then anodizing the silver in a dilute chloride solution. The cell itself contained two arms, the first containing one electrode dipping into a standard chloride solution, the second containing the other electrode in the sample solution. The chloride concentration was related to the potential difference between the two electrodes. Blaedel, Lewis and Thomas[103] using the same technique, were able to determine chloride down to 70 ppb (10^9) in solutions of high ionic strength. A marked improvement, which avoided the need for strict temperature control, was introduced by Malmstadt and Winefordner[104,105] in a technique called null-point potentiometry. This consists of changing the chloride concentration of the unknown solution by addition of standard chloride, while maintaining the ionic strength constant, until it is identical in concentration to a known chloride solution. Indication of this is given by a zero potential. The titration assembly is shown in *Figure 32*.

Another form of null-point potentiometry for chloride is recommended in a British Standards method[106] for analysis of industrial water. Here the chloride is titrated with 0.01M $AgNO_3$ using a half-cell consisting of a length

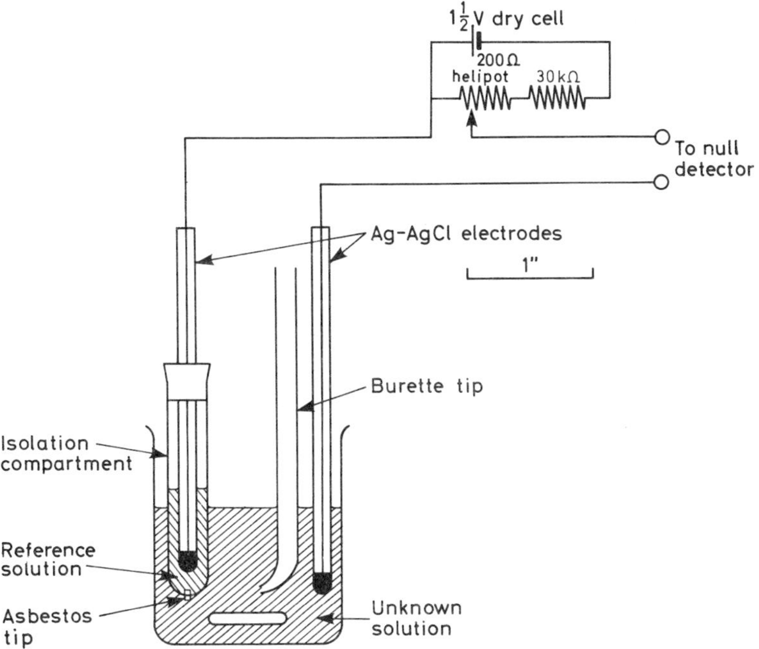

Figure 32 *Precision null-point potentiometric apparatus for chloride determination.* (After Malmstadt and Winefordner[104])

of silver wire dipping into a similar Ag^+ ion concentration as that of the sample at its end-point. The other half of the cell is formed by a second silver electrode dipping into the sample solution. A sensitive galvanometer (sensitivity ~100–200 mm/μA) indicates the end-point. The apparatus is shown in *Figure 33*. The method is suitable for 0.2 mg of Cl^- in a 150 mℓ sample. Bromide and iodide interfere by titrating as chloride. The species

Table 30 Interferences in determination of Cl^- by null-point potentiometry[106]

Species	*Maximum permissible levels* (μg)
SO_3^{2-}	1.5×10^4
SO_4^{2-}	1.5×10^4
PO_4^{3-}	1×10^4
Glassy sodium phosphate[a]	1×10^4
Cu^{2+}	5×10^3
Oil	750
Fe^{3+}	75

[a] Polymeric sodium metaphosphate commonly used in water treatment.

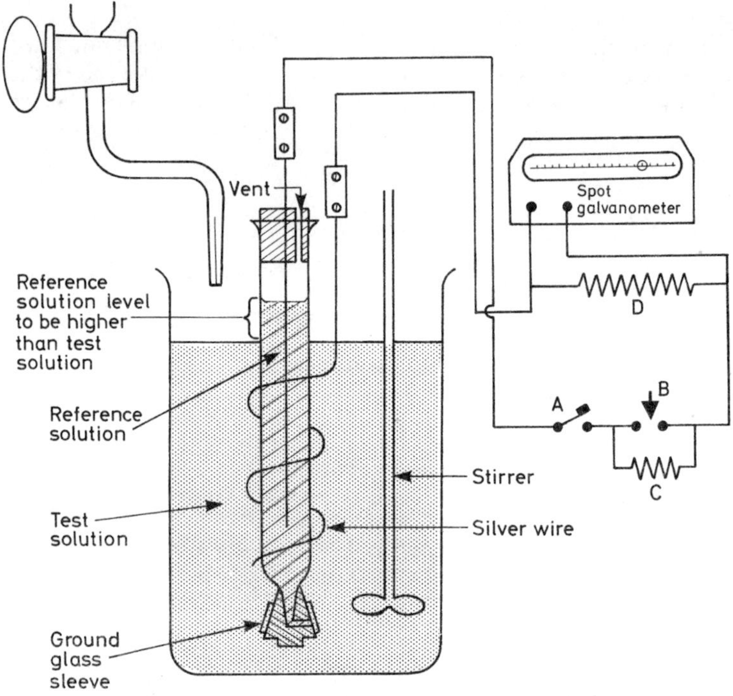

Figure 33 *Null-point potentiometric assembly for chloride determination.* A, *Tapping key;* B, *shorting plug;* C, 1 *MΩ resistance;* D, 10 *kΩ resistance* (After British Standards[106])

given in *Table 30* do not interfere when present in amounts up to the level stated.

Another form of differential potentiometry employing silver or silver chloride electrodes is Differential Electrolytic Potentiometry (DEP) developed by Bishop[107–109]. The essential feature of this form of potentionmetry is that

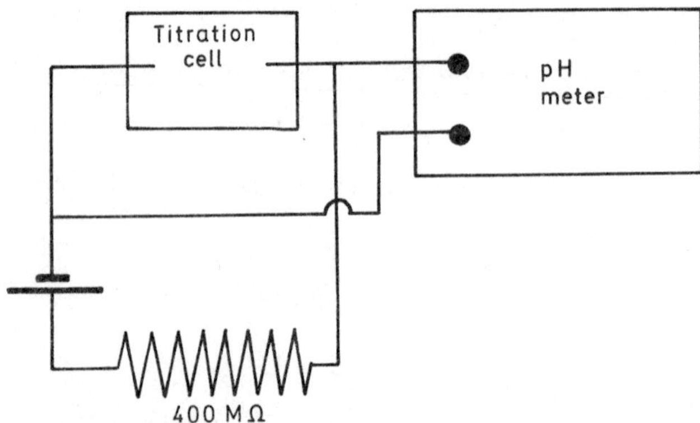

Figure 34 *Simple circuit for micro-titration of* Cl^- *with* $AgNO_3$ *using Differential Electrolytic Potentiometry.* (After Bishop[107])

the potential is observed across a pair of indicator electrodes in a stirred solution during the passage of a minute, heavily stabilized current. The potential shows a sharp and pronounced break at the end-point of the reaction. The simplest form of circuit is shown in *Figure 34*. Micro-scale titration of chloride with $AgNO_3$ using the method gives a precision of ± 2 per cent without difficulty, and ± 0.2 per cent with care. The method comes into its own when chloride levels fall below the concentration at which zero-current electrodes fail to give a Nernstian response. For chloride, the lower limit[110] is 10^{-11} mol. A considerable time is required for analysis using the method. Depending on the number of points taken, a titration may require from 1 to 3 h. This, however, is rapid compared with the 30–100 h for classical potentiometry at concentrations approaching the limit of Nernstian behaviour. A much improved performance is obtained if halide-coated electrodes are used in place of bare silver electrodes. However, the plating process is inconvenient, the electrodes have a restricted life, and adequate cleaning, which becomes necessary at high dilutions, is very difficult. This may well be the reason why Florence[111] has recently reported inability to detect chloride below 7×10^{-6}M using DEP. At low chloride concentrations the capillary microburette originally used becomes tedious to use. Instead, Bishop[112] has recommended insertion of a third microelectrode for coulometric generation of titrant. This form of the method can be referred to as DEP by constant current coulometry[110]. For details of the titration cells and circuits the above reference and others cited in it should be consulted[110]. A great advantage of DEP by constant current coulometry is the short time required. This is in contrast to the much longer periods required in forms of DEP described earlier.

Reverting to direct potentiometry again, several new developments have been reported in recent years. Chou and Sams[113] use a mixed $AgNO_3$–$Th(NO_3)_4$ titrant for simultaneous determination of chloride, bromide, iodide and fluoride. The titration is made at pH 7.2 and 0 °C. Hozumi and Akimoto[114] detect the end-point using a sodium-sensitive glass electrode, utilizing earlier work by Mattock and Uncles[115] indicating that the sodium-sensitive glass electrode is more responsive to Ag^+ than Na^+. Application can be made to chloride, bromide and iodide. The $AgNO_3$ titrant is made up in 80% propan-2-ol; the solution being titrated must contain at least 90% acetone and sodium must be absent. Prokopov[116] has used a platinum indicator electrode in place of the conventional silver electrode.

Although most potentiometric titrations for chloride employ $AgNO_3$ as titrant, $Hg(NO_3)_2$ has been investigated as an alternative[117,118]. The reagent may be used for analysis of Cl^-–Br^-–I^-–SCN^- mixtures.

Recent work by Tomlinson and Torrance[119] indicates that very low concentrations of chloride can be determined automatically by potentiometry. Based on the potential of a Ag–AgCl electrode in relation to a Hg–Hg(I)SO_4 reference electrode, chloride at levels of 0–150 $\mu g\, \ell^{-1}$ can be determined. The method is applied to high-purity power station waters. It appears to be the first continuous method at these levels.

Ion-selective electrodes are now well established in analytical chemistry[120–122]. Chloride can be determined by several different types of electrode. The most used is the solid-state. Here the membrane can be in the form of an AgCl crystal or pressed pellet. This is the homogeneous solid-state membrane characterized by the Orion 94–17 electrode[123]. Other commercial models are available from Corning[124] and Beckman[125]. Another type, the Pungor heterogeneous solid-state membrane electrode (Type OP-Cl-711) incorporates the silver halide precipitate in a polymerized silicone rubber matrix[126]. The Orion 94-17 electrode has a concentration range of 1M to 5×10^{-5}M Cl^-. This may be extended to the ppb (10^9) range if two such electrodes are used in a differential mode[111]. The chloride electrode is normally used in conjunction with a calomel reference electrode using the arrangement shown in *Figure 35*. Combination chloride electrodes are available which incorporate the reference electrode and the chloride-sensing electrode in the same body. The Orion 96-17 is an example of this type.

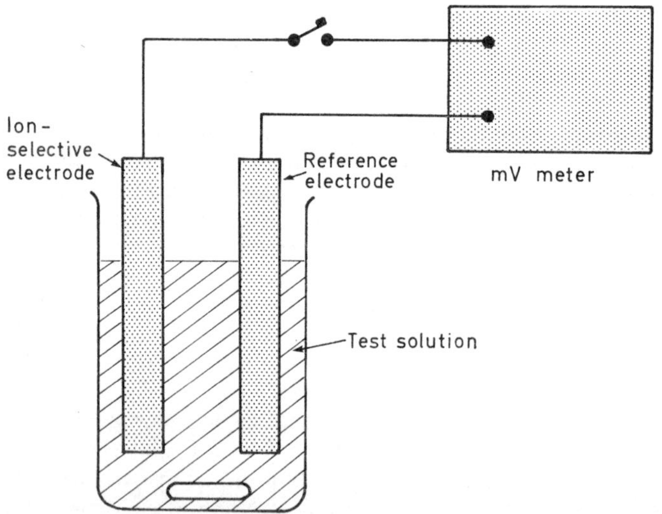

Figure 35 General arrangement for using an ion-selective electrode

Extraneous species forming insoluble salts or stable silver complexes interfere. The degree of interference may be expressed in various ways. In general the Selectivity ratio (or Selectivity constant) is used. This is defined by the empirical equation

$$E = E' \pm \frac{RT}{Z_i F} \ln(a_i + \sum_j K_{ij} a_j^{z_i/z_j})$$

where K_{ij} is the Selectivity Ratio of ion i over j; Z_i is the charge on ion being measured; Z_j is the charge on interfering ion j; E' is a constant; E is the potential of the ion-selective electrode against a standard electrode; a is the activity.

In the case of anions, and where the ion being measured and the interfering ions are univalent, the above equation simplifies to

$$E = E' - \frac{RT}{F} \ln(a_i + K_{ij} a_j)$$

The interference by ion j is therefore determined by the product $K_{ij}a_j$. The lower the value of K_{ij} the lower the interference. If $K_{ij} = 1$ then the ion-selective electrode has the same selectivity for both ions i and j. Referring again to the Orion chloride solid-state electrode, the interferences are given in *Table 31*.

Table 31 Interferences for Orion 94-17 chloride electrode (solid-state)

Interfering ion	*Selectivity constant*
OH^-	1.2×10^{-2}
NH_3	8
$S_2O_3^{2-}$	10^2
Br^-	3×10^2
I^-	2×10^6
CN^-	5×10^6
S^{2-}	Very high. S^{2-} must be absent even in trace amounts

It will be noted that this electrode can also be used for determination of bromide or iodide. The electrode cannot be used in strongly reducing solutions but oxidizing agents are without effect. No interference is given by nitrate, fluoride, bicarbonate, sulphate or phosphate. In some instances interference can be eliminated, for example chloride can be determined in the presence of bromide and iodide if the latter are removed using chromic acid[127]. A complementary method of expressing ISE selectivity is to quote the maximum permissible ratio, on a molar basis, of the interfering ion to the ion being measured. The values on this basis are the reciprocals of selectivity constants. Care chould be exercised in the interpretation of selectivity data published in the literature. This is discussed in the review paper by Moody and Thomas[122]. Interference by extraneous ions in the Pungor chloride electrode differs in some respect from the Orion electrode referred to above.

The use of commercial electrodes is not essential. Mascini and Liberti[128] have provided constructional details of a chloride electrode in which the silver halide is mixed with thermoplastic polymer and then heat treated under pressure. The linear Nernstian response is claimed to be similar to the other types of silver halide electrodes.

There are alternative methods for determination of chloride using ion-selective electrodes. One is to employ the silver-sensitive solid-state electrode, such as the Orion 94-16. Here a known amount of Ag^+ is added to the sample and the residual Ag^+ concentration determined using the silver electrode. Frost[129] has used this method for analysis of boiler cleaning solutions.

In cases where solid-state chloride electrodes are subject to interference, a chloride liquid ion-exchange membrane electrode is sometimes more suitable. An example is the Orion 92-17 electrode for which the selectivity constants are given in *Table 32*. In contrast to the solid-state chloride electrode the 92-17 electrode can be used in the presence of sulphide and ammonium ions as well as in reducing or oxidizing media.

In addition to the technique of preparing a calibration curve and using it

Table 32 Interferences for Orion 92-17 chloride electrode (liquid ion-exchange membrane type)

Interfering ion	*Selectivity constant*
ClO_4^-	32
I^-	17
NO_3^-	4.2
Br^-	1.6
OH^-	1.0
OAc^-	0.32
HCO_3^-	0.19
SO_4^{2-}	0.14
F^-	0.10

for determination of unknown chloride samples, other procedures are possible. Potman and Dahmen[130] apply the silver solid-state electrode to organic microanalysis, using it to detect the end-point when titrating chloride and bromide with Hg^{2+}. The procedure is carried out after initial combustion of the sample. Although the mechanism of the reaction between Hg^{2+} ions and the Ag_2S electrode is not fully clear, there is the distinct advantage that Hg^{2+} ions form strong complexes with halides. Conrad[131] titrates chloride and cyanide argentimetrically in a single sample, again using the Ag_2S electrode (Orion 94-16) to detect end-points. Both chloride and cyanide can be evaluated from the titration curve.

The use of ion-selective electrodes as indicator electrodes in the argentimetric titration of halides has not been accepted without at least one dissenting voice. Masson[132] has argued that in relation to the well-established metallic silver indicator electrode, ion-selective electrodes suffer distinct disadvantages.

One great advantage of ion-selective electrodes is the ease with which continuous analysis can be performed. This is a feature common to many other electroanalytical techniques. A review of continuous analysis by means of Pungor type electrodes, but which is relevant to other types of solid-state electrodes, has been published by Feher *et al.*[133].

Application of chloride ion-selective electrodes is already widespread, extending into industrial, biological, medical, agricultural, environmental and geological areas. Application reviews have been published, and should be consulted for particular cases[134, 135].

A new development in the form of the 'Selectrode', consisting of a thin layer of electroactive material on the surface of hydrophobized graphite, has been described by Ruzicka and Lamm[136]. A pure Nernstian response is given by iodide, bromide and chloride down to 10^{-6}M, 10^{-5}M and 10^{-4}M respectively. No membrane or inner reference solution is involved. The electrode is available commercially[137].

2. *Coulometric methods*

Coulometric analysis using electrogenerated argentous ions has long been established as an effective method for determination of chloride, bromide and iodide. The method is based on measuring the quantity of electricity required to achieve the quantitative reaction,

$$Ag + X^- \rightarrow AgX + e$$

$$\text{where } X^- = Cl^-, Br^-, \text{ or } I^-$$

when the halide is electrolysed with a silver anode. Lingane[138] describes a form of the method in which the equivalence point is detected potentiometrically. The assembly is shown in *Figure 36*. The method is suitable for 0.2–10 mg amounts of chloride, bromide or iodide in 50 mℓ of solution. The

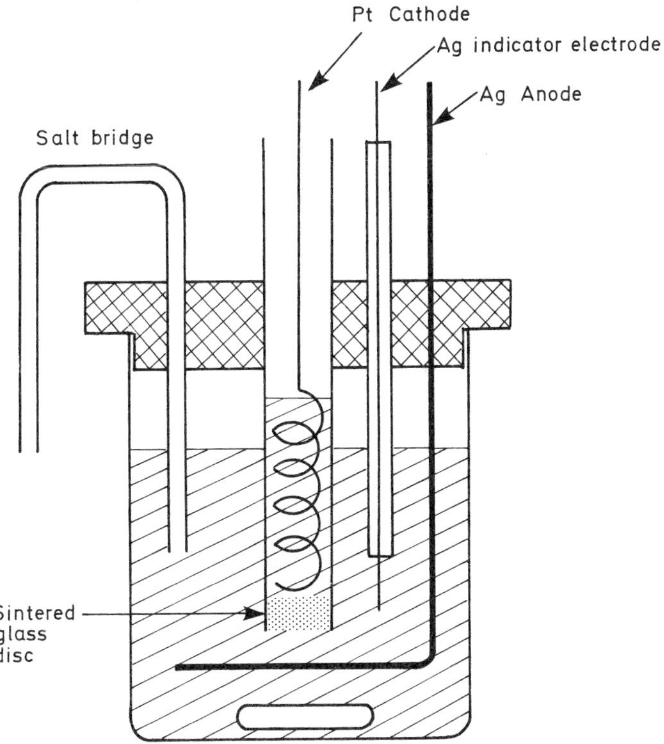

Figure 36 *Cell for coulometric titration of Cl^- with electrogenerated Ag^+ ions.* (After Lingane[138])

accuracy is better than in the conventional $AgNO_3$ titration of halides using indicators. Halide mixtures can be analysed by successive electrolysis at the appropriate potentials. An automatic form of the method has been used by Coulson and Cavanagh[139] for determination of chloride resulting from combustion of organic samples. This method, by which bromide and iodide can also be determined, involves measuring the titration current with an integrator.

A thorough investigation of coulometric generation of Ag^+ on the macro scale has been carried out by Marinenko and Taylor[140], who find it capable of highly accurate determination of chloride, bromide and iodide. The main source of error in very accurate work appears to be photodecomposition of the AgCl precipitate. It has been recommended that determinations at the ultimate precision and accuracy (errors ~0.0012 per cent) should be carried out in the absence of light[141].

The extremely high accuracy of the method has been utilized by Yoshimori and Tanaka[142] for determination of surface moisture and purity of single NaCl crystals. In this work constant current coulometry is used, the electrolysis time being measured using a 50-Hz oscillator based on the frequency of a quartz crystal. Results for three NaCl crystals of 99.988%, 99.993%, and 99.995% with standard deviations of 0.0143 per cent, 0.0138 per cent and 0.0124 per cent respectively, indicate the high degree of precision attained.

Cedergren and Johansson[143] employ coulometric titration with electrogenerated Ag^+ ions for determination of 1–200 nmol of Cl^- in an acetic acid–water (75%:25%) medium. As little as 0.01 ppm Cl^- can be determined in about 10 min. Although Ag^+ ions can be easily generated from a silver anode, the presence of oxidizing agents can cause difficulty by oxidizing the anode independently of the flow of current. Fletcher and Mannion[144] overcome this by generating Ag^+ through a Ag_2S permeable membrane which is inert to chemical oxidation.

Although many forms of the coulometric method require expensive equipment, simpler ones have been described. An example is that recently described by Jacobsen and Tandberg[145]. This employs a battery-operated constant current source, and is capable of chloride determination in the range 0.1–1 ppm. Of the common ions, bromide, iodide, thiocyanate and cyanide must be absent. A bi-amperometric 'dead-stop' end-point is employed.

Recently Lange and Borner[146] have described a new absolute measurement coulometer for determination of chloride. Silver ions are generated at constant current and the end-point detected by means of a second pair of electrodes in the cell. An integrator and digital readout is incorporated. Application is made to determination of chloride in serum.

Electrogenerated mercurous ions for coulometric titration of chloride was investigated by Przybylowicz and Rogers[147]. They substituted a mercury anode for the silver anode and detected the equivalence point potentiometrically using a mercury indicator electrode. Using 0.5M $NaClO_4$ together with 0.02M $HClO_4$ as supporting electrolyte, it was found possible to determine chloride, bromide and iodide individually with high accuracy and precision. However, in the titration of halide mxtures the familiar coprecipitation difficulties found in argentimetric titrations were encountered. In similar studies De Ford and Horn[148] used a mercury pool anode for titration of halides with electrogenerated mercurous ions.

3. *Amperometric methods*

Earlier work on the amperometric titration of chloride is summarized in the monograph by Stock[149]. Recent work is reported by Kreshkov *et al.*[150] who use cadmium nitrate as titrant in an anhydrous acetic acid medium. The method depends on precipitation of cadmium chloride. About 4–6 mg Cl^- can be determined with an accuracy of about 2 per cent. Bromide and thiocyanate can be determined by precipitation of $CdBr_2$ and $Cd(SCN)_2$ respectively.

Ikeda and Musha[151] use $AgNO_3$ as titrant with a rotating platinum electrode, for determination of halides in the presence of cyanide and cyanate. Interference by cyanide in concentrations up to 1500 times that for halide is prevented by adding M formaldehyde which reacts with it giving a cyanohydrin. Interference by excess M-formaldehyde and cyanate in concentrations up to 100 times the halide concentration is avoided by addition of HNO_3 and adjusting the pH to less than 3. The titration, which is applicable to 0.1 mM–10 mM of chloride, bromide or iodide, is made in the presence of gelatin.

4. *Voltammetric methods*

Polarography appears to have been little used in the determination of chloride. Earlier studies were carried out by Kolthoff and Miller[152]. Further investigations are discussed by Milner[153]. For concentrations up to 0.002M the height of the well-developed anodic step from a 0.1M KNO_3 base electrolyte is proportional to the chloride concentration. However, the anodic step becomes poorly defined at higher chloride concentrations. The half-wave potential of this step depends on the chloride concentration. At a concentration of 0.001M the value is +0.25 V *v*. SCE.

Bartik and Kupka[154] use polarography for determination of chloride in biological material after first precipitating protein with sulphosalicylic acid. This subsequently forms a suitable supporting electrolyte for the analysis itself. Gorokhovskii and Ismagilova[155] determine chloride, bromide and iodide using a specially designed silver electrode, this allowing reproducible oscillopolarograms to be obtained in the range 10^{-3}–10^{-6}M.

Calzolari, Gabrielli and Marletta[156] have used a rapid polarographic procedure for determination of halides in algae after initial combustion. The analysis was carried out by recording the anodic waves of chloride and iodide, but the cathodic wave for bromide, this being produced after quantitative oxidation of the ion under controlled conditions. While the results for chloride and bromide agree with those obtained by classical methods, the iodide values are not accurate, this being attributed to the particularly small amount present.

An interesting indirect polarographic procedure for chloride and other anions has been developed by Humphrey and Laird[157]. This is based on familiar displacement of chloranilate ions when chloride reacts with mercuric chloranilate. The reaction has been referred to earlier in this section in connection with a spectrophotometric procedure based on it. Humphrey and Laird utilize the two-electron reversible reduction of both chloranilic acid and chloranilates at the dropping mercury electrode, a process recorded earlier by Weissbart and Van Rysselberghe[158]. The resulting method allows chloride in the range 1×10^{-5}–5×10^{-3}M to be determined. It is noted by the authors that the polarographic procedure could provide a useful alternative where samples containing other absorbing species are present. Analogous methods for cyanide, fluoride, sulphite and sulphate are described.

5. *Miscellaneous electroanalytical procedures*

Colovos, Milson and Moyers[159] use stripping voltammetry for determination of chloride and bromide at concentrations as low as 10^{-5}M. The method is effective only if their concentrations are comparable. Kemula, Kublik and Taraszewska[160] deposit the mercurous salts of chloride, bromide and iodide anodically on to the surface of a hanging mercury drop, and subsequently carry out cathodic stripping. The three anions are determined to $\pm 15\%$ at 10^{-6}–10^{-7}M.

Chronopotentiometry has been used recently both for determination of individual halides and analysis of halide mixtures[161].

Argentimetric high-frequency titration can also be used in the analysis of halide mixtures and individual halides. The method also permits thiocyanate to be determined in some instances[162].

Radiochemical methods

Radiochemical methods for chloride have been based on several systems. Shatalova and Meerov[163] use $^{110}AgNO_3$ for precipitation of chloride, the $^{110}AgCl$ being dissolved in NH_4OH for counting. The method, which gives an accuracy of ± 8 per cent is applied to analysis of plasma and blood. More recently Beaudet and Rygaert[164] used a similar method except that the activity of the supernatant liquid is determined after separation in a centrifuge. No interference is given by sodium, calcium, magnesium, aluminium, iron, sulphate, nitrate, nitrite, phosphate, carbonate, bicarbonate, phenol, pyridine, humic acids, sodium lactate, glycine, pyrogallol, pectins, tannic acid, or sodium dodecylbenzenesulphonate. Bromide and iodide interfere. The method, which was developed for water analysis, is applicable in the range 5–1000 ppm Cl^-.

A method utilizing $^{203}Hg(IO_3)_2$ and based on measuring the activity of the resulting $HgCl_2$ or $HgBr_2$, has been published[165]. Bowen[166] employs a column containing $Ag_2{}^{51}CrO_4$ for determination of chloride as well as sulphide. After passing the sample through the column, the eluate is counted for $^{51}CrO_4{}^{2-}$. Bromide, iodide, cyanide, thiocyanate and sulphite interfere. The range for chloride is 0.8–80 μmol.

Johannesson[167] treats the chloride sample (1–10 μg Cl^-) with a known amount of ^{36}HCl, evaporates to dryness and then determines the activity of the residue. The error for 10–100 μg Cl^- is ± 3 μg and ± 1 μg for 1–10 μg Cl^-. Application is made to analysis of natural waters. The author claims[168] that the method is ten times more sensitive than a sub-stoichiometric method based on precipitation of $Ag^{36}Cl$.

Gas-chromatographic methods

A recent feature of inorganic and organometallic analysis has been the introduction of gas-chromatographic methods. A review of the subject has been published recently by Rodriguez-Vazquez[169]. Several procedures are now available for analysis of halide mixtures.

Ruessel[170] first converts halides (chloride, bromide and iodide) to the corresponding acids using a strongly acidic ion-exchanger. These are reacted with 1,2-olefin oxides in acidic medium to give halogen alcohols. Measurable peaks are obtained at concentrations as low as 0.5×10^{-4}M using flame ionization detection. Another system involves conversion of the halides (bromide, chloride and iodide) by ion-exchange into the tetra-alkylammonium salts. On pyrolysis these decompose giving the trialkylamines and the corresponding alkyl halides. After gas-chromatographic separation, detection is made by thermal conductivity[171].

Matthews, Shults and Dean[172] first extract the halides (bromide, chloride and iodide) from aqueous solution using tetraheptylammonium carbonate in 10% toluene–undecanol solutions. The tetraheptylammonium halides undergo thermal degradation to 1-haloheptanes and triheptylamine above 150 °C. Gas-chromatographic peaks are produced by the halocarbons, and these are used for quantitative analysis of halides at low ppm levels.

In yet another system, Belcher and co-workers[173,174] determine chloride via phenyl mercury(II) chloride, which is extracted into $CHCl_3$ before gas-chromatography. As little as 2.3×10^{-10} g of chloride can be detected using a flame ionization detector. With electron capture detection a further tenfold increase in sensitivity is obtained.

Miscellaneous methods

Methods falling outside the previous categories will now be discussed. Several attempts have been made to develop quantitative or semi-quantitative chromatographic methods for chloride. The well-known ring-oven technique of Weisz has been used for semi-micro determination of chloride, bromide, iodide, thiocyanate, arsenate, dichromate and hexacyanoferrate(III) using a silver sulphide standard scale[174].

Hashmi and Chughtai[176] use circular TLC for semi-quantitative determination of bromide, chloride, iodide, bromate, chlorate, hexacyanoferrate(II), hexacyanoferrate(III), thiocyanate, arsenite and sulphite. The accuracy is ±5 per cent. No interference is given by phosphate, sulphide, nitrite, iodate, thiosulphate, periodate, arsenate or acetate. Another thin-layer method is described by Muto[177], in which silica is suspended in 3% $AgNO_3$ solution and spread on glass. The solvent system is saturated aq. isobutanol–40% ammonium acetate (4:1). The lengths of the bands produced are proportional to the concentrations of chloride, bromide, iodide and phosphate. A rather similar method involves impregnating the chromatographic paper with AgCl or Ag_2O and measuring the distances migrated by chloride, bromide and iodide in 30–45 min of ascending chromatography using 12% aqueous glycerol as the mobile phase[178]. The investigators prefer AgCl for determination of individual halides or bromide and iodide in binary mixtures. Silver oxide gives better results where ternary mixtures are involved. Calibrated graphs are used in evaluating the results. Microgram amounts of halides (as well as thiocyanate) can be determined. As many as 50 samples can be analysed in an hour.

Application of an indirect X-ray fluorescence procedure using bromide or iodide as reference standards, allows the determination of chloride in the range 0.7–4 mg, together with thiocyanate and cyanide. The determination is made[179] after initial precipitation of chloride with $AgNO_3$.

Several attempts have been made to develop amplification methods for chloride. The review by Belcher[180] of amplification methods in general includes an account of some of these methods. One method[181] suitable for 0.05–10 mg of Cl^- includes the following steps:

1. Precipitation of chloride as AgCl followed by metathesis with Na_2S to Ag_2S.
2. Removal of Ag_2S by filtration, the chloride now passing into the filtrate, together with excess sulphide.
3. Oxidation of filtrate S^{2-} to $SO_4{}^{2-}$ with H_2O followed by acidification with HNO_3 and reprecipitation of chloride with $AgNO_3$.
4. Removal of AgCl on original filter containing Ag_2S.
5. Filtrate and washings are discarded. Silver chloride is dissolved by passing minimum amount of 5M NH_4OH through combined Ag_2S plus AgCl precipitates.
6. Filtrate is treated with Na_2S and Ag_2S again collected on original filter.

In this way, arithmetic increments of Ag_2S are collected on the filter. Finally the total amount of Ag_2S is converted to AgCl for weighing. The original amount of chloride is evaluated from the number of amplification steps used. Although at first sight the method might appear tedious, a specially designed glass apparatus simplifies the procedures.

A kinetic-spectrophotometric method for chloride and bromide at low concentrations has been reported by Mentasti and Pelizzetti[182]. The basis is as follows. Thallium(III) oxidizes 4,4′-dihydroxydiphenyl (DHDP) quantitatively to diphenoquinone (DPQ).

$$\mathrm{Tl(III)} + \mathrm{HO{-}C_6H_4{-}C_6H_4{-}OH} \rightarrow \mathrm{Tl(I)} + \mathrm{O{=}C_6H_4{=}C_6H_4{=}O} + 2\mathrm{H^+}$$

Chloride and bromide react with excess thallium(III) to give a strong 1:1 complex which does not oxidize DHDP to DPQ. The resulting method is suitable for chloride or bromide in the range 10^{-4}–10^{-6}M. No interference is given by nitrate or sulphate in 100-fold excess; interference is given by iodide, thiocyanate, sulphite, thiosulphate and species which oxidize DHDP or reduce thallium(III).

Determination of halides by thermometric titration has been reported. Individual halides can be titrated using $AgNO_3$ to a reasonable degree of accuracy, but titration of halide mixtures appears to suffer from the same errors due to coprecipitation that affect potentiometric methods[183].

References

1. FIRSCHING, F.H., *Analyt. Chem.*, **32**, 1876 (1960)
2. RODABAUGH, R.D. and UPPERMAN, G.T., *Analytica chim. Acta*, **60**, 434 (1972)
3. CHWASTOWSKA, J., MARCZENKO, Z. and STOLARCZYK, U., *Chemia. analit.*, **8**, 517 (1963); *Analyt. Abstr.*, **11**, 3662 (1964)
4. DE GEISO, R.C., REEMAN, W. and LINDENBAUM, S., *Analyt. Chem.*, **26**, 1840 (1954)

5. HOLZAPFEL, H. and GURTLER, O., *J. prakt. Chem.*, **35**, 113 (1967); *Analyt. Abstr.*, **15**, 4673 (1968)
6. ZALEVSKAYA, T.L. and STAROBINETS, G.L., *Zh. analit. Khim.*, **24**, 721 (1969); *Analyt. Abstr.*, **19**, 3877 (1969)
7. STAROBINETS, G.L. and ZAKHARTSEVA, E.P., *Izv. Akad. Nauk. beloruss. SSR, Ser. khim. Nauk*, 105 (1970); *Analyt. Abstr.*, **22**, 2264 (1972)
8. RAMALEY, L. and HOLCOMBE, W.A., *Analyt. Lett.*, **1**, 143 (1967)
9. TUSTANOWSKI, S., *J. Chromat.*, **31**, 268 (1967)
10. TUSTANOWSKI, S., *J. Chromat.*, **31**, 270 (1967)
11. HARRISON, B.L. and ROSENBLATT, D.H., *J. Chromat.*, **13**, 271 (1964)
12. MAO, C-H., *Acta chim. Sin.*, **30**, 496 (1964); *Analyt. Abstr.*, **13**, 533 (1966)
13. BARK, L.S., GRAHAM, R.J.T. and MCCORMICK, D., *Analytica chim. Acta*, **35**, 268 (1966)
14. SEILER, H. and SEILER, M., *Helv. chim. Acta.* **50**, 2477 (1967)
15. GAGLIARDI, E. and POKORNY, G., *Mikrochim. Acta*, 699 (1965)
16. SEILER, H. and KAFFENBERGER, T., *Helv. chim. Acta*, **44**, 1282 (1961)
17. PETROVIC, S.M. and CANIC, V.D., *Z. analyt. Chem.*, **228**, 339 (1967); *Analyt. Abstr.*, **15**, 4674 (1968)
18. TAKEUCHI, T. and TSUNODA, Y., *J. chem. Soc. Japan, pure Chem. Sect.*, **87**, 251 (1966); *Analyt. Abstr.*, **14**, 4682 (1967)
19. MUTO, M., *J. chem. Soc. Japan, pure Chem. Sect.*, **85**, 782 (1964); *Analyt. Abstr.*, **13**, 1257 (1966)
20. KAWANABE, K., TAKITANI, S., TIYAZAKI, M. and TAMURA, Z., *Japan Analyst*, **13**, 976 (1964); *Analyt. Abstr.*, **13**, 5385 (1966)
21. ELSHEIMER, H.N., JOHNSON, A.L. and KOCHEN, R.L., *Analyt. Chem.*, **38**, 1684 (1966)
22. ARMSTRONG, G.W., GILL, H.H. and ROLF, R.F., in *Treatise on Analytical Chemistry* (Ed. I.M. Kolthoff and P.J. Elving), Part II, Vol. 7, Interscience, New York (1961)
23. KOLTHOFF, I.M., SANDELL, E.B., MEEHAN, E.J. and BRUCKENSTEIN, S., *Quantitative Chemical Analysis*, 4th edn, MacMillan, London, 580 (1969)
24. LITTLE, K., *Talanta*, **18**, 927 (1971)
25. Imperial Chemical Industries Ltd., Analytical Chemists' Committee, *Analyst*, **75**, 577 (1950)
26. DESAI, M.N., DESAI, K.C. and GANDHI, M.H., *Lab. Pract.*, **18**, 939, 1063(1969)
27. Reference 23, 716
28. FRIESER, H. and FERNANDO, Q., *Ionic Equilibria in Analytical Chemistry*, Chapter XIV, Wiley, New York (1963)
29. LAITINEN, H.A., *Chemical Analysis*, McGraw-Hill, New York (1960)
30. BELCHER, R., MACDONALD, A.M.G. and PARRY, E., *Analytica chim. Acta*, **16**, 524 (1957)
31. BERRY, A.J. and DRIVER, J.E., *Analyst*, **64**, 730 (1939)
32. BISHOP, E. and AYERS, C.A., in *Comprehensive Analytical Chemistry* (Ed. C.L. and D.W. Wilson), Vol. 1B, Chapter VII, Elsevier, London (1960)
33. BLOCK, J. and WATERS, O.B., *Talanta*, **14**, 1130 (1967)
34. WANNINEN, E., *Talanta*, **15**, 717 (1968)
35. ANFAELT, T. and JAGNER, D., *Talanta*, **16**, 555 (1969)
36. *Standard Methods for the Examination of Water, Sewage and Industrial Waters*, The American Public Health Association and the American Waterworks Association, 13th edn, American Public Health Association, New York (1971)
37. SCHULEK, E., PUNGOR, E. and KETHELYI, J., *Analytica chim. Acta*, **8**, 229 (1953)
38. CALDWELL, J.R. and MOYER, H.V., *Ind. Engng Chem. analyt. edn*, **7**, 38 (1935)
39. *British Standard* 4401: Pt 6 (1970)
40. *British Standard* 4550: Pt 2 (1970)
41. FIGG, J.W., *The Analysis of Concretes*, Building Research Station, Department of the Environment, 28, H.M.S.O., London (1970)
42. KAPEL, M., FRY, J.C. and SHELTON, D.R., *Analyst*, **100**, 570 (1975)
43. IKEDA, N., *J. chem. Soc. Japan, pure Chem. Sect.*, **70**, 329 (1949); *Chem. Abstr.*, **45**, 3102 (1951)
44. MEHLIG, J.P., *Chemist Analyst*, **44**, 87 (1955)
45. ARCHER, E.E., *Analyst*, **83**, 571 (1958)
46. KARABASH, A.G., *Zh. analit. Khim.*, **8**, 140 (1953)
47. MACDONALD, A.M.G., *Ind. Chemist*, **36**, 35 (1960)
48. CHENG, F.W., *Microchem. J.*, **3**, 537 (1959)
49. WHITE, D.C., *Mikrochim. Acta*, 449 (1961)

50. WHITE, D.C., *Mikrochim. Acta,* 807 (1961)
51. COLSON, A.F., *Analyst,* **90**, 35 (1965)
52. BELCHER, R., GOUVERNEUR, D. and MACDONALD, A.M.G., *J. chem. Soc.,* 1938 (1962)
53. *Official, Standardised and Recommended Methods of Analysis,* The Society for Analytical Chemistry, London, 351 (1973)
54. STEYERMARK, A., LALANCETTE, R.A. and CONTRERAS, E.M., *J. Ass. off. analyt. Chem.,* **55**, 680 (1972)
55. FLASCHKA, H. and HUDITZ, F., *Z. analyt. Chem.,* **137**, 104 (1952); *Chem. Abstr.,* **47**, 443a (1953)
56. GUSEV, S.I., SOKOLOVA, E.V. and KOZHEVNIKOVA, I.A., *Zh. analit. Khim.,* **17**, 499 (1962); *Analyt. Abstr.,* **10**, 1795 (1963)
57. DE SOUSA, A., *Inf. Quim. Anal.,* **17**, 127 (1963); *Analyt. Abstr.,* **11**, 5476 (1964)
58. DE SOUSA, A., *Chemist Analyst,* **49**, 45 (1960)
59. DE SOUSA, A., *Talanta,* **8**, 782 (1961)
60. DE SOUSA, A., *Analytica chim. Acta,* **24**, 424 (1961)
61. VIEBOCK, F., *Ber.,* **65B**, 493, 586 (1932)
62. FILDES, J.E. and MACDONALD, A.M.G., *Analytica chim. Acta,* **24**, 121 (1961)
63. BELCHER, R., MACDONALD, A.M.G. and NUTTEN, A.J., *Mikrochim. Acta,* 104 (1954)
64. KOLTHOFF, I.M. and BELCHER, R., *Volumetric Analysis,* Volume III, Interscience, New York, 254 (1957)
65. SUMMERSGILL, N., *Chem. Inds, Lond.,* 782 (1961)
66. IWASAKI, I., UTSUMI, S. and OZAWA, T., *Bull. chem. Soc. Japan,* **25**, 226 (1952); *Chem. Abstr.,* **47**, 10407f (1953)
67. IWASAKI, I., UTSUMI, S., HAGENO, K. and OZAWA, T., *Bull. chem. Soc. Japan,* **29**, 860 (1956); *Analyt. Abstr.,* **4**, 3954 (1957)
68. FLORENCE, T.M. and FARRAR, Y.J., *Analytica chim. Acta,* **54**, 373 (1971)
69. BERGMAN, J.G. and SANIK, J., *Analyt. Chem.,* **29**, 241 (1957)
70. ELSHEIMER, H.N. and KOCHEN, R.L., *Analyt. Chem.,* **38**, 145 (1966)
71. BRITT, R.D., *Analyt. Chem.,* **34**, 1728 (1962)
72. DOJLIDO, J. and BIERWAGEN, H., *Chemia. analit.,* **14**, 91 (1969); *Analyt. Abstr.,* **18**, 4413 (1970)
73. *British Standards* 2690: Part 6 (1968)
74. KULHANEK, V. and FISER, C., *Colln Czech. chem. Commun.,* **31**, 1890 (1966); *Analyt. Abstr.,* **15**, 4871 (1967)
75. YAMAMOTO, Y., KUMAMARU, T., TATEHATA, A. and YAMADA, N., *Analytica chim. Acta,* **50**, 433 (1970)
76. ZALL, D.M., FISHER, D. and GARNER, M.Q., *Analyt. Chem.,* **28**, 1665 (1956)
77. GERLACH, J.L. and FRAZIER, R.G., *Analyt. Chem.,* **30**, 1142 (1958)
78. BARNEY, J.E. and BERTOLACINI, R.J., *Analyt. Chem.,* **29**, 1187 (1957)
79. BERTOLACINI, R.J. and BARNEY, J.E., *Analyt, Chem.,* **30**, 202 (1958)
80. BODE, H., EGGELING, W. and STEINBRECHT, V., *Z.analyt. Chem.,* **216**, 30 (1966); *Analyt. Abstr.,* **14**, 2409 (1967)
81. HAMMER, C.F. and CRAIG, J.H., *Analyt. Chem.,* **42**, 1588 (1970)
82. WEST, P.W. and COLL, H., *Analyt. Chem.,* **28**, 1834 (1956)
83. TARAS, M., *Analyt. Chem.,* **19**, 342 (1947)
84. SCHEUBECK, E. and ERNST, O., *Z. analyt. Chem.,* **249**, 370 (1970); *Analyt. Abstr.,* **20**, 1655 (1971)
85. BHATTY, M.K. and UDEN, P.C., *Talanta,* **18**, 799 (1971)
86. BELCHER, R., RODRIGUEZ-VAZQUEZ, J.A. and STEPHEN, W.I., *Analytica chim. Acta,* **61**, 223 (1972)
87. LAMB, A.B., CARLETON, P.W. and MELDRUM, W.B., *J. Am. chem. Soc.,* **42**, 251 (1920)
88. JOHNSON, C.R., *J. phys. Chem., Ithaca,* **35**, 2237 (1931)
89. BOLTZ, D.F. and HOLLAND, W.J., in *Colorimetric Determination of Non-metals* (Ed. D.F. Boltz), Interscience, New York (1958)
90. RAMIREZ-MUNOZ, J., *Analytica chim. Acta,* **74**, 309 (1975)
91. REICHEL, W. and ACS, L., *Analyt. Chem.,* **41**, 1886 (1969)
92. FUJINUMA, H., KASAMA, K., TAKEUCHI, K. and HIRANO, S., *Japan Analyst,* **19**, 1487 (1970); *Analyt. Abstr.,* **22**, 2272 (1972)
93. BELCHER, R., NADJAFI, A., RODRIGUEZ-VAZQUEZ, J.A. and STEPHEN, W.I., *Analyst,* **97**, 993 (1972)
94. DAGNALL, R.M., THOMPSON, K.C. and WEST, T.S., *Analyst,* **94**, 643 (1969)

95. SHINER, V.J. and SMITH, M.L., *Analyt. Chem.*, **28**, 1043 (1956)
96. MARTIN, A.J., *Analyt. Chem.*, **30**, 233 (1958)
97. PROKOPOV, T.S., *Analyt. Chem.*, **42**, 1096 (1970)
98. KUTTEL, D., SZABADKA, O., CSAJVARI, B., MESZAROS, K., HAVAS, J. and PUNGOR, E., *Magy. kém. Foly.*, **75**, 181 (1969); *Analyt. Abstr.*, **19**, 3889 (1970)
99. DIXON, J.P., *Modern Methods in Organic Microanalysis*, Chapter 8, Van Nostrand, London (1968)
100. FREEMAN, R.W., *Analyt. Chem.*, **31**, 214 (1959)
101. REILLEY, C.N., COOKE, W.D. and FURMAN, N.H., *Analyt. Chem.*, **23**, 1223 (1951)
102. FURMAN, N.H. and LOW, G.W., *J. Am. chem. Soc.*, **57**, 1585 (1935)
103. BLAEDEL, W.J., LEWIS, W.B. and THOMAS, J.W., *Analyt. Chem.*, **24**, 509 (1952)
104. MALMSTADT, H.V. and WINEFORDNER, J.D., *Analytica chim. Acta*, **20**, 283 (1959)
105. MALMSTADT, H.V. and WINEFORDNER, J.D., *J. Am. Wat. Wks Ass.*, **51**, 733 (1959); *Analyt. Abstr.*, **7**, 1953 (1960)
106. *British Standard* 2690: Part 6 (1968)
107. BISHOP, E., *Mikrochim. Acta*, 619 (1956)
108. BISHOP, E., *Analyst*, **83**, 212 (1958)
109. BISHOP, E. and DHANESHWAR, R.G., *Analyst*, **87**, 845 (1962)
110. BISHOP, E. and DHANESHWAR, R.G., *Analyt. Chem.*, **36**, 726 (1964)
111. FLORENCE, T.M., *J. electroanal. Chem.*, **31**, 77 (1971)
112. BISHOP, E., *Mikrochim. Acta*, 803 (1960)
113. CHOU, D.H. and SAMS, L.C., *Microchem. J.*, **14**, 507 (1969)
114. HOZUMI, K. and AKIMOTO, N., *Analyt. Chem.*, **42**, 1312 (1970)
115. MATTOCK, G. and UNCLES, R., *Analyst*, **87**, 977 (1962)
116. PROKOPOV, T.S., *Mikrochim. Acta*, 401 (1968)
117. IVANOVA, Z.I. and KOVALENKO, P.N., *Zh. analit. Khim.*, **17**, 739 (1962); *Analyt. Abstr.*, **10**, 2702 (1963)
118. HARZDORF, C., *Z. analyt. Chem.*, **215**, 246 (1966); *Analyt. Abstr.*, **14**, 1966 (1967)
119. TOMLINSON, K. and TORRANCE, K., *Analyst*, **102**, 1 (1977)
120. PUNGOR, E. and TOTH, K., *Analyst*, **95**, 625 (1970)
121. TENYGL, J., in *Ion-selective Electrode Analysis, MTP International Review of Science, Physical Chemistry, Series one*, Vol. 12 (Ed. T.S. West), Butterworths, London, 123 (1973)
122. MOODY, G.J. and THOMAS, J.D.R., *Talanta*, **19**, 623 (1972)
123. Orion Research Incorporated, Cambridge, Massachusetts. Also available from MSE Scientific Instruments, Manor Royal, Crawley, W. Sussex, RH10 2QQ and E.I.L. Ltd., Hanworth Lane, Chertsey, Surrey KT16 9LF
124. Available from D.A. Pitman Ltd., Weybridge, Surrey or Corning-Eel Scientific Instruments, Evans Electroselenium Ltd., Halstead, Essex
125. Available from Beckman Instruments Ltd., Sunley House, 4, Bedford Park, Croydon, Surrey
126. Radelkis Electrochemistry Instruments, Budapest, Hungary. Available from Protech Services Ltd., 40 High Street, Rickmansworth, Herts
127. VAN LOON, J.C., *Analyst*, **93**, 788 (1968)
128. MASCINI, M. and LIBERTI, A., *Analytica Chim. Acta*, **47**, 339 (1949)
129. FROST, J.G., *Analytica chim. Acta*, **48**, 321 (1969)
130. POTMAN, W. and DAHMEN, E.A.M.F., *Mikrochim. Acta*, 303 (1972)
131. CONRAD, F.J., *Talanta*, **18**, 952 (1971)
132. MASSON, M.R., *Talanta*, **22**, 933 (1975)
133. FEHER, Z., NAGY, G., TOTH, K. and PUNGOR, E., *Analyst*, **99**, 699 (1974)
134. BUCK, R.P., *Analyt. Chem.*, **46**, 28R (1974)
135. *Orion Research Incorporated, Analytical Methods Guide*, 9th edn, (1978). Also Orion Newsletters
136. RUZICKA, J. and LAMM, C.G., *Analytica chim. Acta*, **54**, 1 (1971)
137. Radiometer, Copenhagen
138. LINGANE, J.J., *Analyt. Chem.*, **26**, 622 (1954)
139. COULSON, D.M. and CAVANAGH, L.A., *Analyt. Chem.*, **32**, 1245 (1960)
140. MARINENKO, G. and TAYLOR, J.K., *J. Res. natn. Bur, Stand.*, **67A**, 31 (1963)
141. CHAMPION, C.E. and MARINENKO, C., *Analyt. Chem.*, **41**, 205 (1969)
142. YOSHIMORI, T. and TANAKA, T., *Analytica chim. Acta*, **55**, 185 (1971)
143. CEDERGREN, A. and JOHANSSON, G., *Talanta*, **18**, 917 (1971)
144. FLETCHER, K.S. and MANNION, R.F., *Analyt. Chem.*, **42**, 285 (1970)

145. JACOBSEN, E. and TANDBERG, G., *Analytica chim. Acta,* **64**, 280 (1973)
146. LANGE, W. and BORNER, K., *Z. klin. Chem. klin. Biochem.*, **10**, 33 (1972); *Analyt. Abstr.*, **23**, 3646 (1972)
147. PRZYBYLOWICZ, E.P. and ROGERS, L.B., *Analyt. Chem.*, **28**, 799 (1956)
148. DE FORD, D. and HORN, H., *Analyt. Chem.*, **28**, 797 (1956)
149. STOCK, J.T., *Amperometric Titrations,* Chapter 13, Interscience, New York (1965)
150. KRESHKOV, A.P., BORK, V.A., SHVYRKOVA, L.A. and APARSHEVA, M.I., *Zh. analit. Khim.*, **20**, 704 (1965); *Analyt. Abstr.*, **14**, 573 (1967)
151. IKEDA, S. and MUSHA, S., *Japan Analyst,* **16** 445 (1967); *Analyt. Abstr.*, **15**, 6633 (1968)
152. KOLTHOFF, I.M. and MILLER, C.S., *J. Am. chem. Soc.*, **63**, 1405 (1941)
153. MILNER, G.W.C., *Principles and Applications of Polarography,* Longmans, London, 286 (1957)
154. BARTIK, M. and KUPKA, J., *Colln Czech. chem. Commun.*, **25**, 3391 (1960); *Analyt. Abstr.*, **8**, 2960 (1961)
155. GOROKHOVSKII, V.M. and ISMAGILOVA, F.K., *Zh. analit. Khim.*, **21**, 87 (1966); *Analyt. Abstr.*, **14**, 5393 (1967)
156. CALZOLARI, C., GABRIELLI, L.F. and MARLETTA, G.P., *Analyst,* **94**, 774 (1969)
157. HUMPHREY, R.E. and LAIRD, C.E., *Analyt. Chem.*, **43**, 1895 (1971)
158. WEISSBART, J. and VAN RYSSELBERGHE, D., *J. phys. Chem., Ithaca,* **61**, 765 (1957)
159. COLOVOS, G., MILSON, G.S. and MOYERS, J.L., *Analyt. Chem.*, **46**, 1051 (1954)
160. KEMULA, W., KUBLIK, Z. and TARASZEWSKA, J., *Chemia. analit.*, **8**, 171 (1963); *Analyt. Abstr.*, **11**, 1282 (1964)
161. PETERS, D.G. and KINJO, A., *Analyt. Chem.*, **41**, 1806 (1969)
162. GREY, P. and CAVE, G.C.B., *Can. J. Chem.*, **42**, 770 (1964)
163. SHATALOVA, A.A. and MEEROV, G.I., *Biokhimiya,* **25**, 769 (1960); *Analyt. Abstr.*, **8**, 2551 (1961)
164. BEAUDET, C. and RYGAERT, J., *J. radioanal. Chem.*, **1**, 153 (1968); *Analyt. Abstr.*, **17**, 1826 (1969)
165. BANYAI, E., SZABADVARY, F. and ERDEY, L., *Mikrochim. Acta,* 427 (1962)
166. BOWEN, H.J.M., *Radiochem. & radioanal. Lett.*, **3**, 339 (1970)
167. JOHANNESSON, J.K., *J. radioanal. Chem.*, **6**, 27 (1970)
168. JOHANNESSON, J.K., *Analyst,* **86**, 72 (1961)
169. RODRIGUEZ-VAZQUEZ, J.A., *Analytica chim. Acta,* **73**, 1 (1974)
170. RUESSEL, H.A., *Angew. Chem. int. Ed. Engl.*, **9**, 374 (1970)
171. MACGEE, J. and ALLEN, K.G., *Analyt. Chem.*, **42**, 1672 (1970)
172. MATTHEWS, D.R., SHULTS, W.D. and DEAN, J.A., *Analyt. Lett.*, **6**, 513 (1973)
173. BELCHER, R., MAJER, J.R., RODRIGUEZ-VAZQUEZ, J.A., STEPHEN, W.I. and UDEN, P.C., *Analytica chim. Acta,* **57**, 73 (1971)
174. BELCHER, R., RODRIGUEZ-VAZQUEZ, J.A. and STEPHEN, W.I. Unpublished work reported in reference 169
175. CELAP, M.B. and WEISZ, H., *Mikrochim. Acta,* 24 (1962)
176. HASHMI, M.H. and CHUGHTAI, N.A., *Mikrochim. Acta,* 1040 (1968)
177. MUTO, M., *J. chem. Soc. Japan, pure Chem. Sect.*, **86**, 91 (1965); *Analyt. Abstr.*, **14**, 3961 (1967)
178. ALESKOVSKAYA, V.N. and ALESKOVSKII, V.B., *Zh. analit. Khim.*, **24**, 1213 (1969); *Analyt. Abstr.*, **20**, 1657 (1971)
179. STORK, G. and JUNG, H., *Z. analyt. Chem.*, **249**, 161 (1970)
180. BELCHER, R., *Talanta,* **15**, 357 (1968)
181. RAHIM, S.A., ABDULAHED, H. and WEST, T.S., *Mikrochim. Acta,* 111 (1974)
182. MENTASTI, E. and PELIZZETTI, E., *Analytica chim. Acta,* **78**, 227 (1975)
183. HARRIS, R.J.N. quoted in *Thermometric Titrimetry* by H.J.V. Tyrrell and A.E. Beezer, Chapman and Hall, London, 97 (1968)

Chlorite

Chlorites are relatively stable in alkaline solution but rapidly disproportionate in acid solutions giving chloride, chlorate and chlorine dioxide. The commercial product, which has alkali as impurity, contains about 80% of sodium chlorite.

Determination of chlorite is important in connection with drinking water. Chlorites find application in the bleaching industry. The term 'active chlorine' includes chlorite, hypochlorite and chlorine dioxide.

Separation

Paper and thin-layer chromatographic methods are shown in *Table 33*.

Determination

As with several other chlorine-containing anions, chlorite can be reduced by SO_2 to chloride, and then determined in this form. This can be conveniently carried out by adding potassium bisulphite and dilute H_2SO_4 and then boiling off excess SO_2.

Redox titrimetry

1. Iodimetric methods

Chlorite is reduced by iodide in acid solution.

$$ClO_2^- + 4I^- + 4H^+ \rightarrow 2I_2 + Cl^- + 2H_2O$$

The liberated iodine may be titrated with standard thiosulphate. When first developed as a method H_2SO_4 was used. Sulek and Endroi[5] used phosphoric acid, allowing 5 min for the reduction to take place. When acetic acid is used the reaction is very slow[6]. Brown[7] has reported that all three acids give the same result, but that 5 min must be allowed for the reaction to proceed if acetic acid is used.

Hypochlorite reacts in the same way, but may be removed by addition of cyanide in alkaline solution[5].

$$ClO^- + CN^- + H_2O \rightarrow ClCN + 2OH^-$$

The iodimetric method enables chlorite and chlorine dioxide to be determined when present together[8]. The sum of both species is found by the above iodimetric procedure. A colorimetric determination of chlorine dioxide with tyrosine enables each to be evaluated. Chloride, chlorate and chlorite do not interfere in the colorimetric procedure.

An interesting investigation by Norkus[9] has explained why arsenite accelerates the otherwise slow reaction of chlorite and iodide in a bicarbonate

Table 33 Paper and thin-layer chromatographic separation of chlorite

Technique	*Solvent*	ClO_2^- *separated from*	*Ref.*
Paper chromatography	Isopropanol–H_2O–pyridine–NH_3 (0.880) (15:2:2:2)	Cl^-, ClO_3^-, ClO_4^-	1
TLC aluminium oxide G-KeiselgurG (1:1)	Butanol–acetone–aq. NH_3–H_2O (8:10:2:1)	ClO_4^-, ClO_3^-, BrO_3^-, IO_3^-, BrO_2^-	2
TLC	Isopropanol–tetrahydrofuran–NH_3 (0.880) (50:30:20)	Cl^-, ClO_3^-, ClO_4^-	3
Paper and TLC Silufol UV 254 plates	Butanol–pyridine–aq. NH_3 (2:2:1)	ClO^-, ClO_3^-, ClO_4^-	4

medium and in the presence of osmic acid. The mechanism appears to be as follows. Arsenite reduces OsO_4 to Na_2OsO_4 which in turn reduces chlorite to hypochlorite. The latter oxidizes the iodide to iodine, itself being oxidized back to osmium(VIII). The iodine is subsequently titrated with arsenic(III).

A procedure based on the above has been developed[10] for successive determination of chlorine dioxide and chlorite. The same reaction is incorporated in a potentiometric method for chlorite, hypochlorite, chlorate and chloride. This will be described later.

Determination of chlorite in hypochlorite is important. Phenol has been recommended for destruction of hypochlorite but Hashmi and Ayaz[11] observe that phenol also reacts with chlorite. For mixtures of the two ions they recommend destruction of hypochlorite (usually converted to hypobromite prior to analysis) by addition of $(NH_4)_2SO_4$, which reacts in the following way.

$$BrO^- + 2NH_4^+ \xrightarrow{\text{pH 8–9}} 4Br^- + N_2 + 2H_2O$$

Following this, the iodimetric method may be applied and chlorite alone determined.

2. *Using arsenic(III)*

The reaction of chlorite with arsenic(III) is very slow in alkaline medium but a considerable improvement is produced if osmic acid is used as catalyst[7].

$$ClO_2^- + 2AsO_3^{3-} \rightarrow 2AsO_4^{3-} + Cl^-$$

Osmic acid functions both as indicator and catalyst, producing a faint bluish-grey colour at the end-point. The absence of a suitable indicator prevents the reverse titration from being used, i.e. titration of arsenite with sodium chlorite.

Titrimetric determination of chlorite using arsenic(III)[7]

Procedure

To 25 mℓ of $NaClO_2$ solution add 1 g of $NaHCO_3$ and 0.4–0.5 mℓ of 1% osmic acid. Titrate very slowly with 0.05M As(III) allowing 30 s after each drop near the equivalence point. Titrate to the first faint bluish-grey colour as matched against a comparison solution.

Note For preparation of As(III) solutions see p. 9.

---

3. *Using ascorbic acid*

One variation of this is based on the reaction between ascorbic acid and hexacyanoferrate(III) with 2,6-dichlorophenol indophenol as indicator.

$$C_6H_8O_6 + 2[Fe(CN)_6]^{3-} \rightarrow C_6H_6O_6 + 2[Fe(CN)_6]^{4-} + 2H^+$$

For determination of chlorite an excess of hexacyanoferrate(II) is added and the resulting hexacyanoferrate(III) titrated with standard ascorbic acid[12].

$$ClO_2^- + 4[Fe(CN)_6]^{4-} + 4H^+ \rightarrow Cl^- + 4[Fe(CN)_6]^{3-} + 2H_2O$$

Another indirect method consists of adding excess iron(II) to chlorite and titrating the resulting iron(III) with standard ascorbic acid[13].

Spectroscopic methods

Prince[14] has described a method for determination of Cl^-, ClO^-, ClO_2^-, ClO_3^-, ClO_4^- and ClO_2 in composite mixtures. Part of the method involving the chlorite content depends on photometric determination of the iodine (as the tri-iodide ion) evolved by adding the sample to acidified KI. The method is partly empirical and includes titrimetric procedures in addition to the photometric one mentioned.

Hong and Rapson[15] utilize the absorbance of chlorite (and hypochloric acid) at 250 nm in the analysis of mixtures containing ClO_2^-, $HClO_2$, ClO_2, ClO_3^- and Cl_2. As in the previous method, titrimetric procedures also feature.

Triphenylmethane dyes have been applied to the extraction-spectrophotometric determination of chlorite as well as several other anions[16,17]. The principle is chlorite oxidation of excess KI in a strongly acid medium, and interaction of the resulting tri-iodide with the triphenylmethane dye (e.g. malachite green) cation to give an ion-pair. This is extracted into an organic solvent such as benzene and the absorbance measured. In the above instance the molar absorptivity of the complex is 162 000.

Electrochemical methods

1. Potentiometric methods

Reference has already been made to a redox method using arsenic(III) and catalysed by osmic acid[10]. A similar method but using a potentiometric end-point enables mixtures containing chlorite, hypochlorite, chlorate and chloride to be analysed[18]. The chlorite titration is made at pH 8–12 using a platinum indicator electrode and with OsO_4 present. Experimental details are given in the section on chlorate.

Standard NaClO may be used as titrant in the potentiometric determination[19] of chlorite.

$$2ClO_2^- + ClO^- + H^+ + Cl^- \rightarrow 2ClO_2 + 2Cl^- + OH^-$$

The electrodes are compact platinum and calomel; chlorite is determined in the presence of chlorate, chlorine dioxide and chloride.

Potentiometric determination[19] of chlorite in the presence of chlorine dioxide, chlorate and chloride

Reagents

Sodium hypochlorite, 0.04M.
Electrodes: SCE and compact Pt.

Procedure

Acidify the sample, which should be less than 0.01M in $NaClO_2$, with 0.1M HCl. Titrate with 0.04M NaClO while mixing the solution using a magnetic stirrer.

A potential jump from about 830 mV to about 1100 mV indicates the end-point. It is important that the chlorite and HCl concentrations do not exceed 0.01M and that the pH does not exceed 3.5.

---

2. *Polarographic methods*

Hartley and Adams[20] have reported a well-defined but irreversible wave for reduction of chlorite at pH values below 4.5. In the optimum range pH 4.2–4.5 the diffusion controlled wave height is proportional to chlorite concentration within the range 0.2–2.0 mM. When the pH is less than 4.2 the chlorite decomposes too rapidly for analysis.

The polarographic characteristics of chlorite (and chlorine dioxide) have been investigated at a rotating-disc graphite electrode. Chlorite may be determined at pH 7–9 and both species at pH 5.0–5.5 where their stability is adequate[21].

References

1. HARRISON, B.L. and ROSENBLATT, D.H., *J. Chromat.*, **13**, 271 (1964)
2. PESCHKE, W., *J. Chromat.*, **20**, 573 (1965)
3. SEILER, H. and SEILER, M., *Helv. chim. Acta*, **50**, 2477 (1967)
4. THIELEMANN, H., *Mikrochim. Acta*, 746 (1971)
5. SCHULEK, E. and ENDROI, P., *Analytica chim. Acta*, **5**, 245 (1951)
6. KOLTHOFF, I.M., SANDELL, E.B., MEEHAN, E.J. and BRUCKENSTEIN, S., *Quantitative Chemical Analysis*, 4th edn, Macmillan, London (1969)
7. BROWN, E.G., *Analytica chim. Acta*, **7**, 474 (1952)
8. TUMANOVA, T.A., PAKHOMOVA, L.N. and MAIOROVA, L.P., *Zav. Lab.*, **36**, 1036 (1970); *Analyt. Abstr.*, **21**, 183 (1971)
9. NORKUS, P.K., *Zh. analit. Khim.*, **19**, 518 (1964); *Analyt. Abstr.*, **12**, 3875 (1965)
10. NORKUS, P.K., *Zh. analit. Khim.*, **20**, 612 (1965); *Analyt. Abstr.*, **14**, 142 (1967)
11. HASHMI, M.H. and AYAZ, A.A., *Analyt. Chem.*, **35**, 2194 (1963)
12. ERDEY, L. and SVEHLA, G., *Z. analyt. Chem.*, **167**, 164 (1959); *Analyt. Abstr.*, **7**, 122 (1960)
13. ERDEY, L., BAZAS, I. and VIGH, K., *Periodica polytech.*, **3**, 1 (1959); *Analyt. Abstr.*, **6**, 4262 (1959)
14. PRINCE, L.A., *Analyt. Chem.*, **36**, 613 (1964)
15. HONG, C.C. and RAPSON, W.H., *Can. J. Chem.*, **46**, 2061 (1968); *Analyt. Abstr.*, **17**, 2096 (1970)
16. RAMANAUSKAS, E.I., BUNIKENE, L.V., SAPRAGONIENE, M.S., SHULYUNENE, A.K. and ZHILENAITE, M.V., *Zh. analit. Khim.*, **24**, 244 (1969); *Analyt. Abstr.*, **19**, 1022 (1970)
17. SAPRAGONIENE, M.S. and RAMANAUSKAS, E.I., *Nauch. Trudy vyssh. ucheb, zaved. lit. SSR, Khim. khim. Tekhnol.*, **13**, 15 (1971); *Analyt. Abstr.*, **24**, 131 (1973)
18. NORKUS, P.K. and STULG'ENE, S.P., *Zh. analit. Khim.*, **24**, 884 (1969); *Analyt. Abstr.*, **19**, 4862 (1970)
19. KEPINSKI, K.J. and BLASZKIEWICZ, B.G., *Talanta*, **13**, 357 (1966)
20. HARTLEY, A.M. and ADAMS, A.C., *J. electroanal. Chem.*, **6**, 460 (1963)
21. SCHWARZER, O. and LANDSBERG, R., *J. electroanal. Chem.*, **14**, 339 (1967)

Fluoride

The analysis of fluorine-containing materials has a vast literature, probably the biggest for any element. The reason for this is due partly to the widespread interest in the fluorine content of waters, air, biological materials, insecticides, fertilizers, plastics, etc., but also to the characteristic features of fluorine chemistry which make its analysis difficult, and which distinguish it even from the other halogens.

Most fluorides are insoluble to varying degrees; there are difficulties in dissolving fluorine-containing materials. Fluorine is the most electropositive and the most reactive of all the elements. Interference by other ions present in analytical procedures is considerable, either by precipitation as fluorides or by formation of strong metal-fluoride complexes. For this reason separation of fluoride prior to its determination is an important feature of its determination. Separation of fluoride by distillation is time-consuming, and some more recent methods of fluoride analysis have overcome the need for it.

An important potential source of error in fluoride analysis is caused by its interaction with glass. Evaporation of alkaline fluoride solutions from glass can lead to loss of fluoride and this operation should be avoided. The phenomenon was first reported by Reynolds and Hill[1] and confirmed by Rinck[2] who recommended the use of platinum or Jena glass rather than borosilicate glass, and control of pH to between 6 and 8. Specht[3] found that loss of fluoride was not due to evaporation but rather to the fluoride ions being adsorbed on the surface or bound on the lattice.

Extensive reviews [4–8] have appeared on the separation and determination of fluoride and any systematic survey would find these sources an excellent starting point. It is important to note the remark in Macdonald's review[5] that many statements in Elving, Horton and Willard[4] are wrongly attributed and should be checked against the originals.

The above references cover published work to about 1956. Determination of fluoride in the context of organic materials has been reviewed by Ma[9] and many microanalysis procedures are described by Dixon[10].

Fluorine in biological materials presents its own special difficulties, the amount of fluorine involved being usually less than 5 ppm on a dry weight basis. This problem has been discussed by Hall[11, 12]. Plants are more sensitive to fluoride than to most other air pollutants. For this reason the fluoride content of plants is extensively used for the diagnosis of pollution injury and as an air quality standard. Modern techniques for the determination of fluoride in vegetation have been reviewed[13].

With the introduction in 1958 of the reagent Alizarin fluorine blue[14] and the fluoride specific ion electrode[15] in 1966 several older methods for the determination of fluoride will have become obsolete and of academic interest only.

Separations

1. Distillation of fluorosilicic acid

Earlier separations of fluoride were based on the volatility of SiF_4. This became obsolete with the introduction by Willard and Winter[16] in 1933 and independently by Tananaev[17] of steam distillation of fluorosilicic acid (H_2SiF_6)* from perchloric or sulphuric acid at 135 °C and in the presence of glass beads.

* Evidence has been cited[18] to indicate that fluoride is not distilled as H_2SiF_6.

The method has since been investigated by a large number of workers, many of whom were concerned only with quantitative recovery of fluoride from particular materials.

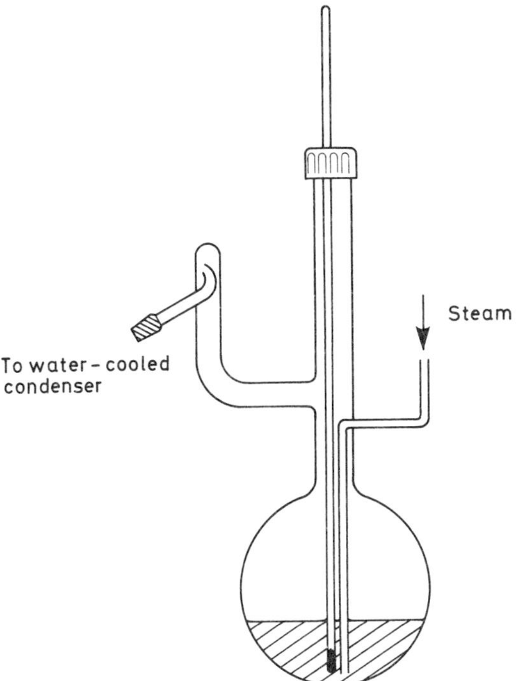

Figure 37 Simple steam-distillation apparatus for separation of fluoride

In its simplest form (*Figure 37*) the apparatus consists of a borosilicate 100–150-mℓ Claissen flask connected to a water-cooled condenser by means of a side tube. The neck carries a thermometer and a steam-inlet tube, both of which nearly reach to the bottom of the flask. This form of the apparatus is recommended for the determination of fluorine in foods[19].

Since its introduction, modifications both to the acid composition in the distillation vessel and to the design of the distillation apparatus have been described. Steam distillation from perchloric acid was found to eliminate interference from phosphate, sulphate and arsenate in the subsequent determination of fluoride. The need to prevent carry-over of sulphate is important where the fluoride is determined by thorium nitrate titration.

Phosphoric acid has been used as the distillation medium but here the possibility of it being carried over into the distillate is great.

Interference by chloride, bromide, and iodide may be prevented by addition of Ag_2SO_4 or $AgClO_4$ to render them involatile. No metallic elements are carried over.

The fact that silica, aluminium, and iron retard volatilization has been confirmed by several investigators. Smith and Parks[20] recommended distillation from sulphuric acid at 150°C, to reduce this effect, having found that if the temperature of distillation from perchloric acid was increased from 135 °C to 139 °C, decomposition products and perchloric acid were carried over into the distillate and interfered with the thorium nitrate titration.

Murty *et al.*[21] found that use of a sulphuric-phosphoric acid mixture was better when these substances were present, but were obliged to precipitate out traces of acid carried over, with silver or barium salts, before the thorium nitrate titration.

Shell and Craig[22], in carrying out the determination of silica and fluoride in fluorosilicates, employed zinc oxide fusion followed by precipitation from

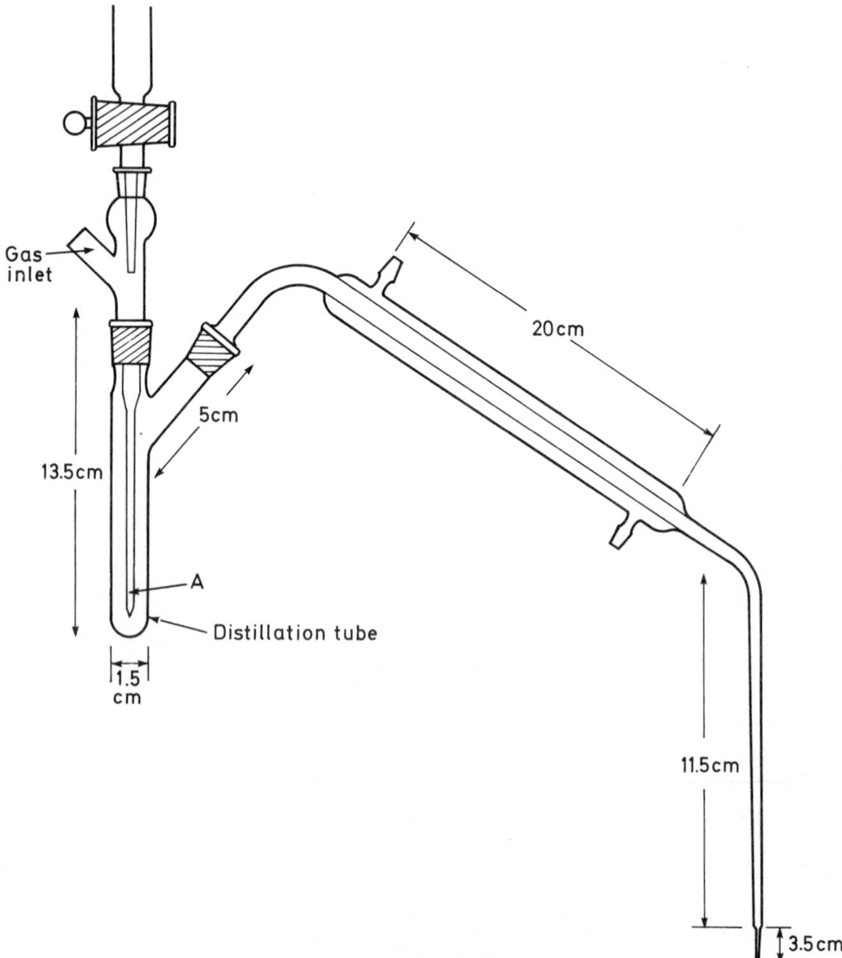

Figure 38 *Apparatus for micro-distillation of fluoride.*
A, *device to conduct nitrogen and water to within 0.5 to 1.0 cm of bottom of distillation tube of still. Condenser core is 8 mm o.d.; delivery tube ends in 5mm o.d. and 1 mm i.d.; capillary tubing is ground to cone-shape at its end.*
(After Singer and Armstrong[29])

an ammoniacal zinc oxide solution. The same investigation revealed an anomalous effect in the presence of boric acid. Low recoveries of fluoride were noted and this was attributed to a non-ionized fluoboric acid or its salt being distilled over. Evaporation of the distillate followed by fusion gave a quantitative recovery of fluoride.

Grimaldi, Ingram and Cuttitta[23] were able to eliminate the effects of silicon and aluminium in the determination of fluoride by fusion with Na_2CO_3/ZnO followed by leaching, filtration, and distillation from phosphoric-perchloric acid mixtures.

The possibility of incomplete recovery of fluoride due to adverse effects of fluoride-complexing metal ions in the original material is, without doubt, a potential source of error. A related source of error arises from interaction of fluoride with the glassware. Peck and Smith[24] confirmed the findings of earlier investigators that some adsorption of fluoride on the glassware of the still takes place. It is largely removed when the flask is cleaned with sodium carbonate solution. Haff, Butler, and Bisso[25] found that such losses gave only a 98% recovery of fluoride using borosilicate glass and distilling from H_2SO_4.

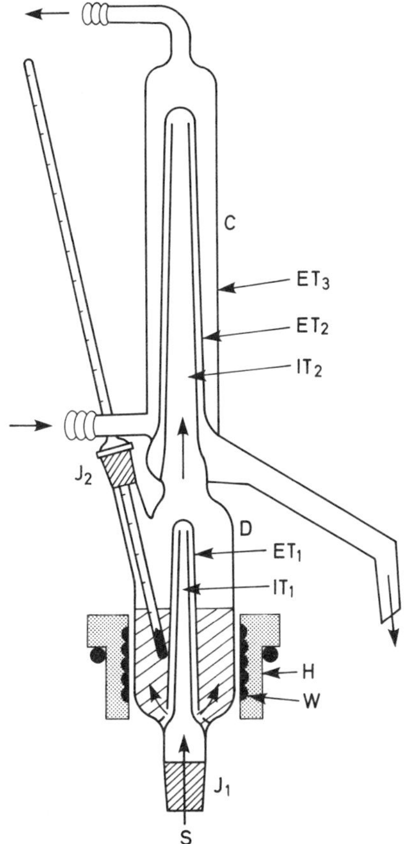

Figure 39 *Upper section of steam-distillation apparatus for fluoride. The original should be consulted for exact dimensions.* (After Ma and Gwirtsman[31]).

Distillation as a method of separating fluoride has several drawbacks, some of which can be minimized or even eliminated. The time involved in the operation makes it impossible to deal with large numbers of samples on a routine basis although automatic forms have been described[26–28].

When micro or sub-micro amounts of fluoride need to be determined the large volume of aqueous distillate required for quantitative recovery of the fluoride results in a very low concentration of fluoride. This makes the determination difficult for evaporation to low volume can result in loss of fluoride. A convenient method for use in such cases has been described by Singer and Armstrong[29]. Nitrogen is used to sweep the fluoride from the microstill into the receiver, and the method is applicable in the range 0–3.0 μg fluoride. An improved distillation flask for use in this method and which minimizes carry-over of phosphate and sulphate, has been developed by Wade and Yamamura[30]. They found that when used in conjunction with the Alizarin fluorine blue method for determination of fluoride, only borate and silicate interfered seriously out of forty-two diverse ions tested in 500:1 molar ratio to fluoride.

The apparatus is shown in *Figure 38*. A form of the distillation procedure widely recommended in the important area of organic microanalysis is that by Ma and Gwirtsman[31,32]. This is shown in *Figure 39*.

Separation of fluoride by steam distillation

The procedure given has been adapted from Ma and Gwirtsman.

Apparatus

The upper section comprises the distillation flask and condenser. Its lower ground glass joint J_1 fits into the lower section, a steam generator consisting of a 1 ℓ flat-bottomed borosilicate flask. The latter is provided with a safety tube and side arm which serves as outlet and which is closed by a screw clip.

Steam S travels through two concentric tubes IT_1 and ET_1, and reaches the distilling flask, D, through the two openings. The vapours enter the condenser, C, which consists of three concentric tubes: in IT_2 and ET_2 the vapours are condensed, and in ET_3 the cooling water circulates. The ground glass joint, J_2, serves as the opening for the introduction of the sodium fluoride solution as well as the seat of a thermometer (150 °C) during distillation. H is an additional heating system consisting of nickel wire, W (resistance 2.120 $\Omega\,ft^{-1}$), 600 cm long. The actual length of the resistance spiral is 420 cm, the rest being used for the terminals (3 × 30 cm bent and twisted at each end). A glass cylinder, 48 mm in diameter, is covered with aluminium foil on which a sheet of asbestos is affixed. The nichrome wire is then wound on the cylinder and covered with a layer of insulating cement. The heating jacket is controlled by means of a Powerstat; the steam generator itself is heated by means of a 500-W hot plate.

Procedure

The sample (containing 0.1–0.5 mg F^-) is decomposed using one of the standard methods, for example a Parr microbomb.

The resulting solution contained in a beaker is transferred quantitatively into the distilling apparatus through a funnel with ground joint fitted to opening J_2. The beaker is then rinsed with 20 mℓ of 70 to 72 % perchloric acid, which is also transferred to the still. One mℓ of 25 % aqueous solution of silver perchlorate solution and 8–10 glass beads are then added, the thermometer is inserted, and the distillation is ready to start.

The hot plate is turned to position 'high' and the Powerstat dial set to deliver 1.5 A at approximately 45 V, and the distillation temperature is maintained at $135° \pm 2$ °C during the entire operation. In about 45 min 250 mℓ of distillate will have collected in the polythene container.

In order to stop the steam distillation, the Powerstat is turned off, and when a drop in temperature is noticeable, the outlet tube of the steam generator is opened and the hot plate switched off.

The distillation apparatus is cleaned by connecting the base of the distillation flask, D, to a water aspirator through a glass tube with ground joint to fit J_1. At the same time the outlet tube of the condenser is fitted with a rubber tube dipping into fluorine-free water. The washing liquid is thus sucked through the entire apparatus.

---

2. *Microdiffusion*

Diffusion as a means of separating fluoride is important in the determination of fluorine in biological materials. The fluoride ions are liberated as HF by mineral acids and absorbed in alkali solutions. The subsequent determination of fluoride is generally by a spectrophotometric method. Usually the amount of fluoride involved is less than 10 µg. A special advantage of diffusion is avoidance of high temperatures. Introduced by Singer and Armstrong[33] in 1954, the operation may be carried out in several ways. Wharton[34] used a polypropylene Conway diffusion unit as shown in *Figure 40*.

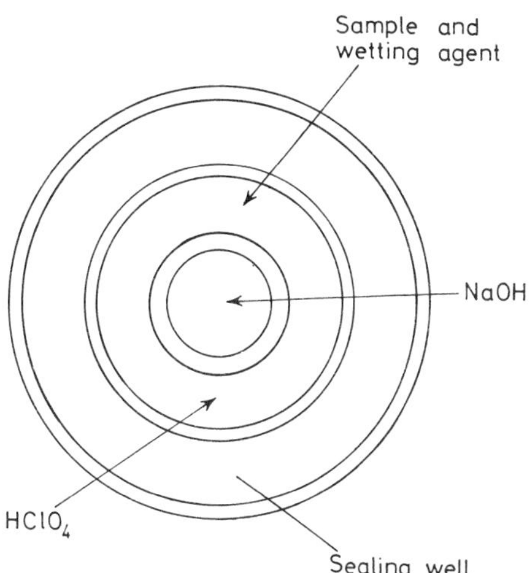

Figure 40 Schematic diagram of microdiffusion cell showing relative locations of materials for fluoride diffusion. (After Wharton[34])

Similar cells were used by Greenland[35] and Frere[36]. Marshall and Wood[37] in the determination of fluoride in air used disposable polystyrene Petri dishes with loose fitting lids which had an alkaline coating deposited on the underside of the lid. In contrast to other investigators they did not find it necessary to seal the lids.

The original work by Singer and Armstrong made use of polythene bottles and this technique has also been advocated by Hall[11, 38–40] who finds it superior to Conway-type diffusion techniques.

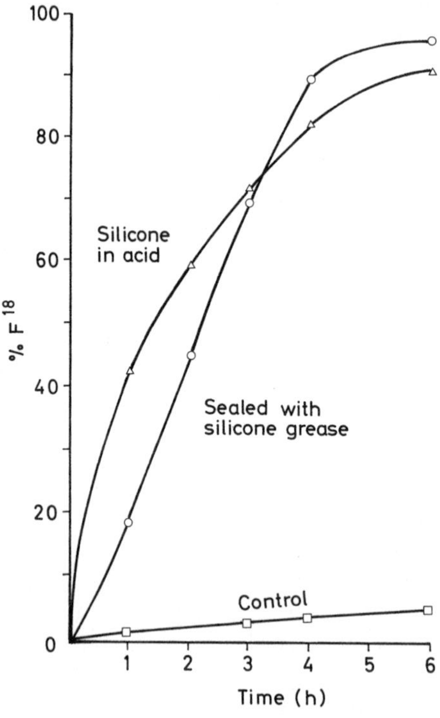

Figure 41 *Room temperature diffusion of radioactive fluorine in presence and absence of a silicone. Control is untreated with silicone and without silicone sealing.* (After Taves[42])

The relatively long time involved in this method of separation, which might be as long as 24 h, is a disadvantage though use of multicell trays[41] combined with overnight diffusion can be used to reduce this.

More recent work has centred on the influence of silicones on the diffusion process. Taves[42, 43] finds that diffusion of fluoride is greatly accelerated in the presence of silicone grease used as sealant in microdiffusion dishes. The results are shown in *Figure 41*.

In the presence of the simplest silicone hexamethyldisiloxane, fluoride is separated from samples in 1 h at room temperature, less than a tenth of the time taken by previous diffusion methods. Taves assumes that trimethylfluorosilane is formed by the reactions

$$HF + (CH_3)_3SiOSi(CH_3)_3 \rightarrow (CH_3)_3SiF + (CH_3)_3SiOH$$

$$HF + (CH_3)_3SiOH \rightarrow (CH_3)_3SiF + H_2O$$

Sulphate and phosphate do not diffuse under these conditions.

An investigation by Sara and Wanninen[44] has combined microdiffusion using hexamethyldisiloxane with determination using the fluoride electrode. Application is made to analysis of toothpastes. In order to ascertain the minimum time required for complete diffusion, Hanocq[45] has carried out a systematic investigation to establish which factors affect the rate. This enables the time required for complete diffusion at a given temperature to be calculated once the cell has been standardized.

Separation of fluoride by microdiffusion

The method described in outline, is by Hall and is recommended by the Society for Analytical Chemistry[46] for the analysis of feeding stuffs.

Hydrofluoric acid is absorbed on to an impregnated filter paper supported in the plastic stopper of a 20 mℓ polythene bottle. The arrangement is shown in *Figure 42*.

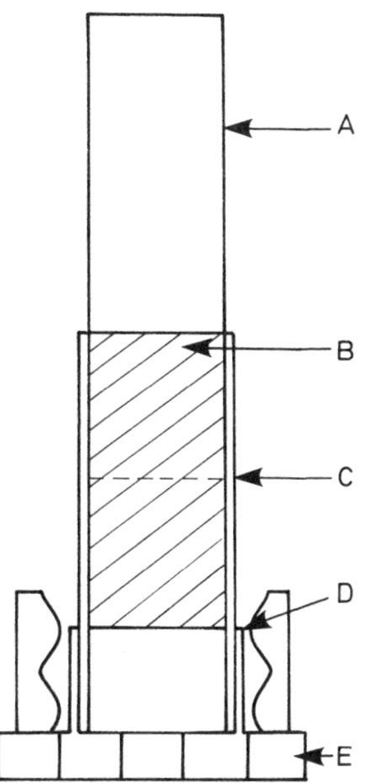

Figure 42 *Sectional diagram of polythene-cap assembly showing filter paper in position.* A, *cylinder of filter paper;* B, *glass rod;* C, *polythene tubing;* D, *well of cap;* E, *bottle cap.* (After Hall[38])

M

Reagents

NaOH, 0.5M, containing 50 %v/v propylene glycol.

Silver sulphate in $HClO_4$:

Approximately 0.25M Ag_2SO_4 in 70 % w/v $HClO_4$: Mix 4 g of finely powdered Ag_2SO_4 with 2 ml of water and 23 ml of 72 % $HClO_4$ in a 250 mℓ Erlenmeyer flask, and heat to about 80°C to dissolve the Ag_2SO_4. Add a further 75 mℓ of 72 % $HClO_4$, and cool.

Procedure [38, 39, 11]

1 mℓ of the solution to be analysed is placed by pipette into the diffusion bottle, and 1 drop of 0.5M NaOH (containg 50 % v/v propylene glycol) placed on the exposed section of the filter paper. Again using a pipette, 2 mℓ of Ag_2SO_4 solution in 70 % w/v $HClO_4$ is immediately added, care being taken to avoid the inside of the bottle neck. The inside of the neck is wiped with a filter paper to ensure that it is absolutely free from $HClO_4$.

The plastic cap containing the treated filter paper is immediately placed into the bottle and tightened. It is then sealed to the neck with carnauba wax in the following way. The bottle is held horizontally with the neck over a container of hot wax and the wax applied from a dropping pipette.

The volume of liquid in the diffusion bottle should not exceed 3 mℓ. The bottle is placed in an oven at 60 °C for 24 h. At the end of this period the bottle is opened, the paper removed using forceps, and its fluoride content determined.

Notes

1. Hall used Alizarin fluorine blue for the spectrophotometric determination of fluoride. If its concentration was above 0.2 ppm the absorbance was measured directly at 615 nm. At lower levels and for precise measurements, extraction into isobutyl alcohol containing an amine was preferred.
2. The propylene glycol used in the impregnation of the filter papers serves to delay drying out.

---

3. Pyrohydrolysis

In the absence of organic matter and of particular relevance to rocks and other refractory materials, pyrohydrolysis is an excellent method of separating fluoride. It involves heating the material with superheated steam and collecting the HF formed.

The reaction may be represented by the equation

$$MF_{2n} + nH_2O\ (gas) \rightleftharpoons MO_n + 2nHF\ (gas)$$

The standard entropy of 2 mol of HF is approximately twice that of 1 mol of steam, so that the forward reaction has a positive standard entropy.

The concept of pyrohydrolysis is not new, the essential technique having been reported by Fremy in 1856. Recent interest is derived from a systematic investigation by Warf, Cline and Tevebaugh[47] who introduced the word 'pyrohydrolysis'. They found that heavier fluorides underwent rapid hydrolysis at 1000 °C. Lighter metal fluorides were slower, but if mixed with an accelerator of U_3O_8, the reaction was complete within a short time.

A modification introduced by Powell and Menis[48] was aimed at reducing the excessive dilution of released fluoride by the condensate which occurs in pyrohydrolysis. Instead of superheated steam moist oxygen was used and the process named 'pyrolysis'. Milligram quantities of fluoride were separated in 20 min or less. Pyrohydrolysis has been used in the analysis of simple and complex fluorides including radioactive materials, rocks, ores, minerals, slags, glass, catalysts, etc. It is more rapid than distillation and for this reason has been recently advocated by Clements, Sergeant and Webb[49] as an alternative to distillation in the routine analysis of rocks and minerals. The apparatus is shown in *Figure 43*.

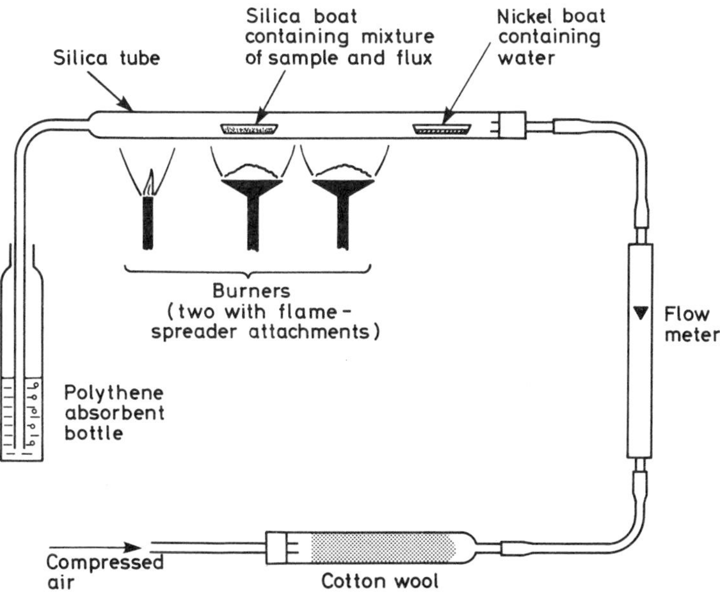

Figure 43 *Apparatus for pyrohydrolytic separation of fluoride prior to its determination.* (After Clements, Sergeant and Webb[49])

The recovered fluoride is determined either using the spectrophotometric alizarin fluorine blue method or by fluoride specific-ion electrode. Fluoride at levels down to 50 ppm may be determined satisfactorily.

Several features of the pyrohydrolysis method may be altered. The furnace can be of platinum, fused silica, or nickel and the carrier gas superheated steam or oxygen. The temperature used, time, nature of the accelerator and end procedure are open to variation.

Pyrohydrolysis of microgram amounts of fluoride present special problems. Low recoveries due to mechanical loss of fluoride may result[50]. This has prompted Davies and Foreman[51] to investigate the optimum conditions for microgram separation using factorial design to indicate and define the important variables. At 2–20 μg fluoride level, fluoride results showed a small negative bias. The end-procedure in this study utilized alizarin fluorine blue.

4. Chromatographic methods including ion-exchange

Ion-exchange and other chromatographic methods may be used to separate both interfering cations and anions before the determination of fluoride. If, for example, the final determination is to be made using alizarin fluorine blue, ions that compete with lanthanum for the alizarin fluorine blue and ions that themselves form complexes with fluoride, e.g. Pb^{2+}, Zn^{2+}, Al^{3+}, Fe^{3+}, etc., have to be removed. This may be done using cation-exchange. Jeffery and Williams[52] use such a method in analysis of deposit-gauge samples for fluoride.

In microanalysis, if the initial decomposition has involved alkali fusion, excess of alkali may be removed by cation-exchange[53].

Needless to say, where metals are involved, they must be in cationic form.

Anion resins enable separation of fluoride from interfering anions particularly phosphate and sulphate which often interfere in the determination of fluoride. Separation of phosphate is particularly important in biological materials and this has been discussed in connection with other methods of separation.

With anions, separation of fluoride may be complicated by the presence of fluoride as complex anions, e.g. $ZrF_6{}^{2-}$, $AlF_6{}^{3-}$, $SiF_6{}^{2-}$, etc., which will not elute with the simple uncomplexed fluoride. Zipkin, Armstrong, and Singer[54] have described the separation of fluoride (25 µg) and phosphate (12.5 mg P) on a Dowex-1 resin using 0.5M NaOH as eluant.

Usually, interfering cations and anions are both present and their removal by separate ion-exchange treatment would increase manipulative errors as well as increase the time required. Newman[55] was able to remove both in one operation by complexing cations with EDTA to give stable negatively charged complexes which are strongly held on a basic resin while fluorides, which are only weakly adsorbed, are quantitatively eluted. The method was successfully applied to phosphate rock with a titrimetric thorium nitrate end procedure for fluoride. It is interesting to see that in a recent paper Edmond[56], noting that fluoride may be determined by specific-ion electrode in strong phosphoric acid, and even in the presence[57] of aluminium, has developed a direct determination of fluoride in phosphate rock without prior separations.

In an investigation of more rapid methods of determination of fluoride in potable water Kelso, Matthews and Kramer[58] use an ion-exchange procedure based on formation of a beryllium fluoride complex $BeF_4{}^{2-}$.

Separation of fluoride and sulphate may be carried out by ion-exchange[59] as described in the textbook on analytical applications of ion-exchange by Inczédy[60]. Funasaka *et al.*[61] have developed an ion-exchange method for separating fluoride, phosphate, sulphate, etc.

Other forms of chromatography have been used to separate fluoride. Zipkin, Armstrong and Singer[54] find that fluoride and phosphate may be easily separated quantitatively by paper chromatography. Halide ions (including fluoride) can be separated by thin layer chromatography on cellulose[62] or silica gel[63]. In paper chromatography and TLC of halides, R_f values generally increase with atomic weight. With conventional ion-exchange material the order for chloride, bromide and iodide is usually reversed.

Gas chromatography has been used for isolating fluoride. Fresen, Cox, and Witter[64] were able to determine 0.01–10 µg mℓ$^{-1}$ of fluoride in urine, serum and other biological materials by selectively extracting with chlorotrimethylsilane in benzene. Fluoride reacts to produce fluorotrimethylsilane which remains in the benzene layer. Direct injection of this (1–3 μℓ) into a stainless steel GLC column containing 20% silicone oil DC 200/50 in Chromosorb P operated at 75° C with nitrogen as carrier gas and flame ionization detector gives a peak corresponding to the fluorotrimethylsilane concentration. Recently this principle has been adapted to determination of total and soluble fluoride in toothpaste[65].

5. Co-precipitation

Shapiro and Kolesnikova[66] have separated fluoride on a $Mg(OH)_2$ suspension. The latter was dissolved in dilute HNO_3 and the fluoride determined photometrically.

Determination

Gravimetric methods

1. Precipitation as calcium fluoride

Gravimetric determination of fluoride as calcium fluoride is over 150 years old. Its drawbacks, which are common to other methods based on precipitation of metal fluorides, include a tendency for the precipitate to be gelatinous, and interference from other ions. Its history and titrimetric variations are described in earlier reviews[4–6]. It is doubtful whether the method finds present day use.

2. Precipitation as lead chlorofluoride

Precipitation of lead chlorofluoride as a means of fluoride determination is one of the earlier fluoride methods. Despite its rather high solubility in water (325 mg ℓ$^{-1}$ at 18 °C) the fact that it may be precipitated in a granular form over a wide range of conditions is advantageous, and it has been used extensively for macro and semi-micro amounts of fluoride.

The determination may be finished gravimetrically or by various titrimetric variations which include a Volhard determination of the precipitated chloride content or the excess chloride, and a corresponding compleximetric determination of lead. Arsenate, phosphate, sulphate and sulphide interfere, as do small amounts of iron and aluminium. There is no interference from arsenite, small amounts of borate and ammonium ions, and fairly large amounts of acetate, perchlorate, nitrate, bromide, iodide, sodium and potassium.

Bournique and Dahmer[67] have carried out a detailed study of the precipitation of lead chlorofluoride and confirm the complexity of the process, which may produce high or low results according to the procedure used. They find that by working in a lower pH range using sodium formate or sodium chloroacetate as buffering agents, good results are possible if conditions are controlled. The optimum pH appears to be 2.0 with low results at lower pH values. Using a gravimetric procedure based on Hoffman and Lundell's original work[68] at pH 4.6 and on which many later versions of the method were based, this investigation found that results could be high by several parts per hundred.

3. Precipitation as lithium fluoride

Precipitation of fluoride as lithium fluoride introduced by Caley and Kahle[69] offers advantages in the determination fluoride in solutions containing 20–200 mg F^-. Owing to incomplete precipitation in aqueous solution, the addition of some miscible organic solvent is necessary. Ethanol is suitable in a minimum concentration of 50% v/v but higher concentrations should be avoided to prevent possible interferences and deterioration in the quality of the precipitate. For lower concentrations of fluoride, a corresponding restriction in the volume of solution is recommended to avoid errors arising from solubility of the precipitate in 50% ethanol.

Determination of fluoride as lithium fluoride[69]

Reagent

Lithium chloride: 30 g ℓ$^{-1}$ in 95% EtOH.

Procedure

Adjust the volume of neutral fluoride solution containing 20–200 mg F^- to 15–40 mℓ according to its estimated F^- content. Heat to 70 °C and add slowly with stirring an equal volume of LiCl solution. Allow to stand until cool and clear. Filter using a medium porosity filter crucible and wash with 50% ethanol saturated with LiF until the filtrate gives a negative reaction for chloride. Wash with 5 mℓ 95% ethanol and dry the crucible for 1 h at 110 °C.

Notes

1. Polyethylene beakers were found to be unsatisfactory for accurate determination of fluoride due to a tendency for the precipitate to adhere to the walls and difficulty in visually detecting residual particles of the precipitate. Borosilicate glass was found to give no significant errors.
2. Sulphate interference, a serious problem in other gravimetric methods for fluoride is not serious for small quantities of both sulphate and fluoride but for larger amounts of fluoride the error becomes more serious, probably due to co-precipitation of Na_2SO_4 or Li_2SO_4 rather than precipitation of these substances in the alcoholic medium. A correction factor could, if necessary, be used for presence of sulphate.
3. No other interferences were investigated but they should be less significant than for calcium fluoride or lead chlorofluoride precipitation in view of the greater solubility of lithium salts.

---

4. Other gravimetric methods

Gravimetric determination of fluoride as LaF_3 has been described by Popov and Knudson[70] and as triphenyltin fluoride by Ballczo and Schiffner[71]. In the latter, a solution of triphenyltin chloride is used as precipitant and the operation carried out at pH 4–9. An advantage is that phosphate, borate, iron, aluminium and zirconium do not interfere. The accuracy on 1–50 mg F^- in synthetic samples and minerals was within ±0.5 per cent.

Titrimetric methods

1. Titration with thorium nitrate

In very dilute solution, thorium(IV) reacts with fluoride ions to form the colourless $(ThF_6)^{2-}$ complex ion by a reaction which may be represented as

$$Th(NO_3)_4 + 6F^- \rightarrow (ThF_6)^{2-} + 4NO_3^-$$

The reaction is non-stoichiometric, with other less stable fluoride complex ions being formed at the same time. If the thorium(IV) solution is added to fluoride in the presence of alizarin red S (sodium alizarin sulphonate) a pink lake is formed between the latter and thorium(IV) ions when all free fluoride ions have been converted to $(ThF_6)^{2-}$. The appearance of the pink colour is by no means distinct or sudden but varies with several factors which include the volume of solution, amount of indicator, pH, etc. The indicator alizarin red S is itself an acid–base indicator (pH 3.7 yellow, pH 5.2 violet) so that pH control would be necessary in such a titration. Direct titration of fluoride with thorium(IV) using alizarin red S is wholly inadequate for reasonably accurate determination of fluoride unless rigid control of conditions is maintained. The back titration of Dahle, Bonnar and Wichmann[72,5] enables 25–350 μg F^- to be determined with an accuracy of ±1 μg though experience would be required to attain this.

If more fluoride is present (~400 μg) a precipitate of thorium fluoride forms and new difficulties appear. The indicator is now adsorbed on the precipitate giving a pink lake which obscures the end-point. A further complication is competition between the indicator and titrant for the low fluoride ion concentration in the vicinity of the end-point.

Interferences by extraneous ions, as in so many fluoride methods, is heavy, consisting of ions which complex with, or precipitate thorium(IV) or fluoride. Thus Ba(II), Fe(II), Al(III), Be(II), Zr(IV), P(V), As(V), As(III), sulphate, and sulphite have to be absent.

Despite inherent defects, the thorium(IV) titration in its countless variations has been the mainstay of fluoride determination, and has found application to a wide range of fluoride-containing materials. Perhaps its most interesting application was to fluoride analysis of the Piltdown skull[73] where it contributed in solving an archaeological problem of long standing. It is a recommended method for determination of fluoride in foods[74].

More recently interest in the method has been revived by an investigation by Selig[75] who advocates methylthymol blue as indicator and a glycine-perchlorate buffer at pH 3.35. A considerable improvement in end-point is obtained and the buffer ensures stoichiometry over the range 1–10 mg F^-. This method has been the subject of a collaborative investigation by the Analytical Methods Committee of the Society for Analytical Chemistry[76], and a modified form recommended for titration of milligram quantities of fluoride.

A conductimetric end-point has been described[77] in the titration of fluoride with Th(IV). Application to rock analysis was made after Willard and Winter distillation.

Titrimetric determination[75] of fluoride with thorium nitrate

Reagents

Buffer solution:

Dissolve 6.7 g of glycine and 11 g $NaClO_4$ in water, add 11 mℓ of M $HClO_4$ and make the volume up to 100 mℓ.

Thorium nitrate 0.02 M:

Dissolve 11.044 g of thorium nitrate tetrahydrate in 0.001M HNO_3, and make up to 1ℓ with 0.001M HNO_3.

Methylthymol blue indicator: 0.2% w/v aq.

Procedure

The sample may contain up to 10 mg fluoride in a volume no larger than 15 mℓ. Acidify with M $HClO_4$ to pH 3.35 ± 0.10 and add 2 mℓ buffer. Add three drops of indicator and titrate with thorium nitrate to a deep blue colour. Standardize the thorium nitrate against a known fluoride solution.

Notes

1. Cations reacting with methylthymol blue interfere. These would include Cu(II), Mg, Zn, Cd, Hg(II), Pb(II), Mn(II), Fe(II), Co(II) and Ni.
2. Sulphate and phosphate interfere. Phosphate may be removed[78] using Ag_2O. Sulphide may be removed by precipitation with benzidine.

---

2. Compleximetric titration

Application of compleximetric procedures is a natural development after initial precipitation of metal fluorides. This can be done in several ways. Belcher and Clark[79] precipitate fluoride with excess standard $CaCl_2$ and, after allowing the precipitate to stand overnight, titrate the excess Ca^{++} ions with standard EDTA, using Eriochrome Black T as indicator. Non-interference by a ten-fold excess of sulphate and phosphate is an advantage, with the long time involved a distinct disadvantage. Precipitation of fluoride as PbClF as a preliminary to an EDTA titration suffers the same drawback, and in addition, a variation in the lead: fluorine ratio, unless strict control is kept on the conditions of precipitation.

Leonard[80] bases a method for the determination of 2–20 mg F^- on initial precipitation of PbClF with excess of standard lead nitrate solution. After filtering off and washing the precipitate the excess of precipitant is titrated with EDTA. Sixteen concurrent determinations carried out on 30–45 mg samples of pure NaF gave a mean recovery of 100.0 per cent with a standard deviation of 0.19 per cent. Interference is caused by ions which precipitate or complex with lead or fluoride, e.g. sulphate and phosphate, which are titrated almost quantitatively as fluoride.

Yamamura, Kussy, and Rein[81] titrate fluoride in inorganic samples containing high levels of metal ions as well as nitrate, chloride, and perchlorate. After preliminary pyrolysis, cerous fluoride is precipitated at pH 1.75 with a measured excess of cerium(III) and the excess back-titrated with EDTA using arsenazo as indicator. Cerium(III) forms a highly insoluble fluoride with a reported value of 1×10^{-15} for the solubility product. Large amounts of chloride and perchlorate do not interfere, neither do smaller amounts of borate and silicate. Sulphate and phosphate interfere seriously but phosphate does not distil in the pyrolysis.

Precipitation of fluoride as samarium fluoride followed by back-titration of excess samarium with EDTA has been described by Combs and Grove[82]. Methylthymol blue was used as indicator for amounts of fluoride from 1 to 4 mg. Phosphate and sulphate interfere by complexing with samarium but most simple anions do not.

Compleximetric titration of fluoride[80]

Procedure

To 2–20 mg F^- in 20 mℓ water add 8.0 mℓ of 0.2M NaCl and 13 mℓ of 95% ethanol. Heat almost to boiling, and add from a burette 25.00 mℓ of standard 0.05M $Pb(NO_3)_2$, dropwise at first, then more rapidly as the precipitate becomes more established. Swirl the solution constantly. Maintain the mixture just at the boiling-point for 1 min to coagulate the precipitate, cool to room temperature, filter, and wash the residue with four 15-mℓ portions of 20% v/v ethanol in aqueous 0.02M NaCl. Titrate the filtrate and washings with standard 0.05M EDTA with xylenol orange as indicator and solid hexamine to bring the pH to approximately 6.

1 mℓ of 0.0500M $Pb(NO_3)_2 \equiv$ 2.10 mg NaF

---

3. *Other titrimetric methods*

Tetraphenylantimony sulphate may be used[83] as an extractant titrant for fluoride. The fluoride is extracted into chloroform as the ion-pair $(C_6H_5)_4SbF$, the residual fluoride ions in the aqueous phase being monitored by a fluoride-sensitive electrode. Phosphate, arsenic(III), arsenic(V), and sulphate do not interfere but sulphite and nitrite must be removed. Curran and Fletcher[84] titrate F^- with electrochemically generated La^{+++} ions. Lanthanum as well as cerium and yttrium have been used by Harzdorf[85] to titrate fluoride to a photometric end-point with 4-(2-pyridylazo)-resorcinol (PAR) as indicator. For 0.1–9 mg F^- the standard deviation is quoted as ± 5 µg. Cerium (III) appears to be as good as lanthanum with yttrium less effective.

The very stable AlF_6^{3-} complex ion has been utilized in fluoride analysis, with aluminium chloride or nitrate being used as titrant. A recent version of the method[86] employs aluminium nitrate with chrome azure S as indicator. The titration, which is carried out at pH 6 and in 50% methanol is made after Willard and Winter distillation. On amounts of fluoride from 1.5 to 120 mg the standard deviation is given as 0.007–0.034 mg.

Spectrophotometric methods

Earlier work (up to 1955) on the determination of fluoride by spectrophotometric methods has been reviewed by Megregian[87].

With the exception of the Alizarin fluorine blue method which is based on a 1:1:1 ternary complex involving the fluoride ion, spectrophotometric methods are indirect procedures based on the ability of the fluoride ion to abstract cations (Zr^{3+}, Al^{3+}, etc.) from strongly absorbing complexes with the liberation of the free dyestuff.

In general the indirect methods suffer from lack of specificity.

1. Alizarin fluorine blue

In aqueous solution at about pH 5 alizarin fluorine blue (alizarin complexan: 1,2-dihydroxyanthraquinon-3-ylmethylamine-NN-diacetic acid; 3-amino-

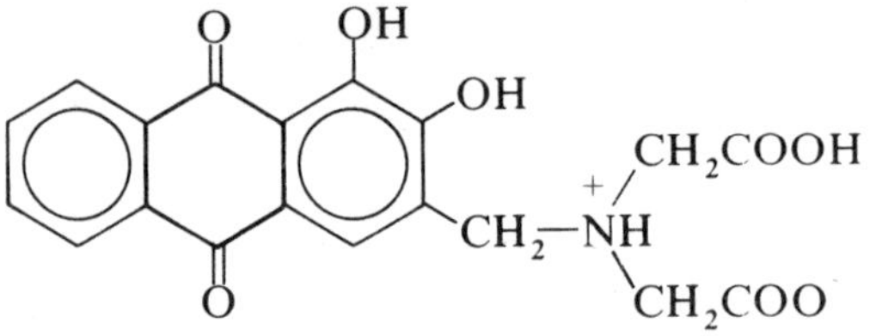

Structure 46 3-aminoalizarin-N,N-diacetic acid (*alizarin fluorine blue*)

alizarin-N, N-diacetic acid) (*Structure 46*) reacts with cerium, lanthanum or praseodymium forming red-mauve complexes of the form shown in *Structure 47*.

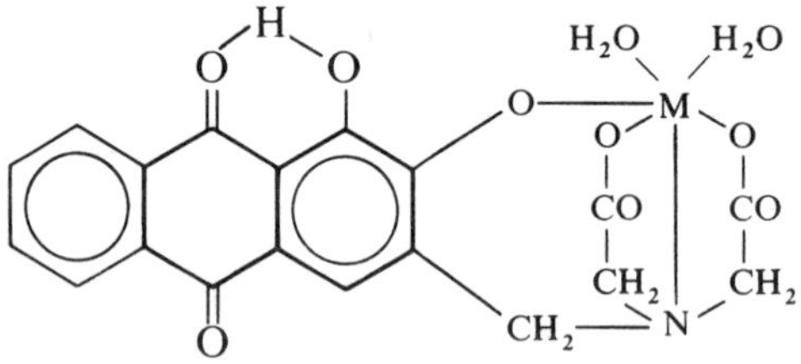

M = Ce, La or Pr

Structure 47 Red–mauve complex with alizarin fluorine blue

Entry of the fluoride ion into the co-ordination sphere by displacement of one of the water molecules results in deprotonation of the 1-hydroxy group in the alizarin molecule, producing a characteristic purple-blue colour. The colour producing mechanism suggested[88] is indicated in *Structure 48*.

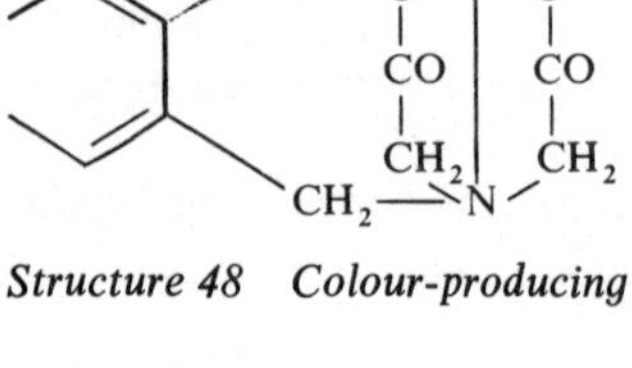

Structure 48 Colour-producing mechanism of alizarin fluorine blue

Other workers have investigated the colour mechanism, including Anfält and Jagner[89] who use photometric and potentiostatic techniques. The reaction, first introduced by Belcher, Leonard, and West[90] quickly established itself as a highly selective and sensitive method for trace determination of fluoride.

Usually, a solution of the reagent is added to the fluoride solution, followed by the buffer, and finally the lanthanum solution, generally as the nitrate. The lanthanum should not be added before the alizarin fluorine blue reagent. After being allowed to stand for a period of time, the absorbance is measured at 625 nm.

Of the lanthanides, the sensitivity was found to be in the order La > Ce > Pr. Further enhancement of the sensitivity was found [91,92] if carried out in an acetone–water medium with the sensitivity increasing up to an acetone concentration of 20% v/v. Several features of the method including the reaction pH, type of buffer and concentration of reactants, have been varied and their effects on the sensitivity and precision of the method noted. For example Hall[39] showed that by replacing the original acetate buffer with succinate, both the sensitivity and speed of the reaction with fluoride was increased.

Recently the Analytical Methods Committee of the Society for Analytical Chemistry[93] has published a report based on a collaborative investigation of the alizarin fluorine blue method for up to 40 μg F^-. The procedure recommended by this report will be given later.

Another valuable study which includes the method is a comparative assessment of five spectrophotometric procedures for the determination of fluoride in water by Crosby, Dennis and Stephens[94]. The conclusion drawn from this work is that the alizarin fluorine blue method has many advantages over the bleaching methods, though the pF electrode, which was evaluated at the same time, was found to surpass all the colorimetric methods with regard to speed, accuracy, and convenience for water analysis.

An important feature of the method is its extension into the sub-micro range, an area of particular significance to biological work. The general approach here is separation of fluoride by microdiffusion followed by its spectrophotometric determination. Hall[11,12,39] has discussed trace fluoride determination in a series of papers. Extraction of the lanthanum chelate into isobutanol containing hydroxylamine hydrochloride was found best for 0.1–1.0 μg F^- in a 2 mℓ sample, with recoveries of over 95 per cent. The procedure, however, is rather tedious, and a simpler one claimed to give about twice the sensitivity for 0.1–1.0 μg F^- in a 4 mℓ sample has been proposed[95].

On the more fundamental aspects of the method, an improved synthesis of the reagent alizarin fluorine blue has been described[96], and the dissociation constants of the reagent have been determined[97], the values being

$$k_1 = 1.28 \pm 0.30 \times 10^{-5}$$

$$k_2 = 2.82 \pm 0.24 \times 10^{-8}$$

$$k_3 = 3.72 \pm 0.19 \times 10^{-11}$$

$$k_4 = 6.39 \pm 0.12 \times 10^{-12}$$

all at an ionic strength of 0.1.

Application of the reagent is widespread and includes, in addition to those already mentioned, atmospheric fluorides[98–100], sea water (automatic)[101,102], urine (automatic)[103], phosphate rock[104], silicate rock[105] and organic compounds[106].

Sulphonated alizarin fluorine blue appears to have several advantages over the parent compound itself. Its solubility (as the potassium salt) is greater, the reaction with fluorine is faster and the analytical range for fluorine is wider[107].

Determination of fluoride (2–40 μg) using alizarin fluorine blue[93]

Reagents

Water:

Further purify glass-distilled water by passing it through a mixture of strongly acidic cation-exchange resin and strongly basic anion-exchange resin.

Succinate buffer, 0.1M, pH 4.6:

Dissolve 5.9 g of succinic acid in 300 mℓ of water and neutralize the solution to pH 4.6 with 0.5M NaOH solution using a pH meter; dilute to 500 mℓ with water. This solution must be prepared freshly before use.

Alizarin fluorine blue solution, approximately 0.0022M.

Triturate 0.44 g of alizarin fluorine blue with 5 mℓ of 0.5M NaOH solution, and dilute to 200 mℓ with water. Add 50 mℓ of 0.1M succinate buffer, pH 4.6, check the pH of the solution with a pH meter and adjust it if necessary to between 4.5 and 4.8. Dilute to 500 mℓ with water and, if necessary, filter. Store this solution in a refrigerator.

Lanthanum nitrate solution, approximately 0.002M:

Dissolve 0.43 g of $La(NO_3)_3$ hexahydrate in 500 mℓ of water.

Lanthanum–alizarin fluorine blue reagent solution:

Mix equal volumes of alizarin fluorine blue solution, approximately 0.0022M, and $La(NO_3)_3$ solution, approximately 0.002M. This mixture must be made up freshly each day.

Acetone.

Fluoride stock solution:

Dissolve 2.2103 g of NaF, previously dried at 140°C for 1 h, in water to produce 1 ℓ. One millilitre of this solution contains 1.00 mg F^-.

Fluoride dilute standard solution:

Dilute 10.0 mℓ F^- stock solution with water to produce 1 ℓ immediately before use. One millilitre of this solution contains 10.0 μg F^-.

Calibration

Transfer suitable volumes of dilute standard fluoride solution, accurately measured to cover the range 0–40 μg of fluoride ion, to a series of standard 50-mℓ calibrated flasks, and dilute each to 10 mℓ with water. Treat the contents of each flask as described below. Add 5.0 mℓ of 0.1M succinate buffer (pH 4.6), 10.0 mℓ of lanthanum–alizarin fluorine blue reagent solution and 10.0 mℓ of acetone, mixing thoroughly and set aside for 30 min. Measure the absorbance of each solution containing fluoride in a 10 mm cell at a wavelength of 625 nm, using in the reference cell the solution prepared as described but containing no added fluoride. By graphical construction or otherwise, establish the relationship between the amount of fluoride and the absorbance (*see* Note 2).

Procedure

Transfer the sample solution previously neutralized to between pH 4 and 5 containing not more than 40 μg of fluoride in a volume of not greater than 20 mℓ to a standard 50-mℓ calibrated flask. Add 5.0 mℓ of 0.1M succinate buffer, pH 4.6, and complete the colour development as described under calibration. At the same time prepare a blank on the reagents in the same way, using water in the place of the sample. Measure the absorbance of the sample solution against the reagent blank solution as reference, as described under calibration. Calculate the amount of fluoride present in the sample by reference to the calibration relationship.

Notes

1. The order of addition of reagents may influence the rate of colour development and the stated order should be strictly observed.
2. For routine purposes, it is necessary to establish the calibration once only for a set of reagents. Fresh calibration is required when reagents are changed or in order to obtain results of the highest possible accuracy.

Interferences

Interference studies were carried out in the collaborative assessment. For the range 2–40 μg F^-, the following can be tolerated in amounts up to those indicated.

Salts:

5.0 g $NaClO_4 \cdot H_2O$.
1.0 g KCl.

Non-metals:

100 mg bromate, bromide, iodide, nitrate, nitrite, selenate, tetraborate.
10 mg sulphate.
1 mg acetate, citrate, silicate, tartrate.
100 μg oxalate, phosphate.
10 μg carbonate, sulphide.

Metals and ammonium ions:

1 mg ammonium, barium, calcium, lithium, magnesium.
200 μg chromate
100 μg copper(II), manganese(II), molybdenum(VI).
50 μg chromium(III).
20 μg beryllium
10 μg cerium(IV), silver, titanium(IV), zinc.
5 μg aluminium, cobalt(II), mercury(II), nickel
3 μg iron(II), iron(III).
2 μg vanadium(V).

For a discussion of these and additional data, the original paper should be consulted.

2. Zirconium–Solochrome Cyanine R

This method, introduced by Megregian[108] depends on the bleaching action of fluoride ion on the red Zr–Solochrome Cyanine R complex resulting from formation of $[ZrOF_2]$. The structure of solochrome cyanine is shown in *Structure 49*.

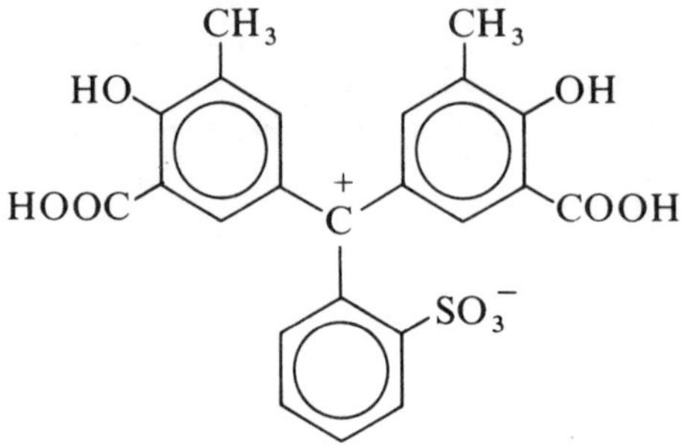

Structure 49 Solochrome cyanine

No simple stoichiometric relationship exists between the fluoride and the zirconium complex with the dyestuff, so that care is needed in controlling the variables in order to obtain good results. The fluoride concentration is measured by the decrease in absorbance at 540 nm by the zirconium complex.

The original method was improved by Sarma[109] and more recently Dixon[110] has applied it to the determination of fluoride in the range 0–2.5 μg. However, Marshall and Wood[37] were unable to reduce the blank to below 1.0 μg F^- in this range.

Without doubt the method has advantages. Its sensitivity, simplicity, speed and ability to operate in fairly strong acid solution without the need for close pH control has made it a popular method. One of the weaknesses is fading of the zirconium complex colour, a factor brought out at the collaborative study carried out by the Analytical Methods Committee of the Society for Analytical Chemistry[93]. It was found necessary to specify short periods of time for both the bleaching action with fluoride and for the solution to remain in the cell before measurement. This was felt to detract from its use in the simultaneous treatment of sample batches. The fading problem does not, however, appear to have affected its widespread application which is second only to alizarin fluorine blue.

Interferences fall into three groups:

1. Metal ions giving colours with solochrome cyanine R. Under the conditions of high acidity used, none of the common metals form coloured complexes.
2. Cations forming strong fluoride complexes in competition with the zirconium, e.g. aluminium(III), iron(III).
3. Anions forming complexes with zirconium, e.g. phosphate, sulphate, citrate, tartrate.

The method may be applied without prior separation of fluoride provided that the ions mentioned fall below certain limits. This is indicated below.

Interference and nature of error	*Amount* (μg) *necessary to give* 10% *error on* 2 μg F^-
Al^{3+}(−ve)	0.4
Fe^{3+}(−ve)	5
PO_4^{3-}(+ve)	0.8
SO_4^{2-}(+ve)	100

Aluminium(III) interference may be eliminated by making the solution alkaline before adding the reagent. Sulphate interference is eliminated by precipitation with $BaCl_2$.

The method has been applied to analysis of minerals and rocks after separation of fluoride by distillation[111], silicate and phosphate rock without separation[112], detection of HF and other inorganic fluorides in air[113], and determination of fluoride in air[114]. Other applications include organic compounds[115], and water[116]. Greenland[35] has used the method for determination of fluoride following separation by microdiffusion.

Spectrophotometric determination[110] of fluoride (0–2.5 μg) using Solochrome Cyanine R

Reagents

Solochrome Cyanine R reagent:

Dissolve 80 mg purified solochrome cyanine R (Note 1) in water, add 1 mℓ of M HCl and dilute to exactly 1ℓ. Solutions of the reagent made up in 0.001M HCl are stable for at least one year.

Acidic zirconium reagent:

The solid zirconyl chloride ($ZrOCl_2 \cdot 8H_2O$) must be white and crystalline. Dissolve 180 mg of zirconyl chloride in a few millilitres of water, add 5 mℓ of 2M HCl and dilute to 100 mℓ in a calibrated flask. Transfer by pipette, 10.0 mℓ into a 1-ℓ calibrated flask, add 53 ± 1 mℓ of conc. HCl (s.gr. 1.18), mix and dilute to mark. The working solution thus contains 5.0 μg mℓ$^{-1}$ of zirconium in 0.62M HCl and should be kept for 48 h before use. It is then stable for at least 1 year (Note 2).

Procedure

To a 25-mℓ calibrated flask add in the following order, sample or standard containing up to 2.5 μg F^- in up to 20 mℓ water, 2.00 mℓ of the acidic zirconium reagent, mix and then 2.00 mℓ of the solochrome cyanine R reagent. Mix and dilute to mark. Allow to stand for about 5 min.

Measure the absorbance within 2 min at 540 nm against water in 2-cm cells.

Notes

1. Most commercial samples of solochrome cyanine R were found to contain about 40% of Na_2SO_4 or NaCl. The following simple procedure

is recommended for obtaining a uniform product from commercial samples.

Dissolve 4 g of the material in 60 mℓ water and add with stirring 40 mℓ conc. HCl (s. gr. 1.18) to liberate the free acid. Filter this off (Buchner funnel) and wash with 6M HCl. Dissolve it in about 100 mℓ $CHCl_3$, and filter the solution to remove any aqueous layer. Extract the $CHCl_3$ with two 100-mℓ portions of distilled water and evaporate the solution to dryness.

Grind the free acid and dry at 60 °C for 1 h.

2. The stability of the working solution was investigated in this work and found to be dependent on the exact procedure used in its preparation. It is important therefore to follow the method described.
3. All glassware, especially the calibrated flasks and optical cells should be fluoride-free. The acidic zirconium reagent is the most suitable for removing the last traces of fluoride from the surface of glass.
4. The volumes of reagents used need to be added reproducibly though not necessarily accurately. Dispensing pipettes were found ideally suited.

---

3. Zirconium–SPADNS

Similar in principle to the solochrome cyanine R method, the Zr–SPADNS method has been investigated by Bellack and Schouboe[117], Wharton[34] and Nicholson[41], the last two applying the method after separation of fluoride by microdiffusion. The structure of SPADNS (4,5-dihydroxy-3-(*p*-sulphophenylazo) 2,7-naphthalene disulphonc acid, trisodium salt) is shown in *Structure 50*.

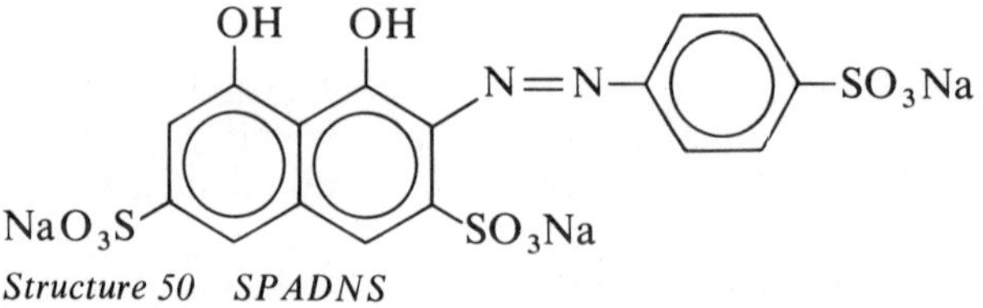

Structure 50 SPADNS

Though its sensitivity is considerably lower than both alizarin fluorine blue and eriochrome cyanine R, it has found application and has been accepted as a standard in water analysis[118].

4. Zirconium–alizarin red S

The complex between zirconium and alizarin red S (sodium alizarin sulphonate) (*Structure 51*) gives a red-brown colour in acid solution if alizarin red S is in excess, and a violet colour if the zirconium is in excess.

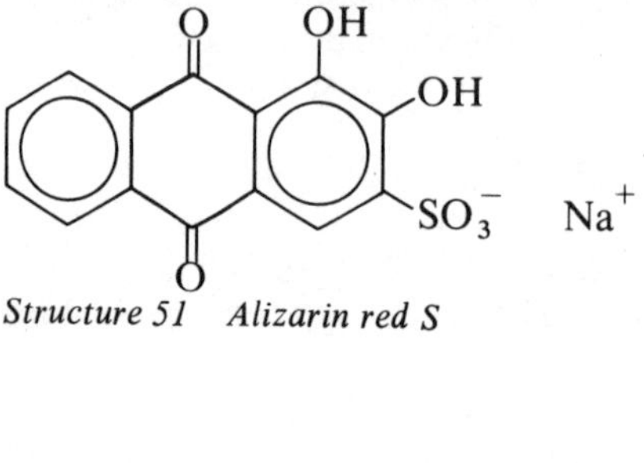

Structure 51 Alizarin red S

The complex is decolorized by fluoride, phosphate, arsenate, sulphate, thiosulphate, and oxalate as well as by hydroxy organic acids. Though of lower sensitivity than the first two spectrophotometric methods discussed, it is suitable for routine determinations because of its simplicity. It has been applied to water analysis[119–122].

As most of the impurities in water influence the results, appropriate modifications are necessary. The method is applicable in the range 0.1–1.0 mg F^-.

5. *Chloranilates*

Insoluble chloranilates have been used for the determination of fluoride, chloride, phosphate, and sulphate. The method depends on the reaction

$$\text{anion}^{n-} + \text{M-chloranilate} + H^+ \rightarrow \underset{\text{(purple)}}{\text{chloranilic acid}} + \underset{\text{(precipitate)}}{\text{M-anion}}$$

After the reaction, excess metal chloranilate and the insoluble metal salt are filtered off, and the purple chloranilate ion in the filtrate is determined spectrophotometrically.

The method is an indirect one with strontium[123], lanthanum[124], and thorium[125] chloranilates recommended for determination of fluoride. Using the lanthanum salt Hayashi, Danzuka and Ueno[124] were able to determine 2–200 ppm F^- with an accuracy of ± 2 per cent, and with no interference from sulphate, chloride, and nitrate if present at levels below 200 ppm.

The use of thorium chloranilate extended the lower limit to 0.2 ppm, but reproducibility was found to be dependent on use of a carefully prepared purple-black form of the thorium salt.

The spectrophotometric determination of fluoride by chloranilates requires carefully controlled conditions and has been criticized on the grounds of high blank values. It is doubtful whether the method has any special advantages.

Electroanalytical methods

Fluoride ion-sensitive electrode

Without doubt, the introduction[15] in 1966 of the fluoride ion-sensitive electrode (or pF electrode) has made a dramatic impact on almost every aspect of fluoride analysis.

Two distinct types of fluoride electrode have been described:

1. Homogeneous solid-state membrane electrodes, or single-crystal membrane electrodes.
   This type contains a doped LaF_3 single crystal.
2. Heterogeneous solid-state membrane electrodes, containing slightly soluble fluoride salts embedded in silicone rubber[126].

The homogeneous LaF_3 form has predominated and the remainder of this section will deal specifically with this type. At least four commercial models are now available* of which the Orion 94-09 has been featured in most investigations. This model has been the subject of a detailed study by Evans, Moody and Thomas[127] who compare it with other models.

A more recent model 94-09A has been introduced, this having the LaF_3 crystal flush with the end of the plastic body. In construction the electrode is similar to the glass electrode except that the glass membrane is replaced by a single crystal of europium-doped lanthanum fluoride.

In the same way that the conventional glass pH electrode measures hydrogen-ion activity, the fluoride electrode measures fluoride-ion activity. Both electrodes develop a potential across a thin layer of ionically conducting material but unlike the glass electrode, the fluoride membrane electrode requires no conditioning in water before use. The Ag/AgCl electrode potential will be determined by the internal chloride ion activity; the internal fluoride ion activity will fix the potential of the inside surface of the crystal.

When immersed in an external fluoride solution a potential difference will exist across the membrane, the magnitude of which will depend on the ratio of the internal and external fluoride-ion activities. The electrode potential is usually measured against a saturated calomel reference electrode giving the following cell:

$$\text{Ag/AgCl, Cl}^-(0.1),\ \text{F}^-\ (0.1)/\text{LaF}_{3(s)}/\text{test solution/SCE}$$

Frant and Ross[15] found that the Nernst type relationship

$$E = \text{constant} + \frac{RT}{F}\ln\frac{(\text{F}^-)_{\text{int}}}{(\text{F}^-)_{\text{ext}}}$$

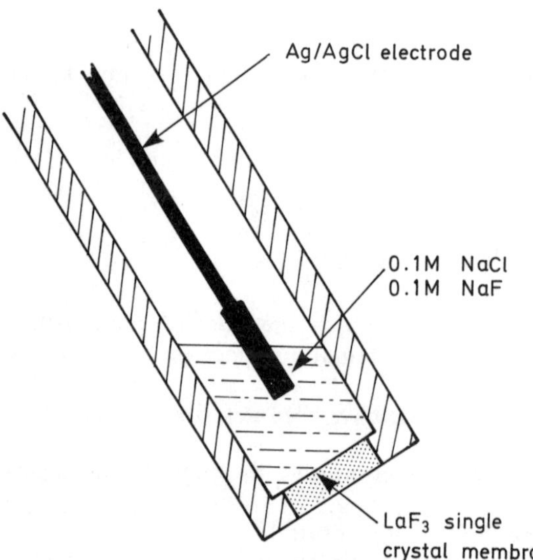

Figure 44 Schematic diagram showing constructional details of LaF_3 solid-state electrode

* Orion 94-09; Beckman No. 39600; Coleman No. 2-803; Corning No. 47604.

where (F^-) = fluoride activity, was obeyed, which is to be expected if lanthanum fluoride is permeable to fluoride ions only. The internal fluoride activity is constant, and the relationship becomes

$$E = \text{constant} - \frac{RT}{F}\ln\,(F^-)_{ext}$$
$$= \text{constant} + 0.05916\,\text{pF at } 25\,^\circ\text{C}$$

where $\text{pF} = -\log(F^-)$. The constant term will depend on the fluoride–chloride activity of the internal solution and the reference electrode, which may be incorporated into the fluoride electrode itself.

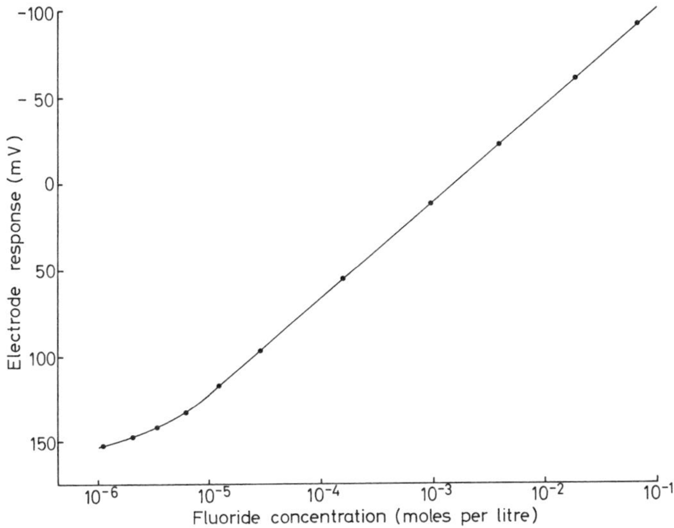

Figure 45 Response of an Orion fluoride-ion electrode to fluoride ion concentration. The calibration curve was made in a TISAB background

A typical electrode response to fluoride ion concentration is shown in *Figure 45*. A change in electrode potential of 59.16 mV will be associated with a ten-fold change in fluoride activity (or concentration if the concentration-activity relationship is regularized by ionic strength adjustment). It will be noted that the response is linear down to 10^{-5}M in fluoride (0.19 ppm) with a deviation from linearity below this concentration. In aqueous solution the response of the electrode is a function of $[H^+]$ due to hydroxide being iso-electronic with fluoride. At low pH values, fluoride activity is affected by the formation of undissociated HF and HF_2^-, while at higher pH values hydroxide interferes. The mechanism of the latter interference is discussed by Evans, Moody and Thomas[127]. The electrode behaves as though it were ten times more sensitive to fluoride than hydroxide. In general, high pH values must be avoided except when the fluoride concentration is high. Further reference to this point will be made later. In very dilute fluoride solutions the working pH should be below 8. This is indicated in *Figure 46*

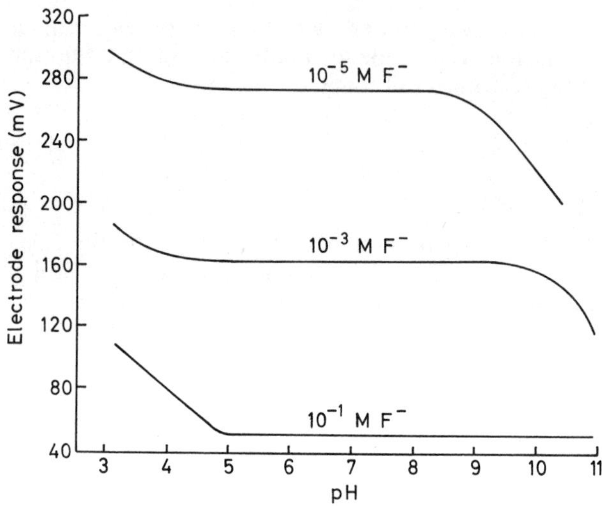

Figure 46 *Effect of pH on the response of a fluoride-ion electrode.* (After Frant and Ross[15])

which shows[15] the dependence of the pF electrode potential on pH for three concentrations of fluoride.

Ion-selective electrodes respond to changes in activity of ions, and the concentration–activity relationship will depend on the ionic strength of the solution. Hence there is need to establish similar ionic strengths for both the sample and standard solution. Frant and Ross[128] have advocated the use of a 'Total Ionic Strength Adjustment Buffer' (TISAB) containing acetic acid and sodium citrate with the pH adjusted to 5.0–5.5 using NaOH. It was applied to the determination of fluoride in water in the ppm range.

Anfält and Jagner[129] have asserted that buffers containing carboxylic acids are unsuitable for all work involving LaF_3 electrodes due to formation of $[La_{(3-x)}Ac_x]$ type complexes which produce a sluggish response and deviation from the Nernstian equation. Further investigations by the same workers[130] report that chelating ligands such as lactate, malonate, citrate, etc., affect the electrode, which can be regenerated by having its crystal surface polished with diamond paste.

Earlier assessments of the pF electrode led to many controversial opinions on its performance, this being in no small measure due to the wide diversity of conditions used. For example, whereas the electrode response time is instantaneous in 10^{-3}M fluoride solutions, a waiting period of about 3 min is required at the 10^{-5}M level. Stirring, another important factor, has been investigated by Lingane[131].

Two methods have been described for using the electrode, a direct potentiometric method where the fluoride concentration is obtained by reference to a calibration curve, and a potentiometric titration of fluoride with lanthanum or thorium nitrate, where the electrode is used to indicate the end-point. The latter approach was investigated by Lingane[131,132] using lanthanum, thorium and calcium salts as titrants. Lanthanum nitrate was found to give the minimum error when the titration was performed in a neutral unbuffered solution. More recently several other workers have confirmed the validity of the method and it has been widely applied. It may be illustrated in the application to the determination of fluorine in organic materials. Francis, Deonarine, and Persing[133] decompose the organic material and titrate the resulting fluoride in 60% v/v 2-propanol with standard lanthanum or thorium nitrate. The titration curves for various amounts of fluoride are shown in *Figure 47*.

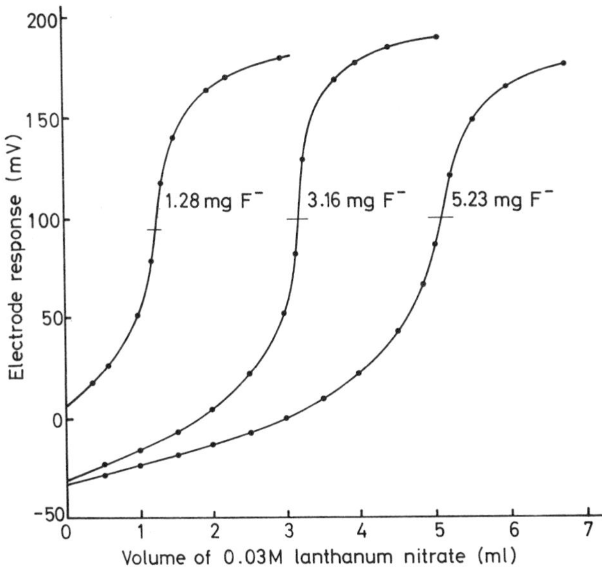

Figure 47 *'Point by point' potentiometric titration of standard amounts of fluoride with lanthanum nitrate using a fluoride-ion electrode.* (After Francis, Deonarine and Persing[133])

For good results, exactly the same procedure must be used for the unknown solution and the standard fluoride solution used in preparing the standard curves.

More recently Eriksson and Johansson[134] have established the optimal conditions for potentiometric titration of fluoride with La and Th in unbuffered solutions. They emphasize that the end-point will differ from the equivalence point, as the curves are asymmetrical, and point out that the end-point will depend on stirring rate.

Hassan[135] has studied application of the potentiometric titration using thorium nitrate, in aqueous–organic solvents. Of the systems investigated, 50% dioxan at pH 5–7 was found to be effective, giving errors of ± 3 per cent.

Direct potentiometric use of the electrode was investigated by Baumann[57] who found that fluoride in the range 10^{-5}–10^{-4}M could be determined.

This work utilized the technique of known addition, i.e. a standard NaF solution is added to the fluoride sample and the potential recorded after each addition. By minimizing changes in factors that might affect activity coefficients, e.g. ionic strength and junction potentials, the relationship between potential and fluoride concentration was found to follow the Nernst equation. In acid solution, total fluoride (free and complexed) may be determined provided that:

1. The hydrogen ion activity remains constant;
2. There are no fluoride complexes other than hydrogen fluoride; and
3. Sufficient free fluoride is available for detection.

For further elaboration of this, the above paper should be consulted. The same investigation was extended to include solutions containing a range of inorganic ions. In the presence of metals which interfere by formation of stable fluoride complexes (e.g. Al^{3+}, UO_2^{2+}, Fe^{3+}, Th^{4+}), precomplexation with H_3PO_4 was found to be effective.

The known addition technique is also used by Selig[136] who employs a Gran plot to evaluate the data. Gran plots normally involve correction of volume to concentration at each stage of the titration. This is extremely tedious. Selig overcomes the problem by utilizing Orion volume-corrected paper. This produces a linear plot of potential against volume of added NaF. The technique is more effective in evaluating the fluoride concentration than the conventional use of sigmoid potentiometric curves.

Application of the direct method to fluoride in water supplies was made by

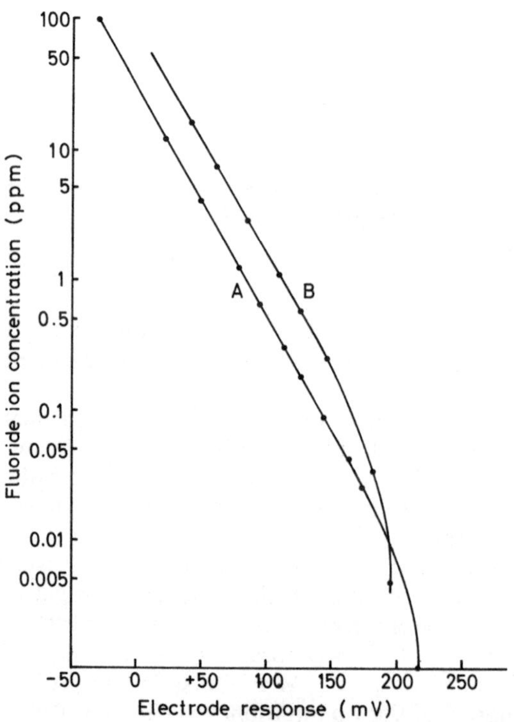

Figure 48 *Calibration curves showing fluoride-ion electrode response against fluoride ion concentration.* A, *pure NaF solution;* B, *NaF in a TISAB background.* (After Frant and Ross[128])

Frant and Ross[127] who were able to compare its performance with the more established SPADNS spectrophotometric method. Fluoride complexed by Al^{3+} or Fe^{3+} was displaced by the citrate content of the TISAB buffer. Their calibration curve is shown in *Figure 48*.

The direct potentiometric method has been applied to organic microanalysis with excellent results[137]. The same work also deals with an important aspect of this approach, namely, day to day variation of the calibration curve intercepts. While the slope remains constant and close to Nernstian response, slight variations in the intercepts make it impossible to use one reference curve over a long period without considerable loss in precision. By standardizing the electrode daily at one fluoride concentration it was found possible to determine fluoride concentrations in all unknown solutions. In a series of 18 NaF solutions containing 0.4–2.0 mg F^-, the standard deviation of the absolute error was found to be 0.17 per cent.

For some time the lower limit of response for the pF electrode was generally accepted as about 10^{-6}M, this being attributed to the background fluoride concentration resulting from dissolution of the lanthanum fluoride membrane. Recently Baumann[138] has investigated an extension of the sensitivity limit of the electrode by introducing fluoride-complexing cations and calculating the residual free fluoride from the stability quotients of the relevant fluoride complexes. The results indicate that Nernstian response is maintained even when the fluoride concentration is extended from one to three decades below the quoted limit of about 10^{-6}M. A related aspect is application of the electrode to minute volumes and hence to very small amounts of fluoride. Durst[139], using a modified electrode and linear null-point potentiometry, has determined amounts of fluoride down to 0.38 ng in 10 μℓ with an error of 0.002 ng F^-.

Mention has been made of interference by the hydroxyl ion. An investigation of the effects of various ions on the electrode response has been made by Bock and Strecker[140]. Non-ionic substances were found to have little effect, but NaCl and $MgSO_4$ caused a change in potential. Iron, borate, and silicate have no effect; Al, Be, Zr, and Ti interfere by forming strong fluoride complexes.

In applying the known addition method to analysis of tea, which can accumulate up to 17000 μg g^{-1} of aluminium, Vickery and Vickery[141] found that Al (and iron) caused serious errors. They report that addition of sodium citrate as masking agent results in good recovery of fluoride in samples containing aluminium, iron, magnesium or silicate.

Not unexpectedly, application of the pF electrode is widespread including, in addition to those mentioned, such materials as phosphate rock[142], toothpaste[44, 143], vegetation[144], serum[145], urine[146], fluorinated carbohydrates[147], silicate rock[148], bone[149], oxides[150], air[151] and tea[141]. Orion Research Inc. have published a methods guide[152] and a series of newsletters providing a regular survey of current applications.

Radiochemical methods

Radiochemical methods fall within the context of this book inasmuch as they may be applied to materials in which the fluorine is in ionic form.

Foreman[153] has given an excellent review of radiometric methods for the determination of fluorine. There are five known isotopes of fluorine, naturally occurring fluorine-19 and four short-lived radioisotopes of which ^{18}F has the longest half-life (109.8 min). Activation methods have utilized thermal[154] and fast neutrons[155], α-particles[156], protons[157], helium-3 nuclei[158] and γ-photons[159,160]. The papers quoted represent but a small proportion of published work in this area of fluoride analysis as the review by Foreman will indicate.

Of recent interest is the determination of fluorine in rock materials including the Apollo II lunar fines, which in the U.K. has been carried out at Harwell[159]. The method employed, utilizing photonuclear activation, is particularly valuable for the determination of light elements including fluorine. In the reaction,

$$^{19}F(\gamma, n)^{18}F$$

the ^{18}F emits positrons, the annihilation of which generates γ-rays of energy 0.51 MeV. The half-life of ^{18}F (109.8 min) is sufficiently long for it to be separated chemically from the irradiated matrix. In the above investigation the ^{18}F was separated by distillation, this being followed by measurement with a NaI (Tl) γ-ray spectrometer. The detection limit was found to be 0.002 μg F. Results were found to be in good agreement with conventional spectrophotometric techniques.

In addition to activation methods, fluorine can be made to react with the radioisotope of another element in such a way that measurement of the latter can be related to the amount of fluorine present. Carmichael and Whitley[161] determined 20–100 μg F^- using a radio-release procedure based on this principle. The fluoride solution was passed down a column containing PTFE–zirconium selenide, the latter material having been irradiated in a neutron flux of 1.2×10^{12} neutrons $cm^{-2}\,s^{-1}$ for 12 h. The reaction

$$Zr(SeO_3)_2 + 6HF \rightarrow ZrF_6^{2-} + 2SeO_3^{2-}$$

takes place and the eluted ^{75}Se is measured by its γ-activity. Phosphate and aluminium interfere.

Isotope dilution is another radiochemical method which has found application to fluoride analysis. Kudahl, Fremlin, and Hardwick[162] have used ^{18}F as tracer to determine submicrogram amounts of fluoride in dental tissue samples of less than 1 mg.

Catalytic methods

Catalytic reactions including enzyme-catalysed reactions have been applied to the determination of very small amounts of fluoride. Apart from the advantage of high sensitivity, there is also the benefit of high selectivity and relative cheapness.

Price and Walker[163] used the principle that the rate of bleaching of the aluminium–haematoxylin lake by fluoride ion to form the stable aluminofluoride ion, is a function of fluoride concentration

$$\text{Al–haematoxylin lake} + 6F^- \rightarrow \text{haematoxylin (yellow)} + AlF_6^-$$

When applied to water analysis, 0–1.5 ppm (in 100 mℓ sample) F^- could be determined with an accuracy of 0.05 ppm. Later Linde[164] utilized the inhibition of enzymatic hydrolysis of ethyl butyrate by fluoride to determine about 0.1 μg mℓ$^{-1}$ F^- in blood, urine and water. This work was extended by McGaughey and Stowell[165] to the estimation of a few nanograms of fluoride in the presence of large amounts of phosphate.

More recently Cabello-Tomas and West[166] determine fluoride in the range 0.5–5 μg (in a final volume of 100 mℓ) by the catalytic effect of fluoride on the reaction between a slightly aged solution of zirconyl chloride and xylenol orange. The technique is termed kinetochromic spectrophotometry. The reaction itself is interesting and based on the known ability of zirconium ions to form polymeric species in aqueous solutions of low acidity.

Whereas a freshly prepared solution of zirconyl chloride gives a red colour immediately with xylenol orange, a 24 h solution forms the red colour slowly, and a solution several weeks old gives no colour except of the xylenol orange. For slightly aged solutions, the red colour is produced in direct proportion to the amount of fluoride present.

The colour has maximum development within 90 min and is stable for a further 60 min with an effective molar absorptivity of 2.0×10^5 for fluoride. Of 32 cations and anions examined only aluminium and iron(II) were found to cause serious interference in 10-fold amounts. However, anion interference is more serious. Phosphate, arsenate, sulphate, citrate and oxalate seriously interfere by also catalysing the reaction. Separation of fluoride is necessary therefore, when these ions are present.

A note of warning is given in this investigation that while the method has a high sensitivity, this is more variable than for conventional absorptiometric techniques, the variations being due to several factors. Attention to detail and daily standardizations to establish the prevailing slope of the calibration curve are essential for the best results. A method by Knapp[167] is very similar, with a lower limit of 0.02 μg F^-.

The zirconium–methyl thymol blue reaction is also catalysed by fluoride. Hems, Kirkbright and West[163] find that it has some advantages over the zirconium–xylenol orange system. For example it is more sensitive, and sulphate does not interfere when present in an equal amount to fluoride.

Another catalytic method in the ppb (10^9) range has been described by Klockow, Ludwig and Giraudo[169]. Based on the inhibiting action of fluoride on the zirconium-catalysed reaction between perborate and iodide, 19–190 ng F^- (in 50 mℓ) can be determined with a standard deviation of ± 7.4 ng.

Thermometric titrimetry

The recent revival of interest in thermometric titrimetry has produced methods for fluoride. Everson and Ramirez[170] found that thermometric titrimetry provided useful information on the general course and nature of metal–fluoride reactions quite apart from analytical applications.

Thorium(IV), cerium(III), aluminium(III), and calcium(II) cations were found to be the best for the titrations. By judicious selection of titrant and pH range, interference from moderate amounts of sulphate, borate, and silicate could be avoided. Most interferences can be eliminated by the time-consuming

Willard–Winter distillation, but the method is not suited to the diluted solution obtained by this procedure.

Johansson[171] has reported the determination of 6–8 mg F^- with an error of $\pm$0.04 mg. The reaction

$$Pb^{2+}{}_{(aq)} + F^-{}_{(aq)} + Cl^-{}_{(aq)} \rightarrow PbFCl_{(s)}$$

was used in this work. It is reasonably fast and accompanied by a fairly large heat effect. The presence of phosphate, sulphate, nitrate, and chloride influence the enthalpy of the reaction. Their removal by ion-exchange is described.

Miscellaneous methods

Fluoride in biological materials can be determined by gas chromatography[64]. Extraction is first made into a solution of chlorotrimethylsilane in benzene. Fluoride reacts to produce fluorotrimethylsilane which remains in the benzene layer. This is used for direct injection into the column. The method is suitable for 0.01–10 μg mℓ$^{-1}$ in the original sample.

A method for determination of fluoride in the 0.2–20 μg mℓ$^{-1}$ level has been described by Bond and O'Donnell[172] based on atomic absorption spectroscopy. Fluoride depresses the absorption of magnesium in an air–coal gas flame, the change in absorption of the 285.2 nm Mg line being proportional to fluoride concentration. Sulphate and phosphate are the principal interferences with aluminium, lanthanum, oxalate and acetate also giving trouble.

The method is considerably more rapid than others and may be used directly without separation of fluoride. Other variations using the same technique are enhancement of zirconium absorption by fluoride in a NO_2–acetylene flame (5–200 μg F^- mℓ$^{-1}$), this method having little interference, and enhancement of titanium (40–400 μg F^- mℓ$^{-1}$) in which there is no interference from either phosphate or sulphate.

Several polarographic methods have been proposed for fluoride. Wallis[173] has based determination of 2–10 μg F^- on the action of fluoride on thorium-*o*-nitrobenzenearsonic acid. Increased amounts of fluoride liberate proportional amounts of the organic constituent, the polarographic wave of which is measured.

Electrochemically generated La^{3+} ions from a lanthanum hexaboride anode may be used to titrate fluoride (or oxalate) potentiometrically[84] From 0.5 to 2.0 mg F^- per 100 mℓ may be determined with an accuracy of a few parts per thousand at pH 5.0. Also based on lanthanum(III) is a gravimetric method proposed by Popov and Knudson[174]. Fluoride is precipitated as LaF_3 with a known amount of $La(NO_3)_3$, the excess being filtered off and its lanthanum content determined gravimetrically with cupferron. Macdonald and Toth[126] found LaF_3 to be a very gelatinous precipitate, though Hislop, Pratchett and Williams[159] used it to determine the chemical yield in the γ-activation determination of fluoride, with no adverse comments.

In an attempt to overcome the poor end-point in the titration of fluoride with $Th(NO_3)_4$ using sodium alizarin sulphonate as indicator, a conductometric end-point has been proposed[175]. Before the end-point, the net change in conductance is due to replacing fluoride ion ($\lambda^0 = 55.4^{-1}$ cm^2 eq) by nitrate ion ($\lambda^0 = 71.4^{-1}$ cm^2 eq) and only a very small increase is expected. After the end-point, the addition of thorium nitrate contributes more causing a sharper increase in conductance. From 0.3 to 5 mg F^- can be titrated with a relative error of 2 per cent. The method was applied to distillates in the Willard–Winter procedure.

A new approach has been described for the determination of small amounts of fluoride in biological materials[176], the technique combining adsorption of fluoride on calcium phosphate with the diffusion method of Hall described earlier. In essence, the method involves boiling the fluoride aliquot for 5–10 min with 20 mg of fluoride-low calcium phosphate. The solution is cooled, centrifuged to remove the calcium phosphate (now containing adsorbed fluoride), and the Hall diffusion technique applied. The investigators applied the method to water, salts, urine, lant extracts, and serum.

Finally, a new and sensitive fluorimetric method[177] has been developed which is capable of reaching 0.01 ppm F^-. This is based on the formation of a 1:1:1 zirconium–calcein blue–fluoride ternary complex. The proposed complex is shown in *Structure 52*.

O O O—Zr CH$_2$—N CH$_3$

Structure 52 Zr-calcein blue-F^- ternary 1:1:1 complex

Formation of the complex enhances the fluorescence. Only phosphate interferes seriously in five-fold concentration, with tungstate, acetate, and tartrate also giving interference at the same level. Molybdate and sulphate give low and high results respectively, in 50-fold concentration. Cations are found to give little interference. Aluminium, manganese and silver interfere slightly in 5-fold concentration; arsenic(V), antimony(III), beryllium, and cobalt give low results in 50-fold concentration.

The method has a precision of ± 3 per cent near the middle range of the calibration curves.

References

1. REYNOLDS, D.S. and HILL, W.L., *Ind. Engng Chem. analyt. Edn,* **11**, 21 (1939)
2. RINCK, G., *Bull. Soc. chim. Fr.*, **15**, 305 (1948)
3. SPECHT, R.C., *Analyt. Chem.*, **28**, 1015 (1956)
4. ELVING, P.J., HORTON, C.A. and WILLARD, H.H., *Fluorine Chemistry* (Ed. J.H. Simons), Vol. II, Academic Press, New York, 51 (1954)
5. MACDONALD, A.M.G., *Comprehensive Analytical Chemistry* (Ed. C.L. Wilson and D.W. Wilson), Vol. 1C, Elsevier, Amsterdam, 319 (1962)
6. HORTON, C.A., *Treatise on Analytical Chemistry* (Ed. I.M. Kolthoff and P.J. Elving), Part II, Vol. 7, Interscience, New York, 207 (1961)
7. KODAMA, K., *Methods of Quantitative Inorganic Analysis—an Encyclopedia of Gravimetric, Titrimetric and Colorimetric Methods,* Interscience, New York, 448 (1963)

8. HORTON, C.A., *Advances in Analytical Chemistry and Instrumentation* (Ed. C.N. Reilley), Vol. 1, Interscience, New York, 151 (1960)
9. MA, T.S., *Treatise on Analytical Chemistry* (Ed. I.M. Kolthoff and P.J. Elving), Part II, Vol. 12, Interscience, New York, 117 (1965)
10. DIXON, J.P., *Modern Methods of Organic Microanalysis,* Van Nostrand, London (1968)
11. HALL, R.J., *Analyst,* **93**, 461 (1968)
12. HALL, R.J., *Proc. Soc. analyt. Chem.,* **3**, 162 (1966)
13. COOKE, J.A., JOHNSON, M.S. and DAVISON, A.W., *Environ. Pollut.,* 257 (1976)
14. BELCHER, R., LEONARD, M.A. and WEST, T.S., *J. chem. Soc.,* 2390 (1958)
15. FRANT, M.S. and ROSS, J.W., *Science,* **154**, 1553 (1966)
16. WILLARD, H.H. and WINTER, O.B., *Ind. Engng. Chem. analyt. Edn,* **5**, 7 (1933)
17. TANANAEV, I., *Zh. prikl. Khim., Leningr.,* **5**, 834 (1932)
18. FOX, E.J., *Analyt. Chem.,* **32**, 1530 (1960)
19. *Official, Standardised and Recommended Methods of Analysis.* The Society for Analytical Chemistry, W. Heffer, Cambridge, England, 123 (1963)
20. SMITH, O.D. and PARKS, T.D., *Analyt. Chem.,* **27**, 998 (1955)
21. MURTY, G.V.L.N., YISWANATHAN, T.S. and RAMAKRISHNA, V., *Analytica., Chim. Acta,* **16**, 213 (1957)
22. SHELL, H.R. and CRAIG, R.L., *Analyt. Chem.,* **26**, 996 (1954)
23. GRIMALDI, F.S., INGRAM, B. and CUTTITTA, F., *Analyt. Chem.,* **27**, 918 (1955)
24. PECK, L.C. and SMITH, V.C., *Talanta,* **11**, 1343 (1964)
25. HAFF, L.V., BUTLER, C.P. and BISSO, J.D., *Analyt. Chem.,* **30**, 984 (1958)
26. ESTILL, W.B. and MOSIER, L.C., *Analyt. Chem.,* **27**, 1669 (1955)
27. SCHALL, E.D. and WILLIAMSON, H.G., *J. Ass. off. agric. Chem.,* **38**, 452 (1955)
28. DEVONSHIRE, L.N. and ROWLEY, H.H., *Proc. Okla. Acad. Sci.,* **34**, 155 (1953)
29. SINGER, L.S. and ARMSTRONG, W.D., *Analyt. Chem.,* **31**, 105 (1959)
30. WADE, M.A. and YAMAMURA, S.S., *Analyt. Chem.,* **37**, 1276 (1965)
31. MA, T.S. and GWIRTSMAN, J., *Analyt. Chem.,* **29**, 140 (1957)
32. *Official Methods of Analysis of the Association of Official Analytical Chemists*, 12th edn, A.O.A.C., Washington, 927 (1975)
33. SINGER, L. and ARMSTRONG, W.D., *Analyt. Chem.,* **26**, 904 (1954)
34. WHARTON, H.W., *Analyt. Chem.,* **34**, 1296 (1962)
35. GREENLAND, L., *Analytica chim. Acta.,* **27**, 386 (1962)
36. FRERE, F.J., *Analyt. Chem.,* **33**, 645 (1961)
37. MARSHALL, B.S. and WOOD, R., *Analyst,* **94**, 493 (1969)
38. HALL, R.J., *Analyst,* **85**, 560 (1960)
39. HALL, R.J., *Analyst,* **88**, 76 (1963)
40. HALL, R.J., *Analyst,* **88**, 899 (1963)
41. NICHOLSON, C.R., *Analyt. Chem.,* **38**, 1966 (1966)
42. TAVES, D.R., *Analyt. Chem.,* **40**, 204 (1968)
43. TAVES, D.R., *Talanta,* **15**, 969 (1968)
44. SARA, R. and WANNINEN, E., *Talanta,* **22**, 1033 (1975)
45. HANOCQ, M., *Mikrochim. Acta,* 729 (1973)
46. *Official, Standardised and Recommended Methods of Analysis,* The Society for Analytical Chemistry, W. Heffer, Cambridge, England, 404 (1963)
47. WARF, J.C., CLINE, W.D. and TEVEBAUGH, R.D., *Analyt. Chem.,* **26**, 342 (1954)
48. POWELL, R.H. and MENIS, O., *Analyt. Chem.,* **30**, 1546 (1958)
49. CLEMENTS, R.L., SERGEANT, G.A. and WEBB, P.J., *Analyst,* **96**, 51 (1971)
50. VALACH, R., *Talanta,* **8**, 629 (1961)
51. DAVIES, A.G. and FOREMAN, J.K., *Proceedings of the Society for Analytical Chemistry Conf.,* Nottingham, W. Heffer, Cambridge, England, 165 (1965)
52. JEFFERY, P.G. and WILLIAMS, D., *Analyst,* **86**, 590 (1961)
53. EGER, C. and YARDEN, A., *Analyt. Chem.,* **28**, 512 (1956)
54. ZIPKIN, I., ARMSTRONG, W.D. and SINGER, L., *Analyt. Chem.,* **29**, 310 (1957)
55. NEWMAN, A.C.D., *Analytica chim. Acta,* **19**, 471 (1958)
56. EDMOND, C.R., *Analyt. Chem.,* **41**, 1327 (1969)
57. BAUMANN, E.W., *Analytica chim. Acta,* **42**, 127 (1968)
58. KELSO, F.S., MATTHEWS, J.M. and KRAMER, H.P., *Analyt. Chem.,* **36**, 577 (1964)
59. FRESEN, J.A., VAN GOGH, H. and VAN PINXTEREN, J.A.C., *Pharm. Weekbl. Ned.,* **95**, 33 (1950)
60. INCZÉDY, J., *Analytical Applications of Ion Exchangers,* Pergamon Press, Oxford, 210 (1966)

61. FUNASAKA, W., KAVANE, M., KUJIMA, T. and MATSUDA, Y., *Japan Analyst,* **4**, 514 (1955); *Analyt. Abstr.,* 3, 2079 (1956)
62. GAGLIARDI, E. and POKORNY, G., *Mikrochim. Acta,* 699 (1965)
63. BARK, L.S., GRAHAM, R.J.T. and MCCORMICK, D., *Analytica chim. Acta,* **35**, 268 (1966)
64. FRESEN, J.A., COX, F.H. and WITTER, M.J., *Pharm. Weekbl. Ned.,* **103**, 909 (1968); *Analyt. Abstr.,* **17**, 3619 (1969)
65. CROPPER, E. and PUTTNAM, N.A., *J. Soc. cosmet. Chem.,* **21**, 533 (1970)
66. SHAPIRO, M. YA. and KOLESNIKOVA, V.G., *Zh. analit. Khim.,* **18**, 507 (1963); *Analyt. Abstr.,* **11**, 1982 (1964)
67. BOURNIQUE, R.A. and DAHMER, L.H., *Analyt. Chem.,* **36**, 1786 (1964)
68. HOFFMAN, F. and LUNDELL, G.E., *J. Res. natn Bur. Stand.,* 3, 589 (1929)
69. CALEY, E.R. and KAHLE, G.R., *Analyt. Chem.,* **31**, 1880 (1959)
70. POPOV, A.I. and KNUDSON, G.E., *Analyt. Chem.,* **26**, 892 (1954)
71. BALLCZO, H. and SCHIFFNER, H., *Z. analyt. Chem.,* **152**, 3 (1956)
72. DAHLE, D., BONNAR, R.U. and WICHMANN, H.J., *J. Ass. off. Agric. Chem.,* **21**, 459 (1938)
73. HOSKINS, C.R. and FRYD, C.F.M., *J. appl. Chem.,* **5**, 85 (1955)
74. *Official Methods of Analysis of the Association of Official Analytical Chemists* 12th edn, A.O.A.C., Washington, 436 (1975)
75. SELIG, W., *Analyst,* **93**, 118 (1968)
76. Analytical Methods Committee of the Society for Analytical Chemistry, *Analyst,* **97**, 734 (1972)
77. ISRAEL, Y., BERNAS, B. and YAHALOM, A., *Analytica chim. Acta,* **36**, 526 (1966)
78. COLSON, A.F., *Analyst,* **88**, 26 (1963)
79. BELCHER, R. and CLARK, S.J., *Analytica chim. Acta,* **8**, 222 (1953)
80. LEONARD, M.A., *Analyst,* **88**, 404 (1963)
81. YAMAMURA, S.S., KUSSY, M.E. and REIN, J.E., *Analyt. Chem.,* **33**, 1655 (1961)
82. COMBS, H.F. and GROVE, E.L., *Talanta,* **17**, 599 (1970)
83. ORENBERG, J.B. and MORRIS, M.D., *Analyt. Chem.,* **39**, 1776 (1967)
84. CURRAN, D.J. and FLETCHER, K.S., *Analyt. Chem.,* **41**, 267 (1969)
85. HARZDORF, C., *Z. analyt. Chem.,* **233**, 348 (1968)
86. HARZDORF, C., *Z. analyt. Chem.,* **227**, 161 (1967)
87. MEGREGIAN, S., In *Colorimetric Determination of Non-metals* (Ed. D.F. Boltz), Interscience, New York (1958)
88. LEONARD, M.A. and WEST, T.S., *J. chem. Soc.,* 4477 (1960)
89. ANFALT, T. and JAGNER, D., *Analytica chim. Acta,* **70**, 365 (1974)
90. BELCHER, R., LEONARD, M.A. and WEST, T.S., *J. chem. Soc.,* 2390 (1958)
91. GREENHALGH, R. and RILEY, J.P., *Analytica chim. Acta.,* **25**, 179 (1961)
92. BELCHER, R. and WEST, T.S., *Talanta,* **8**, 863 (1961)
93. Report prepared by the Fluorine sub-committee of the Analytical Methods Committee of the S.A.C. *Analyst,* **96**, 384 (1971)
94. CROSBY, N.T., DENNIS, A.L. and STEPHENS, J.G., *Analyst,* **93**, 643 (1968)
95. HAARSMA, J.P.S. and AGTERDENBOS, J., *Talanta,* **18**, 747 (1971)
96. AL-ANI, K. and LEONARD, M.A., *Analyst,* **95**, 1039 (1970)
97. LAIRD, C.K. and LEONARD, M.A., *Talanta,* **17**, 173 (1970)
98. WEST, P.W., LYLES, G.R. and MILLER, J.L., *Environ. Sci. & Technol.,* **4**, 487 (1970)
99. BAILEY, D.L.R., KILLICK, C.M. and TROTT, P.E., *Report Warren Springs Laboratory,* LR 129 (AP) (1970)
100. MONTERIOLO, S.C. and PEPE, A., *Pure appl. Chem.,* **24**, 707 (1970)
101. CHAN, K.M. and RILEY, J.P., *Analytica chim. Acta,* **35**, 365 (1966)
102. KLETSCH, R.A. and RICHARDS, F.A., *Analyt. Chem.,* **42**, 1435 (1970)
103. HARGREAVES, J.A., INGRAM, G.S. and COX, D.L., *Analyst,* **95**, 177 (1970)
104. SCHAFER, H.N.S., *Analyt. Chem.,* **35**, 53 (1963)
105. HALL, A. and WALSH, J.N., *Analytica chim. Acta,* **45**, 341 (1969)
106. JOHNSON, C.A. and LEONARD, M.A., *Analyst,* **86**, 101 (1961)
107. LEONARD, M.A., *Symposium on the Determination of Anion-forming Elements,* Analytical Division of the Chemical Society, Swansea, September (1976)
108. MEGREGIAN, S., *Analyt. Chem.,* **26**, 1161 (1954)
109. SARMA, P.L., *Analyt. Chem.,* **36**, 1684 (1964)
110. DIXON, E.J., *Analyst,* **95**, 272 (1970)
111. HUANG, P.M. and JACKSON, M.L., *Am. Miner.,* **52**, 1503 (1967)

112. SEN GUPTA, J.G., *Analytica chim. Acta,* **42**, 119 (1968)
113. *Methods for Detection of Toxic Substances in Air.* H.M. Factory Inspectorate No. 19. H.M.S.O., London (1970)
114. ADAMS, D.F., KOPPE, R.K. and MATZEK, N.E., *Analyt. Chem.,* **33**, 117 (1961)
115. FERRARI, H.J., GERONIMO, F.C. and BRANCONE, L.M., *Microchem. J.,* **5**, 617 (1961)
116. *Manual on Industrial Water and Industrial Waste Water.* A.S.T.M. Special publication No. 148-F, 2nd edn, 1962 printing
117. BELLACK, E. and SCHOUBOE, P.J., *Analyt. Chem.,* **30**, 2032 (1958)
118. *Standard Methods for the Examination of Water and Waste Water.* American Public Health Association, New York, 12th edn, 144–146 (1965)
119. MEYLING, A.H. and MEYLING, J., *Analyst,* **88**, 84 (1963)
120. *British Standards Institute,* B.S. 2690: Pt 4 (1967)
121. PALIN, A.T., *J. Am. Wat. Wks Ass.,* **59**, 255 (1967)
122. Reference 118. p. 142
123. BERTOLACINI, R.J. and BARNEY, J.E., *Analyt. Chem.,* **30**, 202 (1958)
124. HAYASHI, K., DANZUKA, T. and UENO, K., *Talanta,* **4**, 126 (1960)
125. HUTCHINSON, K.A., *Diss. Austr.,* **24**, 4372 (1964)
126. MACDONALD, A.M.G. and TOTH, K., *Analytica chim. Acta,* **41**, 99 (1968)
127. EVANS, P.A., MOODY, G.J. and THOMAS, J.D.R., *Lab. Pract.,* **20**, 644 (1971)
128. FRANT, M.S. and ROSS, J.W., *Analyt. Chem.,* **40**, 1169 (1968)
129. ANFÄLT, T. and JAGNER, D., *Analytica chim. Acta,* **47**, 483 (1969)
130. ANFÄLT, T. and JAGNER, D., *Analytica chim. Acta,* **50**, 23 (1970)
131. LINGANE, J.J., *Analyt. Chem.,* **40**, 935 (1968)
132. LINGANE, J.J., *Analyt. Chem.,* **39**, 881 (1967)
133. FRANCIS, H.J., DEONARINE, J.H. and PERSING, D.D., *Microchem. J.,* **14**, 581 (1969)
134. ERIKSSON, T. and JOHANSSON, G., *Analytica chim. Acta,* **52**, 465 (1970)
135. HASSAN, S.S.M., *Mikrochim. Acta,* 889 (1974)
136. SELIG, W., *Mikrochim. Acta,* 87 (1973)
137. PAVEL, J., KUEBLER, R. and WAGNER, H., *Microchem. J.,* **15**, 192 (1970)
138. BAUMANN, E.W., *Analytica chim. Acta,* **54**, 189 (1971)
139. DURST, R.A., *Analyt. Chem.,* **40**, 931 (1968)
140. BOCK, R. and STRECKER, S., *Z. analyt. Chem.,* **235**, 322 (1968)
141. VICKERY, B. and VICKERY, M.L., *Analyst,* **101**, 445 (1976)
142. EVANS, L., HOYLE, R.D. and MACASKILL, J.B., *N. Z. Jl Sci.,* **13**, 143 (1970)
143. SHANE, N. and MIELE, D., *J. pharm. Sci.,* **57**, 1260 (1968)
144. LEVAGGI, D.A., OYUNG, W. and FELDSTEIN, M., *J. Air Pollut. Control Ass.,* **21**, 277 (1971)
145. SINGER, L. and ARMSTRONG, W.D., *Arch. Oral, Biol.,* **14**, 1343 (1969)
146. TUSL, J., *Clin. chim. Acta,.* **27**, 216 (1970)
147. WOODWARD, B., TAYLOR, N.F. and BRUNT, R.V., *Analyt. Biochem.,* **36**, 303 (1970)
148. JAGNER, D. and PAVLOVA, V., *Analytica chim. Acta.,* **60**, 153 (1972)
149. SINGER, L. and ARMSTRONG, W.D., *Analyt. Chem.,* **40**, 613 (1968)
150. PETERS, M.A. and LADD, D.M., *Talanta,* **18**, 655 (1971)
151. HRABECZY-PÁLL, A., TÓTH, K., PUNGOR, E. and VALLÓ, F., *Analytica chim. Acta,* **77**, 278 (1975)
152. Orion Research Incorp., *Analytical Methods Guide.* 9th edn (1978)
153. FOREMAN, J.K., *Analyst,* **94**, 425 (1969)
154. YULE, H.P., *Analyt. Chem.,* **37**, 129 (1965); **38**, 818 (1966)
155. ENGLAND, E.A.M., HONSBY, J.B., JONES, W.T. and TERREY, D.R., *Analytica chim. Acta,* **40**, 365 (1968)
156. PLASKIN, I.N., BELYAKOV, M.A. and STARCHIK, L.P., *Atomn. Energ.,* **13**, 374 (1962)
157. BEWERS, J.M. and FLACK, F.C., *Analyst,* **94**, 1, 7 (1969)
158. MARKOWITZ, S.S. and MAHONEY, J.D., *Analyt. Chem.,* **34**, 399 (1962)
159. HISLOP, J.S., PRATCHETT, A.G. and WILLIAMS, D.R., *Analyst,* **96**, 117 (1971)
160. KOSTA, L. and SLUNECKO, J., *Analyt. Chem.,* **42**, 831 (1970)
161. CARMICHAEL, I.A. and WHITLEY, J.E., *Analyst,* **94**, 737 (1969)
162. KUDAHL, J.N., FREMLIN, J.H. and HARDWICK, J.L., '*Radioisotopes in the Physical Sciences and Industry',* Vol. II, 317
163. PRICE, M.J. and WALKER, O.J., *Analyt. Chem.,* **24**, 1593 (1952)
164. LINDE, H.W., *Analyt. Chem.,* **31**, 2092 (1959)
165. MCGAUGHEY, C. and STOWELL, E.C., *Analyt. Chem.,* **36**, 2344 (1964)
166. CABELLO-TOMAS, M.L. and WEST, T.S., *Talanta,* **16**, 781 (1969)
167. KNAPP, G., *Mikrochim. Acta,* 467 (1970)

168. HEMS, R.V., KIRKBRIGHT, G.F. and WEST, T.S., *Talanta*, **17**, 433 (1970)
169. KLOCKOW, D., LUDWIG, H. and GIRAUDO, M.A., *Analyt. Chem.*, **42**, 1682 (1970)
170. EVERSON, W.L. and RAMIREZ, E.M., *Analyt. Chem.*, **39**, 1771 (1967)
171. JOHANSSON, C.E., *Talanta*, **17**, 739 (1970)
172. BOND, A.M. and O'DONNELL, T.A., *Analyt. Chem.*, **40**, 560 (1968)
173. WALLIS, C.P., *Talanta*, **5**, 61 (1960)
174. POPOV, A.I. and KNUDSON, G.E., *Analyt. Chem.*, **26**, 892 (1954)
175. ISRAEL, Y., BERNAS, B. and YAHOLOM, A., *Analytica chim. Acta*, **36**, 526 (1966)
176. VENKATESWARLU, P. and SITA, P., *Analyt. Chem.*, **43**, 758 (1971)
177. TAN LAY HAR and WEST, T.S., *Analyt. Chem.*, **43**, 136 (1971)

Hypobromite

Hypobromite solutions are markedly less stable than those of hypochlorite. This has been the subject of several recent investigations[1–3]. Factors that affect the stability include concentration of hypobromite and hydroxide, light, temperature, and presence of foreign ions. The thermodynamic instability causes disproportionation in alkaline solution into bromide and bromate

$$3BrO^- \rightarrow 2Br^- + BrO_3^-$$

Another mode of decomposition is possible both in acid and alkaline media.

$$2HBrO^- \rightarrow 2HBr + O_2$$

$$2BrO^- \rightarrow 2Br^- + O_2$$

Velghe and Claeys[3] investigate the stability of 10^{-1}–10^{-3}N hypobromite solutions stored under various conditions at room temperature. Storage in brown bottles, preferably in the dark is recommended, and becomes essential for stability of solutions $<10^{-2}$N. The above considerations would apply to hypobromite reference standards, samples containing hypobromite for analysis, and hypobromite used as a redox titrant. Hypobromite solutions often contain bromite, bromate and bromide in various amounts. Complete analysis of such solutions is important, and will feature in the methods to be discussed. Hypoiodite solutions are even less stable than those of hypobromite, disproportionating into iodide and iodate.

$$3IO^- \rightarrow 2I^- + IO_3^-$$

A study of its stability is included in the above mentioned investigation by Hashmi *et al*[2].

Determination

Quantitative methods for hypobromite are essentially redox, with either visual or potentiometric end-point.

Hypobromite may be determined using several of the methods given for hypochlorite. In the determination of hypochlorite, potassium bromide is often added to convert it to hypobromite in order to benefit from the more rapid reactions of hypobromite with reducing agents.

$$ClO^- + Br^- \rightarrow BrO^- + Cl^-$$

It is claimed that hypobromite is preferentially destroyed by reaction with phenol or ammonium ions, this being important where species such as bromite and bromate need to be determined in the presence of hypobromite. Recent work has indicated that these expedients are not sufficiently specific for use in quantitative analysis. This will be discussed more fully below.

Like several other bromine-containing anions hypobromite can be reduced by SO_2 to bromide, and then determined in this form. This is conveniently done by adding potassium bisulphite and dilute H_2SO_4 and boiling off the excess SO_2.

Redox titrimetric methods

1. Iodimetric methods

The classical iodimetric method, namely liberation of iodine from KI and its titration with standard thiosulphate is over 50 years old. Though it still features in modern analysis it has been generally superseded by other redox methods capable of giving some measure of selectivity.

2. Ascorbimetric methods

Erdey and Vigh[4] have used ascorbic acid as the basis of indirect redox methods for hypobromite.

In one procedure excess of standard thallium sulphate is added to the hypobromite and the remaining Tl^{3+} ions titrated with standard ascorbic acid using variamine blue as indicator.

$$Tl^{3+} + C_6H_8O_6 \rightarrow Tl^+ + C_6H_6O_6 + 2H^+$$

Experimental details are given in the section on hypochlorite which may also be determined by the same method. Hashmi *et al.*[5] have further examined the method and report that the reaction proceeds via bromine, and that any bromite or bromate present are determined as well. In this respect it is similar to the iodimetric method for hypobromite, being unselective.

Another indirect ascorbimetric method[6] involves the ascorbic acid–hexacyanoferrate(III) reaction. Hypobromite, like hypochlorite, reacts with $K_4Fe(CN)_6$ giving an equivalent amount of $K_3Fe(CN)_6$ which can be titrated with standard ascorbic acid.

$$C_6H_8O_6 + 2[Fe(CN)_6]^{3-} \rightarrow C_6H_6O_6 + 2[Fe(CN)_6]^{4-} + 2H$$

3. Using arsenic(III)

A direct titration of hypobromite with arsenic(III) has been reported by Hashmi *et al.*[5] in which tartrazine is used as indicator. Any bromite present does not react with the arsenic(III) until the hypobromite reaction is complete. The indicator is bleached[7] by hypobromite, but not by bromite or bromate.

The procedure is criticized by later workers for reason of its inconvenient end-point, which requires a preliminary titration with the indicator used externally[8].

Anderson and Madsen[10] use a potentiometric end-point. This is described in the section on electrochemical methods.

The use of arsenic(III) is included in a method by Hashmi and Ayaz[9] for total analysis of solutions containing hypobromite, bromite and bromate. The essential steps are as follows:

1. Iodimetric determination of $BrO^- + BrO_2^- + BrO_3^-$ by titration of iodine liberated from KI with standard thiosulphate.
2. Destruction of hypobromite by addition of ammonium sulphate to a second aliquot, followed by iodimetric determination of $BrO_2^- + BrO_3^-$.

$$4BrO^- + 2NH_4^+ \rightarrow 4Br^- + N_2 + 4H_2O$$

3. Selective reduction of hypobromite and bromite in a third aliquot by addition of excess arsenic(III) followed by a back-titration using standard iodine.
4. Destruction of hypobromite in a fourth aliquot by addition of ammonium sulphate followed by (3) to give hypobromite alone.

The procedure which is given in the bromite section is criticized by Velghe and Claeys[8] on the grounds of the excessive waiting time required, an interfering reaction between ammonium ions and bromite (a fact that had also been reported by earlier workers) and the need for three standard solutions. Anderson and Madsen[10] note that the method was applied only to high hypobromite: bromite ratios, and that it fails where bromite is in excess of hypobromite.

Velghe and Claeys[8] describe a simpler alternative approach to the determination of hypobromite, bromite and bromate in mixtures based on the use of arsenic(III) only. The essential steps are:

1. Determination of hypobromite is based on the fast reaction with arsenic(III) in alkaline medium.

   $$BrO^- + AsO_3^{3-} \rightarrow Br^- + AsO_4^{3-}$$

   In this medium bromate is inactive. Bromite would react slowly according to the reaction

   $$BrO_2^- + 2AsO_3^{3-} \rightarrow Br^- + 2AsO_4^{3-}$$

   but this is avoided when the titration is made by adding arsenic(III) solution from the burette. A reversible indicator which is not quickly destroyed is required. Bromothymol blue, quinoline yellow, or epsilon blue are suitable.
2. Bromite is determined after removal of hypobromite by the arsenic(III) titration. Because of its slow reaction with arsenic(III) its determination is usually based on adding a known excess of arsenic(III) followed by a back-titration. Velghe and Claeys find that a more rapid method can be based on the reaction of bromite with a large excess of iodide.

   $$BrO_2^- + 4I^- + 2H_2O \rightarrow Br^- + 2I_2 + 4OH^-$$

The resulting iodine is titrated with arsenic(III) in weakly alkaline solution.

$$AsO_3^{3-} + I_2 + H_2O \rightarrow AsO_4^{3-} + 2I^- + 2H^+$$

3. Titration of all three anions with arsenic(III) is made in dilute HCl medium using quinoline yellow as reversible indicator.

$$BrO^- + AsO_3^{3-} \rightarrow Br^- + AsO_4^{3-}$$

$$BrO_2^- + 2AsO_3^{3-} \rightarrow Br^- + 2AsO_4^{3-}$$

$$BrO_3^- + 3AsO_3^{3-} \rightarrow Br^- + 3AsO_4^{3-}$$

This titration must be carried out with the sample solution (containing hypobromite, bromite and bromate) in the burette because of the volatility of bromine formed on acidification of hypobromite solutions.

Titrimetric analysis of hypobromite solutions[8] containing bromite and bromate

Reagents

Standard 0.025M (0.1N) arsenic(III) solution:
Molarity stated assumes use of As_2O_3. For preparation of As(III) see p. 9.
Buffer solution: A borax buffer solution of pH 8.3.
Indicator solutions:
Bromothymol blue: 0.05%.
0.05 g of solid dissolved in 100 mℓ of water or 0.04M NaOH.
Quinoline yellow:
Prepare in the same way as bromothymol blue.

Procedure

Determination of hypobromite: Titrate 25.00 mℓ of the hypobromite solution with 0.025M arsenic(III) to about 0.2 mℓ before the end-point. Add 25 mℓ of the pH 8.3 buffer solution and 0.5 mℓ of 0.05% bromothymol blue solution. Continue the titration to a colour change from yellow-green to blue-green.

Determination of bromite: To the reaction mixture after the determination of BrO^-, add 5 mℓ of 20% KI solution and titrate the liberated I_2 using 0.025M arsenic(III), with addition of starch near the end-point. The colour change is from mauve to blue-green.

Determination of hypobromite, bromite and bromate: Add 12 mℓ of 6M HCl and 0.5 mℓ of quinoline yellow to 25.00 mℓ of 0.025M arsenic(III) solution contained in a conical flask. Titrate with the hypobromite solution to a colour change from yellow to colourless.

The bromate content is obtained by subtracting the sum of the hypobromite and bromite from the total of all three anions obtained in the last procedure.

---

4. Miscellaneous redox methods

Erdey and Buzas[11] have used hydrogen peroxide as titrant and lucigenin as indicator for redox titration of hypobromite, this being the most succesful determination[12] for a number of substances with hydrogen peroxide.

Another redox method reported[13] uses vanadium(IV) in an indirect procedure with iron(II).

Electrochemical methods

Anderson and Madsen[10] have reported the use of a potentiometric method for the selective determination of hypobromite and bromite. The selectivity is based on the catalytic effect of osmium tetroxide on the bromite–arsenic(III) reaction. Two alternative procedures are given, one based on the slowness of the reaction between $K_4Fe(CN)_6$ and bromite, which enables hypobromite to be determined in its presence.

The other is based on the effect of osmium tetroxide on the bromite–arsenic(III) reaction. In the absence of the catalyst the reaction is sufficiently slow for hypobromite only to be determined. The procedure, which may also be applied in the presence of bromate and bromide without interference, is given at the end of this section.

An extended form of the method has been described in which any bromate or bromide present are also determined, using potassium permanganate and silver nitrate respectively[14]. This procedure is given in the bromate section.

Fuchs and Landsberg discuss the factors that influence the determination of hypobromite and bromite when present together, and describe methods for their simultaneous determination using chromopotentiometry employing a gold electrode as well as by conventional polarography.

Consecutive micro-potentiometric determination[10] of hypobromite and bromate

Reagents

Arsenic(III), 0.0025M:

Weigh accurately the appropriate amount of As_2O_3 into a solution of 4 g of NaOH dissolved in 25 mℓ of water. Make acid to alizarin with dilute H_2SO_4. Add 100 mℓ of saturated sodium bicarbonate solution and dilute to 1ℓ.

OsO_4 catalyst: 0.1 % solution in 0.3M NaOH.

Electrodes: Platinum and saturated calomel.

Procedure

Dilute 1 mℓ of the BrO^-–BrO_2^- mixture with 8 mℓ of 0.3M sodium bicarbonate. Titrate with the As(III) solution. The titre represents BrO^-. Add 1 mℓ of 1.5M NaOH and 1 drop of 0.1 % OsO_4, and continue the titration.

$$\text{Total titre} \equiv BrO^- + BrO_2^-$$

The basic equations have been given earlier in this section.

Notes

1. The optimum pH for the bromite titration is 9.7–9.9.

2. Addition of OsO_4 to a bromite solution containing undestroyed hypobromite produces incorrect results due to the catalytic effect of OsO_4 on the decomposition of hypobromite.
3. If the hypobromite content is small in relation to bromite an exact determination of hypobromite requires a repeat determination using an arsenic(III) concentration appropriate for good end-point location.
4. The method may be applied in the presence of bromate and bromide without interference.

Determination of hypobromite in the presence of other halogen-containing anions

Several of the hypobromite methods have been discussed in connection with the presence of other halogen-containing ions. For convenience these are summarized in *Table 34*.

Table 34 Determination of hypobromite in presence of other halogen-containing anions

Anions present				
BrO_2^-	BrO_3^-	ClO^-	Br^-	*Ref.*
×	×			9
×	×		×	10
×				15
×	×			8
		×		4
×				7
×	×		×	14

References

1. POLAK, H.L., FEENSTRA, G. and SLAGMAN, J., *Talanta,* **13**, 715 (1966)
2. HASHMI, M.H., AYAZ, A.A., RASHID, A. and ALI, E., *Analyt. Chem.*, **36**, 1379 (1964)
3. VELGHE, N. and CLAEYS, A., *Talanta,* **19**, 1555 (1972)
4. ERDEY, L. and VIGH, K., *Talanta,* **10**, 439 (1963)
5. HASHMI, M.H., RASHID, A., AYAZ, A.A. and CHUGHTAI, N.A., *Analyt. Chem.*, **38**, 507 (1966)
6. ERDEY, L. and SVEHLA, G., *Z. analyt. Chem.*, **167**, 164 (1959); *Analyt. Abstr.*, **7**, 122 (1960)
7. HASHMI, M.H. and AYAZ, A.A., *Analyst,* **89**, 147 (1964)
8. VELGHE, N. and CLAEYS, A., *Analytica chim. Acta,* **60**, 377 (1972)
9. HASHMI, M.H. and AYAZ, A.A., *Analyt. Chem.*, **35**, 908 (1963)
10. ANDERSEN, T. and MADSEN, H.E.L., *Analyt. Chem.*, **37**, 49 (1965)
11. ERDEY, L. and BUZAS, I., *Acta chim. hung.*, **6**, 77 (1955)
12. BERKA, A., VULTERIN, J. and ZYKA, J., *New Redox Titrants,* Pergamon Press, Oxford, 102 (1965)
13. TANDON, J.P. and CHAWIA, K.L., *Bull. chem. Soc. Japan,* **39**, 254 (1966); *Analyt. Abstr.*, **15**, 670 (1968)
14. NORKUS, P.K. and STULG'ENE, S.P., *Zh. analit. Khim.*, **24**, 1565 (1969); *Analyt. Abstr.*, **20**, 3029 (1971)
15. FUCHS, H. and LANDSBERG, R., *Analytica chim. Acta,* **45**, 505 (1969)

Hypochlorite

Determination of hypochlorite is important industrially in connection with bleaching baths and water analysis. In the latter case, the total available chlorine includes hypochlorite as well as molecular chlorine and chloramines.

Classical redox titrimetry is still the principal method in use for analysis of hypochlorites. Recently there has been a tendency to develop electro-analytical methods, these lending themselves more easily to automation.

Separation

Thielemann[24] reports a separation of hypochlorite, chlorite, chlorate and perchlorate by thin layer and paper chromatography. Using Silufol UV 254 plates and butanol–pyridine–aq. NH_3 (2:2:1) as solvent, separation is effected in 30 min.

Determination

Hypochlorite is a powerful oxidant as indicated by the standard potential in alkaline solution.

$$ClO^- + H_2O + 2e \rightleftharpoons Cl^- + 2OH^- \qquad E^0 = +0.89\ V$$

For comparison the potentials for manganate/manganese dioxide and permanganate/manganate in alkaline solution are 0.60 and 0.56 V respectively.

Titrimetric methods

Assay of hypochlorite using sodium arsenite was used as long ago as 1835 by Gay-Lussac. A wide selection of redox reagents has been proposed, some of which are of academic interest only. Two standard texts on redox methods give a comprehensive account of their application to determination of hypochlorite and these should be consulted for additional information[1,2].

In keeping with several other chlorine anions, hypochlorite can be reduced by SO_2 to chloride and then determined in this form. A convenient way of doing this is to add 1% potassium bisulphite solution in a dilute H_2SO_4 medium, and then boil off the excess SO_2.

The present account, while including the more important classical methods, will be largely concerned with contemporary methods.

1. Using iodimetric methods and arsenic(III)

Iodimetric methods may be performed in several ways. Hypochlorite will oxidize iodide to iodine in acid solution and this may be titrated with standard thiosulphate using a starch end-point.

$$ClO^- + 2I^- + 2H^+ \rightarrow Cl^- + I_2 + H_2O$$

This procedure is often recommended for standardization of a sodium hypochlorite solution to be used as redox titrant. It is also applicable to the determination of 'available chlorine' in bleaching powder, this having an indefinite composition but approximating to CaCl(OCl). The 'available chlorine' is equivalent to the amount of iodine liberated on treatment with acetic acid or H_2SO_4, and is expressed as a percentage by weight of the bleaching powder.

Direct visual titration of hypochlorite with standard arsenic(III) is not possible due to destruction of indicators by the hypochlorite. As an alternative to the titration of liberated iodine with thiosulphate, a standard arsenic(III) solution may be used, again with starch to detect the end-point.

A better method is to add excess of a standard arsenic(III) solution to the hypochlorite followed by an excess of sodium bicarbonate, and then determine the amount of unreacted arsenic(III) using standard iodine.

$$H_3AsO_3 + I_2 + H_2O \rightarrow HAsO_4^{2-} + 4H^+ + 2I^-$$

This procedure is not subject to interference from chlorate, chlorite or perchlorate, and is recommended by the Association of Official Analytical Chemists[3] for determination of hypochlorite in pesticide solutions.

The back-titration of arsenic(III) may be made using a standard hypochlorite solution. Here Bordeaux is suitable as an irreversible indicator[4] and Tartrazine as a reversible indicator (provided bromide is added in the latter case to convert hypochlorite to hypobromite)[5].

Titration of a standard arsenic(III) solution by addition of hypochlorite as titrant may be used for determination of the hypochlorite. As well as the two indicators given above bromocresol purple[6] and bromothymol blue[7] function effectively as reversible indicators. Both indicators are used in a borate-buffered medium with osmic acid present as catalyst.

When titrating a reducing agent such as arsenic(III) with hypochlorite, bromide is usually added to the reductant in order to convert the hypochlorite to hypobromite.

$$ClO^- + Br^- \rightarrow BrO^- + Cl^-$$

The reason is that although hypochlorite is a stronger oxidant than hypobromite, hypobromite often reacts more rapidly with reducing agents.

It was noted earlier that direct visual titration of hypochlorite with standard arsenic(III) was not possible due to destruction of indicators by the strongly oxidizing hypochlorite. It is, however, possible to use an external indicator in the form of starch–KI papers. Sodium bicarbonate is added to an aliquot of hypochlorite and a titration made with standard arsenic(III). The end-point is indicated when a drop of solution fails to give a blue colour when added to the paper. The procedure is recommended by British Standards[8] for assay of sodium hypochlorite.

Iodimetric determination of hypochlorite

Procedure
To a 25-mℓ aliquot containing hypochlorite add about 1 g of KI and 10 mℓ of 2M H_2SO_4. Titrate the liberated iodine with standard thiosulphate using starch near the end-point.

---

2. Using ascorbic acid
Analytical methods based on ascorbic acid have been developed for many years by Erdey and co-workers[9–11].

An indirect method for hypochlorite depends on oxidation of hexacyanoferrate(II) to hexacyanoferrate(III) which is subsequently titrated with standard ascorbic acid.

$$ClO^- + 2[Fe(CN)_6]^{4-} + 2H^+ \rightarrow Cl^- + 2[Fe(CN)_6]^{3-} + H_2O$$

$$C_6H_8O_6 + 2[Fe(CN)_6]^{3-} \rightarrow C_6H_6O_6 + 2[Fe(CN_6]^{4-} + 2H^+$$

Dichlorophenolindophenol is used as indicator.

Another procedure depends on oxidation of thallium(I) to thallium(III) by hypochlorite followed by titration of the thallium(III) with standard ascorbic acid.

$$ClO^- + Tl^+ + 2H^+ \rightarrow Tl^{3+} + Cl^- + H_2O$$

$$Tl^{3+} + C_6H_8O_6 \rightarrow Tl^+ + C_6H_6O_6 + 2H^+$$

Variamine blue is employed as indicator. The method may be used for hypobromite in addition to hypochlorite. A particular advantage of the system is that it is not necessary to work in a CO_2 atmosphere. The investigators state that the method suffers no interference from chlorite. This has been confirmed for chlorite:hypochlorite ratios up to 1, and the reaction mechanism clarified[12].

Titrimetric determination of hypochlorite using ascorbic acid[11]

Reagents
Ascorbic acid: 0.05M (0.1N).
  Dissolve 9.0 g of pure ascorbic acid in 1ℓ of distilled water. Standardize against potassium iodate or hexacyanoferrate(III) (Note 1). Stored in air, solutions of ascorbic acid decompose with a 1% daily loss in concentration. This can be reduced if stored under CO_2.
Thallium(I) standard solution: 0.025M (0.1N).
  Dissolve 12.622 g of Tl(I) sulphate in water and make up to 1ℓ.
Acetic acid–acetate buffer.
  Mix 1 volume of 2M sodium acetate with 2 volumes of 2M acetic acid.
Variamine blue indicator mixture:
  Mix 1 part of Variamine blue (4-amino-4′-methoxydiphenylamine hydrochloride) with 400 parts of NaCl. About 0.2 g is used for each titration.

Procedure

To a solution of 25–250 mg ClO^- add excess (10–55 mℓ) of 0.025M Tl_2SO_4. Mix well, add 15 mℓ of 2M HCl and mix again. Add 2M NaOH until a precipitate begins to form, then add 10 mℓ of the buffer.

After addition of about 0.2 g of Variamine blue indicator titrate with 0.05M ascorbic acid until the blue indicator colour vanishes. The procedure is similar at the 0.005M level.

Notes

1. Standardization of ascorbic acid against hexacyanoferrate may be done as follows:
   Weigh $K_3Fe(CN)_6$ (0.6–0.7 g) into a conical flask and dissolve in 15–20 mℓ of water, add 2 g of $KHCO_3$ and 0.5 g of a 1:500 ground mixture of 2,6-dichlorophenolindophenol and NaCl. Titrate the solution with ascorbic acid solution until the blue colour just disappears.
   The equation on which the calculation is based has been given above.
2. The method is suitable for determination of active chlorine in chlorinated lime.

Spectroscopic methods

Hypochlorites may be determined by means of the intense yellow colour formed with benzidine in dilute HCl, but owing to the known carcinogenic properties of benzidine the method should now be discouraged[13].

The absorption maximum for hypochlorite in the UV is 290 nm. However, the absorptivity is rather low and the overlap of related species, namely chlorite and chlorine dioxide, detracts from its use in the selective determination of hypochorite in their presence.

A method based on its reaction with *o*-tolidine has been developed in which the extinction is measured at 436 nm. Like several other reagents including 3,3′-dimethylnaphthidine and NN′–diethyl-*p*-phenylenediamine, the reaction is not specific but depends on the redox potentials involved. The above mentioned reagents are frequently used for determination of 'total available chlorine' in water.

An application of the *o*-tolidine method has been made to determination of hypochlorite in effluents also containing cyanide, chromates, and nitrite. Hypochlorite at levels equivalent to 10 µg of Cl per litre has been determined[14] by measurement of the extinction with *o*-tolidine at 436 nm.

A more selective reagent Syringaldazine (bis-(4-hydroxy-3,5-dimethoxybenzylidene)hydrazine) has recently appeared. This may be applied to 'free chlorine' in water, the reagent having no response to chloramines[15]. The stoichiometry is 1:1 and the optimum conditions pH 7 and 530 nm. The response is rectilinear up to 1 ppm of Cl_2.

Babko, Terletskaya and Dubovenko[16] find that ClO^- produces a 10-fold increase in the fluorescence of a mixture of hydrogen peroxide and luminol (5 amino 2,3-dihydrophthalazine-1,4-dione). A method based on this gives a sensitivity of 0.5 g ClO^- per 10 mℓ of solution.

Electrochemical methods

Considering first potentiometric methods, hypochlorite can be titrated with copper(I) chloride[17].

Another method[18] involves successive potentiometric titration of hypochlorite, chlorite, chlorate and chloride. Hypochlorite is titrated with 0.025M arsenic(III) solution using a platinum indicator electrode at a pH of above 8. Chlorite and chlorate are titrated at pH 8–12 and in a dilute H_2SO_4 medium respectively, osmium tetroxide being employed as catalyst in each instance. The authors claim that for hypochlorite solutions contaminated with small amounts of chlorite, the results are more accurate than using an iodimetric procedure. Experimental details are given in the section on chlorate.

Vulterin and Hovorka[19] use iron(II) for the potentiometric determination of hypochlorite, using platinum and saturated calomel electrodes. Chloride, chlorate, iodate, sulphate and nitrate interfere at high concentration only, chlorite is co-titrated, but bromide, iodide, and phosphate require removal.

Hypochlorite is irreversibly reduced at a dropping mercury electrode at all pH values between 3.6 and 11.0, the half-wave potential in neutral solution being +0.08 V. Drozdetskaya and Il'in[20] have published a polarographic method for hypochlorite employing a platinum micro-electrode and 4M NaCl as supporting electrolyte. Chlorite does not interfere.

Several coulometric methods are available. Gruendler and Holzapfel[21] titrate with 0.1M Fe(II) generated in acetate buffer at pH 4.3–4.7 while passing nitrogen through the solution. Chloride, chlorate, perchlorate and sulphate do not interfere and neither does nitrate up to a 10-fold excess over hypochlorite. Chlorite is titrated with the hypochlorite. Fleet, Ho and Tenygl[22] have recently developed a fully automatic method for determination of sodium hypochlorite (and hydrogen peroxide) in bleaching baths, based on the use of a porous catalytic Ag electrode. In each case oxygen is liberated and measured coulometrically by the electrode. Sodium hypochlorite reacts with hydrogen peroxide in an alkaline medium to liberate oxygen:

$$NaClO + H_2O_2 \rightarrow NaCl + H_2O + O_2$$

At Ag working electrode: $O_2 + 2H_2O + 4e \rightarrow 4OH^-$

At Pt counter electrode: $4OH^- \rightarrow O_2 + 2H_2O + 4e$

Miscellaneous methods

Continuous enthalpimetric titration of hypochlorite in bleaching baths has been proposed using 10% Na_2SO_3 or 5% $Na_2S_2O_3$ as reagents[23]. The respective heats of reaction are 1363 and 961 cal g^{-1}, and the error found ±2.3 per cent.

References

1. KOLTHOFF, I.M. and BELCHER, R., *Volumetric Analysis*, III, Interscience, New York (1957)
2. BERKA, A., VULTERIN, J. and ZYKA, J., *Newer Redox Titrants*, Pergamon Press, Oxford (1965)

3. *Official Methods of Analysis of the Association of Official Analytical Chemists,* 11th edn, 97, 257 (1970)
4. KOLTHOFF, I.M. and STENGER, V.A., *Ind. Engng Chem. analyt. Edn,* **7**, 79 (1935)
5. BELCHER, R., *Analytica chim. Acta,* **4**, 468 (1950)
6. BELCHER, R., EL-KHIAMI, I. and STEPHEN, W.I., *Talanta,* **12**, 775 (1965)
7. CERANA, L.A., *Rev. Facultad. Ing. Quim. Univ. Nac. del Littoral, Argentina,* **29**, 105 (1960)
8. *British Standard* 4426 (1969)
9. ERDEY, L. and SVEHLA, G., *Chemist Analyst,* **52**, 24 (1963)
10. ERDEY, L. and SVEHLA, G., *Z. analyt. Chem.,* **167**, 164 (1959); *Analyt. Abstr.,* **7**, 122 (1960)
11. ERDEY, L. and VIGH, K., *Talanta,* **10**, 439 (1963)
12. HASHMI, M.H., RASHID, A., AYAZ, A.A. and CHUGHTAI, N.A., *Analyt. Chem.,* **38**, 507 (1966)
13. KLUT, H., *Kleine Mitt. Mitgl. Ver. WassVersog.,* **3**, 184 (1927)
14. ZUSE, M., *Galvanotechnik,* **57**, 500 (1966); *Analyt. Abstr.,* **14**, 7933 (1967)
15. BAUSER, R. and RUPE, C.O., *Analyt. Chem.,* **43**, 421 (1971)
16. BABKO, A.K., TERLETSKAYA, A.V. and DUBOVENKO, L.I., *Ukr. khim. Zh.,* **32**, 728 (1966); *Analyt. Abstr.,* **14**, 6807 (1967)
17. KASATKINA, L.A. and YA. SHAPIRO, M., *Zh. analit. Khim.,* **22**, 953 (1967); *Analyt. Abstr.,* **16**, 1253 (1969)
18. NORKUS, P.K. and STULG'ENE, S.P., *Zh. analit. Khim.,* **24**, 884 (1969); *Analyt. Abstr.,* **19**, 4862 (1970)
19. VULTERIN, J. and HOVORKA, J., *Colln Czech chem. Commun. Engl. Edn,* **32**, 4063 (1967); *Analyt. Abstr.,* **16**, 1254 (1969)
20. DROZDETSKAYA, E.P. and IL'IN, K.G., *Zh. analit. Khim.,* **27**, 200 (1972); *Analyt. Abstr.,* **25**, 177 (1973)
21. GRUENDLER, P. and HOLZAPFEL, H., *Talanta,* **17**, 246 (1970)
22. FLEET, B., HO, A.Y.W. and TENYGL, J., *Talanta,* **19**, 317 (1972)
23. STRAFELDA, F. and KROFTOVA, J., *Colln Czech chem. Commun. Engl. Edn,* **33**, 4171 (1968); *Analyt. Abstr.,* **19**, 2226 (1970)
24. THIELEMANN, H., *Mikrochim. Acta,* 746 (1971)

Iodate

Separations

1. Precipitation

Iodate can be separated by precipitation of its sparingly soluble barium salt, a procedure applicable to the analysis of chloride–iodate mixtures where the chloride is to be determined using silver nitrate. Another method utilizes the large tetraphenylarsonium cation, $(C_6H_5)_4As^+$. This precipitates iodate as well as permanganate, perrhenate, perchlorate, periodate, iodide, bromide, fluoride, thiocyanate, chromate, molybdate and tungstate. As well as separating iodate, it can also be used for its determination. This will be discussed at various points within this section.

2. Ion-exchange

Iodate, chlorate and bromate can be separated in millimolar amounts using anion-exchange. Further details are given in the chlorate section.

3. Paper and thin-layer chromatography

Table 25 (in the chlorate section) contains data on several paper and TLC methods for separation of iodate. In addition, the following methods are available.

Palagyi and Zaduban[1] separate iodate, iodide and periodate on silica gel using methanol-25% aq. NH_3–H_2O–10% aq. acetic acid (18:2:2:1). Iodide, iodate, tellurite, phosphate and sulphate are separated on silica gel, Kieselguhr or lanthanum oxide, using acetone–M NH_4OH (1:1) as solvent[2]. More recently Lederer and Polcaro[3] have introduced a TLC method using aluminium oxide, for separation of iodate, periodate, bromate and chromate.

Paper chromatography has been used[4] to separate iodide, iodate and periodate. Whatman No. 4 paper was used, in conjunction with amyl alcohol–pyridine–NH_4OH (3:7:10) as solvent. Glass-fibre chromatography using a number of solvents including isopropanol–1.5 F NH_3 (7:3) is used by Neumann[5] for separation of iodide, iodate and periodate. The author observes that paper chromatography is not satisfactory in this case owing to reduction of periodate, probably to iodate.

4. Coprecipitation

Novikov[6] has reported separation of iodate from periodate by coprecipitation of the latter and ferric hydroxide. By repeating the procedure, a separation of better than 99 per cent is attained.

Determination

Like several other halogen anions, iodate is reduced by SO_2. Determination of the resulting iodide provides an indirect method for iodate determination.

Titrimetric methods

These methods are essentially redox. Several expedients are available for making them more selective, particularly when iodate is accompanied by bromate, chlorate and periodate.

Potassium iodate in pure form is a recognized reference standard in analytical chemistry. As such its reactions with a wide range of reducing species have been the subject of extensive investigation. In many instances, procedures are available for the accurate determination of such species using KIO_3. The same procedures can be used in the reverse sense, namely for determination of iodate.

Iodimetric prcedures are probably the most important ones. They are often capable of giving the selectivity referred to above.

1. Iodimetric

Iodate reacts with iodide in dilute mineral acid giving iodine which can be titrated with standard thiosulphate.

$$IO_3^- + 5I^- + 6H^+ \rightarrow 3I_2 + 3H_2O$$

$$I_2 + 2S_2O_3^{2-} \rightarrow S_4O_6^{2-} + 2I^-$$

The reaction is rapid and capable of high accuracy. Generally it is used for the standardization of thiosulphate solutions, whose strengths can be evaluated in terms of a weight of pure KIO_3. Where iodate is to be determined, a standard solution of thiosulphate is employed.

Titrimetric determination of iodate using sodium thiosulphate

Procedure

To the iodate solution in a volume of 25 mℓ, and containing 0.1–0.15 g IO_3^-, add 2 g of KI and swirl to dissolve. Add 10 mℓ of M HCl and titrate with standard thiosulphate using starch to detect the end-point.

Note

The thiosulphate can be standardized by the same procedure, using an appropriate weight of pure KIO_3 dried at 150 °C.

The above procedure is suitable for assay of $NaIO_3$ or KIO_3 or for analysis of their solutions, but modifications are required if other oxidizing species are present.

Where iodate–periodate mixtures need to be analysed, periodate is usually reduced to iodate in a buffered alkaline solution, using iodide, arsenic(III), manganese(II), sulphate, bromide, etc. Szekeres and co-workers[7,8] have used bromide. In one aliquot the total iodate and periodate are determined by iodimetric titration in the usual way using thiosulphate. In another aliquot periodate is reduced to iodate by addition of KBr and HCl. The solution is made alkaline with $KHCO_3$ and the resulting NaOBr reduced to NaBr by boiling with ethanol. The remaining iodate is titrated iodimetrically as before. In a later improved method, the same investigators use urea in place of ethanol. Belcher and Townshend[9] have developed a method for the same anions, in which periodate is masked with molybdate to give 6-molybdoperiodate. Subsequent demasking is done with oxalic acid. Thus a complete analysis for iodate–periodate can be effected using one aliquot only.

Iodate–bromate mixtures can be analysed in several ways. The sum of both can be determined by iodimetric titration. Then in another aliquot they can be reduced to iodide and bromide by boiling with 1% $KHSO_3$. Iodide can now be determined in the presence of bromide by utilizing its lower redox potential. Details of this are given in the iodide section.

Another approach for iodate in the presence of bromate and chlorate is by reduction in a buffered phthalate solution at pH 5. After 3 min, the resulting iodine is titrated with standard thiosulphate. Bromate and chlorate do not react, but bromate is reduced if a molybdate catalyst is used[10].

Szekeres[11] has described a method by which iodate, periodate, bromate and chlorate in mixtures can be analysed iodimetrically by judicial selection of conditions.

It is also possible to determine iodate iodimetrically by reduction to I^+ under high acidity conditions. In strong acid (4–6M HCl) iodate reacts with iodide in the following way.

$$KIO_3 + 2KI + 6HCl \rightarrow 3ICl + 3KCl + 3H_2O$$

The reaction is the basis of the well-known Andrews method for determination of iodide. Exactly the same procedure can be used for determination of iodate using a known amount of iodide. Details of the experimental procedure are given in the iodide section.

2. Using arsenic(III)

The titration of arsenic(III) with iodate is well established, and constitutes an important method for the determination of arsenic. An accurate standard arsenic(III) solution may be prepared using pure As_2O_3 as reference standard (p. 9), and the iodate–arsenic(III) titration used to determine iodate. Details of the determination are given in the arsenic section.

3. Using hexacyanoferrate(II)

Iodate (as well as bromate and chlorate) reacts with hexacyanoferrate(II) oxidizing it quantitatively to hexacyanoferrate(III). This can be titrated with standard ascorbic acid[12].

$$IO_3^- + 6[Fe(CN)_6]^{4-} + 6H^+ \rightarrow I^- + 6[Fe(CN)_6]^{3-} + 3H_2O$$

Halogens, hypohalites and halites undergo the same reaction. More recent work has employed an improved indicator[13] and an automated potentiometric form of the method has been developed[14].

4. Miscellaneous redox methods

A direct micro titration of iodate using chromium(II) and vanadium(II)–1,10 phenanthroline as redox indicator, has been described[15]. The method is also applicable to analysis of chlorate, bromate and nitrate.

5. Using EDTA

Sparingly soluble compounds containing a metal and the anion to be determined, often form the basis of compleximetric procedures. Vil'borg and Drozdov[16] determine iodate by precipitating lead iodate which is then dissolved in excess standard EDTA in the presence of an ammoniacal buffer. The excess EDTA is back-titrated with zinc sulphate using acid chrome dark blue (C.I. mordant blue 7) as indicator. The same method may also be used for chromate and hexacyanoferrate(III).

Spectrophotometric methods

The iodine liberated when iodate reacts with iodide in acid solution can be used as the basis of a spectrophotometric method for iodate. Lambert and co-workers[17,18] have developed a cadmium iodide–linear starch reagent, the CdI_2 functioning as a source of iodide ions. Further work using the same reagent is reported by Schnepfe[19]. Nitrite is found to interfere but this can be removed using sulphamic acid.

Black and Whittle[20], in a method for halogen residues in swimming pools, use a mixed reagent of leuco crystal violet (4,4′,4″-methylidynetris-(NN-dimethylaniline)) and mercuric chloride for determination of iodine liberated by iodate. The $HgCl_2$ acts as catalyst.

Hashmi, Rashid and Azam[21] are able to determine iodate and bromate simultaneously using a mixture of isoniazid and 2,3,5-triphenyltetrazolium chloride in dilute HCl. This gives a pink colour with iodate at 33 °C; with bromate the colour is only produced at 60 °C. The range for each ion is 10–300 μg in 50 mℓ; the absorbance is measured at 480 nm or 308 nm in each instance. Chlorate does not interfere.

Fuchs, Jungreis, and Ben-Dor[22] use *p*-aminophenol for determination of iodate in amounts of 30 μg and upwards. This reagent is oxidized to the blue indamine dye by mild oxidants. Iodate oxidizes part of the *p*-aminophenol HCl to the quinoneimine, which immediately condenses with unchanged *p*-aminophenol to give the blue dye.

$$O{=}\langle\;\rangle{=}NH + HO{-}\langle\;\rangle{-}NH_2 \rightarrow$$

$$O{=}\langle\;\rangle{=}N{-}\langle\;\rangle{-}NH_2$$

Chlorate and bromate do not interfere, but chloride, bromide, phosphate, Fe^{3+}, and V^{5+} must be absent.

Paslawska[23] has developed a method for traces of iodate (and iodide) using NN′-bis (2-hydroxypropyl)-*o*-phenylenediamine. This forms a red oxidation product with iodate. Iodide present with the iodate is determined after oxidation with bromine, the excess of which is removed using phenol. The range is 0.1–3 μg of iodine $m\ell^{-1}$ (as iodate).

Electroanalytical methods

1. Potentiometric methods

Osmium tetroxide catalyses the reaction between iodate and arsenic(III) or hydrazine sulphate in alkaline medium. Norkus[24] employs a potentiometric titration with platinum and calomel electrodes. At the 20 mg of KIO_3 level, the relative error is ± 0.5 per cent.

Vulterin[25] uses iron(II) as titrant in a phosphoric acid medium, again with osmium tetroxide as catalyst. The iodate is reduced to iodide. A rather different approach is used by Khalifa and Ateya[26]. They react iodate with excess of standard iodide, then back-titrate the excess with standard mercury(II) nitrate.

Ion-selective electrodes have been used for determination of iodate. Iodate is reduced to iodide by heating at 60 °C and at pH 9 with aluminium foil tubes. The resulting iodide is determined using an iodide electrode[27]. Mixtures of iodate and iodide can be analysed over the range 10^{-4}–10^{-5} g $m\ell^{-1}$.

2. Polarographic methods

Both iodate and bromate give single polarographic reduction waves. Reduction processes for iodate in alkaline medium can be summarized by the equation

$$IO_3^- + 6e + 3H_2O \rightarrow I^- + 6OH^-$$

Bromate similarly gives a 6-electron step reduction. Because neither iodate nor bromate interact with sulphite in alkaline medium, they can be determined polarographically in simple vessels open to the air in the presence of sulphite. In addition to eliminating oxygen, the sulphite functions as a supporting electrolyte.

The overvoltage for bromate is much greater than for iodate, thus causing its reduction potential to be much more negative. Their determination can therefore be carried out without mutual interference. Practical details of the determination are given in the monograph by Heyrovsky and Zuman[28]. Neither chlorate nor periodate are reduced at the cathode.

3. Miscellaneous electroanalytical methods

Iodate and iodide can be determined by amperometric titration based on differences in solubility of silver iodate and silver iodide under specified conditions[29].

Kinetic methods

Japanese workers have based an ultra-micro method on the catalytic effect of iodate and iodide on the reduction of the iron(III)–thiocyanate complex[30]. The sum of iodate and iodide is first determined. Then iodide is oxidized to iodine which is extracted into carbon tetrachloride. Iodate remaining in the aqueous phase is determined using the same method. Application of the method has been made to sea water. The range is 0.001–0.01 ppm $IO_3^- + I^-$.

Rodriguez and Pardue[31] utilize the cerium(IV)–arsenic(III) reaction which is catalysed by iodide and osmium. Iodate is inactive but can be determined after reduction to a catalytically active form. Both iodide and iodate can be determined when present together in concentrations down to 10^{-8}M. Relative errors are about 2 per cent. Recent work by Truesdale and Smith[32] on catalysis of the cerium(IV)–arsenic(III) reaction has produced an automatic method for iodide and iodate. It is applied to analysis of river-water.

Miscellaneous methods

An important analytical reaction of iodate is liberation of iodine from acidified KI. Its use in titrimetry is well known. Pennington[33] has used gas-chromatography for evaluating the iodine. The method is suitable for milligram quantities of oxidizing agents capable of liberating iodine from KI quantitatively. A complete determination can be made in 5 min.

A radiometric method has been based on ^{45}Ca-labelled calcium chloride reagent[34]. When the reaction is complete, the aqueous phase shows activity. Oxalate and carbonate react in the same way.

Thermometric titration of KIO_3 in a strong H_2SO_4 medium has been made with 2M potassium thiocyanate. An excellent end-point break is found at a molar ratio of SCN:KIO_3 of 5:7, this corresponding to the reactions

$$5SCN^- + 6IO_3^- + 2H_2O + H^+ \rightarrow 5SO_4^{2-} + 5HCN + 3I_2$$

$$5HCN + 2I_2 + IO_3^- + H^+ \rightarrow 5ICN + 3H_2O$$

A standard deviation of 0.4 per cent was found for 12 determinations[35].

References

1. PALAGYI, S. and ZADUBAN, M., *Chemické. Zvesti*, **23**, 876 (1969); *Analyt. Abstr.*, **20**, 1660 (1971)
2. MOGHISSI, A., *J. Chromat.*, **13**, 542 (1964)
3. LEDERER, M. and POLCARO, C., *J. Chromat.*, **84**, 379 (1973)
4. OBRENOVIC-PALIGORIC, I.D. and CVORIC, J.D., *Bull. Boris Kidrich Inst. nucl. Sci.*, **14**, 95 (1963); *Chem. Abstr.*, **59**, 14555b (1963)
5. NAEUMANN, R., *J. Chromat.*, **18**, 385 (1965)
6. NOVIKOV, A.I., *Zh. analit. Khim.*, **19**, 541 (1964); *Analyt. Abstr.*, **12**, 4534 (1965)
7. SZEKERES, L., KARDOS, E. and RADY, M., *Z. analyt. Chem.*, **160**, 401 (1958); *Analyt. Abstr.*, **5**, 4111 (1958)
8. SZEKERES, L., KARDOS, E. and RADY, M., *Z. analyt. Chem.*, **162**, 430 (1958); *Analyt. Abstr.*, **6**, 1730 (1959)
9. BELCHER, R. and TOWNSHEND, A., *Analytica chim. Acta*, **41**, 395 (1968)
10. KOLTHOFF, I.M. and HUME, D.N., *Ind. Engng Chem. analyt. Edn*, **15**, 174 (1943)
11. SZEKERES, L., *Z. analyt. Chem.*, **172**, 256 (1960); *Analyt. Abstr.*, **7**, 3739 (1960)
12. ERDEY, L. and SVEHLA, G., *Z. analyt. Chem.*, **167**, 164 (1959); *Analyt. Abstr.*, **7**, 122 (1960)
13. ERDEY, L. and KASA, I., *Talanta*, **10**, 1273 (1963)
14. ERDEY, L., SVEHLA, G. and WEBER, O., *Z. analyt. Chem.*, **240**, 91 (1968); *Analyt. Abstr.*, **18**, 12 (1970)
15. LEONARD, M.A., SHAHINE, S.A.E.F. and WILSON, C.L., *Talanta*, **16**, 470 (1969)
16. VIL'BORG, S.S. and DROZDOV, V.A., *Nauch. Dokl Vyssh Shkoty Khim. khim. Teknol.*, 721 (1958); *Analyt. Abstr.*, **7**, 865 (1960)
17. LAMBERT, J.L., ARTHUR, P. and MOORE ,T.E., *Analyt. Chem.*, **23**, 1101 (1951)
18. LAMBERT, J.L., *Analyt. Chem.*, **23**, 1247 (1951)
19. SCHNEPFE, M.M., *Analytica chim. Acta*, **58**, 83 (1972)
20. BLACK, A.P. and WHITTLE, G.P., *J. Am. Wat. Wks Ass.*, **59**, 471 (1967)
21. HASHMI, M.H., RASHID, H.A.A. and AZAM, F., *Analyt. Chem.*, **36**, 2471 (1964)
22. FUCHS, J., JUNGREIS, E. and BEN-DOR, L., *Analytica chim. Acta*, **31**, 187 (1964)
23. PASLAWSKA, S., *Chemia. analit.*, **16**, 951 (1971); *Analyt. Abstr.*, **22**, 3135 (1972)
24. NORKUS, P.K., *Zh. analit. Khim.*, **20**, 88 (1965); *Analyt. Abstr.*, **13**, 3553 (1966)
25. VULTERIN, J., *Colln Czech. Chem. Commun. Engl. Edn*, **31**, 2501 (1966); *Analyt. Abstr.*, **14**, 5398 (1967)
26. KHALIFA, H. and ATEYA, B., *Microchem. J.*, **31**, 147 (1969)
27. PALETTA, B., *Microchem. J.*, **31**, 1210 (1969)
28. HEYROVSKY, J. and ZUMAN, P., *Practical Polarography*, Academic Press, London (1968)
29. MUSHA, S., IKEDA, S. and NISHIDA, G., *Japan Analyst*, **17**, 332 (1968); *Analyt. Abstr.*, **18**, 919 (1970)
30. IWASAKI, I., UTSUMI, S. and YONEHARA, N., *Bull. Chem. Soc. Japan, Pure chem. Sect.*, **85**, 36 (1964); *Analyt. Abstr.*, **12**, 5789 (1965)
31. RODRIGUEZ, P.A. and PARDUE, H.L., *Analyt. Chem.*, **41**, 1376 (1969)
32. TRUESDALE, V.W. and SMITH, P.J., *Analyst*, **100**, 111 (1975)
33. PENNINGTON, S.N., *J. Chromat.*, **36**, 400 (1968)
34. OMBOLY, C., SZARVAS, T. and HORVATH, L., *Radiochem. radioanalyt. Lett.*, **1**, 49 (1969)
35. HARRIES, R.J.N. reported in *Thermometric titrimetry* by Tyrrell, H.J.V. and Beezer, A.E., Chapman and Hall, London (1968)

Iodide

The principal uses of iodides are in photography and pharmaceuticals. In trace amounts iodides are important to animal and plant life. This leads to a minor use as additives.

Basic methods for separation and determination of halides are discussed in the chloride section. To avoid needless repetition these methods will be referred to only in the present section, and emphasis will be directed more to iodide itself.

Separations

Iodide can be separated using a wide range of chromatographic techniques including ion-exchange. These are discussed in the appropriate part of the chloride section. Separation of iodide by solvent extraction has been described by West and Lorica[1]. Here the iodide is complexed with cadmium and extracted in tributylphosphate–butyl methyl ketone. Cyanide and thiocyanate are also extracted and to a lesser extent chloride, bromide, oxalate and nitrate. Fluoride, thiosulphate, sulphate, phosphate, acetate, sulphide, hexacyanoferrate(II) and borate are either poorly extracted or not at all. Several extraction-spectrophotometric methods are known in which the iodide is extracted as the anionic constituent of an ion-pair. Further details of these are given later in this section. Separation of iodide, iodate and periodate by glass-fibre paper chromatography has been described by Naeumann[2]. Various solvent combinations including isopropanol–1.5F NH_3 (7:3) were used. The same ions can be separated on Whatman No. 4 paper using amyl alcohol–pyridine–NH_4OH (3:7:10) as solvent[3].

Where iodide is to be determined in the presence of chloride and bromide. oxidation to iodate can be made without effect on chloride and bromide, this forming the basis of a selective analytical method. An older method for separating these ions was initial precipitation of the silver salts followed by treatment with a mixture of sulphuric and chromic acids. Silver chloride and silver bromide decompose giving chlorine and bromine which can be easily removed. Iodide is oxidized to iodic acid. This is subsequently reduced with SO_2 to iodide and reprecipitated[4] as silver iodide.

Determination

Gravimetric methods

Iodide can be determined gravimetrically as silver iodide using the procedure described for chloride. It is subject to the same interferences. The precipitate has a marked tendency to adsorb various species on its surface. These can be difficult to remove. Application of PFHS has been made by Firsching[5] and this enables a complete analysis of Cl^-–Br^-–I^- mixtures to be made.

Iodide can be selectively precipitated as the palladium salt in the presence of chloride and bromide.

Titrimetric methods

The mercurimetric method described for chloride and bromide is not suitable for iodide due to the relative insolubility of mercury(II) iodide. The first reaction is formation of the tetraiodo complex.

$$4I^- + Hg^{2+} \leftrightharpoons HgI_4{}^{2-}$$

This is followed by precipitation of red mercury(II) iodide

$$Hg^{2+} + HgI_4{}^{2-} \leftrightharpoons 2HgI_2$$

Because the tetraiodo complex dissociates just before the end-point, this comes too soon and does not coincide with the equivalence point.

$$HgI_4{}^{2-} \leftrightharpoons HgI_2 + 2I^-$$

The principal titrimetric methods will now be discussed.

1. Argentimetric methods

Iodide can be determined by the Volhard method using the same procedure described for chloride. The Mohr titration is not suitable for iodide due to adsorption of chromate on the precipitate, this resulting in false end-points.

Titration of iodide using the adsorption indicator method is satisfactory. Eosin (tetrabromofluorescein) is probably the best indicator. As in the titration of bromide, it may be used at a higher acidity than that for fluorescein. Iodide cannot be titrated in the presence of chloride and bromide because these ions are adsorbed on the precipitate surface giving high results. Dextrin, which is often recommended as a protective colloid in the analogous method for chloride, is not suitable for iodide. Recent work by Kapel, Fry and Shelton[6] has investigated a number of surface-active compounds for incorporation in this method. Hydroxypropyl-methyl cellulose is found to give a superior end-point for all three halides (chloride, bromide and iodide); for iodide eosin is confirmed as the best indicator. The investigation indicates that it is not possible to determine the three halides in admixture.

Other indicators recommended for the argentimetric titration of iodide are potassium rhodizonate[7] xylenol orange[8], and *p*-ethoxychrysoidine[9]. Using xylenol orange, it is claimed that iodide can be titrated in the presence of a 10^4-fold excess of chloride. When *p*-ethoxychrysoidine is used, in the presence of excess Ag^+ the indicator is adsorbed as neutral molecules which produce a yellow colour.

2. Using EDTA

De Sousa has developed several compleximetric procedures for determination of iodide in the presence of bromide and chloride. These are described in the chloride section.

Recently Nomura[10] has reported that iodide can be titrated with mercury-(II)-EDTA complex using mercury(II)–methylthymol blue complex as indicator. The determination is based on the formation of a 1:1 complex between mercury(II)–EDTA and iodide (cyanide and thiocyanate form similar complexes). Results are evaluated by reference to a calibration graph which is rectilinear for I^- in the range 0.3–32 mg.

3. Redox

Iodide can be determined by oxidation to iodine, I^+ or iodate. Several reagents have been recommended for this purpose.

1. Oxidation to iodine

   This can be accomplished by nitrite in an acid medium[11].

$$2NO_2^- + 2I^- + 4H^+ \rightarrow 2NO + I_2 + 2H_2O$$

The liberated iodine is titrated with standard thiosulphate. Excess nitrite and nitric oxide are removed with urea. Addition of urea can be made to the acidified solution before the addition of nitrite. This is because the reaction of urea with nitrite and nitric oxide is slow whereas the reaction of iodide with nitrite is rapid. Chloride does not interfere in the procedure but bromide interferes when present in equivalent amounts or more. The method appears to find little current use.

Titrimetric determination of iodide by oxidation to iodine[11]

Procedure

To 25 mℓ of the iodide sample containing 0.15–0.65 g I^- in a 250 mℓ iodine flask, add 1 g of urea, 5 mℓ of 0.5M sodium nitrite solution and 5 mℓ of 2M H_2SO_4. Stopper and allow to stand with frequent shaking, for about 10 min. Cool in an ice-bath, add 1–2 g of KI to dissolve the liberated iodine and titrate with a standard thiosulphate solution using starch near the end-point.

---

2. Oxidation to I^+

   Oxidation of iodide by potassium iodate to iodine monochloride has been used extensively for determination of iodide.

The use of potassium iodate in titrations in which it is reduced to iodine monochloride by the reaction

$$IO_3^- + 6H^+ + 4e \rightarrow I^+ + 3H_2O$$

was introduced by Andrews[12] and further developed by Jamieson[13]. Several species can be determined using the reaction. For iodide the overall reaction can be represented by

$$IO_3^- + 2I^- + 6H^+ + 3Cl^- \rightarrow 3ICl + 3H_2O$$

Two major steps are involved:

$$IO_3^- + 5I^- + 6H^+ \rightarrow 3I_2 + 3H_2O \quad (1)$$

$$IO_3^- + 2I_2 + 5Cl^- + 6H^+ \rightarrow 5ICl + 3H_2O \quad (2)$$

The last equation is an oversimplification; the iodine monochloride is converted into the ICl_2^- ion by the equilibrium

$$ICl + Cl^- \rightleftharpoons ICl_2^-$$

The second step requires a relatively high acidity and the specific presence of chloride ion[14].

In the titration itself an acidity of at least 3M in HCl is required. To detect the end-point the solution is shaken with a few millilitres of carbon tetrachloride. Free iodine produced in the first stage of the reaction imparts a violet colour to the organic phase. The end-point itself is marked by the sudden disappearance of the last trace of violet colour, indicating complete conversion of iodine to iodine monochloride. Bromide does not interfere for concentrations of iodide less than 30 mg per 100 mℓ. For higher concentrations interference by bromide can be eliminated[15] by addition of large amounts of potassium bromide.

When the Andrews titration is applied to reductants other than I^-, for example arsenic(III), antimony(III) and $S_2O_3^{2-}$, the use of dyestuffs such as amaranth and *p*-ethoxychrysoidine have been recommended. In the presence of cyanide, iodide is quantitatively oxidized to iodine cyanide

$$IO_3^- + 2I^- + 3HCN + 3H^+ \rightarrow 3ICN + 3H_2O$$

The analytical procedure based on this has some advantage in that it can be made at a lower acidity, but extreme care is required in view of the toxic properties of hydrogen cyanide.

Titrimetric determination of iodide by potassium iodate (Andrews method)

Procedure

To 25 mℓ of the iodide solution containing up to about 0.2 g I^- and contained in a 250 mℓ iodine flask, add 60 mℓ of concentrated HCl and 5 mℓ of carbon tetrachloride. Titrate with 0.025M KIO_3 until the solution, which first becomes strongly coloured with iodine, turns pale brown. Stopper the flask and shake. The carbon tetrachloride layer will now be violet due to iodine. Continue the titration, shaking vigorously between drops until the last trace of violet colour in the organic phase disappears.

From the equation given earlier it will be seen that
1 mℓ of 0.025M $KIO_3 \equiv$ 0.006345 g of I^-.

---

3. Oxidation to iodate

One of the best methods for fairly small amounts of iodide ($\sim$1 mg) is the amplification method based on quantitative oxidation of iodide to iodate by bromine water.

$$I^- + 3Br_2 + 3H_2O \rightarrow IO_3^- + 6Br^- + 6H^+$$

Excess bromine is destroyed using formic acid

$$Br_2 + HCOOH \rightarrow CO_2 + 2H^+ + 2Br^-$$

An excess of KI is added, and the liberated iodine titrated with standard thiosulphate

$$IO_3^- + 5I^- + 6H^+ \rightarrow 3I_2 + 3H_2O$$

$$I_2 + 2S_2O_3^{2-} \rightarrow 2I^- + S_4O_6^{2-}$$

It will be seen that from the original iodide to the liberated iodine, a six-fold amplification has been accomplished. The reaction is often referred to as the Leipert reaction[16,17] in recognition of his investigations. It has been observed by Belcher[18] that oxidation of iodide to iodate using another halogen was known to others, including Winkler, long before Leipert's work. Apart from the beneficial effects of amplification, the Leipert method has the advantage that bromide and chloride cause no interference unless present in excessive amounts. The same applies to nitrate, sulphate and ammonium. The method has been extensively used in organic microanalysis of halogen-containing compounds and in the Zeisel procedure for alkoxy groups.

Titrimetric determination of iodide using Leipert method

Procedure

Pipette 25 mℓ of the iodide solution, containing up to 2 mg of iodide, into a conical flask and dilute to 100 mℓ with water. Add a few drops of methyl orange. Neutralize with M H_2SO_4, then add 2 mℓ in excess. Add saturated bromine water until the solution remains yellow after swirling, then boil until the yellow colour disappears and for a further 2 min. Cool, wash down the sides of the flask with water, add 2 mℓ of 10% KI, and titrate the liberated iodine with standard 0.02M thiosulphate using a 10-mℓ burette and starch as indicator.

Notes

1. Bromide does not interfere unless present in more than a 20-fold excess.
2. Chloride may be present in amounts up to 5 g.
3. High concentrations of electrolytes decrease the sensitivity of the starch end-point. Malachite green has been recommended as an alternative to starch in such conditions.

---

4. Mercuric oxycyanide method

The mercuric oxycyanide (Vieböck) method suitable for chloride and bromide is also applicable to iodide but appears to have no advantages over alternative methods. Details of the method are given in the chloride section.

Spectroscopic methods

1. Spectrophotometric, visible and UV methods

Spectrophotometric methods for iodide up to about 1951 are reviewed in the monograph by Boltz[19].

Many of the spectrophotometric methods for chloride and bromide can be used for iodide. They include, in terms of the principal reagent used, the following:

1. The mercuric thiocyanate method. A related method[20] based on silver thiocyanate is also available for bromide and iodide.
2. The mercuric diphenylcarbazone/-ide method.
3. The method based on displacement of hydrogen cyanide from mercuric cyanide by a halide.
4. The mercury(II)–EDTA method (for bromide).
5. The method based on phenylmercury(II) halides and their reaction with sodium diethyldithiocarbamate.
6. Methods based on triphenylmethane dyes (for bromide).

In method (4) iodide forms a complex with mercury(II)–EDTA in the pH range 5.0–8.3. The absorbance is measured at 260 nm; the range for iodide is 0.05–2.0 mg. Method (6) based on triphenylmethane dyes has been investigated in a series of papers by Ramanauskas and Bunikiene[21–23]. Both bromide and iodide react with these dyes in the presence of chloramine B, chloramine T or sodium hypochlorite. Brilliant green, acid violet S, crystal violet and malachite green are suitable. The sensitivity for iodide is about 0.01 μg mℓ$^{-1}$. Using crystal violet the maximum absorbance is at 582 nm.

Copper, manganese, calcium, potassium, sodium, chloride and sulphate do not interfere but carbonate, bicarbonate and nitrate do. The basic mechanism of these reactions is oxidation of bromide and iodide to Br^+ and I^+ respectively, which cause a decrease in the colour intensity of the dye.

Later investigations by the same group using malachite green, brilliant green and basic turquoise in the presence of chloramine B, relies on oxidation of iodide to I_3^-. This interacts with the cation of the dye giving an ion-association complex extractable into benzene. For the three dyes mentioned Beer's law holds for 0.032–2.54, 0.031–1.52, and 0.023–2.54 μg mℓ$^{-1}$ I^- respectively. No interference is given by large amounts of chloride, sulphate, nitrate, phosphate, Ca^{2+}, Cu^{2+}, Mn^{2+}, Pb^{2+}, Zn^{2+}, Co^{2+}, Al^{3+}, acetate, and a 10-fold excess of Fe^{3+}. Interference[24] is given by bromide, sulphide and dichromate.

Spectrophotometric determination after preliminary oxidation of iodide to iodine has been the basis of several methods. Bromine, nitrous acid and Fe^{3+} have been used as oxidants. The resulting iodine may be determined using starch, though α-naphthoflavone is more sensitive[25]. Alternatively the iodine can be extracted into chloroform and the absorbance of the organic phase measured. As the extraction is dependent on the presence in the aqueous solution of halides which complex iodine, the calibration should be carried out under the same conditions[26].

Rather than direct oxidation to iodine, the 6-fold amplification reaction based on oxidation to iodate can be employed. This has been discussed already in connection with titrimetric procedures. After destroying excess oxidant, the iodate is reacted with acidified KI to liberate iodine.

In addition to the use of a mercury(II)–EDTA complex for spectrophotometric determination of bromide and iodide, Nomura[27] finds that iodide reacts with mercury(II)–1,2 diaminocyclohexane NNN′N′ tetra-acetate complex. The iodo-complex is formed within 10 min at pH 8.9–9.8 and the absorbance measured at 255 nm. Iodide in the range 0.03–1.5 mg can be determined. There are several interferences including thiocyanate, cyanide, ammonium, silver, copper, sulphide, thiosulphate, iron and mercury. Bromide interferes in concentrations greater than 15 μg in 50 mℓ.

Many of the spectrophotometric methods for halides depend on displacement of a coloured species from a metal complex. Mercury dithizonate has been used in this way by Agterdenbos, Juette and Elberse[28]. The displaced dithizone is extracted into toluene and the absorbance measured at 620 nm. This form of the method is suitable for 2–25 μg of iodide in a 10 mℓ sample. In another method, mercuric iodide is extracted and the residual mercury determined using dithizone.

Novak and Slama[29] have reported that 2–8 μmol of iodide can be determined in the presence of a 1000-fold excess of chloride and bromide, using palladium chloride. The basis of the method is not new. Earlier investigations were made by Martens[30]. A study of the reaction between bromide and iodide with palladous sulphate in aqueous solution was made by Chapman and Sherwood[31] who reported that each halide could be determined. The range for iodide is 1.0–6.0 μg $m\ell^{-1}$ and the optimum wavelength 390 nm.

2. *Molecular emission*

Iodide together with bromide and chloride produces a strong molecular emission in the presence of indium in a cool nitrogen–hydrogen diffusion flame[32]. The method is discussed more fully in the chloride section.

3. *Fluorimetry*

Uranyl acetate has been used by Britton and Guyon[33] for the fluorimetric determination of iodide in amounts of less than 20 μg. The fluorescence is measured at 520 nm with excitation at about 365 nm. Ions that do not affect the determination of 10 μg of iodide when present in 10-mg amounts include Cl^-, BrO_3^-, NO_3^-, SO_3^{2-}, SO_4^{2-}, ClO_3^-, ClO_4^-, Sr^{2+}, Mg^{2+}, Ba^{2+}, Ca^{2+}, Ni^{2+}, Zn^{2+}, Cd^{2+}, NH_4^+, K^+, Na^+ and acetate. For a similar amount of iodide, the following ions interfere in the amounts indicated (in μg): Br^- (150), IO_4^- (110), F^- (80), NO_2^- (60), IO_3^- (50), oxalate (40), SCN^- (2), Al^{3+} (20), WO_4^{2-}, Mn^{2+} and Co^{2+} (2000), Pb^{2+} (500), Cu^{2+} (400) and MoO_4^{2-} (200).

Another method depends on the reaction between iodide and 2′,7′-bis (acetoxymercuri)-fluorescein[34]. The reagent undergoes a decrease in fluorescence due to formation of mercury complexes. Iodide and cyanide may be determined in microgram amounts; chloride and thiocyanate interfere in concentrations greater than 0.005M, with bromide interfering at lower concentrations.

4. *Atomic absorption spectroscopy*

Kirkbright, West and Wilson[35] determine iodide using a fuel-rich nitrogen shielded nitrous oxide–acetylene flame and the 183.0 nm resonance line. The limit of detection, which is about 12 ppm, is independent of whether the solution contains iodide, iodate or periodate. The indirect AAS method developed by Yamamoto *et al.*[36] is related to a spectrophotometric method described earlier. In this, ion-pairs formed between iodide and

1,10-phenanthroline and its derivatives were extracted and the absorbance of the organic phase measured. The AAS method is based on extraction of the bis(1,10-phenanthroline) cadmium(II) iodide complex into nitrobenzene followed by evaluation of Cd by means of its 228.8 nm line.

Electroanalytical methods

1. Potentiometric methods including ion-selective electrodes

The argentimetric and mercurimetric determination of iodide by potentiometric titration is similar to that for bromide and chloride, and these sections should be referred to. Determination of total halides in admixture is relatively easy; determination of individual halides in admixture is more difficult due to mixed crystal formation. One way of resolving the difficulty in binary mixtures[37] is to eliminate iodide (or bromide) in a second aliquot and then titrate the residual chloride.

Null-point potentiometry enables micro amounts of iodide to be determined[38] in the presence of a 2×10^5 excess of chloride. A complete analysis for iodide in the range 5–100 ppm requires 3 min. Silver–silver iodide and platinum electrodes are employed.

Differential Electrolytic Potentiometry (DEP) used in conjunction with constant current coulometry has been developed for sub-micro amounts of bromide and chloride. The technique is unsuitable for iodide due to deposition of insulating iodide films on the generating anode.

It has been noted earlier that due to the lower redox potential in relation to bromide and chloride, iodide can be preferentially oxidized in the presence of these anions. Several visual redox titrimetric procedures, for example the Leipert method, fall into this category.

A wide range of oxidizing reagents have been proposed. Kotkowski and Lassocinska[39] use sodium peroxomolybdate (Na_2MoO_5) prepared by oxidizing a solution of sodium molybdate in dilute sulphuric acid with H_2O_2. Minczewski and Glabisz[40] report the use of chlorite for accurate determination of iodide in the presence of bromide and chloride. The greatest potential change was found to occur in 5.5M HCl.

The strong oxidizing properties of cobalt(III) make it potentially attractive for redox titrimetry. The main obstacle to greater use is its relative instability in aqueous solution. Cobalt(III) acetate has been investigated by several workers[41,42] in this connection. Recently Budesinsky *et al.*[43] describe an electrolytic preparation of cobalt(III) acetate that produces a relatively stable product. The reagent has been applied to several inorganic systems[44] including iodide. The oxidation proceeds stoichiometrically to iodine in 1.5–2.5M H_2SO_4 in contrast to the I^+ state when 4M HCl is used. Although the oxidation is more rapid in 2.5M H_2SO_4, a titration requires 20–25 min. Fifteen to 150 mg of iodide was found to give an average error of +0.36 per cent. A ten-fold excess of bromide or chloride does not interfere, but greater amounts produce a significant decrease in the potential change. This is attributed to formation of the interhalogen compounds iodine bromide or iodine monochloride.

A more general treatment of halide ion-selective electrodes is given in the chloride section. The iodide-selective electrode introduced in 1961 was the first highly selective anion selective electrode[45]. Further studies on heterogeneous solid-state iodide electrodes were published by Pungor and coworkers[46,47] and their findings confirmed by Rechnitz, Kresz and Zamochnick[48]. The Pungor type electrode (OP-I-711) shows the selectivity indicated in *Table 35*.

Table 35 Selectivity of Pungor type OP-I-711 iodide ion-selective electrode[49]

Ion	*Selectivity ratio*[a]
CN^-	1
Br^-	1.8×10^{-4}
SCN^-	3×10^{-5}
$[Fe(CN)_6]^{4-}$	3.5×10^{-6}
SO_3^{2-}	5.5×10^{-7}
Cl^-	3.7×10^{-7}
SO_4^{2-}	1×10^{-7}
OH^-	9.1×10^{-9}
AsO_4^{3-}	2.6×10^{-10}
CrO_4^{2-}	6.6×10^{-11}
PO_4^{3-}	2.5×10^{-11}
NO_3^-	$<10^{-8}$

[a] For a definition and discussion of Selectivity Ratio see p. 318.

The generally low values of the Selectivity Ratios indicate that all the anions listed can be tolerated in large excess in the determination of iodide using the electrode.

Now, in addition to the Pungor type of precipitate-impregnated membrane electrode, the homogeneous single crystal type, for example the Orion 94-53, is commercially available. The concentration range for this electrode is stated[50] to be 10^0–2×10^{-7}M I^-. It may be used without interference in a 1000-fold excess of fluoride, chloride and bromide, but cyanide and sulphide interfere.

Several applications have been reported. Determination of iodide in feeds and plants compares favourably with the more time-consuming standard AOAC method[51]. An application to organic materials and biological samples in the concentration range 10^{-7}–10^{-8} g mℓ^{-1} has been made[52]. The high selectivity of the iodide ion-selective electrode makes the direct determination of iodide in mineral waters possible[53]. An interesting application of the electrode[54] is the direct determination of iodide in the presence of iodate.

2. *Coulometric methods*

Iodide can be determined using a coulometric procedure in the same way as chloride and bromide. The usual titrant is the electrogenerated argentous ion. Individual halides excluding fluoride can be determined in mixtures. The procedures are discussed in the chloride section.

Berraz and Delago[55] use electrogenerated bromine for titrating micro amounts of iodide, which is oxidized to iodate. For 50 μg of iodide the relative error is below 1 per cent. Chloride does not interfere.

3. Amperometric methods

Amperometric argentimetry[56] enables iodide as well as chloride and bromide to be determined in the presence of cyanide and cyanate. Interference by cyanide is prevented by masking with formaldehyde; interference from excess formaldehyde and OCN^- is prevented by addition of HNO_3 to bring the pH to below 3. End-point indication is by platinum electrode. The range for halides is 0.1–10 mM.

An amperometric method based on oxidation of iodide by $K_2Cr_2O_7$ has been developed by Milyaneva and Songina[57]. The titration is made in 2M H_2SO_4. No interference occurs with a 1000-fold excess of chloride or a 2000-fold excess of bromide. For 2–3 mg of iodide the relative error is below 0.4 per cent.

4. Voltammetric methods

Several polarographic methods applicable to chloride and bromide as well as iodide are listed in those sections. One such method developed by Dryhurst and Elving[58], and employing a rotating pyrolytic-graphite electrode, can be used for determination of iodide in the presence of a 100-fold excess of chloride or bromide. Pliska[59] has investigated the oxidation of iodide in the presence of excess chloride and bromide polarographically. One wave only, corresponding to oxidation of iodide to iodine, was observed.

Catalytic methods

The current interest in catalytic methods of analysis tends to suggest that the method is recent in origin. This is not so. Sandell and Kolthoff[60] reported in 1934 that iodide in 0.01–1 μg amounts could be determined by its catalytic effect on the cerium(IV)-arsenic(III) reaction. After an incubation period of several years the whole subject of kinetic and catalytic methods of analysis has opened up and is now established as a valuable part of trace analysis. In the case of iodide catalytic methods are important, enabling it to be determined at ultra-trace level in the presence of many other ions. The high sensitivity overcomes the need for tedious pre-concentration.

In addition to the cerium(IV)–arsenic(III) system, others have been investigated. Svehla[61] has tabulated the important features of several catalytic methods for iodide. An extended form of this is given in *Table 36*.

Some comment on these tabulated methods is pertinent. They have a high tolerance for bromide and chloride, for example in the Toropova and Tamarchenko method no interference is given by a 100-fold excess of bromide and a 1000-fold excess of chloride.

The group of methods based on catalytic decomposition of the monothiocyanate complex (refs. 69 and 70) have been examined by Ottaway, Fuller and Rowston[80], who point out that two widely different iodide concentrations can lead to the same value of the measured parameter, and that only solutions falling in the range 0.001–10 ppm can be analysed without modifying the

Table 36 Catalytic methods for determination of iodide

Reaction used	*Kinetic*[a] *principle*	*Experimental procedure*	*Sensitivity* ($g\,m\ell^{-1}$)	*Ref.*
$2Ce^{4+} + AsO_3^{3-} + H_2O \rightarrow 2Ce^{3+} + AsO_4^{3-} + 2H^+$	f.c.	visual	5×10^{-8}	60
$2Ce^{4+} + AsO_3^{3-} + H_2O \rightarrow 2Ce^{3+} + AsO_4^{3-} + 2H^+$	f.t.	spectric.	1×10^{-8}	62
$2Ce^{4+} + AsO_3^{3-} + H_2O \rightarrow 2Ce^{3+} + AsO_4^{3-} + 2H^+$	automatic	spectric.	1×10^{-8}	63
$2Ce^{4+} + AsO_3^{3-} + H_2O \rightarrow 2Ce^{3+} + AsO_4^{3-} + 2H^+$	i.r.	spectric.	1×10^{-8}	64
$2Ce^{4+} + AsO_3^{3-} + H_2O \rightarrow 2Ce^{3+} + AsO_4^{3-} + 2H^+$	s.c.	visual	1×10^{-8}	65
$2Ce^{4+} + AsO_3^{3-} + H_2O \rightarrow 2Ce^{3+} + AsO_4^{3-} + 2H^+$	f.t.	spectric.	1×10^{-9}	66
$2Ce^{4+} + AsO_3^{3-} + H_2O \rightarrow 2Ce^{3+} + AsO_4^{3-} + 2H^+$	i.r.	spectric.	1×10^{-9}	67
$2Ce^{4+} + AsO_3^{3-} + H_2O \rightarrow 2Ce^{3+} + AsO_4^{3-} + 2H^+$		amperom.	1×10^{-7}	68
$NO_2^- + 2SCN^- + 4H^+ \rightarrow 2NO + (SCN)_2 + 2H_2O$	i.r.	spectric.	1×10^{-9}	69
$NO_2^- + 2SCN^- + 4H^+ \rightarrow 2NO + (SCN)_2 + 2H_2O$		spectric.	1×10^{-9}	70
$NO_2^- + 2SCN^- + 4H^+ \rightarrow 2NO + (SCN)_2 + 2H_2O$		spectric.	2×10^{-9}	73
$2Mn^{3+} + AsO_3^{3-} + H_2O \rightarrow 2Mn^{2+} + AsO_4^{3-} + 2H^+$	f.c.	spectric.	2×10^{-7}	74
$2Ce^{4+} + Sb^{3+} \rightarrow 2Ce^{3+} + Sb^{5+}$	s.c.	visual	1×10^{-9}	65
$3AsO_3^{3-} + IO_3^- \rightarrow 3AsO_4^{3-} + I^-$	f.c.	amperom.	1×10^{-9}	71
$3AsO_3^{3-} + IO_3^- \rightarrow 3AsO_4^{3-} + I^-$	s.c.	visual	1×10^{-6}	72
3,3′-dimethylnaphthidine + H_2O_2	f.c.	spectric.	2×10^{-9}	75
p,p′-tetramethyldiaminodiphenylmethane + chloramine T	i.r.	spectric.	1×10^{-14}	76
$2NO_2^- + S_2O_3^{2-} + 4H^+ \rightarrow 2NO + S_4O_6^{2-} + 2H_2O$	f.c.	visual		77
Ligand substitution Hg(II)–PAR with 1,2-cyclohexanediamine N,N,N′,N′ tetra-acetic acid	f.t.		1×10^{-9}	78
De-inhibition of enzyme-catalysed reaction	f.t.	optical rotation		79

[a] f.c. = fixed concentration.
f.t. = fixed time.
i.r. = initial rate.
s.c. = simultaneous comparison.

methods. Stronger solutions may be diluted to meet this requirement. The Dubravcic form of the cerium(IV)–arsenic(III) method is now listed as a standard method for water analysis[81]. Automatic forms of the cerium(IV)–arsenic(III) method have been developed. Malmstadt and Hadjiioannou[63] use reaction times of 10–100 s only. More recently Truesdale and Smith[82] use an AutoAnalyzer for multisample analysis of river water. At the 20–100 $\mu g\,\ell^{-1}$ level the maximum error in six sets of eleven samples was within ± 0.36 per cent.

A very sensitive catalytic method has been based on a reaction discovered by Feigl and Jungreis[83]. This involves the catalytic effect of iodine or iodide on the reaction between chloramine T and tetra base acetate (acetate of N,N-tetramethyldiaminodiphenylmethane). Chloramine T hydrolyses in water giving hypochlorite, of which the concentration is not sufficient to oxidize the tetra base into the blue quinoid derivative. Very small quantities of I^-/I° catalyse the reaction. The effect is explained by the liberation of free iodine, and the regeneration of iodide on forming the blue derivative.

$$[H_3C-C_6H_4-SO_2NCl]^- + H_2O \rightleftharpoons CH_3-C_6H_4-SO_2NH_2 + ClO^-$$

$$ClO^- + 2I^- + 2H^+ \rightarrow Cl^- + H_2O + 2I^\circ$$

$$(CH_3)_2N-C_6H_4-CH_2-C_6H_4-\underset{H}{N^+}(CH_3)_2 + 2I^\circ \rightarrow$$

$$(CH_3)_2N-C_6H_4-CH{=}C_6H_4{=}N^+(CH_3)_2 + 2I^- + 2H^+$$

The method, developed by Jungreis and Gedalia[84] was applied to drinking water. An improved form of the method has been reported by Ramanauskas[85]. The dilution limit is quoted as $1{:}2.5 \times 10^{10}$ ($0.04\ \mu g\ I\ \ell^{-1}$). Bromide below $0.5\ mg\,\ell^{-1}$ and chloride do not interfere. The blue colour reaches a maximum in 40–50 s and then fades; absorbance measurements must therefore be carried out promptly.

The enzyme-catalysed reaction used by Mealor and Townshend[79] is based on the following. The enzyme β-fructofuranosidase is inhibited in its catalysis of the hydrolysis of such substances as sucrose when certain metal ions such as Ag^+ and Hg^{2+} are present. Small concentrations of selected anions form very strong complexes with Ag^+ and Hg^{2+} and therefore compete with the enzyme for the metals. Such anions (cyanide, sulphide and iodide) decrease the inhibiting effect of the metals.

A knowledge of the mechanism of catalytic reactions is desirable in the development of new analytical procedures. Bontchev[86] has reviewed the subject. One of the most widely used of the catalytic reactions, namely the cerium(IV)–arsenic(III), is thought to proceed in the following sequence:

$$I^- + Ce(IV) \rightarrow Ce(III) + I^\circ$$

$$I^\circ + As(III) \rightarrow \text{intermediate}$$

$$\text{intermediate} + Ce(IV) \rightarrow Ce(III) + As(V) + I^-$$

Radiochemical methods

Neutron activation methods have found several applications in determination of iodide as well as other halides. Iodide and bromide can be determined by irradiation followed by selective extraction[87]. The method permits as little as 0.01 μg of iodide and 0.1 μg of bromide to be determined. Morgan, Black and Mitchell[88] use neutron activation for determination of stable inorganic iodide in body fluids. A complicating factor is that in addition to iodine-128, other γ-emitters are formed on activation with thermal neutrons. In this investigation, separation of iodide on an ion-exchange column is carried out after irradiation. The levels of iodide measured are about 20 μg in 100 mℓ.

Wong and Brewer[89] use a strongly basic anion-exchange column for separation in the analysis of seawater by neutron activation. The eluted iodide is concentrated by precipitation as palladium(II) iodide in the presence of excess palladium(II) with elemental palladium as carrier. Irradiation is for 5 min at a flux of 4×10^{12} neutrons $cm^{-2} s^{-1}$. Concentrations as low as 0.006 μM I^- can be determined.

Isotope-exchange methods have been reported. Richter[90] adds a known amount of 131-iodine to the iodide sample, oxidizes the iodide to I° and extracts into benzene. The radioactivity is distributed between the two phases in direct proportion to the I° and iodide content in each phase. The method, which was applied to natural waters, has a limit of sensitivity of below 1 μg ℓ$^{-1}$.

Gabrielsson and Beronius[91] have based a method on the reaction

$$CH_3I + Na^{131}I \leftrightharpoons CH_3{}^{131}I + NaI$$

25–550 ng I^- can be determined. Determination of 12–2000 ng I^- is possible[92] using an extraction-radiochemical titration with ^{203}Hg-labelled mercury chloride.

Gas chromatographic methods

Small amounts of halides including iodide can be separated and determined using this technique. Further details are given in the chloride and bromide sections.

Miscellaneous methods

Several methods fall outside the above categories. Some of these are also applicable to chloride and bromide and are discussed in those sections. They include use of the Weisz ring oven for semi-quantitative estimation[93] and semi-quantitative circular TLC[94].

In the same category is a paper chromatographic method for micro determination of chloride–thiocyanate–iodide mixtures[95]. After spraying, the exposed spots are cut out and weighed. The authors state that 15–100 μg I^- can be determined to within ± 1.5 per cent.

References

1. WEST, P.W. and LORICA, A.S., *Analytica Chim. Acta,* **25**, 28 (1961)
2. NAEUMANN, R., *J. Chromat.,* **18**, 385 (1965)
3. OBRENOVIC-PALIGORIC, I.D. and COVORIC, J.D., *Bull. Boris Kidrich Inst. nucl. Sci.,* **14**, 95 (1963); *Chem. Abstr.,* **59**, 14555b (1963)
4. BEKK, J., *Chemiker Zeitung,* **39**, 405 (1915); *Chem. Abstr.,* **9**, 2042 (1915)
5. FIRSCHING, F.H., *Analyt. Chem.,* **32**, 1876 (1960)
6. KAPEL, M., FRY, J.C. and SHELTON, D.R., *Analyst,* **100**, 570 (1975)
7. MEHLIG, J.P., *Chemist Analyst,* **44**, 87 (1955)
8. PRIBIL, R. and MARKOVA, V., *Chemiké Listy,* **60**, 89 (1966); *Analyt. Abstr.,* **14**, 2544 (1967)
9. SCHULEK, E. and PUNGOR, E., *Analytica chim. Acta,* **4**, 109, 213 (1950)
10. NOMURA, T., *Bull. Chem. Soc. Japan,* **42**, 952 (1969); *Analyt. Abstr.,* **19**, 218 (1970)
11. ABELEDO, C.A. and KOLTHOFF, I.M., *J. Am. chem. Soc.,* **53**, 2893 (1931)
12. ANDREWS, L.W., *J. Am. chem. Soc.,* **25**, 756 (1903)
13. JAMIESON, G.S., *Volumetric Iodate Methods,* Reinhold, New York (1926)
14. KIPLING, J.J. and GRIMES, G., *Talanta,* **5**, 278 (1960)
15. MUTSCHIN, A., *Z. analyt. Chem.,* **106**, 1 (1936)
16. LEIPERT, T., *Mikrochem. Pregl. Festschr.,* 266 (1929)
17. LEIPERT, T., *Mikrochim. Acta,* **3**, 73, 147 (1938)
18. BELCHER, R., *Talanta,* **15**, 357 (1968)
19. BOLTZ, D.F. (Ed.) *Colorimetric Determination of Non-metals,* Interscience, New York (1958)
20. UTSUMI, S., *J. chem. Soc. Japan,* **74**, 35 (1953); *Chem. Abstr.,* **47**, 6815f (1953)
21. BUNIKIENE, L.V. and RAMANAUSKAS, E.I., *Zh. analit. Khim.,* **23**, 1364 (1968); *Analyt. Abstr.,* **18**, 2396 (1970)
22. RAMANAUSKAS, E.I., BUNIKIENE, L.V. AND ZHILENAITE, M., *Nauch. Trudy vyssh. Ucheb. Zaved. lit. SSR, Khim. khim. Teknol.,* 29 (1968); *Analyt. Abstr.,* **18**, 3962 (1970)
23. BUNIKIENE, L.V., RAMANAUSKAS, E.I. and TAMULYAVICHUTE, M., *Nauch. Trudy vyssh. Ucheb. Zaved. lit. SSR, Khim. khim. Teknol.,* 41 (1970); *Analyt. Abstr.,* **22**, 1568 (1972)
24. NEVERDAUSKIENE, Z., RAMANAUSKAS, E. AND BUNIKIENE, L., *Nauch. Trudy vyssh. Ucheb. Zaved. lit SSR, Khim. khim. Teknol,* 25 (1972); *Analyt. Abstr.,* **26**, 2644 (1974)
25. LAMBERT, J.F., *Analyt. Chem.,* **23**, 1247, 1251 (1951)
26. OVENSTOW, T.C. and REES, W.T., *Analytica chim. Acta,* **5**, 123 (1951)
27. NOMURA, T., *J. chem. Soc. Japan, pure Chem. Sect.,* **88**, 199 (1967); *Analyt. Abstr.,* **15**, 2619 (1968)
28. AGTERDENBOS, J., JUETTE, B.A.H.G. and ELBERSE, P.A., *Talanta,* **17**, 1085 (1970)
29. NOVAK, J. and SLAMA, I., *Colln Czech. chem. Commun. Engl. Edn,* **37**, 2907 (1972); *Analyt. Abstr.,* **24**, 2174 (1973)
30. MARTENS, F.F., *Verh. dt. phys. Ges.,* **4**, 138 (1930)
31. CHAPMAN, F.W. and SHERWOOD, R.M., *Analyt. Chem.,* **29**, 172 (1957)
32. DAGNALL, R.M., THOMPSON, K.C. and WEST, T.S., *Analyst,* **94**, 643 (1969)
33. BRITTON, D.A. and GUYON, J.C., *Microchem. J.,* **14**, 1 (1969)
34. COLVOS, G., HARO, M. and FREISER, H., *Talanta,* **17**, 273 (1970)
35. KIRKBRIGHT, G.F., WEST, T.S. and WILSON, P.J., *Atom. Abs. Newsl.,* **11**, 53 (1972)
36. YAMAMOTO, Y., KUMAMURA, T., HAYASHI, Y. and OTANI, K., *Japan Analyst,* **17**, 92 (1968); *Analyt. Abstr.,* **17**, 2101 (1969)
37. PROKOPOV, T.S., *Analyt. Chem.,* **42**, 1096 (1970)
38. MALMSTADT, H.V. and WINEFORDNER, J.D., *Analytica chim. Acta,* **24**, 91 (1961)
39. KOTKOWSKI, S. and LASSOCINSKA, A., *Chemia analit.,* **11**, 789 (1966); *Analyt. Abstr.,* **14**, 6774 (1967)
40. MINCZEWSKI, J. and GLABISZ, U., *Acta. chim. hung.,* **32**, 133 (1962); *Analyt. Abstr.,* **10**, 1424 (1963)
41. BRICKER, C.E. and LOEFLER, L.J., *Analyt. Chem.,* **27**, 1419 (1955)
42. MINCZEWSKI, J. and PSZONIKA, M., *Chemia analit.,* **9**, 785, 947 (1964)
43. BUDESINSKY, J., DOLEZAL, J., SRAMKOVA, B. and ZYKA, J., *Microchem. J.,* **16**, 121 (1971)
44. HANIF, M., DOLEZAL, J. and ZYKA, J., *Microchem. J.,* **16**, 291 (1971)
45. PUNGOR, E. and HOLLOS-ROKOSINYI, E., *Acta chim. hung.,* **27**, 63 (1961); *Analyt. Abstr.,* **8**, 3561 (1961)
46. PUNGOR, E., HAVAS, J. and TOTH, K., *Acta chim. hung.,* **41**, 239 (1964)
47. PUNGOR, E., HAVAS, J. and TOTH, K., *Instrums Control Syst.,* **38**, 105 (1965); *Analyt. Abstr.,* **13**, 7236 (1966)

48. RECHNITZ, G.A., KRESZ, M.R. and ZAMOCHNICK, S.B., *Analyt. Chem.*, **38**, 973 (1966)
49. PUNGOR, E. and TOTH, K., *Analyst*, **95**, 625 (1970)
50. Orion Research Incorporated, Technical Information
51. HOOVER, W.L., MELTON, J.R. and HOWARD, P.A., *J. Ass. off. analyt. Chem.*, **54**, 760 (1971)
52. PALETTA, B. and PANZENBECK, K., *Clin. chim. Acta*, **26**, 11 (1969)
53. PUNGOR, E., *Analyt. Chem.*, **39**, 28A (1967)
54. PALETTA, B., *Mikrochim. Acta*, 1210 (1969)
55. BERRAZ, G. and DELAGO, O., *Rev. Facultad. Ing. Quim. Univ. Nac. del Littoral Argentina*, **28**, 53 (1959); *Analyt. Abstr.*, **8**, 3275 (1961)
56. IKEDA, S. and MUSHA, S., *Japan Analyst*, **16**, 445 (1967); *Analyt. Abstr.*, **15**, 6633 (1968)
57. MILYANEVA, N.M. and SONGINA, O.A., *Zh. analit. Khim.*, **24**, 1794 (1969); *Analyt. Abstr.*, **21**, 187 (1971)
58. DRYHURST, G. and ELVING, P.J., *J. electroanal. Chem.*, **12**, 416 (1966)
59. PLISKA, V., *Z. analyt. chem.*, **184**, 17 (1961); *Analyt. Abstr.*, **9**, 1898 (1962)
60. SANDELL, E.B. and KOLTHOFF, I.M., *J. Am. chem. Soc.*, **56**, 1426 (1934)
61. SVEHLA, G., *Proc. Soc. analyt. Chem.*, **8**, 80 (1971)
62. STOLC, V., *Mikrochim. Acta*, 710 (1961)
63. MALMSTADT, H.V. and HADJIIOANNOU, T.P., *Analyt. Chem.*, **35**, 2157 (1963)
64. LEIN, A. and SCHWARTZ, N., *Analyt. Chem.*, **23**, 1507 (1951)
65. BOGNAR, J. and SAROSI, SZ., *Mikrochim. Acta*, 1004 (1965)
66. ROGINA, B. and DUBRAVCIC, M., *Analyst*. **78**, 594 (1953)
67. RODRIGUEZ, P.A. and PARDUE, H.L., *Analyt. Chem.*, **41**, 1376 (1969)
68. CZARNECKI, K., *Chemia analit.*, **5**, 875 (1960); *Analyt. Abstr.*, **8**, 2858 (1961)
69. YATSIMIRSKII, K.B., BUDARIN, L.I., BLAGOVESHCHENSKAYA, N.A., SMIRNOVA, P.V., FEDOROVA, A.P. and YATSIMIRSKII, V.K., *Zh. analit. Khim.*, **18**, 103 (1963)
70. IWASAKI, I., URSUMI, S. and OZAWA, T., *Bull. chem. Soc. Japan*, **26**, 108 (1953); *Chem. Abstr.*, **47**, 12123h (1953)
71. TOROPOVA, V.F. and TAMARCHENKO, L.M., *Zh. analit. Khim.*, **22**, 234 (1967)
72. BOGNAR, J. and SAROSI, SZ., *Mikrochim. Acta*, 463 (1969)
73. PROSKURYAKOVA, G.F., *Zh. analit. Khim.*, **22**, 802 (1967); *Analyt. Abstr.*, **16**, 136 (1969)
74. BOGURTH, W. and SCHAEG, W., *Mikrochim. Acta*, 658 (1967)
75. BOGNAR, J. and NAGY, L., *Mikrochim. Acta*, 108 (1969)
76. BALLZO, H., *Z. analyt. Chem.*, **245**, 20 (1969)
77. BAINES, H., *J. Soc. chem. Ind., Lond.*, **49**, 481 (1930)
78. FUNAHASHI, S., TABATA, M. and TANAKA, M., *Analytica chim. Acta*, **57**, 311 (1971)
79. MEALOR, D. and TOWNSHEND, A., *Talanta*, **15**, 1477 (1968)
80. OTTAWAY, J.M., FULLER, C.W. and ROWSTON, W.B., *Analytica chim. Acta*, **45**, 541 (1969)
81. American Public Health Association, American Waterworks Association and Water Pollution Control Federation, *Standard Methods for the Examination of Water and Wastewater*, 14th Edition, American Public Health Assoc., New York (1975)
82. TRUESDALE, V.W. and SMITH, P.J., *Analyst*, **100**, 111 (1975)
83. FEIGL, F. and JUNGREIS, E., *Z. analyt. Chem.*, **161**, 87 (1958)
84. JUNGREIS, E. and GEDALIA, I., *Mikrochim. Acta*, 145 (1960)
85. RAMANAUSKAS, E., *Lietuvos TSR Aukstuju Mokyklu Mokslo Darbai, Chem. ir Chem. Technol.*, **5**, 9 (1964); *Chem. Abstr.*, **61**, 10450b (1964)
86. BONTCHEV, P.R., *Talanta*, **17**, 499 (1970)
87. OHNO, S., *Analyst*, **96**, 423 (1971)
88. MORGAN, D.J., BLACK, A. and MITCHELL, G.R., *Analyst*, **94**, 740 (1969)
89. WONG, G.T.F. and BREWER, P.G., *Analytica chim. Acta*, **81**, 81 (1976)
90. RICHTER, H.G., *Analyt. Chem.*, **38**, 772 (1966)
91. GABRIELSSON, A-B. and BERONIUS, P., *Analytica chim. Acta*, **61**, 123 (1972)
92. JUETTE, B.A.H.G., AGTERDENBOS, J. and ELBERSE, P.A., *Talanta*, **17**, 1130 (1970)
93. CELAP, M.B. and WEISZ, H., *Mikrochim. Acta*, 24 (1962)
94. HASHMI, M.H. and CHUGHTAI, N.A., *Mikrochim. Acta*, 1040 (1968)
95. GANCHEV, N. and KOEV, K., *Mikrochim. Acta*, 87 (1964)

Perbromate

The existence of the perbromate ion and perbromic acid was established[1] in 1968. Gram-quantities of potassium perbromate were synthesized in a later paper[2]. As the ion is relatively new, some account of its synthesis and characteristics is pertinent.

The initial synthesis was by oxidation of bromate electrolytically or using xenon difluoride. Neither method lends itself to large scale work[1]. A later method used fluorine in alkaline solution[2]. Aqueous solutions of perbromic acid of up to about 6M (55% $HBrO_4$) are stable, but decomposition occurs at higher concentrations. The acid itself is a sluggish oxidant intermediate in apparent oxidizing power between perchloric acid and periodic acid. Titration results indicate that perbromic acid is a strong acid with 1 proton per heptavalent bromine like perchloric acid but unlike periodic acid.

Alkali perbromates are prepared by neutralizing the acid potentiometrically with a solution of the appropriate hydroxide. Potassium perbromate decomposes at 280 °C to the bromate. It is isolated by chilling the neutral solution in an ice-bath, filtering, and washing. It can be dried in a vacuum desiccator at room temperature or in an oven at 110 °C. The colourless salt may be recrystallized from hot water. Thermogravimetry and Differential Thermal Analysis on potassium perbromate show an exothermal decomposition at 275–280 °C to bromic acid which itself decomposes at about 390–395 °C to potassium bromide.

Separation

Lederer and Sinibaldi[3] have carried out chromatographic studies. These indicate that:

1. In partition systems, perbromate moves with a high R_f value in solvents such as ethanol–NH_4OH or butanol–pyridine–NH_4OH. Using paper-chromatography the ion is reduced during the run, but on silica-gel it appears to move without decomposition.
2. In ion-exchange paper chromatography perbromate is strongly adsorbed, and moves with R_f values very similar to perchlorate and periodate.
3. Separation of perchlorate, perbromate and periodate can be made using paper electrophoresis. Bromate and perbromate are readily separated both with partition and ion-exchange systems.
4. Separation and identification of perbromate in the presence of all other halides, halates and perhalates is possible using several systems.

Determination

Titrimetric methods

Two redox titrimetric methods have been developed. In the first perbromate is reduced to bromate by 12M hydrobromic acid. The bromate is reacted with KI and the liberated iodine is titrated with standard thiosulphate in the presence of a phosphoric acid–phosphate buffer[2]. In practice the sample is diluted with at least five times its volume of saturated HBr and allowed to stand for 10 min in a stoppered vessel. It is then transferred to at least ten times its volume of 2% sodium iodide solution containing sufficient sodium phosphate to neutralize the acid present. The solution is then titrated immediately with standard thiosulphate.

The HBr concentration is critical. If the reduction is to be completed in 10 min, it must be at least 11.5M.

$$BrO_3^- + 6I^- + 6H^+ \rightarrow Br^- + 3I_2 + 3H_2O$$

A second method in the same publication involves reduction of bromate to bromide using stannous chloride in 6M HCl, with molybdenum(VI) as catalyst. The resulting bromide is oxidized in neutral cyanide solution to cyanogen bromide which further reacts with iodide liberating iodine. This is titrated with standard thiosulphate. Where a perbromate solution contains large amounts of lower bromine oxidation states, these can be reduced by dilute HBr, and the resulting bromine removed by bubbling a suitable gas through the solution. Argon was used in the above work.

Later work indicates that both the above methods are accurate but tedious[4].

Spectrophotometric methods

Brown and Boyd[4] find that the crystal violet extraction method for spectrophotometric determination of perchlorate[5] can be adapted to perbromate. Extraction of the ion-pair in chlorobenzene followed by measurement of the absorbance at 596 nm enables $1–10 \times 10^{-6}$M BrO_4^- to be determined in the presence of 1000-fold amounts of bromate or bromide.

Electroanalytical methods

The perchlorate ion-selective electrode is sensitive to perbromate and may be used for its determination[6]. The titrant used in this investigation was tetraphenylarsonium chloride, and the electrode the Orion 92-81 which responds to perbromate over the range $10^{-1}–10^{-4}$M. In fact, the electrode is more responsive to perbromate than the other perhalates, the order being

$$BrO_4^- > IO_4^- > ClO_4^-$$

The Selectivity Coefficient, which varies according to the perbromate/perchlorate ratio, has a mean value of 1.4.

When the electrode is used for determination of perchlorate, no interference is observed from chloride, chlorate, bromide, bromate, fluoride, sulphate, nitrate and chromate. The investigators assume that the same situation also applies for perbromate.

Polarographic studies on the perbromate ion indicate that like periodate, it is reduced irreversibly at the dropping mercury electrode[7]. At pH values above 3 reduction to bromide is in two steps via bromate. In strongly acid solution, direct reduction to bromide takes place. Polarographic determination of perbromate alone, or in the presence of small amounts of bromate may be made in 0.05M perchloric acid. When large amounts of bromate are present, sodium bicarbonate is added until methyl red gives a yellow colour. Under these conditions reduction of perbromate stops at the bromate stage enabling it alone to be determined. A precision of better than 2 per cent is quoted for determination of perbromate in the presence of bromate.

References

1. APPELMAN, E.H., *J. Am. chem. Soc.,* **90**, 1900 (1968)
2. APPELMAN, E.H., *Inorg. Chem.*, **8**, 223 (1969)
3. LEDERER, M. and SINIBALDI, M., *J. Chromat.*, **60**, 275 (1971)
4. BROWN, L.C. and BOYD, G.E., *Analyt. Chem.*, **42**, 291 (1970)
5. UCHIKAWA, S., *Bull. chem. Soc. Japan,* **40**, 798 (1967)
6. BRAND, J.R. and SMITH, M.L., *Analyt. Chem.*, **43**, 1105 (1971)
7. JASELSKIS, B. and HUSTON, J.L., *Analyt. Chem.*, **43**, 581 (1971)

Perchlorate

Perchlorates find use in several areas, for example in the manufacture of explosives and rocket fuels. The analytical chemistry of perchlorates has been reviewed[1,2].

Separations

1. Precipitation

Perchlorate is quantitatively precipitated by tetraphenylarsonium chloride (TPAC). As well as being separated, it may also be determined gravimetrically using the same reagent. Other ions also precipitated include iodide, periodate, bromide, chromate, thiocyanate and permanganate.

Recently 2,4,6-triphenylpyrylium chloride has been introduced, and is claimed to have advantages over TPAC[3]. Its chemical behaviour is essentially the same as TPAC. It is discussed further as a gravimetric reagent below. Greenhalgh and Riley[4] have separated perchlorate from seawater with TPAC using the corresponding perrhenate as collector.

2. Solvent extraction

Several systems provide a quantitative separation for perchlorate. In some instances a spectrophotometric determination is also possible. The complex with TPAC is 100 per cent extracted[5] into chloroform in the pH range 2–12. The same degree of extraction is given with tetraphenylphosphonium

Table 37 Paper and thin-layer chromatographic separations for perchlorate

Technique	*Solvent*	*Ions separated*	*Ref.*
Paper and TLC Silufol UV 254 plates	Butanol–pyridine–aq. NH_3 (0.880) (2:2:2)	ClO_3^-–ClO^-–ClO_2^-–ClO_4^-	11
Paper	Isopropanol–H_2O–pyridine–aq. NH_3 (0.880) (15:2:2:2)	ClO_3^-–ClO_2^-–Cl^-–ClO_4^-	12
TLC	Isopropanol–tetrahydrofuran–aq. NH_3 (0.880) (50:30:20)	ClO_3^-–ClO_2^-–Cl^-–ClO_4^-	13
TLC Al_2O_3G + Kieselguhr G 1:1	Butanol–acetone–aq. NH_3(0.880)–H_2O (8:10:2:1)	ClO_3^-–ClO_2^-–BrO_3^-–IO_3^-–ClO_4^-	14
TLC Corn starch	Acetone–3M aq. NH_3 (7:3)	ClO_3^-–BrO_3^-–IO_3^-–ClO_4^-– F^-–Br^-–Cl^-–I^-	15

chloride (TPPC)[6] in the pH range 2–11, and triphenylsulphonium chloride (TPSC)[7] in the 2–12 pH range. In contrast, periodate is little extracted into TPAC and TPSC. Bromate is only 32 per cent extracted into TPPC and 28 per cent extracted into TPSC.

Perchlorate is 100 per cent extracted[8] into *n*-butyronitrile by $Fe(phen)_3^{2+}$ at pH 5–10. A spectrophotometric determination is possible, the molar absorptivity being 1.08×10^4 at 510 nm. Extraction into nitrobenzene is also possible[9]. The corresponding $Fe(dipy)_3^{2+}$ ion-pair with perchlorate is extracted into nitrobenzene[10] in the pH range 3.5–8.5. Other extraction systems will be discussed later in the text in connection with spectrophotometric procedures.

3. *Paper and thin-layer chromatography*

Where small amounts of perchlorate are involved, a useful range of separations is possible using chromatographic methods. For convenience, experimental details of some of these are listed in *Table 37*.

4. *Electrophoresis*

Electrophoresis on anion-exchange paper has been used[16] for separating chloride–hypochlorite–chlorate–perchlorate mixtures. The separation is effective at pH 7 using a phosphate buffer and a weakly basic Amberlite WB-2 paper. Using 20 mA per 2.5 cm width, the separation requires 60 min.

Determination

Perchlorates are relatively inert. They cannot be reduced to chloride by SO_2, but reduction to this form can be accomplished using more powerful reductants such as titanium(III). An alternative route to chloride is dry ignition with anhydrous sodium sulphite, sodium nitrite, or sodium peroxide.

Gravimetric methods

Perchlorate is quantitatively precipitated[17] by tetraphenylarsonium chloride as Ph_4AsClO_4. Optimum conditions for the assay of ammonium perchlorate using the reaction were investigated by Glover and Rosey[18] who found that 100 per cent recovery depends on the $Ph_4AsCl:ClO_4^-$ ratio. For 0.006M perchlorate ion and 0.8M HCl, a low recovery results if $Ph_4AsCl:ClO_4^-$ is less than 2:1. When greater than 5:1 results are high. Using values between the two, a 99.8 per cent recovery is possible. Chlorate and bromide do not interfere when present in ammonium perchlorate in amounts up to 0.4%. The precipitate is dried at 110 °C. A factor of 0.2433 is used for perchlorate.

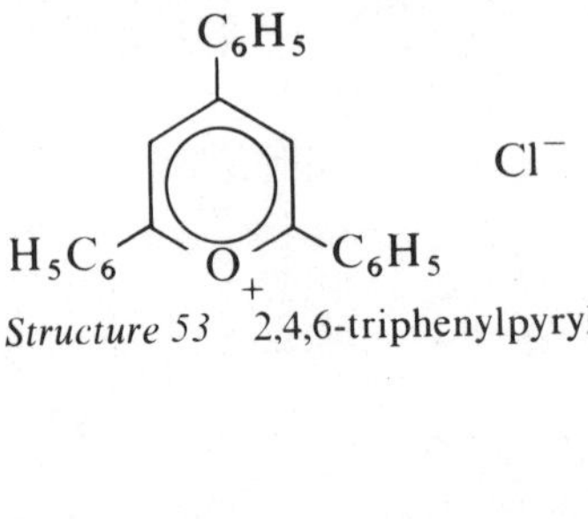

Structure 53 2,4,6-triphenylpyrylium chloride

More recent the reagent 2,4,6-triphenylpyrylium chloride (*Structure 53*) has been investigated as an alternative to TPAC and nitron which behaves similarly[19].

A 2% solution in 0.2M HCl gives precipitates with iodide, thiocyanate, nitrate, perchlorate, permanganate, dichromate, hexacyanoferrate(II), and the chloro-complexes of zinc, lead, cadmium, tin(II), platinum(IV) and gold(III). No precipitate is given with fluoride, bromide, iodate, chlorate, sulphate, oxalate, or the chlorocomplexes of iron(III). The reagent can be used for gravimetric determination of perchlorate in amounts from 40 to 160 mg.

$$(C_6H_5)_3C_5H_2O^+ + ClO_4^- \rightarrow (C_6H_5)_3C_5H_2O{\cdot}ClO_4$$

Tetraphenylphosphonium chloride also precipitates perchlorate quantitatively, and has been used[20] for its determination at ppm level in the presence of a 3000-fold excess of chlorate. Hutton and Stephen[21] use the reagent for analysis of perchlorate–nitrate mixtures. First the perchlorate is precipitated with TPPC and evaluated gravimetrically. Filtrate nitrate is precipitated with N-(4-chlorobenzyl)-1-naphthylmethylamine and evaluated by gravimetry or titrimetry. Satisfactory results are obtained for ratios of nitrate: perchlorate of 1:4.8 to 8.3:1, the widest range tested.

Russian workers[22] have developed gravimetric methods for perchlorate (and periodate) using antipyrine and its derivatives. The sparingly soluble ion-association compounds can be either weighed or titrated potentiometrically with 0.1M NaOH. No interference is given by chloride, chlorate or sulphate, common impurities in perchlorates. The method is applicable to perchlorate in the range 4–50 mg.

Titrimetric methods

Perchlorate can be reduced with a known excess of standard titanium chloride and the excess back-titrated with ferric ammonium sulphate[23]. Experimental details of this determination are also given in a standard text[24].

Aravamudan and Krishnan[25] reduce perchlorate using ferrous sulphate in a strong H_2SO_4 medium and heated to 150–155 °C for 15 min. After cooling and diluting, the unconsumed iron(II) is titrated with $KMnO_4$. An accuracy of about 0.3 per cent is quoted.

Haight[26] used zinc amalgam with molybdenum(VI) as catalyst for reduction of perchlorate to chloride which was subsequently determined by the Volhard method. Possible interference by nitrate and chlorate can be avoided by a preliminary reduction at a much lower temperature and H_2SO_4 concentration. Under these conditions both nitrate and chlorate are reduced leaving perchlorate unaffected by the mild conditions.

Spectroscopic methods

1. Spectrophotometric methods

Perchlorate forms a sparingly soluble violet ion-association complex[27] with methylene blue (*Structure 54*). The system has been used in numerous spectrophotometric procedures, some of which tend to be cumbersome in operation[28]. Nabar and Ramachandran[1] employed an excess of methylene blue and determined its excess after filtering off the precipitate.

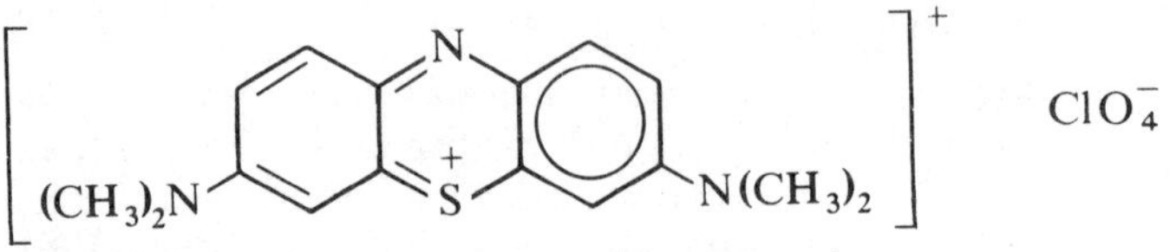

$$\left[(CH_3)_2N\text{—}\text{(phenothiazinium, } \overset{+}{S}\text{, N)}\text{—}N(CH_3)_2 \right]^+ \quad ClO_4^-$$

Structure 54 Methylene blue–perchlorate complex

The complex can be extracted into $CHCl_3$ and other solvents. Iwasaki, Utsumi and Kang[29] were able to eliminate errors due to solubility of the precipitate by extracting into 1,2-dichloroethane. Beer's law holds below 1 ppm. Serious interference is given by chlorate, periodate, nitrate, nitrite, thiosulphate, tungstate, chromate, and magnesium. Some criticism of methylene blue procedures for perchlorate have been made on the grounds of high blank values resulting from lack of a suitable solvent to extract solely the complex of interest.

Several dyestuffs have been applied in addition to methylene blue. Crystal violet forms a complex[30] with perchlorate extractable into chlorobenzene, and giving an absorbance maximum at 595 nm. No interference is given by large amounts of sulphate, iodate or chloride. Details of another method[31] utilizing crystal violet are given in the periodate section.

Other triphenylmethane dyes have been employed. Golosnitskaya and Petraschen[32, 33] use brilliant green and malachite green (*Structure 55*). The complexes are extracted in each case.

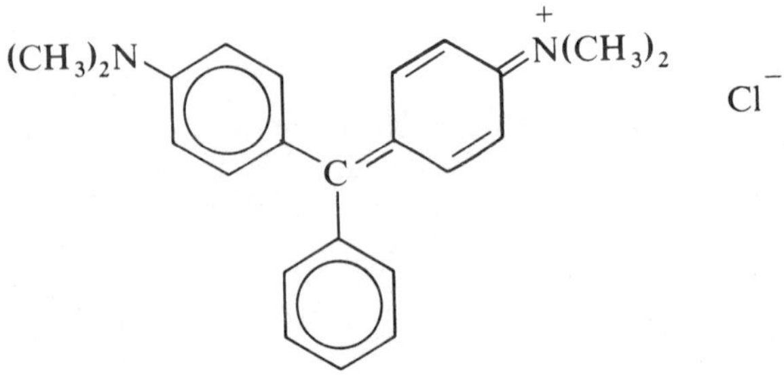

$$(CH_3)_2N\text{—}C_6H_4\text{—}C(C_6H_5)\text{=}C_6H_4\text{=}\overset{+}{N}(CH_3)_2 \quad Cl^-$$

Structure 55 Malachite green

The pH indicator, neutral red, can be used[34] in an extraction-spectrophotometric method for perchlorate. The neutral red cation forms ion-pairs with several anions including thiocyanate. In the case of perchlorate extraction is made into nitrobenzene from a citrate buffer at pH 1–3. The absorbance of the extract is measured at 552 nm. A linear response is given in the range 10^{-6}–10^{-5}M perchlorate. Large amounts of thiocyanate and iodide interfere but these can be removed by addition of silver sulphate.

Fogg, Burns and Yeowart[35] have developed a novel spectrophotometric method for determination of traces of perchlorate in potassium chlorate. First perchlorate is extracted into *o*-dichlorobenzene as the ion-pair with the tetrabutylphosphonium cation. When this is equilibrated with an aqueous solution containing iron(III) thiocyanate complex, an iron(III) thiocyanate–tetrabutylphosphonium complex is formed in the organic layer. Its absorbance is measured at 510 nm. The method was applied to determination of as little as 0.003% perchlorate in potassium chlorate.

Zatko and Kratochvil[36] base a method on a redox reaction in which perchlorate is reduced to chloride by vanadium(III) in the presence of osmium tetroxide. The resulting vanadium(IV) is determined spectrophotometrically. An alternative procedure involves potentiometric titration of the resulting chloride.

Several workers have exploited the extraction of ion-association complexes formed between perchlorate and metal chelates. Thus tris(1,10-phenanthroline)iron(II) perchlorate can be extracted into *n*-butyronitrile and evaluated spectrophotometrically[8]. Yamamoto *et al.*[9] extract the same complex into nitrobenzene. Complete extraction occurs at pH 1.5–10.0, the absorbance maximum is at 516 nm, and a linear range is given from 10^{-6}M to 4×10^{-5}M perchlorate. No interference is given by chloride, sulphate or phosphate even at a $\times 10^4$ excess over perchlorate, but some ions interfere. The tris-2,2′-bipyridyl–iron(II) chelate has been investigated by Yamamoto and Kotsuji[10]. Here the corresponding complex with perchlorate is extracted into nitrobenzene giving an absorbance maximum at 524 nm. Beer's law holds for 0.4–4.0 ppm perchlorate. Chloride. bromide and sulphate do not interfere.

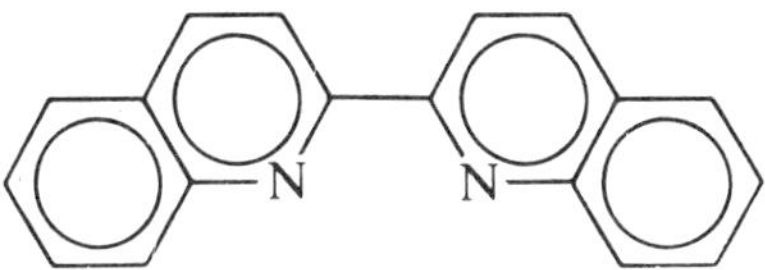

Structure 56 *Cuproine* (2,2′-biquinoline)

More recently Yamamoto, Okamoto and Tao[37] have examined the copper(I) chelate cations of cuproine (2,2′-biquinoline) (*Structure 56*) and neocuproine (*Structure 57*) for spectrophotometric determination of several anions including perchlorate. Extraction is made into methyl ethyl ketone.

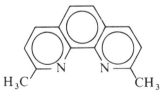

Structure 57 *Neocuproine* (2,9-dimethyl-1,10 phenanthroline)

The absorbance is measured at 456 nm. A linear response holds for 10^{-6}–10^{-5}M ClO_4^-. Chloride, nitrite, thiocyanate, bromide and iodide interfere but this can be largely eliminated by treatment with silver(I) or mercury(II) salts.

Most of the methods discussed involve a precipitation or extraction step prior to measurement. A simple procedure that avoids these steps has been developed by Trautwein and Guyon[38]. The method is indirect, depending on interference by perchlorate with the colour of the rhenium–furildioxime complex formed when perrhenate is reduced with stannous chloride in the presence of α-furildioxime. Several variables affect the colour. The recommended procedure involves two waiting periods of 30 min. Interference occurs in the presence of thiosulphate, copper(II), uranyl, vanadium(V), nitrite and chlorate. Removal of chlorate by heating with HCl is claimed to be effective. No information is provided on the accuracy of the method.

Another novel approach is proposed by Irving and Damodaran[39] based on earlier work by Clifford and Irving[40]. This utilizes a coloured liquid anion-exchanger prepared by equilibrating a solution of tetrahexylammonium iodide in a suitable organic solvent with an aqueous solution of Erdmann's salt, $(NH_4)^+[Co(NH_3)_2(NO_2)_4]^-$. The coloured liquid anion-exchanger has a molar absorptivity of about 10^4. Various anions can displace the coloured erdmannate ion E^- according to the reaction:

$$\{(NR_4)^+E^-\}_{org} + ClO_4^- \rightleftharpoons \{(NR_4)^+ClO_4^-\}_{org} + E^-$$

Accordingly there is a decrease in absorbance of the organic phase and an increase in the aqueous phase. One of the two recommended procedures enables a calibration curve for perchlorate to be constructed using the absorbance of the aqueous phase only. Of particular interest is that any chlorate, hypochlorite, chlorite, nitrite and nitrate which interfere, can be eliminated by a preliminary fuming with HCl. The resulting chloride ions (and many others) do not interfere.

2. *Atomic absorption spectroscopy*

An indirect AAS method has been based on the extracted bis(2,9-dimethyl-1,10-phenanthroline) copper(I)–perchlorate ion pair[41]. The absorbance, using the 324.7 nm copper resonance wavelength, enables perchlorate in the range 0.5–5 ppm to be determined.

3. *Infra-red spectroscopy*

Determination of trace amounts of perchlorate in potassium chlorate has been referred to already in the discussion of spectrophotometric methods. An alternative method employing the infra-red absorption band for perchlorate has been reported[42]. The potassium chlorate sample solution is evaporated nearly to dryness after addition of HCl. Chlorate is reduced to chloride. A disc is prepared from the dried residue. Strong absorption bands at 628 cm^{-1} due to perchlorate enable its content to be evaluated.

Electroanalytical methods

1. *Potentiometric methods including ion-selective electrodes*

Two methods in which a potentiometric titration may be used as an alternative, have been referred to earlier[22,36]. A potentiometric titration has been used for analysis of perchloric acid–nitric acid mixtures[43]. The sequential titration is made in ethyl methyl ketone–methanol (1:1) medium with KOH as titrant and using glass-calomel electrodes. The relative error is less than 1 per cent.

The present situation with regard to ion-selective electrodes is one of rapid development with several new sensor materials being reported[44]. Liquid-type commercial electrodes are available; several solid-state types have been described. Baczuk and DuBois[45] use an Orion type 93-81 liquid-membrane electrode for potentiometric titration of perchlorate with tetraphenylarsonium chloride. A five-fold improvement in the lower concentration limit (to 0.05 mmol in a 50 mℓ sample) was obtained by Smith and Manahan[46] by carrying out the titration at 2 °C. The method is simple and relatively free from interferences. One commercial liquid-type electrode is reported to contain a tris(1,10-phenanthroline derivative)–iron(III) complex[47]. Sharp[48] has reported a solid-state electrode that gives a nearly Nernstian response for perchlorate in the range 10^{-1}–3×10^{-4}M.

2. Coulometric methods

Conversion of perchlorate to chloride by oxygen-flask combustion, followed by coulometric titration of the chloride, has been reported[49].

Miscellaneous methods

The perchlorate–tetraphenylarsonium chloride reaction has been further exploited in a thermometric procedure[50]. Common ions including halides and nitrate do not interfere but permanganate, chlorate, and borofluoride cause large errors. Chlorate interferes but bromate has no adverse effect.

References

1. NABAR, G.M. and RAMACHANDRAN, C.R., *Analyt. Chem.*, **31**, 263 (1959)
2. SCHUMACHER, J.C., *Perchlorates, their Properties, Manufacture and Use,* ACS Monograph No. 146, Reinhold, New York (1960)
3. CHADWICK, T.C., *Analyt. Chem.*, **45**, 985 (1973)
4. GREENHALGH, R. and RILEY, J.P., *J. mar. biol. Ass. U.K.*, **41**, 175 (1961)
5. BOCK, R. and BEILSTEIN, G.M., *Z. analyt. Chem.*, **192**, 44 (1963)
6. BOCK, R. and JAINZ, J., *Z. analyt. Chem.*, **198**, 315 (1963)
7. BOCK, R. and HUMMEL, C., *Z. analyt. Chem.*, **198**, 176 (1963)
8. FRITZ, J.S., ABBINK, J.E. and CAMPBELL, P.A., *Analyt. Chem.*, **36**, 2123 (1964)
9. YAMAMOTO, Y., KOTSUJI, K., KINUWAKI, S. and SAWAMURA, H., *J. chem. Soc. Japan, pure Chem. Sect.*, **85**, 869 (1964); *Analyt. Abstr.*, **13**, 3551 (1966)
10. YAMAMOTO, Y. and KOTSUJI, K., *Bull. chem. Soc. Japan*, **37**, 785 (1964); *Analyt. Abstr.*, **12**, 3307 (1965)
11. THIELEMANN, H., *Mikrochim. Acta*, 746 (1971)
12. HARRISON, B.L. and ROSENBLATT, D.L., *J. Chromat.*, **13**, 271 (1964)
13. SEILER, H. and SEILER, M., *Helv. chim. Acta*, **50**, 2477 (1967)
14. PESCHKE, W., *J. Chromat.*, **20**, 573 (1965)
15. PETROVIC, S.M. and CANIC, V.D., *Z. analyt. Chem.*, **228**, 339 (1967); *Analyt. Abstr.*, **15**, 4674 (1968)
16. TOKUTOMI, M. and KAMIYA, S., *Japan Analyst*, **21**, 81 (1972); *Analyst, Abstr.*, **26**, 31 (1974)
17. SMITH, G.M. and WILLARD, H., *Ind. Engng Chem. analyt. Edn*, **11**, 186 (1939)
18. GLOVER, D.J. and ROSEY, J.M., *Analyt. Chem.*, **37**, 306 (1965)
19. CHADWICK, T.C., *Analyt. Chem.*, **45**, 985 (1973)
20. FUHRMAN, D.L., *Talanta*, **16**, 121 (1969)
21. HUTTON, R.C. and STEPHEN, W.I., *Analyst*, **92**, 501 (1967)

22. AKIMOV, V.K., EMEL'YANOVA, I.A. and BUSEV, A.I., *Zh. analit. Khim.*, **26**, 956 (1971); *Analyt. Abstr.*, **23**, 3148 (1972)
23. BURNS, E.A. and MURACA, R.F., *Analyt. Chem.*, **32**, 1316 (1960)
24. BELCHER, R. and WILSON, C.L., *New Methods of Analytical Chemistry*, 2nd edn, Chapman and Hall, London, 320 (1964)
25. ARAVAMUDAN, G. and KRISHNAM, V., *Talanta*, **13**, 519 (1966)
26. HAIGHT, G.P., *Analyt. Chem.*, **25**, 642 (1953)
27. HAHN, F.L., *Z. angew. Chem.*, **39**, 451 (1926); *Chem. Abstr.*, **20**, 1967 (1926)
28. BOLTZ, D.F. and HOLLAND, W.J., in *Colorimetric Determination of Non-metals* (Ed. D.F. Boltz), Interscience, New York, 176 (1958)
29. IWASAKI, I., UTSUMI, S. and KANG, C., *Bull. chem. Soc. Japan*, **36**, 325 (1963); *Analyt. Abstr.*, **11**, 1979 (1964)
30. UCHIKAWA, S., *Bull. chem. Soc. Japan*, **40**, 798 (1967); *Analyt. Abstr.*, **15**, 4678 (1968)
31. HENDRICK, C.E. and BERGER, B.A., *Analyt. Chem.*, **38**, 791 (1966)
32. GOLOSNITSKAYA, V.A. and PETRASCHEN, V.I., *Zh. analit. Khim.*, **17**, 878 (1962); *Analyt. Abstr.*, **10**, 2264 (1963)
33. GOLOSNITSKAYA, V.A. and PETRASCHEN, V.I., *Tr. Novocherk. Politekhn. Inst.*, **141**, 73 (1964); *Chem. Abstr.*, **64**, 1351e (1966)
34. TSUBOUCHI, M., *Analytica chim. Acta*, **54**, 143 (1971)
35. FOGG, A.G., BURNS, D.T. and YEOWART, E.H., *Mikrochim. Acta*, 974 (1970)
36. ZATKO, D.A. and KRATOCHVIL, B., *Analyt. Chem.*, **37**, 1560 (1965)
37. YAMAMOTO, Y., OKAMOTO. and TAO, E., *Analytica chim. Acta*, **47**, 127 (1969)
38. TRAUTWEIN, N.L. and GUYON, J.C., *Analyt. Chem.*, **40**, 639 (1968)
39. IRVING, H.M.N.H. and DAMODARAN, A.D., *Analyst*, **90**, 443 (1965)
40. CLIFFORD, W.E. and IRVING, H.M.N.H., *Analytica chim. Acta*, **31**, 1 (1964)
41. COLLINSON, W.J. and BOLTZ, D.F., *Analyt. Chem.*, **40**, 1896 (1968)
42. BRIGGS, A.G., HAYES, W.P., HOWLING, P.A. and BURNS, D.T., *Mikrochim. Acta*, 888 (1970)
43. DENISOVA, N.I. and GOLUBEVA, A.A., *Zh. analit. Khim.*, **27**, 1221 (1972); *Analyt. Abstr.*, **25**, 2254 (1973)
44. COVINGTON, A.K., *CRC crit. Rev. analyt. Chem.*, **3**, 355 (1974)
45. BACZUK, R.J. and DUBOIS, R.J., *Analyt. Chem.*, **40**, 685 (1968)
46. SMITH, M.J., and MANAHAN, S.E., *Analytica chim. Acta*, **48**, 315 (1969)
47. ROSS, J.W. in *Ion-Selective Electrodes* (Ed. R.A. Durst), Publn. No. 314, Nat. Bur. Stands, Washington, 73 (1969)
48. SHARP, M., *Analytica chim. Acta*, **61**, 91 (1972)
49. SECOR, G.E., RICCI, B.A. and WHITE, L.M., *Microchem. J.*, **13**, 273 (1968)
50. CARR, P.W. and JORDAN, J., *Analyt. Chem.*, **44**, 1278 (1972)

Periodate

Analytical methods for periodate are essentially redox, and its determination alone is a relatively simple matter. In the presence of other oxidizing species the matter becomes more difficult.

Some years ago it was reported that periodate solutions are unstable[1]. If this were so it would have several analytical implications, for example on the storage of reference solutions and the use of potassium periodate as an analytical reagent. Sufficient evidence is now available to discount this. A recent investigation has indicated that acidic periodate solutions contain two species, tetrahedral periodate and octahedral H_5IO_6. Equilibrium between the two is rapidly attained, and solutions are stable over long periods if stored in amber glass bottles[2].

Table 38 Paper and thin-layer chromatographic separation of periodate

Technique	*Solvent system*	*Ions separated*	*Ref.*
TLC Silica gel	MeOH–25% aq. NH_3–H_2O–10% aq. acetic acid (18:2:2:1)	IO_3^-, I^-, IO_4^-	3
Paper Whatman No. 4	Amyl alcohol–pyridine–aq. NH_3 (0.880) (3:7:10)	IO_3^-, I^-, IO_4^-	4
Paper glass fibre	Several including isopropanol–1.5F NH_3 (7:3)	IO_3^-, I^-, IO_4^-	5
TLC Al_2O_3	Various inorganic solutions	IO_3^-, IO_4^-, BrO_3^-, CrO_4^{2-}	6

Separations

1. Paper and thin-layer chromatography

Some separations are given in *Table 38*. The use of glass fibre paper by Naeumann[5] was found to be necessary. Parallel work on cellulose paper was unsatisfactory due to reduction of periodate, probably to iodate.

2. Thin-layer electrophoresis

Quantitative separation of periodate and iodate by thin-layer electrophoresis on strips of Plaster of Paris has been reported[7].

3. Coprecipitation

Iron(III) hydroxide has been found[8] to be effective for coprecipitation of periodate. This investigation established that periodate could be separated from iodate, the latter remaining in solution. By repeating the procedure a separation in excess of 99 per cent was obtained. Bhattacharyya and Chetia[9] find that aluminium hydroxide will coprecipitate periodate in the presence of large amounts of iodate. The periodate was subsequently determined spectrophotometrically.

Determination

Sulphur dioxide reduces periodate to iodide, and it may be determined in this form. The reduction can be made using gaseous SO_2 or by a dilute solution of potassium bisulphite. Excess SO_2 is boiled off.

Titrimetric methods

1. Iodimetric methods

Periodate is reduced to iodate in buffered alkaline solutions. Several species bring about the reduction including iodide, arsenic(III), and manganese(II) sulphate. With iodide the reaction is as follows:

$$IO_4^- + 2I^- + H_2O \rightarrow IO_3^- + I_2 + 2OH^-$$

Willard and Greathouse[10] recommended a borax–boric acid buffer, with arsenic(III) being used for titrating the liberated iodine. In an acidic solution, periodate is reduced to iodine.

$$IO_4^- + 7I^- + 8H^+ \rightarrow 4I_2 + 4H_2O$$

This can be titrated[11] either with standard thiosulphate or arsenic(III). Mixtures of periodates and iodates can be analysed using the above reactions. Periodate is first determined under alkaline conditions. The sum of periodate and iodate is determined under acidic conditions.

An alternative method for periodate/iodate mixtures is by a modification of the iodimetric procedure. Kahane[12] selectively precipitated periodate by addition of zinc acetate. The precipitate $Zn_5(IO_6)_2$ was filtered off, dissolved in dilute acid and titrated iodimetrically. Iodate in the filtrate was determined by the conventional iodimetric titration.

A more elegant solution to this problem has been described by Belcher and Townshend[13]. Periodate is masked with molybdate by formation of 6-molybdoperiodate $[I(MoO_4)_6]^{5-}$ at pH 3. Iodate is titrated iodimetrically with standard thiosulphate. On addition of oxalic acid the periodate is demasked and the liberated iodine again titrated with standard thiosulphate. The complete analysis requires one aliquot only.

Szekeres has reported the iodimetric analysis of iodate–periodate–bromate–chlorate mixtures[14], and chromate–arsenate–periodate–iodate–bromate–chlorate mixtures[15].

2. Using miscellaneous reductants

Periodate can be titrated directly with arsenic(III) in dilute H_2SO_4 and with ferroin as indicator[16].

Kaushik and Rajendra[17] use the hexacyanoferrate(III)–ascorbic acid reaction in the following way. Excess of hexacyanoferrate(II) is added to the sample in the presence of phosphoric acid. The pH is adjusted by addition of $NaHCO_3$ and the resulting hexacyanoferrate(III) titrated with standard ascorbic acid using 2,4 dichlorophenolindophenol as indicator.

$$IO_4^- + 2[Fe(CN)_6]^{4-} + H_2O \rightarrow IO_3^- + 2[Fe(CN)_6]^{3-} + 2OH^-$$

Iodate does not affect the determination.

Berka and Zyka[18] have shown that periodate can be titrated in the presence of iodate using hydrazine sulphate. Chloramine T has been used in the indirect titration of periodate.

Other redox systems have involved potentiometric end-points. This will be discussed below.

Iodimetric titration of periodate

Procedure

Dissolve the sample in 50 mℓ of water, add 3 g of KI and 3 mℓ of concentrated HCl. Allow to stand for 5 min, then dilute to about 150 mℓ. Titrate with standard thiosulphate using starch.

For more accurate work a blank determination should be made.

$$IO_4^- \equiv 4I_2 \equiv 8S_2O_3^{2-}$$

Spectroscopic methods

2. Spectrophotometric methods, visible and UV

Few spectrophotometric methods exist for periodate and most of them are recent in origin.

The absorption spectra of periodate in aqueous solutions at various pH values have been investigated by Crouthamel *et al.*[20]. This work indicated that periodate can be determined in slightly acidic or alkaline media by means of its absorbance at 222 nm. Subsequent work by Bhattacharyya and Chetia[9] indicated that the system obeys Beer's law over the concentration range 1×10^{-5}–18×10^{-5}M KIO_4 and that the molar absorptivity is 2.87×10^3.

Hendrick and Berger[21] have examined a range of triphenylmethane dyes as well as solvent systems, for determination of periodate. Crystal violet was found to be the best dye, and benzene the best solvent. The range of concentration for which the method is valid is 0.1–1.0×10^{-5}M. Absorbance measurements are made at 615 nm. No interference is given by halates at 10^{-3}M or IO_3^- at 10^{-2}M. Nitrate, bicarbonate, and acetate are not extracted. Thiocyanate interferes when present in concentrations above 10^{-4}M. Sulphite and cyanide interfere by reacting with the dye.

Benzhydrazide has been investigated as a reagent[22]. It had previously been used as titrant for periodate in very dilute H_2SO_4 medium[23]. A linear calibration holds over the range 6.0–14.0×10^{-4}M IO_4^-. Many ions cause severe interference including $[Fe(CN)_6]^{4-}$, $[Fe(CN)_6]^{3-}$, CrO_4^{2-}, I^-, S^{2-}, $S_2O_3^{2-}$, AsO_3^{3-}, Sn^{2+}, Hg^{2+}, Hg_2^{2+}, Pb^{2+}, Ag^+ and Bi^{3+}. Others including iodate, bromate, chlorate and perchlorate can be tolerated when present in molar ratios to periodate of less than 2.5.

Further spectrophotometric methods have been based on *o*-dianisidine[24] and 1,2-bis(4-dimethylaminophenyl)ethane 1,2-diol[25]. It should be noted that *o*-dianisidine is now controlled by the Carcinogenic Substances Regulations[26].

2. Infra-red spectroscopy

Tetraphenylarsonium periodate exhibits a strong and sharp absorption band at 856 cm^{-1}, which is characteristic of the periodate ion. Although several other anions, for example permanganate and chlorate, also form precipitates with TPAC, no resulting bands are produced at this frequency. A method for microgram determination of periodate based on this has been developed by Al-Kayssi and Magee[27]. Periodate is precipitated in slightly acidic solution with TPAC and in the presence of perchlorate as carrier. The precipitate is incorporated into a potassium bromide disc and the absorbance measured at 856 cm^{-1}. No interference is given by permanganate, perchlorate, chlorate, bromate, iodate, or perrhenate. The procedure is lengthy, requiring the precipitate to stand for 24 h in an ice-bath before filtration.

Electroanalytical methods

Potentiometric methods including use of ion-selective electrodes

Periodate in 0.09–70 mg quantities can be titrated potentiometrically in a H_3PO_4 medium, using iron(II) ammonium sulphate as titrant, and osmium tetroxide as catalyst[28]. Several ions interfere depending on the concentrations present. They include fluoride, chloride, bromide, iodide, sulphate, nitrate, phosphate, borate and iodate. Norkus and co-workers[29,30] have used arsenic(III) in the potentiometric titration. In the first paper, K_2RuO_4 is used as catalyst, and the periodate is reduced to iodate in a strong alkaline medium. For 5–200 mg of periodate the error is less than 0.2 per cent. In the second paper the catalyst employed is osmium tetroxide.

References

1. HEAD, F.S.H. and HUGHES, G., *J. chem. Soc.*, 2046 (1952)
2. GALLIFORD, D.J.B., NUTTALL, R.H. and OTTAWAY, J.M., *Talanta*, **19**, 871 (1972)
3. PALAGYI, S. and ZADUBAN, M., *Chemické Zvesti*, **23**, 876 (1969); *Analyt. Abstr.*, **20**, 1660 (1971)
4. OBRENOVIC-PALIGORIC, I.D. and CVORIC, J.D., *Bull. Boris Kidrich Inst. nucl. Sci.*, **14**, 95 (1963); *Chem. Abstr.*, **59**, 14555b (1963)
5. NAEUMANN, R., *J. Chromat.*, **18**, 385 (1965)
6. LEDERER, M. and POLCARO, C., *J. Chromat.*, **84**, 379 (1973)
7. DOBICI, F. and GRASSINI, G., *J. Chromat.*, **10**, 98 (1963)
8. NOVIKOV, A.I. and FINKEL'SHTEIN, E.I., *Zh. analit. Khim.*, **19**, 541 (1964); *Analyt. Abstr.*, **12**, 4534 (1965)
9. BHATTACHARYYA, S.N. and CHETIA, P.K., *Analyt. Chem.*, **39**, 369 (1967)
10. WILLARD, H.H. and GREATHOUSE, L.H., *J. Am. chem. Soc.*, **60**, 2869 (1938)
11. FURMAN, N.H. (Ed.) *Standard Methods of Chemical Analysis*, 6th edn, Vol. 1, Van Nostrand, Princeton, N.J., 522
12. KAHANE, E., *Bull. Soc. chim. Fr.*, 70 (1948)
13. BELCHER, R. and TOWNSHEND, A., *Analytica chim. Acta*, **41**, 395 (1968)
14. SZEKERES, L., *Z. analyt. Chem.*, **172**, 256 (1960); *Analyt. Abstr.*, **7**, 3739 (1960)
15. SZEKERES, L., *Annali Chim.*, **51**, 200 (1961); *Analyt. Abstr.*, **8**, 4932 (1961)
16. GLEN, K. and KATTHAN, W., *Ber.*, **86**, 1077 (1953); *Chem. Abstr.*, **48**, 3834b (1954)
17. KAUSHIK, L. and RAJENDRA, P., *J. indian chem. Soc.*, **47**, 1199 (1970); *Analyt. Abstr.*, **21**, 2567 (1971)
18. BERKA, A. and ZYKA, J., *Čská Farm.*, **8**, 136 (1959); *Analyt. Abstr.*, **6**, 4769 (1959)
19. SINGH, B. and SOOD, K.C., *Analytica chim. Acta*, **13**, 305 (1955)
20. CROUTHAMEL, C.E., MEEK, H.V., MARTIN, D.S. and BANKS, C.V., *J. Am. chem. Soc.*, **71**, 3031 (1949)
21. HENDRICK, C.E. and BERGER, B.A., *Analyt. Chem.*, **38**, 791 (1966)
22. ESCARRILLA, A.M., MALONEY, P.F. and MALONEY, P.M., *Analytica chim. Acta*, **45**, 199 (1969)
23. VULTERIN, J. AND ZYKA, J., *Talanta*, **10**, 891 (1963)
24. GUERNET, M., *Bull. Soc. chim. Fr.*, 478 (1964); *Analyt. Abstr.*, **12**, 3308 (1965)
25. FIELDS, R. and DIXON, H.B.F., *Biochem. J.*, **108**, 883 (1968)
26. *The Carcinogenic Substances Regulations*, H.M.S.O., London (1967)
27. AL-KAYSSI, M. and MAGEE, R.J., *Analytica chim. Acta*, **28**, 176 (1963)
28. VULTERIN, J., *Colln Czech. chem. Commun. Engl. Edn*, **31**, 3529 (1966); *Analyt. Abstr.*, **14**, 7468 (1967)
29. NORKUS, P.K., SIMKEVICHUTE, G.S. and JANKAUSKAS, J., *Zh. analit. Khim.*, **25**, 1673 (1970); *Analyt. Abstr.*, **22**, 1569 (1972)
30. NORKUS, P.K. and SIMKEVICHUTE, G.S., *Zh. analit. Khim.*, **26**, 1076 (1971); *Analyt. Abstr.*, **23**, 3149 (1972)

Part 3

Phosphorus Oxyanions

Before dealing with individual anions within this group, some comment on nomenclature is pertinent. The older obsolete notation dating from Graham's classification of 1833, and according to which phosphates are considered to be either ortho-, pyro-, or meta-, has largely disappeared except in some technological literature. However, recent sources are not always consistent on the meanings they attach to terms. For example, according to Wazer[1] 'metaphosphates' may have chain or cyclic structures, whereas Thilo[2] favours restricting the term to cyclic structures only, and using the term 'chain polyphosphates' to describe linear species.

The terms 'polyphosphate' and 'condensed phosphate' are usually used synonymously although polyphosphoric acids are designated $H_{n+2}P_nO_{3n+1}$ (IUPAC), while metaphosphoric acids, which are usually included in the generic term 'condensed phosphates', are given the general formula $(HPO_3)_n$ (IUPAC).

A full discussion of phosphorus nomenclature is given in the two sources quoted.

References

1. VAN WAZER, J.R., *Phosphorus and its Compounds,* Vol. I, Chapter 8, Interscience, New York (1964)
2. THILO, E., 'Condensed phosphates and arsenates', *Adv. Chem. Radiochem.*, **4**, 1 (1962)

Diphosphate (Pyrophosphate)

There are sufficient additional features in the analytical chemistry of the diphosphate anion to merit a separate treatment. The structure of the ion is shown in *Structure 58.*

```
   O⁻     O⁻
   |      |
⁻O—P—O—P—O⁻
   ‖      ‖
   O      O
```

Structure 58 Diphosphate ion

Alkali diphosphates are stable in neutral and alkaline solutions. With decrease in pH, hydrolysis becomes increasingly rapid.

Diphosphates find application in food processing, water treatment, textile processing, detergents and cleaning compositions.

Separations

1. Precipitation

Tris(ethylenediamine)cobalt(III)chloride will selectively precipitate[1,2] diphosphate in the presence of monophosphate and certain polyphosphates at pH 7.5. However, radioactive studies with ^{32}P indicate that coprecipitation and incomplete precipitation are serious problems especially at low concentrations. One of the most useful separations using this approach is diphosphate and triphosphate. The composition of the precipitated diphosphate is $Coen_3HP_2O_7$. It is doubtful whether the method is as effective as ion-exchange chromatography.

Separation by precipitation features in certain compleximetric methods for diphosphate, for example Kato *et al*[3]. precipitate diphosphate with zinc

Table 39 Separation of diphosphate by paper and thin-layer chromatography

Technique	*Diphosphate separated from*	*Solvent*	*Ref.*
Paper (Whatman 31 DT)	Ortho- and tri-phosphate	Various mixtures of: Dioxan–aqNH_3–trichloro acetic acid–H_2O	4
TLC (silica gel)	Orthophosphate, phosphite and hypophosphite	MeOH–aqNH_3 (0.880)–10% trichloro acetic acid–H_2O (10 : 3 : 1 : 10)	5
TLC (cellulose powder)	Orthophosphate	Dioxan–aqNH_3 (0.880)–trichloro acetic acid–H_2O (65 ml : 0.25 ml : 5 g : 27.5 ml)	6

acetate at about pH 3.8 leaving orthophosphate in solution to be subsequently precipitated with magnesia mixture. Both anions are determined indirectly by compleximetric titration of the metals associated with them. Essentially the same method may be used for mixtures of diphosphates and metaphosphates, namely precipitation of diphosphate as the insoluble zinc salt followed by determination of metaphosphates in the filtrate.

2. Paper and thin-layer chromatography

Several methods involving this technique are listed in *Table 49* in the section on Polyphosphates. Additional separations are given in *Table 39*.

The merits of paper and thin-layer chromatography for the separation of condensed phosphates generally, has been critically discussed by Pollard *et al*[7].

3. Anion-exchange chromatography

This is probably the most useful method particularly where milligram amounts are involved. The method is discussed in the sections on linear and cyclic polyphosphates. *Table 40* indicates the scope of the technique in separating diphosphate from other phosphorus species.

Gel-chromatography on Sephadex G-25 enables diphosphate to be separated from linear phosphates[15] having a degree of polymerization of up to 13.

Determination

Gravimetric methods

Reference has been made[1,2] to separation of diphosphate using tris(ethylenediamine)cobalt(III)chloride. Coprecipitation and incomplete precipitation, especially at low concentrations detracts from its usefulness. A related method[16] precipitates diphosphate as $Na[Co(C_2H_8N_2)_2P_2O_7]$ using cis-dichlorobis(ethylenediamine)cobalt(III)chloride. Diphosphate in the range 20–80 mg is precipitated at pH 11–12, and drying is carried out at 100–120°C. Orthophosphate, triphosphate, trimetaphosphate and tetrametaphosphate do not interfere in ten-fold excess. Of the ions that do interfere, all are masked except Ag^+, Cu^{2+}, VO_2^{2+}, Mg^{2+}, As^{3+}, Bi^{3+}, Ce^{4+} and Th^{4+}.

Titrimetric methods

Diphosphate is hydrolysed to orthophosphate by hot strong acids. The latter may be determined by several titrimetric procedures. Another approach is to titrate the acid liberated when diphosphates are precipitated by zinc sulphate.

$$Na_2H_2P_2O_7 + 2ZnSO_4 \rightarrow Zn_2P_2O_7 + Na_2SO_4 + H_2SO_4$$

Introduced by Britske and Dragunov[17] in 1927, the method has been improved by subsequent investigations. Bell[18] recommended adjusting the pH to 3.8, adding zinc sulphate and titrating the liberated hydrogen

Table 40 Separation of diphosphate from other phosphorus anions by anion-exchange chromatography

Anions separated from $P_2O_7^{4-}$						*Comments*	*Ref.*
Ortho- PO_4	*Tri-* PO_4	*Tetra-* PO_4	*Penta-* PO_4	*Tri-meta* PO_4	*Tetra meta* PO_4		
×	×			×	×		8
×	×	×*		×	×*	*Eluted as mixture	9
×	×			×	×		10
×	×			×		Gradient elution	11
×	×			×	×	Gradient elution	12
×	×			×		Automatic method. Other P species inc. lower P anions also separated	13
×	×	×	×	×	×	Higher linear P anions also separated	14

ions at pH 3.8. It was observed that if the concentration of zinc sulphate was constant, the acidity produced was a function of the triphosphate present. The procedure can be used for determination of triphosphate if diphosphate is absent, or if the latter is determined by another method. Dewald and Schmidt[19] improved the method by adding a zinc sulphate solution adjusted to pH 3.8.

Titrimetric determination of diphosphate[19]

Procedure

Dissolve 0.5 g of diphosphate which contains no polyphosphate or 'hexametaphosphate' in 100 mℓ water and stir for about 2 min. Using 0.1M HCl or 0.1M NaOH, adjust the pH to exactly 3.8. Add 70 mℓ of 12.5% $ZnSO_4 \cdot 7H_2O$ solution previously adjusted to pH 3.8. Stir for 2 min, then titrate with 0.1M NaOH until the pH is again at 3.8. Assume 1 mℓ 0.1M NaOH ≡ 13.23 mg $Na_4P_2O_7$.

The results are not as good if zinc chloride solution is used.

Kato *et al.*[3] precipitate diphosphate quantitatively with zinc acetate at about pH 3.8, dissolve the precipitate in an ammoniacal buffer and titrate with EDTA at pH 10 using Eriochrome black T as indicator. Any orthophosphate present is precipitated as $MgNH_4PO_4$ using magnesia mixture in ammoniacal solution, the precipitate dissolved in HCl, excess EDTA added and the excess titrated with standard Mg^{++}, again using Eriochrome black T as indicator.

Nielsch and Giefer[20] preferred to precipitate the diphosphate as $Mn_2P_2O_7$ at pH 4.1 using excess standard Mn^{2+} solution. After 16 h the precipitate was filtered off and the excess manganese in the filtrate was determined by EDTA titration at pH 10 with Eriochrome black T as indicator. Precipitation was found to be quantitative if the diphosphate concentration was at least 0.2 mg $P_2O_7^{4-}$ per mℓ, and the excess of manganese not less than five-fold. Orthophosphate interferes and must be absent.

Spectrophotometric methods

These methods are indirect ones, in some instances based on the reduction in intensity of a coloured species. Kolloff, Ward and Ziemba[21] base their method for determination of traces of diphosphate in orthophosphate, on the reduction in colour intensity of the iron(III)-thiocyanate complex caused by formation of the iron(III)-diphosphate complex. The absorbance is measured at 435 nm. Maurice[22] describes a similar method in which both diphosphate and triphosphate may be determined by measuring the extinction at two pH values.

Chess and Bernhart[23] base their method on the iron(II)-1,10-phenanthroline complex. Unfortunately iron and aluminium, often present in commercial sodium phosphates, were found to interfere and this could not be prevented by the investigators.

A different principle has been utilized more recently for the determination of diphosphate in orthophosphate[24]. Ferric ions are added to the mixture and the iron(III) diphosphate extracted into dodecylamine in $CHCl_3$ and acetone. The iron content of the extract (and hence the diphosphate content) is determined using sulphosalicylic acid after back-extraction into ammonium hydroxide. The extinction of the aqueous layer is measured at 440–460 nm.

Amperometric method

This method[25], which is unaffected by ortho- and triphosphate, is based on the insolubility of cadmium diphosphate in a 2.5 : 1 water–ethanol mixture at pH 4.

Enzymatic method

Inorganic diphosphate is the product of several biosynthetic processes. Johnson *et al.*[26] have developed an enzymatic method which they use to assay RNA polymerase. Neither orthophosphate nor any of the organic phosphates tested, caused interferences.

References

1. MCKUNE, H.W. and ARQUETTE, G.J., *Analyt. Chem.*, **27**, 401 (1955)
2. WEISER, H.J., *Analyt. Chem.*, **28**, 477 (1956)
3. KATO, T., HAGIWARA, Z., SHINOZAWA, S. and TSUKADA, S., *Technol. Reports Tohuka Univ.*, **19**, 93 (1954); *Analyt. Abstr.*, **2**, 2697 (1955); *Japan Analyst*, **4**, 84 (1955); *Analyt. Abstr.*, **2**, 3025 (1955)
4. KOLLOFF, R.H., *Analyt. Chem.*, **33**, 373 (1961)
5. SEILER, H., *Helv. chim. Acta.*, **44**, 1753 (1961)
6. CLESCERI, N.L. and LEE, G.F., *Analyt. Chem.*, **36**, 2207 (1964)
7. POLLARD, F.H., NICKLESS, G., BURTON, K. and HUBBARD, J., *Microchem. J.*, **10**, 131 (1966)
8. LINDENBAUM, S., PETERS, T.V. and RIEMAN, W., *Analytica chim. Acta.*, **11**, 530 (1954)
9. PETERS, T.V. and RIEMAN, W., *Analytica chim. Acta.*, **14**, 131 (1956)
10. BEAUKENKAMP, J., RIEMAN, W. and LINDENBAUM, S., *Analyt. Chem.*, **26**, 505 (1954)
11. LUNDGREN, D.P. and LOEB, N.P., *Analyt. Chem.*, **33**, 366 (1961)
12. GRANDE, J.E. and BEAUKENKAMP, J., *Analyt. Chem.*, **28**, 1497 (1956)
13. POLLARD, F.H., NICKLESS, G., ROGERS, D.E. and ROTHWELL, M.T., *J. Chromat.*, **17**, 157 (1965); POLLARD, F.H., NICKLESS, G., ROGERS, D.E. and CRONE, D.L., *Proc. Soc. analyt. Chem. Conference*, Nottingham, 1965, W. Heffer & Sons Ltd., Cambridge, 481 (1965)
14. ROTHBART, H.L., WEYMOUTH, H.W. and RIEMAN, W., *Talanta*, **11**, 33 (1964)
15. UENO, Y.Y., YOZA, N.N. and OHASHI, S., *J. Chromat.*, **52**, 481 (1970)
16. SHARMA, C.L., *Z. analyt. Chem.*, **257**, 133 (1971); *Analyt. Abstr.*, **23**, 1393 (1972)
17. BRITSKE, E.V. and DRAGUNOV, S.S., *J. Chem. Ind. U.S.S.R.*, **4**, 49 (1927)
18. BELL, R., *Analyt. Chem.*, **19**, 97 (1947)
19. DEWALD, W. and SCHMIDT, H., *Z. analyt. Chem.*, **134**, 17 (1951)
20. NIELSCH, W. and GIEFER, L., *Z. analyt. Chem.*, **142**, 323 (1955)
21. KOLLOFF, R.H., WARD, H.K. and ZIEMBA, V.F., *Analyt. Chem.*, **32**, 1687 (1960)
22. MAURICE, J., *Bull. Soc. chim. Fr.*, 819 (1959)
23. CHESS, W.B. and BERNHART, D.N., *Analyt. Chem.*, **30**, 111 (1958)
24. SHEVCHUK, I.A., SKRIPNIK, N. A. and YA ENAL'EVA, L., *Zav. Lab.*, **33**, 288 (1967); *Analyt. Abstr.*, **15**, 3289 (1968)
25. SONGINA, O.A., BLIZNYUK, V.M. and OMARKULOVA, G.O., *Zav. Lab.*, **37**, 271 (1971); *Analyt. Abstr.*, **22**, 106 (1972)
26. JOHNSON, J.C., SHANOFF, M., BASS, S.T., BOEZI, J.A. and HANSEN, R.G., *Analyt. Biochem.*, **26**, 137 (1968)

Hexafluorophosphate

Hexafluorophosphates find several applications industrially, for example in catalysis and in the electropolishing of alloys. The synthesis of sodium, potassium and ammonium hexafluorophosphates has been described[1].

Separations

Precipitation with nitron or tetraphenylarsonium chloride will separate hexafluorophosphate from a wide range of ions. This is also the basis of methods for determination of the ion.

Archer and Doolittle[2] have developed a solvent extraction procedure in which ferrous-1,10-phenanthroline hexafluorophosphate is extracted into *n*-butyronitrile. The extraction is quite selective and also forms the basis of a spectrophotometric method.

Determination

Methods for determination of hexafluorophosphate were severely limited until 1963 when Affsprung and Archer[3,4] used tetraphenylarsonium salts to develop gravimetric and amperometric methods.

Gravimetric methods

Prior to 1963 the standard method involved gravimetric determination of the ion with nitron (1,4-diphenyl-endanilodihydrotriazole). This reagent, first introduced for hexafluorophosphate by Lange and Muller[5] was also used extensively for determination of nitrate, but was never satisfactory partly due to its instability. The introduction of tetraphenylarsonium chloride represents a considerable advance. In terms of procedure the method is relatively straightforward.

Any ions forming a precipitate with tetraphenylarsonium chloride will interfere. These include permanganate, perrhenate, perchlorate, bromide, iodide, iodate and thiocyanate. The ions most likely to occur with hexafluorophosphate salts are orthophosphate and monofluorophosphate. These give no precipitate, but difluorophosphates give slight interference. This can be overcome by making the solution basic and boiling for a few minutes to hydrolyse the difluorophosphate into monofluorophosphate. The hexafluorophosphate ion is not affected by this treatment.

Gravimetric determination of hexafluorophosphate using tetraphenylarsonium chloride[3]

Procedure

To an aliquot containing 36–55 mg of potassium hexafluorophosphate, add ammonium hydroxide until basic. A final concentration of ammonium hydroxide in the range 5–11 M is satisfactory, and a total volume of 50 mℓ. Warm to near 50 °C and add about twice the equivalent amount of 0.015M tetraphenylarsonium chloride slowly and with stirring. After allowing to stand for 30 min, filter using a medium porosity sintered glass filter and wash with 50 mℓ of dilute ammonium hydroxide, using 5–10 mℓ portions for each wash.

Dry the precipitate to constant weight at 105–115 °C and weigh as $(C_6H_5)_4AsPF_6$.

Amperometric method

The amperometric titration of hexafluorophosphate ion depends on the formation of $(C_6H_5)_4AsPF_6$ and the subsequent reduction of excess tetraphenylarsonium ion at the mercury drop[4]. Fluoride, hydroxyl, sulphate, chloride, orthophosphate and difluorophosphate do not interfere in ten-fold excess, but ions giving precipitates with the $(C_6H_5)_4As^+$ ion interfere.

The method is applicable in the range 0.0014M–0.01M PF_6^-. Eleven replicate determinations carried out on 0.037 g KPF_6 gave a relative standard deviation of ±0.66 per cent.

Spectrophotometric methods

Reference has already been made[2] to separation of hexafluorophosphate by extraction of ferrous 1,10-phenanthroline hexafluorophosphate into *n*-butyronitrile. A spectrophotometric method based on this is quite selective, the interfering ions being phthalate, bromide, monofluorophosphate (slight), nitrate, nitrite, periodate and thiocyanate. Sodium acetate does not interfere unless present in amounts above 0.5 mmol, but ammonium acetate interferes appreciably in smaller amounts. The absorbance is measured at 505 nm.

Partition titration method

Recently Behrends[6] has based a titration procedure on tetraphenyl arsonium hydroxide as titrant, with extraction into 1,2-dichloroethane. The indicator used is $KMnO_4$, which is transferred completely to the organic layer giving a photometric or visual end-point.

References

1. WOYSKI, M.M., *Inorganic Syntheses* (Ed. L.F. Audrieth) Volume III, McGraw-Hill, 111 (1950)
2. ARCHER, V.S. and DOOLITTLE, F.G., *Analyt. Chem.*, **39**, 371 (1967)
3. AFFSPRUNG, H.E. and ARCHER, V.S., *Analyt. Chem.*, **35**, 1912 (1963)
4. AFFSPRUNG, H.E. and ARCHER, V.S., *Analyt. Chem.*, **35**, 976 (1963)
5. LANGE, W. and MULLER, E., *Chem. Ber.*, **63B**, 1058 (1930)
6. BEHRENDS, K., *Z. analyt. Chem.*, **250**, 246 (1970); *Analyt. Abstr.*, **20**, 2996 (1971).

Hypophosphate

The hypophosphate ion, $P_2O_6^{4-}$ is not easily oxidized. Only dichromate and permanganate in acid solution and at high temperatures effect oxidation, and this is possibly due to the preliminary hydrolysis having produced phosphorous acid. Hypophosphates are very sparingly soluble in water except those of the alkali metals. Dilute solutions of the pure acid can be stored for long periods or even boiled; decomposition of the concentrated solution takes place when heated above 30 °C.

The preparation of tetrasodium hypophosphate, as well as a discussion of analytical methods for hypophosphates, has been given by Palmer[1]. The synthesis of sodium dihydrogen hypophosphate has been published[2].

Separation

1. Precipitation

Precipitation of silver hypophosphate from a medium up to 0.5M in nitric acid separates hypophosphates completely from ortho-, di-, tri-, and tri-metaphosphates[1]. Precipitation of $Ag_4P_2O_6$ preceded by precipitation as zinc hypophosphate is more selective, the only common interfering ion being diphosphate[1].

2. TLC and paper chromatography

The usefulness of paper chromatography and TLC for separation of the oxyacids of phosphorus has been illustrated in other sections. Hypophosphate may be separated using the methods shown in *Table 41*.

3. Ion-exchange chromatography

This approach to the separation of phosphorus anions is discussed in several other sections including polyphosphates, phosphite, and diphosphate, and these should be consulted for further details. Hypophosphate may be separated from ortho- and diphosphate, phosphite, hypophosphite and diphosphite.

Determination

Gravimetric methods

The gravimetric methods of separation[1] given above, may be used for determination of hypophosphates. Silver hypophosphate is dried briefly at 100 °C, then heated until the cream coloured precipitate becomes uniformly grey

$$Ag_4P_2O_6 \rightarrow 2Ag + 2AgPO_3$$

This occurs rapidly at 300 °C. If greater selectivity is required, initial precipitation as zinc hypophosphate is made at pH 4 followed by conversion of this to silver hypophosphate.

Table 41 Separation of hypophosphate by paper chromatography

Technique details	*Solvent*	*Hypophosphate separated from*	*Ref.*
Whatman No. 1 prewashed with 20% HCl	Acidic Isobutanol–acetyl-acetone – trichloroacetic acid–NH_3 (0.880)–H_2O (70 mℓ : 6 mℓ : 2.5 g : 0.2 mℓ : 23.8 mℓ) Basic Isobutanol–isopropanol–NH_3 (0.880)–H_2O (20 mℓ : 40 mℓ : 1 mℓ : 39 mℓ)	Ortho-PO_4 di-PO_4 As(III) As(V)	3
Whatman No. 4 ascending (cylinders)	Isopropanol–H_2O–trichloroacetic acid–NH_3 (0.880) (75 mℓ : 25 mℓ : 5 g : 0.3 mℓ) Isopropanol–isobutanol–H_2O–NH_3 (0.880) (40 mℓ : 20 mℓ : 39 mℓ : 1 mℓ) Other solvents also used	Ortho-PO_4 di-PO_4 tri-PO_4 trimeta-PO_4 tetrameta-PO_4 Phosphite Hypophosphite Pyrophosphite	4
Whatman No. 3 strips	Isopropanol–trichloroacetic acid or Isopropanol–isobutanol–ethanol–aq. NH_3	H_2SO_4 SO_4^{2-} Hypophosphite Condensed phosphates	5

Titrimetric methods

A variation of the above gravimetric method is addition of excess standard silver nitrate solution followed by back-titration[6] with standard thiocyanate. Palmer[1] recommends oxidation by iodic acid at 100 °C in the presence of 40% H_2SO_4, or oxidation with aqueous bromine in the pH range 6–9. The first mentioned method is simple but affected by reducing oxyanions of phosphorus. The bromine oxidation method is unaffected by such anions as phosphite and hypophosphite, these being oxidized only in more acidic solutions.

Titrimetric determination of hypophosphate (0.2–0.25 g) by aqueous bromine[1]

Reagents

Potassium bromate: 3 g $KBrO_3 \ell^{-1}$.
Ammonium molybdate: 2%.
Sodium thiosulphate: 0.1M.

Procedure

Introduce into a glass-stoppered bottle the following in succession: hypophosphate sample dissolved in 20 mℓ of M HCl, 25 mℓ $KBrO_3$, 55 mℓ water containing 5 drops of $(NH_4)_2MoO_4$ solution, and 1 g of KBr.

Stopper the bottle immediately and mix well. Prepare a second bottle in the same way but omitting the hypophosphate. After 30 min open each bottle, quickly introduce 4.5 g borax, and re-stopper. When the borax has dissolved, set the bottles aside for 1 h. Add KI and dilute H_2SO_4 to liberate iodine. Titrate with standard thiosulphate. The one result quoted represents an error of about 0.5 per cent.

Spectrophotometric methods

Hypophosphate may be determined spectrophotometrically in the presence of hypophosphite, phosphite and phosphate using a molybdenum(V)–molybdenum(VI) reagent[7].

When free from other phosphorus anions similarly oxidized, hypophosphate can be oxidized to orthophosphate and this determined either by the molybdenum blue method or by the phosphovanadomolybdate method. The former method was used by Pollard *et al.*[8] in the automatic determination of hypophosphate and other phosphorus anions after anion-exchange chromatography.

References

1. PALMER, W.G., *J. chem. Soc.*, 1079 (1961)
2. BAILAR, J.C. (Ed.), *Inorganic Synthesis*, Vol. IV, McGraw-Hill, New York, 68 (1953)
3. D'AMORE, G., *Ann. Chim. Rome*, **46**, 517 (1956)
4. EBEL, J.P., *Mikrochim Acta*, 679 (1954)
5. RUDNICKI, R., *Chemia. analit.*, **6**, 761 (1961); *Analyt. Abstr.*, **9**, 2731 (1962)
6. MOELLER, T. and QUINTY, G.H., *Analyt: Chem.*, **24**, 1354 (1952)
7. YOZA, N. and OHASHI, S., *Bull. chem. Soc. Japan*, **37**, 33 (1964); *Analyt. Abstr.*, **12**, 2196 (1965)
8. POLLARD, F.H., NICKLESS, G., ROGERS, D.E. and ROTHWELL, M.T., *J. Chromat.*, **17**, 157 (1965)

Hypophosphite

The hypophosphite anion ($H_2PO_2^-$) is strongly reducing so that redox methods feature predominantly in its determination. Hypophosphites find application in several fields, for example in pharmaceutics where its use is apparently diminishing, and in 'electrodeless' metal plating.

Separation

1. Paper and thin-layer chromatography
These are shown in *Table 42*.

2. Ion-exchange chromatography
Anion-exchange chromatography has been shown[5] to be an excellent method for separation of hypophosphite, phosphite, and phosphate. The same workers have developed an automatic chromatographic method by which hypophosphite can be separated from orthophosphate, phosphite, hypophosphate, diphosphate, diphosphite, monothiophosphate, triphosphate and trimetaphosphate[6,7]. This work is more fully described in the section on polyphosphates.

Determination

Titrimetric methods

The corresponding section on phosphite should be consulted. Redox methods involving all the major reagents have been developed for hypophosphite. Details will be found in standard texts[8,9]. Where hypophosphite is in the presence of phosphite, Table 48 on p. 487 provides details of several methods. Additional methods are given in *Table 43*.

Compleximetric methods for hypophosphite have been described. In one the hypophosphite is oxidized with HNO_3. The resulting phosphite is treated with excess bismuth nitrate. After filtering off the precipitate excess bismuth is titrated with EDTA using pyrocatechol as indicator[14].

Fulop and Blazek[15] base their method on the reaction between hypophosphite and the mercury–EDTA complex. When boiled, Hg(II) is reduced to the metal and an amount of EDTA equivalent to the hypophosphite content is released. This is titrated with copper(II) using PAN (1-(2-pyridylazo)-2-naphthol) as indicator.

Spectrophotometric methods

Hypophosphites form a blue complex with ammonium molybdate in the presence of sulphurous acid and this may be utilized as the basis of a

Table 42 Separation of hypophosphite by paper and thin-layer chromatography

Type	*Solvent*	*Hypophosphite separated from*	*Ref.*
Paper (Whatman No. 4)	'Ebel's acidic solvent' and others Isopropanol–trichloroacetic acid–NH_3 (0.880)–H_2O (75 mℓ:5 g:0.3 mℓ:25 mℓ)	Phosphite, pyrophosphite, hypophosphate, ortho-, di-, tri-, trimeta-, and tetrametaphosphates	1
Paper (Whatman No. 3 strips)	Isopropanol–chloroacetic acid or Isopropanol–isobutanol–ethanol–NH_3 aq.	Sulphate, sulphuric acid, phosphite, hypophosphate, and condensed phosphates	2
TLC (silica gel + starch)	Methanol–NH_3 (0.880)–chloroacetic acid 10%–H_2O (10:3:1:10)	Orthophosphate diphosphate and phosphite	3
TLC (MN Polygram sheets CEL 300)	Isopropanol–trichloroacetic acid–tetraethyl ammonium hydroxide –H_2O (750 mℓ:50 g:16 mℓ 20% v/v:250 mℓ) Isopropanol–isobutanol–NH_3 (0.880) (400 mℓ:200 mℓ:10 mℓ)	Orthophosphate, diphosphate, tri-, trimeta-, and tetrametaphosphates, phosphite, polyphosphates n = 20–30, commercial cyclic and linear phosphates	4

Table 43 Redox titrimetric methods for hypophosphite

Oxidant	*Basic procedure*	*Comment*	*Ref.*
Fe(III)	Ten-fold excess Fe(III) About 1.6M in HCl Boil for about 20 min	No interference from phosphite	10
$AgClO_4$ and 85% H_3PO_4	Boil with reagent for 3–3.5 min. Titrate excess Ag^+ potentiometrically with chloride	No interference from phosphite	11
Cr(VI)	Add reagent to strongly acidic (H_2SO_4) sample. Dilute, and titrate excess with Fe(II)	Phosphite also oxidized	12
Ce(IV)	Heat with reagent at 100 °C for 7 min in presence of Mn(II)–Ag(I) catalyst	Phosphite also oxidized	13

spectrophotometric determination[16]. Phosphite does not interfere, but phosphate does. The same reaction is noted and developed into a method by Verbitskaya and Romanova[17] who appear to be unaware of the above work. The disadvantage of phosphate interference has been overcome by Anton[18]. In the original method the absorbance was measured at 470 nm. The modification uses 400 nm and different acidity conditions, enabling hypophosphite to be determined in the presence of phosphate. The phosphate content itself can also be determined if required.

The basis of the method is that phosphate will not form a complex at acidities in excess of 1.6M in HCl. The hypophosphite complex absorbs at 400 nm over a wide range of acidities. If phosphate is to be determined as well, the acidity of a second aliquot is adjusted to 0.14M in HCl and the absorbance measured at 670 nm. If the concentration and absorbance of the hypophosphite are known, its contribution to the absorbance at 670 nm can be calculated. The difference between the contributed absorbance and the total absorbance can be related to the phosphate content. The concentration curves for hypophosphite and monophosphate are shown in *Figure 49*.

Spectrophotometric determination of hypophosphite and orthophosphate when present together[18]

Reagents

Ammonium molybdate reagent:

Dissolve 10 g $(NH_4)_6Mo_7O_{24} \cdot 4H_2O$ in 200 mℓ distilled water to which 60 mℓ conc. HCl has been added. Dilute to 1ℓ.

Sodium sulphite: 20 g in 100 mℓ distilled water.

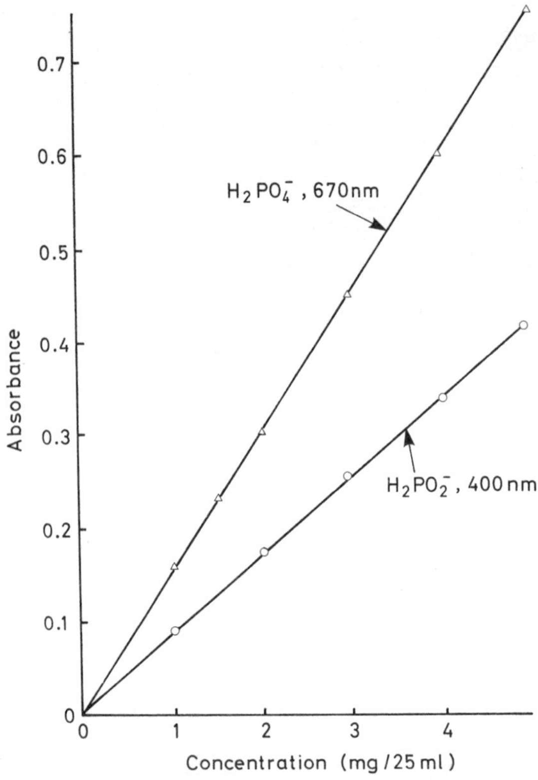

Figure 49 *Concentration curves for $H_2PO_2^-$ and $H_2PO_4^-$. Cell: 1 cm; $H_2PO_2^-$ absorbance in 2.5M HCl recorded after 30 min; $H_2PO_4^-$ absorbance in 0.14M HCl recorded after 30 min.*
(After Anton[18])

Procedure

Transfer an aliquot not exceeding 5 mℓ and not containing more than 5 mg hypophosphite to a 25 mℓ volumetric flask. Add 10 mℓ of 6M HCl, 5 mℓ of the molybdate reagent, and 5 mℓ of the sulphite solution.

Record the absorbance after 30 min at 400 nm in a 1 cm cell against a reagent blank.

The phosphate content in a second aliquot may be determined by excluding the 10 mℓ of 6M HCl and measuring the absorbance at 670 nm after 30 min.

The calibration curve for hypophosphite is constructed by plotting the absorbance at 400 nm within the concentration range 1–5 mg per 25 mℓ. A similar curve for phosphate is constructed as in *Figure 49*.

Miscellaneous methods

Oxidation of hypophosphite to orthophosphate followed by determination of the latter is possible, though this approach is open to interference by other phosphorus anions that respond in the same way. Oxidation of phosphorus anions (including hypophosphite) is a primary step in the method for automatic analysis referred to earlier in connection with ion-exchange separations[6,7]. The various anionic species are separated by anion exchange chromatography and then converted to orthophosphate for colorimetric determination by the molybdenum blue method. For lower oxyanions of phosphorus the conversion is by oxidation.

Two novel analytical methods for hypophosphite depend on evolution of hydrogen. The first was developed for automatic analysis of electrodeless* plating solutions for which conventional methods were unsatisfactory[19]. Palladium black is allowed to catalyse the decomposition of hypophosphite, producing hydrogen.

$$H(H_2PO_2) \xrightarrow{Pd} HPO_2 + H_2$$

$$HPO_2 + H_2O \longrightarrow H_2(HPO_3)$$

The evolved hydrogen is determined by measurement of its combustion flame temperature.

Tischer, Baitsholts and Pryzbylowicz[20] utilize the same reaction but carry it out in a hypodermic syringe. The mixture for analysis, containing Pd^{2+} is drawn into the syringe and excess air expelled. The reaction volume is adjusted to a desired level, the syringe capped and heated in a boiling bath for 10 min. After cooling, the volume of gas, which is proportional to the hypophosphite content, is read off on the syringe scale. The reactions involved are

$$Pd^{2+} + H_2PO_2^- + H_2O \longrightarrow Pd^0 + H_2PO_3^- + 2H^+ \quad (1)$$

$$H_2PO_2^- + H_2O \xrightarrow{Pd^0} H_2PO_3^- + H_2\uparrow \quad (2)$$

Reaction (1) occurs to a very small extent only. A complete analysis takes 15 min.

References

1. EBEL, J.P., *Mikrochim. Acta,* 679 (1954)
2. RUDNICKI, R., *Chemia. analit.,* **6**, 761 (1961); *Analyt. Abstr.,* **9**, 2731 (1962)
3. SEILER, H., *Helv. chim. Acta,* **44**, 1753 (1961)
4. BURNS, D.T. and LEE, J.D., *Mikrochim. Acta,* 206 (1969)
5. POLLARD, F.H., ROGERS, D.E., ROTHWELL, M.T. and NICKLESS, G., *J. Chromat.,* **9**, 227 (1962)
6. POLLARD, F.H., NICKLESS, G., ROGERS, D.E. and ROTHWELL, M.T., *J. Chromat.,* **17**, 157 (1965)
7. POLLARD, F.H., NICKLESS, G., ROGERS, D.E. and CRONE, D.L., *Proc. Soc. Analyt. Chem. Conference, Nottingham,* 1965, W. Heffer & Sons Ltd., Cambridge, 481 (1965)
8. KOLTHOFF, I.M. and BELCHER, R., *Volumetric Analysis,* Volume III, Interscience, New York (1957)
9. BERKA, A., VULTERIN, J. and ZYKA, J., *Newer Redox Titrants,* Pergamon Press, Oxford (1965)
10. KIN'YA OGAWA, *Bull. chem. Soc. Japan,* **42**, 1449 (1969); *Analyt. Abstr.,* **19**, 1192 (1970)
11. ACKERMANN, G. and MENDE, A., *Z. analyt. Chem.,* **232**, 97 (1967); *Analyt. Abstr.,* **16**, 101 (1969)
12. RAO, V.R.S., *Z. analyt. Chem.,* **246**, 384 (1969); *Analyt. Abstr.,* **19**, 2997 (1970)
13. GUILBAULT, G.G. and MCCURDY, W.H., *Analytica chim. Acta,* **24**, 214 (1961)

* An autocatalytic chemical reduction process for continuously plating a metal from a solution of a metal salt containing a reducing agent.

14. CIOGOLEA, G., MORAIT, G. and NGUYEN, H.B., *Farmacia, Bucharest*, **10**, 331 (1962); *Chem. Abstr.*, **58**, 6189b (1963)
15. FULOP, L. and BLAZEK, A., *Farmacia, Bucharest*, **10**, 525 (1962); *Chem. Abstr.*, **58**, 7370b (1963)
16. SCANZILLO, A.P., *Analyt. Chem.*, **26**, 411 (1954)
17. VERBITSKAYA, T.D. and ROMANOVA, N.K., *Zav. Lab.*, **26**, 818 (1960); *Analyt. Abstr.*, **8**, 994 (1961)
18. ANTON, A., *Analyt. Chem.*, **37**, 1422 (1965)
19. GREENFIELD, S. and COOPER, R.M., *Talanta*, **9**, 483 (1962)
20. TISCHER, T.N., BAITSHOLTS, A.D. and PRYZBYLOWICZ, E.P., *Analytica chim. Acta*, **34**, 101 (1966)

Metaphosphates: Trimetaphosphate, Tetrametaphosphate, Hexametaphosphate

The structure of the trimeta- and tetrametaphosphate ions are shown in *Structures 59* and *60*.

Structure 59 $(P_3O_9)^{3-}$

Structure 60 $(P_4O_{12})^{4-}$

The alternative names cyclotriphosphate and cyclotetraphosphate are sometimes used. Alkali salts are soluble; alkaline earth salts are less soluble, though not as insoluble as the corresponding linear polyphosphates which are precipitated from acid solutions by barium ions. Solutions of the metaphosphates of strong bases give a neutral reaction. Solutions of alkali trimetaphosphates are quite stable under neutral conditions.

At lower pH values, hydrolysis takes place, eventually giving monophosphate.

$$\underset{\text{trimeta-}}{(P_3O_9)^{3-}} \rightarrow \underset{\text{tripoly-}}{H_2P_3O_{10}^{3-}} \rightarrow \underset{\text{di-}}{H_2P_2O_7^{2-}} \rightarrow \underset{\text{mono-}}{H_2PO_4^{-}}$$

The presence of cations catalyses the rate of hydrolysis. Metaphosphates are important but much less so than the linear polyphosphates. Apart from some of the applications listed under polyphosphates, sodium trimetaphosphate is used in the modification of starches to prepare starch phosphates. Sodium tetrametaphosphate is used in tanning due to its ability to precipitate proteins at pH 2–3.

The preparation of solutions containing various mixtures of metaphosphates has been described by Thilo and Schulke[1]. The preparation of sodium hexametaphosphate (the single cyclic metaphosphate, not the commercial 'hexametaphosphate') has been given by Griffith and Buxton[2].

Separations

1. Precipitation

Since metaphosphates do not easily form precipitates with Ba^{2+}, methods have been described in which all other phosphates are precipitated as the Ba salts leaving cyclic phosphates in solution. Such methods suffer from incomplete precipitation. For example Dewald and Schmidt[3] show that determination of trimetaphosphate using this method, in the presence of ortho-, di- and triphosphate, gives erratic results. Rothbart and Rieman[4] have demonstrated that while ortho-, di- and triphosphate are incompletely precipitated by Ba^{2+}, higher members are quantitatively precipitated leaving any cyclic phosphates in solution. Thus, in the absence of ortho-, di- and triphosphates, metaphosphates may be determined in the filtrate after removal of these higher polyphosphates.

2. Paper and thin-layer chromatography

As in linear polyphosphates, paper and thin-layer chromatography provides one of the most effective methods for separation of cyclic phosphates. *Table 49* in the polyphosphates section contains some of the more important references on this technique. The merits of paper and thin-layer chromatography are discussed by Pollard *et al.*[5].

3. Anion-exchange chromatography

This is the most commonly used method for separation of both linear and cyclic phosphates, particularly where milligram amounts are involved. Trimeta- and tetrametaphosphate were separated from other polyphosphates by Rieman and co-workers[6, 7]. Moderately cross-linked polystyrene resins containing $—CH_2N^+(CH_3)_3$ ionic groupings were used in this work. A theoretical approach was published from the same source[8].

Pollard *et al.* have developed an automated ion-exchange system based on the AutoAnalyzer, by which mixtures containing trimetaphosphate, linear polyphosphates, lower phosphorus anions, and other phosphorus functions are separated. Details of this work are given in the section on polyphosphates.

Rothbart, Weymouth and Rieman[9] using the anion-exchange resin IRA-400, have isolated three cyclic phosphates from orthophosphate and its linear polymers up to and including tridecaphosphate.

Determination

Spectrophotometric methods

After separation of the individual cyclic phosphates, these may be hydrolysed to give orthophosphate only, and this determined either spectrophotometrically or titrimetrically, depending on the amount involved. The molybdovanadate method is used by some[6, 8, 4]; others have used the molybdophosphate method[10].

Infra-red method

An infra-red method using the KBr pressed-disc technique has been published for the quantitative analysis of condensed phosphates. Four-component mixtures in the form of dry powders can be analysed for three components with an accuracy of ± 0.5 per cent in some cases[11]. The method does not appear to have found extensive use.

References

1. THILO, E. and SCHULKE, U., *Z. Anorg. Allgem. Chem.*, **297**, 431 (1965)
2. GRIFFITH, E.J. and BUXTON, R.L. , *Inorganic Chemistry*, **4**, 549 (1965)
3. DEWALD, W. and SCHMIDT, H.Z., *Z. analyt. Chem.*, **137**, 178 (1952)
4. ROTHBART, H.L. and RIEMAN, W., *Talanta*, **11**, 43 (1964)
5. POLLARD, F.H., NICKLESS, G., BURTON, K. and HUBBARD, J., *Microchem. J.*, **10**, 131 (1966)
6. LINDENBAUM, S., PETERS, T.V. and RIEMAN, W., *Analytica chim. Acta*, **11**, 530 (1954)
7. PETERS, T.V. and RIEMAN, W., *Analytica chim. Acta*, **14**, 131 (1956)
8. BEUKENKAMP, J., RIEMAN, W. and LINDENBAUM, S., *Analyt. Chem.*, **26**, 505 (1954)
9. ROTHBART, H.L., WEYMOUTH, H.W. and RIEMAN, W., *Talanta*, **11**, 33 (1964)
10. POLLARD, F.H., NICKLESS, G., ROGERS, D.E. and ROTHWELL, M.T., *J. Chromat.*, **17**, 157 (1965)
11. CORBRIDGE, D.E.C. and LOWE, E.J., *Analyt. Chem.*, **27**, 1383 (1955)

Monofluorophosphate

The chemistry of the monofluorophosphate ion (PO_3F^{2-}) has been reviewed by Schmutzler[1]. It does not give the characteristic reactions of either orthophosphate or fluoride and has no characteristic reactions of its own, but resembles sulphate chemically. This may be understood in terms of the almost identical Pauling radii of S^{+6} and P^{+5}. Also, the fluoride ion and hydroxyl group are nearly identical in steric terms.

The importance of the monofluorophosphate ion depends mainly on the use of sodium monofluorophosphate as an additive to certain dentifrices to combat dental caries. Alternative fluoride additives include stannous and sodium fluorides. The choice of sodium monofluorophosphate in preference to sodium fluoride has a reason. If the dental polishing agent employed is calcium carbonate, sodium fluoride would cause insoluble calcium fluoride to form on storage with the consequent inactivation of fluoride ions. With sodium monofluorophosphate, which is usually present in amounts less than 1%, free fluoride ions result from hydrolysis which occurs slowly under alkaline conditions, but far more rapidly under acid conditions.

$$H_2PO_3F + H_2O \rightleftharpoons H_3PO_4 + HF$$

Determination of monofluorophosphate involves hydrolysis followed by subsequent analysis for either the resulting fluoride or phosphate. A difficulty here is that in general fluoride and phosphate each interfere in the determination of the other. The problem can only be satisfactorily solved by using recently developed methods.

Synthesis of sodium monofluorophosphate has been described[2] but TLC carried out on the product invariably shows the presence of impurities[3].

Separation

1. Monofluorophosphate can be separated from difluorophosphate ($PO_2F_2^-$) and orthophosphate using electrophoresis[4].

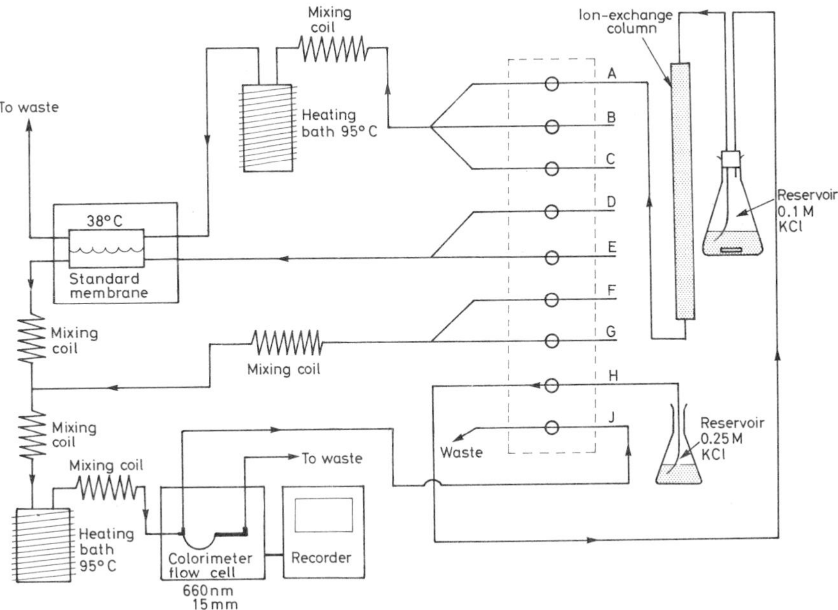

Figure 50 *Flow diagram for automated determination of monofluorophosphate.* A, *sample;* B, *air;* C, *3M H_2SO_4;* D, *air;* E, *distilled water;* F, *hydrazine sulphate;* G, *ammonium molybdate;* H, *eluant;* J, *de-bubbler.* (After Benz and Kelley[6])

2. Monofluorophosphate is precipitated as the silver salt (Ag_2PO_3F) by silver nitrate in a medium of 80% alcohol, but the product is highly contaminated due to coprecipitation[5]. The monofluorophosphate can be subsequently determined by separation of fluoride by distillation from H_2SO_4 or $HClO_4$ solution, followed by titration with thorium(IV) nitrate as described in the section on fluoride. Free fluoride does not affect the precipitation of silver monofluorophosphate owing to the solubility of silver fluoride in the 80% alcohol medium. This method is tedious and probably finds little use in routine analysis at the present time.

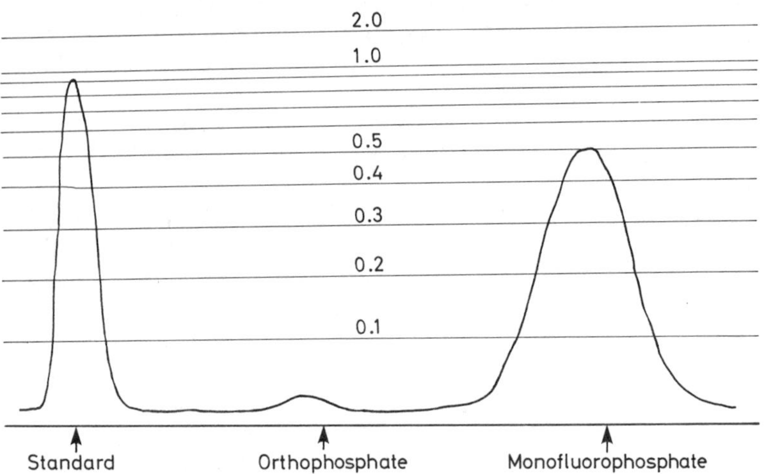

Figure 51 *Separation of orthophosphate and monofluorophosphate by automated ion-exchange.* (After Benz and Kelley[6])

3. Monofluorophosphate is separated from organic substances and other phosphorus species by gradient elution ion-exchange chromatography in an automatic procedure developed by Benz and Kelley[6]. After separation it is hydrolysed, and the resulting orthophosphate determined colorimetrically with molybdate. The separation itself is made on a Dowex 1-X8 resin in chloride form, with potassium chloride solution as eluant. The essential features of the method are shown in *Figure 50*. Measurement of the area under individual peaks enables the concentration of monofluorophosphate to be calculated.

Figure 51 shows the result of applying the method to a sample of commercial sodium monofluorophosphate.

Determination

Analytical methods are based on determination of the orthophosphate or fluoride resulting from hydrolysis of the monofluorophosphate.

Fluoride ion-selective electrode method

This electrode is discussed in the section on fluoride, and this should be consulted for details. Its application to both single monofluorophosphate compounds and aqueous dispersions of toothpastes, enables two important quantities to be determined, namely the 'free' fluoride and the monofluorophosphate content. The 'free' fluoride may be an impurity produced during the original preparation of the material, or the product of partial hydrolysis. The monofluorophosphate content is calculated from the difference between the 'free' fluoride and total fluoride, the latter being measured after complete hydrolysis of the sample.

Shane and Miele[7] describe the application of the pF electrode to the analysis of toothpastes. In this instance the electrode is used to measure 'free' fluoride. If the solution is then made strongly acidic with HCl, hydrolysis of

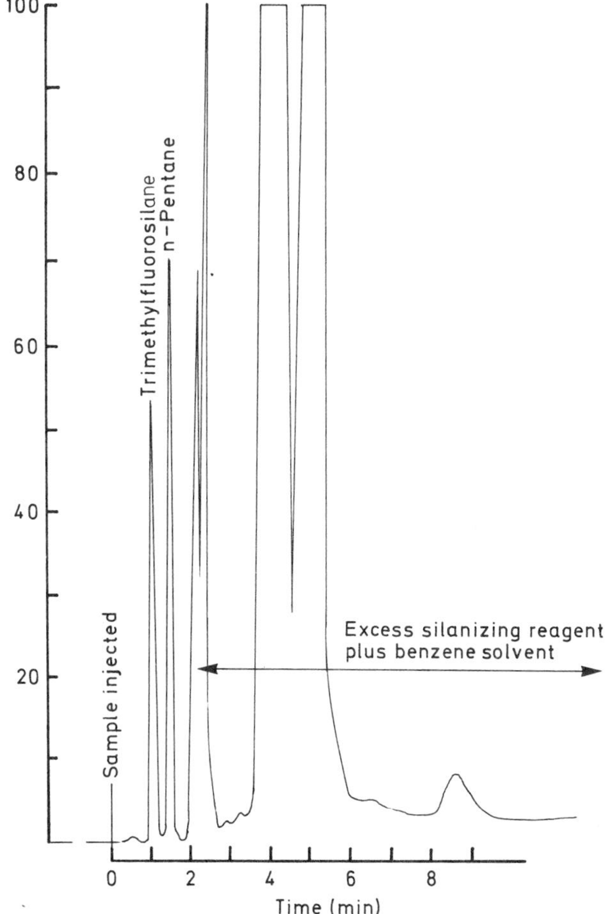

Figure 52 *Typical chromatogram obtained in determination of total and soluble fluorine, expressed as fluoride, in sodium fluoride and sodium monofluorophosphate dental creams.* (After Cropper and Puttnam[9])

monofluorophosphate will be complete in 30 min. A second measurement using the pF electrode enables the total fluoride to be calculated. Appropriate adjustment of ionic strength is essential in order that both standards and samples are measured under similar conditions.

Spectrophotometric method

This is based on spectrophotometric determination of orthophosphate resulting from hydrolysis of monofluorophosphate. This method was used by Benz and Kelley[6] whose work has been already mentioned in connection with ion-exchange separation of monofluorophosphate. The molybdenum blue phosphate method was employed.

Gas chromatographic method

Fresen, Cox, and Witter[8] reported in 1968 that trimethylfluorosilane may be rapidly prepared from trimethylchlorosilane in acid solutions. This reaction has been adapted[9] to provide a rapid means for determination of total and soluble fluoride ('free') in formulations containing sodium monofluorophosphate. The derivative is extracted into benzene containing *n*-pentane as internal standard. Separation is made on a glass column packed with 10% Silicone OVI on 80–100 mesh Celite AWDMCS at 60 °C with nitrogen as carrier. Analyses require less than 30 min and provide an excellent method for determination of monofluorophosphate. A typical chromatogram from the above work is shown in *Figure 52.*

References

1. SCHMUTZLER, R., in *Advances in Fluorine Chemistry* (Ed. M. Stacey, J.C. Tatlow and A.G. Sharpe), Vol. 5, Butterworths, London, 134 (1965)
2. HILL, O.F. and AUDRIETH, L.F., *Inorganic Syntheses* (Ed. L.F. Audrieth), Vol. 3, McGraw-Hill, 106 (1950)
3. WILLIAMS, W.J. and THOMPSON, K.H., unpublished work
4. KLEMENT, R. and KNOLLMULLER, K.O., *Z. analyt. Chem.*, **166**, 193 (1959); *Chem. Abstr.*, 16805h (1959)
5. HILL, H.J. and REYNOLDS, C.A., *Analyt. Chem.*, **22**, 448 (1950)
6. BENZ, C. and KELLEY, R.M., *Analytica chim. Acta,* **46**, 83 (1969)
7. SHANE, N. and MIELE, D., *J. pharm. Sci.*, **57**, 1260 (1968)
8. FRESEN, J.A., COX, F.H. and WITTER, M.J., *Pharm. Weekblad,* **103**, 909 (1968); *Analyt. Abstr.*, **17**, 3619 (1969)
9. CROPPER, E. and PUTTNAM, N.A., *J. Soc. cosmet. Chem.*, **21**, 533 (1970)

Orthophosphate

The determination of orthophosphate has a vast literature extending into such areas as metallurgy, pharmaceutics, food, water, biochemistry, and agriculture. Not unexpectedly, extensive reviews have appeared from time to to time. Amongst the most recent are those by Greenfield[1] and Rieman and Beukenkamp[2].

Many methods for determination of phosphate hinge on the ability of phosphorus to form molybdophosphoric acid. While these will be dealt with in more detail in later parts of this section, it might be relevant at this stage to outline the variety of procedures possible following initial conversion of phosphate to the heteropoly acid. These are shown in *Table 44*. Though the scheme is based on molybdophosphoric acid, it must be borne in mind that several other elements also form heteropoly acids. When phosphorus is accompanied by these, additional steps may be taken to introduce some selectivity. For example, suppression of unwanted species by carboxylic acids prior to spectrophotometric determination, or selective extraction may be used. These will be dealt with in some detail later.

Solutions containing below $20\,\mu g\,\ell^{-1}$ of inorganic phosphate must be stored with care to avoid loss by sorption. An investigation by Ryden, Syers and Harris[3] reports that acid-washed glass containers sorb up to 20% in 1–6 h of contact. Polypropylene and polycarbonate containers behave similarly. Pre-treatment of polycarbonate with phosphate was found to give better results and this is recommended for storing samples of lake waters in bulk subsequent to filtration, which should be done within 6 h of collection.

Separations

Separation of phosphate is often required where it is to be subsequently determined and in analyses where its presence would cause interference. The principal methods of separation are as follows.

1. Precipitation

Conversion of phosphate to the molybdophosphoric acid is the most important method of separating it by precipitation.

Some elements, e.g. bismuth(III), titanium(IV) and zirconium(IV) precipitate as phosphates which then contaminate the heteropoly acid. Other potential interferences are arsenic(V), tungsten(VI), molybdenum(VI), vanadium(V), tellurium, silicon and selenium, but most interferences are eliminated if precipitation is made in a higher concentration of nitric acid.

Use of quinoline and other organic bases in the precipitation can bring some advantages. For example, separation of phosphate and arsenate is possible if the phosphate is precipitated as lutidinium molybdophosphate[4]. Separation of phosphate and silicate is possible if the former is precipitated as ammonium molybdophosphate in the presence of citrate[5].

Apart from its use in the determination of phosphate, precipitation as $MgNH_4PO_4 \cdot 6H_2O$ may be used to separate phosphate, though it is less

Table 44 Analytical procedures based on molybdophosphoric acid

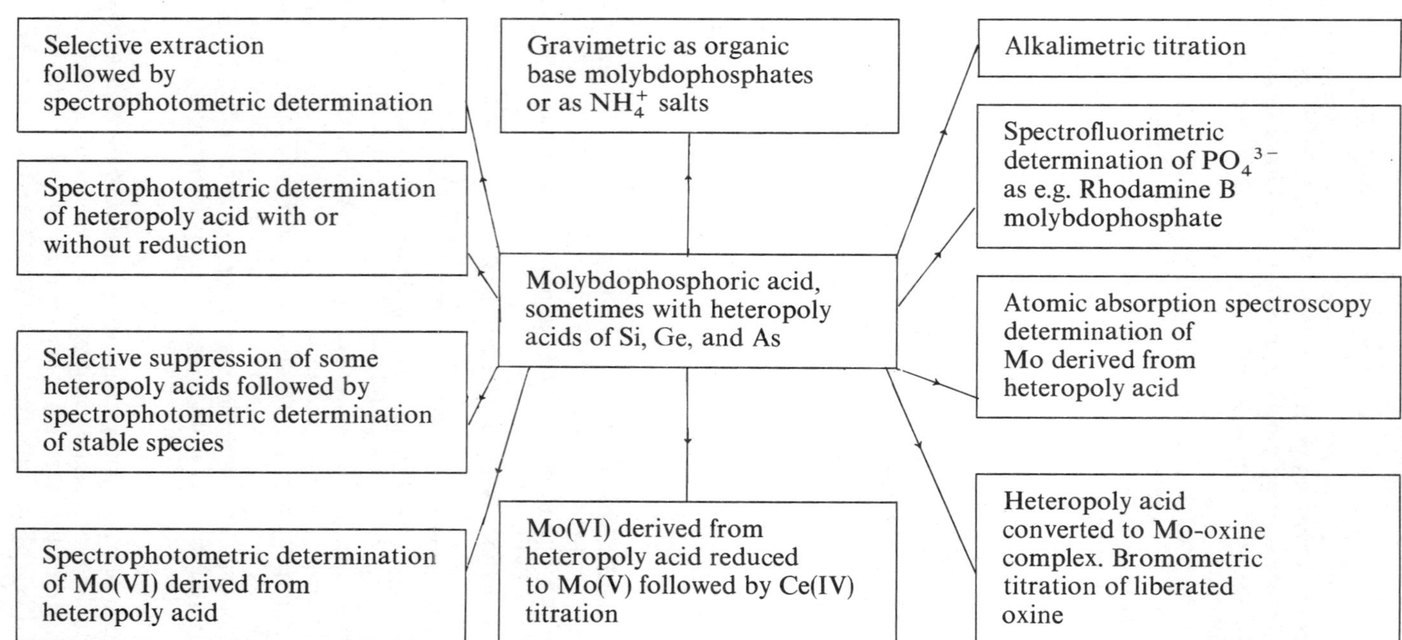

effective in this role as most elements including the alkaline earths precipitate from ammonia solutions. If citric acid is present phosphate may be separated from W, Mo, V, Fe(III), Al, Sn, Zr, Ti, Ca, Zn, Mn, fluoride and traces of silica. Separation from arsenate is not possible as it forms magnesium ammonium arsenate. The method has been used[6] for the removal of phosphate in the microtitration of sulphate using lead nitrate.

Fritz and Yamamura[7] in the titration of sulphate with barium perchlorate, removed phosphate by precipitation with magnesium carbonate; Colson[8] investigating the same method, found that its removal as the insoluble silver salt was better.

Another insoluble form of phosphate used in its separation is the thorium salt. Colson[9] used this method for simultaneous removal of phosphate and fluoride in the mercurimetric titration of chloride. The same procedure was used by Furuya and Tajiri[10] who found that 1–100 mg PO_4^{3-} could be quantitatively precipitated at pH 2.0–3.5 and in the presence of more than 5 g of ammonium acetate per 100 mℓ. Magnesium and calcium in amounts less than 10 mg each, were not precipitated, and could be subsequently determined.

Kinnunen and Wennerstrand[11], finding classical methods of phosphate separation cumbersome, precipitated it with excess beryllium chloride in the presence of ammonium chloride and excess EDTA, the latter to prevent precipitation of cations. In slightly ammoniacal solution $BeNH_4PO_4$ is precipitated, the excess of beryllium forming beryllium hydroxide. One would need to be aware of the toxic hazards of beryllium in using this procedure.

Phosphate may be separated from some elements, especially the alkaline earths, if precipitated as ferric phosphate at pH 5.

2. *Solvent extraction*

Solvent extraction of heteropoly acids by organic solvents has been known for some time, for example it was described by Wu[12] in 1920. Although other systems have been examined, procedures based on heteropoly acid formation are by far the most common.

The most effective extractants are alkyl acetates and mixtures of them with other solvents. Selective extraction of heteropoly acids is particularly suited to the separation of micro amounts of P, Si, As, and Ge. Once extracted, several possibilities exist for the determination of the extracted species.

Table 45 provides data on solvent extraction methods applied to P, As, Si and Ge.

Alternative extraction systems have been studied. Bock and Hummel[24] investigated the extraction of the triphenylsulphonium derivatives of a wide range of anions. Phosphate was found to remain with a large group of anions in the aqueous phase, but its separation from perchlorate, permanganate, and perrhenate was found to be possible.

3. *Chromatography*

Ion-exchange chromatography is a convenient method of separating phosphate from both cations and anions. Separation may be made from most cations[25,26]. Vanadium can be separated if first reduced to V^{3+} or VO^{2+}. Where large amounts of iron(III) are involved, prior reduction to

Table 45 Procedures for determination of phosphorus, arsenic, silicon and germanium based on extraction of heteropoly acids

Present	*Extractant for heteropoly acid*	*Final procedure*	*Comments*	*Ref.*
P	Isobutyl acetate	Reduction of phosphorus to heteropoly blue in solvent phase. Spectrophotometric		13
As		Reduction of arsenic to heteropoly blue in aq. phase. Spectrophotometric		
P	Isobutyl acetate	Reduction of phosphorus to heteropoly blue in solvent phase. Spectrophotometric	Addition of perchloric acid before molybdate prevents formation of molybdosilicic acid.	14
As	—	Reduction of arsenic to heteropoly blue in aq. phase. Spectrophotometric		
Si	—	Reduction of silicon to heteropoly blue in aq. phase. Spectrophotometric	Citric acid used to destroy phosphorus and arsenic heteropoly acids in second aliquot	
P	Chloroform–butanol (4:1)	Spectrophotometric determination of phosphorus via molybdenum(VI) from heteropoly acid	Tungsten(VI) masked. No interference from 100-fold amounts of Si, Ge, As and Sb. Range 1.25–5 μg P	15
Si	—			
Ge	—			
As	—			
Sb	—			
P	Isobutyl acetate pH 0.8–1.0	Reduction of phosphorus to heteropoly blue in solvent phase. Spectrophotometric		16

As	—	Reduction of aq. phase after extraction of phosphorus and germanium. Spectrophotometric determination of arsenic via heteropoly blue		
Ge	2-ethylhexanol pH 0.4	Back extraction into H_2O and spectrophotometric determination of germanium via heteropoly blue		
As	—	Spectrophotometric determination of arsenic in aq. phase via heteropoly blue		16
Si	2-ethylhexanol pH < 0.4	Back extraction into H_2O. Spectrophotometric determination as heteropoly blue		
P As	*n*-butyl acetate (v. slow extraction)	Gravimetric	Applied to phosphorus in steel	17
P	Isobutyl acetate	AAS of molybdenum in heteropoly acid, in organic phase	Range 0.08–1 ppm P	18
As	Butanol	As for phosphorus	Range 0.08–1.2 ppm Si Arsenic and germanium interfere with silicon giving high results	
P	Diethylether, 1M in HCl	Spectrophotometric via molybdenum(VI) in UV or AAS Mo	Range 0.1–0.4 ppm P or Si (UV) 0.1–1.2 ppm P or Si (AAS)	19
Si	Diethylether–pentanol (5:1) 2M in HCl	As for phosphorus		
P	Isobutyl acetate	Heteropoly acid back extracted and degraded in NaOH. $Mo(VI) \xrightarrow{Ag} Mo(V)$ Cerium(IV) titration	No interference from As, Sb, Ge, Si	20

Table 45—(*continued*)

Present	*Extractant for heteropoly acid*	*Final procedure*	*Comments*	*Ref.*
As Sb Ge Si	— — — —			20
P As Si	Isobutyl acetate Ethyl acetate–butanol–isoamyl alcohol Methyl isobutyl ketone–citrate	AAS molybdenum in organic phase	Range of P 1–10 μg Range of As 2–20 μg Range of Si 1–10 μg	21
P As Si	Propylene carbonate–chloroform — —	Spectrophotometric determination of heteropoly acid in organic phase ($\varepsilon = 22\,300$ at 308 nm) or heteropoly blue in organic phase ($\varepsilon = 28\,500$ at 790 nm)	Conditions more rigid for heteropoly blue than heteropoly acid. Range of P 0.4–1.2 ppm. For 0.5 ppm P, maximum permissible amounts As(III), As(V) and Si(IV) are 10, 0, and 50 ppm	22
P As Si	Ethyl, propyl or butyl acetate — —	Spectrophotometric via ion-association complex with crystal violet	Range of P 0.03–0.3 μg P $m\ell^{-1}$. No interference from saturated silicate solution or 10-fold amounts As	23

iron(II) should be undertaken as iron(III) ions might retain some phosphate on the column.

Anion-exchange procedures have been described for separating phosphate from pyro- and tri-phosphate[27], pyrophosphate[28], hypophosphite and phosphite[29], and pyro-, tri-, trimeta, and tetrametaphosphate[30]. Pollard *et al.*[31]. have developed an automatic procedure based on the Technicon AutoAnalyzer for separation and quantitative analysis of a large number of phosphorus-containing anions that include orthophosphate.

Separation of phosphate and fluoride is important, with phosphate being more troublesome in methods for determination of fluoride than the reverse case. Two ion-exchange procedures for their separation have been described[32, 33]. Recently Pinfold and Karger[34] have described a rapid method based on adsorption of phosphate on to a suspension of ground-up resin. This removes all the phosphate from a 0.3 mM solution of disodium hydrogen phosphate within 2 min. Orthophosphate and pyrophosphate may be separated from ATP (Adenosine triphosphate) based on selective adsorption of the latter on charcoal[35].

Paper and thin-layer chromatography are well established techniques for separation of phosphate. Some of the more important separations are indicated in *Table 46*.

Recently gas chromatography has been applied[45] to separation of phosphate. The ammonium salts of phosphate, vanadate, arsenate, oxalate, etc., react with bis(trimethylsilyl)tri-fluoroacetamide, forming derivatives capable of being separated on a GLC column. Detection is by flame ionization, and in the case of phosphate, the derivative is $(TMS)_3PO_4$.

4. *Mercury cathode electrolysis*

This method provides a means of separation of phosphate from iron, cobalt, nickel, molybdenum, etc., with phosphate remaining in solution. Gates[46] has used the technique to separate small amounts of phosphorus from iron in the analysis of high purity iron. A review of the applications of mercury cathode electrolysis has been published by Page, Maxwell and Graham[47].

5. *Coprecipitation*

Separation of traces of phosphate from germanium (IV), silicon(IV), and arsenic(V) has been achieved by coprecipitation of phosphate on aluminium hydroxide. The germanium, silicon and arsenic are volatilized with HF, HCl and HBr with phosphate remaining[48].

6. *Selective suppression of unwanted species*

It has been known for a long time that citric, tartaric or oxalic acids will destroy molybdophosphoric acid but not molybdosilicic acid. Recently Paul[14] has shown that citric acid destroys molybdoarsenic acid, and further, that addition of perchloric acid before the addition of ammonium molybdate prevents the formation of molybdosilicic acid without affecting the formation of the molybdenum and phosphorus heteropoly acids. The same work refers to earlier studies on the effects of carboxylic acids on heteropoly acids. The subject is further discussed by Chalmers[49].

The above reactions may be used with great advantage in the analysis of mixtures containing P, Si, As and Ge. Selective suppression of heteropoly

Table 46 Chromatographic separations involving orthophosphate

Species separated	*Type of chromatography*	*Adsorbent*	*Solvent*	*Ref.*
F^-, NO_2^-, $S_2O_3^{2-}$, SO_4^{2-}, CrO_4^{2-}, PO_4^{3-}, AsO_4^{3-}, AsO_3^{3-}	TLC	Silica gel + 5% corn starch	MeOH–*n*-butanol–H_2O (3:1:1)	36
PO_4^{3-}, $P_2O_7^{4-}$, tri-meta-, tri-phosphate, tetra-meta-, tetra-phosphate	Paper Whatman No. 1 or 3		*For linear* Iso-propyl alcohol–H_2O–trichloroacetic acid–25% aq. NH_3 (75 mℓ:25 mℓ:5 g:0.3 mℓ) *For cyclic* Iso-propyl alcohol–isobutyl alcohol–H_2O–25% aq. NH_3 (40:20:39:1)	37
PO_4^{3-}, $P_2O_7^{4-}$, $P_3O_{10}^{5-}$	TLC and thin layer electrophoresis	Not stated	Dioxan–isopropyl alcohol–10% trichloro-acetic acid–conc. aq. NH_3 (148:128:3:1)	38
PO_4^{3-}, $P_2O_7^{4-}$, HPO_3^{2-}, $H_2PO_2^-$	TLC	Silica gel–starch	MeOH–conc. aq. NH_3–10% trichloro–acetic acid–water (10:3:1:10)	39
PO_4^{3-}, $P_2O_7^{4-}$	TLC	Cellulose	Dioxan–water–trichloroacetic acid–aq. NH_3 (65 mℓ:27.5 mℓ:5 g:0.25 mℓ)	40

PO_4^{3-}, SO_4^{2-}	TLC	Silica gel, Keiselguhr or La_2O_3	Not known	41
PO_4^{3-}, NO_2^-, $S_2O_3^{2-}$, CrO_4^{2-}, N_3^-, CN^-, SCN^-, BO_3^{3-}, S^{2-}, AsO_3^{3-}, AsO_4^{3-}, NO_3^-, SO_4^{2-}	TLC	Corn starch	Acetone–3M NH_4OH (1 : 4)	42
PO_4^{3-}, I^-, Br^-, Cl^-	TLC	Silica gel	Aq. iso-butyl alcohol–40% aq. NH_4 acetate (4:1)	43
PO_4^{3-}, $P_2O_7^{4-}$ tri-phosphate tetra-phosphate penta-phosphate cyclotri-phosphate cyclotetra-phosphate	TLC (linear and circular)	Corn starch	Trichloroacetic acid–isopropyl alcohol–H_2O–0.1M EDTA–aq. NH_3 (5 g:8 mℓ:39 mℓ:1 mℓ 25%:0.3 mℓ) (For PO_4^{3-}, $P_2O_7^{4-}$, tri-, tetra-, penta-, by circular) Isobutyl alcohol–EtOH–H_2O–0.1M EDTA–25% aq. NH_3 (30:30:38:1:1) (For separation cyclic from linear by ascending technique)	44

acid formation permits the spectrophotometric determination of some in the presence of others. This is discussed more fully on p. 467.

Note: In the analysis of traces, preconcentration often becomes important as well as separation. In this connection Rayner[50] has described a 'washing-in' technique using a modification of the Weisz ring oven. It is applied to air-borne phosphoric oxide.

Determination

Gravimetric methods

1. Precipitation as magnesium ammonium phosphate

Determination of phosphate as $MgNH_4PO_4 \cdot 6H_2O$ has been a basic method for over half a century.

$$PO_4{}^{3-} + NH_4{}^{+} + Mg^{2+} + 6H_2O \rightarrow MgNH_4PO_4 \cdot 6H_2O$$

$$2MgNH_4PO_4 \cdot 6H_2O \rightarrow Mg_2P_2O_7 + 2NH_3 + 13H_2O$$

The same reaction, though with a reversed procedure has been the standard method for macro determination of magnesium despite the many potential sources of error.

A detailed discussion of these methods and part of their extensive literature will be found in standard analytical textbooks[1,51,52]. The method consists of adding magnesia mixture* to an acidified phosphate solution, adding ammonia until in slight excess, and then allowing the solution to stand for 4 h or preferably overnight. This is followed by dissolving up the precipitate and re-precipitation. Finally, after filtration and washing the magnesium ammonium phosphate is ignited to the pyrophosphate at about 900 °C and weighed. The seemingly straightforward procedure conceals a host of potential errors.

Magnesium ammonium phosphate is one of the most soluble precipitates used in quantitative analysis. This needs to be borne in mind during the analytical operations. A relatively long time is required for the precipitate to reach constant composition. Usually it is allowed to stand for 4 h or overnight. Recently Zolotavin, Sanatina and Nesterenko[53] have investigated ways of speeding up this aging process, the study being extended to include barium sulphate and thorium oxalate as well as magnesium ammonium phosphate. They found that initial freezing of the precipitate at −18 °C or even −78 °C followed by thawing in hot water (60–70 °C) induced the growth of large precipitate crystals at the expense of smaller ones. The results for $MgNH_4PO_4 \cdot 6H_2O$ indicate that the analysis time may be cut from 7 h to 3 h without loss of accuracy.

Coprecipitation may be heavy in the method, with both positive and negative errors possible depending on the coprecipitated species. For example, adsorbed ammonium phosphate leads to negative errors, whilst magnesium phosphate may lead to positive errors. Related to this is the ignition temperature for conversion to the pyrophosphate. Though pure

* A solution of $MgCl_2 . 6H_2O$ and NH_4Cl, with a slight excess of NH_3.

$MgNH_4PO_4 \cdot 6H_2O$ decomposes[54] at 380–480 °C, a temperature of over 900 °C is generally used to convert some contaminants to the pyrophosphate. Nevertheless, some species, for example $Mg(H_2PO_4)_2$, lose phosphorus pentoxide slowly even at 1150–1200 °C.

A second precipitation is necessary to avoid a large excess of magnesium and ammonium ions. Older work by Lundell and Hoffman[55] indicated no loss of phosphate by this procedure.

As the precipitation is made in ammoniacal solution, much interference is to be expected. Most elements interfere, including the alkaline earths. Lundell and Hoffman[56] successfully used citric acid to mask iron. If substantial amounts of citric acid are present, the determination may be made in the presence of considerable quantities of Ca, Fe, Al, Sn, V, Ti, and Zr. Arsenic interferes by forming a similar salt to phosphate. Schulek and Endroi[57] found that interference by iron and aluminium in amounts greater than 1% could be eliminated by EDTA, which also masked calcium. They claimed that the more troublesome prior separation as the heteropoly acid could be thus avoided. The same approach was used by Huditz, Flaschka and Petzold[58].

Tiron (pyrocatechol-3:5 disulphonic acid) is an alternative masking agent for phosphate in the presence of Al, Cr, Bi, Sb, Sn, Fe(III), U, Ti or Be. Ion exchange chromatography may be used for cation separation before the determination.

Precipitation from homogeneous solution has been applied[59] to determination of phosphate as $MgNH_4PO_4 \cdot 6H_2O$. Slow evolution of NH_3 resulting from the reaction between ammonium chloride and ethylamine causes the slow formation of the precipitate when magnesium ions are present. Interference by calcium is prevented by lactic acid; Fe, Ti and Al may be masked by EDTA. An accuracy of ± 0.4 per cent was claimed using this procedure.

2. *Precipitation as ammonium molybdophosphate*

The addition of excess ammonium molybdate to a solution of phosphate in dilute HNO_3 solution, produces a yellow sparingly soluble precipitate of ammonium molybdophosphate.*

$$PO_4^{3-} + 12H_2MoO_4 + 3NH_4^+ \rightarrow (NH_4)_3[PO_4 \cdot 12\,MoO_3] \cdot 12H_2O$$

The exact composition of the heteropoly acid has been the subject of controversy; Cannon[60] concluded that its composition was $(NH_4)_2HPO_4 \cdot 12MoO_3 \cdot 12H_2O$. Thistlethwaite[61] found the composition to lie between this and the theoretical structure. The latter investigation includes a comprehensive account of earlier work involving the precipitate.

The ability of phosphoric acid to form heteropoly acids has been known since 1826. Many analytical procedures for phosphorus depend on initial precipitation in this form. As precipitated, ammonium molybdophosphate contains HNO_3 and water. Excess reagent is removed by washing with dilute HNO_3, and this is removed by further washing with a solution of ammonium nitrate. The precipitate is decomposed by water. Whether a precipitate of correct composition will be formed will depend on several

* Or more correctly triammonium dodecamolybdophosphate (IUPAC).

factors which include the concentrations of the molybdate solution and the HNO_3 as well as the temperature of precipitation. The presence of ammonium nitrate during precipitation has been recommended to hasten precipitation and to minimize the solubility of the precipitate.

Archer, Heslop and Kirby[62] have investigated the conditions necessary for quantitative determination of phosphate, while in another study involving ^{32}P and ^{99}Mo, the solubility of the precipitate in dilute HNO_3 was determined[63]. The essential conditions reported in the above work are as follows. Phosphate may be quantitatively precipitated with nitromolybdate at any temperature in the range 50–80 °C if the reactants stand for not less than 30 min at this temperature and 30 min at room temperature with stirring every 15 min. Analysis of the precipitate produced at 80 °C indicated a composition agreeing with Thistlethwaite's results. Twice the stoichiometric amount of nitromolybdate reagent was found sufficient to remove 99.9% of the phosphate at 70 °C. The presence of HNO_3 was found to be essential, with the ammonium nitrate having no effect on the removal of phosphate. No interference was found by the presence of perchloric acid, but both HCl and H_2SO_4 interfere.

The precipitate may be dried at 210–410 °C and weighed as $(NH_3)[PO_4 \cdot 12MoO_3]$ though in this form it is hygroscopic. Ignition at 500–700 °C produces molybdophosphoric anhydride, $P_2O_5 \cdot 24MoO_3$, a form which older standard methods recommended for weighing.

The presence of ammonium chloride, ammonium fluoride and ammonium sulphate retard the precipitation, and so also do HCl, HF and H_2SO_4. Arsenic, Se, Si, Te, W, V, Ti and Zr interfere but this may be prevented if the precipitation is made in a higher concentration of HNO_3. The effect of arsenic and the transitional metal ions on the precipitation has been studied[64], the results indicating that phosphate can be quantitatively precipitated at between 50 and 70 °C with 3.5 times the stoichiometric amount of ammonium molybdate, even in the presence of an equivalent amount of arsenic. Radiotracer studies indicate that the precipitation of As is a function of the excess of ammonium nitrate and the precipitation temperature. The same work showed that ferric nitrate inhibits the phosphate precipitation (as well as that of arsenic), with chromium(III), nickel(II) and manganese(II) nitrates having less effect.

From the above discussion it will be apparent that the accurate gravimetric determination of phosphate by this method requires carefully controlled conditions. One of the difficulties, namely the non-stoichiometry of the precipitate, may be overcome by using an empirical factor.

Several alternative approaches have been made. For example, the ammonium molybdophosphate can be dissolved in NH_3 and its molybdate content determined gravimetrically as lead molybdate, a better weighing form. Another procedure involves akalimetric titration of the precipitate. This will be discussed in the section on titrimetric methods.

3. *Organic base molybdophosphates (including quinoline)*

Several organic bases have been examined as alternatives to the NH_4^+ ion. Earlier work has been described in a review[65] and in the textbook by Belcher and Wilson[66]. More recently a range of organic bases has been investigated by Macdonald and Rivero[67] with indication that α-picoline (2-methyl pyridine) has a slight advantage over the well established quinoline, though its use is restricted to a titrimetric finish.

Heslop and Pearson[4] used ^{32}P to study lutidinium and quinolinium molybdates as reagents for the precipitation of phosphate. When the latter was used, arsenic was found to be precipitated under the optimum conditions required for the quantitative precipitation of phosphate. On the other hand, the use of lutidinium molybdate enabled the arsenic to be left in solution.

In order to benefit from its larger molecular weight the iodinium ion $(C_6H_5)_2I^+$ has been examined[68]. Results were comparable with those for quinolinium, with similar interference.

Of the many organic bases examined, quinoline, first introduced by Wilson[69], has been the most successful.

$$H_3PO_4 + 12Na_2MoO_4 + 24HCl \rightarrow H_3[PO_4 \cdot 12MoO_3] + 24NaCl + 12H_2O$$

$$3C_9H_7N\,HCl + H_3[PO_4 \cdot 12MoO_3] \rightarrow (C_9H_7N)_3H_3[PO_4 \cdot 12MoO_3] + 3HCl$$

In the Wilson procedure, a quinoline hydrochloride solution is slowly added to a boiling phosphate solution containing sodium molybdate and acidified with HCl. A coarse crystalline precipitate with good filtration properties is obtained in this way. Wilson was unable to develop a gravimetric procedure, except for very small amounts of phosphate, and resorted to an alkalimetric titration of the precipitate. This form of the method has gained widespread popularity and found extensive application. It will be further discussed in the section on titrimetric methods for phosphate.

Precipitation of phosphate as quinoline molybdophosphate has the following advantages over the ammonium form:

1. It is less soluble.
2. The composition is much closer to theoretical.
3. It is relatively free from coprecipitation.
4. Interferences are less.
5. The general conditions of precipitation, e.g. temperature and excess reagent, are less critical.

Perrin[70] found that ignition at 200–250 °C produced a precipitate corresponding to the theoretical composition $(C_9H_7N)_3 \cdot HPO_4 \cdot 12MoO_3$ and that ignition at 550 °C produced molybdophosphoric anhydride, a less satisfactory weighing form. A thermogravimetric study by Wendlandt and Hoffmann[71] indicated that a stable anhydrous form was produced in the range 155–370 °C.

Interferences with the method follow the general pattern of the ammonium molybdophosphate method. Arsenic, silicon, H_2SO_4, HF and ammonium ions interfere, but this can be prevented if certain steps are taken. Lench[72] in applying the titrimetric and gravimetric forms of the method to determination of phosphorus in iron and steel, was able to overcome interference by Fe, As, Zr, Nb, Ta and W by introducing modifications. Arsenic was removed by volatilization with HBr. Precipitation of iron was avoided by using more reagent or digesting the solution near the boiling point. Interference by silica is prevented by addition of citrate[73] which prevents formation of molybdosilicic acid, though in the microdetermination of phosphate more than 100 mg of citric acid affects the precipitation of the molybdophosphate[74]. If citrate is added, possible interference by ammonium ions is prevented, ammonium molybdophosphate being soluble under these conditions. Interference by ammonium ions is important in the context of fertilizer analysis, an area in which the method has been extensively applied. Acetone may be used to prevent ammonium ion interference by its inclusion as a component of a single 'Quimocial' reagent, this containing quinoline, sodium molybdate, citric and nitric acids, and acetone[75].

The effects of fluoride, which probably interferes by causing silica to be released from glassware, may be overcome by addition of boric acid[74]. Ferric iron has little effect unless the amount of phosphate to be determined is very small. The method is not affected by the presence of calcium, magnesium, aluminium, alkali salts, or citrates, the last mentioned being subject to the conditions stated earlier.

Chromium in 18-fold amounts and titanium in 3.5-fold amounts do not interfere, but the quantity of vanadium present should not be greater than 0.2 of the phosphorus content.

The quinoline molybdophosphate method is generally regarded as accurate, precise, and straightforward. As a potential official method for fertilizer analysis it was subjected to collaborative tests[76] which resulted in its acceptance as a final action method of the Association of Official and Agricultural Chemists[77]. The gravimetric procedure has been applied to semi-micro organic elemental analysis for 2–3 mg amounts of phosphorus, the precipitate being weighed after drying at 160 °C or by a rapid procedure involving washing with dioxan and ether[78].

4. *As silver phosphate*

Silver phosphate may be precipitated from homogeneous solution by the gradual release of silver ions resulting from the breakdown of argentous ammines[79]. As NH_3 escapes from the heated solution, large and easily filtered crystals are precipitated, which contain 7.40% P.

From 3 to 300 mg PO_4^{3-} can be determined within 0.13 mg. Of the interferences studied, potassium, ammonium, nitrate, and acetate produced no significant effects but large amounts of sodium and sulphate ions gave slightly high results. Silicate is a serious interference with arsenate, chromate, tungstate and vanadate giving some interference. Multivalent cations also interfere but may be removed by ion-exchange before the determination. Chloride, bromide, iodide, cyanide, thiocyanate and oxalate, which form insoluble silver compounds may be removed by initial volatilization with HNO_3. After evaporating the solution almost to dryness, which ensures complete elimination of these anions, the resulting salts must be hydrolysed for about 4 h in warm HNO_3 solution to remove any polyphosphate produced during the preliminary treatment.

5. *Miscellaneous methods*

Phosphate may be precipitated as silver thallium(I) phosphate[80], using TlOAc in conjunction with $AgNO_3$. The precipitate shows thermal stability over the exceptionally wide temperature range of 20–720 °C. An alternative titrimetric procedure based on the Volhard method may be used.

Bismuth phosphate is another gravimetric form proposed[81] for determination of phosphate. In 1M HNO_3 there is no interference from Mg, Zn, Mn, Ni or Co.

Gravimetric determination of phosphate as magnesium ammonium phosphate[82]

Reagents

Neutral magnesia mixture:
Dissolve 102 g $MgCl_2 \cdot 6H_2O$ and 53 g of NH_4Cl in distilled water. Add 5 mℓ of NH_4OH (sp. gr. 0.880) and dilute to 1 ℓ with distilled water. Allow to stand overnight and filter.

Hydrochloric acid: 30 %.
Dilute 30 mℓ of HCl (sp. gr. 1.18) to 100 mℓ with distilled water.

Ammonium hydroxide: 10 %.
Dilute 10 mℓ of NH_4OH (sp. gr. 0.880) to 100 mℓ with distilled water.

Ammonium hydroxide: 1 % and 3 %.
Prepare by appropriate dilution of the 10 % solution.

Citric acid: solid.

Methyl red:
Dissolve 0.20 g of methyl red in water containing 1 mℓ of M NaOH solution and dilute to 100 mℓ with distilled water.

Procedure

To a cold solution of between 100 and 200 mℓ containing 10 mℓ of HCl (sp. gr. 1.18) and 0.5–0.75 g of P_2O_5, add 2 g of citric acid and a few drops of methyl red indicator, followed by NH_4OH (sp. gr. 0.880) until the indicator turns yellow. Precipitate, with mechanical stirring, by the dropwise addition throughout, of 100 mℓ of magnesia mixture, followed by sufficient 10 % NH_4OH to bring the final concentration of NH_4OH (sp. gr. 0.880) to 2.5–3.0 % v/v. Allow to stand overnight.

Decant the clear liquor through a Whatman No. 31 filter paper, using suction. Reject the filtrate and dissolve the small amount of precipitate through the filter paper with 30 mℓ of hot 30 % HCl, collecting the extract in the beaker containing the bulk of the precipitate. Wash the filter paper several times with distilled water. To the solution add 2 g of citric acid and 10 mℓ of neutral magnesia mixture (Note 1), then add NH_4OH (sp. gr. 0.880) dropwise with stirring, until a permanent precipitate just appears. If the quantity of precipitate is too great, dissolve the major portion by the dropwise addition of 30 % HCl; this adjustment is essential.

Adjust the total volume to approximately 100 mℓ, cool and add dropwise, with mechanical stirring, 100 mℓ of 1 % NH_4OH followed by 90 mℓ of 10 % NH_4OH, or sufficient to bring the total concentration of NH_4OH (sp. gr. 0.880) to 3 % v/v. Allow to stand for at least 4 h, and preferably overnight.

Filter through a Whatman No. 31 filter paper, removing the precipitate which adheres to the stirrer and the sides of the beaker with a rubber 'policeman'. Wash the paper and precipitate six times with 3 % NH_4OH.

Transfer the paper and precipitate to a weighed platinum crucible and loosen the precipitate from the paper. Add not more than 0.2 g of NH_4NO_3 and char the paper without flaming. Burn off the carbon at a temperature below 900 °C and finally ignite to constant weight, preferably in a muffle, at 1050–1100 °C (Note 2).

$$\mathrm{g\,Mg_2P_2O_7} \times 0.6377 = \mathrm{g\,P_2O_5}$$
$$\mathrm{g\,Mg_2P_2O_7} \times 0.2784 = \mathrm{g\,P}$$

Notes

1. The amounts of citric acid and excess of magnesia mixture recommended should not be varied. Omission of the magnesia mixture will lead to low results.
2. A small amount of magnesium citrate is always coprecipitated with the magnesium ammonium phosphate; this, on ignition gives carbon which can be removed only by careful attention to details.
3. The method is capable of an accuracy of 1 part in 500.

Titrimetric methods

1. Alkalimetric titration of ammonium and quinoline molybdophosphates

Difficulties in the gravimetric methods for determination of phosphate as ammonium molybdophosphate have been discussed. An alternative procedure is the alkalimetric titration of the precipitate using phenolphthalein as indicator.

$$\mathrm{(NH_4)_3[PO_4 \cdot 12MoO_3] + 26NaOH \rightarrow 12Na_2MoO_4 + Na_2HPO_4 + 3NH_3 + 14H_2O}$$

Free NH_3, a product of the reaction, causes a poor end-point. The use of quinoline molybdophosphate rather than the ammonium salt offers many advantages, some of which have been mentioned in the earlier discussion of the gravimetric finish. The advantages indicated in Wilson's original work[69] were quickly verified by later workers, and the method has now become a standard one for both macro and micro amounts of phosphate where high accuracy is required. The equation may be represented thus:

$$\mathrm{(C_9H_7N)_3H_3[PO_4 \cdot 12MoO_3] + 26NaOH \rightarrow Na_2HPO_4 + 12Na_2MoO_4 + 3C_9H_7N}$$

Wilson, who applied the method to analysis of fertilizers, etc., filtered the precipitate using a paper-pulp filter, and after washing it completely free of acid, dissolved it in excess of standard NaOH. The excess was back titrated with standard HCl using a phenolphthalein–thymol blue mixed indicator. Investigation of interferences was restricted to those substances normally found in fertilizers. In general, they are similar to those found in the ammonium molybdophosphate method. The effect of iron(III) is small unless the phosphate content is low. Arsenic is quantitatively precipitated and so is silicate, though interference by the latter is prevented by the presence of citrate[73].

Several of the interferences are in the nature of inhibitory effects on the precipitation, as in the gravimetric procedure. Heslop and Pearson[4] found that increasing the excess of reagent (which does not affect the results) and digesting the precipitate for 2 h, has the effect of counteracting the inhibitory effects of some ions, particularly iron(III).

A considerable improvement was made by Fernlund and Zechner[83] who introduced a composite precipitant which could be kept for about a month instead of the one week lifetime of the original reagent described by Wilson. Titrimetric procedures based on both ammonium and quinoline molybdophosphate have been applied to the analysis of fertilizers. In its original form the alkalimetric method was unreliable in the presence of large amounts of ammonium ions which precluded its use for analysis of neutral and alkaline citrate extracts of fertilizers. This difficulty was overcome by including acetone in the quimocial reagent referred to earlier[75].

One unsatisfactory feature of the method which has caused concern to some users is the tendency of the precipitate to form lumps which dissolve with difficulty. Duncan and Brabson[84] were able, by using additional citric acid, to form larger crystals which did not agglomerate during filtration, and which dissolved readily in alkali. These workers found the method rugged, and favourable in precision and accuracy with the official gravimetric method of the Association of Official Agricultural Chemists. A collaborative study by Cavdill[85] has recommended it for total phosphorus, available phosphorus by direct method, and for citrate-insoluble phosphorus in fertilizers.

Attempts have been made to improve the titrimetric method based on ammonium molybdophosphate but continued evidence of positive bias and lack of precision has confirmed that it is inferior to the quinoline molybdophosphate method[84]. The latter method has been applied to numerous areas of analysis including iron and steel[72], micro organic[74], and submicro organic[86].

Titrimetric determination of phosphate as quinoline molybdophosphate[83]

Reagent

Dissolve 250 g $Na_2MoO_4 \cdot 2H_2O$ in 500 mℓ water, add 460 mℓ concentrated HCl and 1 drop of 30% H_2O_2. To 600 mℓ 1:1 HCl add 28 mℓ quinoline. Mix the two solutions together and heat to boiling. Cool, allow to stand for not less than 24 h, and then filter.

Procedure (for up to 25 mg P)

To the phosphate solution add HCl until 0.9–1.6M and a few drops of 6% $KClO_3$ solution. Heat to boiling and add 10 mℓ of the reagent (20 mℓ for amounts of phosphorus greater than 15 mg). Allow to stand for a few minutes.

Filter through a paper pulp pad and wash with 1M HCl followed by water, until washings are neutral. Wash the precipitate into the original flask (which should also be free of acid) and add excess of standard (0.1M) NaOH. Titrate the excess with standard (0.1 or 0.05M) HCl using phenolphthalein as indicator.

Note
The above reagent keeps for one month compared with the one week of the original reagent proposed by Wilson[69].

---

2. Other titrimetric procedures based on initial formation of molybdo-phosphoric acid
A double amplification* method for use with trace amounts of phosphate has been described[88]. The phosphate is first converted to the 12-molybdo-phosphoric acid, the molybdenum in which is converted into the oxine complex. This is titrated with $KBrO_3$ after addition of KBr.

As each mole of molybdate reacts with two moles of the organic reagent and each of these subsequently consumes four equivalents of a standard bromate solution, an overall amplification of 96 is achieved in terms of the original phosphate.

			Amplification
PO_4^{3-}	$\rightarrow$	$H_3[PO_4 \cdot 12MoO_3]$	$\times$12 (Mo)
Mo(VI)	$\rightarrow$	$MoO_2(C_9H_6ON)_2$	$\times$ 2 (oxine)
C_9H_7OH	$\xrightarrow{2Br_2}$	$C_9H_5Br_2OH + 2HBr$	$\times$ 4 (bromine)

Another approach is described by Kirkbright, Smith and West[20]. In this work the 12-molybdophosphoric acid is selectively extracted into isobutyl acetate, back-extracted into aqueous solution and degraded with alkali. The resulting molybdenum(VI) is reduced to molybdenum(V) by means of a silver reductor column, and the determination completed with a cerimetric titration of molybdenum(V) using ferroin as indicator. A silver reductor which would probably be suitable, has been recently described[89]. Other heteropoly acid forming elements, As, Sb, Ge and Si, do not interfere in this method, neither do a wide range of other ions. The determination of 10^{-6} g of phosphorus using an ordinary burette with titres of several millilitres of 10^{-3}M titrant and visual end-point, is a measure of the advantage derived from an amplification method.

Determination of phosphorus (3–30 μg) by an amplification method based on molybdophosphoric acid[20]

Reagents and apparatus
Reductor column: A 10 cm × 1 cm is used, the silver filling being 7 cm. The latter is prepared as follows. Dissolve 30 g silver nitrate in 400 mℓ water, add a few drops of HNO_3, suspend a sheet of electrolytic copper 10 cm square in the solution, and stir vigorously until the silver has been completely precipitated. Wash by decantation with dilute H_2SO_4 until free from most of the copper. Transfer to the reductor tube with water,

* A full discussion of amplification methods has been given by Belcher[87].

agitate to remove air pockets, and wash with dilute H_2SO_4 until completely free from copper. Maintain the column in 2M HCl at all times, and equilibriate with hot (60–80°C) 2M HCl immediately before use.

Standard orthophosphate solution:
Dissolve 0.1098 g analytical-reagent, grade potassium dihydrogen orthophosphate in distilled water and dilute to 1ℓ.

$$1\ \text{m}\ell\ \text{solution} \equiv 25\ \mu\text{g of phosphorus}$$

Molybdate reagent:
Dissolve 10.69 g of analytical-reagent grade ammonium molybdate tetrahydrate, $(NH_4)_6Mo_7O_{24}\cdot 4H_2O$ in distilled water and dilute to 1ℓ.

Cerium(IV) sulphate solution:
Dilute stock 0.05M solution to 10^{-3}M with M H_2SO_4 as required.

Ferroin indicator solution:
Use a 5×10^{-3}M aq. solution of ferroin, $Fe(C_{12}H_8N_2)_3SO_4$.

Two drops are used in each titration.

Procedure

Transfer the sample solution (up to 5 mℓ) containing between 3 and 30 µg P into a 100-mℓ separating funnel containing 10 mℓ molybdate stock solution and 10 mℓ of water. Add sufficient concentrated HCl to make the solution 0.96M with respect to HCl. Allow the solution to stand for 5 min, add 10 mℓ of isobutyl acetate and shake the funnel for 1 min.

Allow the phases to separate, discard the aqueous phase, and wash the organic phase with 10 mℓ of 2M HCl. Shake the organic phase with 5 mℓ of 4M NH_3 solution, discard the isobutyl acetate and retain the alkaline solution containing the molybdenum(VI).

Transfer the molybdenum solution from the extraction funnel into a 50-mℓ beaker, add sufficient 6M HCl to neutralize the NH_3 and make the solution 2M with respect to HCl. Transfer the solution quantitatively into the top of the reductor column using 2M HCl as wash liquid. Reduce the molybdenum(VI) to molybdenum(V) on this column by eluting the sample three times with 5-mℓ portions of hot 2M HCl and three times with 5-mℓ portions of cold 2M HCl. Collect the eluate (35–40 mℓ) in the titration cell, heat rapidly to boiling, cool the solution to near room temperature, and titrate the molybdenum(V) with standard 10^{-3}M cerium(IV) sulphate, with ferroin as indicator and E.E.L. filter No. 603.

Alternatively, after some experience, the end-point can be detected visually by the disappearance of the last trace of pink colour.

Notes

1. No interference was found for the following ions present in quantities ranging from 1 to 6 mg: Se(IV), Te(IV), Ba(II), Mn(II), Si(IV), Al(III), Pb(II), Co(II), Ni(II), As(V), Ge(IV), Ca(II), Fe(III), Zn(II), Cd(II), Cu(II), Sb(V).
2. The method has been applied to the submicro determination of phosphorus in organic compounds.

3. *EDTA*

Several methods are available for indirect titrimetric determination of phosphate with EDTA. Based on the precipitation of insoluble metal phosphate, they entail either collecting the precipitate and determining its metallic content after dissolution, or adding excess of the metal ions and determining the latter in the filtrate after removing the precipitate.

Earlier work utilized $MgNH_4PO_4 \cdot 6H_2O$ with compleximetric titration of Mg^{++} in ammoniacal buffer and Eriochrome Black T as indicator[58].

$$PO_4{}^{3-} + NH_4{}^+ + Mg^{2+} + 6H_2O \rightarrow MgNH_4PO_4 \cdot 6H_2O$$

An interesting feature of this work is the use of EDTA as masking agent during the precipitation of $MgNH_4PO_4 \cdot 6H_2O$. If added before the precipitation, any polyvalent cations are complexed. On adding the precipitant, consisting of magnesium and ammonium chlorides in ammoniacal solution, the Mg^{++} first reacts with any excess of EDTA and then precipitates $MgNH_4PO_4 \cdot 6H_2O$. The relatively low stability constant of the EDTA–Mg complex prevents it liberating metals from their complexes with the exception of iron, aluminium, thallium and beryllium. The addition of citric acid will mask iron, aluminium and thallium and sulphosalicylic acid masks the beryllium.

There are several unsatisfactory features to the procedure based on $MgNH_4PO_4 \cdot 6H_2O$, for example its appreciable solubility can cause loss of phosphate with resultant errors especially when small amounts of phosphate are involved. Coprecipitation is a potential source of error. This may be overcome by re-precipitation if necessary. A more serious cause of error is variation in composition of the precipitate. A precipitate of constant composition is produced only after a period of standing, and accurate results will depend on the mole ratio of $Mg:PO_4$ being exactly 1:1. Zinc ammonium phosphate has been used as the basis of a procedure by Buss, Kohlschütter and Preiss[90], with the advantages that the final end-point is sharper than for magnesium and with no tendency for the $ZnNH_4PO_4$ to come out of solution at pH 10, at which the titration is carried out.

Precipitation of phosphate in acidic solution has the advantage of improving selectivity. This has been the recent trend with bismuth[91], zirconium[92,93], lanthanum[94], and thorium[95,96] being suggested for this purpose. When bismuth is used, the acidity of the solution must be carefully adjusted; if too acid the bismuth precipitate dissolves, if insufficiently acid a flocculent precipitate results. Riedel[91] evaporates to dryness with HNO_3 and then adjusts the acidity to the optimum value of 0.2M in $HClO_4$. The bismuth solution is added and the back titration done using EDTA with pyrocatechol violet as indicator. Prior removal of sulphate as barium sulphate is required, but any chloride (which would interfere) is removed in the initial treatment. Bassett[97] has extended Riedel's work to the determination of total phosphate and arsenate in a mixture, the arsenate being separately determined iodimetrically. Interfering cations (Pb^{2-}, Fe^{3+}) are removed by ion-exchange, and chloride and sulphate with silver nitrate and barium nitrate respectively.

Budevski *et al.*[92] reported an indirect compleximetric procedure based on precipitation of zirconium phosphate with a known excess of zirconium(IV) in 15–20% H_2SO_4. This was followed by a back titration of zirconium(IV) by EDTA using xylenol orange as indicator. As both the precipitation and titration are done in a strongly acid solution high selectivity is attained. These workers deduced that the Zr:P ratio in the precipitate was 1:2 in contrast to the findings of Sinha, Das Gupta and Kumar[93] who found a 1:1 ratio. The latter investigators concluded on the basis of X-ray diffraction data, that the precipitate was probably zirconyl phosphate, $ZrO(HPO_4)$, as distinct from $Zr(HPO_4)_2$.

The procedure described by Sinha, Das Gupta and Kumar can be used for 0.95–118 mg $PO_4{}^{3-}$ in contrast to the limited range of 35–55 mg specified by Budevski *et al.*, with no interference from iron(III), titanium(IV), thorium (IV) and bismuth(III). Fluoride must be removed if present in excess of 1.4 mg. The indicator used was xylenol orange with the titration being conducted at 90 °C. De Sousa[98] describes an indirect compleximetric method based on initial precipitation of phosphate with silver nitrate in neutral or slightly alkaline solution. The precipitate is reacted with $K_2Ni(CN)_4$, liberating an equivalent amount of Ni^{2+} ions which are titrated with standard EDTA. A micro-method based on the same principle has also been reported.

A rapid compleximetric method based on precipitation of lanthanum phosphate at pH 5.0 has been described by Yofe and Rappart[94]. From 50 to 300 mg $PO_4{}^{3-}$ may be determined in the presence of chloride, sulphate, alkali and alkaline earth metals. The procedure entails adding excess of standard lanthanum chloride to an acidified phosphate solution, and after precipitation of lanthanum phosphate, titrating excess lanthanum with EDTA using xylenol orange as indicator. A slight modification is required when sulphate is present. Small amounts of phosphate may be determined (1–10 mg) if 0.01M lanthanum chloride and EDTA solutions are employed. Concentrations as high as 1930 ppm chloride, 480 ppm Mg^{2+}, 800 ppm Ca^{2+}, 1100 ppm Na^+, 1920 ppm sulphate, and 2740 ppm Ba^{2+} do not interfere. In contrast to the zirconium methods, no filtration of the precipitate is required.

For very small amounts of phosphate (10–50 μg) Kirkbright, Smith and West[95] have described a rapid titrimetric procedure in which thorium phosphate is precipitated. Again, removal of the precipitate is not required. Large amounts of chloride, bromide, iodide, nitrate, sulphate, perchlorate and silicate can be tolerated, but fluoride, borate and arsenate interfere. The precipitant is thorium nitrate, with the back-titration being made at pH 3 using xylenol orange as indicator.

Compleximetric determination of phosphate[93]

Reagents

Zr solution 0.05M:

Dissolve 13.5 g of analytical grade zirconyl nitrate ($ZrO(NO_3)_2 \cdot 2H_2O$), in 140 mℓ of 8M HNO_3. Boil the solution for 5 min to depolymerize any polymerized zirconyl ion and dilute to 1ℓ.

Potassium dihydrogen phosphate solution 0.05M:

Dissolve 3.40 g of analytical grade KH_2PO_4 in 500 mℓ of distilled water. A 0.01M solution is prepared from this solution by dilution.

EDTA 0.05M solution:

Dissolve 18.61 g of EDTA disodium salt, in distilled water and dilute to 1ℓ. The exact molarity is determined using a reliable reference standard, e.g. zinc oxide.

A 0.02M solution is prepared from the above solution by appropriate dilution.

Xylenol orange solution: 0.2%, aqueous.

Procedure

Pipette the phosphate solution, containing between 0.95 and 118 mg PO_4^{3-}, into a 250-mℓ volumetric flask, add 125 mℓ 4M HNO_3 and dilute to nearly 200 mℓ. Add a known excess of 0.05M zirconyl nitrate solution (10–30 mℓ). Heat on a steam bath for 30 min, cool, and make up volume with 1M HNO_3. Mix well.

Filter the precipitate through a dry filter paper and discard the first portion of filtrate. Transfer 100 mℓ of the filtrate to a 500-mℓ conical flask and dilute to 200 mℓ with water. Heat to boiling for 1 min to expel oxides of nitrogen, then titrate the zirconium(IV) slowly with standard EDTA using xylenol orange indicator. The temperature of the solution during the titration should be 90 °C, or more, and the addition of EDTA near the end-point should be at the rate of 1 drop per second. The end-point is indicated by a sharp colour change from pink-red to lemon-yellow.

Determine the exact molarity of the zirconium solution by titrating it with EDTA under the above conditions.

Interferences: Because the precipitation of zirconium phosphate is made in 2–3.5M HNO_3, interference is small, e.g. titanium(IV), bismuth(III), iron(III) and thorium(IV) do not interfere. Fluoride interferes causing high results, presumably by forming a strong complex with zirconium(IV). When present in amounts greater than 1.425 mg the sample should be treated with $HClO_4$ and boric acid to remove it.

Note

The method was successfully applied to fertilizer analysis.

---

4. *Miscellaneous titrimetric procedures*

Phosphate has been determined by titration with bismuth(III) solutions[99, 100]. In the latter paper 50 mg PO_4^{3-} was titrated using methyl thymol blue as indicator. The colour change from green to reddish-violet can be easily observed if chloroform is added and the solution shaken.

Cerium(III) has been recommended for the rapid titration of 5–15 mg P with Eriochrome black T as indicator[101]. Tervalent iron, aluminium, magnesium and calcium interfere but may be removed by ion-exchange. Sulphate interferes when present in amounts equal to or greater than the phosphate. More recently lanthanum nitrate has been recommended for titration of 2–300 μg P with an electrical end-point detection[102].

Spectroscopic methods

1. *Spectrophotometric methods*

Phosphate can be determined by three main methods, as molybdophosphoric acid, its reduction product molybdenum blue, and the yellow vanado-molybdophosphoric complex. In addition, indirect methods based on chloranilates or the molybdate derived from molybdophosphoric acid may be used.

The literature on phosphate determination by heteropoly acid formation is voluminous. Earlier work based on the absorbance of molybdophosphoric acid or its reduction product in aqueous or organic media, has been reviewed by Rieman and Beukenkamp[103]. The sensitivity of spectrophotometric methods based on heteropoly acid formation is not high, and depends on reaction conditions and whether extraction into an organic medium has been employed. The heteropoly acid may be reduced to molybdenum blue and the latter extracted, or it may be extracted first and subsequent reduction carried out in the organic phase.

Extraction is one means of improving selectivity in phosphate determination by this method. The other approach is based on suppression of unwanted hetero species. This has been reviewed recently by Chalmers and Sinclair[49, 104, 105]. The same papers contain a discussion of the analytical implications of the dodecamolybdates existing in two distinct forms. Heslop and Pearson[17] emphasize the same feature, and point out that even the reduced molybdenum blue contains two species, $H_3PO_4 \cdot 10MoO_3 \cdot Mo_2O_5$ and $H_3PO_4 \cdot 8MoO_3 \cdot 2Mo_2O_5$. These factors explain the reported discrepancies in earlier published work on spectrophotometric methods for phosphate, and stress the need to produce one form of the heteropoly acid exclusively.

Suppression of unwanted hetero species will now be considered in more detail. It has been known for a long time that citric, tartaric and oxalic acids destroy molybdophosphoric acid, but not molybdosilicic acid[106]. Paul[14] reported that citric acid destroys molybdoarsenic acid, and furthermore, that if $HClO_4$ is added before ammonium molybdate, molybdosilicic acid is prevented from forming. Related to these were two other rather paradoxical reactions for which explanation was sought:

1. If tartaric acid is added to a mixture of molybdophosphoric and molybdosilicic acids, only the molybdophosphoric acid is destroyed.
2. If a composite reagent containing molybdate and tartaric acid is added to a mixture of phosphate and silicate, only the molybdophosphoric acid is formed.

Chalmers and Sinclair[105] have explained this apparent contradiction in terms of the stability and kinetics of the reacting systems.

$$\text{Molybdophosphoric acid} + \text{tartaric acid} \xrightleftharpoons{\text{fast}} \text{phosphate} + \text{molybdotartrate}$$

$$\text{Molybdosilicic acid} + \text{tartaric acid} \xrightleftharpoons{\text{slow}} \text{silicate} + \text{molybdotartrate}$$

Reaction (1) above is explained by the fast reaction giving the molybdotartrate complex. The molybdosilicate is destroyed far more slowly. Therefore when the tartartic acid is added *finally*, molybdosilicate remains for sufficient time to be measured and reduced to molybdenum blue.

When tartaric acid is added *initially*, in the presence of the molybdotartrate complex, a small amount of molybdophosphate is formed by equilibrium. This is quickly reduced to molybdenum blue in the presence of a reducing agent so that the equilibrium is further shifted to the left-hand side until all the phosphorus is in this form. The molybdosilicate on the other hand, is formed slowly, and does not interfere with the phosphate determination. The experimental facts are thus explained. Chalmers and Sinclair[105] have developed a spectrophotometric procedure for determination of phosphate and silicate based on the above.

The existence of two forms (α and β) of the heteropoly acids was postulated by Strickland[107]. At high acidity and $[H^+]/[MoO_4^{2-}]$ ratio, the unstable β form is produced. It decays spontaneously into the stable α form which is obtained at low acidity and $[H^+]/[MoO_4^{2-}]$ ratio. The β form has a higher extinction coefficient, this explaining the earlier discrepancies reported in phosphate spectrophotometric methods where mixtures of the two forms were probably involved. The β form is stabilized in acetone[104, 105]. Gravimetric methods based on the heteropoly acids are not affected by the two modifications.

A recent study by Pungar and co-workers[108–110] has provided more information on the chemistry of α and β heteropoly modifications. The same study attributes the differences in molar absorptivities and other irregularities found in the various heteropoly spectrophotometric procedures, *not* to the heteropoly acids themselves, but isopolymolybdates formed with them. Despite the many similar characteristics of the four heteropoly acids (P, As, Si and Ge) these investigators find that there are sufficient differences to permit their determination without separation. In order to accomplish this, judicious variation of acid concentration, molybdate concentration, wavelength, α and β modifications, and the medium, is necessary. For example, absorption of the α-molybdoarsenic acid is practically zero at 427 nm whereas that of the other three compounds is considerable. No reduction or extraction is involved.

One further general point is relevant before considering the spectrophotometric methods in more detail, namely the extraction of silicate from glassware, an important source of error where small amounts of phosphorus are to be determined.

Addition of ammonium molybdate solution to an acidified solution of phosphate produces a yellow colour, the absorbance of which may be measured at 380–420 nm. This was used as a means of phosphate analysis by Boltz and Mellon[111]. Interferences include arsenic, silicate, tungstate, vanadate, bismuth, and unless in small amounts, nickel, copper and fluoride. Application has been less than that of the molybdenum blue method.

Recent work by Kennedy and Weetman[112] describes a modified procedure for 1–10 µg phosphate in which absorbance measurements are made at 362 nm. The work of Chalmers and Sinclair[104, 105] on the influence of carboxylic acids on heteropoly acid formation has been referred to. They describe a procedure for the determination of 0.2–1.0 mg P and 0.1–1.0 mg SiO_2 in the same solution[105]. Tartaric acid is used to suppress the formation of molybdosilicic acid in one aliquot. The procedure is relatively simple.

Jakubiec and Boltz[113] extract the molybdophosphoric acid (or its blue reduction product) with propylene carbonate in $CHCl_3$. The molar absorptivity in the propylene carbonate-chloroform phase is 22 300 at 308 nm. Up to 7.5 µg of soluble phosphate may be determined by this procedure.

Reference has been made already to the recent work by Pungor and co-workers[108–110]. In this work, which is restricted to the determination of P, As, Si and Ge, procedures are given for the analysis of all binary combinations as well as mixtures containing P, As and Si, or P, As and Ge. The concentrations involved are approximately 2–17 µg mℓ^{-1} for phosphorus, 3–40 µg mℓ^{-1} for As, 2–19 µg mℓ^{-1} for silicon, and 6–50 µg mℓ^{-1} for germanium.

The blue polymeric species produced when molybdophosphoric acid is reduced, has formed the basis of several colorimetric procedures. Since its introduction by Dickman and Bray[114] in 1940 it has undergone several modifications aimed at increasing the precision, sensitivity and selectivity of phosphate determination. Some reference has been made already to the method in the context of phosphate separation. The blue species may be extracted into oxygen containing organic reagents, or extraction may be carried out on the aqueous phosphate solution before reduction in the organic phase.

The choice of reductant is important, this affecting the time required for the reduction stage as well as the molar absorptivity of the blue product. Recommended reductants include iron(II)[111,115], hydroquinone[116], tin(II) chloride[117], hydrazine sulphate[111,118], 1-amino-2-naphthol-4-sulphonic acid[119], and ascorbic acid[120,121].

Acidity is an important factor. The range 0.4–0.6M in H_2SO_4 has been recommended. A recent study of the reaction stoichiometry and mechanism has clarified the role of acidity in the reaction[122]. For stoichiometric measurement of the amount of blue product, it is not necessary to control the solution acidity as long as it is sufficiently high to prevent direct reduction of molybdenum(VI) which takes place above pH 0.7. As the reaction rate is greater at lower acidities, it is recommended that the analysis is carried out in the range 0.15–0.25M in H_2SO_4 or 0.3–0.5M in HNO_3, the lowest feasible acidity.

The analysis time can be reduced if a catalyst is employed. Kirk and Wilkinson[123] describe a procedure for determination of phosphorus in coke following oxygen-flask combustion. Ascorbic acid is used as reductant with potassium antimonyl tartrate as catalyst, both being combined in the form of a single reagent. The same approach has been used by Shafran *et al.*[124]. and earlier by Murphy and Riley [127] who used it for the analysis of seawater.

If the molybdenum blue method is used without extraction, interference is high. Silicon(IV), germanium(IV) and arsenic(V) interfere. Silicon interference may be eliminated either by increasing the acidity, or by adding citrate. Niobium(V), tantalum(V), tin(IV), tungsten(VI), titanium(IV), zirconium(IV), and bismuth(III) interfere by giving precipitates which adsorb phosphate. Barium(II), strontium(II), and lead(II) precipitate in sulphate solutions. Large amounts of copper(II), nickel(II) and chromium(III) interfere by their colour. Vanadium(V) interferes by forming the vanadomolybdophosphate complex. This can be avoided by reduction to vanadium(IV) in the original solution. Iron should be preferably as iron(II). Nitrite and nitrate interfere. Nitrite may be destroyed using sulphamic acid. Duff and Stuart[125] have eliminated nitrate by reducing it to NH_3 with aluminium metal and NaOH.

A recent study by Tillma and Syers[126] has looked into interference by mercury(II) in the Murphy and Riley[127] form of the method. This can cause significant positive errors. It was found that the effect can be eliminated by treatment with chloride or a metabisulphite–thiosulphate reagent, which complexes with mercury(II). The effects of arsenic(V) interference can also be removed using the metabisulphite–thiosulphate reagent.

With extraction, interference with the method is much less. If we consider the procedure proposed by Lueck and Boltz[128] who first extracted with isobutyl alcohol and then reduced using tin(II) chloride, we find that for 0.6 ppm phosphorus, only arsenic(V), cerium(IV), germanium(IV), gold(III), tungsten(VI), vanadium(V), tin(II) and thiosulphate cause high interference and should be absent or removed before applying the method. The following interfere when present in amounts (ppm) indicated after each: arsenic(III) (60), thiocyanate (60), iodide (60), mercury(I) (20), silicon(IV) (30), and tin(IV) (40).

The sensitivity of the method depends on several factors which include the nature of the reductant. The two most sensitive procedures are those involving 1-amino-2-naphthol-4-sulphonic acid ($\varepsilon = 26\,600$)[119] and hydrazine sulphate ($\varepsilon_{830} = 26\,800$)[129].

Application of the method is widespread. In addition to those mentioned, it includes sub-micro organic analysis[130], micro organic analysis[131], and analysis of Portland cement[132].

Ramírez-Munoz[133] has automated two molybdenum blue procedures for routine use. These are forms of the method which utilize tin(II) and ascorbic acid as reductants. An AMA 40 (Beckman Automatic Materials Analyser) was used, capable of 60 samples per hour. Calibration graphs in the ranges 0–2 and 0–20 ppm were found to be linear, and even in the 0.1–0.01 ppm range the relative standard deviation was below 3 per cent.

Lucci[134] has used it for PO_4^{3-} in the presence of condensed phosphates.

Many other procedures for the molybdenum blue method will be found in the standard IUPAC publication[135] on colorimetric analysis. This source lists the relevant details and includes interferences.

Reference has been made to determination of phosphate in seawater. Here, changes in phosphate concentration may occur in the sample prior to analysis. For example planktonic algae may contain phosphorus which can be released after sampling or even during analysis. Herron[136] has reported a decrease in phosphate concentration on storage which is attributed to bacterial action and not to absorption of phosphate by the polythene container.

In the presence of vanadium(V) and molybdenum(VI), phosphate gives a yellow colour in acid solution due to the vanadomolybdophosphoric acid complex. The reaction was proposed as the basis of a colorimetric method for phosphate by Kitson and Mellon[137]. As a reliable routine method it has some advantages over the molybdenum blue method. The conditions, for example, are not as stringent.

Extraction of the complex is possible, this producing a marked increase in selectivity. The absorption maximum is at 315 nm; the colour is very stable. Optimum acidity for the colour development is about 0.25M in H_2SO_4 (0.5M in HNO_3 or $HClO_4$) with the upper limit of 0.75M in H_2SO_4 (1.5M in HNO_3 or $HClO_4$). Higher acidities retard the colour development.

Interferences (with no extraction of the complex) include the following: Silicon in large amounts, iron(III) (in the presence of chloride and sulphate), reducing agents, chromium(VI), arsenic(V), and citrate. Tin(IV), Nb(V), Ta(V), Ti(IV), Zr(IV), large amounts of W(VI) and V(V) interfere by forming a precipitate which retains phosphorus. Bismuth(III), thorium(IV), chloride and fluoride affect the colour formation.

Silica, when present in large amounts, may be removed by boiling with concentrated $HClO_4$. Iron(III) may be complexed with fluoride, the excess of fluoride being removed with boric acid. Boric acid may also be used to complex fluoride present in the original sample.

The marked reduction in interference on extracting the complex will be apparent from the procedure (Method 2) given at the end of this section. The solvent extraction of the complex has been used as the basis of a substoichiometric method[138] for determination of phosphorus.

Application of the method has been made to all the important groups of phosphorus-containing materials. These include steel[139,140], iron ores[141], aluminium, copper, nickel alloys and white metal[142], water[143,144], and fertilizers[145–147]. The first two fertilizer references are concerned with automated high precision determination of phosphorus using AutoAnalyzers. The third fertilizer reference concerns an assessment of precision obtainable using the Unicam SP3000 system. Measurements were carried out directly rather than by the differential technique often used to increase precision. The results indicate that repeatability of absorbance measurements in the 0–1.2 units range is better than the read-out resolution of 0.001 absorbance units. This would make the method for phosphate more precise than the quinoline molybdophosphate method, with the added advantage of a simpler procedure. Biochemical applications include the determination of phosphate in the presence of labile organic phosphates[148] and inorganic phosphate in the presence of adenosine triphosphate[149]. Schafer[150] has applied the method to phosphate rock analysis. Organic microanalysis has found application for the method following oxygen-flask combustion. This is discussed by Dixon[151] who provides details of a procedure by Saliman[131].

Spectrophotometric determination of phosphate by the vanadomolybdophosphate method

Method 1. Phosphate in water[143]

Reagents

All reagents should be analytical reagent grade.

Vanadium molybdate solution:

Dissolve 0.50 g of ammonium vanadate in warm water, cool, and add 125 mℓ of HNO_3, sp. gr. 1.42. Add a solution of 10.0 g of ammonium molybdate in water, and dilute to 1ℓ.

Nitric acid: 2.0M, approximately.

Standard phosphate solution:
Dissolve 0.716 g of potassium dihydrogen phosphate (dried at 150 °C) in water, and dilute to 1ℓ. Dilute 20 mℓ to 1ℓ as required.
1 mℓ ≡ 10 μg of phosphorus as phosphate.

Preparation of standard graph

Dilute to 50 mℓ appropriate volumes of the standard phosphate solution to the range 0–200 μg of phosphorus as phosphate. To each add 1 mℓ of vanadium molybdate solution, mix well, and set aside at room temperature for 10 min. Measure the absorbance of each test solution in 4 cm cells against distilled water at a wavelength of 370 nm. The plot of absorbance against phosphate concentration should be linear.

Procedure for water samples

Take 50 mℓ of the sample and proceed as above. If the sample is coloured, add 1 mℓ 2M HNO_3 before the vanadomolybdate solution.

Method 2. Phosphorus in aluminium, copper, and nickel alloys, and white metals[142]

This illustrates application of the method in the presence of a high metallic background, in which a solvent extraction procedure is necessary.

Reagents

Standard phosphorus solution:
Prepare a stock solution containing 0.1 mg P per mℓ by dissolving 0.4393 g of potassium dihydrogen phosphate in 1ℓ of water. Prepare a working solution (0.04 mg per mℓ) by diluting 100 mℓ of stock solution to 250 mℓ.

Ammonium molybdate solution: 15 %.
Prepare from ammonium molybdate tetrahydrate and store in a polythene bottle.

Ammonium vanadate solution: 0.25 %.
Dissolve 2.5 g of ammonium metavanadate in 500 mℓ water by heating. Cool and dilute to 1ℓ.

Procedure

Transfer 0.5 g of the sample to a 250-mℓ Teflon beaker and add 20 mℓ of water, 10 mℓ of 15M HNO_3 and 3mℓ of 40 % HF. When dissolved, dilute with water to 35 mℓ and bring to the boil. Add 5 mℓ of 1 % potassium permanganate solution, boil for 2 min, then add 2 mℓ of 5 % sodium nitrite solution and boil for 3 min. Cool, add 10 mℓ of the ammonium vanadate solution and 65 mℓ of the ammonium molybdate solution, and then allow to stand for 15 min. Add 30 mℓ of water, transfer the solution to a 250-mℓ separating funnel and dilute to 150 mℓ with water.
Add 15 mℓ of 50 % citric acid solution, mix, immediately add 40 mℓ of methyl isobutyl ketone and shake for 30 s. Allow the two layers to separate then discard the aqueous layer. Filter the ketone layer through a double-layer rapid filter paper into a small dry beaker and measure the absorbance immediately at a wavelength of 425 nm in 2-cm cells for 50–400 μg of phosphorus, and at 400 nm in 4-cm cells for 0–50 μg of phosphorus. Water is used as a reference solution, the blank value being subtracted.

To prepare a blank and a standard curve in the range 0–400 μg of phosphorus, add 10 mℓ of 15M HNO_3 to aliquots of the standard phosphorus solutions and continue as in the recommended procedure.

Notes

1. Sb and Se must be in the highest valency state. If P is determined in Sb or Se metals add 20 mℓ of 1 % $KMnO_4$ to 0.5 g of the sample to obtain a permanent pink colour. Use 2 mℓ of 5 % sodium nitrite solution to discharge the permanganate colour.
2. The absorbance may be measured between 400 and 480 nm. Both the absorbance of the complex and the blanks increase with decrease in wavelength. Below 0.01 % P, 4-cm cells and a wavelength of 400 nm should be used, at which the sensitivity is nearly twice that obtained at 425 nm.
3. The molar absorptivity of the complex in the organic solvent is 1820 at 425 nm and 3110 at 400 nm. Beer's law is obeyed to at least 38 μg P $m\ell^{-1}$. The colour is stable for at least 1 h and does not change in the temperature range 19–25 °C. After 15 min standing time, an additional filtration step is required.
4. For the determination of 200 μg P, there is no interference for 1 mg As or 0.5 g of the following elements: Ag, Bi, Cd, Ce, Co, Cu, Fe, Hg, La, Mn, Mo, Nb, Ni, Pb, Sb, Se, Sn, Th, Ti, U, W, and Zn.
5. Al up to 0.5 g does not interfere, but because it forms a very strong fluoride complex, silicon is displaced from its fluoride complex and interferes, even in submilligram quantities. Chromium interferes slightly in large amounts (3 % for every 50 mg Cr). Germanium above 1 mg gives a positive error. Vanadium interferes slightly. Zirconium in amounts up to 0.5 g does not interfere except when present together with Si.
6. On a series of 10 standards the standard deviation was found to be ± 0.5 per cent at the 5 μg P $m\ell^{-1}$ level, and ± 1 per cent at the 1.25 μg P $m\ell^{-1}$ level.

Several anions may be determined by means of the purple chloranilate ion liberated in precipitation reactions. Applied to phosphate analysis[152] lanthanum or thorium chloranilates can be used, the relevant reactions being:

$$2PO_4^{3-} + La_2(C_6Cl_2O_4)_3 + 3H^+ \rightarrow 3H\,C_6Cl_2O_4^- + 2\,LaPO_4$$

$$4PO_4^{3-} + 3Th\,(C_6Cl_2O_4)_2 + 6H^+ \rightarrow 6H\,C_6Cl_2O_4^- + Th_3(PO_4)_4$$

Insoluble lanthanum or thorium phosphate is precipitated and the acid chloranilate ion in each instance is proportional to the amount of phosphate in the sample. The method is therefore an indirect one. Absorbance measurements are made at 530 nm. It is possible to determine 3–300 ppm of phosphate with an accuracy of ± 2 per cent with no interference from chloride or nitrate up to 400 ppm. Interference by sulphate can be compensated for by adding a large amount of sulphate to both the sample and standard solution.

Bode[153] has made a study of the dissociation constants of chloranilic acid in various media and described a method for phosphate based on these findings. The chloranilate method does not appear to have found a great deal of application possibly due to the high blank values reported by some investigators.

In the conversion of phosphate to molybdophosphoric acid, 12 mol of molybdenum are produced for each mole of original phosphate. Clearly, if the resulting molybdophosphoric acid is broken down and its molybdenum content determined by a spectrophotometric procedure, this would lead to a sensitive indirect method for phosphate determination. Djurkin, Kirkbright and West[15] used 2-amino-4-chlorobenzene thiol in chloroform. Depending on the procedure, an effective molar absorptivity for phosphorus of 96 900 or 359 000 is obtained, enabling as little as 0.2 μg (0.008 ppm) of phosphorus to be determined even in the presence of large amounts of Si, Ge, As and Sb. Tungsten(VI) in 30-fold amount interferes, but a simple masking procedure eliminates this. After breakdown of the heteropoly acid with alkali the green complex with 2-amino-4-chlorobenzene thiol is extracted into chloroform–butanol and absorbance measurements made at 710 nm.

Hurford and Boltz[19] first separated phosphorus and silicon by selective extraction and finally measured the molybdate absorbance in the UV at 230 nm. 0.1–0.4 ppm of phosphorus and silicon can be determined.

Another approach is to react the heteropoly acid derived from phosphate with various organic dyestuffs to form ion-association complexes. Babko and co-workers[154, 23] examined a range of dyestuffs and recommend iodine green or crystal violet for the extraction-spectrophotometric determination of phosphate. Other methods based on malachite green[155] and safranine[156] have been published.

A novel method has recently appeared for the analysis of biological, pharmaceutical and food products[157]. This entails precipitation of phosphate as magnesium uranyl phosphate, which is dissolved in H_2SO_4. The liberated UO_2^{2+} ions reacted with hexacyanoferrate (II) as shown below.

$$2Na_3PO_4 + 2Mg(UO_2)(CH_3CO_2)_4 \rightarrow Mg(UO_2)_2(PO_4)_2 + 6NaCH_3CO_2 + Mg(CH_3CO_2)_2$$

$$UO_2^{2+} + K_4[Fe(CN)_6] \rightarrow (UO_2)_2[Fe(CN)_6] + 2K_2SO_4$$

The sensitivity of this spectrophotometric method is 0.01 mg P and the average error 1 per cent.

Though not a conventional colorimetric method, phosphate in air may be determined by comparing the intensities of coloured stains[158]. The sample (1 μℓ) is washed into the heated zone of a Weisz ring oven. After drying it is sprayed with a reagent containing *o*-dianisidine, anhydrous acetic acid and sodium molybdate. The brown ring obtained is compared with standards prepared from potassium hydrogen phosphate. Elements commonly present in air do not interfere.

2. *Flame emission spectroscopy*

Like sulphur, phosphorus has its principal atomic resonance lines in the far UV region of the spectrum (1775, 1783, 1788 Å). Because of the almost total absorption by air, flame gases, and quartz optics in this region, application of atomic absorption spectroscopy and atomic fluorescence spectroscopy is not possible in their normal modes.

Indirect emission spectroscopic methods have been suggested. Dippel, Bricker and Furman[159] used the depressive effect of phosphate on the emission of calcium and magnesium. Their method is restricted in range and sensitivity. Szebenyi-Gyory *et al.*[160] use a similar system except that a second metal, e.g. barium, is introduced to partially displace calcium from the non-excitable species. The emission is measured for calcium in a solution containing phosphate and barium such that the total metal concentration is always constant. Then, if the relative emission for calcium at 630 nm is plotted against the concentration of calcium, the slope is proportional to the phosphate concentration. The method is claimed to be suitable for rapid determinations. Serious interference is caused by 10-fold amounts of Al, Cr, Co, Fe, Sr, Sn, and nitrate. Equimolar amounts of zinc and mercury cause medium interference, and so do 10-fold amounts of Mn, K and Na.

A direct emission method has recently appeared[161] based on an earlier gas-chromatographic method for the determination of phosphorus in organophosphorus compounds[162]. In this work a cool nitrogen–hydrogen diffusion flame is used, with several advantages being derived. The background radiation is less than for pre-mixed flames; the relatively low temperature results in very low excitation, even in the alkali metals. The flame has high reducing properties. Furthermore, because of the low temperature and the limited supply of oxygen, species are observed which are not usually found in normal premixed flames. With phosphorus, an intense green emission due to HPO is observed. This is caused by HPO, formed in an excited state by a chemiluminescence reaction, returning to its lower electronic state. *Figure 53* shows the emission spectrum of HPO obtained by nebulizing a 1.2×10^{-2}M orthophosphoric acid solution into the nitrogen–hydrogen diffusion flame.

The intensity at 528 nm exhibits a linear response with orthophosphoric acid in the 0.2–500 ppm P range. Metallic phosphates give a weak signal due

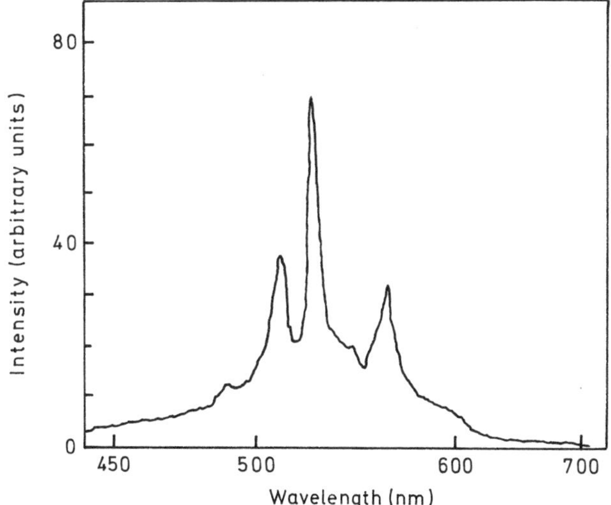

Figure 53 *Emission spectrum of HPO species obtained by nebulizing a* 1.2×10^{-2} *M solution of orthophosphoric acid into the nitrogen–hydrogen diffusion flame.* (After Dagnall, Thompson and West[161])

to lack of dissociation in the relatively cool flame. The depressive matrix effect of cations may be readily overcome by a preliminary ion-exchange separation. Fifty-fold amounts of acetic, hydrobromic, hydrochloric, nitric, oxalic, sulphuric, and tartaric acids have no effect.

Application of this method has been made to phosphorus-containing detergent materials after preliminary ion-exchange[163]. Results for materials containing up to 20% phosphate (expressed as P_2O_5) give precisions of 2–4 per cent. The method is rapid and simple. When the band emission from HPO is monitored over a narrow spectral region, sensitivity is lost. In a recent paper, Aldous, Dagnall and West[164] report a considerable improvement using a modified filter photometer containing a broad band-pass filter and modified burner. The detection limit for phosphorus is improved 100-fold to 0.007 ppm; application is made to determination of phosphorus in organic and aqueous matrices after preliminary batch ion-exchange removal of cations.

3. *Fluorimetric methods*

Phosphate has long been known to interfere in fluorimetric procedures, and this has been exploited for analytical purposes. Land and Edmunds[165] utilized the quenching effect of phosphate on the complex formed between aluminium and morin. Many interferences were found, some of which could be overcome by initial fuming with perchloric acid or ion-exchange. Kirkbright, Narayanaswary, and West[166] have attempted to exploit the potentially high sensitivity of solution spectrofluorimetry, while retaining the selectivity for determination of phosphate available for earlier work. This is achieved in the following way.

Phosphate is converted to the molybdophosphoric acid which is reacted with the basic dyestuff Rhodamine B, to form an ion-association complex. After extraction of excess dye reagent into chloroform, the Rhodamine B molybdophosphate is extracted into chloroform–butanol (4:1 v/v) and the intensity of fluorescence in this solution measured at 575 nm with excitation at 350 nm. Interference studies on 37 foreign ions indicated the methods to be highly selective. Large amounts of silicate do not interfere. Arsenic(III) and vanadium(V) may be tolerated in 25 and 50-fold amounts respectively. The method is applicable to 0.04–0.6 μg P. An investigation into the nature of the ion-association complex indicated a combining ratio of 3 moles of Rhodamine B to 1 of molybdophosphate, suggesting an uncharged complex of the type $[RhB^+]_3[PMo^{-3}]$.

The same investigators[167] have recently reported a similar method involving the organic base quinine. This has the additional advantage that quinine has a high fluorescence intensity and stability in solutions of H_2SO_4; quinine is frequently used as a standard for the calibration of spectrofluorimeters. The method, which is capable of phosphorus determination in the range 0.02–1.2 μg has a selectivity comparable with the previously described method.

X-ray fluorescence (or X-ray emission spectroscopy) can be regarded as a special case of fluorimetry. It is pertinent then to indicate its application to phosphate determination here. Small amounts of phosphate (as well as chloride, thiocyanate, cyanide, bromide or iodide) can be determined by this technique after precipitation or coprecipitation with a heavier reference element[168]. For phosphate, 1–10 mg is coprecipitated by thallium(I) and silver nitrate. The mixed precipitate is analysed directly on the filter.

4. Atomic absorption spectroscopy

While atomic absorption spectroscopy may be used for many elements, until recently it could not be used directly for traces of phosphorus, arsenic or silicon because the resonance lines lie in the vacuum UV, or because of the formation of refractory compounds which fail to dissociate completely in flames. A direct method has been reported by Kirkbright and Marshall[169] who use a nitrogen-separated nitrous oxide–acetylene flame and a microwave-excited phosphorus electrodeless discharge source. The reported sensitivities are 4.8 and 5.4 μg mℓ$^{-1}$ at the 177.5 and 178.3 nm lines respectively. However, an indirect approach may be made by applying atomic absorption spectroscopy to the molybdenum content of molybdophosphoric acid. Zaugg and Knox[170] have described one such method, but it suffers interference from both arsenic and silicon.

Later, Kirkbright, Smith and West[18] reported the sequential determination of phosphorus and silicon using a nitrous oxide–acetylene flame. Briefly, the phosphorus heteropoly acid is extracted quantitatively into isobutyl acetate, and, after adjustment of acidity, the silicon is extracted into butanol. In each case the molybdenum is determined by atomic absorption. 0.08–1.0 ppm of phosphorus may be determined. The method is highly selective due to the extraction procedure.

Arsenic(V) and germanium(IV) do not interfere in the determination of phosphorus but they affect the silicon determination giving high results. Ten-fold amounts of tungsten(VI) give no interference in the determination of phosphorus, but 100-fold amounts do.

Other procedures have been described by Ramakrishna, Robinson and West[21] and Hurford and Boltz[19]. In the former paper phosphorus, arsenic and silicon are determined; the procedure is given below. In the latter paper, phosphorus and silicon are determined, again after selective extraction.

Determination of phosphate (1–10 μg), arsenate and silicate using atomic absorption spectroscopy[21]

Reagents

Molybdate solution:

Dissolve 10 g ammonium molybdate tetrahydrate in 100 mℓ distilled water.

Citrate solution:

Dissolve 100 g citric acid in about 800 mℓ distilled water, adjust to pH 3.2 with NaOH and dilute to 1ℓ.

Procedure

Transfer 10 mℓ of sample or an aliquot containing not more than 10 μg each of phosphorus and silicon and 20 μg of As into a separating funnel. Dilute if necessary to 10 mℓ with distilled water. Add 1 mℓ of molybdate solution and 2 mℓ of dilute HNO_3 or sufficient acid to bring the pH to about 0.7 and mix well. Allow the contents of the funnel to stand for about 20 min for the complete formation of molybdophosphoric acid, molybdoarsenic acid, and molybdosilicic acid.

Determination of phosphorus: Add 10 mℓ iso-butyl acetate and shake the funnel for 1 min. After the separation of phases, carefully transfer the lower aqueous phase (A) into another separating funnel for subsequent determination of arsenic and/or silicon. Measure the absorbance due to molybdenum in the iso-butyl acetate extract under conditions listed in the Notes, using a blank prepared in a similar way to set the zero of the instrument.

Determination of arsenic: To the aqueous phase (A) or, in the absence of phosphorus, to the sample treated as given under Procedure, add 5 mℓ of 1:1 ethyl acetate–butanol mixture and shake for 1 min. Add 5 mℓ of iso-amyl acetate and extract once again for about 30 s. Allow the phases to separate and drain the aqueous phase (B) into another funnel for the determination of silicon. Wash the organic phase twice by shaking it vigorously for 1 min with 10 mℓ portions of wash solutions to remove the free molybdate reagent. Measure the absorption due to molybdenum in the organic phase as described for phosphorus.

Determination of silicon: To the aqueous phase (A + B) or to the sample, add 2 mℓ of citrate solution; mix well and allow to stand for 2 min. Extract the molybdosilicic acid with 10 mℓ of methyl iso-butyl ketone by inverting the funnel for about 30 s, and measure the molybdenum absorbance as before against a solvent blank.

The concentrations of phosphorus, arsenic and silicon were determined by means of calibration curves prepared from standard solutions containing 1–10 µg of P, 2–20 µg As, and 1–10 µg Si and treated as above.

Notes

1. No interference was found in the following, present in amounts of 200 µg each, for quantities of 2.5 µg each of P and Si, and 5 µg As.
   Group 1. Li^+, Na^+, K^+, Cs^+, Cu^{2+}, Ag^+.
   Group 2. Be^{2+}, Ca^{2+}, Sr^{2+}, Mg^{2+}, Zn^{2+}, Cd^{2+}, Hg^{2+}, Hg_2^{2+}.
   Group 3. $B_4O_7^{2-}$, Al^{3+}, Ce^{4+}.
   Group 4. Sn^{4+}, Pb^{2+}.
   Group 5. VO_3^-, Sb^{5+}, Bi^{3+}.
   Group 6. SO_3^{2-}, SO_4^{2-}, Cr^{3+}, SeO_3^{2-}, TeO_3^{2-}, WO_4^{2-}, UO_4^{2-}.
   Group 7. F^-, Cl^-, Br^-, I^-, Mn^{2+}.
   Group 8. Fe^{3+}, Co^{2+}, Ni^{2+}, Pd^{2+}.
2. Ti^{4+} and Zr^{4+} caused low recoveries for phosphorus. Germanium did not affect the determination of phosphorus or arsenic but interfered in the determination of silicon.
3. Instrumental conditions for the AAS determination of molybdenum were:

Wavelength	313.2 nm
Slit	2 Å (0.3 mm)
Lamp current	40 mA
Nitrous oxide	15 psi
Acetylene	Adjusted to give a rose red inner core about 1–2 cm in height above the burner head during aspiration of the organic phase.

4. All solutions were stored in polythene bottles to avoid silicon contamination.

Electrical methods

1. Potentiometric methods

Several potentiometric methods have been described for the determination of phosphate. Cullum and Thomas[171] determined the total orthophosphate content of detergent powders by conversion of phosphate to the diacid form, precipitation as $AgPO_4$, and potentiometric titration of the liberated acid.

$$NaH_2PO_4 + 3AgNO_3 \rightarrow Ag_3PO_4\downarrow + NaNO_3 + 2HNO_3$$

Borate, carbonate, silicate, and sulphate do not interfere.

Another method involves potentiometric titration in a borate-buffered solution with precipitation of Ag_3PO_4 at a silver electrode[172]. Although the reaction departs from ideal stoichiometry, the precision is such that good results may be obtained. Nitrate, sulphate, and acetate do not interfere, and neither does fluoride, which interferes in many phosphate methods.

Direct titrimetric determination of phosphate is possible with a silver nitrate solution, or Ag^+ generated coulometrically from a silver anode in 80% ethanol–0.1M sodium acetate medium[173]. Here, the end-point is detected potentiometrically for solutions down to 2×10^{-4}M in phosphate, or amperometrically down to 1.7×10^{-3}M. Halides interfere by coprecipitation. Equimolar amounts of sulphate can be tolerated but calcium(II), aluminium(III) and iron(III) must be absent.

Potentiometric microdetermination of phosphate has been reported recently[174]. Orthophosphate forms one of the most insoluble lead salts

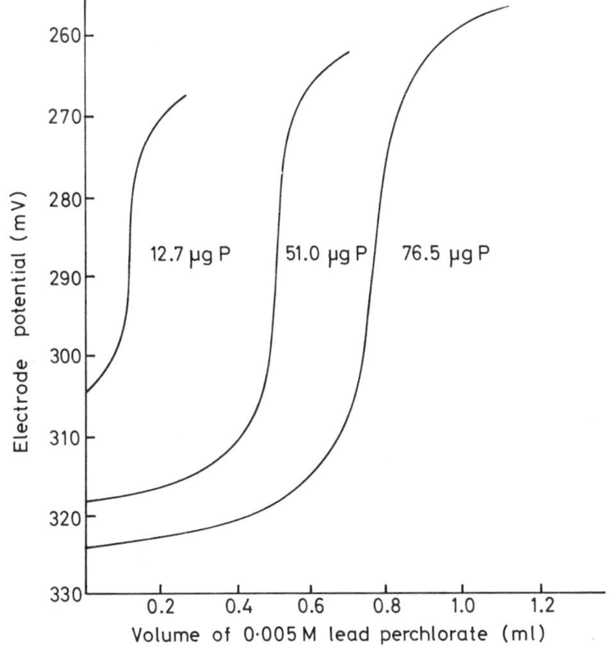

Figure 54 *Microtitration of various amounts of orthophosphate with* 0.005 *M lead perchlorate using a lead ion-selective electrode.* (After Selig[174])

($-\log K_{sp} = 42.1$ at 25 °C). The method utilizes lead perchlorate as titrant, and the Orion Model 94-82 lead ion-selective electrode. Solutions are buffered to pH 8.25–8.75. The potential response for various amounts of phosphate is shown in *Figure 54.*

Sulphate and nitrate do not interfere; chloride and fluoride cause slightly high results. Silicate should not exceed the amount of phosphate present. Anions which form insoluble lead salts with solubility products smaller than that of lead sulphate ($-\log K_{sp} = 8$) should be absent. These include molybdenum(VI), tungsten(VI), and chromium(VI). Interference by carbonate and bicarbonate is eliminated by acidifying to pH 4, boiling briefly, and then re-adjusting the pH.

For the range 0.5–1.5 mg P, 0.01M lead perchlorate is used. For smaller amounts down to 0.01 mg P, 0.005M lead perchlorate is recommended. More recent studies by Selig[175] have provided additional information on interferences and the lower limit of the method for phosphate, again using the lead ion-selective electrode. Sulphate does not interfere up to a sulphur/phosphorus ratio of 320, and neither does fluoride up to a fluorine/phosphorus ratio of 133. Using a 0.001N lead perchlorate solution, the lower practical limit is given as about 10 µg. The same investigation reports that if silver nitrate is used as titrant in conjunction with a Ag/S^{2-} electrode, borate-buffered solutions are more satisfactory than sodium acetate–methanol if the titration is carried out in partially non-aqueous systems.

Earlier studies on phosphate ion-selective electrodes involving bismuth phosphate, were not successful due to potential drift and lack of selectivity. Nanjo, Rohm and Guilbault[176] have developed liquid ion-exchange electrodes based on quaternary ammonium, arsonium and phosphonium salts, as well as triphenyl tin salts. These showed good sensitivity but again lacked selectivity. The same workers[177] have used the alternative approach of enzyme-based electrodes. Here an enzyme selectively catalyses a reaction involving phosphate and the response is followed electrically. Two enzymes are concerned, the reactions being

$$\text{glucose-6-phosphate} \xrightarrow{\text{alkaline phosphatase}} \text{glucose} + \text{phosphate}$$

$$\text{glucose} \xrightarrow[O_2]{\text{glucose oxidase}} \text{gluconic acid} + H_2O_2$$

2. *Amperometric methods*

Phosphate can be titrated amperometrically using iron(II). Bixler and Colwell[178] have re-investigated the method recently, and find the useful range to be 2–55 ppm. Errors range from −7 to +8 per cent and average at 4 per cent. Chloroacetic acid is used as supporting electrolyte.

Radiochemical methods

When tungstate is added to molybdophosphoric acid it becomes part of the molybdophosphate complex. On extraction the amount of tungsten(VI) extracted with the heteropoly acid will be proportional to the amount of heteropoly acid, and therefore to the amount of phosphate. Hahn and

Schmitt[179] used ^{185}W in their procedure to form 185-tungstomolybdophosphoric acid. This was extracted and the tungsten activity determined by means of its β emission. Arsenic, silicon and niobium interfere, but not germanium. The method was applied to water analysis in the range 0–0.54 ppm PO_4^{3-}.

Other methods include the use of isotope dilution with ^{32}P-labelled $Mg_2P_2O_7$ for analysis of phosphate rock[180], and a neutron-activation method for phosphorus in silicate rock by direct β counting.

Kinetic methods

In recent years the distinctive advantages offered by kinetic methods have attracted a great deal of attention. These include high sensitivity and selectivity and relative cheapness. Although many of the methods are concerned with metals, quite a number have appeared in the determination of non-metal anions.

No doubt the idea of kinetic methods is still associated with long periods of data collecting and lengthy calculations. Many of the recently published methods utilize automatic systems which enable the analysis time to be reduced to seconds. Crouch and Malmstadt[181] have developed a method based on their mechanistic study of the molybdenum blue reaction[122]. Under controlled conditions the initial rate of formation of molybdenum blue from phosphate, molybdate and ascorbic acid is directly proportional to the phosphate concentration. Automatic instrumentation is used to provide a digital readout proportional to the phosphate concentration, with 1–12 ppm P being determined with a relative error of 1–2 per cent. Only 20–30 s of reaction time is required for each sample. In a later publication[182], an automatic fast reaction-rate system is employed which produces digital data on phosphorus concentration (0.1–5.00 ppm P) in blood serum in about 100 ms.

A further extension of the method enables silicate (1–10 ppm) and phosphate (1–10 ppm) to be determined simultaneously. In this work an automated differential kinetic procedure is used. Kriss, Rudenko and Kurbatova[184] using the same reaction, indicate that it may be used for small amounts of phosphate in the presence of condensed phosphates.

Other reactions have also provided kinetic methods for phosphate. For example, the rate of reaction between KI and ammonium molybdate in the presence of starch and at pH 0.6 is rectilinearly proportional to the concentration of phosphate acting as catalyst[185].

Miscellaneous methods

One of the newest techniques to find application in phosphate analysis is gas-chromatography. The ammonium salts of phosphate and several other anions (vanadate, arsenate, oxalate, etc.) are reacted with bis(trimethylsilyl) trifluoracetamide and the trimethyl silyl derivatives subjected to gas chromatography with a flame ionization detector. The phosphate derivative is $(TMS)_3PO_4$. Sodium and potassium salts are first converted to the ammonium salts by ion-exchange[45].

References

1. GREENFIELD, S., in *Comprehensive Analytical Chemistry* (Ed. C.L. Wilson and D.W. Wilson), Vol. 1C, Elsevier, Amsterdam, 220 (1962)
2. RIEMAN, W. and BEUKENKAMP, J., in *Treatise on Analytical Chemistry* (Ed. I.M. Kolthoff and P.J. Elving), Part II, Vol. 5, Academic Press, New York, 317 (1961)
3. RYDEN, J.C., SYERS, J.K. and HARRIS, R.F., *Analyst,* **97**, 903 (1972)
4. HESLOP, R.B. and PEARSON, E.F., *Analytica chim. Acta,* **37**, 516 (1967)
5. MACDONALD, A.M.G. and VAN DER VOORT, F.H., *Analyst,* **93**, 65 (1968)
6. WHITE, D.C., *Mikrochim. Acta,* 254 (1959)
7. FRITZ, J.S. and YAMAMURA, S.S., *Analyt. Chem.,* **27**, 1461 (1955)
8. COLSON, A.F., *Analyst,* **88**, 26 (1963)
9. COLSON, A.F., *Analyst,* **90**, 35 (1965)
10. FURUYA, M. and TAJIRI, M., *Japan Analyst,* **12**, 1139 (1963); *Analyt. Abstr.,* **12**, 1141 (1965)
11. KINNUNEN, J. and WENNERSTRAND, B., *Chemist Analyst,* **44**, 51 (1955)
12. WU, H., *J. biol. Chem.,* **43**, 189 (1920)
13. PAUL, J., *Mikrochim. Acta,* 830 (1965)
14. PAUL, J., *Mikrochim. Acta,* 836 (1965)
15. DJURKIN, V., KIRKBRIGHT, G.F. and WEST, T.S., *Analyst,* **91**, 89 (1966)
16. PAUL, J., *Analytica chim. Acta,* **35**, 200 (1966)
17. HESLOP, R.B. and PEARSON, E.F., *Analytica chim. Acta,* **39**, 209 (1967)
18. KIRKBRIGHT, G.F., SMITH, A.M. and WEST, T.S., *Analyst,* **92**, 411 (1967)
19. HURFORD, T.R. and BOLTZ, D.F., *Analyt. Chem.,* **40**, 379 (1968)
20. KIRKBRIGHT, G.F., SMITH, A.M. and WEST, T.S., *Analyst,* **93**, 224 (1968)
21. RAMAKRISHNA, T.V., ROBINSON, J.W. and WEST, P.W., *Analytica chim. Acta,* **45**, 43 (1969)
22. JAKUBIEC, R.J. and BOLTZ, D.F., *Mikrochim. Acta,* 1199 (1970)
23. BABKO, A.K., SHKARAVSKII, YU. F. and IVASHKOVICH, E.M., *Zh. analit. Khim.,* **26**, 854 (1971); *Analyt. Abstr.,* **23**, 2420 (1972)
24. BOCK, R. and HUMMEL, C., *Z. analyt. Chem.,* **198**, 176 (1963)
25. YOSHINO, Y., *Japan Analyst,* **3**, 121 (1954); *Chem. Abstr.,* **48**, 9867 (1954)
26. KINDT, B.H., BALIS, E.W. and LIEBHAFSKY, H.A., *Analyt. Chem.,* **24**, 1501 (1952)
27. OHASHI, S. and TAKADA, S., *Bull. chem. Soc., Japan,* **34**, 1516 (1961); *Analyt. Abstr.,* **9**, 1866 (1962)
28. WINAND, L., *J. Chromat.,* **7**, 400 (1962)
29. POLLARD, F.H., ROGERS, D.E. and ROTHWELL, M.T., *J. Chromat.,* **9**, 227 (1962)
30. GRANDE, J.A. and BEUKENKAMP, J., *Analyt. Chem.,* **28**, 1497 (1956)
31. POLLARD, F.H., NICKLESS, G., ROGERS, D.E. and CRONE, D.L., *Proc. Soc. analyt. Chem. Conference,* Nottingham (1965), Heffer and Sons Ltd., Cambridge, 481 (1965)
32. ZIPKIN, I., ARMSTRONG, W.D. and SINGER, L., *Analyt. Chem.,* **29**, 310 (1957)
33. NEWMANN, A.C.D., *Analytica chim. Acta,* **19**, 471 (1958)
34. PINFOLD, T.A. and KARGER, B.L., *Separation Sci.,* **5**, 183 (1970)
35. HUANG, K.P., *Analyt. Biochem.,* **38**, 383 (1970)
36. KAWANABE, K., TAKITANI, S., MIYAZAKI, M. and TAMURA, Z., *Japan Analyst,* **13**, 976 (1964); *Analyt. Abstr.,* **13**, 5385 (1966)
37. IONOVA, L.A. and POSTNIKOV, N.N., *Khim. Prom.,* 198 (1969); *Analyt. Abstr.,* **18**, 2344 (1970)
38. WAGNER, E.F., *Seifen-Ole-Fette-Wachse,* **94**, 27 (1968); *Analyt. Abstr.,* **16**, 2969 (1969)
39. SEILER, H., *Helv. chim. Acta,* **44**, 1753 (1961)
40. CLESCERI, N.L. and LEE, G.F., *Analyt. Chem.,* **36**, 2207 (1964)
41. MOGHISSI, A., *J. Chromat.,* **13**, 542 (1964)
42. CANIC, V.D., TURCIC, M.N. and BURGARSKI-VOJINOVIC, M.B., *Z. analyt. Chem.,* **229**, 93 (1967)
43. MUTO, M., *J. chem. Soc. Japan, pure Chem. Sect.,* **85**, 782 (1964); *Analyt. Abstr.,* **13**, 1257 (1966)
44. CANIC, V.D., TURCIC, M.N., PETROVIC, S.M. and PETROVIC, S.E., *Analyt. Chem.,* **37**, 1576 (1965)
45. BUTTS, W.C., *Analyt. Lett.,* **3**, 29 (1970)
46. GATES, O.R., *Analyt. Chem.,* **26**, 730 (1954)
47. PAGE, J.A., MAXWELL, J.A. and GRAHAM, R.P., *Analyst,* **87**, 245 (1962)
48. LEVINE, H., ROWE, J.J. and GRIMALDI, F.S., *Analyt. Chem.,* **27**, 258 (1955)
49. CHALMERS, R.A., *Proc. Soc. analyt. Chem.,* **3**, 157 (1966)
50. RAYNER, L.W.W., *Mikrochim. Acta,* 214 (1970)
51. KOLTHOFF, I.M., SANDELL, E.B., MEEHAN, E.J. and BRUCKENSTEIN, S., *Quantitative Inorganic Analysis,* 4th edn, Macmillan, London, 642 (1969)

52. BELCHER, R., NUTTEN, A.J. and MACDONALD, A.M.G., *Quantitative Inorganic Analysis*, 3rd edn, Butterworths, London, 107 (1970)
53. ZOLOTAVIN, V.L., SANATINA, V.N. and NESTERENKO, V.P., *Zh. analit. Khim.*, **21**, 1289 (1966)
54. DUVAL, C., *Inorganic Thermogravimetric Analysis*, 2nd edn, Elsevier, New York (1963)
55. LUNDELL, G.E.F. and HOFFMAN, J.I., *J. Ass. off. agric. Chem.*, **8**, 188 (1924)
56. LUNDELL, G.E.F. and HOFFMAN, J.I., *Ind. Engng Chem. analyt. Edn*, **15**, 44, 171 (1923)
57. SCHULEK, E. and ENDROI, A., *Magy. kém. Foly.*, **66**, 139 (1960); *Analyt. Abstr.*, **8**, 505 (1961)
58. HUDITZ, F., FLASCHKA, H. and PETZOLD, I., *Z. analyt. Chem.*, **135**, 333 (1952)
59. DE SAINT CHAMANT, H. and VIGIER, R., *Bull. Soc. chim. Fr.*, **21**, 180 (1954); *Analyt. Abstr.*, **1**, 1232 (1954)
60. CANNON, P., *Talanta*, **3**, 219 (1960)
61. THISTLETHWAITE, W.P., *Analyst*, **72**, 531 (1947)
62. ARCHER, D.W., HESLOP, R.B. and KIRBY, R., *Analytica chim. Acta*, **30**, 450 (1964)
63. ARCHER, D.W. and HESLOP, R.B., *Analytica chim Acta*, **30**, 582 (1964)
64. HESLOP, R.B. and PEARSON, E.F., *Analytica chim. Acta*, **33**, 522 (1965)
65. MACDONALD, A.M.G., *Ind. chem. Manuf., London*, **35**, 88 (1959)
66. *New Methods of Analytical Chemistry*. Belcher, R. and Wilson, C.L. in association with West, T.S., 2nd edn, Chapman and Hall, London, 323 (1964)
67. MACDONALD, A.M.G. and RIVERO, A-M., *Analytica chim. Acta*, **37**, 525 (1967)
68. BOWD, A.J. and BURNS, D.T., *Mikrochim. Acta*, 560 (1967)
69. WILSON, H.N., *Analyst*, **76**, 65 (1951)
70. PERRIN, C.N., *J. Ass. off. Agric. Chem.*, **41**, 758 (1958); **42**, 567 (1959)
71. WENDLANDT, W.W. and HOFFMANN, W.M., *Analyt. Chem.*, **32**, 1011 (1960)
72. LENCH, A., *Analyt. Chem.*, **35**, 1695 (1963)
73. WILSON, H.N., *Analyst*, **79**, 535 (1954)
74. BELCHER, R. and MACDONALD, A.M.G., *Talanta*, **1**, 185 (1958)
75. DAHLGREN, S.E., *Z. analyt. Chem.*, **189**, 243 (1962); *Analyt. Abstr.*, **10**, 1230 (1963)
76. HOFFMAN, W.M. and BREEN, H.J., *J. Ass. off. agric. Chem.*, **47**, 413 (1964)
77. *J. Ass. off. Agric. Chem.*, **48**, 210 (1965)
78. FENNELL, T.R.F. and WEBB, J.R., *Talanta*, **2**, 105 (1959)
79. FIRSCHING, F.H., *Analyt. Chem.*, **33**, 873 (1961)
80. SPACU, G. and DIMA, L., *Z. analyt. Chem.*, **120**, 317 (1940)
81. KEŠANS, A., *Z. analyt. Chem.*, **128**, 215 (1948)
82. GREENFIELD, S., in *Comprehensive Analytical Chemistry* (Ed. C.L. Wilson and D.W. Wilson), Vol. 1C, Elsevier, Amsterdam, 225 (1962)
83. FERNLUND, U. and ZECHNER, S., *Z. analyt. Chem.*, **146**, 111 (1955); *Analyt. Abstr.*, **2**, 2695 (1955)
84. DUNCAN, R.D. and BRABSON, J.A., *J. Ass. off. agric. Chem.*, **49**, 1201 (1966)
85. CAVDILL, P.R., *J. Ass. off. agric. Chem.*, **52**, 587 (1969)
86. BELCHER, R., MACDONALD, A.M.G., PHANG, S.E. and WEST, T.S., *J. chem. Soc.*, 2044 (1965)
87. BELCHER, R., *Talanta*, **15**, 357 (1968)
88. BELCHER, R. and UDEN, P.C., *Analytica chim. Acta*, **42**, 180 (1968)
89. SALAM KHAN, M.A. and STEPHEN, W.I., *Analyst*, **93**, 26 (1968)
90. BUSS, H., KOHLSCHÜTTER, H.W. and PREISS, M., *Z. analyt. Chem.*, **193**, 264 (1963)
91. RIEDEL, K., *Z. analyt. Chem.*, **168**, 106 (1959)
92. BUDEVSKI, O., PENCHEVA, L., RUSINOVA, R. and RUSEVA, E., *Talanta*, **11**, 1225 (1964)
93. SINHA, B.C., DAS GUPTA, S. and KUMAR, S., *Analyst*, **93**, 409 (1968)
94. YOFE, J. and RAPPART, B.R., *Analytica chim. Acta*, **43**, 346 (1968)
95. KIRKBRIGHT, G.F., SMITH, A.M. and WEST, T.S., *Analyst*, **94**, 321 (1969)
96. KINNUNEN, J. and WENNERSTAND, B., *Chemist Analyst*, **46**, 92 (1957)
97. BASSETT, J., *Analyst*, **88**, 238 (1963)
98. DE SOUSA, A., *Analytica chim. Acta*, **67**, 234 (1973).
99. SALMON, J.E. and TERRY, H., *J. chem. Soc.*, 2813 (1950)
100. BAKACS, E., *Z. analyt. Chem.*, **190**, 373 (1962)
101. TAVLLI, T.A. and IRANI, R.R., *Analyt. Chem.*, **35**, 1060 (1963)
102. GRIEPINK, B. and SLANINA, J., *Mikrochim. Acta*, 241 (1967)
103. Reference 2, p. 348
104. CHALMERS, R.A. and SINCLAIR, A.G., *Analytica chim. Acta*, **33**, 384 (1965)
105. CHALMERS, R.A. and SINCLAIR, A.G., *Analytica chim. Acta*, **34**, 412 (1966)
106. ALIMARIN, I.P. and SVEREV, V.S., *Mikrochemie*, **22**, 89 (1937)
107. STRICKLAND, J.D.H., *J. Am. chem. Soc.*, **74**, 862, 868, 872 (1952)

108. HALASZ, A. and PUNGOR, E., *Talanta,* **18**, 557 (1971)
109. HALASZ, A. and PUNGOR, E., *Talanta,* **18**, 569 (1971)
110. HALASZ, A., PUNGOR, E. and POLYAK, K., *Talanta,* **18**, 577 (1971)
111. BOLTZ, D.F. and MELLON, M.G., *Analyt. Chem.,* **20**, 749 (1948)
112. KENNEDY, J.F. and WEETMAN, D.A., *Analytica chim. Acta,* **55**, 448 (1971)
113. JAKUBIEC, R.J. and BOLTZ, D.F., *Mikrochim. Acta,* 1199 (1970)
114. DICKMAN. S.R. and BRAY, R.H., *Ind. Engng Chem. analyt. Edn,* **12**, 665 (1940)
115. CHALMERS, R.A. and THOMSON, D.A., *Analytica chim. Acta,* **18**, 575 (1958)
116. GING, N.S., *Analyt. Chem.,* **28**, 1330 (1956)
117. LAWS, E.Q. and WEBLEY, D.J., *Analyst,* **84**, 28 (1959)
118. HAGUE, J.L. and BRIGHT, H.A., *J. Res. natn. Bur. Stand.,* **26**, 405 (1941)
119. GRISWOLD. B.L., HUMOLLER, F.L. and MCINTYRE, A.R., *Analyt. Chem.,* **23**, 192 (1951)
120. CHEN, P.S., TORIBARA, T.Y. and WARNER, H., *Analyt. Chem.,* **28**, 1756 (1956)
121. FOGG, D.N. and WILKINSON, N.T., *Analyst,* **83**, 406 (1958)
122. CROUCH, S.R. and MALMSTADT, H.V., *Analyt. Chem.,* **39**, 1084 (1967)
123. KIRK, B.P. and WILKINSON, H.C., *Talanta,* **19**, 80 (1972)
124. SHAFRAN, I.G., PAVLOVA, M.V., TITOVA, S.A. and YAKUSHAVA, L.D., *Trudy Vses. Nauch-Issled. Inst. Khim. Reakt.,* 66 (1966); *Analyt. Abstr.,* **14**, 6767 (1967)
125. DUFF, E.J. and STUART, J.L., *Analyst,* **96**, 802 (1971)
126. TILLMA, R.W. and SYERS, J.K., *Analyst,* **100**, 322 (1975)
127. MURPHY, J. and RILEY, J.P., *Analytica chim. Acta,* **27**, 31 (1962)
128. LUECK, C.H. and BOLTZ, D.F., *Analyt. Chem.,* **28**, 1168 (1956)
129. BOLTZ, D.F. and MELLON, M.C., *Analyt. Chem.,* **19**, 873 (1947)
130. BELCHER, R., MACDONALD, A.M.G., PHANG, S.E. and WEST, T.S., *J. chem. Soc.,* 2044 (1965)
131. SALIMAN, P.M., *Analyt. Chem.,* **36**, 112 (1964)
132. NESTORIDIS, A., *Analyst,* **95**, 51 (1970)
133. RAMIREZ-MUNOS, J., *Analytica chim. Acta,* **78**, 431 (1975)
134. LUCCI, G.C., *Annali Chim.,* **56**, 1343 (1966); *Analyt. Abstr.,* **15**, 737 (1968)
135. I.U.P.A.C., *Spectrophotometric Data for Colorimetric Analysis,* Butterworths, London (1963)
136. HERRON, J., *Limnol. & Oceanogr.,* **7**, 316 (1962); *Analyt. Abstr.,* **11**, 5764 (1964)
137. KITSON, R.E. and MELLON, M.G., *Ind. Engng Chem. analyt. Edn,* **16**, 379 (1944)
138. HESLOP. R.B. and RAMSEY. A.C., *Analytica chim. Acta,* **47**, 305 (1969)
139. LINDLEY, G., *Analytica chim. Acta,* **25**, 334 (1961)
140. B.S. 1121: Pt 45:(1966), British Standards Institute, London
141. B.S. 4158: Pt 2:(1970), British Standards Institute, London
142. PAKALNS, P., *Analytica chim. Acta,* **51**, 497 (1970)
143. ABBOTT, D.C., EMSDEN, G.E. and HARRIS, J.R., *Analyst,* **88**, 814 (1963)
144. B.S. 2690: Pt 3:(1966), British Standards Institute, London
145. DOCHERTY, A.C., *Lab. Pract.,* **18**, 47 (1969)
146. JORDAN, D.E., *J. Ass. off. agric. Chem.,* **52**, 581 (1969)
147. DOCHERTY, A.C., FARROW, S.G. and SKINNER, J.M., *Analyst,* **97**, 36 (1972)
148. PARVIN, R. and SMITH, R.A., *Analyt. Biochem.,* **27**, 65 (1969)
149. UEDA, I. and WADA, T., *Analyt. Biochem.,* **37**, 169 (1970)
150. SCHAFER, H.N.S., *Analyt. Chem.,* **35**, 53 (1963)
151. DIXON, J.P., *Modern Methods in Organic Microanalysis,* Van Nostrand, London, 160 (1968)
152. HAYASHI, K., DANZUKA, T. and UENO, K., *Talanta,* **4**, 244 (1960)
153. BODE, H., EGGELING, W. and STEINBRECHT, V., *Z. analyt. Chem.,* **216**, 30 (1966)
154. BABKO, A.K., SHKARAVSKII, YU. F. and KULIK, V.I., *Zh. analit. Khim.,* **21**, 196 (1966); *Analyt. Abstr.,* **14**, 6067 (1967)
155. ITAYA, K. and UI, M., *Clin. chim. Acta,* **14**, 361 (1966)
156. DUCRET, L. and DROUILLAS, M., *Analytica chim. Acta,* **21**, 86 (1959)
157. GHIMICESUC, G.H. and DORNEANU, V., *Talanta,* **19**, 261 (1972)
158. SACHDEV, S.L. and WEST, P.W., *Atmos. Envir.,* **2**, 331 (1968)
159. DIPPEL, W.A., BRICKER, C.E. and FURMAN, N.H., *Analyt. Chem.,* **26**, 553 (1958)
160. SZEBENYI-GYORY, E., SLEVIN, P.J., SVEHLA, G. and ERDEY, L., *Talanta,* **17**, 1167 (1970)
161. DAGNALL, R.M., THOMPSON, K.C. and WEST, T.S., *Analyst,* **93**, 72 (1968)
162. BRODY, S.S. and CHANEY, J.E., *J. Gas Chromat.,* **4**, 42 (1966)
163. ELLIOTT, W.N. and MOSTYN, R.A., *Analyst,* **96**, 452 (1971)
164. ALDOUS, K.M., DAGNALL, R.M. and WEST, T.S., *Analyst,* **95**, 417 (1970)
165. LAND, D.B. and EDMUNDS, S.M., *Mikrochim. Acta,* 1013 (1966)

166. KIRKBRIGHT, G.F., NARAYANASWARY, R. and WEST, T.S., *Analyt. Chem.*, **43**, 1434 (1971)
167. KIRKBRIGHT, G.F., NARAYANASWARY, R. and WEST, T.S., *Analyst*, **97**, 174 (1972)
168. STORK, G. and JUNG, H., *Z. analyt. Chem.*, **249**, 161 (1970); *Analyt. Abstr.*, **20**, 1523 (1971)
169. KIRKBRIGHT, G.F. and MARSHALL, M., *Analyt. Chem.*, **45**, 1610 (1973)
170. ZAUGG, W.S. and KNOX, R.J., *Analyt. Chem.*, **38**, 1759 (1966)
171. CULLUM, D.C. and THOMAS, D.B., *Analytica chim. Acta*, **24**, 205 (1961)
172. MCCOLL, D.H. and O'DONNELL, T.A., *Analyt. Chem.*, **36**, 848 (1964)
173. CHRISTIAN, G.D., KNOBLOCK, E.C. and PURDY, W.C., *Analyt. Chem.*, **35**, 1869 (1963)
174. SELIG, W., *Mikrochim. Acta*, 564 (1970)
175. SELIG, W., *Mikrochim. Acta*, II, 9 (1976)
176. NANJO, M., ROHM, T.J. and GUILBAULT, G.G., *Analytica chim. Acta*, **77**, 19 (1975)
177. GUILBAULT, G.G. and NANJO, M., *Analytica chim. Acta*, **78**, 69 (1975)
178. BIXLER, J.W. and COLWELL, L.F., *Analytica chim. Acta*, **85**, 185 (1976)
179. HAHN, R.B. and SCHMITT, T.M., *Analyt. Chem.*, **41**, 359 (1969)
180. RIJKHEER, J., *J. South. Afr. Chem. Inst.*, **13**, 1 (1960); *Analyt. Abstr.*, **8**, 86 (1961)
181. CROUCH, S.R. and MALMSTADT, H.V., *Analyt. Chem.*, **39**, 1090 (1967)
182. JAVIER, A.C., CROUCH, S.R. and MALMSTADT. H.V., *Analyt. Chem.*, **41**, 239 (1969)
183. INGLE, J.D. and CROUCH, S.R., *Analyt. Chem.*, **43**, 7 (1971)
184. KRISS, E.E., RUDENKO, V.K. and KURBATOVA, G.T., *Zh. analit. Khim.*, **26**, 1000 (1971)
185. ALEKSEEVA, I.I., NEMZER, I.I. and TOLSTYKH, E.A., *Zav. Lab.*, **35**, 1305 (1969); *Analyt. Abstr.*, **19**, 3835 (1970)

Phosphite

Phosphite (HPO_3^{2-}) is a strongly reducing anion, though less so than hypophosphite with which it is often connected in analysis. Redox titrimetric methods feature considerably in its determination.

Separations

1. Paper and thin-layer chromatography

Table 47 provides the relevant data on four methods in this category.

2. Anion-exchange chromatography

Where larger amounts of phosphite are involved, anion exchange chromatography offers a good method of separation. Pollard *et al.*[5] used gradient elution with KCl on a Dowex-1 X8 column. The separation of phosphite was excellent in the two systems studied, one at pH 6.8, the other at pH 11.4. A sequel to this work was an automatic ion-exchange analysis of phosphorus anion mixtures using an AutoAnalyzer[6,7]. In this procedure the separated anions (including phosphite) are converted to orthophosphate and this continuously monitored using a colorimetric procedure based on molybdenum blue. More details of this will be found in the section on polyphosphates.

Table 47 Chromatographic separation of phosphite

Technique	*Solvent*	*Phosphite separated from*	*Ref.*
Paper. Whatman No. 3 strips	Isopropanol–chloroacetic acid or Isopropanol–isobutyl alcohol–ethanol–aq. NH_3	H_2SO_4, SO_4^{2-}, hypophosphite, hypophosphate, condensed phosphates	1
Paper. Whatman No. 4 ascending (cylinders)	Isopropanol–trichloroacetic acid–NH_3 (0.880) (75 mℓ: 5 g in 25 mℓ: 0.3 mℓ) ('Ebel's acidic solvent') Also several other solvents used including basic ones	Hypophosphite, pyrophosphite, hypophosphate, {*o*-PO_4, di-PO_4, tri-PO_4, trimeta-PO_4, tetrameta-PO_4}	2
TLC MN Polygram sheets CEL 300	Isopropanol–trichloroacetic acid – tetraethyl ammonium hydroxide–H_2O (750 mℓ: 50 g: 16 mℓ 20% v/v: 250 mℓ) and Isopropanol–isobutanol–NH_3 (0.880) (400 mℓ: 200 mℓ: 10 mℓ)	*o*-PO_4 di-PO_4 tri-PO_4 trimeta-PO_4 tetrameta-PO_4 hypophosphite polyphosphate $n = 20–30$ commercial cyclic and linear phosphate products	3
TLC Silica gel and starch	Methanol–NH_3 (0.880)–10% chloroacetic acid–H_2O (10:3:1:10)	*o*-PO_4 di-PO_4 hypophosphite	4

Determination

Redox titrimetric methods

Almost all the principal oxidizing reagents used in quantitative analysis have been applied to determination of phosphite. These include permanganate, cerium(IV), iodine, vanadate, chromate, hypochlorite and hypobromite. Many of the methods require strict control of experimental conditions or heating for prolonged periods in order to obtain satisfactory results. A detailed treatment of methods has been given in standard texts[8,9].

Table 48 Redox titrimetric methods for phosphite and hypophosphite in common solution

Phosphite plus hypophosphite	*Phosphite*	*Hypophosphite*	*Ref.*
Boil with excess Ce(IV) Back titrate with Fe(II)	By difference	Oxidation to phosphite with excess Ce(IV) in sulphuric acid 1.5 h at room temp. 30 min at 60°C. Back titration with Fe(II)	15
Reflux with vanadate for 20 min or Cr(VI) for 1 h. Back-titrate excess vanadate with Fe(II)	By difference	Boil with excess Fe(III) in 1.5-2.0M HCl. Fe(II) titrated with vanadate	16
	Oxidation to orthophosphate at b.pt in few min in 2–6M HCl	Oxidation to phosphite with Cu(II) in about 6M HCl at room temp. in 2–3 min. Potentiometric or visual titration of excess Fe(II) equivalent to Cu(I) with various oxidizing agents	17
Oxidation to orthophosphate by vanadate with Ag(I) catalyst. Potentiometric	By difference	In absence of Ag(I) catalyst, only hypophosphite oxidized to orthoposphate	18

Related to the determination of phosphite on its own is determination of phosphite and hypophosphite when present together. The reaction of these anions with different oxidizing agents is slow and complicated, but several methods are now available, and will be discussed below. Recent work has considerably reduced the time required for the quantitative oxidation of phosphite.

Guilbault and McCurdy[10] confirmed earlier findings by RaO and RaO[11] that silver(I) catalyses the cerium(IV) oxidation of phosphite (as well as hypophosphite), and themselves recommended a mixed catalyst containing manganese(II) and silver(I) nitrates. Using this, the time for oxidation of phosphite and hypophosphite is reduced to 10 and 7 min respectively.

Hypochlorite as oxidant for phosphite has been re-investigated recently by Masalovich *et al.*[12]. When added to a phosphate-buffered solution in a closed vessel at pH 7, phosphite is oxidized in 3 min. Addition of KI and titration of liberated iodine completes the determination. Norkus, Lunyatskas and Tsarankute[13] have developed a rapid iodimetric procedure based on oxidation in a saturated solution of aqueous sodium bicarbonate, disodium hydrogen phosphate or sodium tetraborate. A two-fold excess of iodine in about 1.7% KI oxidizes the phosphite in 5 min. Excess iodine is titrated with arsenic(III).

A much clearer picture of the optimum conditions for oxidation of phosphites by iodine has emerged from the fundamental study by Masalovich *et al.*[14]. Their factorial designed study indicates that the optimum parameters are as follows:

Oxidation time:	10.6 min	pH:	7.28
Temperature:	22.5 °C	Excess iodine:	180.3%
KI content:	4.7%		

with pH and temperature having the greatest effect.

When phosphite and hypophosphite are to be determined in common solution, several methods may be used. The bases of some are shown in *Table 48*.

Determination of phosphite by redox titrimetry[10]

Reagents

Iron(II) sulphate: standard solution.
Cerium(IV) sulphate: standard solution.
Catalyst: 1.2 mℓ 50% manganese(II) nitrate solution and 5.0 g silver(I) nitrate dissolved in 100 mℓ 1M perchloric acid.
Indicator: Ferroin.

Procedure

To a solution containing 10–100 mg phosphite add 2 mℓ catalyst solution, 5.5 mℓ conc. H_2SO_4 for each 100 mℓ solution, and a 70–150% excess of standard cerium(IV) sulphate. Heat on a hot plate for 10 min at 100 °C, quench the reaction by cooling, add 10 mℓ conc. H_2SO_4 and titrate with a standard iron(II)sulphate solution using ferroin as indicator.

Note

The Standard Deviation is ±0.17 for 15–100 mg phosphite.

Spectrophotometric methods

As with several other phosphorus anions, phosphite may be oxidized to orthophosphate and this determined spectrophotometrically, preferably as molybdenum blue or using the phosphovanadomolybdate method. The latter method was used by Pollard *et al.*[5] to monitor the phosphite fraction eluted by anion-exchange chromatography. The molybdenum blue method was the basis of the subsequent automatic method[6,7].

References

1. RUDNICKI, R., *Chemia analit.*, **6**, 761 (1961); *Analyt. Abstr.*, **9**, 2731 (1962)
2. EBEL, J.P., *Mikrochim. Acta*, 679 (1954)
3. BURNS, D.T. and LEE, J.D., *Mikrochim. Acta*, 206 (1969)
4. SEILER, H., *Helv. chim. Acta*, **44**, 1753 (1961)
5. POLLARD, F.H., ROGERS, D.E., ROTHWELL, M.T. and NICKLESS, G., *J. Chromat.*, **9**, 227 (1962)
6. POLLARD, F.H., NICKLESS, G., ROGERS, D.E. and ROTHWELL, M.T., *J. Chromat.*, **17**, 157 (1965)
7. POLLARD, F.H., NICKLESS, G., ROGERS, D.E. and CRONE, D.L., *Proc. Soc. Analyt. Chem. Conference*, Nottingham, 1965, W. Heffer and Sons Ltd., Cambridge, 481 (1965)
8. KOLTHOFF, I.M. and BELCHER, R., *Volumetric Analysis*, Vol. III, Interscience, London (1957)
9. BERKA, A., VULTERIN, J. and ZYKA, J., *Newer Redox Titrants*, Pergamon Press, London (1965)
10. GUILBAULT, G.G. and MCCURDY, W.H., *Analytica chim. Acta*, **24**, 214 (1961)
11. RAO, K.B. and RAO, G.G., *Z. analyt. Chem.*, **147**, 274, 279 (1955)
12. MASALOVICH, V.M., AGASYAN, P.K., MASALOVICH, N.S. and NIKOLAEVA, E.R., *Zav. Lab.*, **35**, 257 (1969); *Analyt. Abstr.*, **18**, 3898 (1970)
13. NORKUS, P.K., LUNYATSKAS, A.M. and TSARANKUTE, S.P., *Zh. analit. Khim.*, **20**, 753 (1965); *Analyt. Abstr.*, **14**, 662 (1967)
14. MASALOVICH, N.S., AGASYAN, P.K., MASALOVICH, V.M. and NIKOLAEVA, E.R., *Zav. Lab.*, **33**, 1053 (1967); *Analyt. Abstr.*, **15**, 7236 (1968)
15. BERNHART, D.N., *Analyt. Chem.*, **26**, 1798 (1954)
16. VERBITSKAYA, T.D. and ROMANOVA, N.K., *Zav. Lab.*, **26**, 818 (1960); *Analyt. Abstr.*, **8**, 994 (1961)
17. NORKUS, P.K. and MARKEVICHIENE, R.M., *Zh. analit. Khim.*, **22**, 1527 (1967); *Analyt. Abstr.*, **17**, 126 (1969)
18. MATSUO, T., SHIDA, J. and KUDO, K., *Japan Analyst*, **18**, 488 (1969); *Analyt. Abstr.*, **19**, 2998 (1970)

Polyphosphates: Triphosphate, Tetraphosphate and Higher Members

The nomenclature of linear and cyclic phosphates has been discussed on page 422. Polyphosphates can be represented by the general formula $H_{n+2}P_nO_{3n+1}$. The term is often used synonymously with condensed phosphate. The present treatment will be confined mainly to triphosphate (*Structure 61*) and tetraphosphate (*Structure 62*).

```
 O⁻     O⁻     O⁻                  O⁻     O⁻     O⁻     O⁻
 |      |      |                   |      |      |      |
O⁻—P—O—P—O—P—O⁻                  O⁻—P—O—P—O—P—O—P—O⁻
 ||     ||     ||                  ||     ||     ||     ||
 O      O      O                   O      O      O      O
```

Structure 61 *Triphosphate* $(P_3O_{10})^{5-}$ *Structure 62* *Tetraphosphate* $(P_4O_{13})^{6-}$

Diphosphate (pyrophosphate) is dealt with in a separate section, though it will feature to some extent in the present discussion.

Polyphosphates find extensive use in commerce and industry. These include water softening (due to their complexing action, especially with the alkaline earths), the food industry, as fertilizer components, in the manufacture of surface acting detergents, in pharmaceutical preparations, in cleaning compositions, in the textile and paper industries, and as deflocculants. At the present time, there is concern over the ecological effects of some of these applications.

The most important of the linear polyphosphates are sodium tetraphosphate and Calgon (Graham's salt—a mixture of higher polyphosphates with 13–25 phosphorus atoms per molecule, and often misleadingly called 'hexametaphosphate', this implying a cyclic configuration). The general chemistry of condensed phosphates is authoritatively dealt with by Van Wazer[1] and Thilo[2].

In aqueous solution at room temperature and at a pH of 7–9, polyphosphates are stable almost indefinitely. At higher acidities and with increase in temperature, hydrolysis becomes increasingly rapid giving mono- and diphosphate.

$$[P_3O_{10}]^{5-} \xrightarrow{H_2O} [HP_2O_7]^{3-} + [HPO_4]^{2-}$$

Polyphosphates are precipitated from acid solution by barium ions. This has been used as a general method of separating them from metaphosphates, which are more soluble.

Separations

1. Precipitation

It is now accepted that precipitation with Ba^{2+} as a means of separating linear phosphates from cyclic phosphates is not quantitative except in certain cases. The difficulties are due to incomplete precipitation and coprecipitation especially when small amounts are involved. Chromatography is the method most used at present for these separations.

Complex cobalt salts have been investigated as precipitants for condensed phosphates, with some advantages in certain instances[3]. Tris(ethylenediamine) cobalt(III)chloride enables triphosphate and diphosphate to be separated[4,5] by precipitating the former at pH 3.6, though ^{32}P studies have indicated that coprecipitation and incomplete precipitation occur even under carefully controlled conditions.

2. Paper and thin-layer chromatography

Paper chromatography was originally applied to inorganic phosphates by Ebel[6,7]. His comprehensive paper[8] on the separation of the phosphorus oxyacids has been the basis of much of the subsequent work using this technique. *Table 49* contains some of the more important separations involving linear and cyclic phosphates by paper and thin-layer chromatography.

Three main factors affect the extent of hydrolysis of condensed phosphates during the chromatographic separation, time, temperature, and pH of the solvent. The investigation by Iida and Yamabe[14] listed above makes a comparative study of the influence of solvents. The merits of paper and thin-layer chromatography in the separation of phosphates has been discussed by Pollard *et al.*[18].

Table 49 Paper and thin-layer chromatographic separation of linear and cyclic phosphates

Ions separated	*Paper chromatography*						*TLC*		
Orthophosphate	X	X	X	X	X		X	X	X
Diphosphate	X	X	X	X	X	X	X	X	X
Triphosphate	X	X	X		X	X	X	X	X
Tetraphosphate		X	X		X	X		X	
Pentaphosphate		X	X		X			X	
Hexaphosphate		X	X		X				
Heptaphosphate		X	X		X				
Octaphosphate			X		X				
Trimetaphosphate	X	X	X	X		X	X	X	X
Tetrametaphosphate	X	X	X			X	X	X	X
Hypophosphate	X								X
Hypophosphite	X								X
Phosphite	X								X
Pyrophosphite	X								
Solvents and other materials	(a)	(b)	(c)	(a) and (j)	(g) and (a)	(a) and (e)	(k)	(f)	(h) and (i)
Reference	8	9	10	11	12	15	14	16	17

(a) Isopropanol–trichloroacetic acid–ammonia (0.880)
75 ml:5 g in 25 ml water:0.3 ml
Notes 1. This is 'Ebel's acidic reagent'
2. Other acidic and basic solvents also used in this work. Details in original paper or reviev

(b) As (a). Also basic solvent.
Isopropanol–isobutanol–H_2O–ammonia (0.880)
400 mℓ:200 mℓ:390 mℓ : 10 mℓ

(c) As (a). Also
Isopropanol–trichoroacetic acid–H_2O—ammonia (0.880)
70 mℓ:20 mℓ 20%: 10 mℓ : 0.3 mℓ

(e) For cyclic phosphates
Isopropanol–isobutanol–H_2O–ammonia (25%)
40:20:39:1
Also Ebel's acidic reagent for linear phosphates.

(f) For separation of linear phosphates by circular TLC.
Isopropanol–trichloroacetic acid–0.1M EDTA–H_2O–ammonia (25%)
8 mℓ:5 g:1 mℓ 25%:39 mℓ:0.3 mℓ
For separation of cyclic from linear
Ethanol–isobutanol–0.1M EDTA–H_2O–ammonia (25%)
30:30:1:38:1
Absorbent: corn starch.

(g) Isopropanol–monochloroacetic acid–H_2O–ammonia (0.880)
250 mℓ:12.5 g:350 mℓ : 15 mℓ

(h) Isopropanol–trichloroacetic acid–tetraethyl ammonium hydroxide–H_2O
750 mℓ:50 g:16 mℓ 20% : 250 mℓ
Thin-layer plates: MN Polygram CEL 300.

(i) **Isopropanol–isobutanol–ammonia (0.880)**
400 mℓ:200 mℓ:10 mℓ
Thin-layer plates: MN Polygram CEL 300.

(j) Tert-butanol–H_2O–formic acid
80 mℓ:20 mℓ : 5 mℓ

(k) 21 variations used based on
Isopropanol–isobutanol–trichloroacetic acid–H_2O–ammonia
Adsorbent: Avicel.

Ohashi and Van Wazer[19] have applied paper chromatography to the separation of very long chain phosphates (up to $n = 5000$). Ebel's acidic solvent was used in this work.

Gel-chromatography has been applied[20] to linear phosphates with degrees of polymerization from 1 to 13. A sephadex G-25 column was used with 0.1M KCl as eluant.

3. *Ion-exchange chromatography*

This is probably the most useful method for separation of both linear and cyclic phosphates. It often enables adjacent members of the series to be isolated and determined, a task not possible using classical wet chemical methods for oligomers greater than trimer.

Whereas paper and thin-layer chromatography permits the separation of microgram quantities of condensed phosphates, ion-exchange chromatography allows milligram amounts to be isolated.

Several condensed phosphates were separated by Rieman and co-workers[21,22] using moderately cross-linked polystyrene resins containing $—CH_2N^+(CH_3)_3$ ionic groupings. A theory of ion-exchange behaviour of condensed phosphates was published[23] in 1954.

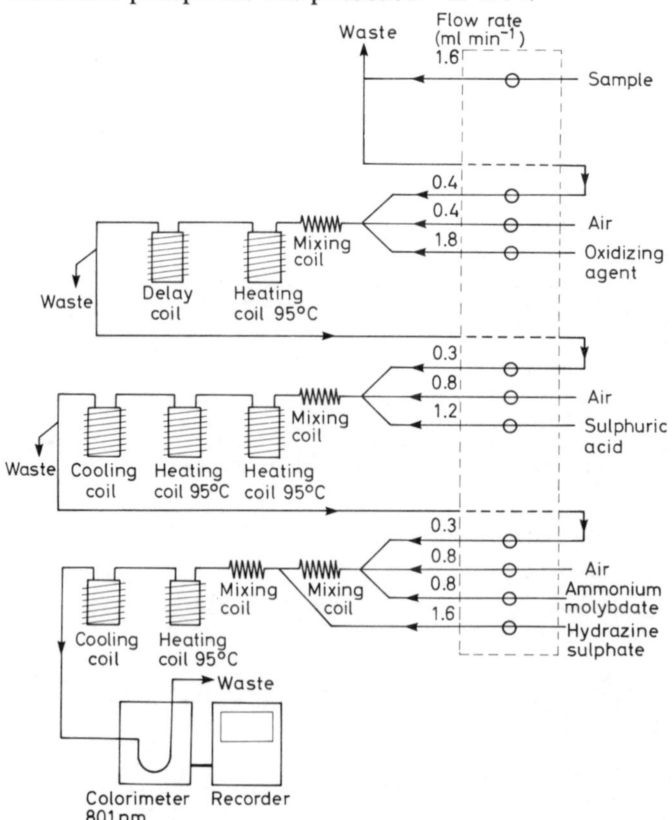

Figure 55 *Technicon AutoAnalyzer module for phosphorus anions.* (After Pollard *et al.*[27])

Lundgren and Loeb[24] have described an automated form of the ion-exchange procedure based on earlier work by Grande and Beukenkamp[25]. In this gradient elution system, the column effluent containing the condensed phosphates is hydrolysed at 95 °C after being mixed with 3.4M H_2SO_4, to convert phosphate species into orthophosphate. This is determined on a continual basis by a colorimetric procedure based on molybdenum blue. Since phosphate is present only as orthophosphate, the system does not have to be calibrated for each phosphorus anion.

Pollard *et al.*[26, 27] have extended this work so that analysis of mixtures containing lower phosphorus anions as well as condensed phosphates can be made on an automatic basis. The details are essentially as follows. The phosphate mixture is subjected to gradient elution on a column of DOWEX-1 X 10 per cent D.V.B. The eluted anions are passed through a Technicon AutoAnalyzer as shown in *Figure 55*. Typical elution curves are shown in *Figure 56*.

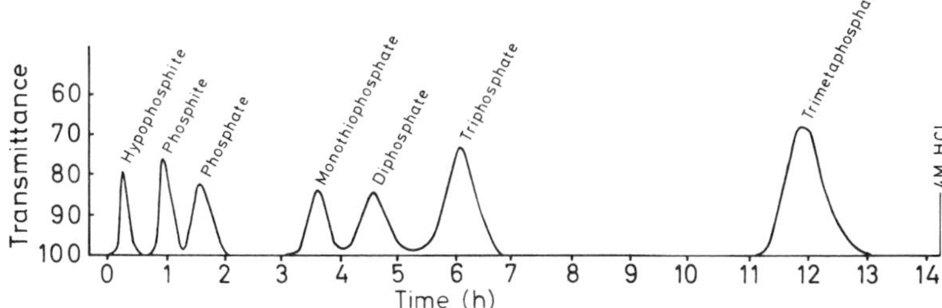

Figure 56 *Separation of simple and complex phosphorus-containing anions by automatic anion exchange chromatography.* (After Pollard *et al.*[26])

Quantitative evaluation of the elution curves is based on the phosphorus concentration in the column being a Gaussian function of time, in which case the area under the curves is directly proportional to the product of the peak maximum and the width of the peak at half-maximum. Another evaluation method involves division of the peaks into narrow strips of equal width, and the subsequent calculation and summation of the optical densities.

$$\text{Phosphorus load} = K \sum_{t=t_1}^{t=t_2} \log_{10} \frac{T_0}{T}$$

where t_2 and t_1 are the times for the end and beginning of the peaks respectively. T is the transmittance at time t. K is a constant which includes the width of the strips. The above investigation also includes the development of a Datex encoder apparatus for recording the elution data directly on to punch tape, and computer evaluation of the results. The original papers should be consulted for further details.

Separation of mixtures consisting of orthophosphate and many of its linear and cyclic polymers have been accomplished by Rothbart, Weymouth and Rieman[28] using the resin IRA-400 and KCl as eluant. A nearly perfect separation of ortho-, di-, the linear polymers as far as trideca-, and the three cyclic compounds trimeta-, tetrameta- and one unidentified (probably pentametaphosphate), was obtained.

Determination

1. pH or end-group titration

This approach is based on the different acid strengths of the hydrogens in mono- and condensed phosphates, depending on their position in the molecule[29, 30]. We see this indicated below:

```
         O
         ||
(vw)HO—P—OH(w)
         |
         OH
         (s)

        O           O          O
        ||          ||         ||
(w) HO—P—O—    [ —P—O— ]     —P—OH (w)
        |           |          |
        OH          OH         OH
        (s)         (s)   n    (s)

          O     OH(s)
           \\  /
             P
           /   \
          O     O
(s)HO     |     |   //O
      \   P     P
  O//      \ O /   \OH(s)
```

(s) strongly acidic; (w) weakly acidic; (vw) very weakly acidic.

The two weakly acidic hydrogens in linear polyphosphates are referred to as end-groups.

For orthophosphoric acid:

$$pKa_1 = 2.23;\ pKa_2 = 7.20;\ pKa_3 = 12.40.$$

When titrated with sodium hydroxide the strongly acidic hydrogens will give an end-point at about pH 4.5 and the weakly acidic ones at about pH 9.

Total hydrolysis of polyphosphates (linear and cyclic) will produce orthophosphate only. The third hydrogen in orthophosphate is not normally titratable, but on addition of silver nitrate to precipitate the orthophosphate, it is released and can be subsequently titrated.

Essentially the pH method consists of the following steps. Dilute HCl is added to the phosphate mixture in order to convert the species to the corresponding acids. The solution is then titrated with standard NaOH. Two inflections appear in the titration curve, the first at pH 4.5, the second at pH 9. This is shown in *Figure 57*.

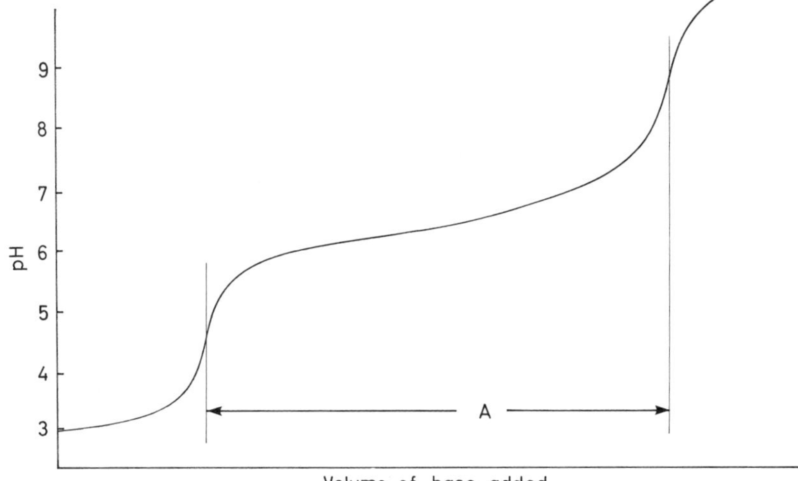

Figure 57 Titration of weakly acid function in orthophosphate and linear phosphates

Titre A is equivalent to the weakly acid function in orthophosphate and linear phosphates.

The same solution is treated with excess HCl, again reconverting the neutralized phosphates to the corresponding acids. The excess HCl and strongly acidic hydrogens are again titrated with standard NaOH to just beyond the pH 4.5 inflection point and then excess silver nitrate is added. The pH drops to about 3. The titration is now continued to beyond pH 5. This is shown in *Figure 58*.

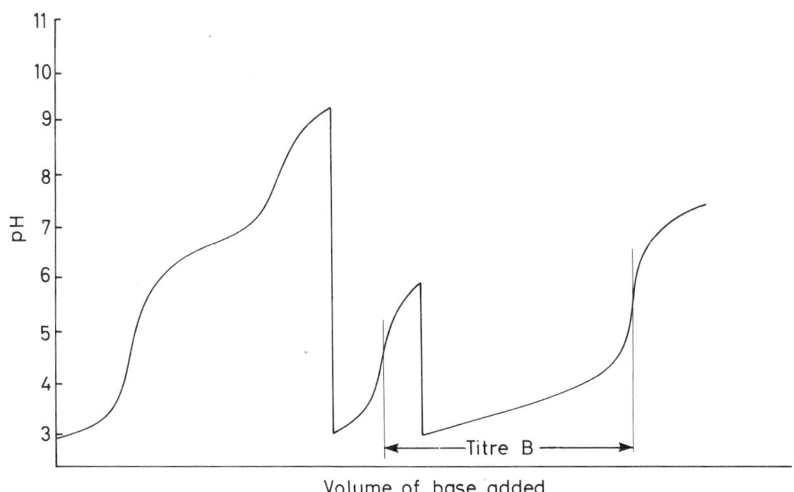

Figure 58 Titration of phosphorus acid function by silver precipitation method

Titre B = weakly acidic H directly titratable plus weakly acidic function of orthophosphate not directly titratable.

Finally a second aliquot is totally hydrolysed. The original procedure[29] involved refluxing with HCl for at least 8 h. An improved method[30] enables this to be accomplished in less than 1 h. Again a pH titration is carried out on the resulting orthophosphate as described above, inflections appearing at pH 4.5 and 9.0. This is shown in *Figure 59*.

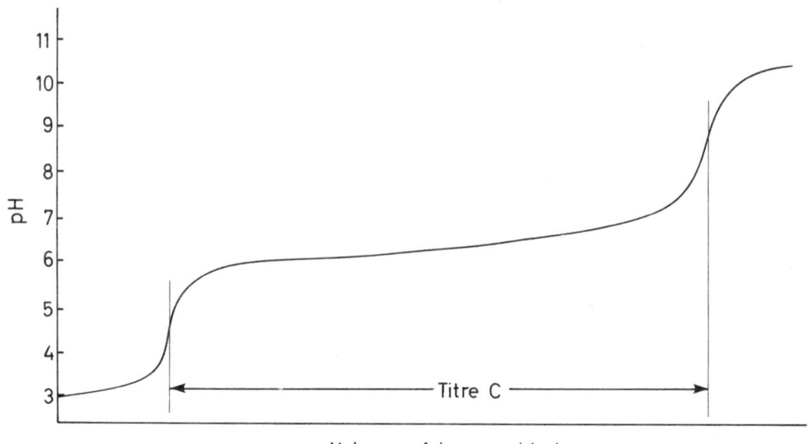

Figure 59 *Titration of phosphorus acid function after complete hydrolysis to orthophosphate*

Titre C gives the total phosphorus content. In this way, three titrations (before and after hydrolysis, and after addition of silver nitrate) can be used for the analysis of ortho- and polyphosphates. It will be seen that the presence of ring metaphosphates, with one strongly acidic hydrogen per P atom, will complicate the above considerations. They should therefore be absent.

If linear polyphosphates only are present, the average chain length $\bar{n}$ is derived from

$$\bar{n} = \frac{2(\text{total P})}{\text{end-group P}}$$

pH titration may be used to classify an unknown phosphate into the linear or cyclic categories. Rothbart, Weymouth and Rieman[28] in their ion-exchange studies, isolated an unknown phosphate on which they carried out a potentiometric micro-titration with sodium hydroxide. The single inflection obtained indicated that it had no weakly ionized hydrogens, and that it was therefore cyclic. This was confirmed by two-dimensional chromatography.

It should be noted that the pH titration method can only be applied in the absence of weakly acidic anions other than phosphate.

2. *Colorimetric determination of chromatographic spots*

Ascending paper chromatography followed by colorimetric determination of total phosphorus in each spot after hydrolysis to orthophosphate, is one of the most accurate methods for determination of condensed phosphates in their mixtures[12]. The colorimetric procedures used have been generally based on molybdenum blue.

3. *Polarography*

An indirect polarographic method for determination of triphosphate ions in the presence of other polyphosphates has been described by Shaw and Townshend[31]. While phosphates and polyphosphates are not themselves reducible at the dropping mercury electrode, this study indicates that tripolyphosphate ions form a soluble complex with mono-octyltin cations, and consequently produce a diminution in the polarographic wave height of the octyltin. From 2×10^{-4} to 4×10^{-3}M tripolyphosphate may be determined in the presence of 2×10^{-3}M ortho-, di-, trimeta-, and 10^{-3}M tetraphosphate, together or in any combination. The basis of the method is shown in *Figure 60* and the calibration curve in *Figure 61.*

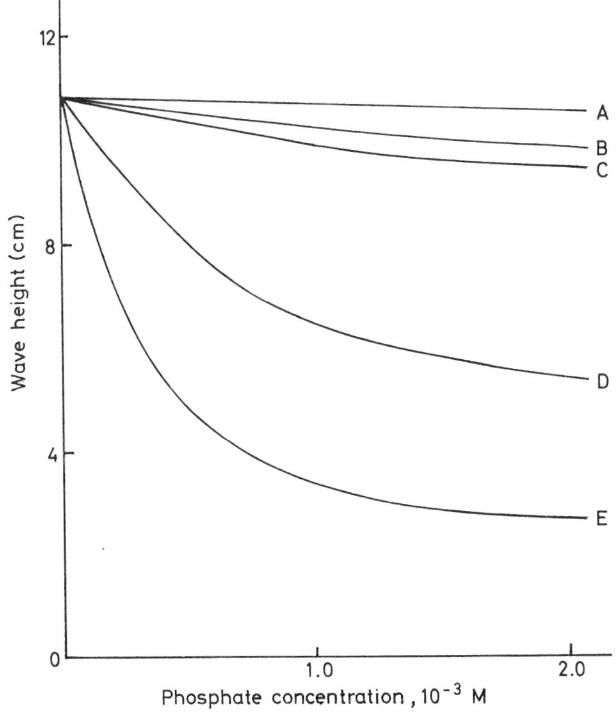

Figure 60 *Effect of phosphorus anions on wave height of* 3×10^{-4} *M mono-octyltin in 50% v/v aqueous 2-propanol, 1M in* $HClO_4$ *and 0.25M in HCl. Conditions as in Figure 60.* A, *orthophosphate;* B, *pyrophosphate;* C, *trimetaphosphate;* D, *tetrametaphosphate;* E, *tripolyphosphate.* (After Shaw and Townshend[31])

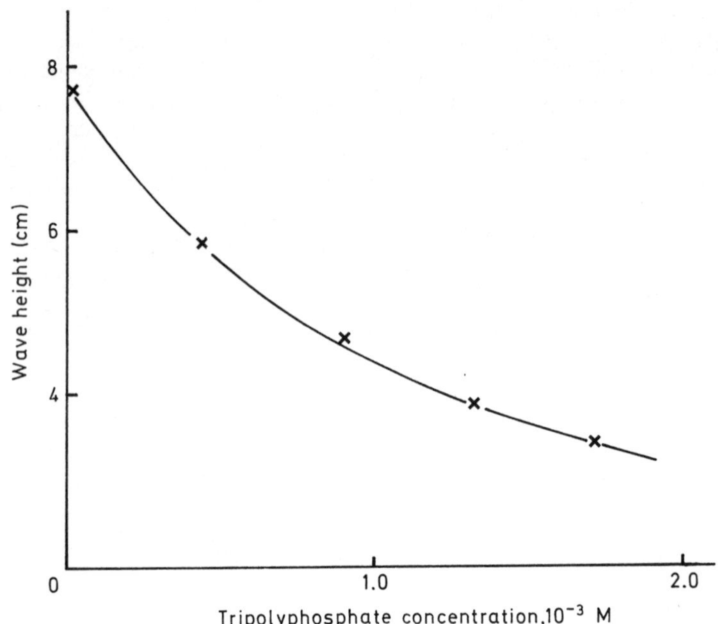

Figure 61 *Calibration curve of tripolyphosphate concentration as a function of polarographic wave height. Conditions: Sensitivity, 1.5 μA full-scale deflection; drop time, 1.0 s; blanking, 30 %.* (After Shaw and Townshend[81])

The method is described as simple, rapid, and acceptably precise. Non-interference by orthosphosphate, sulphate, calcium and magnesium ions make the method equally applicable to detergent preparations and effluent samples.

4. *Miscellaneous methods*

Precipitation of tripolyphosphates by zinc followed by compleximetric determination of the zinc has been suggested[32]. Another proposed method of analysis of condensed phosphates depends on examination of the nuclear magnetic resonance spectra[33, 34]. Relative amounts of orthophosphate, end-groups, middle-groups and probably branching chains can be determined with reasonable accuracy.

References

1. WAZER, J.R. VAN, *Phosphorus and its Compounds,* Vol. 1, Interscience, New York (1964)
2. THILO, E., *Adv. Inorg. Chem. Radiochem.,* Vol. 4, Academic Press, New York, 1 (1962)
3. MCCUNE, H.W. and ARQUETTE, G.J., *Analyt. Chem.,* **27**, 401 (1955)
4. GOLUBCHIK, E.M., *Zav. Lab.,* **35**, 926 (1969); *Analyt. Abstr.,* **19**, 2193 (1970)
5. WEISER, H.J., *Analyt. Chem.,* **28**, 477 (1956)

6. EBEL, J.P., *Bull. Soc. chim. Fr.*, **20**, 991, 998 (1953)
7. EBEL, J.P., *Compt. rend.*, **234**, 621 (1952)
8. EBEL, J.P., *Mikrochim. Acta,* 679 (1954)
9. KARL-KROUPA, E., *Analyt. Chem.*, **28**, 1091 (1956)
10. THILO, E. and GRUNZE, H., *Die Papierchromatographie der kondensierten Phosphate,* Akademie-Verlag, Berlin (1955)
11. MEHROTRA, R.C. and GUPTA, V.S., *J. Polymer Sci.*, Pt. A2, 3959 (1964)
12. WOODIS, T.C., TRIMM, J.R. and DUNCAN, R.D., *Analytica chim. Acta,* **65**, 469 (1973)
13. LEDERER, M. and MAJANI, C., *Chromatog. Rev.*, **12**, 239 (1970)
14. IIDA, T. and YAMABE, T., *J. Chromat.*, **54**, 413 (1971)
15. IONOVA, L.A. and POSTNIKOV, N.N., *Khim. Prom.*, 198 (1969); *Analyt. Abstr.*, **18**, 2344 (1970)
16. CANIC, V.D., TURCIC, M.N., PETROVIC, S.M. and PETROVIC, S.E., *Analyt. Chem.* **37**, 1576 (1965)
17. BURNS, D.T. and LEE, J.D., *Mikrochim. Acta,* 206 (1969)
18. POLLARD, F.H., NICKLESS, G., BURTON, K. and HUBBARD, J., *Microchem. J.*, **10**, 131 (1966)
19. OHASHI, S. and VAN WAZER, J.R., *Analyt. Chem.*, **35**, 1984 (1963)
20. UENO, Y., YOZA, N. and OHASHI, S., *J. Chromat.*, **52**, 481 (1970)
21. LINDENBAUM, S., PETERS, T.V. and RIEMAN, W., *Analytica chim. Acta,* **11**, 530 (1954)
22. PETERS, T.V. and RIEMAN, W., *Analytica chim. Acta,* **14**, 131 (1956)
23. BEUKENKAMP, J., RIEMAN, W. and LINDENBAUM, S., *Analyt. Chem.*, **26**, 505 (1954)
24. LUNDGREN, D.P. and LOEB, N.P., *Analyt. Chem.*, **33**, 366 (1961)
25. GRANDE, J.E. and BEUKENKAMP, J., *Analyt. Chem.*, **28**, 1497 (1956)
26. POLLARD, F.H., NICKLESS, G., ROGERS, D.E. and ROTHWELL, M.T., *J. Chromat.*, **17**, 157 (1965)
27. POLLARD, F.H., NICKLESS, G., ROGERS, D.E. and CRONE, D.L., *Proc. Soc. Analyt. Chem. Conference,* Nottingham, 1965, W. Heffer and Sons Ltd., Cambridge, 481 (1965)
28. ROTHBART, H.L., WEYMOUTH, H.W. and RIEMAN, W., *Talanta,* **11**, 33 (1964)
29. VAN WAZER, J.R., GRIFFITH, E.J. and MCCULLOUGH, J.F., *Analyt. Chem.*, **26**, 1755 (1954)
30. GRIFFITH, E.J., *Analyt. Chem.*, **28**, 525 (1956)
31. SHAW, S. and TOWNSHEND, A., *Talanta,* **20**, 332 (1973)
32. AKIYAMA, T., FUJIWARA, M., OKAMOTO, H. and FUSAKA, K., *Bull. Kyoto Coll. Pharm.*, 19 (1955)
33. CALLIS, C.F., VAN WAZER, J.R. and SHOOLERY, J.N., *Analyt. Chem.*, **28**, 269 (1956)
34. VAN WAZER, J.R., CALLIS, C.F. and SHOOLERY, J.N., *J. Am. chem. Soc.*, **77**, 4945 (1955)

Part 4
Sulphur Anions

Disulphite

Disulphite ($S_2O_5^{2-}$) (also known as metabisulphite and pyrosulphite) exists in the solid state only and has the structure shown in *Structure 63*.

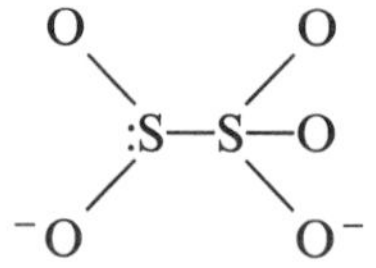

```
O        O
 \      /
  :S—S—O
 /      \
⁻O       O⁻
```

Structure 63 Disulphite ion ($S_2O_5^{2-}$)

When dissolved in water it hydrolyses to bisulphite.

$$Na_2S_2O_5 + H_2O \rightleftharpoons 2NaHSO_3$$

Conversely, careful evaporation of bisulphite solutions will produce anhydrous sodium disulphite. Moderately strong acids convert bisulphide to H_2SO_3. Bases or salts of weak acids convert them to normal sulphites.

The aqueous analytical chemistry of disulphite is therefore essentially the analytical chemistry of bisulphite and sulphite.

Titration with standard iodine is a standard method, for example this is the method recommended by British Standards[1] for the assay of photographic grade sodium metabisulphite.

In the determination of sulphite (produced from disulphite) it is essential to add it to the excess iodine and not the reverse, or low results are obtained. The unconsumed iodine is titrated with standard thiosulphate[2].

$$SO_3^{2-} + I_2 + H_2O \rightarrow SO_4^{2-} + 2H^+ + 2I^-$$

When disulphite has to be determined in the presence of thiosulphate and tetrathionate, their different behaviour on oxidation with halogens can be utilized[3]. With iodine oxidation, disulphite and thiosulphate react. With bromine all three react. If the iodine oxidation is made in the presence of formaldehyde, disulphite is masked and only sulphite reacts.

References

1. *British Standard* 3834: London (1964)
2. *Standard Methods of Chemical Analysis*, Ed. N. H. Furman, 6th Edition, Vol. 1, 1016, Van Nostrand, Princeton, N. Jersey (1962)
3. SZEKERES, L. and SUGAR, E. *Magyar Kem. Lapja*, **16**, 434 (1961); *Analyt. Abstr.*, **9**, 1453 (1962)

Dithionate

Because of its comparative resistance to oxidation, it is convenient to discuss the determination of dithionate ($S_2O_6^{2-}$) and polythionates separately. Dithionates are resistant to cold oxidizing agents, hydroxyl, and many other reagents. For this reason, methods for its determination are restricted.

The synthesis of sodium dithionate has been described[1]. The determination of dithionate is included in several reviews of the analytical chemistry of sulphur compounds[2–4].

Separations

Dithionate can be separated from other sulphur-containing anions by paper chromatography[5]. Using *n*-butanol–water (3:1) as solvent a separation from sulphite, peroxodisulphate, disulphate, and tetrathionate can be achieved. With isopropanol–water (3:1) separation from sulphate, thiosulphate, sulphide, disulphite and hydrogen sulphate is possible in addition to these anions.

Determination

Titrimetric methods

Oxidation of dithionate to sulphate forms the basis of most titrimetric methods. Both wet and dry methods of oxidation have been investigated. In acid medium at elevated temperatures, dithionates undergo decomposition according to the reaction

$$S_2O_6^{2-} \rightarrow SO_4^{2-} + SO_2$$

This forms the basis of another titrimetric procedure by which the SO_2 evolved is expelled by a continuous stream of CO_2 and determined iodimetrically.

1. Oxidation using dichromate/sulphuric acid

Dithionate is oxidized to sulphate by standard dichromate in a strong H_2SO_4 medium[6, 7].

$$3S_2O_6^{2-} + Cr_2O_7^{2-} + 2H^+ \rightarrow 2Cr^{3+} + 6SO_4^{2-} + H_2O$$

The excess of dichromate is determined iodimetrically. Murthy[8] includes the dichromate oxidation as part of a procedure for determination of dithionate in the presence of sulphide, sulphite, thiosulphate and polythionate. The sample is boiled with alkaline potassium permanganate to oxidize sulphide, sulphite, thiosulphate and polythionate. Excess potassium permanganate is removed by boiling with manganous sulphate in neutral solution. Precipitated manganese dioxide is filtered off. The solution is made 5M in H_2SO_4 and the dichromate oxidation applied for determination of dithionate.

Although other oxidants have been recommended for the titrimetric determination of dithionate, doubts have been expressed about their effectiveness, and it has been claimed[3] that correct results are only achieved using the dichromate/H_2SO_4 procedure.

2. *Iodimetric determination of expelled SO_2*

Soffer[9] has developed a method for analysis of $S_2O_6^{2-}$–SO_3^{2-}–SO_4^{2-} mixtures based on treatment of the sample with HCl. The expelled SO_2 is carried by CO_2 into a cooled excess of standard iodine. Any SO_2 resulting from sulphite can be expelled before the determination or determined independently, and a correction made to the dithionate result. Sulphite is determined iodimetrically after masking interfering cations with EDTA. Sulphate is determined compleximetrically via barium sulphate after removal of interfering cations by ion-exchange. The method was applied to leach liquors containing 3–70 g ℓ^{-1} of dithionate, up to 11 g $SO_2\,\ell^{-1}$ (this including sulphite and SO_2) and 110–240 g $SO_4^{2-}\,\ell^{-1}$.

3. *Using miscellaneous oxidants*

Oxidation of dithionate by vanadate in H_2SO_4 media has been proposed[10]. The method is a modification of an earlier one by Lang and Kurtenacker[11] in which the time required is reduced. Vanadium(IV) produced in the reaction is titrated with standard $KMnO_4$.

Recently cerium(IV) has been proposed as oxidant[12]. The authors report that ceric sulphate in a boiling acid medium oxidizes dithionate, as well as tri- and tetrathionates, to sulphate. For dithionate alone, the oxidation is quantitative in M H_2SO_4 at boiling temperature in 30 min. The same result is obtained in 6M or 9M H_2SO_4. For tri- and tetrathionates complete oxidation requires 6M H_2SO_4 under the same conditions.

Hexacyanoferrate(III) has been investigated as oxidant by Solymosi and Varga[13]. In addition to dithionate, sulphite, bisulphite, sulphide, thiosulphate, disulphite and tetrathionate are oxidized to sulphate by an excess of hexacyanoferrate(III) in 4–5M alkali medium at 50–60 °C, and with osmic acid as catalyst.

Colorimetric and spectrophotometric methods

A colorimetric method[14] has been based on the dichromate/H_2SO_4 oxidation of dithionate. The sample is heated on a water-bath with a known amount of potassium dichromate in 5M H_2SO_4, for 15 min. The absorbance is then measured against a reagent blank. Beer's Law holds for up to 75 mg of $Na_2S_2O_6\cdot 2H_2O$. Alternatively, the excess of dichromate can be determined polarographically. The same investigation gives a similar method based on vanadium(V) oxidation. Using this, up to 80 mg of dithionate can be determined in the presence of sulphite after a preliminary oxidation by $KMnO_4$ in alkaline medium.

Ozawa[15] has developed a spectrophotometric method for dithionate based on its conversion to sulphate by evaporation with M sodium carbonate, followed by fusion of the residue at 900–950 °C for 5 min. The resulting sulphate is evaluated spectrophotometrically. A procedure is given for the preliminary removal of any sulphate in the sample.

References

1. FERNELIUS, W. C. (Ed.), *Inorganic Synthesis*, Vol. 2, McGraw-Hill, New York, 170 (1946)
2. BLASIUS, E., HORN, G., KNOCHEL, A., MUNCH, J. and WAGNER, H., in *Inorganic Sulphur Chemistry* (Ed. G. Nickless), Elsevier, Amsterdam, 221 (1968)
3. SZEKERES, L., *Talanta*, **21**, 2 (1974)
4. HAFF, L.V., in *The Analytical Chemistry of Sulphur and its Compounds* (Ed. J.H. Karchmer), Part 1, Wiley-Interscience, New York, 237 (1970)
5. SERVIGNE, Y. and DUVAL, C., *Compt. Rend.*, **245**, 1803 (1957); *Analyt. Abstr.*, 5, 1833 (1958)
6. YOSHIDA, J., *J. chem. Soc. Japan, pure Chem. Sect.*, **63**, 1533 (1942); *Chem. Abstr.*, **41**, 3016 (1947)
7. GLASSTONE, S. and HICKLING, A., *J. chem. Soc.*, 5 (1933)
8. MURTHY, A.R.V., *Current Sci., India*, **22**, 371 (1953); *Chem. Abstr.*, **48**, 6912g (1954)
9. SOFFER, N., *Analyst*, **86**, 843 (1961)
10. CROSSLAND, H. and HOFMANN-BANG, N., *Acta. Chem. Scand.*, **15**, 1064 (1961)
11. LANG, R. and KURTENACKER, H., *Z. analyt. Chem.*, **123**, 81 (1942)
12. NAIR, V.R. and NAIR, C.G.R., *Talanta*, **18**, 432 (1971)
13. SOLYMOSI, F. and VARGA, A., *Analytica chim. Acta*, **17**, 608 (1957)
14. VEREK-SISKA, J., ECKSCHLAGER, K. and WAGNEROVA, D.W., *Chemiké Listy*, **59**, 1479 (1965); *Analyt. Abstr.*, **14**, 1952 (1967)
15. OZAWA, T., *J. chem. Soc. Japan, pure Chem. Sect.*, **87**, 859 (1966); *Analyt. Abstr.*, **14**, 7454 (1967)

Dithionite

Sodium dithionite ($Na_2S_2O_4$), sometimes known by the older names sodium hydrosulphite and sodium hyposulphite, finds use as a bleaching agent in the textile and paper industries, and in the dyeing of cellulose fibres.

Dithionites are extremely powerful reducing agents, even stronger than bisulphites, to which they are oxidized in aqueous solution.

Dry and anhydrous alkali dithionites are stable. On heating to about 190 °C they are converted to sulphite and thiosulphate with evolution of SO_2. Hydrated salts and aqueous solutions are rapidly oxidized in air to sulphate and bisulphite. In the absence of air such solutions are still unstable and disproportionate into bisulphite and thiosulphate.

$$2Na_2S_2O_4 + H_2O \rightarrow 2NaHSO_3 + Na_2S_2O_3$$

The rate of disproportionation is dependent[1] on temperature, concentration and pH. An investigation of the anaerobic decomposition of aqueous solutions of sodium dithionite has been reported recently[2].

The determination of dithionite is included in several accounts of the general analytical chemistry of sulphur compounds[3–5].

Determination

Titrimetric methods

1. Iodimetric methods

Dithionite is oxidized to sulphate by iodine

$$S_2O_4^{2-} + 3I_2 + 4H_2O \rightarrow 2SO_4^{2-} + 6I^- + 8H^+ \tag{1}$$

Dithionite also undergoes an important reaction with formaldehyde in which formaldehyde bisulphite and formaldehyde sulphoxylate are formed.

$$S_2O_4^{2-} + 2HCHO + H_2O \rightarrow HCHO\cdot HSO_3^- + HCHO\cdot HSO_2^- \tag{2}$$

Formaldehyde bisulphite does not react with iodine but the sulphoxylate is oxidized thus:

$$HCHO\cdot HSO_2^- + 2I_2 + 2H_2O \rightarrow SO_4^{2-} + 4I^- + 3H^+ + HCHO \tag{3}$$

A further point of interest is that formaldehyde masks any bisulphite present leaving only formaldehyde sulphoxylate to react with iodine.

A method based on the above reactions was published by Merriman[6] and this was subsequently recommended by the American Association of Textile Chemists and Colorists[7]. It is not applicable when significant amounts of thiosulphate, sulphite and other oxidizable impurities, not masked by formaldehyde, are present.

An extended form of this method was developed by Wollak[8] for dithionite, bisulphite, and thiosulphate. Three iodimetric procedures are involved:

1. An excess of standard iodine is added to the sample in the presence of formaldehyde. Excess iodine is titrated with standard thiosulphate. Dithionite undergoes the reactions shown in equations (2) and (3). Thiosulphate present reacts in its normal manner with iodine.
2. The calculated equivalent amount of iodine is added to another aliquot, followed by excess of sulphite. The latter reacts with tetrathionate formed by thiosulphate and iodine

$$S_4O_6^{2-} + SO_3^{2-} \rightarrow S_3O_6^{2-} + S_2O_3^{2-} \tag{4}$$

   Excess sulphite is masked by formaldehyde and the thiosulphate formed in (4) is titrated with I_2.
3. A third aliquot is added to a known excess of standard I_2 and a back-titration made with standard thiosulphate. Dithionite reacts according to equation (1). Bisulphite reacts thus:

$$HSO_3^- + I_2 + H_2O \rightarrow HSO_4^- + 2HI \tag{5}$$

A critical evaluation of the Wollak method has been carried out by Danehy and Zubritsky[2], who validate it, and derive the explicit relations between the titres by which the concentrations of the three components can be evaluated. The experimental procedure is given below.

Nair and Nair[9] have developed a modification of the Wollak method, using Chloramine-T.

Other iodimetric approaches have been used in the development of analytical procedures. Schulek and Maros[10] utilize the disproportionation of aqueous solutions of dithionite into disulphite and thiosulphate. Inspection of the appropriate equations will indicate that whereas 1 mol of dithionite reacts with 6 equivalents of iodine, the disproportionation products react with 5 equivalents only. Any disulphite and thiosulphate originally present remain unchanged.

Szekeres[11] has utilized the decomposition reaction of dithionite in the presence of HCl, for analysis of $S_2O_4^{2-}$–$S_2O_3^{2-}$–SO_3^{2-} mixtures.

Titrimetric analysis of sodium dithionite for dithionite, bisulphite and thiosulphate[8, 2]

Reagents

Formaldehyde solution: approx. 37%.
Acetic acid: 20%.
Iodine: approx. 0.05M (0.1 N). Standardized.
Sodium thiosulphate: approx. 0.1 M. Standardized.
Sodium sulphite solution: 25 g anhydrous $Na_2SO_3 \ell^{-1}$.

Procedure

(1) Add 35 mℓ of formaldehyde solution to 50 mℓ of boiled and cooled distilled water and add 0.3 g of $Na_2CO_3 \cdot 10H_2O$ which brings the pH to about 9. To this solution add a weighed solid sample or an aliquot of the sample, and swirl.

Add 25 mℓ of water and 5 mℓ of 20% aqueous acetic acid. Mix and then titrate with the standard iodine.

Milliequivalents of iodine consumed = Titre A.

(2) Add an aliquot to an excess of standard iodine (75 mℓ is sufficient for about 0.2 g of $Na_2S_2O_4$) in which about 1 g of hydrated sodium acetate has been dissolved. Slowly add Na_2SO_3 solution until the iodine solution is decolorized, and then add an additional 30 mℓ. Add two drops of phenolphthalein solution, and neutralize with approximately 1M NaOH. After 5 min add 10 mℓ of the formaldehyde solution and 10 mℓ of the 20% aqueous acetic acid. Mix and titrate with the standard iodine solution.

Milliequivalents of iodine consumed = Titre B.

(3) Add an aliquot of the dithionite sample to a known volume of standard iodine in which about 1 g of hydrated sodium acetate has been dissolved. Titrate the excess iodine with standard thiosulphate.

Milliequivalents of iodine consumed = Titre C.

Calculation

$$\text{m mol } S_2O_3^{2-} = 2B$$

$$\text{m mol } S_2O_4^{2-} = \frac{(A - 2B)}{4}$$

$$\text{m mol } HSO_3^{-} = \frac{(2C - 3A + 2B)}{4}$$

Note
The original papers should be consulted for the derivation of these expressions.

---

2. Other redox methods
Although iodimetric procedures are the most commonly used, a wide range of other redox reagents have been proposed for the determination of dithionite. These include hexacyanoferrate(III), Fe^{3+}, potassium iodomercurate(II) diammineargentate(I), tetraaminocuprate(II), and methylene blue. In some cases potentiometric end-points are employed.

Considering first ferrimetric procedures, Hahn[12] used a neutral ferric chloride solution with a mixture of hexacyanoferrate(II) and thiocyanate as indicator. A deep red colour due to the ferric thiocyanate complex is observed near the end-point. At the end-point itself the solution turns blue. The titration can be performed rapidly and without an inert atmosphere. Errors are quoted as less than 0.1 per cent.

Spencer[13], in a study of the kinetics of the air-oxidation of dithionite in aqueous solutions, found that titration with ammoniacal copper sulphate was the most satisfactory method.

$$2Cu(NH_3)_4^{2+} + S_2O_4^{2-} + 2H_2O \rightarrow 2Cu^+ + 2SO_3^{2-} + 4NH_4^+ + 4NH_3$$

The same reagent was investigated by Patel and Rao[14]. Reliable results are claimed even in the presence of large amounts of bisulphite–sulphite.

A method utilizing methylene blue as titrant was found to be effective by Rinker *et al.*[15,16]. During the titration the intense blue colour of the reagent is reduced to the almost colourless leuco-form. Experimental details are sparse, but indication is given that bisulphite, sulphite, and thiosulphate do not interfere.

Periodate is used by Kaushik and Rajendra[17]. Here, a measure of selectivity is attained by the presence of formaldehyde, as formaldehyde sulphoxylate formed from dithionate (equation (2) above) reacts with periodate but not the formaldehyde bisulphite.

Titration of dithionite with hexacyanoferrate(III) is one of the better known methods.

$$S_2O_4^{2-} + 2[Fe(CN)_6]^{3-} + 4OH^- \rightarrow 2SO_3^{2-} + 2[Fe(CN)_6]^{4-} + 2H_2O$$

Earlier forms of the method[18] employed iron(II) as indicator. Wawrzyczek and Rychcik[19] use an argon atmosphere with ferrous dimethylglyoximate as indicator. De Groot[20], again using hexacyanoferrate(III) as titrant, finds that methylene blue is an effective indicator.

Titrimetric determination of dithionite in technical sodium dithionite[20]

Procedure

To 90 mℓ of water in a titration flask, add 10 mℓ of approximately 0.1M NaOH, 10 mℓ of methanol and 1 mℓ of 0.2% aqueous methylene blue. Connect to a supply of oxygen-free nitrogen, and pass a stream of the gas through the solution continuously.

To remove oxygen from the solution, add a little sodium dithionite, then add 0.02M $K_3Fe(CN)_6$ to a pale blue colour.

Add the sample of dithionite (containing about 250 mg of $Na_2S_2O_4$) and titrate the solution with 0.1M $K_3Fe(CN)_6$ to the reappearance of a blue colour.

Note

Sulphide interferes and must be removed. No interference is given by the following in the amounts stated.

Na_3PO_4	(0.2 g)	$Na_2S_2O_3$	(0.5 g)
$Na_4P_2O_7$	(0.2 g)	EDTA	(0.5 g)
$Na_5P_3O_{10}$	(0.2 g)	Na_2SO_3	(1 g)
Na_2SO_4	(0.2 g)	$Na_2S_3O_6$	(0.1 g)

NaCl, Na_2CO_3, urea and wood flour do not interfere.

Spectroscopic methods

Colorimetric methods are based on the ability of dithionite to reduce certain dyes to the colourless form. Goebel and Roseira[21] used inanthrene yellow G (C.I. 1118). Dithionite induces a hypsochromic shift which may be measured by comparison with a colour scale. The same investigators developed other methods based on decomposition of azorubine (C.I. 179) and amaranth.

Whaley and Gyan[22] used naphthol yellow S for semi-quantitative colorimetric estimation of dithionite. On adding the dithionite sample to the dye, the colour immediately turns from yellow to red. The time taken for restoration of the yellow colour is a semi-quantitative measure of the dithionite present. No interference is given by sulphite, sulphate, sulphide, sulphur dioxide, chloride, hydroxyl or alkoxide.

An indirect method by Buscarons, Artigas and Rodriguez-Roda[23] utilizes the red complex formed between chromate and *o*-dianisidine. In this method dithionite is allowed to react with a known excess of chromate, and the remaining chromate reacted with *o*-dianisidine. After an interval the absorption is measured at 470 nm. The method, which is both rapid and simple, is applicable to 0.1–4 μg mℓ$^{-1}$ of dithionite. It should be noted that *o*-dianisidine is carcinogenic.

Electroanalytical methods

1. Potentiometric methods

Potentiometric procedures have been based on hexacyanoferrate(III), iron-(III), and thallium(III).

Dithionite is oxidized to sulphite by hexacyanoferrate(III) under mild conditions. The potentiometric end-point can be observed at this stage. If the sample also contains sulphite, further oxidation in strongly alkaline solution at 50–60 °C in the presence of OsO_4 as catalyst, converts[24, 25] to sulphate. The method allows the simultaneous determination of dithionite, sulphite, and thiosulphate with an accuracy within 0.4 per cent.

Iron(III) has been used by Berterolle and Giuffre[26].

Wawrzyczek, Tylzanowska and Jacyk[27] find that potential changes of 300 mV or more are produced at the inflection point in the titration of $Na_2S_2O_4$ with thallium(III) chloride using platinum and calomel electrodes. The same response occurs when Na_2SO_3 and $Na_2S_2O_5$ are titrated with the reagent. A visual titration using starch–iodide is also possible.

2. Polarographic methods

Automatic polarographic determination of dithionite in the presence of NaOH has been reported[28]. Application is made to reduction solutions in the dyestuff industry. In the absence of oxygen dithionite gives an oxidation wave at -0.45 V *vs.* SCE. No interference is given by thiosulphate, sulphate, HSO_4^-, or less than 0.01 % of dyes in the indanthrene series.

Lem and Wayman[29] report the continuous polarographic determination of dithionite in a 0.5M $(NH_4)_2HPO_4$–0.5M aq. NH_3 basal electrolyte containing a drop of wetting agent. An amperometric titration is made using 0.2N Rubine (C.I. Acid Red 14).

References

1. JELLINEK, K. and JELLINEK, E., *Z. phys. Chem.*, **93**, 325 (1919)
2. DANEHY, J.P. and ZUBRITSKY, C.W., *Analyt. Chem.*, **46**, 391 (1974)
3. SZEKERES, L., *Talanta*, **21**, 2 (1974)
4. BLASIUS, E., HORN, G., KNOCKEL, A., MUNCH, J. and WAGNER, H., in *Inorganic Sulphur Chemistry* (Ed. G. Nickless), Elsevier, Amsterdam, 220 (1968)
5. HAFF, L.V., in *The Analytical Chemistry of Sulphur and its Compounds* (Ed. J.H. Karchmer), Part 1, Wiley-Interscience, New York, 244 (1970)
6. MERRIMAN, R. W., *Chem. Ind., Lond.*, **42**, 290 (1923)
7. *Am. Dyestuff Reptr*, **46**, 443 (1957); *Analyt. Abstr.*, **5**, 1498 (1958)
8. WOLLAK, R., *Z. analyt. Chem.*, **80**, 1 (1930)
9. NAIR, V.R. and NAIR, C.G.R., *Res. Ind.*, **16**, 47 (1971); *Chem. Abstr.*, **76**, 54069s (1972)
10. SCHULEK, E. and MAROS, L., *Acta. chim. hung.*, **17**, 273 (1958); *Analyt. Abstr.*, **6**, 1279 (1959)
11. SZEKERES, L., *Z. analyt. Chem.*, **203**, 178 (1964); *Analyt. Abstr.*, **12**, 5130 (1965)
12. HAHN, F.L., *Analytica chim. Acta*, **3**, 62 (1949)
13. SPENCER, M.S., *Trans. Faraday Soc.*, **63**, 2510 (1967)
14. PATEL, C.C. and RAO, M.R.A., *Proc. natn. Inst. Sci. India*, **15**, 115 (1949)
15. RINKER, R.G., GORDON, T.P., MASON, D.M., SAKAIDA, R.R. and CORCORAN, W.H., *J. phys., Chem., Ithaca*, **64**, 573 (1960)
16. RINKER, R. G., LYNN, S., MASON, D. M. and CORCORAN, W. H., *IEC Fundam.*, **4**, 282 (1965)
17. KAUSHIK, R. L. and RAJENDRA, P., *J. Indian chem. Soc.*, **46**, 405 (1969)
18. *Ciba Rev.*, **4**, 1391 (1941)

19. WAWRZYCZEK, W. and RYCHCIK, W., *Chemia analit.*, **8**, 539 (1963); *Analyt. Abst.* **11**, 3639 (1964)
20. DE GROOT, D. C., *Z. analyt. Chem.*, **229**, 335 (1967); *Analyt. Abstr.*, **15**, 6122 (1968)
21. GOEBEL, E.F. and ROSEIRA, A., *Rev. Quim. Ind. Rio de Janerio*, **26**, 20 (1957); *Analyt. Abstr.*, **5**, 1832 (1958)
22. WHALEY, T.P. and GYAN, J.A., *Analyt. chem.*, **29**, 1499 (1957)
23. BUSCARONS, F., ARTIGAS, J. and RODRIGUEZ-RODA, C., *Analytica chim. Acta*, **23**, 214 (1960)
24. SOLYMOSI, F. and VARGA, A., *Analytica chim. Acta*, **17**, 608 (1957)
25. SOLYMOSI, F. and VARGA, A., *Magy. kém. Foly.*, **65**, 52 (1959); *Analyt. Abstr.*, **6**, 4746 (1959)
26. BERTEROLLE, E. and GUIFFRE, L., *Tinctoria*, **51**, 364 (1954)
27. WAWRZCZEK, W., TYLZANOWSKA, D. and JACYK, A., *Chemia analit.*, **13**, 575 (1968); *Analyt. Abstr.*, **17**, 2635 (1969)
28. OKA, S., *Japan Analyst*, **10**, 774 (1961); *Analyt. Abstr.*, **10**, 3193 (1963)
29. LEM, W.J. and WAYMAN, M., *J. Soc. Dyers Colour.*, 277 (1967); *Analyt. Abstr.*, **15**, 5957 (1968)

Peroxodisulphate

Peroxodisulphates are derived from peroxodisulphuric acid (Marshall's acid). The $S_2O_8^{2-}$ ion (*Structure 64*) is also known by the alternative names persulphate, peroxidisulphate and peroxydisulphate:

$$\left[\begin{array}{ccccccc} & & \text{O} & & & \text{O} & \\ & & | & & & | & \\ \text{O}- & & \text{S}-\text{O}- & \text{O}- & & \text{S}- & \text{O} \\ & & | & & & | & \\ & & \text{O} & & & \text{O} & \end{array}\right]^{2-}$$

Structure 64 *Peroxodisulphate* $(S_2O_8)^{2-}$

When dry and free from water of crystallization, alkali peroxodisulphates are quite stable. Aqueous solutions are moderately stable. During hydrolysis hydrogen peroxide is produced. Peroxodisulphates usually contain this compound as impurity. Several methods have been developed for analysis of mixtures containing the two species.

As strong oxidants, peroxodisulphates find application in bleaching and dyeing. Other uses are to be found in medicine and the cosmetic industry. Ammonium or potassium peroxodisulphates are often added in small quantities ($\sim$ 110 ppm) to flour as improvers.

The analytical chemistry of peroxodisulphate is included in several reviews covering the analysis of sulphur compounds[1–3]. Behrends[4] in a paper on gravimetric and spectrophotometric methods for determination of $S_2O_8^{2-}$, includes a survey of analytical procedures with 146 references.

Separations

Peroxodisulphate can be separated from sulphuric acid, sulphate, hypophosphite, phosphite, hypophosphate and condensed phosphates by paper chromatography[5]. Both isopropanol–chloroacetic acid and isopropanol–iso-butanol–ethanol–aq. NH_3 can be used as mobile solvents.

Thin-layer chromatography on silica gel–starch has been used to separate sulphate, thiosulphate, sulphite and peroxodisulphate, using methanol–propanol–0.880 NH_3–H_2O (10:10:1:2) as solvent[6].

Determination

Analytical methods for peroxodisulphate rely almost exclusively on redox reactions.

Gravimetric methods

Behrends[4] has investigated compounds of the type $[R_3P(CH_2)_nPR_2]^{2+}$ where R = aryl or aralkyl radicals as precipitating reagents for peroxo-disulphate. Using $[(C_6H_5)_3P(CH_2)_4P(C_6H_5)_3]Br_2$ as reagent 20–70 mg of peroxodisulphate can be determined gravimetrically by precipitation as $[(C_6H_5)_3P(CH_2)_4P(C_6H_5)_3]S_2O_8 \cdot 2H_2O$. The anhydrous form is weighed after drying at 150 °C.

Titrimetric methods

1. Iodimetric methods

Earlier studies on liberation of iodine from KI by peroxodisulphate suggested that the reaction was too slow for analytical work.

$$S_2O_8{}^{2-} + 2I^- \rightarrow 2SO_4{}^{2-} + I_2$$

Wahba, El Asmar and El Sadr[7] proposed the use of ferric chloride as catalyst. Indelli and Prue[8] used traces of iron as catalyst, a large excess of KI, and a 24 h reaction time.

Gupta[9,10] employed the alternative approach of hydrolysis in strong H_2SO_4 followed by titration of the resulting H_2O_2 with $KMnO_4$ or iodine. A subsequent study of the peroxodisulphate–iodide reaction by Frigerio[11] showed it to be pH-dependent, and that in neutral solution I^- is quantitatively oxidized to iodine rapidly, without heat, catalysts, or interference by atmospheric oxygen. The method based on these findings is rapid and simple. Where micro amounts of peroxodisulphate are involved, an alternative spectrophotometric procedure is provided. The macro procedure is given below.

The iodimetric method has been utilized for the analysis of peroxo-disulphate–hydrogen peroxide mixtures, an important determination for reasons given earlier. First the peroxide is selectively reduced with hypo-chlorite, the excess of this being eliminated with cyanide. After removing excess cyanide in a stream of CO_2 the peroxydisulphate is determined iodimetrically[12].

Iodimetric titration of peroxodisulphate[11]

Reagents

Potassium iodide: 6M.
Sodium thiosulphate: 0.1M.
Phosphate buffer: pH 6.85; 0.05 mol KH_2PO_4 plus 0.05 mol $K_2HPO_4 \ell^{-1}$.

Procedure

Accurately weigh out samples containing 1–2 mmol of peroxodisulphate and dissolve them in 20 m of the buffer solution. Add 10 mℓ of 6M KI and titrate with standard thiosulphate until the yellow iodine colour just disappears. Starch may be used as indicator if necessary.

---

2. Using Fe(II)

In acid medium, peroxodisulphate is reduced by ferrous sulphate.

$$S_2O_8^{2-} + 2Fe^{2+} \rightarrow 2SO_4^{2-} + 2Fe^{3+}$$

Kolthoff and Carr[13] have concluded that of the available titrimetric procedures the iodimetric and ferrometric ones are superior. Excess ferric sulphate can be back-titrated with standard ceric sulphate. In a variation of the method, Erdey, Buzas and Vigh[14] used ascorbic acid for the titration of Fe^{3+} ions produced in the reduction.

3. Using miscellaneous reductants

Arsenic(III) has been used[15,16] for the quantitative reduction of peroxodisulphate. In the first paper an iodimetric end-procedure is used; the second employs $KMnO_4$.

The well-established hexacyanoferrate(III)–ascorbic acid reaction has been applied by Erdey and Svehla[17]. The method permits determination of both peroxodisulphate, hydrogen peroxide and their mixtures.

4. Compleximetric methods

One procedure is simply an extension of (2) above. Excess Fe^{2+} is oxidized by peroxodisulphate to Fe^{3+} and this titrated with standard EDTA[18] using salicylic acid as indicator. The method is applicable to 10–270 mg of peroxodisulphate.

Another approach is to decompose peroxodisulphate into sulphate which is determined indirectly with EDTA. This has been employed by de Sousa[19]. The decomposition was produced by boiling an aqueous solution. Excess barium chloride was added to precipitate the sulphate, and the excess was determined by titration with EDTA.

Spectroscopic methods

1. Colorimetric and spectrophotometric methods

The iodimetric procedure by Frigerio[11] discussed earlier can be adapted to spectrophotometry where micro amounts of peroxodisulphate are involved.

A pH 6.85 buffer solution is added to the sample and the absorbance measured at 355 nm. The method is suitable for 0.01–0.15 μmol of peroxodisulphate.

Behrends[4] utilizes the reaction of peroxodisulphate with the tetraphenylarsonium cation. The resulting bis(tetraphenylarsonium)peroxodisulphate is extracted into 1,2-dichloroethane, treated with iodide and the absorbance measured at 366 nm. Mariano[20] has reported that peroxodisulphate, peroxosulphate, and hydrogen peroxide can be determined rapidly and accurately, in mixtures, using ceric and ferrous sulphate solutions. When all three are present the procedure consists of adding arsenic(III). This allows hydrogen peroxide to be determined with cerium(IV) by the reaction:

$$2Ce^{4+} + H_2O_2 \rightarrow 2Ce^{3+} + 2H^+ + O_2$$

Addition of iron(II) to the same sample, followed by measurement of the iron(III) formed, gives the peroxodisulphate content. Finally the total oxidizing power of another aliquot is found by addition of iron(II) followed by measurement of iron(III) spectrophotometrically. Peroxosulphate is found by difference.

The extent to which Alcian blue (C.I. 74,240) is irreversibly oxidized and decolorized has been used for determination[21] of peroxodisulphate. No interference is given by an 8-fold molar excess of potassium bromate over peroxodisulphate.

A very sensitive method for the indirect determination of peroxodisulphate using triphenylmethane dyes has appeared[22]. Several other oxidizing species can be determined using the same principle. The method is based on the reaction of iodide or bromide with certain triphenylmethane dyes, in the presence of chloramine-T. The resulting I^+ or Br^+ cations cause a decrease in colour intensity of the dye. Application to peroxodisulphate (and other oxidants) is by their reaction with iodide. The sensitivity is about 0.01 $\mu g\, m\ell^{-1}$.

2. *Other spectroscopic methods*

A fluorimetric method has been based on re-oxidation of leuco-fluorescein to fluorescein through the action of peroxodisulphate[23]. Applicable to as little as 5–10 ppm of $(NH_4)_2S_2O_8$ the method was used for the determination of peroxodisulphate in flour. Under controlled conditions the intensity of fluorescence is proportional to the peroxodisulphate content. Bromate interferes.

Infra-red methods have been reported[24,25] for the identification of the peroxodisulphate ion.

Molecular emission cavity analysis (MECA) has been applied to several sulphur anions including peroxodisulphate. The technique[26] enables ng amounts to be determined in samples of a few microlitres. A brief account of the technique is given in the sulphide section. Peroxodisulphate alone gives a weak sulphur emission. This is enhanced in the presence of phosphoric acid. The response is very similar to that for sulphate.

Electroanalytical methods

1. *Potentiometric methods*

Peroxodisulphate can be titrated potentiometrically in strongly alkaline solution using the arsenite–iodine system[27]. Excess arsenic(III) is added to the sample and the solution titrated with standard iodine at 60–70 °C, using platinum and standard calomel electrodes.

The use of photosensitizing catalyst systems in conjunction with a light source has featured in studies by Sierra and Monzon[28]. Peroxodisulphate is titrated with iron(II) in the presence of iodide, Ag^+, and erythrosine B under illumination from a 150 W lamp. A similar system employs mercurous nitrate as titrant[29].

2. Polarographic methods

Polarography is capable of discriminating[30] between $H_2S_2O_8$, H_2SO_5, and H_2O_2. Using a platinum micro-electrode in conjunction with a mercurous sulphate reference electrode, in M $HClO_4$, HNO_3, or H_2SO_4 acids, three distinct waves appear between −1.4 and −0.2 V. These correspond to reduction of H_2SO_4, oxidation–reduction of H_2O_2, and reduction of $H_2S_2O_8$.

Potassium peroxodisulphate–alkali halide systems have been studied by d.c. and a.c. (sine wave) polarography[31]. A peak, probably due to a product of interaction between peroxodisulphate and the halide close to the surface of the dropping mercury electrode, is proportional to the peroxodisulphate concentration provided the halide ion concentration is kept within limits.

Gas chromatographic methods

Peroxodisulphate can be determined by a simple gas chromatographic procedure[32] after reduction to hydrogen sulphide. A 20% solution of stannous chloride in strong phosphoric acid is used as reductant.

References

1. SZEKERES, L., *Talanta*, **21**, 2 (1974)
2. BLASIUS, E., HORN, G., KNOCHEL, A., MUNCH, J. and WAGNER, H., *Inorganic Sulphur Chemistry* (Ed. G. Nickless), Elsevier, Amsterdam, 199 (1968)
3. HAFF, L.V., in *The Analytical Chemistry of Sulphur and its Compounds* (Ed. J.H. Karchmer), Part 1, Wiley-Interscience, New York, 255 (1970)
4. BEHRENDS, K., *Z. analyt. Chem.*, **226**, 1 (1967); *Analyt. Abstr.*, **15**, 2598 (1968)
5. RUDNICKI, R., *Chemia analit.*, **6**, 761 (1961); *Analyt Abstr.*, **9**, 2731 (1962)
6. SEILER, H. and ERLENMEYER, H., *Helv. chim. Acta*, **47**, 264 (1964)
7. WAHBA, N., EL ASMAR, M.F. and EL SADR, M.M., *Analyt. Chem.*, **31**, 1870 (1959)
8. INDELLI, A. and PRUE, J.E., *J. chem. Soc.*, 107 (1959)
9. GUPTA, Y.K., *Analytica chim. Acta*, **24**, 415 (1961)
10. GUPTA, Y.K., *Z. analyt. Chem.*, **180**, 260 (1961); *Analyt. Abstr.*, **8**, 4604 (1961)
11. FRIGERIO, N.A., *Analyt. Chem.*, **35**, 412 (1963)
12. SCHULEK, E., PUNGOR, E. and TROMPLER, J., *Acta. chim. hung.*, **4**, 393 (1954); *Analyt. Abstr.*, **2**, 612 (1954)
13. KOLTHOFF, I. N. and CARR, E. M., *Analyt. Chem.*, **25**, 298 (1953)
14. ERDEY, L., BUZAS, I. and VIGH, K., *Periodica Polytech.*, **3**, 1 (1959); *Analyt. Abstr.*, **6**, 4262 (1959)
15. GUPTA, Y.K. and GHOSH, S., *Analytica chim. Acta*, **17**, 379 (1957)
16. PRASAD, G. and GUPTA, Y.K., *Z. analyt. Chem.*, **198**, 173 (1963); *Analyt. Abstr.*, **11**, 4827 (1964)
17. ERDEY, L. and SVEHLA, G., *Analytica chim. Acta*, **27**, 164 (1962)
18. KELLNER, A. and SZEKERES, L., *Chemist Analyst*, **54**, 75 (1965)
19. DE SOUSA, A., *Inf. Quim. Anal.*, **15**, 91 (1961); *Analyt. Abstr.*, **9**, 1028 (1962)

20. MARIANO, M.H., *Analyt. Chem.*, **40**, 1662 (1968)
21. VILLEGAS, E., POMERANZ, Y. and SHELLENBERGER, J.A., *Analytica chim. Acta*, **29**, 145 (1963)
22. RAMANAUSKAS, E.I., BUNIKIENE, L.V., SAPROGONENE, M.S., SHULYUENE, A.K. and ZHILENAITE, M.V., *Zh analit. Khim.*, **24**, 244 (1969); *Analyt. Abstr.*, **19**, 1022 (1970)
23. AUERBACH, M.E., ECKERT, W. and ANGELL, E., *Cereal. Chem.*, **26**, 490 (1949); *Chem. Abstr.*, **44**, 2135c (1950)
24. AL-KAYSSI, M. and MAGEE, R.J., *Talanta*, **9**, 667 (1962)
25. KYRTI, J.R., *Acta chem. fenn.*, **38B**, 51 (1965); *Chem. Abstr.*, **63**, 16g (1965)
26. BELCHER, R., BOGDANSKI, S.L., KNOWLES, D.J. and TOWNSHEND, A., *Analytica chim. Acta*, **77**, 53 (1975)
27. NORKUS, P.K. and SHIMKAYAVICHYUTE, G.S., *Zh. analit. Khim.*, **27**, 1419 (1972)
28. SIERRA, J.F. and MONZON, E., *An. R. Soc. esp. Fis Quim. B*, **63**,51 (1967); *Analyt. Abstr.*, **15**, 3303 (1968)
29. SIERRA, J.F. and SANCHEZ-PEDRENO, C., *An. R. Soc. esp. Fis Quim. B*, **63**, 1111 (1967); *Analyt. Abstr.*, **16**, 1845 (1969)
30. RASPI, G. and VENTURINI, M., *Chimica Ind., Milano*, **50**, 536 (1968); *Chem. Abstr.*, **69**, 49018a (1968)
31. HAKOILA, E., *Talanta*, **15**, 55 (1968)
32. ITO, S., *J. chem. Soc. Japan, pure Chem. Sect.*, **90**, 1027 (1969); *Analyt. Abstr.*, **19**, 4842 (1970)

Polysulphide

Though not an anion as such, the inclusion of polysulphide is justified in view of its important connections with other sulphur anions. Alkali and ammonium polysulphides have the general formula M_2S_x where $x > 1$. Sodium members Na_2S_2, Na_2S_4, and Na_2S_5 are known; potassium members up to hexa- are known.

Polysulphides are important in connection with the pulping industry. A common method in alkaline pulping is to employ a sulphate digestion liquor. The active constituents of this 'white liquor' include sodium hydroxide and sodium sulphide with smaller amounts of sodium carbonate, sodium sulphate, sodium thiosulphate and sodium sulphite.

Sulphate pulping requires a recovery process for the digestion liquor, this involving separation of 'black liquor' from the pulp, and its evaporation and combustion to recover the inorganic constituents. A solution of the combustion smelt is referred to as 'green liquor', this containing ferrous sulphide, manganese dioxide etc. This is subsequently converted to 'white liquor' for further digestion of pulp[1].

Polysulphides also find application in plant protection and as chemical intermediates. Determination of polysulphides (and other sulphur species) is often required in industrial water used on blast furnace slags.

Polysulphides are invariably accompanied by other sulphur-containing species, usually sulphide (monosulphide), thiosulphate and sulphite. Accordingly, the present discussion will give emphasis to determination of polysulphide in such mixtures. In the analysis of polysulphides it is normal to differentiate between total sulphur, monosulphide-S, and polysulphide-S.

Analytical methods have evolved from essentially classical gravimetric procedures to classical titrimetry, and more recently to potentiometric titrimetry. Nevertheless, many of the older basic reactions used for separating and differentiating between the various species, remain in current use.

Determination

The analytical chemistry of polysulphide has been reviewed by Ahlgren and Harler[2]. It is also included in several recent reviews of the analytical chemistry of sulphur compounds[3–5].

Many polysulphide analytical procedures, particularly those applicable to mixtures containing polysulphide, rely on certain basic reactions. In order to avoid repetition later, the more important basic reactions will be summarized below.

Polysulphide-sulphur reacts with sulphite in neutral solution at 50 °C to form thiosulphate.

$$Na_2SS_x + xNa_2SO_3 \rightarrow Na_2S + xNa_2S_2O_3 \qquad (1)$$

Elemental and polysulphide-sulphur are hydrolysed by hot water to give hydrogen sulphide and thiosulphate. This takes place rapidly in alkaline solution.

$$4S + 3H_2O \rightarrow S_2O_3^{2-} + 2H_2S + 2H^+ \qquad (2)$$

Iodine in acid medium only oxidizes the monosulphide moiety of polysulphide.

$$H_2SS_x + I_2 \rightarrow 2H^+ + 2I^- + (x + 1)S \qquad (3)$$

Thiosulphate is also oxidized

$$2S_2O_3^{2-} + I_2 \rightarrow S_4O_6^{2-} + 2I^-$$

The total sulphur content of polysulphide can be measured by oxidation with alkaline peroxide solution. The excess of alkali is back-titrated with standard sulphuric acid.

$$Na_2S_x + (2x - 2)NaOH + (3x - 1)H_2O_2 \rightarrow xNa_2SO_4 + 4xH_2O \qquad (4)$$

Polysulphide reacts with alkaline cyanide under anaerobic conditions to give 1 thiocyanate for each polysulphide-sulphur atom.

$$Na_2SS_x + xCN^- \rightarrow Na_2S + xSCN^- \qquad (5)$$

In boric acid medium hydrogen sulphide is produced and excess hydrogen cyanide is removed by boiling in acid. Thiocyanate and thiosulphate remain unaffected by this treatment.

Bromine (bromate/bromide) or hypobromite oxidize monosulphide and polysulphide-sulphur as well as thiosulphate, to sulphate.

$$S^{2-} + 4H_2O + 4Br_2 \rightarrow SO_4^{2-} + 8H^+ + 8Br^- \qquad (6)$$

$$S + 4H_2O + 3Br_2 \rightarrow SO_4^{2-} + 8H^+ + 6Br^- \qquad (7)$$

When present with polysulphide, sulphite may be masked with formaldehyde and the polysulphide determined without interference.

$$HCHO + SO_3^{2-} + H^+ \rightarrow CH_2OH \cdot SO_3^- \qquad (8)$$

Thiocyanate is oxidized by bromine but not iodine in acidic solution.

$$SCN^- + 4H_2O + 4Br_2 \rightarrow SO_4^{2-} + 8H^+ + 7Br^- + BrCN \qquad (9)$$

Gravimetric methods

Polysulphide-sulphur is easily converted to elemental sulphur which can be evaluated gravimetrically[6]. This is accomplished by neutralizing an aqueous solution of polysulphide to methyl orange, or by heating in benzene or carbon disulphide followed by evaporation of the organic solvent.

Another gravimetric procedure involves total sulphur. Here oxidation is carried out with alkaline peroxide or bromine, the resulting sulphate being evaluated gravimetrically as barium sulphate. The above procedures do not take account of the thiosulphate content of polysulphide, and this is invariably present. Gravimetric procedures are sometimes used in conjunction with iodimetric titration which gives the monosulphide moiety only. Alternatively, monosulphide can be separated and determined gravimetrically as cadmium sulphide.

Modern methods tend to avoid the more time-consuming gravimetric procedures.

Titrimetric methods

1. Iodimetric methods

A standard method for determination of polysulphide was introduced by Schulek[7] in 1925.

The sample solution is boiled with alkaline cyanide in a boric acid medium. Hydrogen sulphide is produced as well as one thiocyanate for each polysulphide-sulphur atom (basic reaction (5)). Excess cyanide is removed by boiling the acidified solution. Thiocyanate and any thiosulphate present remain unaffected by this treatment. Thiocyanate is oxidized to bromine cyanide by bromine, the excess bromine being destroyed with phenol. On adding KI, iodine is liberated and titrated with standard thiosulphate.

$$BrCN + 2I^- \rightarrow CN^- + I_2 + Br^-$$

1 mℓ of 0.1M thiosulphate ≡ 1.603 mg of polysulphide-sulphur.

If thiosulphate is present, the solution is transferred to a volumetric flask after the boiling with alkaline cyanide stage. Polysulphide-sulphur is determined in one aliquot using the above method. Thiosulphate is determined on a second aliquot by acidifying with HCl, treating with excess iodine, and back-titrating with standard thiosulphate.

1 mℓ 0.05M iodine ≡ 6.40 mg thiosulphate-sulphur.

Another iodimetric method was introduced by Kurtenacker and Bittner[8]. Here the polysulphide-sulphur is allowed to react with sodium sulphite at about 50 °C in neutral solution. Thiosulphate is formed (reaction (1)). Sulphide, which is also produced in the reaction, is precipitated by addition of zinc acetate, and is filtered off. Addition of formaldehyde destroys excess sulphite (reaction (8)). The solution is acidified with acetic acid, and the thiosulphate titrated with standard iodine. If the original sample is thought to contain thiosulphate, and this is very likely in polysulphide solutions, a correction can be made by carrying out the above procedure omitting the sulphite.

Analysis of mixtures containing polysulphides and other sulphur-containing species, is important. Szekeres[9] has developed methods for polysulphide, sulphide and thiosulphate when present together. One procedure utilizes the fact that iodine oxidizes only monosulphide-sulphur and thiosulphate in acid medium, but bromine oxidizes polysulphide-sulphur in addition. The reactions are (3) and (6) above. One aliquot is oxidized by excess iodine, the excess being determined by thiosulphate titration. The titre represents monosulphide-sulphur and thiosulphate. Treatment of a second aliquot with bromine gives polysulphide-sulphur, monosulphide-sulphur and thiosulphate. A third aliquot is treated with alkaline cyanide and boric acid according to equation (5). This masks polysulphide-sulphur as thiocyanate and prevents its hydrolysis on heating the solution with boric acid. The latter treatment removes the monosulphide moiety as hydrogen sulphide. A fourth aliquot is boiled with boric acid to expel hydrogen sulphide, and then treated similarly to the second. The amount of each of the species present is calculated using equations.

Similar reactions have been employed recently in a method for analysis of industrial water used on blast-furnace slags[10]. Such samples may contain sulphate, thiosulphate, sulphide, polysulphide, sulphite and trithionate.

An alternative method for sulphide, polysulphide and thiosulphate has been developed by Szekeres[11]. This includes conversion of polysulphide-sulphur to sulphide, and its precipitation as cadmium sulphide, followed by an iodimetric titration.

A method based on iodimetric, compleximetric and acidimetric procedures enables polysulphide, thiosulphate and total sulphide-sulphur to be evaluated[12]. First polysulphide is precipitated as ZnS_x using ammoniacal zinc sulphate. This is filtered off and boiled with HCl. The resulting element sulphur is oxidized with alkaline peroxide, the excess of this being back-titrated with standard acid. 1 mℓ M HCl ≡ 0.016033 g polysulphide-sulphur. Any thiosulphate is removed during the ZnS_x filtration and can be determined iodimetrically. Total sulphide-sulphur is determined by conversion to sulphate using bromine, precipitating this as barium sulphate, and then evaluating it compleximetrically. Low values for polysulphide-sulphur can be caused[4] by some of the polysulphide-sulphur being converted to sulphide on boiling with HCl.

Wronski[13] has described several methods for determination of the monosulphide moiety in polysulphide. In one method, the polysulphide is treated with sodium sulphite (reaction (1)) and the resulting monosulphide titrated with *o*-hydroxymercuribenzoic acid. Details of the latter titration are given in the sulphide section.

2. *Acid–base titration*

Oxidation of polysulphide with alkaline peroxide enables the total sulphur content of polysulphide to be determined (reaction (4)). Feher and Berthold[14] have based a titrimetric procedure on this principle. The excess of sodium hydroxide is titrated with standard H_2SO_4.

Electroanalytical methods

Mixtures containing polysulphide, sulphide, and thiosulphate as ammonium salts have been analysed using the 'dead-stop' amperometric method with Pt electrodes[15]. The sulphide is titrated with ammoniacal silver nitrate without interference from thiosulphate. In a second aliquot, sulphide is removed by boiling with boric acid and the residual thiosulphate titrated with standard mercuric chloride. Finally, in a third aliquot, polysulphide is converted by sulphite to thiosulphate, and this determined after masking excess sulphite with formaldehyde.

Several potentiometric methods can be used for mixtures containing sulphur anions with polysulphide. White, green and black liquors can be analysed for polysulphide, thiosulphate, sulphite, and effective alkali using a mercury pool and saturated calomel electrode[16]. Essentially the same basic reactions are used. Polysulphide is converted by excess sulphite to sulphide and thiosulphate. After precipitation of sulphide as ZnS and masking sulphite with formaldehyde (reaction (8)), thiosulphate is titrated potentiometrically with standard $HgCl_2$.

The same workers[17] have published an automated micro method based on much the same method, but including sulphide. A more recent application of potentiometry has involved the sulphide ion-selective electrode[18, 19]. The same basic reactions are again used, with $HgCl_2$ as titrant. A Radelkis OP-S-711 sulphide ion-selective electrode is used to indicate end-points. The method is applied to white, green and black liquors containing polysulphide, sulphide, thiosulphate, sulphite and thiols.

References

1. TOMLINSON, G.H., in 'Pulp', *Kirk-Othmer Encyclopaedia of Chemical Technology*, 2nd edn, Vol. 16, Wiley, New York, 708 (1968)
2. AHLGREN, P. and HARLER, N., *Svensk. kem. Tidskr.*, **78**, 404 (1966); *Chem. Abstr.*, **66**, 25679d (1967)
3. BLASIUS, E., HORN, G., KNOCHEL, A., MUNCH, J. and WAGNER, H., *Inorganic Sulphur Chemistry*, (Ed. G. Nickless), Elsevier, Amsterdam, 199 (1968)
4. SZEKERES, L., *Talanta*, **21**, 2 (1974)
5. HAFF, L.V., in *The Analytical Chemistry of Sulphur and its Compounds* (Ed. J.H. Karchmer), Part 1, Wiley-Interscience, New York, 347 (1970)
6. GRIFFIN, R.C., *Technical Methods of Analysis*, McGraw-Hill, New York, 60 (1921)
7. SCHULEK, E., *Z. analyt. Chem.*, **65**, 352 (1925)
8. KURTENACKER, A. and BITTNER, K., *Z. analyt. Chem.*, **142**, 115 (1925); *Chem. Abstr.*, **19**, 2000 (1925)
9. SZEKERES, L., *Z. analyt. Chem.*, **178**, 81 (1960); *Analyt. Abstr.*, **8**, 2387 (1961)
10. BLASIUS, E., WAGNER, H. and ZIEGLER, K., *Arch. Eisenhütt Wes.*, **42**, 473 (1971); *Analyt. Abstr.*, **22**, 3164 (1972)
11. SZEKERES, L., *Pharm. Zentralhalle Dtl.*, **102**, 6 (1963); *Analyt. Abstr.*, **10**, 5137 (1963)
12. LEGRADI, L., *Analyst*, **86**, 854 (1961)
13. WRONSKI, M., *Analyt. Chem.*, **32**, 133 (1960)
14. FEHER, F. and BERTHOLD, H.J., *Z. analyt. Chem.*, **138**, 245 (1953)
15. KISS, S.A., *Z. analyt. Chem.*, **188**, 341 (1962), *Analyt. Abstr.*, **10**, 112 (1963)
16. DANIELSEN, A.J., JOHNSEN, K. and LANDMARK, P., *Norsk Skogind.*, **23**, 378 (1969); *Analyt. Abstr.*, **21**, 1252 (1971)
17. DANIELSEN, A.J., JOHNSEN, K. and LANDMARK, P., *Meddr. Pap Ind. Forsk. Inst.*, No. 232 (1969); *Norsk Skogind.*, **23**, 77 (1969); *Analyt. Abstr.*, **19**, 395 (1970)
18. PAPP, J. and HAVAS, J., *Magy kém. Foly.*, **76**, 307 (1970); *Analyt. Abstr.*, **20**, 4439 (1971)
19. PAPP, J., *Cellulose Chem. Technol.*, **5**, 147 (1971); *Analyt. Abstr.*, **22**, 2404 (1972)

Polythionates

When hydrogen sulphide is allowed to react with sulphite solutions over a period of days, a series of complex reactions takes place, the product being known as Wackenroder's solution. This contains trithionate ($S_3O_6{}^{2-}$), tetrathionate ($S_4O_6{}^{2-}$) and pentathionate ($S_5O_6{}^{2-}$) as well as thiosulphate.

Such mixtures occur in several industrial situations, for example in the cellular fabric industry. The analysis, both for individual and total polythionates, is important.

Determination of polythionates in the presence of other sulphur-containing anions is also important. Several analytical schemes have been proposed for mixtures containing tri- to hexa- together with sulphur oxy-acids. One investigation suggests the presence of polythionates with more than six sulphur atoms per molecule in many of the reaction mixtures previously studied[1]. Owing to the nature of the analytical methods themselves, this would throw doubt on their validity, if such species existed.

Determination of individual polythionates in pure form is relatively easy, but analysis of mixtures is more difficult. Titles of publications are not always indicative of their content. Some refer to 'determination of tetrathionate', implying some measure of selectivity, when other polythionates are also determined by the method.

Dithionate ($S_2O_6{}^{2-}$) is different in several respects to other members of the series, for example it is not easily oxidized. For this reason, dithionate is treated separately elsewhere and will only feature in this section when its determination is involved with other polythionates.

The preparation of potassium trithionate is described by Krause and Bush[2]. The preparation of the corresponding tetrathionate and pentathionate are given by Stamm, Goehring and Feldmann[3,4].

The analytical chemistry of sulphur compounds including polythionates has received considerable attention in recent years. Authoritative accounts appear in the monographs edited by Karchmer (Haff[5]) and Nickless (Blasius *et al.*[6]). The last mentioned account is comprehensive and includes much of the earlier work. Analysis of polythionates is included in a review of the analytical chemistry of sulphur acids by Szekeres[7].

Separations

The polythionates are so similar chemically that analysis of mixtures by classical methods is lengthy and liable to give erroneous results. Pollard, Jones and Nickless[8] have discussed the advantages of chromatographic separation prior to analysis. Chromatography in its various forms has made an important impact on the analysis of mixtures,though some of the methods are not without problems.

1. Based on fractional crystallization

Fractional crystallization of their benzidine[1] or pyridinocuprate complexes[9] has been reported.

Table 50 TLC methods for separation of polythionates

Technique	*Solvent system*	*Species separated*	*Ref.*
TLC silica gel–starch	Methanol–dioxan–conc. NH_3–H_2O (3:6:1:1)	$S_2O_6^{2-}$, $S_3O_6^{2-}$, $S_4O_6^{2-}$, $S_5O_6^{2-}$	11
TLC silica gel	Ethanol–butanol–conc. NH_3–H_2O (75:75:8–10:10–30 mℓ)	$S_3O_6^{2-}$, $S_4O_6^{2-}$, $S_5O_6^{2-}$, $S_2O_3^{2-}$	12
TLC Gelman SA and SG sheets	Butanol–pyridine–acetic acid–water (15:10:3:12)	$S_3O_6^{2-}$, $S_4O_6^{2-}$, SO_4^{2-}, $S_2O_3^{2-}$, SCN^-	13

2. *Based on solubility*

Mangan[10] has based a separation method on differences in solubility of lead thionates.

3. *Paper and thin-layer chromatography*

Experimental data on some TLC methods are given in *Table 50*. Several paper chromatographic methods have been published but the long time required for separation results in secondary reactions occurring on the paper itself. The technique is mainly restricted to qualitative work involving low concentrations of polythionates. When these concentrations are exceeded the size of the zones is such that a quantitative separation is no longer attained, i.e. overloading occurs. This is discussed in depth by Pollard, Jones and Nickless[8]. In some instances it is possible to perform quantitative analysis using paper chromatography. This is discussed later in this section.

4. *Anion-exchange chromatography*

Iguchi[14], using Dowex 1-X2 in chloride form has separated di-, tri-, tetra- and pentathionates, as well as the constituents of Wackenroder's solution. Dithionate is eluted with M HCl, trithionate with 3M HCl, tetrathionate with 6M HCl, and finally pentathionate with 9M HCl. In order to avoid high acidities, in which polythionates are less stable, Pollard, Nickless and Glover[15] begin the elution with potassium hydrogen phthalate. Their method enables the lower polythionates to be separated from thiosulphate and sulphite. Schmidt and Sand[16] found that separation of trithionate to hexathionate was not possible by ion-exchange, due to decomposition of hexathionate on the column. However, mixtures of SO_3^{2-}–$S_2O_3^{2-}$–$S_3O_6^{2-}$ and $S_3O_6^{2-}$–$S_4O_6^{2-}$–$S_5O_6^{2-}$ were separated without difficulty using NaCl or HCl as eluents.

5. *High performance liquid chromatography*

The recent application of high performance chromatography (HPLC) to polythionates found in Wackenroder's solution has produced encouraging results[17]. Trithionate to pentathionate and thiosulphate are separated and determined in 15 min. Further details appear later in this section.

Determination

Three aspects of polythionate analysis must be distinguished, the determination of individual members in pure form, the determination of total polythionate (or collective analysis) and the analysis of polythionate mixtures.

Determination of individual polythionates is not difficult, but analysis of mixtures has been extremely difficult. Haff[18] has noted that 'there appears to be no satisfactory method for the determination of individual polythionates in the presence of each other'. Recently HPLC has provided an elegant solution to this problem. Older methods are time-consuming. This has caused doubt as to whether decomposition of some species occurs during the analysis.

Before going on to particular methods, some of the basic reactions on which the methods depend will be reviewed.

Alkali sulphites react with higher thionates (tetrathionate, pentathionate, hexathionate) giving trithionate and thiosulphate.

$$S_{x+3}O_6^{2-} + xSO_3^{2-} \rightarrow S_3O_6^{2-} + xS_2O_3^{2-} \qquad (1)$$

Alkali cyanides react with higher thionates (cyanolysis) according to the equation

$$S_{x+3}O_6^{2-} + (x+2)CN^- + H_2O \rightarrow SO_4^{2-} + xSCN^- + 2HCN + S_2O_3^{2-} \qquad (2)$$

With tetrathionate, pentathionate and hexathionate the reaction is fast: with trithionate the reaction is slow at room temperature.

Alkali sulphides reduce polythionates

$$S_xO_6^{2-} + S^{2-} \rightarrow (x-3)S + 2S_2O_3^{2-} \qquad (3)$$

Again, the reaction with trithionate is slow at room temperature. Higher thionates (S_4^-, S_5^- and S_6^-) are hydrolysed by dilute alkalis at room temperature.

$$4S_4O_6^{2-} + 6OH^- \rightarrow 5S_2O_3^{2-} + 2S_3O_6^{2-} + 3H_2O \qquad (4)$$

$$2S_5O_6^{2-} + 6OH^- \rightarrow 5S_2O_3^{2-} + 3H_2O \qquad (5)$$

$$S_6O_6^{2-} \rightarrow S_5O_6^{2-} + S \qquad (6)$$

Equation (5) can be extended using equation (6). Trithionate is unaffected under the above conditions, but undergoes hydrolysis with more concentrated alkalis.

$$2S_3O_6^{2-} + 6OH^- \rightarrow S_2O_3^{2-} + 4SO_3^{2-} + 3H_2O \qquad (7)$$

The above reactions have been used singly and in groups, as the main basis of analytical methods. Other methods are based on oxidation, quantitative scanning chromatography, and polarography.

In keeping with the general treatment used throughout the book, methods are classified according to the nature of the final procedure.

Gravimetric methods

One of the earliest methods for determination of individual polythionates was oxidation to sulphate which was then determined gravimetrically. Another method, used for trithionate on its own, was treatment with cupric sulphate to give cupric sulphide and H_2SO_4. The former was determined gravimetrically after ignition to copper oxide. The latter was determined[9] alkalimetrically or gravimetrically as barium sulphate. It is doubtful whether these methods find current use.

Titrimetric methods

1. Kurtenacker–Goehring method

This is the classical method for analysis of polythionates. In its earlier form[20] aliquots are allowed to react with sulphite, cyanide, and sulphide in accordance with equations (1), (2) and (3). In each case the liberated thiosulphate is titrated with standard iodine. Three simultaneous equations can be set up and from these the amounts of tri-, tetra- and pentathionate in the mixture evaluated. Hexathionate will also react in the above manner. Goehring, Feldmann and Helbing[21] were able to extend the method to include this by incorporating the hydrolysis of polythionates under controlled conditions. This is indicated in equations (4)–(7).

The Kurtenacker–Goehring method usually gives high results. Its general unreliability can be attributed to the following causes. Tripolythionate reacts slowly with sulphide and the reaction is non-stoichiometric. Alkaline sulphide always contains some thiosulphate and other sulphur compounds, these giving a high titre for iodine. Furthermore, colloidal sulphur, often found with polythionates, reacts with sulphite giving thiosulphate. This increases the titre for iodine in reaction (1). Trithionate appears to be the only reliable result using the method. Some workers have limited themselves to a calculation of *n*, the average number of sulphur atoms per mole, but this information is of limited value. The Kurtenacker–Goehring method has been extended to include thiosulphate, sulphite and sulphide.

2. *Alkalimetric*

Jay[22] has based a method on the acidity liberated on treating polythionates with mercuric chloride.

$$2S_xO_6^{2-} + 3HgCl_2 + 4H_2O \rightarrow HgCl_2 \cdot 2HgS + 8H^+ + 4Cl^- + 4SO_4^{2-} + (2x - 6)S$$

Tri-, tetra- and pentathionates react producing 4 mol of acidity per mol of polythionate. Dithionate does not react. The free acid is titrated in the presence of KI, this being required to keep excess mercuric chloride in solution by complexation as the pH is raised near the end-point. Thiosulphate and sulphide interfere with this method.

3. *Redox*

Several titrimetric methods have been based on oxidation of polythionates. Hofman-Bang and Christiansen[23] use an excess of standard hypochlorite in boiling alkaline solution. The excess is subsequently determined iodimetrically. Their results indicate that dithionate is not oxidized, trithionate is oxidized to the extent of 30–40 %, tetrathionate is quantitatively oxidized and pentathionate almost quantitatively (~98 %).

Chloramine-T has been used for polythionate determination[24]. Again the procedure is not applicable to dithionate. Hepta- and octathionates are oxidized at 45–50 °C.

Sodium periodate can be used in much the same way[25] as hypochlorite. The method is applicable to tri- and tetrapolythionates, hydrosulphide (SH^-) and polysulphide. The authors state that various binary mixtures can be analysed, but experimental details are scanty.

Cerium(IV) in 2M perchloric acid oxidizes thiosulphate, tri-, tetra- and pentathionate quantitatively[26] to sulphate. Halides, dithionate and highly coloured ions interfere. Nair and Nair[27] use the same reagent in H_2SO_4 media. In about 1M sulphuric acid dithionate is quantitatively oxidized.

Unconsumed oxidant is titrated with standard iron(II) using ferroin as indicator. Quantitative oxidation of tri- and tetrathionate is complete in 30 min on boiling in a strongly acidic medium (6M H_2SO_4). For dithionate, 2 mol of cerium(IV) are consumed per mol of dithionate.

$$S_2O_6^{2-} + 2H_2O \leftrightharpoons 2SO_4^{2-} + 4H^+ + 2e$$

The corresponding amounts for tri- and tetrathionate are 8 and 14 respectively.

$$S_3O_6^{2-} + 6H_2O \leftrightharpoons 3SO_4^{2-} + 12H^+ + 8e$$

$$S_4O_6^{2-} + 10H_2O \leftrightharpoons 4SO_4^{2-} + 2OH^+ + 14e$$

The method is suitable for individual polythionates and dithionate. As the Chloramine-T method described earlier has no effect on dithionate, a combination of this with the above method would give the amount of dithionate and polythionates in mixtures. The method suffers interference from other reductants, for example sulphide, sulphite and thiosulphate.

Cerimetric titration of polythionates (tri- and tetra-)[27]

Reagents

Ceric ammonium sulphate:

Standardize with iron(II) in the usual way.

Ferroin indicator:

Dissolve 0.468 g of phenanthroline monohydrate in 100 mℓ water containing 0.278 g $FeSO_4 \cdot 7H_2O$

Procedure

To a 40 mℓ aliquot of cerium(IV) solution in a 500-mℓ conical flask add sufficient H_2SO_4 to bring about an overall acidity of 6M. Add the polythionate solution (containing about 0.25 mmol of tri- or about 0.12 mmol of tetrathionate) and boil for 30 min. Cool, and determine the unconsumed cerium(IV) by titration against standard iron(II) using a drop of ferroin as indicator.

Notes

1. No blank determination is required.
2. Sulphide, sulphite and thiosulphate interfere. Allowance for these may be made after carrying out a separate iodimetric determination.
3. The moles of cerium(IV) consumed per mole of thionate are 8.0 for tri- and 14.0 for tetrathionate.
4. Dithionate may be titrated, but under different conditions of acidity. The original paper should be consulted.

Spectrophotometric methods

Spectrophotometric methods can be applied to separated individual polythionates. Alternatively it may be applied, with selectivity in some instances, to polythionate mixtures.

Spectrophotometric methods have been based on thiocyanate produced in the cyanolysis of polythionates (reaction (2)) or the thiosulphate produced by reacting polythionates with sulphite (reaction (1)).

The cyanolysis reaction was employed by Nietzel and De Sesa[28], who then used the familiar iron(III)-thiocyanate spectrophotometric procedure to complete the determination. Penta- and hexathionate react in the same manner. More recently, Kelly, Chambers and Trudinger[29] have used the same reaction for the determination of trithionate in mixtures with thiosulphate and tetrathionate. In this work copper(II) is used as catalyst, this causing the reaction with thiosulphate to proceed rapidly at room temperature. The use of copper(II) as catalyst in this reaction was reported in earlier work by Urban[30]. In addition, Kelly, Chambers and Trudinger utilize the fact that cyanolysis of trithionate occurs only at boiling temperature. The reactions are shown in equations (8)–(10).

$$S_4O_6^{2-} + 3CN^- + H_2O \rightarrow S_2O_3^{2-} + SO_4^{2-} + 2HCN + SCN^- \quad (8)$$

$$S_2O_3^{2-} + CN^- \xrightarrow[\text{catalyst}]{\text{Cu}} SO_3^{2-} + SCN^- \quad (9)$$

$$S_3O_6^{2-} + 3CN^- + H_2O \rightarrow SO_3^{2-} + SO_4^{2-} + 2HCN + SCN^- \quad (10)$$

Reaction (8) takes place at 5 °C. $S_4O_6^{2-} \equiv 1SCN^-$.
Reaction (9) takes place at 5 °C in the presence of copper(II).

$$S_4O_6^{2-} \equiv 2SCN^-$$

$$S_2O_3^{2-} \equiv 1SCN^-$$

Reaction (10) takes place at boiling temperature in the presence of copper(II).

$$S_4O_6^{2-} \equiv 2SCN^-$$

$$S_2O_3^{2-} \equiv 1SCN^-$$

$$S_3O_6^{2-} \equiv 1SCN^-$$

Data obtained under the three conditions allows the amount of each constituent to be evaluated.

Japanese workers[31–33] have published several papers on spectrophotometric determination of polythionates based on thiocyanate produced by cyanolysis. Tetra-, penta-, and hexathionate can be determined alone. The same workers[34] have developed a method for micro-determination of two species of tetra-, penta- and hexathionate when present together. This employs copper(II) as catalyst to convert thiosulphate into additional thiocyanate. A further and recent development[35] has produced a 60-fold increase in sensitivity allowing 3.3×10^{-7}–1.0×10^{-5} M tetrathionate, 1.7×10^{-7}–5.0×10^{-6} M pentathionate, and 1.0×10^{-7}–3.3×10^{-6} M hexathionate, to be determined. This is achieved by extracting the complex between thiocyanate (equivalent to polythionate) and methylene blue with 1,2-dichloroethane before spectrophotometric evaluation. The absorbance is measured at 657 nm. Copper(II), bromide, iodide, nitrate, perchlorate and sulphide interfere.

A rapid and sensitive method for tetrathionate and thiosulphate (singly or together) has been published[36]. The procedure involves cyanolysis in the absence of copper(II), followed by spectrophotometric determination of the thiocyanate as the iron(III) complex. Application has been made to analysis of soil extracts. Large amounts of sulphate do not affect the method. For 100 μg of tetrathionate or thiosulphate, there is no interference from 2 mg amounts of sodium nitrate, sodium sulphate, sodium nitrite, disodium hydrogen phosphate, sodium bicarbonate, magnesium chloride, calcium chloride, lithium chloride, aluminium chloride, potassium acetate, cystine, methionine, sulphamic acid or sulphanilic acid.

The basic reaction for cyanolysis (equation (2)) indicates that each mole of polythionate produces one mole of thiosulphate as well as thiocyanate. Koh and Taniguchi[37] have developed a method based on adding excess iodine to the thiosulphate formed and measuring this excess spectrophotometrically. This gives the total amount of polythionate (tetra-, penta and hexa-) in mixtures. A modified procedure enables the total polythionate to be determined in the presence of thiosulphate and sulphite.

As an alternative to cyanolysis the sulphitolysis reaction indicated in equation (1) can be utilized[38]. Excess sodium sulphite is added to the polythionate. When the reaction is complete, unconsumed sulphite is masked with formaldehyde, and an excess of iodine added. The excess is evaluated spectrophotometrically by means of its absorbance at 372 or 440 nm. Sulphitolysis is also used by Koh and Taniguchi[39] for microdetermination of hexathionate in mixtures containing thiosulphate and sulphite. At the 0.5 μmol level, the relative standard deviation is reported as 2.2 per cent.

Electroanalytical methods

Direct potentiometric titration of polythionates can be made with hexacyanoferrate(III) using OsO_4 as catalyst[40]. The titration is made in strongly alkaline conditions at 50–60 °C. Sulphite, sulphide and thiosulphate are also oxidized under these conditions.

A rapid coulometric method for microdetermination of polythionate has been described by Blasius and Muench[41]. This involves degradation with sulphite or cyanide (equations (1) and (2)) followed by coulometric titration of the resulting thiosulphate. The method, which is applicable to tetra-, penta- and hexathionates, is claimed to give a much better precision than alternative methods.

Several polarographic methods have been reported. Though different polarographic responses are given by individual polythionates these appear to be too small for analytical use. Cathode-ray polarography has been investigated by Schmidt and Sand[42].

Chromatographic methods

Quantitative chromatographic methods have been referred to briefly earlier in this section. Pollard *et al.*[43] describe a scanning technique for use in conjunction with paper chromatographic separation of polythionates. The method consists of producing uniform layers of silver sulphide and sulphur by decomposition of the silver thionates formed when the chromatograms are sprayed with a silver nitrate solution. The absorbance of the layers is measured using a scanning device. Mixtures containing tri-, tetra-, penta- and hexathionates can be analysed.

More recently[17] the polythionates found in Wackenroder's solution have been separated and determined using High Performance Liquid Chromatography (HPLC). The separation is made on a 4-foot stainless steel column

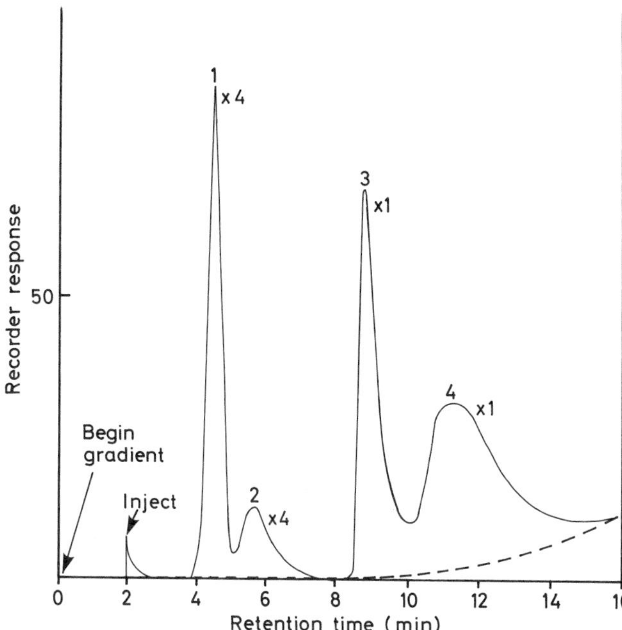

Figure 62 *Separation of thionates in Wackenroder's solution using High Performance Liquid Chromatography*. (After Chapman and Beard[17])

Peak	*Identity*
1	$S_2O_3^{2-}$ = 25 μg
2	$S_3O_6^{2-}$ = 125 μg
3	$S_4O_6^{2-}$ = 50 μg
4	$S_5O_6^{2-}$ = 39 μg

containing 200–270 mesh activated carbon. Detection is by UV absorbance at 254 nm. Optimization conditions include the use of tetrahydrofuran to decrease retention time and sharpen the peaks. A completed chromatogram is shown in *Figure 62*. The slight positive base-line drift indicated by the dotted line has no effect if peak areas are measured by a digital peak analysis technique. A measure of the precision obtained is given in *Table 51*.

Table 51 Precision obtained in analysis for Wackenroder's sulphur species by peak area determination[17]

Sulphur species	*Relative standard deviation* (%)	μg injected *in* 50 mℓ
$Na_2S_2O_3$	2.5	50
$K_2S_3O_6$	3.6	100
$K_2S_4O_6$	3.0	50
$K_2S_5O_6 \cdot 1\frac{1}{2}H_2O$	2.3	39

References

1. WEITZ, F. and SPOHN, K., *Ber.*, **89**, 2332 (1956)
2. KRAUSE, R.A. and BUSCH, D.H., *Analyt. Chem.*, **30**, 1817 (1958)
3. STAMM, H., GOEHRING, M. and FELDMANN, U., *Z. anorg. allg. Chem.*, **250**, 226 (1942)
4. GOEHRING, M. and FELDMANN, U., *Z. anorg. allg. Chem.*, **257**, 223 (1948)
5. HAFF, L.V., in *The Analysis of Sulphur and its Compounds* (Ed. J.H. Karchmer), Part 1, Wiley-Interscience, New York, 238 (1970)
6. BLASIUS, E., HORN, G., KNOCHEL, A., MUNCH, J. and WAGNER, H., *Inorganic Sulphur Chemistry* (Ed. G. Nickless), Elsevier, Amsterdam, 199 (1968)
7. SZEKERES, L., *Talanta*, **21**, 2 (1974)
8. POLLARD, F.H., JONES, D.J. and NICKLESS, G., *J. Chromat.*, **15**, 393 (1964)
9. HEINZE, G., *Z. anorg. allg. Chem.*, **276**, 146 (1954)
10. MANGAN, J.L., *N. Z. J. Sci. Technol.*, **30B**, 323 (1949); *Chem. Abstr.*, **45**, 5069h (1951)
11. SEILER, H. and ERLENMEYER, H., *Helv. chim. Acta*, **47**, 264 (1964); *Analyt. Abstr.*, **12**, 1703 (1965)
12. NAITO, K., TAKEI, S. and OKABE, T., *Bull. chem. Soc. Japan*, **43**, 1360 (1970); *Analyt. Abstr.*, **20**, 3012 (1971)
13. KELLY, D.P., *J. Chromat.*, **51**, 343 (1970)
14. IGUCHI, A., *Bull. chem. Soc. Japan*, **31**, 597 (1958); *Analyt. Abstr.*, **6**, 1706 (1959)
15. POLLARD, F.H., NICKLESS, G. and GLOVER, R.B., *J. Chromat.*, **15**, 533 (1964)
16. SCHMIDT, M. and SAND, T., *Z. anorg. Chem.*, **330**, 188 (1964); *Analyt. Abstr.*, **12**, 5754 (1965)
17. CHAPMAN, J.N. and BEARD, H.R., *Analyt. Chem.*, **45**, 2268 (1973)
18. Reference 5, p. 241
19. JOSEPHY, E., *Z. anorg. allg. Chem.*, **135**, 21 (1924)
20. KURTENACKER, A. and GOLDBACH, E., *Z. anorg. allg. Chem.*, **166**, 177 (1927)
21. GOEHRING, M., FELDMANN, U. and HELBING, W., *Z. analyt. Chem.*, **129**, 346 (1949)
22. JAY, R.R., *Analyt. Chem.*, **25**, 288 (1953)
23. HOFMAN-BANG, N. and CHRISTIANSEN, M.T., *Acta chem. Scand.*, **15**, 2061 (1961); *Analyt. Abstr.*, **9**, 1881 (1962)
24. SHARADA, K. and MURTHY, A.R.V., *Z. analyt. Chem.* **177**, 401 (1960); *Analyt. Abstr.*, **8**, 2388 (1961)
25. KAUSHIK, R.L. and PROSAD, R., *Indian. J. Chem.*, **8**, 462 (1970); *Analyt. Abstr.*, **20**, 3775 (1971)
26. KRAUSE, R. A. and BUSCH, D. H., *Analyt. Chem.*, **30**, 1817 (1958)
27. NAIR, V.R. and NAIR, C.G.R., *Talanta*, **18**, 432 (1971)
28. NIETZEL, O.A. and DE SESA, M.A., *Analyt. Chem.*, **27**, 1839 (1955)
29. KELLY, D.P., CHAMBERS, L.A. and TRUDINGER, P.A., *Analyt. Chem.*, **41**, 898 (1969)
30. URBAN, P.J., *Z. analyt. Chem.*, **179**, 422 (1961); *Analyt. Abstr.*, **8**, 4149 (1961)
31. KOH, T., *Bull. chem. Soc. Japan*, **38**, 1510 (1965); *Analyt. Abstr.*, **14**, 685 (1967)
32. KOH, T. and IWASAKI, I., *Bull. chem. Soc. Japan*, **38**, 2135 (1965); *Analyt. Abstr.*, **14**, 1953 (1967)
33. KOH, T. and IWASAKI, I., *Bull. chem. Soc. Japan.*, **39**, 352 (1966); *Analyt. Abstr.*, **14**, 3144 (1967)
34. KOH, T. and IWASAKI, I., *Bull. chem. Soc. Japan*, **39**, 703 (1966); *Analyt. Abstr.*, **14**, 4667 (1967)
35. KOH, T., SAITO, N. and IWASAKI, I., *Analytica chim. Acta*, **61**, 449 (1972)
36. NOR, Y.M. and TABATABAI, M.A., *Analyt. Lett.*, **8**, 537 (1975)
37. KOH, I. and TANIGUCHI, K., *Analyt. Chem.*, **45**, 2018 (1973)
38. IWASAKI, I. and SUZUKI, S., *Bull. chem. Soc. Japan*, **39**, 576 (1966); *Analyt. Abstr.*, **14**, 3951 (1967)
39. KOH, I. and TANIGUCHI, K., *Analyt. Chem.*, **46**, 1679 (1974)
40. SOLYMOSI, F. and VARGA, A., *Acta chim. hung.*, **20**, 295 (1959); *Analyt. Abstr.*, **6**, 2938 (1959)
41. BLASIUS, E. and MUENCH, J., *Z. analyt. Chem.*, **261**, 198 (1972); *Analyt. Abstr.*, **24**, 2163 (1973)
42. SCHMIDT, M. and SAND, T., *J. inorg. nucl. Chem.*, **26**, 1185 (1964)
43. POLLARD, F.H., NICKLESS, G., JONES, D.J. and GLOVER, R.B., *J. Chromat.*, **15**, 407 (1964)

Sulphate

Sulphate is a major anion with relevance to industrial chemistry, environmental chemistry including pollution, biochemistry and mineralogy, as well as several other areas. The fact that sulphur in several other forms is ultimately determined after conversion to sulphate further enhances the importance of sulphate determination.

Not unexpectedly, the analytical chemistry of sulphate has been the subject of a large number of investigations and this has produced an extensive literature. Many reviews have been published[1–5]. The ones quoted have been restricted to those which have appeared during the past 20 years. It should be noted that each of the above reviews covers the analysis of a wide range of sulphur compounds, with sulphate determination forming a part. Several reviews have appeared on particular aspects of sulphate determination. These will be referred to where appropriate.

Separations

Removal of interfering cations facilitates both titrimetric and spectrophotometric determination of sulphate. This is of particular importance in water analysis.

1. Ion-exchange chromatography

In its simplest form the sample is passed through a cation-exchange column before analysis[6]. An indirect method is reported by Ryabinin and Bogatyrev[7] in which sulphate and nitrate are passed through a cation-exchange column in lead form. Lead sulphate is precipitated and retained on the column; the eluted lead nitrate is titrated with EDTA.

Several anion-exchange separations have been reported[8–10], including sulphate and chromate, sulphate and large amounts of phosphate, and sulphate, sulphite, thiosulphate and sulphide. Mikes and Szanto[11] use an anion-exchange resin in chloride form, titrating the displaced chloride using the Mohr or Volhard methods.

2. Adsorption chromatography

The ability of acid-washed alumina columns to separate sulphate from cations and most anions was reported by Nydahl[12,13]. It was subsequently used by Fritz, Yamamura and Richard[14] as a preliminary step before titration of sulphate with barium perchlorate.

3. Thin-layer chromatography

The most important sulphate separations using this technique are shown in *Table 52*.

4. Gas-chromatography

This is discussed later under determination of sulphate.

Table 52 Separation of sulphate by TLC

Adsorbent	*Solvent*	*Sulphate separated from*	*Ref.*
Silica-gel–starch	Methanol–propanol–NH_3 (0.880)-H_2O (10:10:1:2)	$S_2O_3^{2-}$, SO_3^{2-}, $S_2O_8^{2-}$	15
Gelman prepared thin sheets SA and SG	Several, but following preferred: butanol–pyridine–acetic acid–H_2O (15:10:3:12)	$S_2O_3^{2-}$, $S_3O_6^{2-}$, $S_4O_6^{2-}$, SCN^-	16
Silica-gel Kieselguhr or La_2O_3	Acetone–1M NH_4OH (1:1)	PO_4^{3-}	17
Maize starch	Acetone–3M aq. NH_3 (1:4)	NO_2^-, $S_2O_3^{2-}$, CrO_4^{2-}, N_3^-, CN^-, SCN^-, BO_3^{3-}, S^{2-}, AsO_3^{3-}, AsO_4^{3-}, NO_3^-, PO_4^{3-}	18
Silica-gel + 5% corn starch	Methanol–*n*-butanol–H_2O (3:1:1)	F^-, NO_2^-, $S_2O_3^{2-}$, CrO_4^{2-}, PO_4^{3-}, AsO_4^{3-}, AsO_3^{3-}	19

5. *Miscellaneous*

Of the many other separation methods available for sulphate, several depend on the general chemistry of the sulphate anion. Separation as barium sulphate is always possible subject to the restrictions discussed later in the gravimetric determination of sulphate in this form. The precipitate may be analysed by a compleximetric procedure.

Addition of ammonium hydroxide will remove a number of elements including iron; mercury cathode electrolysis will free sulphate from a wide range of elements.

Boiling with conc. HCl will eliminate sulphite as SO_2 and sulphide as hydrogen sulphide. This principle has been used by de Sousa[20,21] for mixtures containing sulphate, sulphite and sulphide.

Finally, mention should be made of separation of sulphate as hydrogen sulphide after reduction. The hydrogen sulphide is absorbed and may be subsequently determined, for example, by the methylene blue spectrophotometric procedure. This method, which is highly selective, is discussed more fully in the section on spectrophotometric methods for sulphate.

Determination

Most methods currently used are based on the insolubility of barium sulphate. Formerly the gravimetric procedure was the most commonly used. In recent years titrimetric procedures based on barium sulphate have tended to displace it except in cases where a high degree of accuracy is required.

Gravimetric methods

1. *As $BaSO_4$*

Gravimetric determination of sulphate by addition of barium chloride to a sulphate solution has long been established as a reference method.

$$SO_4^{2-} + BaCl_2 \rightarrow BaSO_4 + 2Cl^-$$

The white precipitate is filtered, washed, ignited and weighed. At first sight the method might appear to be straightforward. In practice it is subject to countless sources of error, due mainly to coprecipitation. The final result will depend on a variety of experimental conditions which include concentration and rate of addition of reagents, temperature, digestion and ignition of the precipitate, and the nature of extraneous cations and anions present. Generally, good results will depend on strict adherence to experimental details.

In the present treatment it is not proposed to deal in detail with the theoretical and other aspects of the determination. These are discussed at length in standard texts[22–24]. The first mentioned source of Kolthoff, Sandell, Meehan and Bruckenstein is particularly useful, providing several important references to earlier work on the method.

The more important factors are as follows. Coprecipitation of both cations and anions takes place with the contaminants largely present throughout the interior of the primary particles of the precipitate rather than at the external surface. This is the result of occlusion, by which is meant the incorporation into the precipitate crystals of ions or molecules adsorbed during the growth of the precipitate. Water may be occluded in this way, and is not quantitatively removed by the usual method of heating to about 100 °C.

Occlusion occurs by two mechanisms, namely solid solution formation, or ion-entrapment. In addition to occlusion, coprecipitation may occur by adsorption on the surface of crystal particles. This may consist of salts having an ion in common with barium sulphate, in which case the behaviour is largely, though not entirely, determined by the Paneth–Fajans–Hahn adsorption rule. Salts having no common ion with the precipitate undergo exchange adsorption. Other factors that contribute in addition to the Paneth–Fajans–Hahn rule are electrical dissociability of adsorbed compounds and deformability of the adsorbed ions.

The solubility of barium sulphate in water is small though not negligible. Although the solubility in water increases with temperature, hot water may be used to wash it with very little error resulting. Usually precipitation is made in a dilute HCl solution. The presence of HCl produces a denser precipitate which is easier to filter. It also prevents precipitaton of other barium salts such as the carbonate or phosphate. The presence of HCl (or HNO_3) results in an increase in solubility of barium sulphate. A solution of about 0.05M in HCl may be used with no significant loss on this account.

Cations are coprecipitated as sulphates or bisulphates. When the barium solution is added to the sulphate, cation coprecipitation predominates over anion coprecipitation. The reverse is true if an alkali sulphate solution is added to an acidified barium chloride solution.

Coprecipitation of the alkali metals, ammonium sulphate, and H_2SO_4 increases with the concentration of the cation involved, and decreases with increase in rate of precipitation and time of digestion. Sodium ions produce errors only when present in large amounts: potassium ions cause coprecipitation errors in relatively low amounts. The presence of ammonium ions is of interest as it demonstrates that coprecipitation must be seen in conjunction with the fate of the coprecipitated species on ignition. Coprecipitated ammonium sulphate produces large negative errors due to its volatility on ignition at 950–1100 °C. If sodium ions are present, rapid addition of barium chloride decreases coprecipitation of sodium sulphate.

Divalent metals are all coprecipitated to a greater or lesser extent. Salts having a common ion follow the Paneth–Fajans–Hahn adsorption rule as mentioned earlier. This is illustrated by the fact that calcium ions are adsorbed to a greater extent than magnesium because calcium sulphate is less soluble than magnesium sulphate. Calcium is the most serious interference of the divalent metals.

Moving on to the tervalent ions Fe^{3+} causes serious errors unless preventative steps are taken. The reason here is largely due to the formation, on hydrolysis, of a positively charged basic ferric salt which is strongly adsorbed on the negatively charged barium sulphate.

On the other hand Cr^{3+} ions cause errors due to incomplete precipitation of barium sulphate resulting from partial retention of sulphate as a complex.

Two approaches may be used to eliminate cationic interferences. EDTA can be used to complex M^{2+} and M^{3+} cations[25]. Alternatively, the sample solution can be passed through a cation-exchange resin.

Several anions cause serious errors due to occlusion. Again the Paneth–Fajans–Hahn rule offers guidance, indicating that the less soluble the barium salt with the anion, the greater the tendency for occlusion by that anion. For example, barium nitrate is less soluble than barium chloride, and nitrate is therefore more strongly occluded than chloride. Both nitrate and chlorate cause serious errors unless removed. This is usually done by evaporation of the solution to dryness two or three times with concentrated HCl.

$$NO_3^- + 3Cl^- + 4H^+ \rightarrow Cl_2 + NOCl + 2H_2O$$

$$ClO_3^- + 5Cl^- + 6H^+ \rightarrow 3Cl_2 + 3H_2O$$

The finest filter paper or preferably a pulp pad should be used in filtering the precipitate, and hot water for washing it. Before ignition at about 800–1000 °C, the precipitate should be dried at about 110 °C. Care must be taken that the filter paper does not catch fire. The final ignition should be carried out in excess air to avoid the possibility of the precipitate being reduced to sulphide by the carbon of the paper.

Despite its voluminous literature, the method continues to be the subject of new investigations. Nishimura[26] has eliminated the ignition and other heating stages by drying the precipitate, contained in a sintered crucible, by washing with ethanol and ether. Air is then drawn through it for 20 min and the weighing carried out after a 5–10 min period in a desiccator. A considerable saving of time is effected with little apparent difference in result. When applied to a sample of pyrite, the average result was 54.1 % sulphur compared with 54.0% for the ordinary procedure involving ignition.

Other investigations have focused on the complex aging processes that occur after the initial precipitate has been formed. In the normal procedure it is recommended that the precipitate is allowed to stand for several hours, preferably overnight, for these processes to take place. This adds considerably to the time. Not unexpectedly, attempts have been made to achieve similar results, namely a better chemical composition and an easily filterable precipitate, in less time. Zolatavin *et al.*[27] find that freezing the precipitate in solid carbon dioxide–acetone for 15 min followed by thawing in hot water at 60–70 °C for 15 min produces an effect similar to that of prolonged aging at room temperature. The technique was also applied to magnesium ammonium phosphate and thorium oxalate in addition to barium sulphate. A time reduction from 10 h to 2 h is claimed for a complete gravimetric sulphate determination.

More recently Pleskach and Chirkova[28] have investigated the effects of pH, excess Ba^{2+}, and sulphate and Ba^{2+} concentration, on the rate of formation, dimension and settling rate of barium sulphate crystals. The investigation indicated that crystals of maximum size formed at the maximum rate when the pH was in the range 3.0–3.5.

The influence of foreign ions on the particle size of barium sulphate precipitates has been investigated recently by Liteanu and Lingner[29] who find that sodium chloride, sodium nitrate, potassium bromide, potassium nitrate, and other salts at high concentration hinder the growth of crystals even at high supersaturation.

Precipitation from homogeneous solution is possible in the case of barium sulphate. Sulphamic acid or dimethyl sulphate may be used[30].

$$NH_2SO_3H + H_2O \rightarrow SO_4^{2-} + NH_4^+ + H^+$$

$$(CH_3)_2SO_4 + 2H_2O \rightarrow SO_4^{2-} + 2CH_3OH + 2H^+$$

Gravimetric determination of sulphate as barium sulphate

Notes

1. This procedure assumes that interfering ions have been removed as indicated earlier in the text. If cation-exchange is to be used, a 2-cm diameter 10-cm long column of strongly acidic resin (e.g. Zeo-Karb 225) equilibriated with 4–6M HCl would be suitable. After passing the sulphate through slowly, the column is washed through with 200 mℓ of de-ionized water. If alkali metals are present in appreciable amounts dilute the barium chloride solution (10 mℓ of 10% solution diluted to about 100 mℓ), heat to the boil, and add rapidly. This diminishes the effects of coprecipitation by the alkali metals.
2. If the sulphate solution is already acidified with HCl, adjust the acidity to about 0.05M.

Procedure

Dilute the sulphate solution, containing about 0.3 g SO_4^{2-} to about 250 mℓ and add 2 mℓ concentrated HCl. Heat nearly to the boiling point, then add slowly with stirring, 10 mℓ of 10% barium chloride solution. Allow the precipitate to settle, then test for complete precipitation by adding a little more of the reagent. Leave it on a hot plate for at least 2 h, but preferably longer, and even overnight if possible.

Filter through a fine paper or pulp pad or a fine porcelain filter crucible. Wash the precipitate with hot water in small portions until free from HCl (silver nitrate). If a filter paper or pulp pad is used, dry and then carefully ignite without allowing the paper to catch fire. If a filter crucible is employed place in an oven until dry. Finally, ignite at about 900 °C until constant in weight, then cool and weigh.

---

2. *Using organic reagents*

The weak base benzidine (4,4′,diaminobiphenyl) (*Structure 65*) was proposed as a gravimetric reagent for sulphate by Vaubel[31] in 1896. Its hydrochloride,

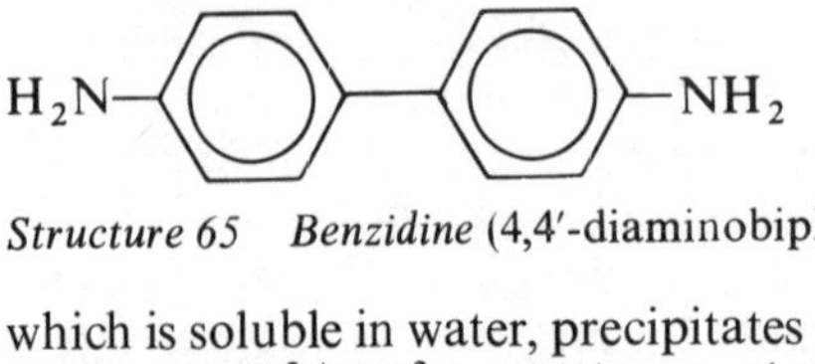

$$H_2N-C_6H_4-C_6H_4-NH_2$$

Structure 65 *Benzidine* (4,4′-diaminobiphenyl)

which is soluble in water, precipitates sulphate giving an insoluble compound $C_{12}H_{12}N_2H_2^{2+}SO_4^{2-}$ which may be weighed or titrated. Its solubility in water of 98 mg ℓ$^{-1}$, with an even greater solubility in HCl, has been a major disadvantage. It appears to find little present day use. No doubt its known carcinogenicity has contributed to this. An account of benzidine as a sulphate reagent has been given by Stephen[32]. Related titrimetric procedures exist, and will be discussed later in this section.

3. *Miscellaneous*

Hexamine cobalt(III) halides were examined by Mahr and Kraus[33] as precipitants for sulphate. The tribromide salt was found to be the best, this giving a precipitate of $(NH_3)_6CoBrSO_4$. It may be weighed after drying at 80 °C. The solubility is reduced by the common-ion effect and may be further reduced by the presence of ethanol and acetone. Titrimetric and spectrophotometric procedures were described in the same work.

Belcher and Gibbons[34] developed a gravimetric sulphate method based on the Werner complex octammine-μ-amino-μ-nitrodicobalt(III) tetranitrate (*Structure 66*).

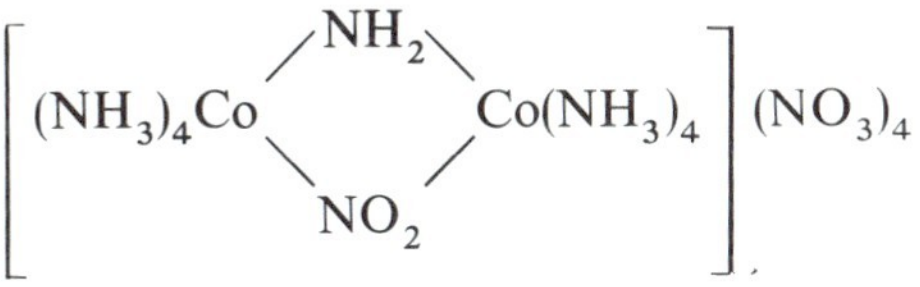

$$\left[(NH_3)_4Co\begin{matrix} \diagup NH_2 \diagdown \\ \\ \diagdown NO_2 \diagup \end{matrix}Co(NH_3)_4\right](NO_3)_4$$

Structure 66 Octammine-μ-amino-μ-nitrodicobalt (III) tetranitrate

The solubility of the resulting precipitate in water is 22.4 mg ℓ$^{-1}$ at room temperature, but is probably much less in the presence of excess reagent and the 25% organic solvent used in the procedure. Sulphate in the range 1–100 mg may be determined. Phosphate (at pH 5 or below), fluoride, nitrate and peroxide have no effect when present in moderate amounts.

Titrimetric methods

1. *Using barium*

Numerous attempts have been made to develop rapid titrimetric methods for sulphate based on the insolubility of barium sulphate. Most of the earlier methods entailed back-titration of an excess of Ba^{2+} ions. Rhodizonic acid was one of the most satisfactory of the earlier indicators but in general the sharpness was poor with resulting loss of accuracy.

The most successful of current methods are based on the work of Fritz and co-workers[35–37] in 1954–57. Essentially the method consists of titrating sulphate with barium perchlorate in a medium containing 30–40% alcohol, at an apparent pH of 2.3–3.7. Alizarin Red S is used as an adsorption indicator when the sulphate is present in macro or semi-micro amounts: for micro quantities of sulphate the indicator recommended is Thorin (Thoron: 1-(*o*-arsonophenylazo)-2-naphthol-3,6-disulphonic acid) (*Structure 67*). The choice of barium perchlorate in preference to the chloride was made on the basis of coprecipitation considerations.

Fritz and Freeland[35] established that the order of coprecipitation of anions on a barium sulphate precipitate was

$$NO_3^- > Cl^- > Br^- > ClO_4^-$$

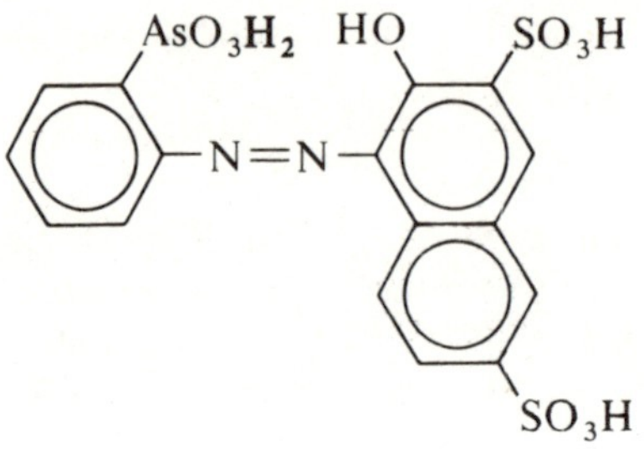

Structure 67 Thorin

this being the reverse order of the molar solubilities of the corresponding barium salts of these anions. This conforms to the Paneth–Fajans–Hahn adsorption rule. In several recently published procedures the chloride continues to be used nevertheless.

The alcoholic medium is essential, and has an optimum effect at the 30–40% concentration. If lower, the end-point is less distinct; if higher, the equilibrium is slow in being attained and false end-points arise which slowly fade causing difficulties. The presence of alcohol also has an effect on the nature of the precipitate itself. Barium sulphate precipitated under aqueous conditions is usually fine and crystalline. In the presence of alcohols it is light, flocculent and somewhat gelatinous.

A less satisfactory feature of the precipitate is its ability to strongly co-precipitate both cations and anions. This tendency is far more marked than in the gravimetric procedure due to the different conditions under which it is produced. Removal of cations is best done using ion-exchange.

The adjustment of pH to 2.3–3.7 is essential. At lower pH values an indistinct end-point is obtained and results are slightly low. In practice chloroacetic acid or pyridine may be used for the adjustment. If a cation-exchange procedure has been carried out, the resulting solution may be partly neutralized with magnesium acetate before the titration.

Alizarin Red S (sodium alizarin sulphonate) is an acid–base indicator of pH range 3.7–5.2. In the present method, however, it functions as an adsorption indicator, probably in the following manner. During the titration barium sulphate adsorbs sulphate ions on to its surface, this giving a negative charge. When excess Ba^{2+} ions are present, the precipitate becomes positively charged due to adsorption of Ba^{2+} ions on to the surface. When this happens the negatively charged Alizarin Red S ion is attracted to the surface where it forms a weak pink barium complex.

If micro amounts of sulphate are involved, the quantity of precipitate is insufficient for the indicator action to be observed. The colour change for thorin is from yellow to pink. This is not always easy to observe especially in artificial light. Methylene blue is effective in screening out the pinkish tinge of thorin[38]. A mixture of thorin and methylene blue is now incorporated into several current versions of the method.

Phosphate causes serious interference and should be removed. The original workers[36] recommended magnesium carbonate as a precipitant for phosphate. Colson[39] found that precipitation as silver phosphate by addition of silver oxide was an effective method of overcoming phosphate interference.

The resulting silver sulphate is decomposed on an ion-exchange resin and the free H_2SO_4 titrated with barium perchlorate. This particular work was in connection with the micro-determination of sulphur in organic compounds after oxygen-flask combustion, an important application of sulphate determination.

Phosphate is by far the greatest of the anionic interferences. Sulphite interference may be overcome by titrating it to sulphate with standard iodine and subtracting the sulphate equivalent of the iodine from the total sulphate found.

When the method is used for micro-quantities of sulphate (0.12 mg–12.0 mg SO_4^{2-} per 10 mℓ) some changes in the procedure become necessary. The titration is now carried out in 80% alcohol. The apparent pH range is 2.5–4.0, this being automatically attained on passing the sample through a cation-exchange column, unless the foreign salt content is too high. The

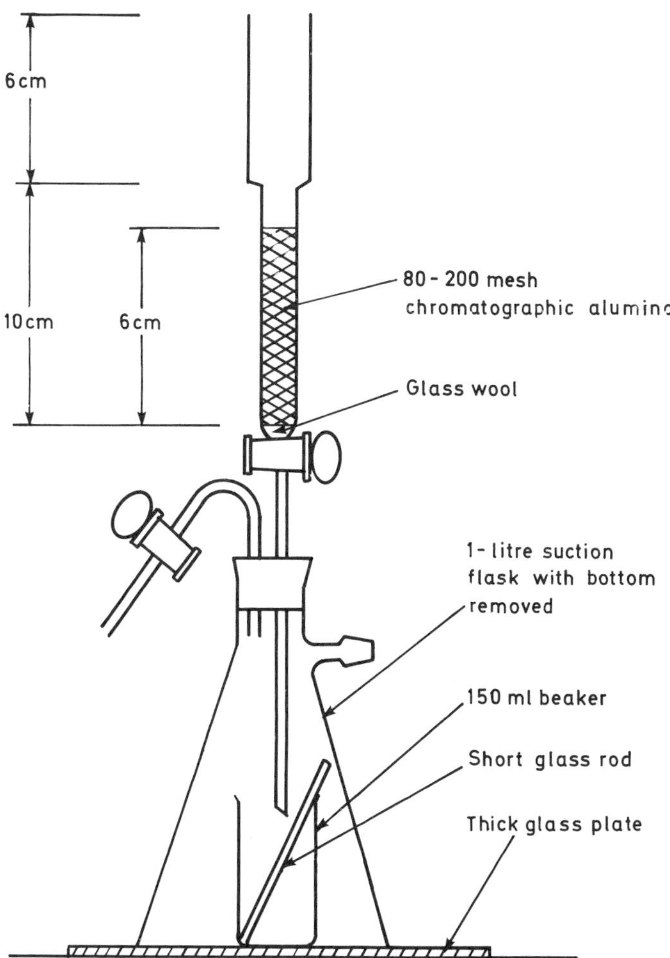

Figure 63 Apparatus for chromatographic separation of sulphate on an activated alumina column. (After Fritz, Yamamura and Richard[37])

Table 53 Indicators for titration of sulphate with barium

Trivial name	*Chemical name*	*Comments*	*Ref.*
Thorin [Thoron; APANS]	1-(*o*-arsonophenylazo)-2-naphthol-3,6-disulphonic acid	Colour change yellow → pink	36 38
Carboxyarsenazo	3-(*o*-arsonophenylazo)-6-(*o*-carboxyphenylazo)-4,5-dihydroxy-2,7-naphthalene disulphonic acid	Colour change violet → blue Medium: 2+1 acetone–water solution buffered with pyridine and $HClO_4$(approx. pH 5.8). PO_4^{3-} interferes	41 42 43
Nitchromazo [Nitro-orthanilic S; Dinitrosulphonazo (III)]	3,6 bis-(4-nitro-2-sulphophenyl azo) 4,5 dihydroxy-2,7 naphthalene-disulphonic acid	Colour change violet → blue Functions in presence ×5 PO_4^{3-} and ×4 AsO_4^{3-}. No interference from F^-, Cl^-, NO_3^-, ClO_4^-	44 45 46 47
Arsonazo III	2,7-bis-(2-arsonophenylazo)-1,8-dihydroxy naphthalene 3,6-disulphonic acid	Colour change blue → red	48 49
Sulphonazo III	3,6-bis-(2-sulphophenylazo)-4,5 dihydroxy-2,7-naphthalene disulphonic acid	Colour change purple red → blue Medium: slightly acidic 1 + 1 water–acetone. Ref. 43 finds end-point sluggish	50 51 52 43

Dimethylsulphonazo III	3,6-bis-(4-sulpho-*p*-tolylazo)-4,5-dihydroxy-2,7 naphthalene disulphonic acid	Colour change violet blue → blue grey. Salts > 0.1 mM interfere. PO_4^{3-}, AsO_4^{3-}, EDTA and NaCl have smallest effect. Ref. 43 find end-point sluggish	53 54 43
Orthanil K [Orthanilic K; Carboxysulphazo III]	3-(2-carboxyphenylazo)-6-(2-sulphophenylazo)-4,5-dihydroxy-2,7 naphthalene disulphonic acid	Almost all cations require prior removal (ion-exchange). Very selective for effluents containing F^- and $C_2H_3O_2^-$ Medium; water-acetone 1:1 pH 4	55 56
Chlorophosphonazo III	3,6-bis-(4-chloro-2-phosphonophenyl azo) 4,5-dihydroxy 2,7 naphthalene disulphonic acid	Colour change wine red → blue Of 21 cations and 10 anions investigated, only Y, La, Zr, Hf, Th, U(IV) and U(VI) interfere	57
Dibromosulphonazo III	3,6-bis-(4-bromo-2-sulphophenylazo)4,5-dihydroxy 2,7 naphthalene disulphonic acid	Colour change red → blue	53
Carboxyazo III	3,6-bis-(2-carboxy phenylazo)-4,5 dihydroxy 2,7 naphthalene disulphonic acid	Colour change purple pink → green blue For titrimetric and photometric (685 nm) Medium: 75% EtOH pH 2.55 Back-titration recommended	58
Carboxysulphonazo	3-(2-carboxyphenylazo)-6-(2-sulphonylazo) 4,5-dihydroxy 2,7 naphthalene disulphonic acid	Colour change purple pink → green blue For titrimetric and photometric (645 nm) Medium: 75% EtOH pH 2.1 Back titration recommended	58

maximum concentration of this is approximately 5–10 times the molar concentration of sulphate. If exceeded, the pH would be below the range quoted. In the micro method, the titrant is also made up in 80% alcohol.

A chromatographic method of separating sulphate on an alumina column was described by Fritz, Yamamura and Richard[36]. The technique (*Figure 63*) allows as little as 0.5 ppm SO_4^{2-} to be separated from large amounts of chloride, nitrate and perchlorate, and from most metal ions. The sulphate is eluted from the column with dilute ammonium hydroxide, passed through a small cation-exchange column, and then titrated. Fluoride and phosphate are not separated on the alumina column. Fluoride interference is eliminated by addition of boric acid[40]. Removal of phosphate has been dealt with above.

Sulphate is not satisfactorily separated from chromium(III), zirconium(IV) and thorium(IV) by the above method due to formation of slow reacting sulphate complexes. A method of overcoming this difficulty is to pre-treat the sample with Entol (N-Hydroxyethylenediaminetriacetic acid) which forms strong complexes with the metals concerned. The resulting solution then responds to the alumina separation. EDTA is unsatisfactory as a substitute for Entol due to instability of the metal complex on the column.

In addition to thorin as indicator, several derivatives of chromotropic acid have been suggested as alternatives, and some comparative studies on these have been reported. Various criteria such as sharpness of end-point, time for reaching equilibrium, accuracy and selectivity have been included in these studies. Data on several indicators, including thorin, are given in *Table 53*.

The comparative study by Budesinsky and Krumlova[54] is particularly informative. This concludes that dimethylsulphonazo(III) is the best indicator both for visual and photometric titration. Furthermore, phosphate, arsenate, EDTA and NaCl have the smallest effect when this indicator is used. The structures of selected indicators for Ba^{2+} titration of sulphate are shown in *Structures 68–70*.

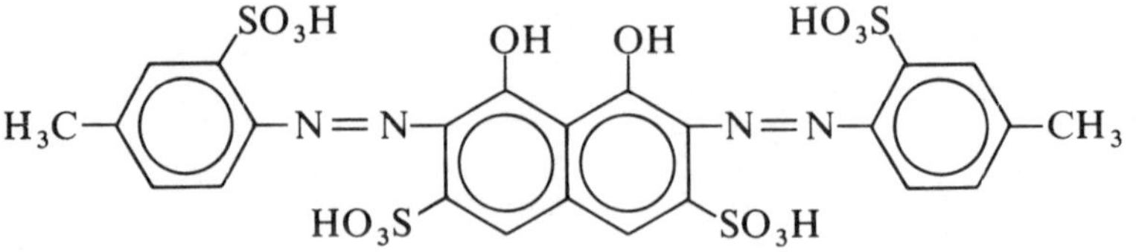

Structure 68 Dimethylsulphonazo III

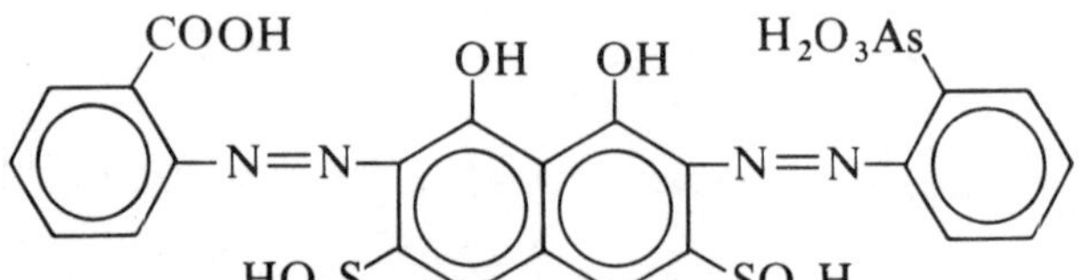

Structure 69 Carboxyarsenazo

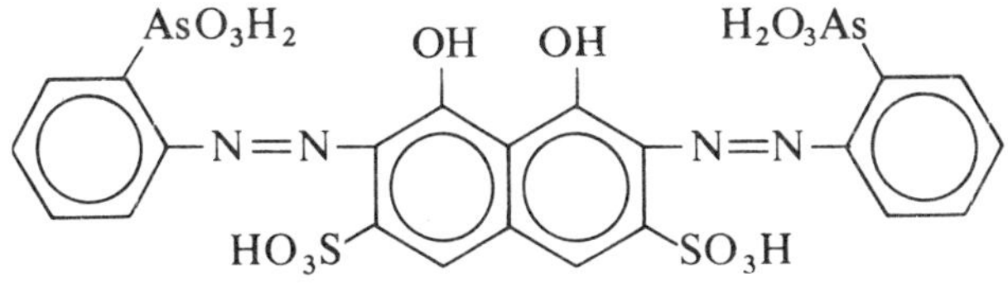

Structure 70 Arsenazo III

The accuracy obtained using various indicators is shown[54] in *Table 54*. This indicates that thorin gives less accurate results than the alternative indicators. The results are in agreement with the molar absorptivities determined in the same study.

Table 54 Accuracy obtained using various indicators in titrimetric assay of potassium sulphate

Indicator	*Sulphate found*[a] (%)	SD (%)
Thorin	99.4	±0.15
Carboxyarsenazo	99.6	±0.14
Sulphonazo	100.4	±0.10
Dinitrosulphonazo III	100.5	±0.12
Dimethylsulphonazo III	99.8	±0.08
Dibromosulphonazo III	100.2	±0.10

[a] Average of 10 determinations.

In contrast to this work, Archer, White and Mackison[43] prefer carboxyarsenazo and find dimethylsulphonazo III slow to attain equilibrium. Hozumi and Umemoto[48] claim that Arsenazo III is better than either Sulphonazo III or Thorin[48].

The lengthy account of the titration of sulphate with Ba^{2+} ions is justified by its extensive application in several important areas of analytical chemistry. Determination of sulphur in organic compounds on the semi-micro, micro and sub-micro scale following oxygen-flask combustion is an example[40]. White[59] has described an application to simultaneous determination of sulphur and chlorine in organic compounds, the chlorine being titrated as chloride with mercuric nitrate. Belcher *et al.*[60] have extended the method into the sub-micro region, enabling 10–30 μg of sulphur to be determined in organic compounds. A lower limit of 0.5 μg SO_4^{2-} is attained in another study[61].

Other applications of the method involve oil[62], coal[63], food[64] and water[65].

Titrimetric determination of sulphate using barium perchlorate

Reagents

Barium perchlorate: 0.1 M.

Prepare an approximately 0.1 M solution,

adjust the pH to 3.0–3.5 and standardize against a standard solution of H_2SO_4 using the macro procedure.

Barium perchlorate: 0.01 M.

Dissolve 3.9 g $Ba(ClO_4)_2 \cdot 3H_2O$ in 200 mℓ water. Add 800 mℓ isopropanol. Standardize against 0.005 M H_2SO_4.

Ethanol or methanol may be used as alternatives to isopropanol, but the latter is preferred due to its slower rate of evaporation.

Alizarin Red S: 0.2% aqueous.

Thorin: 0.2% aqueous.

General procedure (macro)

The solution should contain 2–4 mmol of sulphate in 45 mℓ water. Add 40 mℓ methanol and adjust the pH to 3.0–3.5 with dilute magnesium acetate ($\sim$0.25 M) or perchloric acid.

Rapidly add about 90 per cent of the barium perchlorate required, add 5 drops of the Alizarin Red S indicator, and titrate to the first permanent pink allowing a time lapse of 3–5 s between the addition of the last few increments.

Note

For the semi-micro scale (0.2–0.8 mmol SO_4^{2-}) add 10 mℓ of water, 10 mℓ of methanol and 1 drop of indicator.

General procedure (micro)

To 10 mℓ of solution add 40 mℓ alcohol and 1 drop of thorin indicator. Ensure that the apparent pH is 2.5–4.0. Titrate with 0.01 M barium perchlorate to the first permanent pink. The bulk of titrant should be added rapidly, but 2–3 s allowed between final additions.

Micro-procedure involving preliminary separation

The sample containing 0.12–12.0 mg SO_4^{2-} is adjusted to pH 0.5–1.0 with dilute HCl or perchloric acid. It is passed through an alumina column at an approximate rate of 120 drops per min, washed with 10 mℓ of 5% v/v HCl and 25 mℓ of water added in several portions.

The sulphate is eluted by adding successively 5 mℓ of 1 M ammonia, 20 mℓ of 0.1 M ammonia, 20 m of 0.1 M ammonia in 5 mℓ portions, and about 25 mℓ of water.

The sulphate-containing effluent is passed through the ion-exchange column, the effluent being collected in a 100 mℓ volumetric flask. The column is washed with sufficient water to fill the volumetric flask to the mark.

A 10 mℓ aliquot is titrated as described in the general micro procedure.

Notes

1. Thorin solution deteriorates on keeping and should be replaced after one month. It may be screened by adding one drop of 0.05% aqueous methylene blue in addition to the drop of thorin.
2. The ion-exchange column should be 2.5 cm in diameter and filled with 7–8 cm of a cation-exchange resin (Dowex 50-X8 20–50 mesh, or equivalent) in H form.
3. The alumina column is prepared as follows: Chromatographic alumina (80–200 mesh) is washed in a beaker and allowed to settle. The supernatant liquid is removed by decanting and the process repeated to remove very fine particles. After transferring the alumina to the column

it is washed with 50 mℓ of 1 M ammonia, several 5 mℓ portions of 1 M ammonia, several portions of 0.1 M ammonia and about 50 mℓ of water. Finally it is washed with 10 mℓ of HCl or $HClO_4$ of the same strength used in the sulphate sample to be passed through. The column should never be allowed to run dry.

4. In the presence of chromium(III), thorium(IV) or zirconium(IV) the following treatment is required: Add an excess of Entol solution (0.5M: dissolve 69.5 g Entol in water, adding NaOH pellets to aid dissolution. The pH should not be more alkaline than 5 or 6. Dilute to 1ℓ), raise the pH to between 5 and 6. Heat to boiling then allow to cool. Acidify if only zirconium is present. If chromium or thorium are present boil for 10–15 min before cooling and acidifying, to ensure complete complex formation.

---

2. *Using lead nitrate as titrant*

The titrimetric determination of sulphate using lead nitrate as titrant offers a simple and versatile method. Introduced by Archer[66] and Nechiporenko[67] it depends on lead sulphate being virtually insoluble in water–acetone mixtures. A slight excess of the reagent causes a sharp change from green to the purple-red of lead dithizone.

Further studies by White[68, 69] extended the method into the micro- and sub-micro region and established the optimum conditions for highest accuracy. In addition, interference studies were carried out and the method applied to sulphur in organic compounds.

Heavy metals interfere by interaction with dithizone, but may be removed by cation-exchange. Potassium interferes when present in amounts equivalent to the sulphate. This is attributed to the low solubility of potassium sulphate in water–acetone mixtures. Nechiporenko[70] has established upper limits for non-interference by a range of elements when the method is used without cation-exchange. For 0.25–50 mg SO_4^{2-} the error is within 1.5 per cent for Si, Hg, Ag, Co, Zn, Ni, Fe, Al and Mn in concentrations of 500, 0.1, 0.1, 5, 20, 40, 100, 100 and 2000 mg per mℓ respectively.

Phosphate interferes and may be removed by precipitation as $MgNH_4PO_4$. Chloride interferes only when present in larger amounts. White recommends its removal when in excess of 2 mg per 25 mℓ. Nechiporenko[67] states that chloride interferes when present in 7-fold excess of the sulphate concentration. Nitrite interferes by oxidizing the indicator: it may be destroyed with urea before the titration. Nitrate is tolerated unless in large quantities. Perchlorate does not interfere.

In a series of papers, Nechiporenko[71–74] has described the use of diphenylcarbazone as an alternative indicator to dithizone. Its lead complex is less stable than the corresponding lead dithizonate. The medium recommended is ethanol–water. Interferences are essentially the same, requiring ion-exchange removal of cations. For 0.01 and 0.025 mg SO_4^{2-} the errors are quoted as less than 3 and 2 per cent respectively. The method lends itself to simultaneous determination of trace amounts of sulphate and chloride in a single tap-water sample. First the sulphate is titrated with standard lead nitrate solution, the solution is made slightly more acid, and the chloride titrated with standard mercuric nitrate. A further modification in the same investigation includes a preconcentration of sulphate[37] on an alumina column similar to that used by Fritz, Yamamura and Richard[37]. The usefulness of the above method has been confirmed by Lewis[75] in an analysis of rain and bore-hole waters, and Parker[76] who finds it both rapid and accurate. Calcium interferes in both the dithizone and diphenylcarbazone forms of the method due to insolubility of calcium sulphate in the medium.

A photometric end-point for the dithizone form of the method has been suggested by Niwa and Parry[77] in which 20 ppm in sulphate may be titrated directly.

Microtitration of sulphate using lead nitrate[68, 69]

Reagents

Lead nitrate 0.005 M.
It should not be more acid than corresponds to the green colour of bromophenol blue.

Acetone–acetic acid: 0.5% w/v of glacial acetic acid in acetone.
The acetone must be free from all but the smallest traces of heavy metals.

Dithizone: 0.05% w/v in acetone. Prepare fresh daily.

Ammonium hydroxide: 0.02M approximately.

Nitric acid: 0.02M approximately.
Prepare from dilute (2M) acid which has been at that concentration for some time. (This is to avoid the possibility of traces of nitrous acid by directly diluting the concentrated acid. Nitrous acid would rapidly oxidize dithizone.)

Procedure

To the sample containing a maximum of 5 mg SO_4^{2-} add if necessary an excess of dilute ammonium hydroxide and evaporate to dryness on a water bath. Dissolve the residue in 1 mℓ of water, add 1 drop of bromophenol blue and adjust to a yellow-green colour by careful addition of dilute ammonium hydroxide or HNO_3. The solution must not attain the blue colour. Add 18 mℓ of the acetone–acetic acid mixture followed by about 0.4 mℓ of the dithizone indicator.

Titrate with 0.005M lead nitrate solution at a fast rate and using mechanical stirring. When near the end-point add a further 2 mℓ of the acetone–acetic acid solution and continue dropwise to a colour change from emerald green, through a blue and purple to a permanent red-purple which marks the end-point. Addition of excess lead gives a red colour.

For more accurate work, the value of the small but definite indicator blank titre may be determined and a correction made.

Notes

1. The acetic acid is incorporated in the acetone for greater simplicity and in order to keep the acetic acid concentration constant when adding more acetone near the end-point.
2. Although a wide variation in water concentration at the end-point is possible without undue effect on the precision, too much water reduces the sharpness at the end-point and the precision suffers. For

this reason, addition of acetone–acetic acid is made near the end-point to maintain the water concentration at about 25%, the optimum value.

3. The appearance of a pink or red colour on addition of the first few drops of dithizone to the sample solution indicates the presence of a heavy metal impurity. Addition of excess dithizone will mask small amounts. If the amount is large, an ion-exchange separation must be made.

---

3. Using EDTA

Since the first published[78] compleximetric method for determination of sulphate in 1950 many other methods have appeared, several of which are reviewed in the monograph by Schwarzenbach and Flaschka[79]. Relatively few basic principles are involved, but a number of fundamental difficulties are inherent in the method and much of the literature consists of modifications aimed at overcoming these.

The main approach is centred on precipitation of sulphate with standard barium chloride, filtering off the precipitate and back-titrating the excess barium with standard EDTA. It will be apparent that the precipitation stage will have the significance, and require the same attention as in the gravimetric determination of sulphate. As the sulphate content will depend on the excess of Ba^{2+} ions, a precipitate very close to theoretical stoichiometry is essential.

An interesting feature of barium sulphate is that when it is precipitated in the presence of EDTA, the coprecipitation of many ions is prevented. Furthermore when excessive amounts are already present, if the precipitate is dissolved in ammoniacal EDTA and re-precipitated by acidification, a pure precipitate is obtained[80].

The solubility of barium sulphate can be reduced by addition of alcohol or another suitable water-miscible solvent. A further difficulty in this form of the method is that the back-titration of excess Ba^{2+} ions would also titrate other metals present. Cation-exchange is one solution to this problem though the increase in volume resulting from this step makes the titration more difficult.

The solubility of barium sulphate in ammoniacal EDTA followed by titration of excess EDTA has been the basis of another approach[81]. Back titration of the excess EDTA is made with standard magnesium chloride solution using Eriochrome Black T as indicator. The same workers[82] applied the method to the determination of sulphur in steel.

When the amount of sulphate is large, there is some difficulty in completely dissolving it in the ammoniacal EDTA. Rumler, Herbolsheimer and Wolf[83] have suggested 5% tri- or mono-ethanolamine as an alternative to ammonia. Morris[34] has recommended sodium hydroxide but if this is used there would be the possibility of interference caused by ions dissolved from the glassware.

Another way of carrying out a compleximetric determination of sulphate is by initial precipitation of lead sulphate. This has much better properties as a precipitate than barium sulphate, and its relatively high solubility can be reduced by addition of alcohols. The procedure may be carried out in several ways. Iritani, Tanaka and Oishi[85] treat the sulphate sample (5–350 μg SO_4^{2-}) with a known excess of $Pb(NO_3)_2$ solution in a medium containing acetic acid and 25–30% ethanol. After filtration the filtrate is back-titrated with standard EDTA using Cu–PAN complex as indicator. There is no interference from NH_4^+, K^+, Na^+, Mg^{2+}, Cl^- or CO_2, but Ca^{2+} and PO_4^{3-} interfere by coprecipitation.

The precipitated lead sulphate can be dissolved in ammoniacal EDTA of known concentration and the excess back-titrated. This procedure was employed by Sporek[86] who carried out the initial precipitation in an acidic solution containing isopropyl alcohol. Back-titration of excess EDTA was made with standard zinc chloride solution using Eriochrome Black T as indicator. Only 30–45 min is required for a complete analysis, this including a period of 15 min during which the precipitate is set aside. The method is applicable in the macro range. A modification by Ashbrook and Ritcey[87] allows the precipitate to stand for 3 h before filtration which is done using two Whatman No. 3 filter papers instead of the fine-porosity frit used by Sporek. This is claimed to give a greatly increased accuracy and precision. Phosphate, molybdate and selenate interfere giving high results. Arsenic and antimony give no interference.

Another variation in the procedure is to dissolve the lead sulphate in a highly specific complexing agent, for example sodium acetate or ammonium tartrate, and then titrate the lead(II) with standard EDTA.

Tanaka and Tanabe[88] use ammonium acetate. When the precipitate has dissolved the pH is adjusted to 5 and the lead(II) titrated using Xylenol Orange as indicator. The coefficient of variation found was 2 per cent, 0.5 per cent, and less than 0.2 per cent for 1 mg, 10 mg and 50 mg SO_4^{2-} respectively. A similar method is described by Odler and Gebauer[89]. In this procedure fluoride, iodide, chromate, phosphate, oxalate and arsenate interfere, with chloride giving high results when present in excess of 500 mg.

Several simple procedures are available for determination of sulphate and other species when present together. Sulphate, sulphide and sulphite are determined in the following way[90]. Sulphide is precipitated with copper nitrate solution, the unconsumed Cu^{2+} being titrated with standard EDTA. In a second aliquot sulphate is determined by precipitation as barium sulphate followed by titration of excess Ba^{2+} with standard EDTA. In a third aliquot sulphide and sulphite are oxidized to sulphate with bromine and the total sulphate determined as above. The total composition can then be evaluated.

An alternative procedure for sulphate and sulphide present together has been given by de Sousa[91]. One aliquot is boiled with HCl to expel the sulphide as H_2S. The sulphate, which is unaffected, is determined using EDTA. A second aliquot is oxidized with bromine. The sulphide is converted to sulphate which is then determined with the sulphate already present, and the sulphide content obtained by difference.

The same worker[92] has described an analogous method for sulphate and sulphite, involving removal of sulphite as SO_2 and a similar oxidation of sulphite to sulphate with bromine.

Determination of sulphate and phosphate when present together can be made compleximetrically[93]. First the phosphate is precipitated as magnesium ammonium phosphate, filtered off and the magnesium content titrated with EDTA. Sulphate in the filtrate is precipitated as lead sulphate and again titrated with EDTA.

Applications of compleximetric determination of sulphate is widespread and includes analysis of cement[94], fertilizers[95], steel[82] and reagent chemicals[96]. Several other applications are given in the monograph by Schwarzenbach and Flaschka[79].

4. *Titration of sulphide produced by reduction of sulphate*

Reduction followed by separation of H_2S provides the basis for both separation and determination of sulphate. Reducing agents proposed have included titanium phosphoric acid[97] and various mixtures[98] containing hydriodic acid. The resulting H_2S is absorbed in solutions of zinc or cadmium salts, or NaOH, and subsequently determined by titrimetry or spectrophotometry. Archer[99] employed mercuric acetate as titrant with dithizone as indicator.

Quartermain and Hill[97] used a variation of the method for determination of trace amounts of sulphate in high purity chemicals. After reduction using titanium in phosphoric acid, the sulphide is titrated with mercuric acetate using diphenylthiocarbamate as indicator. Essentially a trace method, it has the ability to determine 10 μg of sulphate in a wide variety of substances, with an accuracy of ±10 μg.

More recently the reduction method has been used by Beswick and Johnson[100] in the analysis of foodstuffs. Initial decomposition of the samples was by oxygen-flask. The results, on 26 different types of food, indicate that the method is more accurate and precise than the turbidimetric method for sulphate, and that it is particularly suitable for samples high in mineral content. A disadvantage is that each analysis requires 3 h.

Murphy and Sergeant[101] find that precipitation of mercuric sulphide tends to mask the dithizone end-point, and prefer to use 2-(hydroxy-mercuri)-benzoic acid as titrant, again with dithizone as indicator. This procedure is based on earlier work by Wronski[102]:

$$2\;C_6H_4(COO^-)(HgOH) + S^{2-} \rightleftharpoons {}^-OOC{-}C_6H_4{-}Hg{-}S{-}Hg{-}C_6H_4{-}COO^- + 2OH^-$$

They apply the method to sulphur in rocks in the range 5–2000 mg kg^{-1} S. The procedure consists of oxidizing the sulphur to sulphate, reducing this to sulphide using a five-component reduction mixture, absorbing the H_2S in potassium hydroxide solution, and then titrating with the above reagent.

5. *Miscellaneous titrimetric procedures*

Several titrimetric procedures have been based on the sulphate–benzidine reaction. In view of the carcinogenic properties of benzidine they should no longer be used.

4-amino-4′-chlorobiphenyl (CAD) has been shown to be a most sensitive reagent for sulphate, for example it will produce turbidity with 0.0005M H_2SO_4 whereas barium chloride will not[103]. The precipitation of sulphate by this reagent has been developed into a titrimetric procedure for direct determination of 2.5–100 mg sulphate. The reagent is added at pH 1.0–2.0, the precipitate boiled for 1 min and then titrated with standard sodium hydroxide using a mixed phenol red–bromothymol blue indicator. Nitrate does not interfere, but oxidizing agents decompose the reagent. Aluminium forms an insoluble complex salt containing sulphate. It may be masked using tartaric acid. Phosphate, oxalate, selenate, and tellurite form insoluble salts with the reagent. Phosphate may be removed as magnesium ammonium phosphate. Application of the method has been made to sulphur in coal[104]. The reagent is not carcinogenic. Some doubts have been thrown on the method on the grounds of solubility errors[105] but using the sensitivity of the reagent as a criterion, there is little doubt that it has advantages in this respect.

Amplification methods exist for several anions. The subject has been reviewed by Belcher[106]. One of the earliest titrimetric methods for sulphate based on treatment with barium chromate dissolved in HCl was, in fact, an amplification method, though not described as such at the time[107]. Recently Weisz and Fritsche[108] have developed an amplification method based on exchange of sulphate with barium iodate in an acetonitrile-containing medium. The liberated iodate is determined using a standard titrimetric procedure. In another method capable of twelve-fold amplification, the principal step involves addition of excess barium bromate to the sulphate solution. First barium sulphate is precipitated. Addition of acetone causes the excess barium bromate to precipitate out. After filtration this is reacted with KI and the liberated iodine titrated with standard thiosulphate[109]. The method is applied to micro-determination of sulphur in organic compounds.

Sulphate in seawater has been determined by a photometric titration, with HCl in dimethylsulphoxide[110]. Most conventional sulphate methods fail when applied to seawater owing to the high salt content. The amount of sulphate normally found in seawater would suggest use of the gravimetric barium sulphate method. However, errors would arise due to coprecipitation, mainly by calcium and alkali salts. In the above method the sulphate is titrated to H_2SO_4 using bromocresol green as indicator. The end-point is evaluated graphically.

Spectroscopic methods

1. Spectrophotometric methods—visible and UV

The sulphate ion forms few coloured systems. This results in a dearth of direct spectrophotometric methods. Indirect methods often depend on the displacement of a chromogenic species from an insoluble compound. Another approach involves measurement of the excess of a compound or ion that reacts with sulphate giving an insoluble compound. Such methods tend to be inconvenient, and often lack sensitivity as well as being prone to interference by other anions. Methods based on benzidine will not be discussed owing to its carcinogenic nature.

4-amino-4′-chlorobiphenyl was introduced[103] as a precipitant for sulphate but was later applied to its spectrophotometric determination in the submicro range[112]. The amine cation has a molar absorptivity of about 23 000 at 254 nm, and the procedure involves measuring the amount of amine remaining in solution after precipitation and removal of the amine sulphate. The latter operation is best carried out using a centrifuge, this reducing the possibility of solubility errors that might arise from filtering and washing the precipitate. Ahmed and Lawson[113] adapted the method to the milligram scale and applied it to the analysis of coals and related material. In the range 3–7.5 mg SO_4^{2-} recoveries within 1% of theoretical amounts were reported.

A similar method is reported[114] using 2-aminoperimidine, which was later used[115] in the nephelometric determination of sulphate. Again the reagent absorbs strongly in the UV, giving a double peak at 200–230 nm and a rather broad peak at 305 nm. The latter peak is suitable for analytical work. The procedure consists of adding a known amount of the reagent to the sulphate sample solution, allowing 30 min for the precipitate to form, and then measuring the absorbance at 305 nm of the clear supernatant liquid after centrifuging. Sulphate in the range 4–120 ppm may be determined. For 50 ppm of sulphate, interference by fluoride, nitrate and phosphate at 100 ppm is only slight.

As with 4-amino-4′-chlorobiphenyl, 2-aminoperimidine is recommended for the determination of sulphate in rain and surface waters. Synthesis of the reagent is described in the original work by Stephen[114]. An improved synthesis of the reagent has been given by McClure[116].

Barium chloranilate was introduced as a colorimetric reagent for sulphate by Bertolacini and Barney[117]. The method involves the application of a general principle which may be also applied to chloride and phosphate.

$$Y + MA(\text{solid}) \rightarrow A^- + MY(\text{solid}), \qquad \text{where } A^- = \text{chloranilate ion}$$

In the case of sulphate, insoluble barium chloranilate reacts with the anion giving barium sulphate and releasing an equivalent amount of the highly coloured chloranilic acid (2,5-dichloro-3,6-dihydroxy-*p*-quinone) which gives a broad absorbance peak at 530 nm.

$$SO_4^{2-} + BaC_6Cl_2O_4 + H^+ \rightarrow HC_6Cl_2O_4^- + BaSO_4$$

The reaction is carried out in 50% aqueous ethanol buffered to pH 4. Buffering is necessary as the absorbance of chloranilic acid is a function of pH. Presence of ethanol increases the sensitivity to about 2 ppm of sulphate, by decreasing the solubilities of barium sulphate and barium chloranilate.

In the original work cations were found to interfere by forming insoluble chloranilates. Their removal by cation exchange is straightforward. Chloride, nitrate, bicarbonate, phosphate and oxalate do not interfere at the 100 ppm level. Further investigations[118] indicated that phosphate and fluoride do not interfere unless present in amounts greater than 10 mg. The method has been subject to criticism on several grounds. The relatively high values of the blanks has been unacceptable to several workers, for example Haslam, Hamilton and Squirrel[119] in the analysis of plastics. The original phthalate buffer has been replaced by others because it is frequently incapable of maintaining the required pH value after cation-exchange[146, 147]. The blank value is related to the exact method of preparing the reagent[120, 121] and this may partly explain the diversity of opinion on the method. A mathematical treatment of the equilibria has been carried out by Agterdenbos and Martinius[122]. This has raised further controversy[120, 123].

It has been pointed out[124] that the molar absorptivity of chloranilic acid is much greater at 280–350 nm than at 530 nm. Another pertinent factor is that changes in ionic strength can produce proportional errors when measurements are made in the UV region[125].

Despite the criticisms outlined above, the method has found extensive use. Application has been made to a wide variety of materials including soil[126], urine[127], foods[64] and water[128]. It has been adapted to automatic determination of sulphate in the 5–400 ppm range[129].

Two newer developments are of interest. Kudo and Tanaka[130] employ the barium complex of 3,6-dihydroxy-2-methyl-*p*-benzoquinone, which is related to chloranilic acid. In this case the liberated anion is evaluated at 515 nm, and gives a rectilinear graph for 5–70 μg SO_4^{2-} per mℓ.

Yamamoto, Hirro and Tanaka[131] extract the chloranilate ion in the presence of tris-(1,10-phenanthroline)-iron(II) ions, into nitrobenzene. The extinction at 516 nm is proportional to the concentration of chloranilate ion, and this permits determination of sulphate in the range 4×10^{-6}M to 4×10^{-5}M. No interference is given by phosphate, fluoride, hexacyanoferrate(II), nitrite, sulphite and acetate. Metal ions except those of the alkali metals, interfere as in the normal method. Application of chloranilates to the determination of other anions has been reviewed by Bark[132].

Reduction of sulphate to sulphide followed by spectrophotometric evaluation of the latter as methylene blue (*Structure 71*) is one of the most

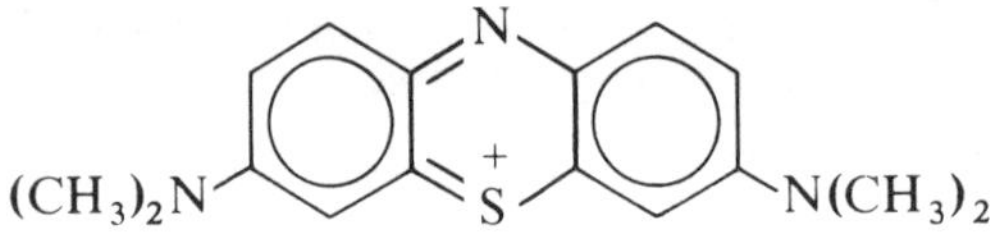

$(CH_3)_2N$ — N — $\overset{+}{S}$ — $N(CH_3)_2$

Structure 71 Methylene blue

sensitive of the indirect methods. The formation of methylene blue depends on the reaction between H_2S and an acidic solution of *p*-aminodimethylaniline in the presence of Fe^{3+} ions. Several reducing agents have been proposed[97,98] including titanium in phosphoric acid, and hydriodic and hypophosphorous acids in acetic acid solution. Earlier work on the method is summarized by Beswick and Johnson[133]; it is also discussed in the monograph on colorimetric analysis by Boltz[134]. A comprehensive study of the method was carried out by Gustafsson[98].

When nitrogenous materials are analysed, low recoveries are obtained. This has been attributed to formation of volatile products which interfere with the formation of methylene blue[98,135]. This may be satisfactorily dealt with[136] by adding zinc acetate, evaporating to dryness, and igniting at 320 °C for 1 h. The treatment is based on the fact that zinc nitrate is decomposed by this treatment whereas zinc sulphate is stable.

The methylene blue method is sensitive[135] ($\varepsilon = \sim 34\,000$) but the colour fades rapidly in sunlight. Published work on the method indicates that its range is restricted and that it is basically unreliable, probably due to the spectrophotometric properties of methylene blue solutions. An attempt to improve the linearity of the method by addition of pyridine has been made by Kirsten and Patel[137]. Unquestionably the reduction of sulphate to sulphide is an attractive basis for a simple selective and sensitive method. Quantitative transfer and absorption in alkaline solution presents no problems. Apart from the methylene blue method for determination of the resulting sulphide several other methods have been proposed including iodimetric titration, precipitation titration, and other spectrophotometric methods. A recent micro-method based on the bright orange tris(1,10-phenanthroline) iron(II) complex, is described by Davis and Lindstrom[138]. Details appear later in this section.

Several sulphate methods are based on release of ligands from complexes with barium, thorium and zirconium. When sulphate reacts with solutions or suspensions of these complexes the coloured ligand is released and evaluated spectrophotometrically. Until recently no direct procedure existed. Goguel[139] has developed such a method based on absorption of the $FeSO_4^+$ complex at between 325 and 360 nm. It allows rapid determination of sulphate in the range 10–500 mg ℓ^{-1}. A study of interferences is included in the work, this indicating that low concentrations of phosphate, fluoride, Fe^{3+} and other ions do not affect the accuracy thus making the method suitable for the analysis of natural waters. Where brines are involved corrections are necessary.

Kanno[140] has proposed an indirect method based on barium molybdate.

$$SO_4^{2-} + BaMoO_4 \rightarrow BaSO_4 + MoO_4^{2-}$$

The released molybdate is complexed with thioglycollic acid and the absorbance measured at 365 nm. Ethanol is used to suppress the solubility of barium sulphate. The molar absorptivity is stated to be ten times greater than that of the barium chloranilate method. A linear calibration curve is given below 25 μg SO_4^{2-} mℓ^{-1}.

Barium chromate has found similar use, and the method has been applied to soil analysis[141]. Phosphate interferes but it can be coprecipitated with calcium carbonate, allowing 1 mg SO_4^{2-} to be determined[142] in the presence of 500 ppm of phosphate.

Barium ions form a 1:2 complex with the rhodizonate anion which, in the absence of chloride exhibits a maximum absorbance at 480 nm. Babko and Litvinenko[143] have utilized this as the basis for a spectrophotometric method for sulphate. The sulphate is allowed to react with a bright red suspension of barium rhodizonate at pH 2–3.8. Barium sulphate is precipitated with release of an equivalent amount of rhodizonic acid. The sensitivity is reported as 0.5–0.8 μg SO_4^{2-} mℓ^{-1}.

Reduction of sulphate to sulphide followed by determination of the latter has already been discussed. While the initial reduction and separation of H_2S is selective, the spectrophotometric end-procedure utilizing methylene blue has defects. Davis and Lindstrom[138] have replaced this step with a procedure based on reduction of Fe^{3+} ions by H_2S in the presence of 1,10-phenanthroline. The resulting Fe^{2+} ions form a stable complex with the reagent, tris-(1,10-phenanthroline) iron(II). Spectrophotometric evaluation of the highly coloured complex provides a very sensitive method for the H_2S produced ($\varepsilon = 11\,000$) and hence for the original amount of sulphate. Of over 20 common ions only nitrite and those ions forming H_2S under the same conditions, interfere.

Ducret and Ratouis[144] use an ion-exchange resin to exchange sulphate with thiocyanate, this being subsequently determined by extracting its methylene blue complex into 1,2-dichloroethane at pH 1.

$$\underset{\text{(resin)}}{2SCN^-} + \underset{\text{(solution)}}{SO_4^{2-}} \rightleftharpoons \underset{\text{(resin)}}{SO_4^{2-}} + \underset{\text{(solution)}}{2SCN^-}$$

A rapid and simple spectrophotometric method for analysis of strong

H_2SO_4 in the range 85–99% has been published[145]. Quinalizarin (1,2,5,8 tetrahydroxyanthraquinone) is used as reagent. The acid concentration, which is accurate to about ±0.3%, is evaluated from the ratio of absorbances at 535 and 630 nm.

A photometric titration of sulphate with barium chloride and using thorin as indicator has been recommended for determination of sulphate in industrial waters[65].

Spectrophotometric determination of sulphate using barium chloranilate[117]

Reagents

Barium chloranilate: Reagent grade (commercial product).

It may be prepared as follows: mix 1ℓ of 0.1% aqueous chloranilic acid with 1ℓ of 5% aqueous barium chloride and allow to stand overnight at room temperature. Wash the aged precipitate with water until free of chloride ion. Remove water by centrifuging the precipitate three times with ethanol and once with diethyl ether. Finally dry the solid for 1 h at 60 °C in a vacuum oven.

Buffer, pH 4.0: 0.05M reagent grade potassium hydrogen phthalate.

Ion exchange resin: Dowex 50 × 8 (H^+ form) 20–50 mesh.

Procedure

Pass an aqueous solution containing sulphate through a column 1.5 cm in diameter and 15 cm long containing the cation resin. Adjust the effluent to pH 4 with dilute HCl or NH_4OH.

To an aliquot containing up to 40 mg of sulphate in less than 40 mℓ in a 100 mℓ volumetric flask add 10 mℓ of buffer solution and 50 mℓ of 95% ethanol. Dilute to volume with distilled water, add 0.3 g of barium chloranilate and shake for 10 min. Remove excess barium chloranilate and the precipitated barium sulphate by filtration or by means of a centrifuge.

Measure the absorbance at 530 nm against a blank prepared in the same manner. A calibration curve is prepared using standard potassium sulphate.

Note

The system obeys Beer's law up to at least 400 μg mℓ$^{-1}$ of sulphate. In the original work a 1 cm cell was used. With 5 cm cells the sensitivity is 2 ppm of sulphate in the original solution.

---

2. *Turbidimetric and nephelometric methods*

The lack of entirely satisfactory routine spectrophotometric methods for small amounts of sulphate has been largely responsible for the extensive investigation of turbidimetric and nephelometric methods. Earlier studies were based on barium sulphate suspensions, but more recently organic reagents have resulted in a great improvement. In the turbidimetric method, a barium chloride solution is added to an acidified solution of the sulphate, with the aim of producing a uniform finely divided precipitate. Several stabilizing agents have been proposed for the purpose, including starch, gum-ghatti, and 'Tween 80' (polyoxyethylene sorbitol). Several others are listed by Beswick and Johnson[64] who themselves compare the turbidimetric method with others in the determination of sulphur in foodstuffs, the sulphate being produced by oxygen-flask combustion. They recommend the method if high precision is not required and where interference by phosphate, iron, calcium and magnesium would otherwise provide a problem. Wimberley[148] has reported that results can be as good even when additives are omitted.

Turbidimetric methods have been applied to determination of sulphate in a wide variety of materials. In addition to the application to food already mentioned, these include plant material[149] and water, where it remains a standard method for routine analysis[150].

In turbidimetric analysis the light intensity is measured in the direction of the incident beam. In nephelometry, which is generally more sensitive, light scattered by the precipitate is measured at an angle (generally 90°) to the incident beam. As in turbidimetry the technique is critically dependent on the physical characteristics of the precipitate particles. Several procedures have been based on the rather low solubility of barium sulphate, particularly in mixed solvents consisting of water and polyhydric alcohols.

A fundamental study of the method has been carried out by Toennies and Bakay[151]. More recent work has tended to look at alternative precipitants for sulphates. Reference has been already made[103, 112] to the high sensitivity of CAD(4-amino-4′-chlorobiphenyl) to sulphate. The finely divided precipitate makes it ideal for both turbidimetric and nephelometric procedures. A semi-quantitative procedure was used by Haslam, Hamilton and Squirrel[152] in the analysis of plastic materials. A more detailed study has been carried out by Martin and Stephen[153] who developed a nephelometric method suitable for 2.5–25 ppm of sulphate in test volumes of 10 mℓ. Gum-ghatti, a polysaccharide containing L-arabinose, D-xylose, D-galactose, D-mannose and glucuronic acid, is used as stabilizer. Any phosphate present is removed as magnesium ammonium phosphate. Results for a batch of 11 determinations (5.0–30.0 ppm) give an average error of ± 2.8 per cent. An improved colloidal stabilizer prepared from gum-ghatti is also described in the same work. Using this the measurable range for sulphate is 1–25 ppm, this showing an increase in sensitivity at the lower end of the scale. An interesting application of the method[154] is determination of sulphate in the presence of barium. This is accomplished by masking the Ba^{2+} ions with EDTA.

An important feature of this reagent and related ones, is the use of solubility of the precipitate salt in water as a criterion of its analytical usefulness. This is not a valid criterion for the methods being considered, for they do not require isolation of the precipitate, and a precipitate as such is much less soluble in the solution, than in water, due to the common ion effect. Accordingly, errors arising from loss of precipitate by simple mechanical processes or from increased solubility in wash liquids, are eliminated.

4-amino-4′-chlorobiphenyl was originally assumed to be carcinogenic in common with its parent 4-aminobiphenyl. Physiological studies, however, have shown this not to be so, and its analytical application should not be restricted on this account.

A new reagent, 2-aminoperimidine hydrochloride has appeared recently[114] for the nephelometric determination of sulphate. Reference has already been made to it in connection with spectrophotometric determination of sulphate in the UV. The parent heterocyclic perimidine (*Structure 72*) forms sparingly soluble salts with several acids, but the behaviour is much more pronounced with the 2-amino derivative (*Structure 73*). As little as 0.05 ppm of SO_4^{2-} can be detected by precipitation of the corresponding amine sulphate. Suspensions of the precipitate have remarkable stability, and make the addition of stabilizers unnecessary.

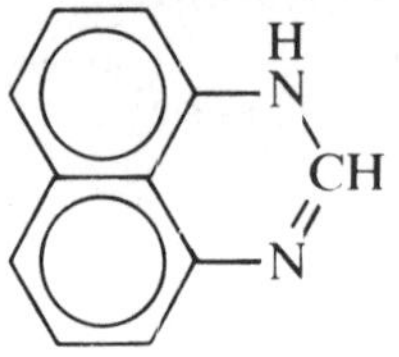

Structure 72 Perimidine

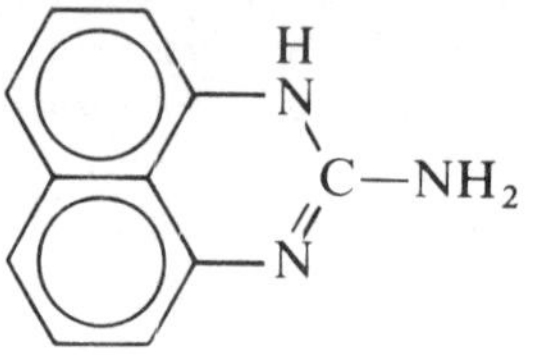

Structure 73 2-amino perimidine

2-Aminoperimidine is similar to several other salt-forming reagents in that it shows poor selectivity. In high concentrations, many ions form precipitates. However, under the conditions in which sulphate is determined, few common ions interfere, and the above study by Martin and Stephen[153] indicates that most common anions can be tolerated in at least ten-fold amounts without effect. The method is particularly suitable for determination of very small amounts of sulphate in natural waters.

The solubility of the amine sulphate is 0.020 g ℓ^{-1} compared with 0.098 and 0.155 g ℓ^{-1} for the corresponding sulphates of benzidine and 4-amino-4′-chlorobiphenyl, but as stated above, the sensitivity of the reagent is a more important factor.

Both the preparation of the reagent and its recovery after use, are described in the above paper. An improved synthesis has been published[116].

Nephelometric determination of sulphate using 2-aminoperimidine[114]

Reagents

2-Aminoperimidine hydrochloride solution:

Dissolve 0.5 g of the amine salt in 100 mℓ of warm distilled water, filter the hot solution and store in an amber-coloured reagent bottle. The reagent is sensitive to oxidants, and some deterioration of the reagent solution occurs if it is left exposed to air and light for some days. If it is stored in a stoppered dark glass bottle, little or no change occurs for some time, and the reagent can be used for at least 4 days, giving exactly the same calibration graph.

Stock potassium sulphate solution, 10 ppm:

Dissolve 18.14 mg of freshly dried Analytical Reagent grade salt in 1ℓ of freshly distilled water.

Apparatus:

An 'EEL' nephelometer comprising the EEL nephelometer head and EEL Unigalvo Type 20 (Evans Electroselenium Ltd., Essex, England) is suitable. Test tubes (10 mm i.d., capacity 12 mℓ) provided with the instrument are used for holding the suspensions in the nephelometer.

General procedure

For 0–5 ppm of sulphate, transfer 1.0 to 5.0 mℓ of standard SO_4^{2-} solution to each of five 10-mℓ volumetric flasks. Dilute to about 5 mℓ with distilled water, add 4 mℓ of the 2-aminoperimidine hydrochloride solution, and dilute the contents to the mark. Mix well by inverting the flask several times and leave the suspensions for 5–10 min. Transfer to the nephelometer tube and measure the light scattering of each solution after setting the zero reading on a blank solution and the sensitivity to give a reading of about 80 per cent full scale deflection for the most concentrated sulphate solution. At the lower sensitivity settings of the instrument, distilled water and a reagent blank solution give essentially the same reading. Plot the galvanometer readings against the concentration of sulphate in the 10 mℓ test solution.

For 0–1 ppm or 0–0.5 ppm of sulphate, proceed in exactly the same way but use higher instrumental sensitivities.

Note

The reagent may be recovered in the following way. All solutions and suspensions containing the reagent are stored in a residues bottle to which a quantity of 5% sodium sulphate solution has been added. On standing, the precipitate of the amine sulphate settles out and the supernatant liquid is periodically decanted off. More sulphate solution is added to maintain a sufficient concentration in the aqueous phase. When an appreciable amount of the precipitate has been collected, it is filtered off on a large sintered glass filter funnel, washed with water and then suspended in water. After addition of 4M sodium hydroxide, the mixture is thoroughly shaken up and the free base is filtered off. This is dissolved in the minimum amount of hot acetone. The acetone solution is then treated with sufficient 4M HCl to precipitate completely the hydrochloride of the base. This is filtered off, drained well, washed on the filter with a small volume of acetone followed by diethyl ether, and finally air-dried on the filter. The product can be further purified by dissolving it in 40 times the weight of water with warming, filtering the hot solution and treating with a saturated aqueous solution of potassium chloride until precipitation is complete. The precipitate is filtered off, washed with a little dilute potassium chloride solution and then with acetone and diethyl ether as previously. The hydrochloride is obtained as a greyish-white crystalline powder which dissolves readily in warm water. The solution gives an immediate silky white precipitate when treated with 0.05% potassium sulphate solution.

---

3. *Spectrofluorimetry*

In recent years several spectrofluorimetric methods for sulphate have appeared. Guyon and Lorah[155] developed a method based on the inhibiting effect of sulphate on the fluorescence of the thorium–morin complex in 80% ethanolic solution at pH 2.35. Although the sensitivity is high, several species including fluoride, phosphate, tungstate, molybdate, As(III), Fe^{3+} and Al^{3+}

interfere seriously. Another spectrofluorimetric method is based on enhancement of the fluorescence of the zirconium–calcein blue complex. Excitation and fluorescence maxima occur at 350 and 410 nm respectively. The method is applicable[156] in the range 0.2–12 mg sulphate. Fluoride and phosphate interfere, as do several other cations and anions.

4. *Infra-red spectroscopy*

Several polyatomic anions including sulphate exhibit characteristic infra-red bands which enable their identification and determination to be accomplished. Haba and Wilson[157] were able to determine as little as 20 μg SO_4^{2-} in the presence of hexacyanoferrate(II), hexacyanoferrate(III), cobalticyanide, metavanadate and chromate using 1 mm potassium bromide discs.

Underwood, Miller and Howe[158] investigated the accuracy and selectivity of infra-red spectroscopy applied to aqueous solutions containing nitrate, nitrite and sulphate. Relative errors of about 3 per cent were found for amounts ranging from 1 to 50 mg mℓ^{-1}. The main interferences were found to be organic compounds, ammonium salts, borate, carbonate, phosphate and perchlorate. The method was found to have limited value only. Chasan and Norwitz[159] have used infra-red to determine barium, strontium, sodium and potassium sulphates by the potassium bromide disc technique. Peak heights are measured for $BaSO_4$ and $SrSO_4$ at 983 and 993 cm^{-1} respectively; both Na_2SO_4 and K_2SO_4 are measured at 619 cm^{-1}. Barium and strontium sulphate can be determined when present together in ratios from 1:20 to 20:1. Carbonate and nitrate do not interfere but sodium and potassium cause fogging of the discs due to their hygroscopicity, and this causes erratic results. Recently the method has been applied[160] to determination of sulphate in up to a 400-fold molar excess of nitrate and a 60-fold molar excess of nitrite.

5. *Atomic spectroscopy*

Elements normally present as anions in dilute aqueous solution are not easy to determine using conventional flame spectroscopy. This is because the wavelengths for measurement by both emission and absorption lie in the far or vacuum UV region of the electromagnetic spectrum. The determination of non-metals by analytical flame spectroscopy has been reviewed by Gilbert[161]. This includes a consideration of S, B, Si, P, As, Se, Te, Cl, Br and I. Difficulties associated with direct determination can be overcome by resorting to indirect methods. In the case of sulphate such methods are largely centred on measurement of the Ba^{2+} ion.

Flame emission spectroscopy (FES) can be used for determination of sulphate either by measurements on the excess of Ba^{2+} ions after precipitation of barium sulphate or on the Ba^{2+} ions derived from the precipitate itself. The former method is used in recent work by Pleskach and Chirkova[162] who employ the 499.3 nm Ba line for sulphate below 200 ppm. Shaw[163] used the same procedure for the analysis of water and soil extracts, some samples containing as much as 1000 mg of Na^+, K^+ or Mg^{2+} per litre. Several methods have been based on the Ba^{2+} content of barium sulphate precipitates. Cullum and Thomas[164] separate the precipitate using a centrifuge and then subject a suspension in 1% starch solution to analysis by FES. In a modified version the precipitate is dissolved in an EDTA solution, the advantage being that the tendency of the precipitate to settle out during aspiration no longer presents a problem[165]. In both cases the method was applied to the analysis of detergents.

Earlier work on the determination of sulphate using FES was handicapped by the effects of interference and the relatively low sensitivity of methods for determination of Ba^{2+}. Recent work[166] utilizing the nitrous oxide–acetylene flame enables 0.5–10.0 ppm of sulphate to be determined with interference only from calcium. The procedure, which is a simple one, involves the precipitation of barium sulphate in a 50% solution of propan-2-ol. This reduces the solubility to an acceptable level, and enables spraying to be carried out without instability.

Atomic absorption spectroscopy has been used for both direct and indirect determination of sulphate at low concentrations. As with FES, methods can be based on the excess of Ba^{2+} ions or on the Ba^{2+} ions derived from precipitated barium sulphate after dissolving it in EDTA. The former procedure is used by Varley and Chin[167] for the determination of sulphate in soils. Dissolution of the isolated barium sulphate in EDTA followed by AAS is used by Wollin[168].

Rose and Boltz[169] have described an analogous method based on the precipitation of lead sulphate in an ethanolic solution. The 283.3 nm lead resonance line is used in the subsequent AAS.

A new and important development in the direct determination of sulphate by atomic spectroscopy employs a microwave-excited electrodeless discharge lamp and a nitrogen-separated nitrous oxide–acetylene flame[170]. Sulphate in the range 50–700 ppm sulphur can be determined using the 180.7 nm resonance line for sulphur. No significant chemical or physical interference occurs in the signal from 200 ppm of sulphur when the following species are present in 50-fold excess by weight: Al^{3+}, Cu^{2+}, K^{+}, Mg^{2+}, Mn^{2+}, Mo(VI), Na^{+}, Ni^{2+}, Zn^{2+}, F^{-}, $PO_4{}^{3-}$, Cl^{-}, Br^{-} and I^{-}.

6. *Molecular emission spectroscopy including MECA*

In recent years considerable interest has been shown in the molecular emission at about 394 nm due to the S_2 species. Dagnall, Thompson and West[171] generated the species in a cool diffusion flame. This is achieved in a nitrogen-diluted hydrogen diffusion flame burning in air, or in a pre-mixed air–hydrogen flame burning inside a cooled sheath. The use of nitrogen (or argon) not only reduces the temperature of the flame but at the same time causes an appreciable reduction in the background emission of such species as hydroxyl. The temperature most suitable for conversion of sulphur species (including sulphate) into S_2 is 390 °C. *Figure 64* shows the emission spectrum from S_2. Being a band emission, a considerable loss of sensitivity occurs if a monochromated instrument is used to measure the radiation over a narrow spectral region. This difficulty has been overcome by employing a simple filter photometer. The resulting detection limit is increased about 100-fold giving a value of 0.08 ppm S in aqueous solutions[172]. However, interferences are considerable; for example most cations interfere by producing depressive matrix effects. This can be overcome by a preliminary ion-exchange separation.

Sulphur-containing species, including sulphate, give the blue emission response due to S_2 when subjected to Molecular Emission Cavity Analysis (MECA)[173–175]. Experimental details of the equipment are given in the section on sulphide.

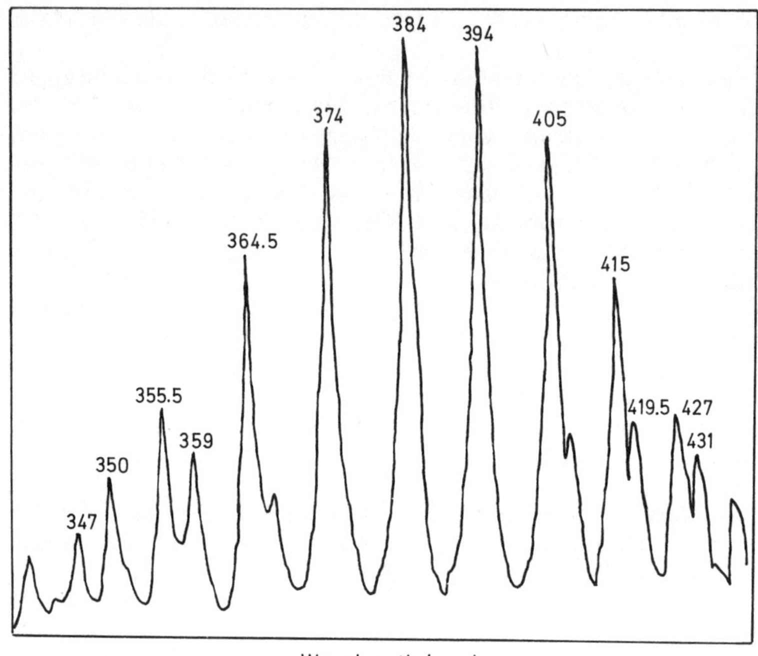

Figure 64 *Emission spectrum of S_2 species obtained by nebulizing a 5×10^{-3} M aqueous solution of sulphur dioxide into a hydrogen–nitrogen diffusion flame.* (After Dagnall, Thompson and West[171])

When the technique was applied to sulphate it became apparent that the response depends on the nature of the cations present. Thus for sulphate present as the salts of Na^+, NH_4^+, Fe^{2+}, Mn^{2+} and H^+, the time interval between inserting the sample cavity into the flame and achieving the maximum emission intensity (t_M) increases with the thermal stability of the compounds;

i.e. $Na^+ > Fe^{2+} > Mn^{2+} > NH_4^+ > H^+$

Furthermore the emission intensity decreases as t_M increases. For a series of metal sulphates, addition of H_3PO_4 before MECA analysis is found to enhance the S_2 signal, presumably by forming refractory salts with the cations present. The best signal for sulphate is given in a medium 0.10M in H_3PO_4. Sulphate and sulphide give completely resolved responses, allowing each to be determined in the presence of the other. The technique permits ng amounts of sulphate to be determined in μℓ samples.

Electroanalytical methods

1. Potentiometric including use of ion-selective electrodes

In recent years ion-selective electrodes have made an impressive impact on analytical chemistry[176]. At least four different types of electrode have been proposed for determination of sulphate:

1. The lead selective electrode which allows the potentiometric detection of end-points in the titration of sulphate with standard lead solutions.
2. Barium sulphate-impregnated silicone rubber membrane electrodes.
3. Membrane electrodes based on a four-component mixture of lead sulphate, lead sulphide, silver sulphide and copper sulphide.
4. Electrodes based on iron(III)/sulphate complex ion equilibria.

It should be pointed out that (3) and (4) are recent in origin whereas (1) and (2) have been subjected to a more widespread assessment over a longer period of time. The principles and performances of each type will now be discussed in more detail.

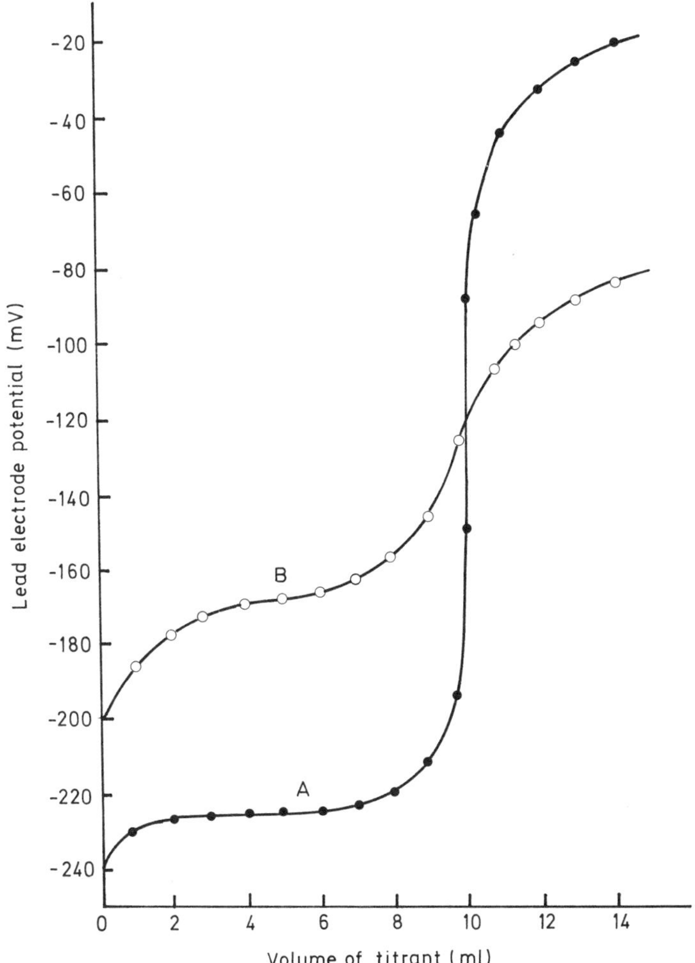

Figure 65 *Potentiometric titration of sulphate with lead perchlorate using a lead ion-selective electrode.* A, *titration of 100 ml of* 10^{-3} *M* Na_2SO_4 *with* 10^{-2} *M* $Pb(ClO_4)_2$ *(50% dioxane solution);* B, *titration of 100 ml of* 5×10^{-5} *M* Na_2SO_4 *with* 5×10^{-4} *M* $Pb(ClO_4)_2$ *(50% dioxane solution).* (After Ross and Frant[177])

Several publications have appeared featuring the lead-selective electrode introduced by Ross and Frant[177] for the potentiometric titration of sulphate. These workers used the ORION 94-82 Pb electrode in conjunction with the ORION double junction 90-02 reference electrode. The presence of dioxane was found to be more effective than ethanol in lowering the solubility of lead sulphate and its inclusion was recommended for this purpose. A titration curve using lead perchlorate and in 50% dioxane solution, is shown in *Figure 65*. A limit on the lower concentration for useful titration is set by the solubility of lead sulphate. This is about 5×10^{-5}M.

Interference is caused by Cu^{2+}, Hg^{2+}, Ag^{+}, and a 10-fold molar excess of chloride, nitrate and hydrogen carbonate. The adverse effect of hydrogen carbonate can be eliminated by adjusting the sample pH to 4. Titration curves in the absence of carbonate are independent of pH in the range pH 3.0–6.5.

More recently Mascini[178] has used a similar electrode for the titration of sulphate in mineral and seawaters. Samples were initially passed through a cation-exchange resin in Ag form to remove chloride ions, followed by a second in H^{+} form to remove excess silver. Sulphate in the range 20–3000 ppm could be determined. Another useful application of the lead solid-state ISE has been the micro and semi-micro determination of sulphur in organic compounds[179]. In this work any fluoride present is treated either by addition of boric acid or by boiling with perchloric acid. Nitrogen and halogens do not interfere, but phosphorus must be absent. The results for 10 different compounds were within ± 0.3 per cent absolute, limits considered to be acceptable in microanalysis. Further applications of the electrode include analysis of petroleum[180] and nickel plating baths[181].

Barium sulphate-impregnated silicone rubber membrane electrodes were introduced by Pungor and Havas[182] and subjected to rigorous examination by later workers including Rechnitz, Lin and Zomochnick[183]. The response was found to be linear over the range 10^{-1}–10^{-4}M SO_4^{2-} and the reproducibility ± 5 per cent, but chloride concentrations greater than 10^{-3}M caused interference. These investigators concluded that the electrode was of limited use.

The observation has been made that while it is relatively easy to achieve a Nernstian potentiometric response to sulphate ion, it is extremely difficult to attain potentiometric selectivity[184]. Rechnitz and co-workers[184,185] have described a sulphate ISE based on lead sulphate, lead sulphide, silver sulphide and copper sulphide mixtures. The second paper provides details of the preparation and properties of the electrode. Although the mechanism is obscure, the electrode gives a linear response and is selective.

Electrode type (4) is recent in origin but is included in the present discussion because of its novel principle. Based on the Fe^{3+}–SO_4^{2-} complex-ion equilibrium, it is manufactured from Fe-1173 glass, an iron-doped chalcogenide glass of composition $Ge_{28}Sb_{12}Se_{60}$. It responds to Fe^{3+} ions, which form stable complexes with sulphate. If Ba^{2+} ions are added incrementally, these complexes are broken down by precipitation of barium sulphate and the liberated Fe^{3+} ions produce an electrode response. The end-point is indicated by a constant potential[186,187].

In addition to methods based on ion-selective electrodes, other potentiometric methods for sulphate have appeared. Wagner[111] has described a rapid method for sulphate, nitrate and chloride in which all three are first converted to the corresponding acids by ion-exchange. The three acids are titrated potentiometrically with barium hydroxide. Titration with potassium palmitate gives nitrate plus chloride. Finally potentiometric titration with silver nitrate gives chloride alone.

Goldstein, Menis and Manning[188] determine 1–6 mg sulphate by addition of an excess of standard barium acetate followed by potentiometric titration of the excess with perchloric acid in glacial acetic acid. Acetic anhydride is used to eliminate water. The procedure, which was used to determine sulphate in reactor fuels, suffers no interference from UO_2^{2+}, Fe^{3+}, and other ions.

Of the more recent methods, Jovanovic, Gaa'l and Bjelica[189] employ a polarized bismuth electrode system for titration of sulphate with a mixture of lead and barium nitrate. Baudisch, Beilstein and Nevenhausen[190] also use the same mixture as titrant but detect the end-point by a pH change of 1 to 3 units measured using glass and calomel electrodes. Several ions interfere including phosphate, diphosphate, sulphide, sulphite, thiosulphate and acetate.

2. *Amperometric methods*

Several other amperometric methods for sulphate have been reported since the systematic study by Kolthoff and Pan[191] of the titration with lead nitrate. These report an accuracy of about ± 0.3 per cent, with calcium, potassium and chloride interfering if present in large amounts. An automatic amperometric method has been described based on a Ag–AgCl reference electrode and a stationary mercury pool indicator eletrode. Sulphate solutions down to 0.001 mM can be titrated[192] with 0.002M $Pb(NO_3)_2$.

3. *Polarographic methods*

Sulphate is not directly reduced at the dropping mercury electrode but several indirect polarographic methods exist[193–195], some based on lead sulphate. In one, sulphate in the range 0.2–2 mM is precipitated with lead nitrate from a water–acetone or water–dioxan mixture (the latter if chloride is present) and the precipitate dissolved in saturated ammonium chloride. The resulting Pb^{2+} ions are determined polarographically[195].

An analogous method utilizes the excess of Ba^{2+} ions after precipitation of barium sulphate. This has been applied to determination of sulphate following oxygen-flask combustion of organic sulphur compounds[196].

Sulphate polarographic methods often require pre-concentration. In order to overcome this necessity, Mayer, Hluchan and Abel[197] developed a method based on exchange of sulphate for chromate, using barium chromate as reagent. The method was applied to water samples in which such substances as Fe^{2+} and sulphide needed pre-oxidation.

Humphrey and Laird[198] have developed an interesting polarographic technique based on sulphate displacing an equivalent amount of chloranilate ion which is determined by means of its polarographic reduction. This forms a useful alternative to the spectrophotometric end-procedure generally employed in indirect determination of chloride, phosphate, fluoride, etc.

Sulphate may also be determined by oscillographic polarography[199].

4. *Conductimetric methods*

Sulphate in the range 2–5 mg has been determined by precipitation of barium sulphate with excess standard barium acetate in an acetic acid medium, followed by conductimetric titration of the excess with standard perchloric acid. The results are comparable with a potentiometric variation of the method. A conductimetric titration of sulphate has advantages in some circumstances. Bowley[201] has applied the technique to Portland cement clinker after first decomposing the sample with a cation-exchange resin. The sulphate, in the form of H_2SO_4, is titrated with standard KOH using a high frequency titrimeter.

Kinetic methods

The reaction between zirconium and methylthymol blue in acidic solution proceeds very slowly in a chloride medium. Certain anions, for example sulphate, fluoride and phosphate, catalyse the reaction possibly due to formation of labile complexes with zirconium. This has formed the basis of a catalytic method[202] for sulphate in the range 0.1–2.4 ppm. An important feature of the method is the need to use a zirconium solution which has been allowed to age for a minimum period of time. Such solutions may be used for a limited period of time only. Many cations interfere but treatment with a cation ion-exchanger overcomes this. Interference by equimolar ratios of arsenic(V), fluoride and phosphate is prevented by prior treatment with magnesium oxide.

Radiochemical methods

Armento and Larson[203] have developed a method based on ^{51}Cr-labelled barium chromate. More recently Bowen[204] determines 2–100 μmol of sulphate (60–3200 μg) in aqueous solution, by passing the solution through a column of ^{131}I-labelled barium iodate and measuring the γ activity of the filtrate. The presence of 20% methanol reduces the blank value. The method, which is simple and rapid, gives a precision of ± 2.5 per cent. No interference studies are reported. Johannesson[205] reports a substoichiometric isotope dilution method. A preliminary ion-exchange treatment converts sulphate to H_2SO_4 to which is added ^{35}S-labelled H_2SO_4. Following precipitation with barium nitrate, a measurement of the β-activity enables sulphate in the range 10–100 μg to be determined.

Miscellaneous methods

There has been a marked revival of interest in thermometric titrimetry in recent years. In the case of sulphate, use can be made of the exothermic nature of its precipitation as barium sulphate. This was first utilized in a thermometric method over 50 years ago by Dean and Watts[206]. Williams and Janata[207] find that the direct thermometric titration of sulphate with barium perchlorate is rapid, relatively free from interferences, but critically dependent on the concentration of ethanol in the titrating medium. The range for sulphate is 1–25 mg; the accuracy is lower than in other instrumental methods. In another thermometric method also based on Ba^{2+}, a precision of better than 0.5 per cent is claimed[208].

Gas-chromatographic methods have been developed for determination of sulphate. Ito and Hara[209] first reduce sulphate to H_2S using 20% $SnCl_2$ in strong orthophosphoric acid at 250–317 °C. The resulting H_2S is submitted to gas chromatography on a 2-m column of silica gel with hydrogen as carrier gas.

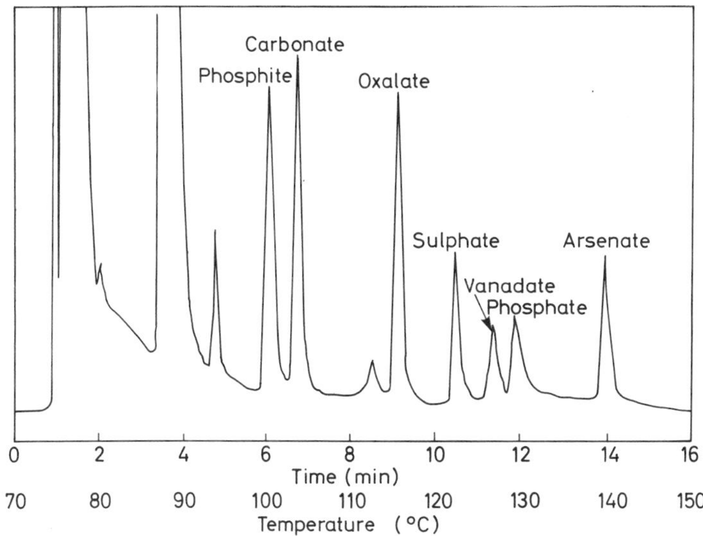

Figure 66 Gas chromatographic separation of trimethylsilyl (TMS) derivatives of seven anions including sulphate. (After Butts and Rainey[211])

Butts[210, 211] has published studies on trimethylsilyl derivatives of several anions including sulphate. The general method for preparation of the compounds is reacting the ammonium salts (of the anions) at 25 °C with trifluorobis(trimethylsilyl) acetamide in dimethylformamide. The separation is made in a 6-ft glass column containing SE-30 on Chromosorb W(HP) at 70–150 °C. It should be pointed out that the above derivatives are not formed by the sodium or potassium salts, but these are easily converted to the ammonium form by ion-exchange. Bisulphate gives the same chromatographic peak as sulphate and so does sulphite, which is apparently oxidized. The separation of eight anions, including sulphate, is shown in *Figure 66*.

References

1. HEINRICH, B.J., GRIMES, M.D. and PUCKETT, J.E., in *Treatise on Analytical Chemistty* (Ed. I.M. Kolthoff and P.J. Elving), Part II, Vol. 11, Interscience, New York, 1–35 (1961)
2. HADDOCK, L.A., in *Comprehensive Analytical Chemistry* (Ed. C.L. Wilson and D.W. Wilson), Vol. 1c, Elsevier, Amsterdam, 282 (1962)
3. HAFF, L.V., in *Analytical Chemistry of Sulphur and its Compounds* (Ed. J.H. Karchmer), Part 1, Wiley-Interscience, New York, 183 (1970)
4. BLASIUS, E., HORN, G., KNOCHEL, A., MUNCH, J. and WAGNER, H., in *Inorganic Sulphur Chemistry* (Ed. G. Nickless), Elsevier, Amsterdam (1968)
5. SZEKERES, L., *Talanta*, **21**, 2 (1974)

6. INCZEDY, J., *Analytical Applications of Ion-exchange,* Pergamon, Oxford, 135 (1966)
7. RYABININ, A.I. and BOGATYREV, V.L., *Zh. analit. Khim.,* **23**, 894 (1968); *Analyt. Abstr.,* **18**, 875 (1970)
8. SUBBOTINA, A.I., ARKHANGEL'-SKAYA, E.A. and PETROV, A.M., *Trudy Khim. i khim. Teknol., Gor'kii,* 118 (1963); *Analyt. Abstr.,* **12**, 1149 (1965)
9. SHIRAISHI, N,, IBA, T. and MORISHIGE, T., *Japan Analyst,* **14**, 450 (1965); *Analyt. Abstr.,* **14**, 126 (1967)
10. IGUCHI, A., *Bull. chem. Soc. Japan,* **31**, 600 (1958); *Analyt. Abstr.,* **6**, 1705 (1969)
11. MIKES, J.A. and SZANTO, J., *Talanta,* **3**, 105 (1959)
12. NYDAHL, E. and GUSTAFSSON, L., *Acta chem. scand.,* **7**, 143 (1953)
13. NYDAHL, E., *Analyt. Chem.,* **26**, 580 (1954)
14. FRITZ, J.S., YAMAMURA, S.S. and RICHARD, M.J., *Analyt. Chem.,* **29**, 158 (1957)
15. SEILER, H. and ERLENMEYER, H., *Helv. chim. Acta,* **47**, 264 (1964)
16. KELLY, D.P., *J. Chromat.,* **51**, 343 (1970)
17. MOGHISSI, A.J., *J. Chromat.,* **13**, 542 (1964)
18. CANIC, V.D., TURCIC, M.N. and BUGARSKI-VOJINOVIC, M.B., *Z. analyt. Chem.,* **229**, 93 (1967); *Analyt. Abstr.,* **15**, 5211 (1968)
19. KAWANABE, K., TAKITANI, S., MIYAZAKI, M. and TAMURA, Z., *Japan Analyst,* **13**, 976 (1964); *Analyt. Abstr.,* **13**, 5385 (1966)
20. DE SOUSA, A., *Inf. quim. Anal., Madrid,* **15**, 121 (1961); *Analyt. Abstr.,* **9**, 1454 (1962)
21. DE SOUSA, A., *Inf. quim. Anal., Madrid,* **16**, 177 (1962); *Chem. Abstr.,* **60**, 22g (1964)
22. KOLTHOFF, I.M., SANDELL, E.B., MEEHAN, E.J. and BRUCKENSTEIN, S., *Quantitative Chemical Analysis* 4th edn, MacMillan Co., London (1969)
23. BELCHER, R. and NUTTEN, A.J., *Quantitative Inorganic Analysis,* 3rd edn, Butterworths, London (1970)
24. LAITINEN, H.A., *Chemical Analysis,* McGraw-Hill, New York (1960)
25. PRIBIL, R. and MARINCOVA, D., *Chemiké Listy,* **46**, 542 (1952)
26. NISHIMURA, M., *Analytica chim. Acta,* **34**, 246 (1966)
27. ZOLOTAVIN, V.L., SANATINA, V.N. and NESTERENKO, V.P., *Zh. analit. Khim.,* **21**, 1289 (1966); *Analyt. Abstr.,* **15**, 4513 (1968)
28. PLESKACH, L.I. and CHIRKOVA, G.D., *Zh. analit. Khim.,* **26**, 2290 (1970); *Analyt. Abstr.,* **24**, 3362 (1973)
29. LITEANU, C. and LINGNER, H., *Talanta,* **19**, 945 (1972)
30. WAGNER, W.F. and WUELLNER, J.A., *Analyt. Chem.,* **24**, 1031 (1952)
31. VAUBEL, W., *Z. analyt. Chem.,* **35**, 163 (1896)
32. STEPHEN, W.I., *Ind. Chemist,* **37**, 551 (1961)
33. MAHR, C. and KRAUS, K., *Z. analyt. Chem.,* **128**, 477 (1948)
34. BELCHER, R. and GIBBONS, D., *J. chem. Soc.,* 4216 (1952)
35. FRITZ, J.S. and FREELAND, M.Q., *Analyt. Chem.,* **26**, 1593 (1954)
36. FRITZ, J.S. and YAMAMURA, S.S., *Analyt. Chem.,* **27**, 1461 (1955)
37. FRITZ, J.S., YAMAMURA, S.S. and RICHARD, M.J., *Analyt. Chem.,* **29**, 158 (1957)
38. WAGNER, H., *Mikrochim. Acta,* 19 (1957)
39. COLSON, A.F., *Analyst,* **88**, 26 (1963)
40. MACDONALD, A.M.G., *Analyst,* **86**, 3 (1961)
41. NOVIKOVA, K.F., BASARGIN, N.N. and CYANKOVA, M.F., *Zh. analit. Khim.,* **16**, 348 (1961); *Analyt. Abstr.,* **9**, 175 (1962)
42. NOVIKOVA, K.F. and BASARGIN, N.N., *Trudy Kom. Anal. Khim. Akad. Nauk. USSR,* **13**, 27 (1963); *Analyt. Abstr.,* **11**, 2175 (1964)
43. ARCHER, E.E., WHITE, D.C. and MACKISON, R., *Analyst,* **96**, **879** (1971)
44. KUZNETSOV, V.I. and BASARGIN, N.N., *Zav. Lab.,* **31**, 538 (1965); *Analyt. Abstr.,* **13**, 4801 (1966)
45. AKIMOV, V.K., BRAGINA, S.I. and BUSEV, A.I., *Vest. mosk. gos. Univ., Ser. Khim.,* 70 (1968); *Analyt. Abstr.,* **18**, 1043 (1970)
46. BASARGIN, N.N. and NOVIKOVA, K.F., *Zh. analit. Khim.,* **21**, 473 (1966); *Analyt. Abstr.,* **15**, 1143 (1968)
47. BASARGIN, N.N. and NOGINA, A.A., *Zh. analit. Khim.,* **22**, 394 (1967); *Analyt. Abstr.,* **15**, 6998 (1968)
48. HOZUMI, K. and UMEMOTO, K., *Microchem. J.,* **12**, 46 (1967)
49. UMEMOTO, K., INOUE, K. and NISHII, A., *Japan Analyst,* **19**, 450 (1970); *Analyt. Abstr.,* **21**, 3362 (1971)
50. BUDESINSKY, B., *Analyt. Chem.,* **37**, 1159 (1965)

51. BUDESINSKY, B. and VRZALOVA, D., *Z. analyt. Chem.*, **210**, 161 (1965)
52. SEDLAK, M., COWELL, W.H. and MILNER, O.I., *Microchem. J.*, **16**, 59 (1971)
53. BUDESINSKY, B. and VRZALOVA, D., *Chemist Analyst*, **55**, 110 (1966)
54. BUDESINSKY, B. and KRUMLOVA, L., *Analytica Chim. Acta*, **39**, 375 (1967)
55. SAVVIN, S.B., AKIMOVA, T.G., DEDKOVA, V.P. and VARSHAL, G.M., *Zh. analit. Khim.*, **24**, 1868 (1969); *Analyt. Abstr.*, **21**, 669 (1971)
56. PETROVA, E.I., *Zh. analit. Khim.*, **26**, 402 (1971); *Analyt. Abstr.*, **22**, 3641 (1972)
57. BUDESINSKY, B., *Microchem. J.*, **14**, 242 (1969)
58. ARMEANU, V. and DRAGUSIN, I., *Revue rumm. Chim.*, **14**, 1511 (1969): *Analyt. Abstr.*, **20**, 74 (1971)
59. WHITE, D.C., *Mikrochim. Acta* 807 (1962)
60. BELCHER, R., CAMPBELL, A.D., GOUVERNEUR, P. and MACDONALD, A.M.G., *J. chem. Soc.*, 3033 (1962)
61. McGILLIVRAY, R. and WOODGER, S.C., *Analyst*, **91**, 611 (1966)
62. LONSDALE, M., *Proc. Soc. analyt. Chem.*, **7**, 12 (1970)
63. NELLIST, G.R. and EDWARDS, A.H., *Proc. Soc. analyt. Chem.*, **2**, 144 (1965)
64. BESWICK, G. and JOHNSON, R.M., *Talanta*, **17**, 709 (1970)
65. British Standards 2690: Part 6 (1968) London
66. ARCHER, E.E., *Analyst*, **82**, 208 (1957)
67. NECHIPORENKO, G.N., *Izv. Akad. Nauk. SSSR, Otd. Khim Nauk*, 359 (1958); *Analyt. Abstr.*, **6**, 135 (1959)
68. WHITE, D.C., *Mikrochim. Acta*, 254 (1959)
69. WHITE, D.C., *Mikrochim. Acta*, 280 (1960)
70. NECHIPORENKO, G.N., *Gidrokhim. Mater.*, **33**, 143 (1961); *Analyt. Abstr.*, **10**, 2673 (1963)
71. NECHIPORENKO, G.N., *Gidrokhim. Mater.*, **29**, 214 (1959); *Analyt. Abstr.*, **8**, 1500 (1961)
72. NECHIPORENKO, G.N., *Gidrokhim. Mater.*, **26**, 207 (1957); *Analyt. Abstr.*, **5**, 2008 (1958)
73. MATVEEV, A.A. and NECHIPORENKO, G.N., *Gidrokhim. Mater.*, **33**, 134 (1961); *Analyt. Abstr.*, **10**, 2934 (1963)
74. NECHIPORENKO, G.N., *Gidrokhim. Mater.*, **33**, 151 (1961); *Analyt. Abstr.*, **10**, 2937 (1963)
75. LEWIS, W.M., *Proc. Soc. Wat. Treat. Exam.*, **16**, 287 (1967)
76. PARKER, S., *Proc. Soc. analyt. Chem.*, **4**, 102 (1967)
77. NIWA, U. and PARRY, E.P., *Chemist Analyst*, **49**, 102 (1960)
78. MUNGER, J.R., NIPPLER, R.W. and INGOLS, R.S., *Analyt. Chem.*, **22**, 1455 (1950)
79. SCHWARZENBACH, G. and FLASCHKA, H., *Complexometric Titrations*, 2nd edn, Methuen, London (1969)
80. PRIBIL, R. and MARICOVA, D., *Chemiké Listy*, **46**, 542 (1952)
81. BELCHER, R., GIBBONS, D. and WEST, T. S., *Chem. Inds, London*, 127 (1954)
82. BELCHER, R., GIBBONS, G. and WEST, T.S., *Analyst*, **80**, 751 (1955)
83. RUMLER, F., HERBOLSHEIMER, R. and WOLF, G., *Z. analyt. Chem.*, **166**, 23 (1959); *Analyt. Abstr.*, **6**, 3953 (1959)
84. MORRIS, A.G.C., *Chemist Analyst*, **48**, 76 (1959)
85. IRITANI, N., TANAKA, T. and OISHI, H., *Japan Analyst*, **8**, 30 (1959); *Analyt. Abstr.*, **7**, 102 (1960)
86. SPOREK, K.F., *Analyt. Chem.*, **30**, 1032 (1958)
87. ASHBROOK, A.W. and RITCEY, G.M., *Analyst*, **86**, 740 (1961)
88. TANAKA, T. and TANABE, H., *Japan Analyst*, **8**, 826 (1959); *Analyt. Abstr.*, **8**, 192 (1961)
89. ODLER, I. and GEBAUER, J., *Chemiké Zvesti*, **15**, 563 (1961); *Analyt. Abstr.*, **9**, 1450 (1961)
90. BURRIEL-MARTI, F. and ALVAREZ-HERRERO, C., *Quim. analit. pura apl. Ind.*, **18**, 142 (1964); *Analyt. Abstr.*, **13**, 132 (1966)
91. DE SOUSA, A., *Inf. quim. Anal.*, **15**, 121 (1961); *Analyt. Abstr.*, **9**, 1452 (1962)
92. DE SOUSA, A., *Inf. quim. Anal.*, **16**, 177 (1962); *Analyt. Abstr.*, **10**, 3667 (1963)
93. IRITANI, N. and TANAKA, T., *Japan Analyst*, **9**, 1 (1960); *Analyt. Abstr.*, **8**, 4603 (1961)
94. NESTORIDIS, A., *Analyst*, **95**, 51 (1970)
95. CAMPBELL, A.D., HUBBARD, D.P. and TIOH, N.H., *Analyst*, **99**, 519 (1974)
96. JANGIDA, B.L., VARDE, M.S. and VENKATASUBRAMANIAN, V., *Indian J. Chem.*, **2**, 149 (1964); *Analyt. Abstr.*, **12**, 3847 (1965)
97. QUARTERMAIN, P.G. and HILL, A.G., *Analyst*, **85**, 211 (1960)
98. GUSTAFSSON, L., *Talanta*, **4**, 227, 236 (1960)
99. ARCHER, E.E., *Analyst*, **81**, 181 (1956)
100. BESWICK, G. and JOHNSON, R.M., *J. Sci. Fd Agric.*, **21**, 565 (1970)
101. MURPHY, J.M. and SERGEANT, G.A., *Analyst*, **99**, 515 (1974)

102. WRONSKI, M., *Analyst,* **83**, 314 (1958)
103. BELCHER, R., NUTTEN, A.J. and STEPHEN, W.I., *J. chem. Soc.,* 1334 (1953)
104. WILKINSON, H.C., *Analyst,* **81**, 9 (1956)
105. BENGTSSON, T.A., *Analytica chim. Acta,* **18**, 353 (1958)
106. BELCHER, R., *Talanta,* **15**, 357 (1968)
107. KOLTHOFF, I.M. and BELCHER, R., *Volumetric Analysis,* Vol. III, Interscience, New York, 339 (1957)
108. WEISZ, H. and FRITSCHE, U., *Mikrochim. Acta,* 638 (1970)
109. GAWARGIUS, Y.A. and FARAG, A.B., *Talanta,* **19**, 641 (1972)
110. JAGNER, D., *Analytica chim. Acta,* **52**, 483 (1970)
111. WAGNER, A., *Mitt. Ver. Grosskesselbesitzer,* 50 (1958); *Analyt. Abstr.,* **6**, 4187 (1959)
112. JONES, A.S. and LETHAM, D.S., *Analyst,* **81**, 15 (1956)
113. AHMED, M.N. and LAWSON, G.J., *Talanta,* **1**, 142 (1958)
114. STEPHEN, W.I., *Analytica chim. Acta,* **50**, 413 (1970)
115. JONES, P.A. and STEPHEN, W.I., *Analytica chim. Acta,* **64**, 85 (1973)
116. MCCLURE, G.L., *Analytica chim. Acta,* **64**, 289 (1973)
117. BERTOLACINI, R.J. and BARNEY, J.E., *Analytica Chem.,* **29**, 281 (1957)
118. JENEMANN, H. and ZIMMERMANN, G., *Glastech. Ber.,* **34**, 191 (1961); *Analyt. Abstr.,* **10**, 1441 (1963)
119. HASLAM, J., HAMILTON, J.B. and SQUIRRELL, D.C.M., *Analyst,* **86**, 239 (1961)
120. AGTERDENBOS, J. and MARTINIUS, N., *Talanta,* **12**, 426 (1965)
121. PROCHAZKOVA, L., *Z. analyt. Chem.,* **182**, 103 (1961); *Analyt. Abstr.,* **9**, 885 (1962)
122. AGTERDENBOS, J. and MARTINIUS, N., *Talanta,* **11**, 878 (1964)
123. BARNEY, J.E., *Talanta,* **12**, 425 (1965)
124. SPENCER, B., *Biochem. J.,* **75**, 435 (1960)
125. SUTHERLAND, I.T., *Clinica chim. Acta,* **14**, 554 (1966)
126. MAGAR, W.Y. and POLLARD, A.G., *Chem. Inds, London,* 505 (1961)
127. WAINER, A. and KOCH, A.L., *Analyt. Biochem.,* **3**, 457 (1962)
128. CARLSON, R.M., ROSELL, R.A. and VALLEJOS, W., *Analyt. Chem.,* **39**, 688 (1967)
129. GALES, M.E., KAYLOR, W.H. and LONGBOTTOM, J.E., *Analyst,* **93**, 97 (1968)
130. KUDO, H. and TANAKA, Y., *Japan Analyst,* **19**, 99 (1970); *Analyt. Abstr.,* **21**, 1061 (1971)
131. YAMAMOTO, Y., HIRRO, K. and TANAKA, T., *Japan Analyst,* **17**, 206 (1968); *Analyt. Abstr.,* **17**, 2440 (1969)
132. BARK, L.S., *Ind. Chem.,* **40**, 153 (1964)
133. BESWICK, G. and JOHNSON, R.M., *J. Sci. Fd Agric.,* **21**, 565 (1970)
134. BOLTZ, D.F. (Ed.), *Colorimetric Determination of Non-metals,* Interscience, New York (1958)
135. JOHNSON, C.M. and NISHITA, H., *Analyt. Chem.,* **24**, 736 (1952)
136. SINCLAIR, A., THORBURN BURNS, D., HALL, R.D. and HAYES, W.P., *Talanta,* **18**, 972 (1971)
137. KIRSTEN, W.J. and PATEL, V.J., *Microchem. J.,* **17**, 277 (1972)
138. DAVIS, J.B. and LINDSTROM, F., *Analyt. Chem.,* **44**, 524 (1972)
139. GOGUEL, R., *Analyt. Chem.,* **41**, 1034 (1969)
140. KANNO, S., *Japan Analyst,* **8**, 180 (1959); *Analyt. Abstr.,* **7**, 469 (1960)
141. NEMETH, K., *Z. PflErnähr Dung. Bodenk.,* **103**, 193 (1963); *Analyt. Abstr.,* **12**, 3069 (1965)
142. OZAWA, T., *J. chem. Soc. Japan, pure Chem. Sect.,* **87**, 855 (1966); *Analyt. Abstr.,* **14**, 7451 (1967)
143. BABKO, A.K. and LITVINENKO, V.A., *Zh. analit. Khim.,* **18**, 237 (1963); *Analyt. Abstr.,* **11**, 948 (1964)
144. DUCRET, L. and RATOUIS, M., *Analytica chim. Acta,* **21**, 91 (1959)
145. ZIMMERMAN, E. and BRANDT, W.W., *Talanta,* **1**, 374 (1958)
146. STOFFYN, P. and KEANE, W., *Analyt. Chem.,* **36**, 397 (1964)
147. BARNEY, J.E., *Talanta,* **12**, 425 (1965)
148. WIMBERLEY, J.W., *Analytica chim. Acta,* **42**, 327 (1968)
149. GARRIDO, M.L., *Analyst,* **89**, 61 (1964)
150. *Standard Methods for the Examination of Water and Waste Water,* 13th edn, American Public Health Association, Washington, D.C., 334 (1971)
151. TOENNIES, G. and BAKAY, B., *Analyt. Chem.,* **25**, 160 (1953)
152. HASLAM, J., HAMILTON, J.B. and SQUIRRELL, D.C.M., *Analyst,* **86**, 239 (1961)
153. MARTIN, J.M. and STEPHEN, W.I., *Analytica chim. Acta,* **39**, 175, 525 (1967)
154. MENDES-BEZERRA, A.E. and UDEN, P.C., *Analyst,* **94**, 308 (1969)
155. GUYON, J.C. and LORAH, E.J., *Analyt. Chem.,* **38**, 155 (1966)
156. TAN, L.H. and WEST, T.S., *Analyst,* **96**, 281 (1971)
157. HABA, F.R. and WILSON, C.L., *Talanta,* **9**, 841 (1962)

158. UNDERWOOD, A.L., MILLER, M.W. and HOWE, L.H., *Analytica chim. Acta*, **29**, 79 (1963)
159. CHASAN, D.E. and NORWITZ, G., *Talanta*, **18**, 499 (1971)
160. MEEHAN, B.J. and TARIQ, S.A., *Talanta*, **20**, 1215 (1973)
161. GILBERT, P.T., in *Analytical Flame Spectroscopy* (Ed. R. Mavrodineanu), Macmillan, London, 181 (1970)
162. PLESKACH, L.I. and CHIRKOVA, G.D., *Zav. Lab.*, **37**, 168 (1971)
163. SHAW, W.M., *Analyt. Chem.*, **30**, 1682 (1958)
164. CULLUM, D.C. and THOMAS, D.B., *Analyst*, **84**, 113 (1959)
165. CULLUM, D.C. and THOMAS, D.B., *Analyst*, **85**, 688 (1960)
166. FORBES, E.A., *Analyst*, **98**, 506 (1973)
167. VARLEY, J.A. and CHIN, P.Y., *Analyst*, **95**, 592 (1970)
168. WOLLIN, A. *Atom. Abs. Newsl.*, **9**, 43 (1970)
169. ROSE, S.A. and BOLTZ, D.F., *Analytica chim. Acta*, **44**, 239 (1969)
170. KIRKBRIGHT, G.F. and MARSHALL, M., *Analyt. Chem.*, **44**, 1288 (1972)
171. DAGNALL, R.M., THOMPSON, K.C. and WEST, T.S., *Analyst*, **92**, 506 (1967)
172. ALDOUS, K.M., DAGNALL, R.M. and WEST, T.S., *Analyst*, **95**, 417 (1970)
173. BELCHER, R., BOGDANSKI, S.L. and TOWNSHEND, A., *Analytica chim. Acta*, **67**, 1 (1973)
174. BELCHER, R., BOGDANSKI, S.L., KNOWLES, D.J. and TOWNSHEND, A., *Analytica chim. Acta*, **77**, 53 (1975)
175. BELCHER, R., BOGDANSKI, S.L., KNOWLES, D.J. and TOWNSHEND, A., *Analytica chim. Acta*, **79**, 292 (1975)
176. TENYGL, J., *MTP International Reviews of Science, Physical Chemistry, Series one*, Vol. 12 (Ed. T. S. West) Butterworths, London, 123 (1973)
177. ROSS, J.W. and FRANT, M.S., *Analyt. Chem.*, **41**, 967 (1969)
128. MASCINI, M., *Analyst*, **98**, 325 (1973)
179. SELIG, W., *Mikrochim. Acta*, 168 (1970)
180. HEISTAND, R.N. and BLAKE, C.T., *Mikrochim. Acta*, 212 (1972)
181. FRANT, M.S., *Plating*, 686 (1971)
182. PUNGOR, E. and HAVAS, J., *Acta. chim. hung.*, **50**, 77 (1966); *Analyt. Abstr.*, **15**, 2422 (1968)
183. RECHNITZ, G.A., LIN, Z.F. and ZOMOCHNICK, S.B., *Analyt. Lett.*, **1**, 29 (1967); *Analyt. Abstr.*, **16**, 118 (1969)
184. RECHNITZ, G.A., FRICKE, G.H. and MOHAN, M.S., *Analyt. Chem.*, **44**, 1098 (1972)
185. MOHAN, M.S. and RECHNITZ, G.A., *Analyt. Chem.*, **45**, 1323 (1972)
186. JASINSKI, R. and TRACHTENBERG, I., *Analyt. Chem.*, **44**, 2373 (1972)
187. JASINSKI, R. and TRACHTENBERG, I., *Analyt. Chem.*, **45**, 1277 (1973)
188. GOLDSTEIN, G., MENIS, O. and MANNING, D.L., *Analyt. Chem.*, **33**, 266 (1961)
189. JOVANOVIC, M.S., GAA'L, F.F. and BJELICA, L.J., *Mikrochim. Acta*, 778 (1971)
190. BAUDISCH, J., BEILSTEIN, G. and NEVENHAUSEN, H.E., *Z. analyt. Chem.*, **235**, 231 (1968); *Analyt. Abstr.*, **17**, 143 (1969)
191. KOLTHOFF, I.M. and PAN, Y.D., *J. Am. chem. Soc.*, **62**, 3332 (1940)
192. MYERS, S.A. and SWANN, W.B., *Talanta*, **12**, 133 (1965)
193. OHLWEILER, O.A., *Analytica chim. Acta*, **9**, 476 (1953)
194. LONG, M.I.E., *Analyst*, **93**, 339 (1968)
195. BARANOWSKI, R. and GREGOROWICZ, Z., *Chemia analit.*, **10**, 125 (1965); *Analyt. Abstr.*, **13**, 2323 (1966)
196. BISHARA, S.W., *Microchem. J.*, **15**, 211 (1970)
197. MAYER, J., HLUCHAN, E. and ABEL, E., *Analyt. Chem.*, **39**, 1460 (1967)
198. HUMPHREY, R.E. and LAIRD, C.E., *Analyt. Chem.*, **43**, 1895 (1971)
199. GLADISHEV, V.P., *Zav. Lab.*, **28**, 1063 (1962); *Analyt. Abstr.*, **10**, 1774 (1963)
200. GOLDSTEIN, G., MANNING, D.L. and ZITTEL, H.E., *Analyt. Chem.*, **34**, 1169 (1962)
201. BOWLEY, M.J., *Analyst*, **94**, 787 (1969)
202. HEMS, R.V., KIRKBRIGHT, G.F. and WEST, T.S., *Talanta*, **16**, 789 (1969)
203. ARMENTO, W.J. and LARSON, C.E., *Analyt. Chem.*, **35**, 918 (1963)
204. BOWEN, H.J.M., *Analyst*, **95**, 665 (1970)
205. JOHANNESSON, J.K., *Analyst*, **92**, 766 (1967)
206. DEAN, P.M. and WATTS, O.O., *J. Am. chem. Soc.*, **46**, 855 (1924)
207. WILLIAMS, M.B. and JANATA, J., *Talanta*, **17**, 548 (1969)
208. PERCHEC, H. and GILOT, B., *Bull. Soc. chim. France*, 619 (1964); *Analyt. Abstr.*, **12**, 3610 (1965)
209. ITO, S. and HARA, T., *J. chem. Soc. Japan, pure Chem. Sect.*, **90**, 1027 (1969); *Analyt. Abstr.*, **19**, 4842 (1970)
210. BUTTS, W.C., *Analyt. Lett.*, **3**, 29 (1970)
211. BUTTS, W.C. and RAINEY, W.T., *Analyt. Chem.*, **43**, 538 (1971)

Sulphide

Determination of sulphide is important in many connections. Its extreme toxicity as hydrogen sulphide is well known. In solution, a concentration of a few tenths of a milligram per litre causes an objectionable odour. Its existence in this form can result from microbial action on organic matter under anaerobic conditions.

Sulphides are often present in industrial effluents. In this connection automatic methods for continuous monitoring are important. In industrial processes themselves, particularly where ores and minerals are concerned, determination of sulphide, as well as other sulphur anions, is a routine requirement. Some industrial implications of sulphide are more subtle. For example, when steam is used as a raw material it is often necessary to ensure the absence of sulphur compounds, especially hydrogen sulphide, which is a well known catalyst poison.

$Na_2S \cdot 9H_2O$ is generally used as a reference standard. Recently Blair[1] has recommended potassium di-isopropyl phosphorodithioate as an alternative standard. Its preparation in pure form is described in the same source.

The analytical chemistry of sulphide is included in several recent reviews of the general analytical chemistry of sulphur compounds[2–5].

Separations

1. Gaseous as hydrogen sulphide

The most widely used technique for separation is to acidify the mixture containing sulphide and sweep out the liberated hydrogen sulphide with air, carbon dioxide, or preferably nitrogen. The gas is retained in a suitable absorbent. Zinc or cadmium acetate solutions are generally used, the corresponding sulphide being precipitated. The method is particularly suited to the separation of small amounts of sulphide, and it now forms part of recommended methods for sulphide determination[6,7].

Evaluation of sulphide is often made iodimetrically after separation by this method. The separation has importance outside the area of sulphide analysis. Trace amounts of sulphate can be determined by reduction to sulphide using hydriodic and hypophosphorous acids[8,9]. The sulphide is then separated as hydrogen sulphide before being determined.

2. Direct precipitation as cadmium sulphide or zinc sulphide

This is related to the previous method but avoids the generation of hydrogen sulphide. It is more suitable when substantial amounts of sulphide are present. Pomeroy[10] added zinc acetate to the sample, plus sodium hydroxide to produce a substantial carrier precipitate. The precipitate can be filtered off or the supernatant liquid carefully decanted.

Precipitation of sulphide is applicable when it is accompanied by sulphite or thiosulphate, as neither is precipitated. However, a potential difficulty here is coprecipitation of thiosulphate on the bulky zinc or cadmium sulphide precipitate. A precipitate of smaller surface area, and therefore causing less coprecipitation, is produced by adding a fresh suspension of zinc or cadmium carbonates[11].

An iodimetric procedure involving initial separation of sulphide as cadmium sulphide is given later in this section.

3. *Ion-exchange methods*

Iguchi[12] has separated sulphate, sulphite, thiosulphate and sulphide using an anion-exchanger in nitrate form. Elution is made with various solutions. Sulphite and sulphide are eluted in that order by 0.1 M ammonium nitrate–30% acetone, at pH 9.7.

Ultramicro amounts of hydrogen sulphide in gaseous mixtures or in water have been separated on Amberlite IRA 400 anion-exchange resin, followed by elution with 4M NaOH and spectrophotometric determination by the methylene blue method[13]. The resin retains sulphide for about ten days without loss.

4. *Thin-layer chromatography*

TLC on maize-starch and using acetone–3M aq. NH_4OH (1:4) as solvent, enables sulphide to be separated[14] from nitrite, thiosulphate, chromate, azide, cyanide, thiocyanate, borate, arsenite, arsenate, nitrate, sulphate and phosphate.

5. *Microdiffusion*

Determination of constituents in biological samples when present at ultra-trace levels, is often difficult. Separation of sulphide in such materials can be made by microdiffusion using standard Conway units[15]. To avoid etching the inner well surfaces by the 40% NaOH used to absorb the hydrogen sulphide, small polythene cups can be used. This is shown in *Figure 67*. A period of 3 h is required for complete separation. The polythene inserts, together with contents, are transferred to stoppered tubes for analysis by the methylene blue method.

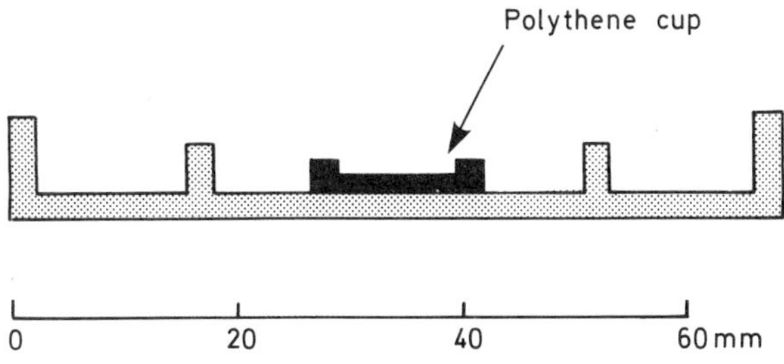

Figure 67 Polythene inserts for use with Conway units. (After Patel and Spencer[15])

A rapid microdiffusion method[16] based on the Conway technique enables complete diffusion to occur within 15 min.

6. *Miscellaneous methods*

Hydrogen sulphide in very low concentration can be extracted from air using silver nitrate-impregnated papers[17]. The method is applicable to 5 parts per trillion (10^{-12}). The analysis is completed using a fluorimetric technique.

Separation by gas-chromatography has been reported. An account of this is included in the analytical methods for determination of sulphide.

Wronski has reported separation of hydrogen sulphide as $(C_2H_5)_3Pb{-}S{-}Pb(C_2H_5)_3$ by extraction with *n*-hexanol. The separation forms part of a method for microgram determination of hydrogen sulphide in natural water using *o*-hydroxymercuribenzoic acid. A fuller discussion is given on p. 572.

Determination

Gravimetric methods

Sulphide can be oxidized to sulphate and then determined gravimetrically in that form as barium sulphate. The oxidation is best carried out with alkaline hydrogen peroxide. Other oxidants include hypobromite and bromine in HCl.

Although sulphide can be precipitated quantitatively as CdS, this is non-stoichiometric and its value lies in separation rather than determination.

Titrimetric methods

1. Iodimetric methods

This is the most important titrimetric method for sulphide although it contains several potential sources of error. The reaction can be represented by the equation:

$$H_2S + I_2 \leftrightharpoons S\downarrow + 2I^- + 2H^+$$

Direct titration can lead to errors. The general procedure recommended is addition of excess standard iodine to the sulphide sample followed by a back-titration with standard thiosulphate. If the sulphide has been separated by generation of hydrogen sulphide and absorption in zinc acetate, the excess of iodine can be added directly to the acidified suspension, and this followed by a back titration.

In the reaction represented by the above equation, the pH value of the solution is important. If slightly alkaline, even in a weak bicarbonate solution, partial oxidation of sulphide to sulphate occurs.

$$S^{2-} + 4I_2 + 8OH^- \rightarrow SO_4{}^{2-} + 8I^- + 4H_2O$$

On the other hand, if a slightly acid solution of sulphide is titrated directly with iodine, some loss of hydrogen sulphide by volatilization may result. If solutions are dilute, the precipitated sulphur does not affect the titration. When more concentrated solutions are used, iodine is occluded by the precipitate.

Any sulphite and thiosulphate present will be titrated with sulphide. Sulphide solutions are often contaminated with its oxidation products which also react with iodine. Several methods involving iodimetry have been developed for mixtures of sulphur anions including sulphide. Umland and Janssen[18] determine sulphite and sulphide in the presence of sulphate as follows. Treatment with perchloric acid in the presence of mercuric chloride liberates

SO_2 and retains sulphide as mercuric sulphide. The SO_2 is absorbed in aqueous alkaline peroxide. It can now be titrated iodimetrically. After removing SO_2 the mercuric sulphide is treated with stannous chloride and HCl to liberate hydrogen sulphide which is absorbed in cadmium acetate and determined iodimetrically.

Szekeres[19] uses the iodimetric method for analysis of sulphide–sulphite–thiosulphate mixtures. Four aliquots are required. One is treated with iodine and the second with bromine (a bromide/bromate mixture). Bromine reacts with the species in the following manner.

$$S^{2-} + 4H_2O + 4Br_2 \rightarrow SO_4^{2-} + 8H^+ + 8Br^-$$

$$S_2O_3^{2-} + 5H_2O + 4Br_2 \rightarrow 2SO_4^{2-} + 10H^+ + 8Br^-$$

$$SO_3^{2-} + H_2O + Br_2 \rightarrow SO_4^{2-} + 2H^+ + 2Br^-$$

Sulphide is removed from the remaining two aliquots by boiling with boric acid. Then one is titrated with iodine, and the other with bromine.

In other publications, the iodimetric analysis of sulphide–thiosulphate–polysulphide mixtures is described[20–22]. Further details are given in the polysulphide section.

Iodimetric titration of sulphide in industrial effluents[23]

Reagents

Cadmium acetate solution: 250 g cadmium acetate dihydrate per litre.

Potassium iodide solution: 100 g KI per litre. Store in a dark bottle.

Sulphuric acid, dilute: 1 volume of 98 % acid diluted cautiously by adding to 3 volumes of water.

Iodine: 0.0625M.

Dissolve 25 g of KI in about 50 mℓ of water in a glass-stoppered 1ℓ volumetric flask. Weigh 15.9 g of iodine into a weighing bottle and transfer by means of a small, dry funnel into the 1ℓ flask. Stopper and shake the flask until all the iodine has dissolved, then dilute to 1ℓ. Standardize against 0.125M sodium thiosulphate as described below.

Potassium iodate: 0.020M.

Dry about 5 g of potassium iodate at 120 °C. Weigh accurately about 4.3 g of the dry material, dissolve in water and make up to 1ℓ. Calculate the exact molarity.

Sodium thiosulphate: 0.125M.

Dissolve 31.2 g of sodium thiosulphate pentahydrate in 1ℓ of freshly boiled and cooled water. Add 3 drops of chloroform to stabilize the solution, Store in a dark bottle, and allow to stand for several days before use. Standardize against potassium iodate solution as described below.

Starch indicator solution:

Grind 5 g of soluble starch with a little cold water into a smooth paste and pour into 1 litre of boiling water with constant stirring. Boil for 1 min and allow to cool before use.

Standardization of 0.125M thiosulphate

Add 5 mℓ of KI solution to a conical flask followed by 100 mℓ of water. Pipette 25.0 mℓ of 0.020M KIO_3 into the flask. Add 10 mℓ of dilute

H_2SO_4. Titrate immediately with the 0.125M thiosulphate adding starch near the end-point.

Standardization of 0.0625M iodine

Pipette 25.0 mℓ of the iodine solution into a conical flask and dilute with 100 mℓ of water. Titrate with the standardized thiosulphate adding starch near the end-point.

Titration of sulphide in sample

Add 10.0 mℓ of sample (*see* Note 1) to 100 mℓ of water and 10 mℓ of cadmium acetate solution. Allow the precipitate to settle, decant the clear supernatant liquid through the filter paper, transfer the precipitate to the paper and wash with water. Into a 250 mℓ wide-mouth bottle place about 100 mℓ of water, 10 mℓ of dilute H_2SO_4 and 25 mℓ of 0.0625M iodine. Drop the filter paper into the bottle and quickly insert the stopper. Shake vigorously to completely dissolve the sulphide. Titrate the excess iodine with sodium thiosulphate, adding starch solution near the end-point.

$$\text{Sulphide as } S^{2-} = \frac{2000V_1}{V_2}\ \text{mg}\,\ell^{-1}$$

where

V_1 is the volume of 0.0625M iodine consumed (mℓ);
V_2 is the volume of the sample.

Notes

1. A 10 mℓ sample has been recommended. If the approximate sulphide content is known the optimum volume of sample to be taken is $16\,000/C$ mℓ where C is the concentration of sulphide in mg ℓ^{-1}.
2. If the concentration is to be expressed in terms of hydrogen sulphide a factor of 2125 should be used in place of 2000 in the calculation formula.

---

2. Using o-*hydroxymercuribenzoic acid*

A number of useful titrimetric procedures have been based on this reagent. Initial work was reported by Wronski[24] in 1958. The basic reaction in alkaline medium is:

$$2\ C_6H_4(COO^-)(HgOH) + S^{2-} \longrightarrow C_6H_4(COO^-)\text{Hg—S—Hg}(^-OOC)C_6H_4 + 2OH^-$$

Several indicators have been used. Thiofluorescein gives a blue colour in alkaline solution which disappears with the first excess of reagent as titrant. Other indicators are dithizone, sodium nitroprusside, diphenylcarbazone, and monomercuriphenolphthalein. References to the many investigations are given in a review by Szekeres[2] already cited, and in a recent paper by Wronski[25]. A special advantage of the reagent is that sulphite and thiosulphate do not interfere. Interferences generally depend on the indicator used. The reaction itself also depends on the indicator in some instances. Thus when sodium nitroprusside is used, the titre obtained agrees with the following reaction:

$$C_6H_4(COO^-)(HgOH) + S^{2-} \longrightarrow C_6H_4(COO^-)(HgS^-) + OH^-$$

The titration of sulphide can be conducted on the macro scale using a 0.05M solution of the reagent.

Another related observation of analytical significance reported by Wronski is the quenching of fluorescence in mercurated fluorescein by sulphide. This can be used in two ways. A calibration curve can be prepared in the presence of excess mercurated fluorescein, or a fluorimetric titration performed. The former method has been used to determine sub-ppb (10^9) levels of hydrogen sulphide in air[26]. Air is drawn through a 0.1–1.0M NaOH solution for up to 60 min and the solution analysed. An automatic recorder has been developed[27]. The second approach, the fluorimetric titration, has several advantages. Interference by thiols, cyanide, xanthates, etc., which alter the fluorescence of mercurated fluorescein, do not affect the titration. In addition, calculations are based on the mercury content of mercurated fluorescein and no standardization is required.

Wronski[25] has developed a solvent extraction procedure for initial separation of hydrogen sulphide as triethyllead sulphide $(C_2H_5)_3Pb–S–Pb(C_2H_5)$, before titration with tetramercurated fluorescein. A graphical representation of the titration is shown in *Figure 68*. No interference is given by common ions found in water samples. Several procedures are given. The original work should be consulted for details.

3. *Miscellaneous methods*

EDTA methods for sulphide have been reported. There is little evidence that they find widespread use. Kivalo[29] was the first to develop an indirect method. This was based on the observation that when an alkaline sulphide is added to a neutral or weakly acidic solution of copper perchlorate, a sulphide of stoichiometric composition is formed. Excess copper in the filtrate is titrated with EDTA using murexide as indicator.

Sulphide–sulphate–sulphite mixtures have been analysed by compleximetric titration[30]. First S^{2-} is determined by adding excess of copper nitrate which precipitates copper sulphide. Excess copper is determined by EDTA. In a second aliquot sulphate is precipitated by addition of excess barium chloride and the excess back-titrated with EDTA. Finally sulphide and sulphite are oxidized to sulphate and this determined as before. The three components can now be evaluated.

The problem of sulphide and sulphite when present together has also been approached in another way[31]. Sulphide is separated from sulphite by extraction with ethanol. Residual sulphite is oxidized to sulphate with bromine, then determined with EDTA using barium chloride. A second aliquot

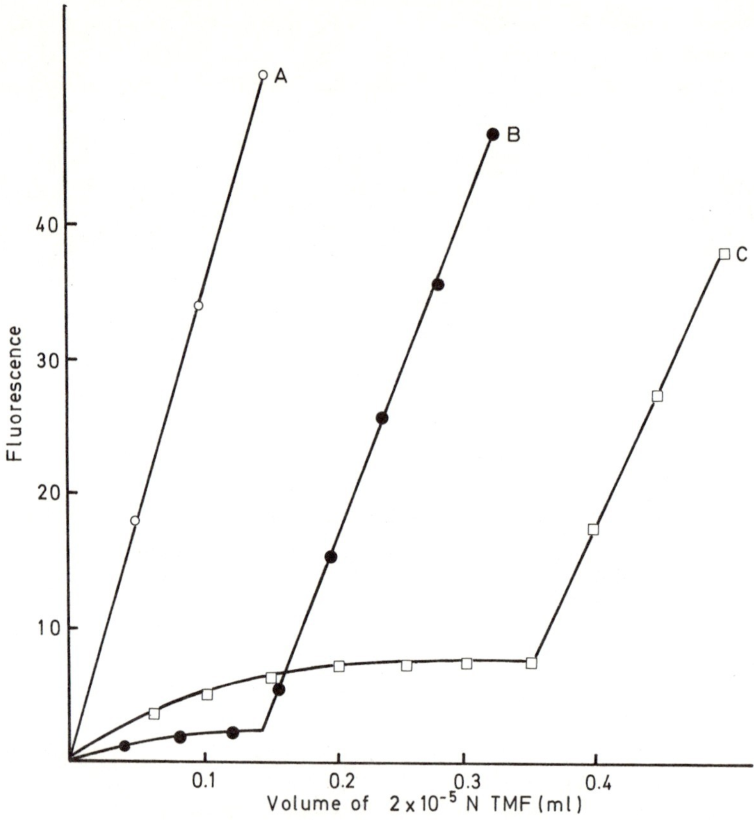

Figure 68 *Fluorimetric titration of hydrogen sulphide as triethyllead sulphide with tetramercurated fluorescein in hexanol–ethanol mixtures.* A, *added* 0, *found 0* H_2S; B, *added 0.0514 μg, found 0.0510 μg* H_2S; C, *added 0.120 μg, found 0.119 μg* H_2S. (After Wronski[25])

is oxidized to sulphate and determined in the same way, this representing sulphide plus sulphite.

The same worker[32] has provided a compleximetric method for sulphide and sulphate when present together. First sulphide is expelled as hydrogen sulphide by boiling with HCl. Residual sulphate is determined by EDTA using barium chloride. In a second aliquot sulphide is oxidized to sulphate using bromine. This plus the original sulphate are determined as before.

In addition to iodine, several other oxidizing reagents have been recommended for determination of sulphide. These include bromine, hypochlorite, iodate, hexacyanoferrate(III), permanganate and periodate. In most cases no obvious advantage is apparent. Most of the reagents have to be standardized independently. An exception to this is N-bromosuccinimide proposed by Sarwar *et al.*[33]. N-bromosuccinimide oxidizes sulphide to elemental sulphur. A solution of the reagent is stable for several days if kept refrigerated and in the dark. The titration is direct with KI present and using starch as indicator.

N-bromosuccinimide selectively oxidizes iodide to iodine, which in turn reacts with sulphide.

$$Br^+ + 2I^- \rightarrow I_2 + Br^-$$

$$H_2S + I_2 \rightarrow 2H^+ + 2I^- + S$$

It is assumed that the mechanism of the reaction is via hypobromous acid formed by the hydrolysis of N-bromosuccinimide:

```
     O                      O
     ||                     ||
CH2—C                  CH2—C
 |     \                |     \
 |      NBr + H2O →     |      NH + HBrO
 |     /                |     /
CH2—C                  CH2—C
     ||                     ||
     O                      O
```

The range for sulphide is 0.6–13 mg. Experimental details of the titration are given below.

A precipitation titration using Zn^{2+} has been reported[34]. In aqueous solution the solubility of zinc sulphide causes errors. A titration in the presence of ethanol with methylthymol blue as indicator is recommended. The end-point can be detected potentiometrically if required. No interference is given by sulphate, sulphite, thiosulphate, carbonate or phosphate, but Ca^{2+} and Mg^{2+} must be masked with EDTA. Results are slightly higher than those given by the iodimetric method. An interesting extension of the method enables the sulphide content of polysulphide solutions to be determined. Here use is made of the reaction between S_x^{2-} and sodium sulphite.

$$Na_2S_x + (x - 1)Na_2SO_3 \rightarrow Na_2S + (x - 1)Na_2S_2O_3$$

The resulting sulphide is titrated using the above method[35]. Szekeres has described several methods for analysis of sulphide–polysulphide–thiosulphate mixtures, including iodimetric procedures. These are discussed elsewhere.

Titrimetric determination of sulphide using N-bromosuccinimide[33]

Reagent

0.005M. Dissolve 0.2225 g of the recrystallized compound in water and make up to 250 mℓ.

Procedure

Pipette 0.5–100.0 mℓ of the sample solution into a 250 mℓ iodine flask, add 1.0 mℓ of 10% KI and a few drops of starch solution. Acidify with a few drops of 2M HCl, then titrate with N-bromosuccinimide with constant stirring. The end-point is indicated by a blue colour which persists for 30 s.

$$CO\cdot CH_2\cdot CH_2\cdot CO\cdot NBr \equiv Br^+ \equiv I_2 \equiv H_2S$$

Spectroscopic methods

1. Spectrophotometric methods—visible and UV

Determination of sulphide as methylene blue is still the most important and widely used spectrophotometric method for trace amounts of sulphide, despite the fact that the reaction has been known[36] since 1883. The reaction is between sulphide and an acid solution of NN-dimethyl *p*-phenylenediamine (also known as *p*-aminodimethyl aniline) in the presence of Fe^{3+}. At first the solution is red. It later turns to blue as the dye forms. The reaction can be represented as follows:

$N(CH_3)_2$

H_2N

$+ H_2S + 6FeCl_3 \longrightarrow$

H_2N

$N(CH_3)_2$

$N(CH_3)_2$

N S $+ 6FeCl_2 + NH_4Cl$

$+ 4HCl$

$N(CH_3)_2Cl$

The reaction is almost specific for hydrogen sulphide, and probably the most sensitive. Absorbance measurements are usually made at about 670 nm, but the absorbance peak can vary with conditions[37]. Strict control of conditions are required for reproducible results, for example the temperature should not vary by more than 2 °C. An investigation by Mecklenburg and Rosenkranzer[38] indicates that complete formation of the blue colour requires as long as 3 h.

The method has been subjected to numerous investigations. Of these the study by Gustafsson[39] is particularly important. Application of the method can be made to atmospheric hydrogen sulphide after absorption in a suitable solution. Zutshi and Mahadevan[37] have recently established optimum conditions for application of the method to gaseous sulphide in the environment. Earlier studies gave a value of 34×10^3 for the molar absorptivity at 670 nm. Normal application of the method to water samples enables 0.5–100 µg S^{2-} to be determined[40]. If an anion-exchange technique is used to isolate and pre-concentrate the sulphide, estimation of hydrogen sulphide in concentrations as low as 70 parts per milliard (10^9) in air and 0.1 parts per milliard in water, is possible[13].

The method is almost specific for sulphide. Sulphite and thiosulphate interfere only when present in excess of 10 mgℓ^{-1}. Strong reducing agents interfere.

Application of the method is widespread, particularly to air and water. For water, it has been recommended as a standard method[40,6]. Its use for determination of ultratrace amounts of sulphate after preliminary reduction to sulphide has already been noted. Automatic forms of the method have been described. In one such method Grasshoff and Chan[41] find that owing to its extreme sensitivity, dilution of the sample is required before analysis by AutoAnalyzer. An accurate method for doing this is described.

Rees, Gyllenspetz and Docherty[42] in developing an automatic method for trace sulphide in condensed steam, find that NN-diethyl-*p*-phenylenediamine is preferable to the dimethyl homologue normally used. A procedure using methylene blue is given below.

Other spectrophotometric methods for sulphide have been reported. The nitroprusside method is based on a transient violet colour produced in alkaline solution[43]. The same reaction is used by Casapieri, Scott and Simpson[44] in an automatic procedure for 1–10 ppm of S^{2-}. The tolerance limits for sulphite, thiosulphate, phenol, and formaldehyde are 500, 2000, 100 and 100 ppm respectively. This compares, in the case of sulphite and thiosulphate with only about 40 ppm for the methylene blue method. Bethea and Bethea[45] found several problems in the method including significant fading of colour at the recommended flow rates. With modification, good results were obtained with Beer's law holding up to 40 μg S^{2-} $m\ell^{-1}$.

The chloranilate method, used initially for chloride, fluoride and phosphate, has been adapted[46] to sulphide. Mercury(II) chloranilate is added to the sulphide. The liberated chloranilate ion is evaluated spectrophotometrically. Humphrey and Hinze[47] have drawn attention to the benefit of enhanced sensitivity if the absorbance is measured at 330 nm rather than 525 nm. The apparent molar absorptivity for sulphide is 3.2×10^4 at 330 nm.

Triphenylmethane dyes form the basis of several methods. Lambert and Manzo[48] use the crystal-violet–tetraiodomercurate(II) ion-association compound as reagent for sulphide in the range 0–6.0 ppm. The compound is sufficiently insoluble for use in a column technique.

Russian workers[49] obtain high sensitivities using crystal violet in the presence of KI and chloramine B. Extraction is made into benzene and the absorbance measured at 610 nm. Beer's law holds for 0.023–0.082 μg S^{2-} $m\ell^{-1}$ with a sensitivity of 2 ng S^{2-}.

Sulphide can be determined by separation as hydrogen sulphide and passing this into an acidified solution of ammonium molybdate. Molybdenum blue is formed and its concentration determined spectrophotometrically at 700 nm. The method is recommended for sulphide in industrial effluents[7].

Direct analysis of sulphur anion mixtures by spectrophotometry in the UV has been reported[50]. Aqueous solutions of sulphide, thiosulphate, sulphite and sulphate have absorbed maxima at 230, 220, 230, and 210 nm, respectively. By using suitable equations and measuring at the maxima (but at 240 nm for sulphite to avoid interference from sulphide) the concentration of each can be derived. The sensitivity for sulphide is 35 ng per 50 mℓ of solution.

A new absorptiometric method has been introduced by Rahim and West[51]. This is based on the green colour produced when sulphide ions are treated in ammoniacal solution with iron(III) and an excess of nitrilotriacetic acid. The range of application is from 1200 down to 8 ppm S^{2-}. Of 17 anions examined the only serious interference is given by selenium(IV). At 100-fold excess, interference is given by oxalate, citrate, tartrate and chromate, but these can be tolerated at lower levels. The absorbance must be measured within 2 and 12 min of mixing the components. More recently a method based on the reaction of sulphide and iron(III) in the presence of 1,10-phenanthroline has appeared[52].

Spectrophotometric determination of sulphide (in steam condensate) by the methylene blue method[40]

Reagents

Deoxygenated water: Prepare by purging water with nitrogen.
Ammonium ferric sulphate: 180 g ℓ^{-1}. Filter if necessary to remove suspended matter.
NN-diethyl-*p*-phenylenediamine(DPD) solution: Dissolve 2.0 g of NN-diethyl-*p*-phenylenediamine sulphate in 100 mℓ of 9M H_2SO_4. This solution is stable for at least one month. It should be stored in the dark.
Sulphuric acid, 9M reagent solution: Dilute concentrated H_2SO_4 (98% w/w) by adding to an equal volume of water.
Zinc acetate dihydrate: 25 g ℓ^{-1} solution.
Iodine, 0.00313M standard solution: Measure, using a microburette, 6.25 mℓ of 0.05M iodine into a 100 mℓ volumetric flask and dilute to the mark with water. This solution should be prepared as required.
Sulphide standard solution: 1. Sulphide, standard solution A: Dissolve 2–3 g of $Na_2S \cdot 9H_2O$ in deoxygenated water and dilute to approximately 1ℓ. Determine the sulphide content of the solution by direct titration with 0.00313M iodine solution using starch as indicator. For each 1 mℓ of sulphide solution approximately 3 mℓ of iodine solution will be needed.

Take a volume of this solution calculated to contain 10 mg of sulphide (as sulphur) and dilute immediately with about 500 mℓ of the deoxygenated water. Then add 20 mℓ of the zinc acetate solution and make up to exactly 1000 mℓ in a volumetric flask using the deoxygenated water.

Standardize this solution with the 0.00313M iodine solution and adjust the concentration if necessary.

Sulphide standard solution A, 1 mℓ ≡ 10 μg of sulphide as sulphur.

2. Sulphide, standard solution B: Dilute 10.0 mℓ of sulphide standard solution A with 50 mℓ deoxygenated water and then add about 2 mℓ of the zinc acetate solution and make up to exactly 100 mℓ with the deoxygenated water in a volumetric flask, to give a solution containing 0.5 gℓ^{-1} zinc acetate dihydrate.

Sulphide standard solution B, 1 m ≡ 1.0 μg of sulphide as sulphur.

Both standard sulphide solutions should be used within 1 h of preparation.
Starch indicator solution: Prepare in the usual way.

Preparation of calibration graph

A fresh calibration graph should be prepared for each new batch of ammonium ferric sulphate and DPD. For range 0.5–10 μg of sulphide: Into a series of seven 100 mℓ graduated, stoppered measuring cylinders, each containing about 50 mℓ of deoxygenated water and 2 mℓ of the zinc acetate solution, introduce accurately measured volumes of the sulphide standard solution B corresponding to 0, 1.0, 2.0, 5.0, 7.0, 9.0 and 10 μg of sulphide as sulphur. Dilute the contents of each cylinder to about 97 mℓ with water and mix gently; add from a pipette 1.0 mℓ of DPD solution and mix. Allow each solution to stand for 60 ± 30 s, then add from a pipette 1.0 mℓ of the ammonium ferric sulphate solution; mix and dilute to 100 mℓ with water.

Allow the solutions to stand for at least 10 min, then measure the absorbance of each solution using 40 mm cells at a known temperature of between 20 and 25 °C in a spectrophotometer at the wavelength corresponding to maximum absorption (approximately 670 nm, but the exact wavelength should be checked for each spectrophotometer). Use water in the compensating cell.

Deduct the reading for the blank containing no added S^{2-} from those obtained for the standard solutions and plot a graph of the net absorbances against the corresponding micrograms of sulphur.

Note

The absorbance given by 10 µg of sulphide (S) in the total volume of test solution is approximately 0.6.

For the range 10–100 µg of sulphide: Proceed in a similar manner to the previous procedure but use accurately known volumes of the sulphide standard solution A corresponding to 0, 10, 20, 50, 70, 90, and 100 µg of sulphide and measure the absorbances in 5 mm cells.

Sampling

The temperature of the sample should not be greater than 20 °C and, if sampling from a flowing stream, the flow rate should be between 20 mℓ min^{-1} and 50 mℓ min^{-1}. A stainless steel cooling coil should be used.

Procedure

Determine the volume of sample to be collected using the following preliminary test.

To a 100 mℓ graduated, stoppered measuring cylinder add 2.0 mℓ of the iodine solution and 1 mℓ of the starch indicator solution. Collect a sample of water by means of a dip tube reaching below the surface of the reagents. Note the volume at which the blue colour is discharged. This volume will contain 200 µg sulphide and sulphite (expressed as sulphur) and not more than this volume should be taken for the test. If the colour is not discharged when 95 mℓ of sample has been collected, this volume can be used in the test.

Collect the appropriate volume of the sample in a 100 mℓ graduated stoppered cylinder containing 2 mℓ of the zinc acetate solution. Use a glass dip tube such that the tip is below the surface of the zinc acetate solution.

If necessary make up the volume to 97 mℓ with water and mix gently. Add from a pipette 1.0 mℓ of the DPD solution and mix. Allow to stand for 60 ± 30 s and then add from a pipette 1.0 mℓ of the ammonium ferric sulphate solution. Mix and dilute to 100 mℓ with water.

Allow the solution to stand for at least 10 min, then measure the absorbance of the sample solution, using a 40 mm or 5 mm cell, according to the concentration of sulphide, in the spectrophotometer at a temperature within 1 °C of that at which the calibration graph was prepared and at the same wavelength. Use water in the compensating cell.

Prepare a reagent blank solution by introducing into a 100 mℓ graduated stoppered cylinder 2 mℓ of the zinc acetate solution, 95 mℓ water, 1 mℓ of the DPD solution and 1 mℓ of the ammonium ferric sulphate solution. Make up the volume to 100 mℓ with water and mix well.

Prepare a colour blank solution by introducing into a second 100 mℓ graduated stoppered cylinder, 2 mℓ of the zinc acetate solution and a volume of the sample equal to that collected and make up, if necessary, to 97 mℓ. Add 1 mℓ of the H_2SO_4, make up the volume to 100 mℓ with water and mix well.

Measure the absorbance of the reagent blank solution and the colour blank solution under the same conditions using the same size cells as were used for the sample. Use water in the compensating cell.

Calculation

Deduct the readings obtained for the reagent blank and the colour blank from that obtained for the sample and read off the sulphide content of the sample in micrograms from the calibration graph.

$$\text{Sulphide (as sulphur), ppm} = \frac{\mu\text{g of sulphur}}{\text{m}\ell\text{ of sample}}$$

---

2. *Fluorimetric methods*

Sulphide reacts with mercury(II)-2,2′-pyridylbenzimidazole giving HgS and releasing an equivalent amount of the fluorescent organic ligand. This has been used by Bark and Rixon[53] as the basis of a highly sensitive method for sulphide. Apart from the sensitivity, other advantages are the high stability of the reagent and the possibility of measuring the luminescence up to 48 h after the reaction.

An indirect method reported by Vernon and Whitham[54] employs 2-(*o*-hydroxyphenyl)benzoxazole as reagent. This exhibits a bright green fluorescence in acetone solution, the fluorescence being attenuated in the presence of copper(II) ions by complex formation. The effect of sulphide on the system enables its determination to be made in the concentration range 0–100 ng mℓ$^{-1}$, with a limit of detection of 1 ng.

3. *Molecular emission cavity analysis (MECA)*

MECA, introduced by Belcher *et al.*[55] has been applied to determination of several sulphur anions including sulphide. The basis of measurement is the intensity of their S_2 emission measured at 384 nm.

The general form of the cavity holding apparatus is shown in *Figure 69*. Emission from the cavity is passed via an 8.5 nm slit and a grating monochromator to a photomultiplier, the output of which is fed to a fast-response potentiometric recorder. Peaks are measured either by triangulation or using electronic integration. A commercially available MECA spectrophotometer is now available. The above study, which includes a description of the technique itself, indicates that sodium sulphide alone gives a broad emission peak extremely rapidly. Addition of phosphoric acid, which is beneficial to the signal in the case of other sulphur anions, is of no value to sulphide due to loss of hydrogen sulphide. The use of an ammonium phosphate buffer at pH 7 does not affect the maximum emission intensity, but gives a much sharper peak. The maximum limit for linearity is 0.65 µg S^{2-} using the above buffer.

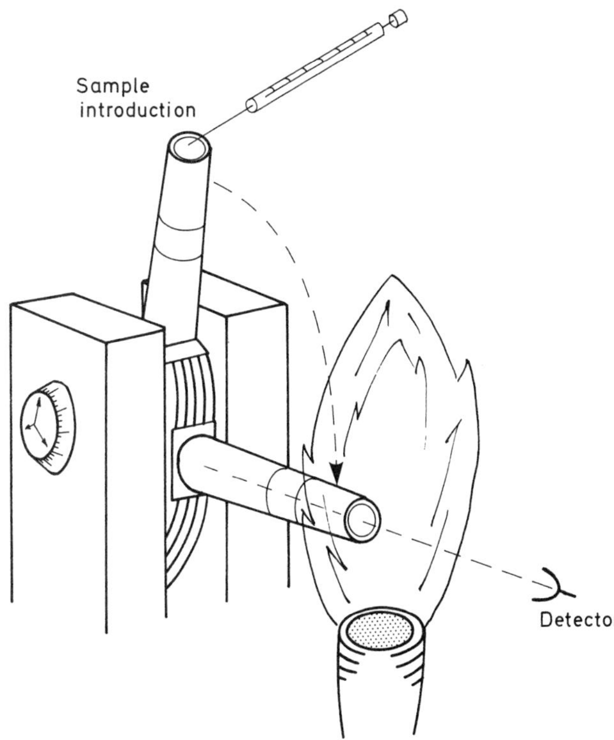

Figure 69 Molecular Emission Cavity Analysis (MECA). Addition of sample to cavity and introduction of cavity into flame. (After Belcher *et al.*[54])

Electroanalytical methods

1. Potentiometric methods, including ion-selective electrodes

A titrimetric method for sulphide using zinc in ammoniacal solution and metallochromic indicators has been referred to already. This titration can be performed potentiometrically[56].

Hexacyanoferrate(III) reacts with sulphide under strongly alkaline conditions and with osmium tetroxide present as catalyst.

$$S^{2-} + 2[Fe(CN)_6]^{3-} \rightarrow S + 2[Fe(CN)_6]^{4-}$$

The end-point can be detected using the 'dead-stop' technique, or using the normal potentiometric procedure[57].

Silver(I) has been used for analysis of sulphide-containing mixtures by potentiometric titration. Kiss[58] used this method for sulphide–polysulphide–thiosulphate mixtures. Ammonium sulphide was titrated with ammoniacal silver nitrate. Thiosulphate was next titrated with mercuric chloride after removal of sulphide by boiling with aqueous boric acid. Finally polysulphide was converted to thiosulphate by sulphite, and titrated in that form. Platinum electrodes were used; the end-point was detected using the 'dead-stop' technique. For this reason the method would be more accurately described as amperometric rather than potentiometric.

The same worker[59] has used cadmium acetate for direct titration of alkali sulphide, again using the 'dead-stop' technique. Hydroxyl and cyanide ions interfere. Nitrite, chloride and sulphur acids are tolerated.

A detailed study of the potentiometric titration of sulphide using Ag^+ in strongly alkaline ammoniacal solution has been carried out by Liu and Shen[60]. A rotating silver sulphide or silver indicator electrode, and a calomel reference electrode were used. The potential reaches equilibrium rapidly. From 0.2 to 4 mg of sulphide in the concentration range 5×10^{-4}–1×10^{-2}M can be determined to within 0.2–0.4 per cent.

Iodine in strongly alkaline medium has been used[61]. This method enables analysis of sulphide–cyanide mixtures to be carried out. Where sulphide is accompanied by polysulphide, sulphite, and thiosulphate, a potentiometric method using mercury chloride as titrant is suitable[62]. Details of this method are given in the polysulphide section.

Silver sulphide solid-state electrodes are now commercially available[63]. They enable sulphide (or Ag^+) to be determined down to 10^{-7}M. Mercury(II) interferes, and must be absent. Cyanide interferes unless present in concentrations[64] less than mM. Evaluation of the ORION 94-16 electrode has been carried out by Light and Swartz[65]. Bock and Puff[66] have found that sulphide at low levels (10^{-5}–10^{-6}M) can only be satisfactorily determined if its oxidation is negligible. In this connection, addition of ascorbic acid was found to be effective.

No interference is given by fluoride, chloride, sulphate, carbonate, hydroxyl or phosphate. Absence of interference by halides makes the electrode particularly useful in the potentiometric titration of sulphide and halides in photographic materials. Halide ion-selective electrodes cannot be used for this purpose due to poisoning by sulphide released from the gelatin.

Sulphur–anion mixtures containing sulphide can be analysed using ion-selective electrodes. Papp[67,68] has described analysis of polysulphide–sulphide–sulphite–thiosulphate mixtures using mercuric chloride as titrant. In this case the sulphide electrode is used to monitor the Hg^{2+} concentration. Further details appear in the polysulphide section.

Potentiometric titration of sulphide with silver nitrate using the silver sulphide electrode fails at low concentrations due to hydrolysis of sulphide and formation of silver hydroxide. The use of sodium plumbate(II) as titrant permits determination of sulphide in concentrations down to 1 ppm in the presence of a 10^5–10^6-fold excess of chloride, bromide, iodide, sulphite, thiosulphate or thiocyanate. Cyanide must be absent[69]. Slanina and co-workers use lead(II) as titrant for automatic potentiometric titration of ng amounts of sulphide[70]. At the 90 ng level, the standard deviation is reported as 2 per cent. No interference is given by halides, acetate, sulphate, cyanide, nitrate, phosphate or ammonium. The same investigators[71] report application of the above method to determination of sulphur in organic compounds. After combustion in a current of H_2 the sulphur is reduced over a platinum catalyst at 900 °C and the resulting hydrogen sulphide absorbed in a designed titration vessel. Automatic titration of the sulphide is done using Pb^{2+} with the end-point being located by a sulphide ion-selective electrode.

2. *Coulometric methods*

Cadersky[72] reports a coulometric method for 4–85 μg of sulphide using electrogenerated Ag^+ in a basic cyanide medium. The end-point is located by zero current potentiometry or amperometrically. A 100-fold excess of chloride, bromide, iodide, thiocyanate, or thiosulphate over sulphide can be tolerated. In another method Pribyl and Slovak[73] titrate traces of sulphide with electrogenerated iodine, using an automatic procedure. The method is suitable for 1–50 µg of sulphur as hydrogen sulphide, in a 10 mℓ sample.

3. *Polarographic methods*

Earlier studies on direct polarography of sulphide were made by Kolthoff and Miller[74] who reported a well-defined wave at the dropping mercury electrode. However, anodic current methods have not been entirely satisfactory. Rapid direct polarographic methods, in which mercury drops are dislodged from a capillary at short intervals of time, offer advantages over conventional polarography. This has been applied to sulphide determination by Canterford[75]. *Figure 70* shows a comparison of polarograms obtained by the rapid and conventional procedures. The same capillary with the same head of mercury is used in each case. Only the drop time and the scan rate is different. A notable advantage of the method is non-interference by cyanide which affects several other sulphide methods.

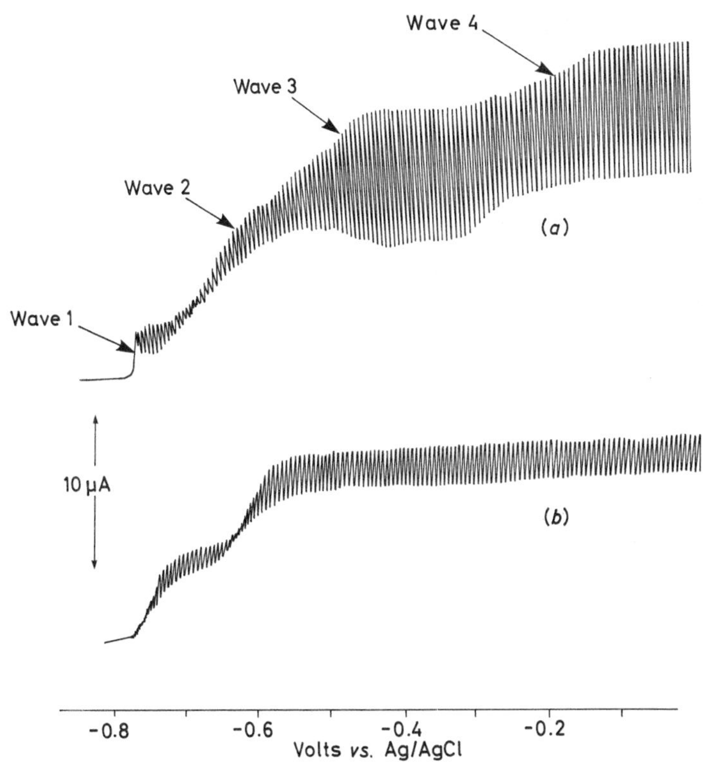

Figure 70 *Conventional and rapid dc polarograms of* 1.5×10^{-3} *M sulphide in 1 M sodium perchlorate. Conditions: (a) drop time 2.9 s; (b) drop time 0.16 s.* (After Canterford[75])

Indirect polarographic methods have been described. One is based on the reaction between methyl mercury(II) iodide and sulphide[76]. Less than 1 ppm of sulphide can be determined with a precision of ± 5 per cent or less. Several common anions do not interfere but cyanide does. Hasebe and Kambara[77] use the methylene blue reaction, that is the reaction between sulphide and NN-dimethyl-*p*-phenylenediamine in the presence of iron(III). Here the height of the a.c. polarographic peak for methylene blue at -0.2 V (*v*. Hg pool) is measured. The calibration graph is linear over the range 10–90 μM S^{2-}. Halides interfere.

Kinetic and catalytic methods

A catalytic method for sulphide based on a fixed time spectrophotometric procedure utilizes the reaction

$$Fe^{2+} + Ag^{+} \rightarrow Fe^{3+} + Ag$$

A sensitivity of 1×10^{-13} g mℓ$^{-1}$ is reported[78].

The iodine–azide reaction forms the basis of another method[79].

$$3N_3^- + I_2 \rightarrow 3N_2 + 2I^-$$

Here amperometry using a rotating platinum electrode is used to follow the reaction rate. Sulphide can be determined in three ranges, 10^{-15}, 10^{-14} and 10^{-13} g mℓ$^{-1}$. The same reaction has also been used for determination of thiocyanate and thiosulphate.

An enzymatic method has been developed by Mealor and Townsend[80] for sulphide, cyanide and iodine. Its basis is as follows. The enzyme *β*-fructofuranosidease (invertase) is inhibited in its catalysis of the hydrolysis of substrates such as sucrose, by the presence of certain metal ions. If small concentrations of certain anions that form strong complexes with these metals are present, competition takes place with the enzyme for the metals. In such circumstances the anions decrease the inhibitory effect. For sulphide, the range which can be determined is $1–2.5 \times 10^{-7}$ M. The measured parameter is optical rotation. Slow aging of the enzyme necessitates a new calibration curve each day.

Miscellaneous methods

Nanogram quantities of sulphide have been determined by release of radioactive iodide in the reaction

$$2Ag^{131}I + S^{2-} \rightarrow Ag_2S + 2^{131}I^-$$

Two procedures are given[81]. In the first, labelled silver iodide is fixed on a filter paper disc which is shaken with the sulphide solution until equilibrium is attained. In the second, which requires a larger sample, the solution is passed through the filter disc or a labelled silver iodide precipitate. The *γ*-radiation is counted using a sodium iodide detector and single-channel analyser.

Bowen[82] has used a ^{51}Cr-labelled silver chromate column to determine sulphide (and chloride). From 0.4 to 40 μmol of sulphide in aqueous solution can be determined using a 25 mm × 10 mm column. Bromide, iodide, iodate, cyanide, thiocyanate and sulphite interfere. The method is unsuitable for solutions of pH greater than 4.0.

Gas-chromatography has now been applied to determination of several anions[83]. Mixtures of sulphide, sulphite and carbonate can be analysed by means of the gaseous products evolved on acidification[84]. These are injected into the gas-chromatograph, where detection is made using thermal conductivity. The sensitivity is low, being 1–10 mg for sulphide and 2–18 mg for sulphite.

The same anions are determined in another gas-chromatographic method[28]. In this case an acidifying device is connected to the column inlet.

References

1. BLAIR, J.S., *Analyt. Chem.*, **41**, 1497 (1969)
2. SZEKERES, L., *Talanta*, **21**, 2 (1974)
3. BLASIUS, E., HORN, G., KNOCHEL, A., MUNCH, J. and WAGNER, H., in *Inorganic Sulphur Chemistry* (Ed. G. Nickless), Elsevier, Amsterdam, 199 (1968)
4. HANLEY, A.V. and CZECH, F.W., in *The Analytical Chemistry of Sulphur and its Compounds*, Part 1 (Ed. J. H. Karchmer), Wiley-Interscience, New York, 285 (1970)
5. LOWENHEIM, F.A., in *Encyclopedia of Industrial Chemical Analysis* (Ed. F. D. Snell and L. S. Ettre), Vol. 18, Interscience, New York, 392 (1973)
6. American Public Health Association, American Waterworks Association, and Water Pollution Control Federation, *Standard Methods for the Examination of Water and Wastewater*, 13th edn, American Public Health Association, New York (1970)
7. *Official, Standardised and Recommended Methods of Analysis*, Compiled and Edited by N. W. Hanson, 2nd edn, The Society for Analytical Chemistry, London, 462 (1973)
8. BESWICK, G. and JOHNSON, R.M., *J. Sci. Fd Agric.*, **21**, 565 (1970)
9. GUSTAFSSON, J., *Talanta*, **4**, 236 (1960)
10. POMEROY, R., *Analyt. Chem.*, **26**, 571 (1954)
11. KOLTHOFF, I.M. and BELCHER, R., *Volumetric Analysis*, Vol. III, Interscience, New York, 295 (1957)
12. IGUCHI, A., *Bull. chem. Soc. Japan*, **31**, 600 (1958); *Analyt. Abstr.*, **6**, 1705 (1959)
13. PAEZ, D.M. and GUAGNINI, O.A., *Mikrochim. Acta*, 220 (1971)
14. CANIC, V.D., TURCIC, M.N., BUGARSKI-VOJINOVIC, M.B. and PERISIC, N.U., *Z. analyt. Chem.*, **229**, 93 (1967); *Analyt. Abstr.*, **15**, 5211 (1968)
15. PATEL, S.S. and SPENCER, C.P., *Analytica chim. Acta*, **27**, 278 (1962)
16. DEBEVERE, J.M. and VOETS, J.P., *Lab. Pract.*, 713 (1972)
17. NATUSCH, D.F.S., KLONIS, H.B., AXELROD, H.D., TECK, R.J. and LODGE, J.P., *Analyt. Chem.*, **44**, 2067 (1972)
18. UMLAND, F. and JANSSEN, A., *Z. analyt. Chem.*, **224**, 413 (1967); *Analyt. Abstr.*, **15**, 2600 (1968)
19. SZEKERES, L., *Analytica chim. Roma*, **52**, 67 (1962); *Analyt. Abstr.*, **9**, 5140 (1962)
20. SZEKERES, L., *Z. analyt. Chem.*, **178**, 81 (1960); *Analyt. Abstr.*, **8**, 2387 (1961)
21. SZEKERES, L., *Acta. chim. hung.*, **26**, 167 (1961)
22. SZEKERES, L., *Pharm. Zentralhalle Dtl.*, **102**, 6 (1963); *Analyt. Abstr.*, **10**, 5137 (1963)
23. *Official, Standardised and Recommended Methods of Analysis*, Compiled and Edited by N.W. Hanson, 2nd edn, The Society for Analytical Chemistry, London, 460 (1973)
24. WRONSKI, M., *Analyst*, **83**, 314 (1958)
25. WRONSKI, M., *Analyt. Chem.*, **43**, 606 (1971)
26. AXELROD, H.D., CARY, J.H., BONELLI, J.E. and LODGE, J.P., *Analyt. Chem.*, **41**, 1856 (1969)
27. ANDREWS, T.R. and NICHOLS, P.N.R., *Analyst*, **90**, 367 (1965)
28. MCDONALD, K.L., *Analyt. Chem.* **44**, 1298 (1972)
29. KIVALO, P., *Analyt. Chem.*, **27**, 1809 (1955)
30. BURRIEL-MARTI, F. and ALVAREZ HERRERO, C., *Inf. quim. analit. pura apl. Ind.*, **18**, 142 (1964); *Analyt. Abstr.*, **13**, 132 (1966)

31. DE SOUSA, A., *Inf. quim. analit.*, **17**, 51 (1963); *Analyt. Abstr.*, **11**, 1266 (1964)
32. DE SOUSA, A., *Inf. quim. analit,* **15**, 121 (1961); *Analyt. Abstr.*, **9**, 1452 (1962)
33. SARWAR, M., ELAHI, M., ANWAR, M. and HANIF, M., *Mikrochim. Acta*, 846 (1970)
34. SZEKERES, L., KARDOS, E. and SZEKERES, G.L., *Chemist Analyst*, **53**, 115 (1964)
35. SZEKERES, L., KARDOS, E. and SZEKERES, G.L., *Chemist Analyst*, **54**, 70 (1965)
36. FISCHER, E., *Ber.*, **16**, 2234 (1883)
37. ZUTSHI, P.K. and MAHADEVAN, T.N., *Talanta*, **17**, 1014 (1970)
38. MECKLENBURG, M. and ROSENKRANZER, F., *Z. anorg. Chem.*, **86**, 143 (1914)
39. GUSTAFSSON, L., *Talanta*, **4**, 227 (1960)
40. *British Standards* 2690: Part 14 (1972), London
41. GRASSHOFF, K.M. and CHAN, K.M., *Analytica chim. Acta*, **53**, 442 (1971)
42. REES, T.D., GYLLENSPETZ, A.B. and DOCHERTY, A.C., *Analyst*, **96**, 201 (1971)
43. BERNSTEIN, V.N. and BILIKER, V.G., *Russian chem. Revs.*, **30**, 227 (1961)
44. CASAPIERI, P., SCOTT, R. and SIMPSON, E.A., *Analytica chim. Acta*, **45**, 547 (1969)
45. BETHEA, N.J. and BETHEA, R.M., *Analytica chim. Acta*, **61**, 311 (1972)
46. HOFFMAN, E., *Z. analyt. Chem.*, **185**, 372 (1962); *Analyt. Abstr.*, **9**, 3016 (1962)
47. HUMPHREY, R.E. and HINZE, W., *Analyt. Chem.*, **43**, 1100 (1971)
48. LAMBERT, J.L. and MANZO, D.J., *Analytica chim. Acta*, **48**, 185 (1969)
49. RAMANAUSKAS, E. and GRIGONIENE, K., *Nauch. Trudy Vyssh. Ucheb. Zaved. lit. SSR Khim khim Teknol.*, **13**, 21 (1971); *Analyt. Abstr.*, **24**, 114 (1973)
50. EREMIN, YU.G. and KISELEVA, K.S., *Zh. analit. Khim.*, **24**, 1201 (1969); *Analyt. Abstr.*, **20**, 978 (1971)
51. RAHIM, S.A. and WEST, T.S., *Talanta*, **17**, 851 (1970)
52. RAHIM, S.A., SALIM, A.Y. and SHEREEF, S., *Analyst*, **98**, 851 (1973)
53. BARK, L.S. and RIXON, A., *Analyst*, **95**, 786 (1970)
54. VERNON, F. and WHITHAM, P., *Analytica chim. Acta*, **59**, 155 (1972)
55. BELCHER, R., BOGDSNSKI, S.L., KNOWLES, D.J. and TOWNSHEND, A. *Analytica chim. Acta*, **77**, 53 (1975)
56. GALLUS, J., *Chemia analit.*, **2**, 249 (1957)
57. SOLYMOSI, F. and VARGA, A., *Analytica chim. Acta*, **17**, 608 (1957)
58. KISS, S.A., *Z. analyt. Chem.*, **188**, 341 (1962); *Analyt. Abstr.*, **10**, 112 (1963)
59. KISS, S.A., *Talanta*, **8**, 726 (1961)
60. LIU, C.H. and SHEN, S., *Analyt. Chem.*, **36**, 1652 (1964)
61. NORKUS, P. and SHEMKYAVICHUTE, G., *Zh. analit. Khim.*, **26**, 39 (1971); *Analyt. Abstr.*, **22**, 2234 (1972)
62. DANIELSEN, A.J., JOHNSEN, K. and LANDMARK, P., *Meddr. Pap Ind. Forsk Inst.*, No. 232 (1969); *Norsk skogind.*, **23**, 77 (1969); *Analyt. Abstr.*, **19**, 395 (1970)
63. Orion 94-16 electrode, Orion Research Inc. U.S. Available from E.I.L. Ltd, Chertsey, England. Radelkis OP-S-711, Radelkis, Hungary
64. VESELY, J., JENSEN, O.J. and NICOLAISEN, B., *Analytica chim. Acta*, **62**, 1 (1972)
65. LIGHT, T.S. and SWARTZ, J.L., *Analyt. Lett.*, **1**, 825 (1968)
66. BOCK, R. and PUFF, H-J., *Z. analyt. Chem.*, **240**, 381 (1968); *Analyt. Abstr.*, **18**, 159 (1970)
67. PAPP, J., *Cellulose Chem. Technol.*, **5**, 147 (1971); *Analyt. Abstr.*, **22**, 2404 (1972)
68. PAPP, J. and HAVAS, J., *Magy. kém. Foly.*, **76**, 307 (1970); *Analyt. Abstr.*, **20**, 4439 (1971)
69. NAUMANN, R. and WEBBER, C., *Z. analyt. Chem.*, **253**, 111 (1971); *Analyt. Abstr.*, **21**, 4071 (1971)
70. SLANINA, J., BUYSMAN, E., AGTERDENBOS, J. and GRIEPINK, B.F.A., *Mikrochim. Acta*, 657 (1971)
71. SLANINA, J., AGTERDENBOS, H. and GRIEPINK, B.F.A., *Mikrochim. Acta*, 1225 (1970)
72. CADERSKY, I., *Z. analyt. Chem.*, **239**, 14 (1968); *Analyt. Abstr.*, **17**, 3420 (1969)
73. PRIBYL, M. and SLOVAK, Z., *Mikrochim. Acta*, 119 (1963)
74. KOLTHOFF, I.M. and MILLER, C.S., *J. Am. chem. Soc.*, **63**, 1405 (1941)
75. CANTERFORD, D.R., *Analyt. Chem.*, **45**, 2414 (1973)
76. GRUEN, L.C., *Analytica chim. Acta*, **52**, 123 (1970)
77. HASEBE, K. and KAMBARA, T., *Bull. chem. Soc. Japan*, **43**, 2110 (1970); *Analyt. Abstr.*, **20**, 3772 (1971)
78. BABKO, A.K. and MAKSIMENKO, T.S., *Zh. analit. Khim.*, **22**, 570 (1967); *Analyt. Abstr.*, **15**, 6621 (1968)
79. MICHALSKI, E. and WTORKOWSKA, A., *Chemia analit.*, **7**, 691 (1962); *Analyt. Abstr.*, **10**, 2244 (1963)
80. MEALOR, D. and TOWNSHEND, A., *Talanta*, **15**, 1477 (1968)

81. KRIVAN, V., PAHLKE, S. and TOLG, G., *Talanta*, **20**, 391 (1973)
82. BOWEN, H.J.M., *Radiochem. radioanalyt. Lett.*, **3**, 339 (1970)
83. RODRIGUEZ-VAZQUEZ, J.A., *Analytica chim. Acta*, **73**, 1 (1974)
84. BIRK, J.R., LARSEN, C.M. and WILBOURN, R.G., *Analyt. Chem.*, **42**, 273 (1970)

Sulphite and Sulphur Dioxide

Sulphite is an anion of major importance. In the metallurgical industry the use of sulphide ores has analytical implication for sulphite both during the process itself and in air and liquid effluent control resulting from it. In steam generation, sodium sulphite is often added to boiler feedwater in order to reduce dissolved oxygen to a minimum. Technically, sulphite is important as a reducing agent and in bleaching. Its use in food preservation is well known. Large quantities are used in the production of paper pulp.

Sulphite is often produced as an intermediate step in the analysis of sulphur-containing materials. Examples would be determination of sulphur in oil[1] or food[2] after oxygen-flask combustion. In such analyses the resulting sulphite is oxidized, usually by hydrogen peroxide, and the SO_4^{2-} formed determined by barium perchlorate titration. Oxidation to sulphate followed by its determination is a method that can be often applied to sulphite. Aqueous bromine is a suitable oxidant. The procedure is often used when sulphite is accompanied by other sulphur anions. The analysis of such mixtures will be referred to throughout the section.

Sulphite is masked using formaldehyde.

$$Na_2SO_3 + HCHO + H_2O \rightarrow CH_3(OH)SO_3Na + NaOH$$

The reaction finds extensive use in analysis of sulphite-containing mixtures.

Several reviews[3–5] covering the analytical chemistry of sulphur compounds include a treatment of sulphite. The present treatment of sulphite will include some consideration of the determination of SO_2. The role of SO_2 as a serious air pollutant is well known and needs no further emphasis. Although reference is made to SO_2 determination at several points in this section, a fuller discussion of the topic is included as a sub-section at the end.

Separations

1. As SO_2

Sulphites liberate SO_2 on acidification. This can be swept out using an inert carrier gas, and absorbed in an alkaline solution. Alternatively it can be displaced by boiling the solution. Sulphur dioxide separated in this manner can be determined iodimetrically, or if in trace amounts, using a spectrophotometric method. West and Gaeke[6] used a mercuric chloride solution for collecting traces of SO_2. It was subsequently determined spectrophotometrically.

If thiosulphate is also present with sulphite, SO_2 will be liberated from this by mineral acid, but not from an acetate–acetic acid buffer.

2. *Ion-exchange*

Sulphite, sulphate, thiosulphate and sulphide can be separated using anion-exchange, eluting with nitrate solutions of various strengths[7]. Sulphite and sulphide are eluted in that order by 0.1 M ammonium nitrate–30% acetone at pH 9.7.

Pollard, Nickless and Glover[8] separate sulphite, thiosulphate and lower polythionates by anion-exchange chromatography using De-Acidite FF resin. Sulphite and thiosulphate are eluted and separated with 2M potassium hydrogen phthalate.

3. *Thin-layer chromatography*

TLC on silica-gel/starch with methanol–propanol–conc. NH_3–H_2O (10 :10 : 1 : 2) as solvent, enables sulphite, sulphate, thiosulphate and peroxodisulphate to be separated[9]. In another method by Handa and Johri[10] sulphide, sulphite, sulphate and thiosulphate are separated by TLC on microcrystalline cellulose using *n*-propanol–1M aq. NH_3–acetone (30:20:2) as solvent. Quantitative evaluation of the separated species is made using the Weisz ring-oven technique.

4. *Miscellaneous methods*

Potentially interfering species can sometimes be removed from sulphite by precipitation. A case in point is sulphide. When both ions occur in mixtures, sulphide can be precipitated using zinc or cadmium carbonates. Addition of glycerol is recommended to prevent oxidation of sulphite when the sulphide precipitate is being filtered off.

The use of formaldehyde as a masking agent for sulphite has been referred to earlier. This device is often used in the analysis of mixtures such as sulphite–thiosulphate. In this particular example the sum of both species can be determined iodimetrically in one aliquot. A second aliquot is treated with formaldehyde and the thiosulphate determined alone using the same method. Sulphite is evaluated by difference.

Determination

Several workers, for example Sengar and Gupta[11], have concluded that none of the existing methods for macro determination of sulphite are entirely satisfactory. When used with care, the iodimetric method is probably the most reliable.

Gravimetric methods

Sulphite is readily converted to sulphate after which it can be determined gravimetrically as barium sulphate. Several oxidants are suitable including bromine water, ammoniacal hydrogen peroxide and sodium hypobromite. Excess oxidant can be removed by boiling. The method suffers from the general disadvantages of gravimetric procedures and can be recommended only in circumstances where the more rapid titrimetric methods fail.

Titrimetric methods

1. Iodimetric methods

The iodimetric method for determination of sulphite is well over 100 years old. Nevertheless, it remains as probably the most used method for macro amounts.

$$SO_3^{3-} + I_2 + H_2O \rightarrow SO_4^{2-} + 2I^- + 2H^+$$

A potential source of error is partial oxidation of sulphite by atmospheric oxygen. In order to minimize this certain procedures have been recommended. The sample can be added to excess of standard iodine and a back-titration made with thiosulphate. This is the generally used procedure. The reverse titration, i.e. addition of sulphite from a burette, has been recommended[12]. This is far less convenient. Another recommendation is that the sulphite sample is delivered with the tip of the pipette below the surface of the iodine. Further studies have indicated that this is unnecessary.

Luminol has been proposed as indicator, based on its chemiluminescence in the presence of iodine in alkaline solutions. This is quenched[13] by sulphite. Using this indicator, amounts down to 0.1 mg of sodium sulphite can be determined in the presence of strongly coloured substances. For 25 mg amounts of sodium sulphite the reported errors range from 0.01 to 0.06 mg.

Application of the iodimetric determination of sulphite has been widespread. A British Standards method[14] for sulphite in industrial water recommends acidifying the sample, adding excess of a standard KIO_3–KI solution, and back-titrating the iodine with standard thiosulphate. Virtually the same procedure is recommended by the Society for Analytical Chemistry[15]. A similar procedure is given in the standard U.S. source *Standard Methods for the Examination of Water and Wastewater*[16], the difference being that the titration is made directly with a KIO_3–KI titrant.

The iodimetric method can be adapted to determination of atmospheric SO_2. A known volume of air is bubbled through a NaOH solution, which is then acidified and titrated with standard iodine. A disadvantage in this case is interference given by NO_2, ozone and reducing agents such as hydrogen sulphide.

Sulphite can be determined in the presence of other sulphur anions using the method. Szekeres[17] has applied it to sulphite in the presence of sulphide and thiosulphate. Umland[18] has used it for sulphite and sulphide in the presence of sulphate. Details of these methods are given in the sulphide section. Soffer[19] applied the method to sulphite–dithionate–sulphate mixtures. This is discussed in the dithionite section. Further applications have been made by Szekeres[20, 21] to analysis of sodium dithionite containing sulphite and thiosulphate in addition to the main constituent, and to the analysis of sulphite–thiosulphate–tetrathionate mixtures. In the latter work use is made of the fact that only sulphite and thiosulphate are oxidized by iodine whereas all three anions are oxidized by bromine. Sulphite and thiosulphate are differentiated by masking sulphite with formaldehyde.

In 1930 Wollak[22] described a simple iodimetric procedure for determination of dithionite, bisulphite and thiosulphate when present together. A critical re-examination of this has been carried out recently by Danehy and Zubritsky[23], who conclude that the method is effective. Explicit relationships between the titres are derived enabling the concentrations of each component to be calculated.

Iodimetric titration of sulphite

Procedure

Pipette an excess of standard iodine (according to the presumed sulphite content) into an iodine flask. Add the sample, preferably as a solid, stopper and swirl until it dissolves. Titrate the excess iodine with standard thiosulphate using starch near the end-point.

Notes

1. Interference is possible from several species including iron(II), mercury(I), and arsenic(III). Several anions interfere.
2. To determine sulphite in the presence of other reducing species, titrate one aliquot normally. The titre corresponds to all the reducing species present. Add formaldehyde to a second aliquot before the titration. Here sulphite is masked and the difference in titres corresponds to the sulphite present[24].

---

2. Other redox methods

Several redox reagents including potassium permanganate, potassium dichromate, ceric sulphate, chloramine-T, sodium chlorite, thallium(III) perchlorate, and potassium hexacyanoferrate(III) have featured in the determination of sulphite. These are discussed in standard texts[25,26]. However, no single reagent appears to have emerged with clear advantages over the iodimetric method.

Thallium(III) perchlorate has been investigated recently by Sharma and Gupta[27]. A mild oxidant, it reacts almost instantaneously with sulphite, thiosulphate, or thiourea. These species can be determined directly using *p*-ethoxychrysoidine as indicator, or indirectly.

$$\text{Tl(III)} + SO_3^{2-} + H_2O \rightarrow \text{Tl(I)} + 2H^+ + SO_4^{2-}$$

Interference is given by chloride and bromide which form strong complexes with thallium(III). Copper(II) and iron(II) interfere in the indirect determination. In subsequent work the reagent is applied to analysis of sulphide–sulphite–thiosulphate mixtures, this time using indigo carmine as indicator[28]. When applied to the separate determination of these anions, results are reasonable; when the reagent is substituted for iodine in the older Kurtenacker and Wollak procedure, errors are larger. The advantages of the reagent are that it maintains its strength over long periods and is unaffected by air and light.

3. Compleximetric methods

EDTA forms a stable complex with thallium(III) but not with thallium(I). An excess of standard thallium(III) can therefore be added to sulphite and a back-titration made with standard EDTA at pH 6.0 and with xylenol orange as indicator[29].

Other EDTA procedures utilize the fact that sulphate is readily determined by EDTA titrations if initially precipitated as barium sulphate. Burriel-Marti and Alvarez-Herrero[30] use this approach in the analysis of sulphate–sulphide–sulphite mixtures. Additional details are given in the sulphate section.

De Sousa[31] employs a similar method for sulphide–sulphite mixtures. Sulphite is oxidized by aqueous bromine and the resulting sulphate determined compleximetrically after treatment with barium chloride. In another method for sulphite–sulphate mixtures, sulphite in one aliquot is expelled as SO_2 and the residual sulphate determined with EDTA. In a second aliquot sulphite is oxidized to sulphate using aqueous bromine and the total sulphate determined by EDTA titration. The sulphite content is obtained by difference[32].

Spectroscopic methods

1. Spectrophotometry—visible and UV

Sulphite reacts with *p*-rosaniline hydrochloride (*Structure 74*) and formaldehyde to give a red-purple product, *p*-rosaniline methyl sulphonic acid. The reaction finds extensive use in the determination of atmospheric SO_2.

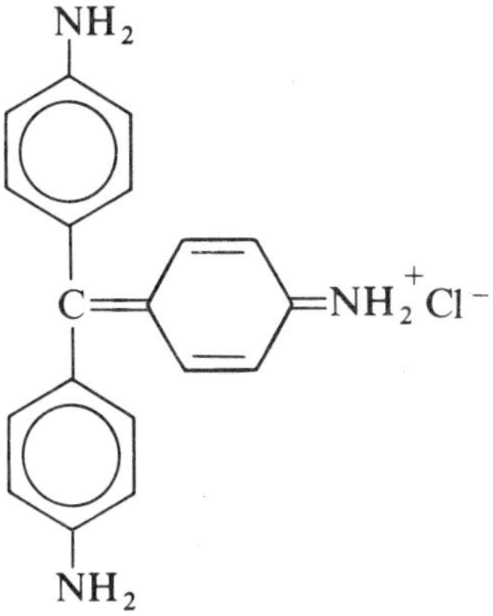

Structure 74 *p*-Rosaniline hydrochloride

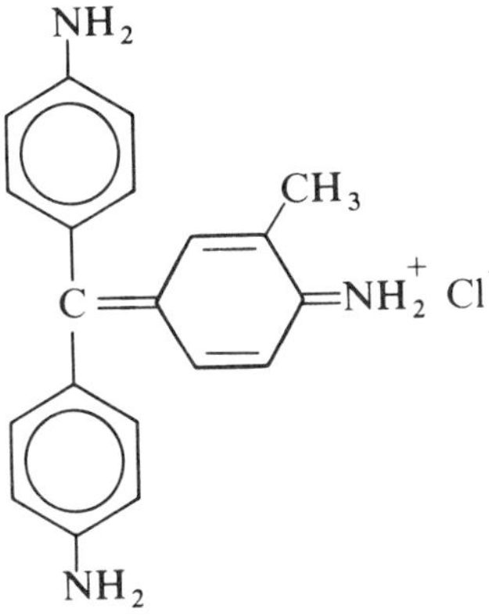

Structure 75 Rosaniline hydrochloride (*magenta*)

This work is derived from a highly specific test for bisulphite developed by Steigmann[33], who employed acid-bleached fuchsin (magenta, rosaniline hydrochloride) (*Structure 75*) to give an intense violet colour. Acid-bleached fuchsin is simply a solution of dye to which acid is added to produce discoloration. Urone, Boggs and Noyes[34] applied the reaction to determination of SO_2 in air. West and Gaeke[35], whose names are often associated with the method, employed a solution of tetrachloromercurate(II) for trapping the SO_2, and substituted *p*-rosaniline in place of the original fuchsin.

$$SO_2 + H_2O + [HgCl_4]^{2-} \rightarrow [HgCl_2SO_3]^{2-} + 2H^+ + 2Cl^-$$

The resulting dichlorosulphitomercurate(II) is remarkably stable and prevents oxidation of SO_2 to SO_3 during sampling and storage. It is subsequently evaluated using the *p*-rosaniline method referred to above.

A recurring problem in the method has been impurity of the reagent dyes and the effect of this on the sensitivity and reproducibility. Pate, Lodge and Wartburg[36] assayed 18 samples of *p*-rosaniline hydrochloride spectrophotometrically and accepted only those giving spectral maxima similar to a compound of known purity. Scaringelli, Saltzman and Frey[37] used a countercurrent distribution technique to purify *p*-rosaniline. In this case the resulting method showed an improvement in sensitivity, reproducibility and working range compared with the West–Gaeke method. Furthermore, interference from nitrogen oxides, ozone and heavy metals were minimized. The *p*-rosaniline sulphonic acid was found to exhibit a hypsochromic spectral shift giving a 575 nm peak at pH 1.2 ± 0.1 and a 548 nm peak at pH 1.6 ± 0.1.

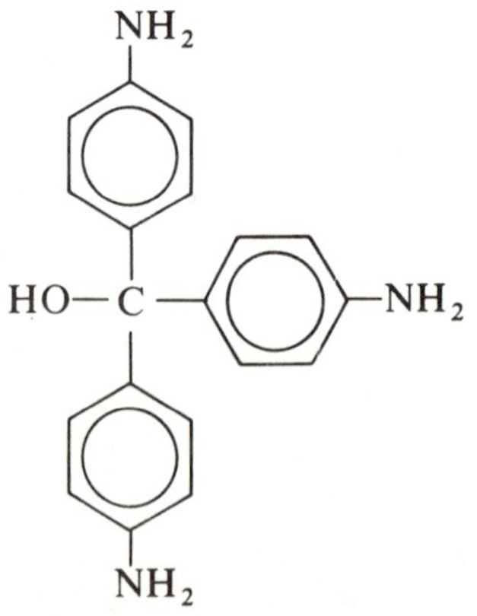

NH_2

HO—C— —NH_2

NH_2

Structure 76 p-Rosaniline base

King and Pruden[38] purified both rosaniline hydrochloride (fuchsin) and *p*-rosaniline hydrochloride using paper chromatography. Analyses for sulphite carried out using the purified materials indicated that *p*-rosaniline was the better of the two owing to its low blanks. A linear calibration curve was obtained for up to 80 μg of SO_2 with the HCl–formaldehyde reaction at pH 1.1. The same workers point out that paper chromatographic purification is not suitable for routine work. They find that *p*-rosaniline base (*Structure 76*), produced by treating acid-bleached *p*-rosaniline hydrochloride with sodium hydroxide, has advantages and can be substituted for the parent dye. It can be purified by recrystallization from aqueous methanol, this giving a reproducibly pure and stable reagent.

Reference has been made to interference by nitrogen oxides. This can be eliminated by addition of sulphamic acid to the absorbing solution.

Several other spectrophotometric procedures have been described. Sussman and Portnoy[39] proposed adding excess dichromate to sulphite and then measuring the decrease in absorbance. The method is subject to many interferences. Stephens and Suddeth[40] develop a method based on reduction of iron(III) in a solution containing 2,4,6-tri(pyridyl)-1,3,5-triazole and propylene carbonate. Iron(II) produced in the reaction with sulphite reacts with the triazone giving violet bis[2,4,6-tri-(2-pyridyl)1,3,5-triazine]–iron(II) complex ion which shows maximum absorbance at 593 nm. Beer's law holds for 3–57 μg SO_2. Hydrogen sulphide and manganese(II) interfere seriously.

Attari, Igilski and Jaselkis[41] describe a similar method based on iron(III) in the presence of 1,10-phenanthroline, this being a modification of earlier work by Stephens and Lindstrom[42].

The ubiquitous chloranilate ion has featured in a method by Humphrey and Hinze[43]. Here it is presumed that the reaction of sulphite and mercuric chloranilate gives non-dissociated mercuric sulphite:

$$HgCh + SO_3^{2-} \rightarrow HgSO_3 + Ch^{2-} \qquad Ch = \text{chloranilate}$$

Absorbance measurements can be made at 525 nm or 330 nm, the corresponding ranges for sulphite being 5–100 μg mℓ$^{-1}$ and 0.5–8.0 μg mℓ$^{-1}$.

The same workers[44] have developed other spectrophotometric methods. One based on 4,4′dithiopyridine or 5,5′dithiobis(2-nitrobenzoic acid) has a range of 0.2–6.0 μg mℓ$^{-1}$ of SO_2. Another[45] is analogous to the mercuric thiocyanate method for chloride. Although no reaction occurs in water alone, thiocyanate equivalent to sulphite or SO_2 is released in ethanol or methanol, and this can subsequently react with iron(III) to give the familiar ferric thiocyanate complex.

Mixtures of sulphite, thiosulphate and polythionates (tetra-, penta- and hexa-) can be analysed spectrophotometrically using a relatively simple procedure[46]. This is discussed on p. 608.

Eremin and Kiseleva[47] use direct UV analysis for sulphite–sulphate–sulphide–thiosulphate mixtures. Further details are given in the sulphide section. Scoggins[48] employed a simple UV procedure for determination of sulphite or SO_2. In this, the sulphite solution is acidified with H_2SO_4 and the absorbance measured at 276 nm. Bhatty and Townshend[49] observe that the sensitivity is low and recommend making the measurements at 198 nm instead. This provides a 4-fold increase in sensitivity. The procedure allows 1 μg of SO_2 mℓ$^{-1}$ to be determined. At 276 nm the only interferences are sulphide and nitrite. At 198 nm no interference is given by fluoride, sulphate, phosphate, chloride and cyanide, but sulphide, nitrite, thiosulphate, bromide, nitrate, thiocyanate and iodide absorb. Interference can be overcome by sweeping out the SO_2 from an acidified solution with a stream of nitrogen and re-absorbing it in an alkaline EDTA solution[48].

Okutani, Ito and Utsumi[50] utilize the 1:2 complex formed between sulphite and mercury(II) in 0.05–1.0M H_2SO_4. The maximum absorbance is given at 237 nm.

Spectrophotometric determination of sulphur dioxide with *p*-rosaniline hydrochloride[38]

Reagents

Bleached *p*-rosaniline reagent solution:

The base is purified as follows. Dissolve 1 g of *p*-rosaniline hydrochloride in 250 mℓ of 2.5M HCl. After allowing this to stand for 2 h, filter the bleached solution through a Whatman No. 1 filter paper. Add a slight excess of 2.5M NaOH to the filtrate to precipitate the base. Filter through a sintered-glass plate of porosity 3, and wash thoroughly with distilled water to remove sodium chloride and excess sodium hydroxide. Recrystallize by dissolving in 70 mℓ of methanol at the boiling point, adding 300 mℓ of water at 80 °C and allowing the solution to cool to room temperature. The yield of recrystallized product is about 64%. Dissolve 1.0 g of the purified *p*-rosaniline base in 60 mℓ of conc. HCl and dilute to 1ℓ with water. The reagent is stable for at least 6 weeks if kept in the dark.

Potassium tetrachloromercurate solution:

A solution of 27.2 g of mercury(II) chloride and 14.9 g of potassium chloride in water is diluted to 1ℓ.

Formaldehyde solution: 0.2%:

5 mℓ of 40% formaldehyde solution is diluted to 1ℓ.

Standard sulphite solution:

A solution of 0·4 g of anhydrous sodium sulphite in 500 mℓ of water is prepared, corresponding to between 300 and 400 μg of SO_2 $mℓ^{-1}$. The concentration of sulphite is determined by iodimetric titration.

$$1\ mℓ\ 0.05\ M\ \text{iodine} \equiv 3.2030\ mg\ SO_2.$$

Immediately after analysis the sulphite solution is stabilized by dilution with potassium tetrachloromercurate solution. Ten mℓ of sulphite solution diluted to 500 mℓ with the tetrachloromercurate gives a solution corresponding to between 6 and 8 μg of SO_2 $mℓ^{-1}$.

Procedure

Transfer aliquots of the dilute sulphite solution corresponding to not more than 80 μg of SO_2, to a 50 mℓ volumetric flask, and add 10 mℓ each of bleached *p*-rosaniline reagent and formaldehyde. Dilute the solutions to the mark and allow to stand for 20 min. Measure the absorbance in a 1 cm glass cell at 572 nm against a reagent blank. Treat the sample solution the same way.

---

2. *Fluorimetric methods*

The Schiff reaction developed by West and Gaeke has been further extended by Axelrod, Bonelli and Lodge[51] into a fluorimetric method for sulphite. Reaction of the formaldehyde–bisulphite complex with 5-amino fluorescein gives a non-fluorescent product according to the proposed reaction:

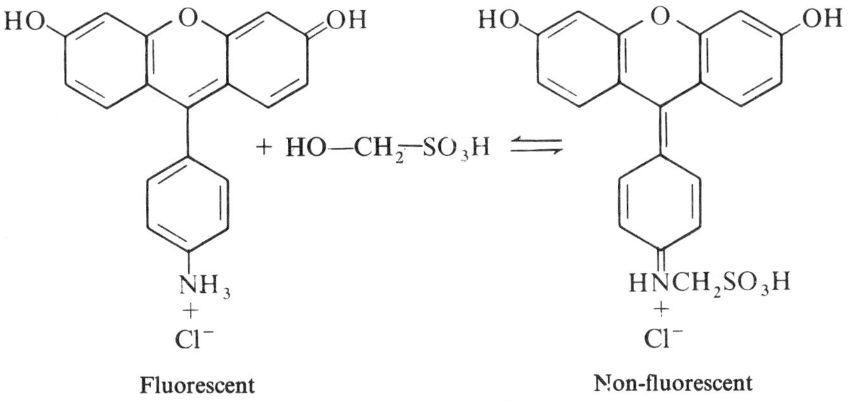

HO O OH HO O OH

+ $HO{-}CH_2{-}SO_3H \rightleftharpoons$

NH_3 + Cl^- $HNCH_2SO_3H$ + Cl^-

Fluorescent **Non-fluorescent**

The method is applicable to SO_2 collected in solutions of tetrachloromercurate(II). No interference is given by nitrate, sulphate, hydrogen peroxide, iron(II), or ammonium ions in 10^{-2}M concentration. A 5 per cent error is given by potassium, calcium, magnesium, copper(II), acetate and nitrite at a concentration of 10^{-2}M. The same error is produced by 10^{-3}M iodide. Iron(III) gives a 45 per cent error at 10^{-2}M. The lower limit for the method is 0.02 μg SO_2 $m\ell^{-1}$ in tetrachloromercurate(II).

3. *Atomic absorption spectroscopy*

Indirect AAS methods for sulphite have been based on mercury(II) and lead(II). In the former case sulphite is added to a mercury(II) oxide suspension, this causing transference of mercury from the solid phase to the highly stable $[Hg(SO_4)_2]^{2-}$ complex[52]. Iodide, thiosulphate and thiocyanate behave similarly to sulphite, and interfere. No interference is given by ammonia, sulphate, nitrite, bromide or cyanide. The method is suitable for concentrations of sulphite up to 83 ppm.

Rose and Boltz[53] base their method on the excess of lead(II) after precipitation of lead sulphate. Preliminary oxidation of sulphite to sulphate is done using hydrogen peroxide. The range is 2–20 ppm of SO_2. At the 5 ppm level no interference is given by 500 ppm of chloride, nitrite, nitrate, perchlorate, Na^+, K^+, $NH_4{}^+$, Ca^{2+} or Mg^{2+}. The following species are permissible at the levels (ppm) indicated: acetate (250), EDTA (20), Ba^{2+} (10), Al^{2+} (10). Iron(III) and phosphate should be absent.

4. *MECA*

Molecular Emission Cavity Analysis is applicable to sulphite as well as other sulphur anions[54, 55]. The basic technique, which depends on the blue S_2 emission at 384 nm, is discussed more fully in the sulphide section. Sulphite and sulphate give completely resolved responses and can therefore be determined simultaneously. The same does not apply to thiosulphate and sulphite which give similar responses. The range for sulphite is 3–300 ppm using samples from 3 to 5 μℓ.

Electroanalytical methods

1. Potentiometric methods including ion-selective electrodes

Direct potentiometric titration of sulphite using sodium chlorite has been described[56]. The pH range of 4–4.6 is critical. Below pH 4 loss of SO_2 occurs; above pH 5 the reaction is slow and incomplete. Even in the narrow pH range proposed, recovery of sulphite is only 94.0–94.2 per cent, so that an empirical standardization of the reagent is required.

Norkus and Shemkyavichute[57] conduct the potentiometric titration of sulphite in 2–10M NaOH using iodine as titrant and platinum and calomel electrodes. Mixtures containing sulphite, polysulphide and thiosulphate, and sulphite, polysulphide, thiosulphate and sulphide can be analysed potentiometrically with mercuric chloride as titrant[58, 59]. Details of both methods are given in the section on polysulphide.

Some application of ion-selective electrodes has been made to determination of sulphur. Papp and Havas use a pS^{2-} electrode in the potentiometric titration of sulphide–thiosulphate–sulphite–polysulphide mixtures. Mercuric chloride is used as titrant [60, 61]. Additional details are given in the polysulphide section.

The lead ion-selective electrode has been applied to determination of SO_2 in flue-gases[62]. In this case, the gases are passed through 3% hydrogen peroxide and a potentiometric titration done using 0.01M Pb^{2+} as titrant. Results using the method are claimed to be comparable to those obtained by the Ba^{2+}– thorin titration. Sulphite ion-selective electrodes are now commercially available [63, 64]. The range is 10^{-6}–10^{-2}M $SO_3{}^{2-}$. For 10^{-4}M $SO_3{}^{2-}$ interferences are hydrofluoric acid (3×10^{-3}M), acetic acid (5×10^{-3}M) and HCl ($>$1M)[64].

2. Polarography

Polarography is a sensitive method for sulphite but thiosulphate and other sulphur species interfere. In acid solution reduction produces one or more steps depending on the pH of the electrolyte. The wave in 1M HCl corresponds to reduction to dithionite. At pH 6 this is reduced[65] to thiosulphate.

Aulenbach and Balmat[66] were able to overcome difficulties due to extraneous species present in waste water in the following way. Nitrogen was passed through a neutral or alkaline sulphite solution to remove O_2, but without loss of SO_2. After acidification, further passage of N_2 removed the resulting SO_2. The difference between the diffusion current immediately after acidification, and after removal of SO_2, was found to be directly proportional to the sulphite concentration.

Ciaccio and Cotsis[67] investigated polarography of Na_2HgCl_4 solutions used to trap gaseous SO_2 in the form of the $[HgCl_2SO_3]^{2-}$ complex ion. The reduction wave in such solutions was found to be obscured by the wave for the $[HgCl_4]^{2-}$ moiety. This difficulty was overcome by reduction of the complex to elemental mercury in basic medium followed by its removal. After pH re-adjustment to 1.0, the reduction wave due to SO_2 could be measured.

Strafelda and Dolezal[68] apply automatic polarography to analysis of concentrated sulphite solutions produced by absorbing industrial waste gases in aqueous ammonia. The basal electrolyte in this case is 3.5M H_2SO_4. A well-defined wave is given for up to 0.1M $SO_3{}^{2-}$.

Spectrophotometric determination of chloride, cyanide, fluoride, sulphate and sulphite using metal chloranilates is now an established feature of their analytical chemistry. Humphrey and Laird[69] have proposed polarographic determination of the released chloranilate ion as an alternative to its spectrophotometric evaluation. Their method is based on the reversible 2-electron reduction of chloranilate at the dropping mercury electrode, this having been reported in earlier work by Wessbart and Rysselberghe[70]. The resulting current is proportional to the concentrations of the anions involved. For sulphite the range is 5×10^{-5}M–5×10^{-3}M. Mercuric chloranilate is recommended as reagent. Glycerol is added to retard oxidation of sulphite. The method is of value where coloured species are involved, or where other ions absorb.

3. *Coulometric methods*

Coulometry is now established as one of the most important methods for determination of sulphur compounds, particularly at low concentration. An example of current practice is micro-coulometric determination of trace amounts of sulphur in light petroleum products[71]. Sulphur dioxide formed by combustion of the sample enters a cell where it reacts with electrogenerated iodine.

$$I_3^- + SO_2 + H_2O \rightarrow SO_3 + I^- + 2H^+$$

$$3I^- \rightarrow I_3^- + 2e$$

The current required to regenerate I_3^- is fed through a precision series resistor to a recorder and displayed on a strip chart as a peak. Hydrocarbons are burned to CO_2 and H_2O and do not affect the titration. The results are calculated using an expression based on Faraday's laws:

$$W = \frac{QM}{96\,493n} \times 10^9$$

where W = weight of substance titrated in ng; M = formula weight of substance titrated; Q = number of coulombs used; n = number of Faradays corresponding to one formula weight.

Q is evaluated using the expression

$$Q = It = \frac{v}{R} \times 10^3 \times 60 \times S \times A$$

where I = current in amperes; t = time in seconds; v = recorder sensitivity in mV inch^{-1}; R = resistance of series resistor; S = chart speed in minutes inch^{-1}; A = area under peak.

Other coulometric procedures for determination of sulphur in petroleum products have been described by Dixon[72] and Carter[73]. The former method, like the ones previously mentioned, employs variable current coulometry. The latter method by Carter utilizes a simple and inexpensive constant current coulometer. Sulphur in oils in the range 0.01–1.0% can be determined. In each of the above methods combustion of the sample produces SO_2 which is swept into the coulometric cell.

A coulometric method for SO_2 developed by Bailey and Bishop[74] uses Differential Electrolytic Potentiometry for end-point location.

Miscellaneous methods

Methods for determination of sulphite and sulphide in mixtures are often tedious and time consuming. Birk, Larsen and Wilbourne[75] describe a gas-chromatographic technique which depends on evolution of hydrogen sulphide, SO_2 and CO_2 from sulphide, sulphite and carbonate respectively on acidification. The method is applicable to mg amounts of sulphite.

Sodium sulphite and bisulphite can be determined by thermometric titration using the familiar iodine–thiosulphate reaction[76].

Determination of atmospheric SO_2

Reference to determination of atmospheric SO_2 has been made throughout the present section.

Modifications of the West–Gaeke method using sodium tetrachloromercurate(II) for trapping gaseous SO_2 are important, and recommended by the American Society for Testing and Materials[77]. The sensitivity is 0.005–0.2 ppm using an appropriate volume of air sample.

An important study of the parameters of the West–Gaeke procedure has been carried out by Scarangelli and co-workers[37,78]. One of their procedures has been adapted to parallel photometric analysis[79]. This technique, which employs an ORNL GeMSEC (General Medical Sciences—Atomic Energy Commission) Photometric Analyser, has been described by Anderson[80]. It is based on spectrophotometric absorption, the special feature being that reagent addition, mixing and absorbance measurements on 15 test portions are accomplished in identical manner. Thus there is no need to wait for the chromogenic reaction to attain equilibrium before making the measurements. The technique employs a rotor containing 15 cells spinning past a beam of light. The signal, in the form of a peak for each cell, is displayed continuously on an oscilloscope. Results indicate a considerable saving in time where the West–Gaeke procedure is used for routine determination of SO_2. The range for SO_2 is 0.25–2.5 ppm.

The iodimetric method is applicable to determination of SO_2 in air, with NaOH used in the trapping solution. After acidification, a titration is done with standard iodine. Several gases interfere, notably NO_2, hydrogen sulphide, and ozone.

A relatively simple procedure consists of passing the sample through a dilute hydrogen peroxide solution at pH 5. The resulting H_2SO_4 is titrated with standard NaOH. Several species interfere.

A flame-photometric detector for SO_2 has been described[81]. It may be used for gas-chromatographic detection of sulphur compounds at levels below 1 ppm. The detector itself is based on photometric detection of the flame emission of the sulphur compounds in a hydrogen–air flame. Stevens and O'Keeffe[82] describe application of the detector to continuous recording of atmospheric SO_2 at levels below 0.06 ppm.

References

1. LONSDALE, M., *Proc. Soc. analyt. Chem.*, **7**, 12 (1970)
2. BESWICK, G. and JOHNSON, R.M., *Talanta*, **17**, 709 (1970)
3. SZEKERES, L., *Talanta*, **21**, 2 (1974)
4. BLASIUS, E., HORN, G., KNOCHEL, A., MUNCH, J. and WAGNER, H., in *Inorganic Sulphur Chemistry* (Ed. G. Nickless), Elsevier, Amsterdam, 199 (1968)
5. HAFF, L.V., in *The Analytical Chemistry of Sulphur and its Compounds* (Ed. J. H. Karchmer), Part 1, Wiley-Interscience, New York, 223 (1970)
6. WEST, P.W. and GAEKE, G.C., *Analyt. Chem.*, **28**, 1816 (1956)
7. IGUCHI, A., *Bull. chem. Soc. Japan*, **31**, 600 (1958); *Analyt. Abstr.*, **6**, 1705 (1959)
8. POLLARD, F.H., NICKLESS, G. and GLOVER, R.B., *J. Chromat.*, **15**, 533 (1964)
9. SEILER, H. and ERLENMEYER, H., *Helv. chim. Acta*, **47**, 264 (1964); *Analyt. Abstr.*, **12**, 1703 (1965)
10. HANDA, A.C. and JOHRI, K.N., *Talanta*, **20**, 219 (1973)
11. SENGAR, H.G.S. and GUPTA, Y.K., *Talanta*, **12**, 185 (1965)
12. KOLTHOFF, I.M., *Z. analyt. Chem.*, **60**, 448 (1921)
13. LUKOVSKAYA, N.M. and MARKOVA, L.V., *Zh. analit. Khim.*, **24**, 1893 (1969); *Analyt. Abstr.*, **21**, 162 (1971)
14. *British Standards* 2690: Part 2 (1965), London
15. HANSON, N.W. (Ed.), *Official, Standardised and Recommended Methods of Analysis*, The Society for Analytical Chemistry, London, 463 (1973)
16. American Public Health Association, American Waterworks Association, Water Pollution Control Federation, *Standard Methods for the Examination of Water and Wastewater*, 13th edn, American Public Health Association, New York, 337 (1971)
17. SZEKERES, L., *Ann. chim. Roma*, **52**, 67 (1962); *Analyt. Abstr.*, **9**, 5140 (1962)
18. UMLAND, F., *Z. analyt. Chem.*, **224**, 413 (1967); *Analyt. Abstr.*, **15**, 2600 (1968)
19. SOFFER, N., *Analyst*, **86**, 843 (1961)
20. SZEKERES, L., *Z. analyt. Chem.*, **203**, 178 (1964); *Analyt. Abstr.*, **12**, 5130 (1965)
21. SZEKERES, L. and SUGAR, E., *Magy. Kém. Lap.*, **16**, 434 (1961); *Analyt. Abstr.*, **9**, 1453 (1962)
22. WOLLAK, R., *Z. analyt. Chem.*, **80**, 1 (1930)
23. DANEHY, J.P. and ZUBRITSKY, C.W., *Analyt. Chem.*, **46**, 391 (1974)
24. PRATER, A.N., JOHNSON, C.M., POOLE, M.F. and MACKINNEY, G., *Ind. Engng Chem. analyt. Edn*, **16**, 153 (1944)
25. BERKA, A., VULTERIN, J. and ZYKA, J., *Newer Redox Titrants*, Pergamon Press, Oxford (1965)
26. KOLTHOFF, I.M. and BELCHER, R., *Volumetric Analysis*, Vol III, Interscience, New York (1957)
27. SHARMA, P.D. and GUPTA, Y.K., *Talanta*, **21**, 168 (1974)
28. SHARMA, D.N., SHARMA, P.D. and GUPTA, Y.K., *Talanta*, **23**, 326 (1976)
29. SZEKERES, L. and KELLNER, A., *Chemist Analyst*, **55**, 77 (1966)
30. BURRIEL-MARTI, F. and ALVAREZ-HERRERO, C., *Inf. quim. analit.*, **18**, 142 (1964); *Analyt. Abstr.*, **13**, 132 (1966)
31. DE SOUSA, A., *Inf. quim. analit.*, **17**, 51 (1963); *Analyt. Abstr.*, **11**, 1266 (1964)
32. DE SOUSA, A., *Inf. quim. analit.*, **16**, 177 (1962); *Analyt. Abstr.*, **10**, 3667 (1963)
33. STEIGMANN, A., *Analyt. Chem.*, **22**, 492 (1950)
34. URONE, P., BOGGS, W.E. and NOYES, C.M., *Analyt. Chem.*, **23**, 1517 (1951)
35. WEST, P.W. and GAEKE, G.C., *Analyt. Chem.* **28**, 1816 (1956)
36. PATE, J.B., LODGE, J.P. and WARTBURG, A.F., *Analyt. Chem.*, **34**, 1660 (1962).
37. SCARINGELLI, F.P., SALTZMAN, B.E. and FREY, S.A., *Analyt. Chem.*, **39**, 1709 (1967)
38. KING, H.G.C. and PRUDEN, G., *Analyst*, **94**, 43 (1969)
39. SUSSMAN, S. and PORTNOY, I.L., *Analyt. Chem.*, **24**, 1652 (1952)
40. STEPHENS, B.G. and SUDDETH, H.A., *Analyst*, **95**, 70 (1970)
41. ATTARI, A., IGILSKI, T.P. and JASELKIS, B., *Analyt. Chem.*, **42**, 1282 (1970)
42. STEPHENS, B.G. and LINDSTROM, F., *Analyt. Chem.*, **36**, 1308 (1964)
43. HUMPHREY, R.E. and HINZE, W., *Analyt. Chem.*, **43**, 1100 (1971)
44. HUMPHREY, R.E., WARD, M.H. and HINZE, W., *Analyt., Chem.*, **42**, 698 (1970)
45. HINZE, W., ELLIOTT, J. and HUMPHREY, R.E., *Analyt. Chem.*, **44**, 1511 (1972)
46. KOH, T. and TANIGUCHI, K., *Analyt. Chem.*, **45**, 2018 (1973)
47. EREMIN, YU.G. and KISELEVA, K.S., *Zh. analit. Khim.*, **24**, 1201 (1969); *Analyt. Abstr.*, **20**, 978 (1971)
48. SCOGGINS, M.W., *Analyt. Chem.*, **42**, 1091 (1970)

49. BHATTY, M.K. and TOWNSHEND, A., *Analytica chim. Acta,* **55**, 263 (1971)
50. OKUTANI, T., ITO, S. and UTSUMI, S., *J. chem. Soc. Japan, pure Chem. Sect.*, **88**, 1296 (1967); *Analyt. Abstr.*, **16**, 1849 (1969)
51. AXELROD, H.D., BONELLI, J.E. and LODGE, J.P., *Analyt. Chem.*, **42**, 512, 743 (1970)
52. JUNGREIS, E. and ANAVI, Z., *Analytica chim. Acta*, **45**, 190 (1969)
53. ROSE, S.A. and BOLTZ, D.F., *Analytica chim. Acta,* **44**, 239 (1969)
54. BELCHER, R., BOGDANSKI, S.L., KNOWLES, D.J. and TOWNSHEND, A., *Analytica chim. Acta*, **77**, 53 (1975)
55. BELCHER, R., BOGDANSKI, S.L., KNOWLES, D.J. and TOWNSHEND, A., *Analytica chim. Acta,* **79**, 292 (1975)
56. MINCZEWSKI, J. and GLABISZ, U., *Talanta*, **5**, 179 (1960)
57. NORKUS, P. and SHEMKYAVICHUTE, G., *Zh. analit. Khim.*, **26**, 39 (1971); *Analyt. Abstr.*, **22**, 2234 (1972)
58. DANIELSEN, A.J., JOHNSEN, K. and LANDMARK, P., *Norsk. Skogind.*, **23**, 378 (1969); *Analyt. Abstr.*, **21**, 1252 (1971)
59. DANIELSEN, A.J., JOHNSEN, K. and LANDMARK, P., *Meddr. Pap Ind. Forsk Inst.*, No. 232; *Norsk. Skogind.*, **23**, 77 (1969); *Analyt. Abstr.*, **19**, 395 (1970)
60. PAPP, J. and HAVAS, J., *Magy kém. Foly.*, **76**, 307 (1970); *Analyt. Abstr.*, **20**, 4439 (1971)
61. PAPP, J., *Cellulose Chem. Technol.*, **5**, 147 (1971); *Analyt. Abstr.*, **22**, 2404 (1972)
62. YOUNG, M., DRISCOLL, J.N. and MAHONEY, K., *Analyt. Chem.*, **45**, 2283 (1973)
63. E.I.L. Electrode No. 8010, E.I.L. Hanworth Lane, Chertsey, Surrey, England
64. Orion Electrode No. 95-64, MSE Scientific Instruments, Manor Royal, Crawley, West Sussex, England
65. KOLTHOFF, I.M. and MILLER, C.S., *J. Am. chem. Soc.,* **63**, 1405 (1941)
66. AULENBACH, D.B. and BALMAT, J.L., *Analyt. Chem.*, **27**, 562 (1955)
67, CIACCIO, L.L. and COTSIS, T., *Analyt. Chem.*, **39**, 260 (1967)
68. STRAFELDA, F. and DOLEZAL, J., *Colln Czech. chem. Commun. Engl. Edn,* **32**, 2707 (1967); *Analyt. Abstr.*, **15**, 6622 (1968)
69. HUMPHREY, R.E. and LAIRD, C.E., *Analyt. Chem.*, **43**, 1895 (1971)
70. WESSBART, J. and RYSSELBERGHE, D., *J. phys. Chem., Ithaca*, **61**, 765 (1957)
71. KILLER, F.C.A. and UNDERHILL, K.E., *Analyst*, **95**, 505 (1970)
72. DIXON, J.P., *Analyst*, **97**, 612 (1972)
73. CARTER, J.M., *Analyst*, **97**, 929 (1972)
74. BAILEY, P.L. and BISHOP, E., *Analyst*, **97**, 311 (1972)
75. BIRK, J.R., LARSEN, C.M. and WILBOURNE, R.G., *Analyt. Chem.*, **42**, 273 (1970)
76. PRIESTLEY, P.T., *Analyst*, **88**, 194 (1963)
77. ASTM D2914-70T, American Society for Testing and Materials, Philadelphia, Pa. (1972)
78. SCARANGELLI, F.P., ELFERS, L., NORRIS, D. and HOCHHEISER, S., *Analyt. Chem.*, **42**, 1818 (1970)
79. COLEMAN, R.L., SHULTS, W.D., KELLEY, M.T. and DEAN, J.A., *Analyt. Lett.*, **5**, 169 (1972)
80. ANDERSON, N.G., *Analyt. Biochem.*, **28**, 545 (1969)
81. BRODY, S.S. and CHANEY, J.E., *J. Gas Chromat.*, **4**, 42 (1966)
82. STEVENS, R.K. and O'KEEFFE, A.E., *Analyt. Chem.*, **42**, 143A (Feb.) (1970)

Thiosulphate

The principal use of thiosulphate is in photography. Its reducing properties also find use in bleaching.

Analytically, the importance of thiosulphate needs little emphasis. Despite a long history of use and the introduction of newer reagents, the iodine–thiosulphate titration continues to find extensive application. Thiosulphate is a stronger reductant than sulphite. In neutral solutions mild oxidizing agents such as iodine oxidize thiosulphate to tetrathionate. Hydrogen peroxide, bromine and chlorine oxidize it to sulphate. Thiosulphate solutions are unstable when slightly acidified, forming free sulphur, sulphite and polythionate.

Separations

1. Precipitation by silver ions
Silver ions precipitate thiosulphate in dilute nitric acid solution. This may be used to separate thiosulphate from species which are soluble under these conditions.

2. Ion-exchange
Ion-exchange provides several methods. Iguchi[1] separated sulphate, sulphite, thiosulphate and sulphide using an anion-exchanger in nitrate form. Elution was done using various solutions. For mixtures of sulphate, sulphite and thiosulphate the column was first eluted with ammoniacal sodium nitrate solution to remove sulphate and sulphite. Elution with neutral sodium nitrate solution removes the thiosulphate.

Schmidt and Sand[2] separate thiosulphate, sulphite and trithionate by anion-exchange on a Dowex 1-XZ column using NaCl or HCl as eluant.

Anion-exchange is also used by Pollard, Nickless and Glover[3] to separate thiosulphate, sulphite and lower polythionates (trithionate, tetrathionate and pentathionate).

3. Thin-layer chromatography
Several thin-layer chromatographic separations include thiosulphate. Details of some are given in *Table 55*.

4. Solvent extraction
Few extraction procedures have been published for separation of thiosulphate. Extraction by basic dyes followed by its spectrophotometric determination is reported by Grigoniene, Ramanauskas and Butkevicius[45]. Additional details are given in the discussion of spectrophotometric methods.

5. High-performance liquid chromatography
High performance liquid chromatography (HPLC) has been used to separate thiosulphate and polythionates[66]. Further details are given in the section on polythionates.

Determination

An account of the analytical chemistry of thiosulphate is included in several reviews covering sulphur anions[8–11].

Table 55 Separation of thiosulphate by TLC

Technique	*Solvent system*	*Thiosulphate separated from*	*Ref.*
TLC (silica gel-starch)	(1) Methanol–propanol–NH_3(0.880)–H_2O (10:10:1:2) (2) Methanol–dioxan–NH_3(0.880)–H_2O (3:6:1:1)	(1) SO_4^{2-}, SO_3^{2-}, $S_2O_8^{2-}$ (2) lower polythionates	4
TLC (maize-starch)	Acetone–3M sq. NM_3	NO_2^-, SCN^-, CrO_4^{2-}, N_3^-, CN^-, BO_3^{3-}, S^{2-}, AsO_3^{3-}, AsO_4^{3-}, NO_3^-, SO_4^{2-}, PO_4^{3-}	5
TLC (Gelman SA and SG)	Several including butanol–pyridine–acetic acid–H_2O (15:10:3:12)	SO_4^{2-}, SCN^-, $S_3O_6^{2-}$, $S_4O_6^{2-}$	6
TLC (silica gel)	Ethanol–butanol–NH_3(0.880)–2M ammonium acetate–H_2O (75:75:8–10:20–40:10–30)	$S_3O_6^{2-}$, $S_4O_6^{2-}$, $S_5O_6^{2-}$	7

Gravimetric methods

The principal method depends on oxidation of thiosulphate by hydrogen peroxide or bromine to sulphate, followed by gravimetric determination of this as barium sulphate. Other sulphur compounds interfere and the method suffers from the general disadvantages associated with gravimetric procedures.

Titrimetric methods

1. Iodimetric methods

Of the redox methods, determination by iodimetric titration is the most important and widely applied despite its antiquity.

$$2S_2O_3^{2-} + I_2 \rightarrow S_4O_6^{2-} + 2I^-$$

Before discussing its specific application to determination of thiosulphate, some comments on the reaction itself are pertinent. Extensive studies over several years have clarified the conditions necessary for accurate results. Much of this is reported and discussed in standard texts[12,13]. In the normal titration, i.e. addition of thiosulphate to iodine, the iodine solution is neutral or slightly acid. Alkaline iodine solutions react with hydroxyl ions giving hypiodous acid

$$I_2 + OH^- \leftrightharpoons HIO + I^-$$

or hypiodite ion (IO^-)

$$I_2 + 2OH^- \leftrightharpoons IO^- + I^- + H_2O$$

Hypiodous acid is known to oxidize thiosulphate to sulphate

$$4HIO + S_2O_3^{2-} + 6OH^- \leftrightharpoons 4I^- + 2SO_4^{2-} + 5H_2O$$

The situation is further complicated by disproportionation of hypiodous acid into iodate and iodide. An important consequence of the above is that when even a slightly alkaline solution of iodine is titrated with thiosulphate, the latter is partially oxidized to sulphate, this giving a negative error.

If the iodine is excessively acidified, two sources of error appear. In the first place there is a possibility that the thiosulphate will decompose. Some sources report that it is possible to titrate a rather strongly acidified solution of I_2 provided the thiosulphate is added slowly and with stirring.

A second source of error is air-oxidation of iodide, which occurs more readily with increasing acidity. The iodine solution, therefore, requires to be slightly acidified but not excessively so. The above discussion concerns the titration of iodine with thiosulphate. If the reverse titration is considered, i.e. the iodine being added, then the thiosulphate must be no more than slightly acid to avoid decomposition. If on the other hand it is alkaline, the added iodine would oxidize it beyond the tetrathionate stage with consequent error. One solution in this situation, would be to carry out the reverse titration, i.e. titrate with the thiosulphate sample.

In many cases, for example in the assay of commercial grade sodium thiosulphate, the sample would be neutral, and the sources of error discussed above would not arise. Such is the case in the assay of anhydrous sodium thiosulphate used as a photographic material[14]. Commercial thiosulphate sometimes contains sulphite as impurity. This can be masked using formaldehyde and the thiosulphate titrated with iodine without error. The end-point of the iodine–thiosulphate reaction can be detected by observing the appearance or disappearance of the iodine colour. However, it is more usual to employ starch, which gives an intense blue colour partly due to an adsorption complex with iodine.

Starches can be separated into two major fractions, amylose a straight chain fraction and amylopectin which has a branched structure. These forms occur in different proportions depending on the origin of the starch. Potato starch contains a high proportion of amylose. It is the amylose that forms the blue complex with iodine. Amylopectin forms a reddish-purple complex instead. The intense blue colour, which provides an extremely sharp end-point, is given with freshly prepared starch solutions. Older solutions impart a reddish colour and the resulting end-point is sluggish. A recent kinetic study of the amylose–iodine reaction by Thompson and Hamori[15] indicates that the rate-determining step in producing the blue complex consists in the formation of an eleven-atom polyiodine chain I_{11}^{3-} inside the amylose helix.

A starch solution is prepared in the following way. Mix about 2 g of starch with a little water and pour the slurry into about 200 mℓ of boiling distilled water. Continue to heat, with stirring, until the solution becomes clear. Cool and dilute to about 1ℓ with distilled water.

Several preservatives have been recommended. If used, care is needed that they do not interfere with the subsequent reactions. One way of overcoming the instability of starch solutions is to use a solid solution. Clark[16] has reported that a solid 5% solution of starch in urea dissolves immediately in aqueous solutions. The solid preparation keeps very well and gives excellent end-points. A commercial product known as Thyodene is available.

A standard iodine solution for evaluating thiosulphate solutions can be prepared by accurately weighing out suitable amounts of pure iodine. This is inconvenient and rarely carried out. In practice, a better method is to prepare an iodine solution of approximately known strength and standardize this using pure arsenious oxide:

$$As_2O_3 + 2I_2 + 5H_2O \rightleftharpoons 2HAsO_4^{2-} + 4I^- + 8H^+$$

The procedure is given later in this section. The most convenient method, and the one generally used, is to generate a known quantity of iodine by adding an accurately weighed amount of KIO_3 to an acidified excess of KI.

$$IO_3^- + 5I^- + 6H^+ \rightarrow 3I_2 + 3H_2O$$

The liberated iodine is titrated with the thiosulphate solution to be standardized. Potassium dichromate can be used as an alternative to the iodate, but the reaction is slow at low acidities.

$$Cr_2O_7^{2-} + 6I^- + 14H^+ \rightleftharpoons 2Cr^{3+} + 3I_2 + 7H_2O$$

If the acidity is increased, air oxidation of iodide becomes a source of error. Although KIO_3 has an advantage over potassium dichromate in this respect, it suffers from the disadvantage that only relatively small weights are required.

Thus for a titre of 25 mℓ of 0.1M thiosulphate, the corresponding weight of KIO_3 required to liberate the requisite amount of iodine is 0.0892 g. Weighing errors, using a ±0.1 mg balance, would introduce significant errors. It is usually recommended that 250 mℓ or 500 mℓ of KIO_3 solution is prepared using correspondingly larger amounts, and that aliquots from this are used in the standardization.

Furman and Wallace[29] first introduced the titration of thiosulphate with cerium(IV), in the presence of KI. In this method the KI is added to the thiosulphate before the titration.

$$2Ce(IV) + 2I^- \rightarrow I_2 + 2Ce(III)$$

$$I_2 + 2S_2O_3^{2-} \rightarrow 2I^- + S_4O_6^{2-}$$

The end-point is detected visually using starch. Griepink and Cysouw[30] have observed that the method fails when applied on the microscale, but a modified form gives satisfactory results.

The iodimetric determination of thiosulphate is featured in several methods developed for analysis of mixtures of sulphur anions. Of the older methods, the Wollak method for analysis of dithionite–bisulphite–thiosulphate mixtures is probably the best known. This method is discussed in some detail in the section on dithionite. Since its introducton, it has been re-investigated by several workers. Recent work by Latimer[17] indicates that in modified form it is capable of determining thiosulphate directly in mixtures containing iodine-oxidizable sulphur compounds.

Many of the iodimetric methods capable of analysing mixtures containing thiosulphate and other sulphur anions are discussed in other sections. For convenience they are listed in *Table 56*.

Table 56 Iodimetric procedures for determination of thiosulphate in mixtures with other sulphur anions

Mixture	*Comments*	*Ref.*
Polysulphide–SCN^-–$S_2O_3^{2-}$	Details in polysulphide section	18
$S_2O_4^{2-}$–SO_3^{2-}–$S_2O_3^{2-}$	Details and experimental procedure in $S_2O_4^{2-}$ section	19 20 21
$S_2O_4^{2-}$–SO_3^{2-}–$S_2O_3^{2-}$	Bromimetric procedure also involved	22
S^{2-}–SO_3^{2-}–$S_2O_3^{2-}$	Details in S^{2-} section	23
Polysulphide–S^{2-}–$S_2O_3^{2-}$	Details in polysulphide section. Bromimetric procedure also involved	24 25 26
Polysulphide–S^{2-}–$S_2O_3^{2-}$		27
Polysulphide–SO_4^{2-}–S^{2-}–$S_2O_3^{2-}$	Similar reactions to Refs. 24–26	28

Titrimetric determination of thiosulphate by iodimetric procedures

Procedure 1. Direct titration
Add 2 mℓ starch indicator to the thiosulphate solution. Titrate with standard iodine until the first permanent blue colour appears.

Procedure 2. Reverse titration
Titrate an aliquot of standard iodine with thiosulphate until the iodine colour becomes pale yellow. Dilute the solution to about 200 mℓ, add 2 mℓ of starch solution and continue the titration until the colour changes from blue to colourless.

Note
The iodine solution used in the above procedure is best standardized against pure As_2O_3.

$$H_3AsO_3 + I_2 + H_2O \rightarrow H_3AsO_4 + 2I^- + 2H^+$$

For accurate work this should be dried either by heating at 110 °C for 1 h, or by allowing it to stand over concentrated H_2SO_4 in a desiccator, preferably overnight. The quantity of As_2O_3 prescribed in the following procedure is appropriate for iodine solutions of about 0.1M.

Accurately weigh out about 2.5 g of dry As_2O_3 into a beaker and dissolve it in 10 mℓ of 2M NaOH. Add dilute HCl or H_2SO_4 dropwise until the solution is just acid to litmus (paper). Make up to exactly 500 mℓ in a volumetric flask. Pipette 25 mℓ of the As(III) solution (using a rubber suction bulb) into a conical flask. Add 1 g of sodium hydrogen carbonate and 2–3 mℓ of starch indicator. Titrate with the iodine solution until the first permanent blue colour is produced.

From the above equation it will be seen that $As_2O_3 \equiv 4I$.

Procedure 3. Using pure KIO_3 as reference standard
Dry the KIO_3 by heating in an oven for 1 h at 180 °C. Accurately weigh out about 0.90 g of KIO_3, dissolve in water and make up to exactly 250 mℓ in a volumetric flask. To a 25 mℓ aliquot, add 1 of KI and 5 mℓ of 1M H_2SO_4. Titrate with the thiosulphate solution until the iodine colour is pale yellow, add 2–3 mℓ of starch solution and continue the titration until the solution becomes colourless.

$$KIO_3 \equiv 3I_2 \equiv 6S_2O_3{}^{2-}$$

Note
The weight of KIO_3 quoted is appropriate for a thiosulphate solution of about 0.1M.

---

2. Other redox methods
Potassium permanganate, potassium manganate, copper(III), hypohalites, vanadium(V), iodine monochloride, chloramine-T, hexacyanoferrate(III), thallium(III), perchlorate, cerium(IV), sodium periodate, and lead tetra-acetate can be used[8,9,31] in the redox titration of thiosulphate. In some cases

the procedures are complicated or involve critical conditions. The use of cerium(IV) has been briefly referred to already. Krause and Busch[32] found that thiosulphate (and several polythionates) are rapidly oxidized to sulphate by cerium(IV) in 2M $HClO_4$ at 85 °C. The excess of cerium(IV) was subsequently back-titrated with standard sodium oxalate. Singh and Singh[33] employed standard iron(II) with ferroin as indicator for the back-titration.

Thallium(III) appears to have some marked advantages[34]. The reagent is stable, unaffected by light and air, and is non-hygroscopic. Oxidation of thiosulphate is instantaneous.

$$Tl(III) + 2S_2O_3^{2-} \rightarrow Tl(I) + S_4O_6^{2-}$$

Direct titration of thiosulphate is made using *p*-ethoxychrysoidine as indicator. An indirect iodimetric procedure is also possible. Chloride and bromide interfere in the direct determination by forming strong complexes with thallium(III) and thus preventing its reaction with thiosulphate.

Copper(II) and iron(II) interfere in the indirect procedure but chloride and bromide do not.

3. *Miscellaneous*

De Sousa[34, 35] has developed a compleximetric method by which thiosulphate can be determined in thiosulphate–sulphide mixtures. Both anions are oxidized by Br_2 to sulphate which is determined using EDTA in the usual way. In a second aliquot sulphide is removed as cadmium sulphide and the thiosulphate determined as before. Sulphate and sulphite interfere.

Wronski[36] has employed *o*-hydroxymercuribenzoic acid for titration of thiosulphate and sulphide in the presence of dithionite. A rapid and direct titration of thiosulphate in the presence of sulphite has been based on the fact that when the respective barium salts are oxidized with hydrogen peroxide, thiosulphate produces H_2SO_4 which can be titrated with standard NaOH, but sulphite does not. If the two anions are present as the sodium salts, initial conversion to the insoluble barium salts is required.

Spectrochemical methods

1. *Spectrophotometric methods—visible and UV*

Thiosulphate reacts with cyanide to give thiocyanate which can then react with iron(III) giving the intensely red ferric-thiocyanate complex[37]. The absorbance is measured at 496 nm. Interference by polythionates is prevented[38] by working at pH 5. A further investigation by Nor and Tabatabai[39] indicates that thiosulphate (and tetrathionate) can be determined spectrophotometrically in the absence of copper(II). Their method is rapid, sensitive and accurate, and permits microgram amounts of either species to be determined even in the presence of very large amounts of sulphate. For 100 µg of either, no interference is given by the presence of 2 mg amounts of $NaNO_3$, Na_2SO_4, $NaNO_2$, Na_2HOP_4, $NaHCO_3$, $MgCl_2$, $CaCl_2$, LiCl, $AlCl_3$, $KC_2H_3O_2$, cystine, methionine, sulphamic acid or sulphanilic acid. Application was made to soil analysis.

Spectrophotometric methods for thiosulphate have been based on oxidation with excess iodine followed by measurement of the excess iodine at 365 nm. Ozawa[40] developed such a method for concentrations of thiosulphate below 10^{-3}M. Possible interference by sulphite and nitrite was prevented. Koh and Taniguchi[41] report a method for analysis of mixtures containing polythionates (tetra-, penta-, hexa-), thiosulphate and sulphite. Here again the basis is spectrophotometric determination of an excess of iodine. Polythionates are converted to thiosulphate by cyanolysis according to the equation

$$S_xO_6^{2-} + (x-1)CN^- + H_2O \rightarrow SO_4^{2-} + 2HCN + (x-3)SCN^- + S_2O_3^{2-}$$

$x = 4$, 5 and 6.

The procedure includes determination of the thiosulphate before and after cyanolysis and masking the sulphite present with formaldehyde.

Okutani and co-workers[42,43] use the mercury(II)–diphenylcarbazone reaction as the basis of a method. In its simplest form 0.1–1 ppm $S_2O_3^{2-}$ is shaken with a solution of mercuric nitrate in HNO_3, KI, benzene and diphenylcarbazone. The absorbance is measured at 562 nm. The second paper extends the method to the determination of thiosulphate and sulphide in the presence of large quantities of chloride.

Several other spectrophotometric methods have been proposed including the use of chloranilates[44] and triphenylmethane dyes[45]. In the latter paper, which involves an extraction procedure, large amounts of acetate, sulphate and sulphite, and limited amounts of sulphide and chloride, do not interfere. The minimum determinable concentration of thiosulphate is 0.02 $\mu g\ m\ell^{-1}$.

Mixtures containing sulphide, sulphate, sulphite and thiosulphate can be analysed by direct measurement in the UV. Further details are given in the sulphide section.

2. *MECA (Molecular Emission Cavity Analysis)*

Sodium thiosulphate gives a rapid multi-peaked emission response when subjected to MECA[47]. The method permits ng amounts of thiosulphate to be determined. The usual procedure of adding perchloric or phosphoric acids to enhance the emission intensity is not feasible owing to decomposition of thiosulphate in acid solutions. However, some increase in intensity is given using an ammonium phosphate buffer. Thiosulphate gives an identical response to sulphite so that simultaneous determination of these anions in mixtures is not possible. Details of the technique itself are given in the sulphide section.

Electroanalytical methods

1. *Potentiometric and amperometric methods*

Several potentiometric procedures have been published for thiosulphate. In some, thiosulphate can be determined in the presence of other sulphur anions. The familiar thiosulphate–iodine titration can be conducted potentiometrically. In a recent investigation by Norkus and Shemkyavichute[48], direct potentiometric titration with iodine is made in 2–10M NaOH using platinum and calomel electrodes.

Rencova and Zyka[49] develop both direct and indirect potentiometric procedures with lead(IV) acetate as titrant. In the indirect procedure an excess of the acetate is added and back-titration made with hydroquinone. When this procedure is used, the back-titration must be made within 35 min to prevent hydrolysis of the acetate in aqueous medium. The potential change at the equivalence point is about 70 mV for 0.02–0.05M solutions of lead(IV) acetate.

Potentiometric procedures involving the hexacyanoferrate(III)–thiosulphate system have been investigated by several workers notably Solymosi and Varga[50, 51] who develop methods for mixtures containing dithionite, thiosulphate and sulphite. End-points are determined potentiometrically or by the 'dead-stop' technique. Osmium tetroxide is used as catalyst. While the above titrations are made in NaOH media, Rao and Sarma[52] conduct the reaction in an acidic medium and in the presence of zinc(II) and copper(II) which act as catalysts.

Hanif, Dolezal and Zyka[53] use cobalt(III) acetate for the potentiometric titration of thiosulphate. Preparation of the reagent is described in another publication[54]. The titration, in which platinum and calomel electrodes are used, is performed in a nitrogen atmosphere, and is quantitative only in a solution saturated with sodium acetate. Oxidation of thiosulphate to tetrathionate takes about 40 min. The average error for 70–240 mg $S_2O_3^{2-}$ was found to be −0.15 per cent.

Mercuric chloride has been reported as titrant for thiosulphate, with the advantage that sulphate, sulphite and nitrite do not interfere[55]. In a later publication the same worker[56] reports analysis of thiosulphate–sulphide–polysulphide mixtures using the 'dead-stop' technique. Further details are given in the polysulphide and sulphide sections.

Mercuric chloride is also used by Danielsen *et al.*[57, 58] for the potentiometric analysis of thiosulphate–sulphite–polysulphide, and thiosulphate–sulphite–sulphide–polysulphide mixtures. Additional details are given in the polysulphide section.

Papp and Havas[59, 60] use the same reactions but employ a sulphide ion-selective electrode to detect the end-points. The method is applicable to mixtures containing thiosulphate, sulphite, sulphide, polysulphide and thiols.

Amperometric titration of thiosulphate can be made[61] using KIO_3, thallium(III), $KBrO_3$, $K_2Cr_2O_7$ or $KMnO_4$. When $KMnO_4$ and thallium(III) are used, sulphate, nitrate, $H_2PO_3^-$, H_3BO_3, chloride, carbonate, acetate and tartrate do not interfere, but large amounts of molybdate interfere seriously. An automatic amperometric titration of thiosulphate has been reported[62].

Catalytic methods

The azide–iodide reaction

$$2N_3^- + I_2 \rightarrow 3N_2 + I^-$$

provides the basis of a catalytic method[63] for thiosulphate in the ultramicro range (10^{-11}–10^{-13} g $Na_2S_2O_3$ mℓ^{-1}). The reaction rate is followed amperometrically using a rotating platinum and calomel electrodes. Similar methods exist for thiocyanate and sulphide. Utsumi and Okutani[64] employ the same reaction for determination of thiosulphate in the range 0.01–0.15 ppm but in this case a spectrophotometric method is used to monitor the disappearance of iodine. Iron(III), copper(II), sulphite and cyanide interfere.

Miscellaneous methods

Wackenroder's solution, formed in the reaction between hydrogen sulphide and sulphite, contains thiosulphate, trithionate, tetrathionate and pentathionate. Until recently its analysis was extremely difficult[65]. High speed liquid chromatography has now provided an elegant solution to the problem. A complete separation and determination can be made in 15 min. Further details are given in the section on polythionates.

Gas-chromatography has been applied to determination[67] of thiosulphate. The basis here is initial conversion to barium sulphate using barium hydroxide and bromine. This allows separation from acetate, nitrate and chloride which interfere with the method. The sulphate is subsequently reduced to hydrogen sulphide by 20% stannous chloride in strong H_3PO_4 before gas-chromatography.

A novel micro-gravimetric method on paper has been described by Ganchev and Koev[68]. Between 20 and 200 μg of thiosulphate contained in 0.01 mℓ is applied to a narrow filter-paper strip impregnated with AgCl. Migration occurs on treatment with H_2O in a special apparatus. After drying, the white spots are cut out and weighed. Comparison with standards allows determination of thiosulphate to be made to within ±1.5%. Bromide, iodide or cyanide interfere, but chloride, sulphate, carbonate, nitrate, sulphite, chromate, tetrathionate or oxalate, do not.

Titration of thiosulphate has been carried out thermometrically with cerium(IV) using a digital thermometric titrator[69]. Construction of the titrator is described in the same paper.

References

1. IGUCHI, A., *Bull. chem. Soc. Japan*, **31**, 600 (1958); *Analyt. Abstr.*, **6**, 1705 (1959)
2. SCHMIDT, M. and SAND, T., *Z. anorg. Chem.*, **330**, 188 (1964); *Analyt. Abstr.*, **12**, 5754 (1965)
3. POLLARD, F.H., NICKLESS, G. and GLOVER, R.B., *J. Chromat.*, **15**, 533 (1964)
4. SEILER, H. and ERLENMEYER, H., *Helv. chim. Acta*, **47**, 264 (1964); *Analyt. Abstr.*, **12**, 1703 (1965)
5. CANIC, V.D., TURCIC, M.N., BUGARSKI-VOJINOVIC, M.B. and PERISIC, N.U., *Z. analyt. Chem.*, **229**, 93 (1967); *Analyt. Abstr.*, **15**, 5211 (1968)
6. KELLY, D.P., *J. Chromat.*, **51**, 343 (1970)
7. NAITO, K., TAKEI, S. and OKABE, T., *Bull. chem. Soc. Japan*, **43**, 1360 (1970); *Analyt. Abstr.*, **20**, 3012 (1971)
8. SZEKERES, L., *Talanta*, **21**, 2 (1974)
9. BLASIUS, E., HORN, G., KNOCHEL, A., MUNCH, J. and WAGNER, H., in *Inorganic Sulphur Chemistry* (Ed. G. Nickless), Chapter 6, Elsevier, Amsterdam (1968)
10. LOWENHEIM, F.A. in *Encyclopedia of Industrial Chemical Analysis* (Ed. F.D. Snell and L.S. Ettre), Vol. 18, Interscience, New York, 429 (1973)
11. HEINRICH, B.J., in *Treatise on Analytical Chemistry* (Ed I.M. Kolthoff and P.J. Elving), Part II, Vol. 7, Interscience, New York, 84 (1961)

12. KOLTHOFF, I.M. and BELCHER, R., *Volumetric Analysis*, Vol III, Interscience, New York and London, 213 (1957)
13. LAITINEN, H.A. and HARRIS, W.E., *Chemical Analysis*, 2nd edn, McGraw-Hill, New York (1975)
14. *British Standards* 3302: (1960)
15. THOMPSON, J.C. and HAMORI, E., *J. phys. Chem., Ithaca*, **75**, 272 (1971)
16. CLARK, E.D., *Nature*, **168**, 876 (1951)
17. LATIMER, G.W., *Talanta*, **13**, 321 (1966)
18. SCHULEK, E., *Z. analyt. Chem.*, **65**, 352 (1925)
19. WOLLACK, R., *Z. analyt. Chem.*, **80**, 1 (1930)
20. GOEHRING, M., *Z. analyt. Chem.*, **128**, 341 (1949)
21. DANEHY, J.P. and ZUBRITSKY, C.W., *Analyt. Chem.*, **46**, 391 (1974)
22. SZEKERES, L., *Z. analyt. Chem.*, **203**, 178 (1964); *Analyt. Abstr.*, **12**, 5130 (1965)
23. SZEKERES, L., *Ann. chim. Roma.*, **52**, 67 (1962); *Analyt. Abstr.*, **9**, 5140 (1962)
24. SZEKERES, L., *Z. analyt. Chem.*, **178**, 81 (1960); *Analyt. Abstr.*, **8**, 2387 (1961)
25. SZEKERES, L., *Acta. chim. hung.*, 167 (1961)
26. SZEKERES, L., *Pharm. Zentralhalle Dtl.*, **102**, 6 (1963); *Analyt. Abstr.*, **10**, 5137 (1963)
27. LEGRADI, L., *Analyst*. **86**, 854 (1961)
28. BLASIUS, E., WAGNER, H. and ZIEGLER, K., *Arch. Eisenhütt Wes.*, **42**, 473 (1971); *Analyt. Abstr.*, **22**, 3164 (1972)
29. FURMAN, N.H. and WALLACE, J.H., *J. Am. chem. Soc.*, **53**, 1283 (1931)
30. GRIEPINK, B.F.A. and CYSOUW, H.A., *Mikrochim. Acta*, 1033 (1963)
31. BERKA, A., VULTERIN, S.J. and ZYKA, J., *Newer Redox Titrants*, Pergamon Press, Oxford, England (1965)
32. KRAUSE, R.A. and BUSCH, D.H., *Analyt. Chem.*, **30**, 1817 (1958)
33. SINGH, B. and SINGH, S., *Analytica chim. Acta*, **14**, 505 (1956)
34. DE SOUSA, A., *Chemist Analyst*, **50**, 76 (1961)
35. DE SOUSA, A., *Inf. quim. analit.*, **17**, 139 (1963); *Analyt. Abstr.*, **11**, 3070 (1964)
36. WRONSKI, M., *Z. analyt. Chem.*, **179**, 350 (1961); *Analyt. Abstr.*, **8**, 4151 (1961)
37. SORBO, B.H., *Biochim. Biophys. Acta*, **23**, 412 (1957)
38. URBAN, P.J., *Z. analyt. Chem.*, **179**, 415 (1961); *Analyt. Abstr.*, **8**, 4191 (1961)
39. NOR, Y.M. and TABATABAI, M.A., *Analyt. Lett.*, **8**, 537 (1975)
40. OZAWA, T., *J. chem. Soc. Japan, Pure Chem. Sect.*, **87**, 576 (1966); *Analyt. Abstr.*, **14**, 6084 (1967)
41. KOH, T. and TANIGUCHI, K., *Analyt. Chem.*, **45**, 2018 (1973)
42. OKUTANI, T., UTSUMI, S., SHIBATA, K. and IWASAKI, I., *J. chem. Soc. Japan, Pure Chem. Sect.*, **86**, 831 (1965); *Analyt. Abstr.*, **14**, 3949 (1967)
43. OKUTANI, T. and UTSUMI, S., *J. chem. Soc. Japan, Pure Chem. Sect.*, **86**, 1149 (1965); *Analyt. Abstr.*, **14**, 3950 (1967)
44. HOFFMANN, E., *Z. analyt. Chem.*, **185**, 372 (1962); *Analyt. Abstr.*, **9**, 3016 (1962)
45. GRIGONIENE, K., RAMANAUSKAS, E. and BUTKEVICIUS, J., *Zh. analit. Khim.*, **27**, 2028 (1972); *Analyt. Abstr.*, **26**, 2629 (1974)
46. EREMIN, YU.G. and KISELEVA, K.S., *Zh. analit. Khim.*, **24**, 1201 (1969); *Analyt. Abstr.*, **20**, 978 (1971)
47. BELCHER, R., BOGDANSKI, S.L., KNOWLES, D.J. and TOWNSHEND, A., *Analytica Chim. Acta*, **77**, 53 (1975); **79**, 292 (1975)
48. NORKUS, P. and SHEMKYAVICHUTE, G., *Zh. analit. Khim.*, **26**, 39 (1971); *Analyt. Abstr.*, **22**, 2234 (1972)
49. RENCOVA, J. and ZYKA, J., *Chemist Analyst*, **56**, 27 (1967)
50. SOLYMOSI, F. and VARGA, A., *Analytica chim. Acta*, **17**, 608 (1957)
51. SOLYMOSI, F. and VARGA, A., *Magy. kém. Foly.*, **65**, 52 (1959); *Analyt. Abstr.*, **6**, 4746 (1959)
52. RAO, V.P.R. and SARMA, B.V.S., *Chemist Analyst*, **55**, 110 (1966)
53. HANIF, M., DOLEZAL, J. and ZYKA, J., *Microchem. J.*, **16**, 291 (1971)
54. BUDESINSKY, J., DOLEZAL, J., SCRAMKOVA, B. and ZYKA, J., *Microchem. J.*, **16**, 121 (1971)
55. KISS, S.A., *Z. analyt. Chem.*, **182**, 251 (1961); *Analyt. Abstr.*, **9**, 1029 (1962)
56. KISS, S.A., *Z. analyt. Chem.*, **188**, 341 (1962) *Analyt. Abstr.*, **10**, 112 (1963)
57. DANIELSEN, A.J., JOHNSEN, K. and LANDMARK, P., *Norsk. Skogind.*, **23**, 378 (1969); *Analyt. Abstr.*, **21**, 1252 (1971)
58. DANIELSEN, A.J., JOHNSEN, K. and LANDMARK, P., *Meddr. Pap Ind. Forsk. Inst.*, No. 232; *Norsk. Skogind.*, **23**, 77 (1969); *Analyt. Abstr.*, **19**, 395 (1970)
59. PAPP, J. and HAVAS, J., *Magy. kém. Foly.*, **76**, 307 (1970); *Analyt. Abstr.*, **20**, 4439 (1971)

60. PAPP, J., *Cellulose Chem. Technol.*, **5**, 147 (1971); *Analyt. Abstr.*, **22**, 2404 (1972)
61. ZHDANOV, A.K. and AKHMEDOV, G., *Uzbek. khim. Zh.*, 6 (1971); *Analyt. Abstr.*, **24**, 771 (1973)
62. MYERS, S.A. and SWANN, W.B., *Talanta*, **12**, 133 (1965)
63. MICHALSKI, E. and WTORKOWSKA, A., *Chem. Anal., (Warsaw)*, **7**, 783 (1962); *Analyt. Abstr.*, **10**, 1773 (1963)
64. UTSUMI, S. and OKUTANI, T., *J. chem. Soc. Japan, Pure Chem. Sect.*, 75 (1973); *Chem. Abstr.*, **78**, 92122c (1973)
65. HAFF, L.V., in *The Analytical Chemistry of Sulphur and its Compounds* (Ed. J.H. Karchmer), Part 1, Wiley-Interscience, New York, 241 (1970)
66. CHAPMAN, J.N. and BEARD, H.R., *Analyt. Chem.*, **45**, 2268 (1973)
67. ITO, S. and HARA, T., *J. chem. Soc. Japan, Pure Chem. Sect.*, **90**, 1027 (1969); *Analyt. Abstr.*, **19**, 4842 (1970)
68. GANCHEV, N. and KOEV, K., *Mikrochim. Acta*, 97 (1964)
69. PRIESTLEY, P.T., *Analyst*, **88**, 194 (1963)

Table of atomic weights 1975

(Scaled to the relative atomic mass, $A_r(^{12}C) = 12$)

Published in *Pure and Applied Chemistry*, **47**, 80–81 (1976) and reproduced by permission of the International Union of Pure and Applied Chemistry.

Name	*Symbol*	*Atomic number*	*Atomic weight**
Actinium	Ac	89	227.0278
Aluminium	Al	13	26.98154
Americium	Am	95	(243)
Antimony	Sb	51	121.75
Argon	Ar	18	39.948
Arsenic	As	33	74.9216
Astatine	At	85	(210)
Barium	Ba	56	137.33
Berkelium	Bk	97	(247)
Beryllium	Be	4	9.01218
Bismuth	Bi	83	208.9804
Boron	B	5	10.81
Bromine	Br	35	79.904
Cadmium	Cd	48	112.41
Caesium	Cs	55	132.9054
Calcium	Ca	20	40.08
Californium	Cf	98	(251)
Carbon	C	6	12.011
Cerium	Ce	58	140.12
Chlorine	Cl	17	35.453
Chromium	Cr	24	51.996
Cobalt	Co	27	58.9332
Copper	Cu	29	63.546
Curium	Cm	96	(247)
Dysprosium	Dy	66	162.50
Einsteinium	Es	99	(254)
Erbium	Er	68	167.26
Europium	Eu	63	151.96
Fermium	Fm	100	(257)
Fluorine	F	9	18.998403
Francium	Fr	87	(223)
Gadolinium	Gd	64	157.25
Gallium	Ga	31	69.72
Germanium	Ge	32	72.59
Gold	Au	79	196.9665
Hafnium	Hf	72	178.49
Helium	He	2	4.00260

* Values in parentheses indicate the mass number of the most stable known isotope.

Name	*Symbol*	*Atomic number*	*Atomic weight**
Holmium	Ho	67	164.9304
Hydrogen	H	1	1.0079
Indium	In	49	114.82
Iodine	I	53	126.9045
Iridium	Ir	77	192.22
Iron	Fe	26	55.847
Krypton	Kr	36	83.80
Lanthanum	La	57	138.9055
Lawrencium	Lr	103	(260)
Lead	Pb	82	207.2
Lithium	Li	3	6.941
Lutetium	Lu	71	174.97
Magnesium	Mg	12	24.305
Manganese	Mn	25	54.9380
Mendelevium	Md	101	(258)
Mercury	Hg	80	200.59
Molybdenum	Mo	42	95.94
Neodymium	Nd	60	144.24
Neon	Ne	10	20.179
Neptunium	Np	93	237.0482
Nickel	Ni	28	58.70
Niobium	Nb	41	92.9064
Nitrogen	N	7	14.0067
Nobelium	No	102	(259)
Osmium	Os	76	190.2
Oxygen	O	8	15.9994
Palladium	Pd	46	106.4
Phosphorus	P	15	30.97376
Platinum	Pt	78	195.09
Plutonium	Pu	94	(244)
Polonium	Po	84	(209)
Potassium	K	19	39.0983
Praseodymium	Pr	59	140.9077
Promethium	Pm	61	(145)
Protactinium	Pa	91	231.0359
Radium	Ra	88	226.0254
Radon	Rn	86	(222)
Rhenium	Re	75	186.207
Rhodium	Rh	45	102.9055
Rubidium	Rb	37	85.4678
Ruthenium	Ru	44	101.07

Name	*Symbol*	*Atomic number*	*Atomic weight**
Samarium	Sm	62	150.4
Scandium	Sc	21	44.9559
Selenium	Se	34	78.96
Silicon	Si	14	28.0855
Silver	Ag	47	107.868
Sodium	Na	11	22.98977
Strontium	Sr	38	87.62
Sulphur	S	16	32.06
Tantalum	Ta	73	180.9479
Technetium	Tc	43	(97)
Tellurium	Te	52	127.60
Terbium	Tb	65	158.9254
Thallium	Tl	81	204.37
Thorium	Th	90	232.0381
Thulium	Tm	69	168.9342
Tin	Sn	50	118.69
Titanium	Ti	22	47.90
Tungsten (Wolfram)	W	74	183.85
Uranium	U	92	238.029
Vanadium	V	23	50.9414
Xenon	Xe	54	131.30
Ytterbium	Yb	70	173.04
Yttrium	Y	39	88.9059
Zinc	Zn	30	65.38
Zirconium	Zr	40	91.22

* Values in parentheses indicate the mass number of the most stable known isotope.

Index